PHYSICS

THE MACMILLAN COMPANY
NEW YORK · CHICAGO
DALLAS · ATLANTA · SAN FRANCISCO
LONDON · MANILA
BRETT-MACMILLAN LTD.
TORONTO

PHYSICS

John Stewart Marshall

PROFESSOR OF PHYSICS,
McGILL UNIVERSITY

Elton Roy Pounder

ASSOCIATE PROFESSOR OF
PHYSICS, McGILL UNIVERSITY

THE MACMILLAN COMPANY
NEW YORK

PREFACE

This textbook covers the major branches of physics at a level suitable to the first and second years of a University course. Sufficient material is included for a two-year course, but it is felt that the book will serve as the text for a one-year introductory course by judicious omission of the more difficult parts. The order in which material is covered can be altered considerably at the discretion of the instructor with the exceptions that an appreciable familiarity with mechanics is assumed in all later work and that the discussion of wave motion in sound should precede the study of light.

Calculus is not needed for an understanding of the text. The careful introduction of the concept of infinitesimals at many points, however, provides the student with a mature approach to elementary physical processes. At the same time, it gives him an insight into the elegance and power of calculus methods, as applied to physics, which should be of considerable benefit in the study of calculus as a mathematical discipline. Largely for the benefit of the student who is studying calculus concurrently, formal calculus notation and derivations are used in a number of sections, usually at the ends of chapters. With the exception of the chapter on alternating-current theory, these sections summarize material developed earlier in the text, and may be omitted without loss of continuity.

The mks system of metric units is introduced at the beginning and used almost exclusively in the sections on mechanics (except for parallel use of the fps gravitational system) and in electricity. Both mks and cgs units appear in other parts of the book where appropriate.

We wish to express our indebtedness to Professor Jack Bordan, for his skilled and careful preparation of the illustrations. We also wish to thank Professor Sydney Wagner for helpful discussions regarding the content and sequence of much of the book.

J. S. MARSHALL
E. R. POUNDER

McGill University, Montreal

CONTENTS

MECHANICS

CHAPTER 1. Introduction   3
         2. Kinematics   19
         3. Force   44
         4. Statics   74
         5. Energy and Power   88
         6. Friction and Machines   105
         7. Angular Motion   123
         8. Simple Harmonic Motion   152
         9. Elasticity   168
        10. Gravitation   181
        11. Fluid Mechanics   196

HEAT

CHAPTER 12. Relative Temperature   231
        13. Gas Thermometers and the Molecular Theory
            of Gases   243
        14. The Kinetic Theory of Gases   261
        15. The Expansion of Gases   284
        16. Heat Engines and the Laws of Thermo-
            dynamics   316
        17. Sizable and Attractive Molecules   332
        18. The Solid and Liquid States   342
        19. Evaporation   359
        20. Water Substance   375
        21. Heat Transfer by Conduction and Convection   390
        22. Radiation   401

vii

SOUND

CHAPTER 23.   The Vibrations of Particles   417
24.   Wave Motion   431
25.   Standing Waves and Vibrating Systems   461
26.   Acoustics   484

LIGHT

CHAPTER 27.   Light and Color   507
28.   Reflection, Refraction, and Dispersion   517
29.   Lenses and Mirrors   531
30.   Simple Lens Systems   562
31.   Illumination and Optical Instruments   577
32.   Diffraction, Interference, and Polarization   602

ELECTRICITY AND MAGNETISM

CHAPTER 33.   Electric Current   633
34.   Resistance   649
35.   Chemical Effects of Current   672
36.   Magnetostatics   688
37.   Magnetic Effects of Current   708
38.   Magnetic Flux Density   723
39.   Electromagnetic Induction   741
40.   Electrostatics   757
41.   Alternating Currents   781
42.   Electronics   808

ATOMIC PHYSICS

CHAPTER 43.   Atomic Physics   831
44.   Nuclear Physics   857

APPENDIX A.1   Atomic Weights on the Physical Scale   881
A.2   The Periodic System   884

ANSWERS TO ODD-NUMBERED PROBLEMS   887
INDEX   893

MECHANICS

1

Introduction

1.01 NATURE OF PHYSICS

The savage ascribes a supernatural cause to every event which takes place in the physical world. He believes in an assortment of devils, sprites, and gods who must be propitiated to ensure that the sun will rise, the rain will fall, and the hunting will be good. This view of the world has gradually been displaced over a period of thousands of years by the concept of natural law—the assumption that the world is organized on rational lines and that understanding of its laws is possible. That the change in viewpoint is not complete is witnessed by the survival of superstitions—the danger of breaking a mirror, the malevolence of black cats, and so on.

Physical science is the study of material phenomena with a view to the discovery of the natural laws governing the events in question. As science grew it became convenient to classify it into various branches and subjects, especially when the body of known facts and more-or-less-proven theories became too great for any one man to know. The boundaries of the various subjects are always vague and constantly shifting, and any attempt to set up watertight compartments for the various sciences is both futile and dangerous. Nevertheless, certain classic fields make up the subject known as physics. They include the structure of inanimate matter and the energy changes resulting from interactions of matter. That this general description of physics applies almost equally well to chemistry merely serves to point out the similarity of these twin fundamental sciences.

There are two valid reasons for the study of physics. The first is curiosity—the great physicists of the past seem to have been drawn to the subject largely by an urge to find out why things work as they do. This curiosity or urge for knowledge has had an amazing effect on the

3

lives of all of us.   It is probable that the last century has seen a greater change in the lives and habits of mankind than the preceding thousand years, and this change is largely the result of the application of physical science to the means of production, transportation, and communication. Thus, the second reason for the study of physics is a desire to apply the ability it gives us to control nature.

1.02 DIVISIONS OF PHYSICS

In the nineteenth century physics was divided into four relatively independent compartments, **electricity and magnetism, heat, light,** and **sound**—four different manifestations of energy.   The fifth classic branch was **mechanics,** which treats of force and energy and their effect on matter and so serves as a base for the other four.   In 1864 James Clerk Maxwell (1831)* developed a theory which showed that light and radiant heat were electromagnetic fields moving through space, and shortly after this, experiments began to reveal the complex structure of atoms, leading to a new branch of physics sometimes called "modern" physics or **atomic physics,** which has tended to give a unifying explanation of all physics (and chemistry) in terms of subatomic particles. Nevertheless it has remained most satisfactory, in beginning the study of physics, to follow the classical divisions and to appeal occasionally to atomic physics for explanations.   Accordingly we start with mechanics.

1.03 MEASUREMENT AND NEED OF UNITS

Physics is an exact science.   This does not mean that physical theories are exactly right—in fact, most physicists believe the contrary, that *all* our theories are only imperfect descriptions of reality which will be improved in time but never reach exact truth, whatever that may be. It is worth noticing, moreover, that frequently, even when more exact refinements are known, the earlier, simpler theory is often very useful— giving results quite accurate enough for many purposes.   An example may help.   The gas law $PV = RT$ (pressure times volume is proportional to absolute temperature) was established about 1800, but later measurements showed that it wasn't quite right.   These measured deviations from the simple gas law led to a more exact law, called van der Waals'

* The date after Maxwell's name is the year of his birth.   Birth dates of prominent scientists will be shown in this manner throughout the text to give an indication of the period during which they lived.   Details of the careers of most of these men can be found in any standard encyclopedia.

Equation, which is available when very accurate computations are needed, but probably ninety-five per cent of the arithmetic done in connection with gases is based on $PV = RT$. Similarly, $PV = RT$ is very useful in theoretical work, provided one recognizes that slight modifications of the results obtained may be necessary. We may sum up the situation this way: $PV = RT$ is *never* exact, *always* important.

The improvements in physical theories result from exact measurements, that is, careful observations with well-constructed instruments. The reduction of an observation to a *number* is almost a fetish with physicists, but it works. A qualitative description of a physical phenomenon may lead to some understanding of it but rarely to the exact knowledge which allows the phenomenon to be used. Now stating a result as a number implies comparison with some standard. If a stone has a mass of 5 pounds, according to me, this result is meaningless unless someone else interested knows what I mean by a pound, that is, has access to the same (or equivalent) pound with which I compared my stone. Obviously, every laboratory, grocery store, and industrial plant cannot have access to the same standard pound. Hence elaborate precautions must be taken to see that the standard pounds used in various places are alike. (Of course the "standards" do not have to be equally accurate for all commodities. If your grocer inadvertently short weighs your pound of sugar by $\frac{1}{10}$ ounce, worth $\frac{1}{16}$ cent, you will care less than if you pay for 1 pound of gold and receive $15\frac{9}{10}$ ounces. The difference there amounts to about \$3.50.)

1.04 FUNDAMENTAL UNITS

In mechanics we shall see that it is possible to express all the quantities we encounter in terms of three so-called fundamental quantities—mass, length, and time. These are not the only possible choices and their selection may be explained perhaps as an attempt to avoid having to define these three abstruse concepts, whose nature we intuitively think we understand but which are so difficult to define.

1.05 METRIC UNITS

The unit of length in the metric system is the *meter*, which is defined as the distance between two hairlines on a certain bar of metal when that bar is at a specified temperature. This particular bar is carefully preserved in Paris and is the only exact meter standard in the world. All other metersticks and other metric scales of length are more-or-less exact copies of the original.   Similarly, the unit of mass is the *kilogram*, which is the mass of a certain block of metal kept in Paris.   It was duplicated as skillfully as possible to provide secondary standards which are kept at standards laboratories throughout the world (for example, at the National Bureau of Standards in Washington and the National Research Council in Ottawa).   These secondary standards are in turn the basis of our standard masses as used in laboratories, factories, shops, and so on.

It will be realized that the meter and the kilogram as thus defined are quite arbitrary in size.   When the metric system of units was designed, however, the sizes were chosen to correspond to useful physical quantities. Thus, the meter was intended to be one ten-millionth part of the distance from the North Pole of the earth to the equator as measured on the meridian through Paris.   More accurate measurements of the earth made later show that the circumference of the earth is slightly greater than 40 million meters.   This made a choice necessary.   Should the meter be defined in terms of the size of the earth?   If this were done, all units based on the meter would have to be revised every time a more accurate survey of the earth was made.   The alternative, which was chosen, was to keep the meter as an arbitrary unit.   Similarly, the kilogram was intended to be the mass of 10^{-3} cubic meters of water at a temperature of four degrees centigrade; although this is not precisely true, the error involved is negligible for most work.   Thus, there is a simple relationship in the metric system between the mass and volume of water.

The third fundamental unit is the *second*, which is based on astronomical observation.   The interval of time between successive meridian passages of the sun (meridian passage at a position in our latitudes is the instant when the sun is directly south of us) is called a day.   The length of the day varies slightly throughout the year, and its average over the year is taken as the mean solar day.   The second is 1/86,400 of a mean solar day, the day being divided into 24 hours, the hour into 60 minutes, and each minute into 60 seconds.   The use of these somewhat strange numbers is a heritage from the ancient Babylonians, who were rather fond of the number 12.   No clock yet built keeps perfect time indefinitely, so our time system is constantly checked against astronomical observations.   (Just recently new types of clocks have been invented which for short periods of time, say a few months or even years, seem to be more consistent timekeepers than the rotation of the earth.   So perhaps a few years hence the second will be as arbitrary as the meter.   One of the reasons for the interest in this is that astronomers tell us the day is gradually lengthening—at the leisurely rate of a few seconds per day in a hundred years. That seems trivial, but in a few thousand years it would amount to something measurable, and we try to take the long view in science.)

In the metric system multiples and submultiples of the basic "name" units (that is, the gram, the meter, the second, etc.) are all powers of ten, and a uniform system of nomenclature is used. It is important to become thoroughly familiar with this system as soon as possible. It is shown in Table 1.01. The prefixes which are most widely used are shown in boldface type, and the standard abbreviations are also shown.

TABLE 1.01   Nomenclature of Metric Units.

Multiple Unit Prefix				Submultiple Unit Prefix			
deca	= dk	= 10	= 10^1	deci	= d	= 1/10	= 10^{-1}
hecto	= h	= 100	= 10^2	**centi**	= c	= 1/100	= 10^{-2}
kilo	= k	= 1000	= 10^3	**milli**	= m	= 1/1000	= 10^{-3}
mega	= M	= 1,000,000	= 10^6	**micro**	= μ	= 1/1,000,000	= 10^{-6}
				nona	= n	= 10^{-9}	
				micromicro (or pica)	= $\mu\mu$ (or p)	= 10^{-12}	

Example I.   One one-thousandth part of a meter is called a *milli-meter*, written 1 mm, the second "m" being an abbreviation for meter.

Example II.   One thousand *watts* is an amount of power and may be abbreviated as 1000 w or 1 kw.

Example III.   10.6 $\mu\mu$f represents a capacitance. The basic unit of capacitance is the *farad* (f), and the unit $\mu\mu$f is one one-millionth of a millionth of a farad.

A *system* of units is any self-consistent set, based preferably on the minimum possible number of independent units. The minimum number in mechanics is three, and if the meter, kilogram, and second are chosen, the result is called the *mks* system. When electrical quantities enter the equations a fourth independent unit is needed, and the *ampere* the fundamental unit of electric current, is added. Similarly, in discussing heat a fifth independent unit, the *degree centigrade*, is introduced. These five units, together with further ones derived from them, constitute the *mks* or *mksa* system, which will be the principal one used in this book.

Many equations will work with any unit chosen. Thus two capacitors in series have an equivalent capacitance of $C = C_1C_2/(C_1 + C_2)$, and any unit of capacitance will serve here—farads, microfarads, or statfarads. Many of the equations of physics are of this balanced type, but with many others correct results depend on consistent use of units. The basic equation of mechanics is that force is the product of mass and acceleration ($F = ma$), and unless all the units used belong to one of the self-consistent systems, this equation will give seriously wrong answers.

In the mks system, it will be noted that two of the mechanical units are basic "name" units and the third, the kilogram, is a multiple of a "name" unit. This is a rather illogical feature of the system, but it has historical precedent and should cause the student little trouble. The use of the mks system of units is relatively new, having been recommended in 1935 by the International Electrotechnical Commission, but it has certain special advantages, particularly in electrical work, and its adoption in books and papers on physics is increasing rapidly.

The system of metric units which was used exclusively prior to 1935, and which the student may have encountered already, is called the *cgs* system, after the initial letters of the three fundamental units, the *centimeter* for length, the *gram* for mass, and the *second* for time. Its use leads to mechanical units differing from the mks ones only by factors of powers of ten, but it gives rise to several different types of electrical units whose use can be quite confusing. Occasionally, throughout this text, conversion factors between mks and cgs units will be given.

1.06 BRITISH UNITS

The metric system was specifically designed for scientific work and is the most convenient one for this purpose. It is also used in everyday life on the continent of Europe, but here in North America and in the United Kingdom we tend to use it only for scientific work while retaining the far older British system in engineering and commerce. This duality is unfortunate, but such matters are not settled entirely by logic (the authors readily admit that a length of a half-mile conveys a far more exact impression of distance to them than a length of 800 meters). The unit of length is the *foot*, which legend has it was originally the length of King Henry VIII's foot, but as this original standard is now unavailable the unit is defined in terms of a standard bar kept in London. The *pound*, the unit of mass, is similarly a particular block of metal in London. The unit of time, the *second*, is the same as in the metric system. This *fps* system is noted for its extraordinarily large number of units and for the awkwardness of its conversion factors. Thus length may be measured in inches, feet, yards, fathoms, perches, poles, rods, furlongs, and miles, and

$$12 \text{ inches} = 1 \text{ foot} \qquad 3 \text{ feet} = 1 \text{ yard} \qquad 1760 \text{ yards} = 1 \text{ mile}$$

to give only the conversion factors between the more commonly used units of length. Fortunately there are no electrical units in the fps system, as the study of electrical phenomena had made little progress before the metric system was introduced.

The relations between the British and metric units ultimately are a matter of comparing the standards. The conversion factors that you will need, together with the abbreviations that will be used in this book, are:

$$1 \text{ inch (in.)} = 2.54 \text{ centimeters (cm)}$$
$$1 \text{ foot (ft)} = 30.48 \text{ cm}$$
$$1 \text{ yard (yd)} = 0.9144 \text{ m}$$
$$1 \text{ meter (m)} = 39.37 \text{ in.}$$
$$1 \text{ kilometer (km)} = 0.6214 \text{ miles}$$
$$1 \text{ mile} = 1.609 \text{ (km)}$$
$$1 \text{ kilogram (kgm)} = 2.205 \text{ pounds}$$
$$1 \text{ pound (lb)} = 453.6 \text{ grams (gm)}$$

It is necessary to be able to convert from one system of units to another and from larger to smaller units, etc., but it should be stressed that this is really an arithmetical drill, no more closely related to an understanding of physics than learning to manipulate a slide rule, and about equally important.

EXAMPLES OF CONVERSION OF UNITS

Example I. The distance from Berlin to Paris is 540 miles. Express this distance in kilometers.

$$1 \text{ mile} = 5280 \text{ ft} = 5280 \times 12 \text{ in.}$$
$$= 5280 \times 12 \times 2.54 \text{ cm}$$
$$= 5280 \times 12 \times 2.54 \times 10^{-2} \text{ m}$$
$$= 5280 \times 12 \times 2.54 \times 10^{-2} \times 10^{-3} \text{ km}$$
$$= 1.609 \text{ km}$$

therefore $\quad 540 \text{ miles} = 869 \text{ km}$

Example II. The mass of 1 gallon of water is 10 lb. Express this mass in kilograms.

$$1 \text{ lb} = 453.6 \text{ gm} = 453.6 \times 10^{-3} \text{ kgm}$$

therefore $\quad 10 \text{ lb} = 4.536 \text{ kgm}$

Example III. The density of lead is 11,350 kgm m^{-3}. Express this in pounds per cubic foot.

$$1 \text{ kgm m}^{-3} = \frac{2.205 \text{ lb}}{(39.37 \text{ in.})^3}$$

$$= \frac{2.205}{\left(\dfrac{39.37}{12}\right)^3} \text{ lb ft}^{-3}$$

$$= 0.6243 \text{ lb ft}^{-3}$$

therefore $\quad\quad 1.135 \times 10^4 \text{ kgm m}^{-3} = 708.7 \text{ lb ft}^{-3}$

1.07 EQUATIONS IN PHYSICS

Physical ideas, physical laws, or definitions of physical entities may be stated in words or they may be expressed in algebraic form. In this latter form they are called equations and are useful for calculations. Boyle's Law, for example, states that for a gas the pressure (P) and the volume (V) are inversely proportional.

Algebraically this becomes

$$P \propto \frac{1}{V}$$

or $\quad\quad\quad\quad P = \dfrac{C}{V} \quad\quad (C = \text{constant})$

or $\quad\quad\quad\quad PV = C$

This last statement of the law is compact and well suited to quantitative work. The equation is the same statement as the proportionality, since $P \propto 1/V$ means that if P is doubled, $1/V$ is doubled. That is, V is reduced by a factor 2, and these two changes leave the left-hand side of the last equation unchanged or constant.

An example of an equation arising from the definition of a physical quantity is that for velocity (v), which may be defined as distance (s) per unit time (t) for straight-line motion. Algebraically,

$$v = \frac{s}{t}$$

Example. A boy on a bicycle travels at a uniform velocity of 8 miles per hour (mph) for 2 hours. How far does he travel? From the above equation,

$$s = vt$$

$$= \frac{8 \text{ miles}}{\text{hr}} \times 2 \text{ hr} = 16 \text{ miles}$$

It will be noted in the above problem that units are treated as algebraic quantities. The "hour" appearing in the numerator cancels the "hour" appearing in the denominator.

In the two equations above, the symbols represent "arithmetic quantities" or "absolute values", i.e., they are tacitly assumed to be always positive. Fuller use can be made of equations by letting the symbols represent algebraic quantities which may be either positive or negative.

For example, New York, Philadelphia, and Washington lie on a straight line. If a is the distance from New York to Philadelphia, b the distance from Philadelphia to Washington, and c the distance from New York to Washington,

$$a + b = c$$

is an obvious equation connecting these arithmetic quantities. Instead of distance, let us use an algebraic quantity called displacement, which is numerically equal to distance but has a sign attached to it, positive, say, if measured from New York toward Washington, negative if measured in the opposite direction. If s_{NP} is the displacement from New York to Philadelphia, then in an obvious notation

$$\left. \begin{array}{l} s_{NP} = -s_{PN} = a \\ s_{PW} = -s_{WP} = b \\ s_{NW} = -s_{WN} = c \end{array} \right\} \tag{1.01}$$

This seems to be complicating the situation unnecessarily, but it permits a very simple type of equation connecting the various displacements. The equation

$$s_{NP} + s_{PW} = s_{NW} \tag{1.02}$$

replaces

$$a + b = c \tag{1.03}$$

but we can also write

$$s_{PW} = s_{PN} + s_{NW} \tag{1.04}$$

or any combination we like, provided the first subscript letter is the same in the first term on each side of the equation and also the last subscript letter of the last term on each side is the same. Equation (1.04) means physically that if you travel from Philadelphia to New York and then from New York to Washington, your final position is the same as if you had gone directly from Philadelphia to Washington. Equations

(1.02), (1.03), and (1.04) are illustrated in Figure 1.01(a), 1.01(b), and 1.01(c), respectively.

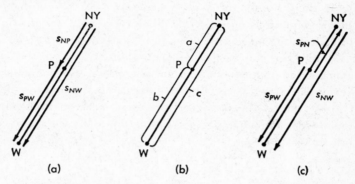

Fig. 1.01. Various methods of showing distances between New York, Philadelphia, and Washington and the relations between them.

Two points of mathematical notation are important. Vertical bars on either side of a quantity mean that we take the size of the quantity with a positive sign. This is called the absolute value.

$$|s_{NP}| = |s_{PN}| = a$$

The symbol $\sum_n s_n$ means that we add up all n quantities, of which s_n is a typical sample, paying proper attention to whether they are positive or negative. Thus, if $n = 3$ and $s_1 = 15$, $s_2 = 10$, $s_3 = -8$,

$$\sum_n s_n = s_1 + s_2 + s_3 = 15 + 10 - 8 = 17$$

The symbol $\sum_n s_n$ is read as the algebraic sum of the n quantities s.

Algebraic quantities are closely related to vector quantities, which will be discussed in the next chapter.

1.08 ARITHMETIC OF EXPERIMENTAL DATA

Throughout the field of physics the theories that arise or the ideas put forward must be substantiated by experiment. Now experiments involve measurements, and the accuracy with which we can effect such measurements determines the exactness of our proof of the theory or idea in question. Since there is no such thing as a perfect measurement, our object in the following sections will be to put down and explain a few of the rules which determine the accuracy of a physical measurement.

These rules are based on experience and apply to the measurements of any physical quantity, whether it be temperature, pressure, time, or length, etc.

(1) ESTIMATED FIGURE

To illustrate the rules and their application, we will consider the measurement of length.   Suppose that we want to measure the length l of a metal bar, using a meterstick divided into hundredths of a meter, namely, centimeters.   If we place one end of the bar at the zero of the

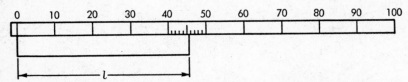

Fig. 1.02.   Meterstick subdivided into centimeters and metal bar to be measured below it.

meterstick, the position of the other end of the bar relative to the scale determines its length.   Referring to the figure, we see that the length is between 45 cm and 46 cm.   Now we make use of a rule for obtaining a more exact measurement.

Rule I.   *Every measurement should include one estimated figure.   The estimate should usually be made to one-tenth part of the smallest division.*
In our illustration this means that we mentally divide the distance between the 45-cm and 46-cm marks into ten equal divisions (millimeters) and then make an estimate of which one of these divisions coincides with the end of the bar.   (This is probably a bit more than we can do accurately, so we call the result an estimate or reasonable guess.)   Suppose we decide that this occurs at the sixth millimeter mark; then

$$l = 45.6 \text{ cm} \qquad \text{(or 456 mm)}$$

At this stage we can make two observations:

(a) The length l as quoted above (45.6 cm) is not the *exact* length of the bar because the final number is only an estimate.
(b) Despite the fact that our final reading is not perfect, nevertheless a reading of 45.6 cm is an improvement over either 45 cm or 46 cm.   It is quite common practice in writing down a measurement to depress the

final or estimated figure.   This is a reminder that it is an estimate only, thus

$$l = 45._6 \text{ cm} \qquad \text{(or } 45_6 \text{ mm)}$$

(2) POSSIBLE ERROR

Let us suppose that three different observers are asked to measure the length of the bar and that each one uses the same meter stick.   It is not inconceivable that three independent observers will arrive at different values of the estimated figure, and we might get three different answers as follows:

$$l = 45._5 \text{ cm}$$
$$= 45._6 \text{ cm}$$
$$= 45._7 \text{ cm}$$

We do not know which of these answers is the correct one, but any one of them might be.   For the sake of argument, suppose $l = 45._5$ cm is correct; then the third observer has made an overestimate or error of $0._2$ cm.   Similarly, if we argue that $l = 45._7$ cm is correct, then the first observer has made an underestimate or error of $-0._2$ cm.   It is customary to include this information when writing the result, thus:

$$l = 45.6 \text{ cm} \pm 0.2 \text{ cm}$$

This is an alternative way of showing that the result quoted is not exact. The 0.2 cm is called the possible error.   Thus the statement means that l is almost certainly between 45.4 cm and 45.8 cm.   "Possible error" is therefore a reasonable guess of the *maximum* error likely to be made in a careful observation.   It might be called the estimated maximum possible error but is abbreviated to possible error (or P.E.).

Rule II.   *The possible error in a measurement is usually taken as plus or minus one-fifth of the smallest division of the scale used.*

On the meter stick we are using, the smallest division is 1 cm, therefore the possible error is $\pm\frac{1}{5}$ of 1 cm, which is ± 0.2 cm as given above.

(3) COMPOUNDING OF POSSIBLE ERRORS

1. Addition or Subtraction.   Consider two length measurements,

$$l_1 = 45.6 \text{ cm} \pm 0.2 \text{ cm}$$
$$l_2 = 31.73 \text{ cm} \pm 0.02 \text{ cm}$$

Maximum value of $l_1 + l_2$ = 45.8 cm + 31.75 cm = 77.55 cm
Minimum value of $l_1 + l_2$ = 45.4 cm + 31.71 cm = 77.11 cm

The best guess at the value of $l_1 + l_2$ is halfway between the maximum and minimum, that is, the average value, and this leads to

$$l_1 + l_2 = 77.33 \text{ cm} \pm 0.22 \text{ cm}$$

This is identically the same as saying that the maximum and minimum values of $l_1 + l_2$ are 77.55 cm and 77.11 cm, respectively.

In actual practice our final statement of the result of this addition is "rounded off" as follows:

$$l_1 + l_2 = 77.3 \text{ cm} \pm 0.2 \text{ cm}$$

"Rounding off" a result and its possible error consists of getting rid of all estimated figures but one.

The above final result can be arrived at more quickly by rounding off l_1 and l_2 and their possible errors to the same number of decimal places. This ensures that the sum of the two has only *one* estimated figure.   Thus:

$$l_1 = 45.6 \text{ cm} \pm 0.2 \text{ cm}$$
$$l_2 = 31.7 \text{ cm} \pm 0.0 \text{ cm}$$
$$l_1 + l_2 = 77.3 \text{ cm} \pm 0.2 \text{ cm}$$

as above.   Similarly,

$$l_1 - l_2 = 13.9 \text{ cm} \pm 0.2 \text{ cm}$$

(Note that in rounding off $l_2 = 31.73$ we drop the 3; if the number to be dropped is 5 or greater, then we increase the number to its left by one, e.g., $l_2 = 31.78$ becomes 31.8.)

As a result of the foregoing discussion we can quote a third rule.

Rule III.   *For addition or subtraction, the accuracy of the result is governed by the* last *figure of the least accurate measurement.   The possible error of the result is the sum of the possible errors of the component measurements.*

2. Multiplication or Division.   The rules for multiplication or division will be quoted without proof.

It is first necessary to say what is meant by the number of **significant figures** in a measurement.   As the name implies, it is the number of figures in a measurement which have a real meaning and which were arrived at by an actual reading from a scale.   For example, the estimated figure is one of the significant figures because it has a real meaning in a measurement even though it is not an exact measurement.

Consider the measurement

$$2.03 \text{ cm} \pm 0.02 \text{ cm}$$

which has three significant figures. This measurement could equally well be written as

$$0.0203 \text{ m} \pm 0.0002 \text{ m}$$

This still has only three significant figures. The first zero to the right of the decimal place is there because of the size of the unit chosen to express the measurement.

Rule IV. *When two measurements are multiplied or divided, the number of significant figures in the result should be equal to the number of significant figures in the factor containing the least number.*

This rule may be illustrated by four examples:

$$34.5_6 \times 2.8_1 = 87.1136 = 87._1$$
$$34.5_6 \times 3.8_1 = 131.6736 = 13_2$$
$$34.56 \div 2.8_1 = 12.29 = 12._3$$
$$34.56 \div 3.8_1 = 9.092 = 9.0_9$$

In each of the four examples the number of significant figures in the measurements to be multiplied or divided is three and four, respectively. Therefore the answer in each case contains only three significant figures (Rule IV).

The next step is to find the possible error in the result. This is done by first determining the per cent possible error in the individual measurements before they are multiplied or divided. Consider the following: For $l_1 = 34.56$ cm ± 0.02 cm:

$$\text{Per cent possible error} = \pm \frac{0.02}{34.56} \times 100 = \pm 0.057 = \pm 0.06$$

For $l_2 = 2.81$ cm ± 0.02 cm:

$$\text{Per cent possible error} = \pm \frac{0.02}{2.81} \times 100 = \pm 0.71 = \pm 0.7$$

Rule V. *The total per cent possible error in the answer when two measurements are multiplied or divided is the sum of the individual per cent possible errors.*

$$l_1 \times l_2 = 34.5_6 \text{ cm} \times 2.8_1 \text{ cm} = 87.1 \text{ cm}^2 \pm (0.06\% + 0.7\%)$$
$$= 87.1 \text{ cm}^2 \pm 0.76\%$$
$$= 87.1 \text{ cm}^2 \pm 0.8\% \quad \text{(rounded off)}$$

$$0.8\% \text{ of } 87.1 \text{ cm}^2 = 87.1 \times \tfrac{8}{1000} = \frac{696.8}{1000} = 0.6968 = 0.7 \text{ cm}^2$$

Therefore we have, finally,

$$l_1 \times l_2 = 87.1 \text{ cm}^2 \pm 0.7 \text{ cm}^2$$

Similarly,

$$\frac{l_1}{l_2} = \frac{34.5_6 \text{ cm}}{2.8_1 \text{ cm}} = 12.29 = 12._3 \pm 0.8\%$$

$$0.8\% \text{ of } 12.3 = 12.3 \times \tfrac{8}{1000} = \frac{98.4}{1000} = 0.0984 = 0.1$$

Therefore we obtain

$$\frac{l_1}{l_2} = 12.3 \pm 0.1$$

(The above rules show how to obtain the possible error in simple cases. Possible error is a maximum likely error, found by adding up all the possible inaccuracies in the measurements, that is, taking the "worst" case. Another useful concept in science is "probable error", an estimate of just how much the result *is* likely to be wrong. It can be found by the methods of statistics when the number of measurements is large but is mentioned here for completeness only, as we shall not attempt to calculate probable errors in this book.)

In the problems throughout the book we have attempted to quote a reasonable number of significant figures in the data given and in the answers. This also applies to worked-out examples. Complete consistency is impossible (e.g., if 99 cm has two significant figures, does 100 cm contain three and if so, why is a measurement of just over a meter more accurate than one just less than a meter?), and we apologize for any shortcomings of this type. In the solution of problems attention should be paid continually to the number of significant figures.

PROBLEMS

1. The distance from Cairo to Capetown is 8000 km. Express this distance in miles.

2. The density of water is 62.4 lb ft^{-3}. Express this as a density in grams per cubic centimeter.

3. The speed of a car is 30 mph. Express this speed in feet per second.

4. A man has a mass of 60 kgm. What is his mass expressed in pounds?

5. Astronomical distances are expressed in light-years. A light-year is the distance light will travel in a year. The velocity of light is 186,000 miles sec^{-1}. Express the light-year in (a) miles, (b) kilometers.

6. The pressure of the atmosphere is 1033 gm cm^{-2}. What is the pressure in pounds per square inch?

7. The acceleration caused by gravity is 32 ft sec^{-2}. Express this acceleration in centimeters per second per second.

8. Density (D) is defined as mass (M) divided by volume (V). Express this as an equation.
   (a) Find the density of a substance whose mass is 10 lb and whose volume is 3 ft^3.
   (b) Find the mass of a substance whose density is 2 gm cm^{-3} and whose volume is 180 cm^3.

9. A field measures 200.0 ft $\pm$ 0.2 ft by 100.0 ft $\pm$ 0.2 ft. Find the area, the per cent possible error, and the possible error in the area.

10. The radius of a circle is 0.60 m $\pm$ 0.02 m. Find the area of the circle, the per cent possible error, and the possible error.

11. The radius of a sphere is 0.60 m $\pm$ 0.02 m. Find the volume of the sphere, the per cent possible error, and the possible error.

12. An automobile travels with a uniform velocity in a straight line. The automobile covers a distance of 608 miles $\pm$ 2 miles in 15 hr 15 min $\pm$ 2 min. Find the velocity, the per cent possible error, and the possible error.

13. In an experiment, the volume of a certain quantity of water is found to be 0.0012 m^3 $\pm$ 0.0002 m^3, and the mass is found to be 1.26 $\pm$ 0.02 kgm. Find the density (mass/volume), the per cent possible error, and the possible error.

14. The maximum and minimum Fahrenheit temperatures on a certain day are 101.6F $\pm$ 0.2F and 57.7F $\pm$ 0.02F. Find the temperature variation, the per cent possible error, and the possible error.

15. A wholesale chemist has 9.4 lb $\pm$ 0.2 lb of sodium nitrate in stock. He receives a shipment of 650 lb $\pm$ 2 lb. What is his total stock, the per cent possible error and the possible error?

16. Small items such as screws are often still sold by number but for convenience are handled by weighing. By counting and weighing a number of random samples it is found that 144 screws (one gross) of a certain size have a mass of 55.34 $\pm$ 0.06 gm. A packaging machine is adjusted to measure out the screws in lots of mass 56 $\pm$ 1 gm, and this package is sold as one gross. What are the minimum and maximum number of screws you would expect to find in "one-gross" packages?

2

Kinematics

The branch of physics called **mechanics** is an attempt to describe in consistent and accurate terms how bodies (i.e., baseballs, jet aircraft, planets, electrons, etc.) move and what causes them to move. A special case is that of bodies which are at rest or are moving in a straight line at constant speed. This division of mechanics is called **statics** and is of great importance in civil engineering. The remainder of the subject is called **dynamics** and deals with bodies undergoing accelerated motion. Dynamics is further subdivided into **kinematics,** which concerns itself solely with describing movement, and **kinetics,** which includes both motion and its causes (that is, motion and force).

Mechanics is an old branch of physics and some of the greatest scientists, from Galileo Galilei (1564) to Albert Einstein (1879), have contributed to its present formulation. Its successes have been enormous both in engineering and in the understanding of the universe around us. The laws we are about to study do describe accurately the motion of bodies ranging in size from the molecules of a gas, which are so small that 10^{20} of them may be contained in a cubic centimeter, to the entire world. Only in the last fifty years when scientists have discovered the strange world inside the atom has it been necessary to modify these laws, and the resulting modifications will be referred to briefly later in this book.

2.01 DISPLACEMENT

If a body moves with respect to a reference point, we define its **displacement** at any instant of time as the line joining the reference point and the body. Thus in Figure 2.01 O is the reference point and $OABC$ the path followed by the body, which is at A, B, and C at times t_1, t_2, and t_3, respectively. Then the displacement is OA at time t_1, OB at t_2, and OC at t_3. Displacement thus measures the position of the body

19

at a given time with respect to a reference point. The reference point O is normally a point fixed on the surface of the earth, although this is not necessarily always the case since O itself may be a moving point; but this is a complication which we need not consider now. We are all aware that even if O is fixed on the earth, it is not at rest because of the earth's daily rotation, its annual revolution about the sun, and the motion through space of the solar system; but again, this point of view will rarely be needed.

How do we describe a displacement numerically? Consider the time t_2 when the body is at B. We can measure the distance OB, which is, say, 27.36 m. The number 27.36 m does not, however, locate the point B, it merely restricts us to a circle of this radius with O as center. To find the point B and hence the displacement OB, we need another number to represent direction. To get it, we need a reference direction such as the line OX, which, again, will normally be fixed on the surface of the earth and unchanging with time.

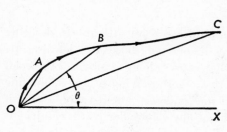

Fig. 2.01.

Then the direction OB is specified by the angle $\theta =$ angle XOB, measured counterclockwise by convention. In the diagram $\theta = 38°$. Then

$$\text{Displacement } OB = 27.36 \text{ m}, \ 038°$$

Similarly, $$\text{Displacement } OC = 56.01 \text{ m}, \ 022°$$

(Figure 2.01 is of course a map, or diagram of the actual problem, in which distance on the earth has been represented to scale so that 1 mm on the paper represents 1 m on the earth. Since the scale of the map is the same in all directions, the angles are represented correctly in size.)

Displacement is the first of many similar quantities we shall encounter which require two numbers to specify them, one number to measure size and one to give direction. They are referred to as **vector** quantities and are to be contrasted with most of the familiar quantities in everyday life which have size or magnitude only. Such things as the mass of a bag of sugar, the volume of a room, the number of students in a class, the amount of money in your pocket are completely described by a number together with the unit in which the number is measured. These are called **scalar** quantities. This distinction is vital in physics and bears repeating.

Vector quantities have size and direction and require *two* numbers, together with their units, for a complete description. They are shown in boldface type.

Scalar quantities have size only and are completely described by *one* number and a unit.

2.02 ADDITION OF SCALARS

Most scalar quantities are intrinsically positive; thus a negative mass or a negative volume has no meaning to us. We add scalars by the ordinary rules of arithmetic, 4 lb of sugar plus 3 lb of sugar equals 7 lb of sugar. Subtraction of scalars, or the difference of two scalar quantities, presents no difficulties. Some scalar quantities, to be introduced later, can be negative. For example, electric charges are of two kinds which neutralize each other. They are called positive and negative electricity, and if $+6$ microcoulombs and -4 microcoulombs are added (put together physically), the total or net charge is $+2$ microcoulombs.

2.03 ADDITION OF VECTORS

The addition or compounding of vector quantities (referred to for brevity as "vectors") is different from that of scalars since both the size and direction of the quantities must be taken into consideration. First we must ascribe a physical meaning to the process or operation of addition. Consider a body which is at O at time $t = 0$, at A at $t = t_1$, and at B at $t = t_2$. (See Figure 2.02.) Then **OA** is displacement at $t = t_1$. If A is now treated as origin, **AB** is displacement at $t = t_2$ with respect to A, and **OB** is displacement with respect to O. As a result of the successive displacements **OA** and **AB** there is a total displacement **OB**.

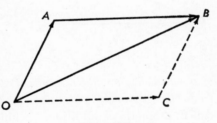

Fig. 2.02.

Thus it is reasonable to speak of **OB** as the "sum" of **OA** and **AB**. This is written as

$$\mathbf{OA} + \mathbf{AB} = \mathbf{OB} \qquad (2.01)$$

where the boldface symbols are an indication of the vector nature of the quantities being added. By addition of vectors we shall therefore mean the calculation of the single vector which is equivalent in its action to the two or more original vectors.

Draw *OC* parallel to *AB* and *CB* parallel to *OA*.   Then *OC* is equal in magnitude to *AB* and has the same direction.   Hence it represents a displacement equal to *AB* but starting from the point *O*.   Similarly *CB* is a displacement equal to *OA* but starting from *C*.   Now

$$\mathbf{OC} + \mathbf{CB} = \mathbf{OB} \tag{2.02}$$

and so we deduce from (2.01) and (2.02) that the order of the addition of displacements does not affect the result.

A special case of interest is the obvious result

$$\mathbf{OA} + \mathbf{AO} = 0, \qquad \text{i.e.,} \quad \mathbf{AO} = -\mathbf{OA}$$

which stated in words is "multiplying a displacement by -1 is equivalent to reversing its direction".   This enables us to define subtraction:

$$\mathbf{OB} - \mathbf{AB} = \mathbf{OB} + (-\mathbf{AB}) = \mathbf{OB} + \mathbf{BA} = \mathbf{OA}$$

a result which could be obtained directly by transposing terms in equation (2.01) according to the ordinary rules of algebra.

The next question is whether the results deduced above for displacements apply to all forms of vectors.   This question can ultimately be settled only by experiment, and countless experiments show that they do—all vector quantities *must* be combined or added as we have treated displacements. This important result is stated formally as the **parallelogram law of vector addition:**

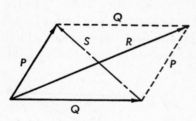

Fig. 2.03.

If two vectors **P** *and* **Q** *acting on a body are represented to scale as the adjacent sides of a parallelogram, their resultant* **R** *is represented by the diagonal drawn from the common point of the sides P, Q.* This is sometimes called geometrical addition.   Symbolically **P** + **Q** = **R**.   The student should verify for himself that **P** − **Q** = **S**, where **S** is the other diagonal of the parallelogram.

Triangle of Vectors.   A modification of the parallelogram law is this: If the vector **P** is plotted to scale and the vector **Q** is drawn from the end of **P**, then the resultant **R** is obtained by drawing the vector from the beginning of **P** to the end of **Q**.   The upper left half of Figure 2.03 illustrates this method while the lower right half shows that the same result is obtained by reversing the order of addition.

Polygon of Vectors. The method of the triangle of vectors can be extended to any number of vectors, the resultant figure being a polygon. This method is illustrated in Figure 2.04, where **P, Q, R,** and **S** are vectors acting on a body. By the triangle law, **OB** is the resultant of **P** and **Q, OC** is the resultant of **OB** and **R, OD** is the resultant of **OC** and **S**; i.e., **OD** is the resultant of **P, Q, R,** and **S**. Clearly there is no need of drawing the dotted lines *OB, OC* to find the resultant vector.

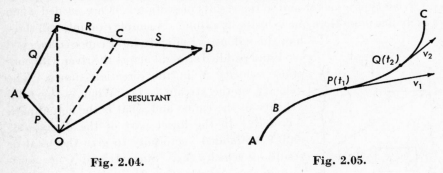

Fig. 2.04.   Fig. 2.05.

2.04 VELOCITY

The time rate of change of displacement is called the **velocity** of the body. In other words, displacement measures position, velocity measures the rate at which position is changing with time. Velocity is a vector, the two numbers describing it being the scalar speed (so many miles per hour or meters per second) and the direction of motion. If the body moves along the path *ABC* (Figure 2.05) and *P* is its position at time t_1, then the direction of the velocity at t_1 is the direction of the tangent to the curve *ABC* at the point *P*. Similarly the body is at *Q* at t_2 and the direction of its velocity is as shown.

The simplest possible type of motion is that in which both speed and direction of motion remain unchanged with time. In Figure 2.06 a body

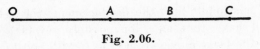

Fig. 2.06.

is moving at constant speed along the straight line *ABC*, the origin for displacement measurements being *O*. Constant speed means that if distance *AB* equals distance *BC*, the time intervals for the body to go from *A* to *B* and from *B* to *C* are equal. This case of constant velocity can be described very compactly in algebraic form. If *v* is the magnitude of the velocity (the speed) and s is the magnitude of the displacement, $v = s/t$ and $s = vt$ provided that at $t = 0$ the body was at O. Usually velocity will not be constant, and it is important to notice that any change in *either* speed *or* direction is a change in velocity. For instance, a man running at constant speed around a circular track is changing his velocity all the time. We shall return to this when we talk about rotation in Chapter 7.

Velocity is a vector and so the results of section 2.03 are needed when a body has more than one velocity at a time. A simple example will show how this is done. In Figure 2.07 a canoe is launched at A and paddled straight across the river with constant velocity **V** in the direction shown. The velocity of the stream is **U**. What is the total velocity of the canoe and what is the actual path followed? In the lower part of the diagram **U** and **V** are added vectorially to give the total or resultant velocity $\mathbf{V}_R$. Since **U** and **V** are constant in size and direction, $\mathbf{V}_R$ is a constant. The direction of motion at any time is the direction of $\mathbf{V}_R$, and since this is unchanging, the canoe moves in a straight line starting from A. We can find the path followed by drawing a straight line through A parallel to the direction of $\mathbf{V}_R$, that is, the line AB.

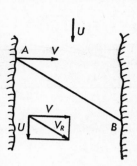

Fig. 2.07.

2.05 ACCELERATION

When the velocity of a body changes with time, we say that the body is being accelerated. The change in velocity may be a change in either speed or direction or both—in all three cases the body has an **acceleration.** This acceleration is defined as the time rate of change of velocity and may be either positive or negative. If it is negative, it is sometimes called a retardation. Acceleration is a vector, and if motion takes place in a straight line, the displacement, the velocity, and the acceleration all have the same (or possibly reverse) directions. In Figure 2.06, if the body moves from O to C with constant velocity, the displacement and velocity at any time during this period are in the direction OC. The acceleration is zero and has no direction. If after passing C the body speeds up, displacement, velocity, and acceleration are all in the same direction OC. If it starts to slow down, the acceleration is in the direction CO.

In general, however, the direction of acceleration is different from that of velocity, just as the direction of the velocity is not necessarily the same as that of the displacement. (For example, if Figures 2.01 and 2.05 describe the same motion, the velocity at t_1 is in the direction shown in the second figure, but the direction of the displacement is OP.)

Since acceleration is a vector, if a body has two or more accelerations at the same time, these must be added by vectorial addition. Acceleration may be a constant or its value may depend on time, but as a wide range of useful problems exist in which the acceleration is constant, we shall restrict ourselves to this case for the time being.

Units. So far in this chapter we have said little about units, but as they are vital in setting up any meaningful relation between measured quantities and in solving problems, we shall now review the units in which displacement, velocity, and acceleration are measured. Note that all three are vectors and hence have direction, normally measured in degrees from a fixed reference direction. The units usually given are the units in which the magnitudes of the various vectors are measured. Displacement is distance and so is measured in meters or feet. Velocity is distance per unit time, and acceleration is increase of velocity per unit time. Thus if the velocity at a given time is 10 meters per second and the velocity one second later is 14 meters per second, the velocity has increased by 4 meters per second in that second. We write acceleration in this case as 4 meters per second per second or by an obvious algebraic abbreviation 4 m/sec^2. These units are summarized in Table 2.01 for the two systems we shall use. Of course, any ratio of length over time is a unit of velocity, for example, miles per hour or feet per year (which would be appropriate for a glacier).

TABLE 2.01.

Quantity	mks Unit	fps Unit
Displacement	m	ft
Velocity	m/sec	ft/sec
Acceleration	m/sec^2	ft/sec^2

Acceleration of Gravity. It is common experience that bodies released above the surface of the earth will fall with rapidly increasing speed. For thousands of years it was believed that heavier bodies fall more rapidly than light ones, but no one thought to put this idea to an experimental test. There is a possibly apocryphal story that Galileo climbed the Leaning Tower of Pisa and dropped two objects of different weights simultaneously. He saw that they struck the ground at practically the same instant and correctly ascribed the slight lag of the lighter body to the greater effect of air resistance on it. If this experiment is repeated in a vacuum to eliminate air resistance, it is found that a feather and a piece of lead fall the same distance in the same time and that furthermore the acceleration of either body is constant. Whether Galileo actually performed the Pisa experiment is unimportant. He *did* realize from his many experiments that the acceleration of gravity is a constant, and he *was* one of the pioneers of the experimental method. The concept of an experiment was largely foreign to the thinking of the classical and pre-Renaissance world, and the introduction of this powerful method by Galileo and others marks the real beginning of modern science. The idea of an experiment is simple but may not be fully understood by those commencing the study of science. Take a situation, possibly quite complicated, and judge as far as possible what are the factors which control or influence that situation. Attempt to keep all but *one* of these factors constant. Vary the remaining factor and *measure* the effect of this variation on the situation. Repeat for all the factors which can be varied, altering only one factor at a time. Virtually every conclusion arrived at in this book is based on experiments of this type.

The acceleration of gravity is represented in equations as g and being an important constant has been measured many times by many different methods. The obvious direct method of timing a falling body is inaccurate because of the large speeds and short times involved. One simple laboratory method using a pendulum is described in Chapter 8. The result of accurate measurements is that g is about 9.80 m/sec² or 32.0 ft/sec², which are the values we shall use in problems. The value of g varies slightly with latitude (increasing from 9.78 m/sec² at the equator to 9.83 m/sec² at the poles) and decreases slightly with height above the surface (by about 0.2% in 10 km).

Thus if a body is released with zero velocity and allowed to fall freely, its velocity after 1 sec is 9.80 m/sec, after 2 sec it is 19.6 m/sec, and so on. For the first 2 sec the average velocity is $(0 + 19.6)/2 = 9.80$ m/sec, and hence the distance fallen in this time is $9.80 \times 2 = 19.6$ m. Relations between time, velocity of fall, and distance fallen can be worked out in this way and are given in Table 2.02 in both our principal systems of units.

TABLE 2.02   Speed and Distance of Free Fall.

Time (sec)	Velocity at End of Time (m/sec)	(ft/sec)	Distance Fallen (m)	(ft)
0.00	0.00	0.00	0.00	0.00
1.00	9.80	32.0	4.90	16.0
2.00	19.6	64.0	19.6	64.0
3.00	29.4	96.0	44.1	144
4.00	39.2	128	78.4	256
5.00	49.0	160	122	400
10.0	98.0	320	490	1.60×10^3
25.0	245	800	3.06×10^3	1.00×10^4
100	980	3.20×10^3	4.90×10^4	1.60×10^5

The first three or four lines of Table 2.02 describe quite accurately what happens to a falling body, but as the time increases the figures become progressively higher than those which are actually observed, because air resistance prevents "free" fall. Air resistance produces a retardation which is a complicated function, increasing with velocity. For moderate speeds this retardation is proportional to velocity. Since the retardation increases with velocity, eventually the retardation equals the acceleration of gravity, so that the net acceleration is zero and the body falls at a constant speed known as the **terminal velocity.** For a man this terminal velocity is about 120 mph. A parachute increases the air resistance greatly, so that the same man jumping from an aircraft and coming down with an open parachute has a terminal velocity of about 15 mph. This is the sort of velocity reached on hitting the ground after a jump of about 8 ft (without benefit of parachute), and so the shock is considerable but rarely leads to serious injury. Another fortunate effect of terminal velocity applies to raindrops and especially hailstones. These often originate in clouds two miles or more above the surface of the earth, and so if they came down in "free" fall as in Table 2.02, they would be highly lethal weapons.

2.06 EQUATIONS OF MOTION FOR CONSTANT ACCELERATION

As was done in deriving Table 2.02, "common-sense" arithmetic can be used in any problem where the acceleration is constant. It is an advantage to express this common-sense logic in algebraic form. Let a stand for the constant acceleration, u for the initial velocity, v for the velocity at time t, and s for the distance covered in time t.

Initial velocity $= u$
Velocity after 1 sec $= u + a$
Velocity after 2 sec $= u + 2a$
Velocity after t sec $= v = u + at$ (2.03)

The distance covered equals average velocity times time:

$$s = \bar{v}t$$

where $\bar{v}$ is average velocity.   Since velocity varies linearly with t in this case, the average is easy to calculate—it is just the arithmetic mean of the initial and final velocities:

$$\bar{v} = \frac{u + u + at}{2} = u + \tfrac{1}{2}at$$
$$s = ut + \tfrac{1}{2}at^2 \qquad\qquad (2.04)$$

It is sometimes convenient to have an equation not involving time. Solve (2.03) for t, giving

$$t = \frac{v - u}{a}$$

Substitute in (2.04):

$$s = \frac{u(v - u)}{a} + \tfrac{1}{2}a\,\frac{v^2 - 2uv + u^2}{a^2}$$
$$2as = 2uv - 2u^2 + v^2 - 2uv + u^2 = v^2 - u^2$$
$$v^2 = u^2 + 2as \qquad\qquad (2.05)$$

Equations (2.03) to (2.05) are sometimes called the equations of motion for constant acceleration.   They provide a complete description of such a motion.   Note in particular that nothing in the proof places a restriction on the directions of u and a.   If they have the same (or reverse) directions, these equations reduce to algebraic relations since the motion takes place in a straight line.   If u and a are inclined at an angle to each other, the plus signs must be read as signifying geometrical addition of vectors.

Example I.   Let us use these equations to verify some of the results of Table 2.02.   Here we take $u = 0$, $a = g = 9.80$ m/sec^2, and we measure distance downward from the point of release as positive.   After 5.00 sec

$$v = 0 + 5.00 \times 9.80 = 49.0 \text{ m/sec}$$
$$s = 0 \times 5.00 + \tfrac{1}{2} \times 9.80 \times (5.00)^2 = 122._5 \text{ m}$$

Example II.   A boy throws a ball straight up into the air with an initial velocity of 80 ft sec^{-1}.   Find

    (a) the time taken for the ball to reach its highest point
    (b) the maximum height reached by the ball
    (c) the total time the ball is in the air
    (d) the velocity with which the ball strikes the ground

Solution (a) and (b):

$$u = \text{initial velocity} = 80 \text{ ft sec}^{-1}$$
$$v' = \text{velocity at maximum height} = 0$$
$$g = \text{acceleration} = -32 \text{ ft sec}^{-2}$$
$$h_1 = \text{maximum height of ball (ft)}$$
$$t_1 = \text{time taken to reach maximum height (sec)}$$

This is a case of straight-line motion and can be solved algebraically by assigning signs to the various quantities.   The quantities u and h_1 are in the same direction (upward) and have been taken as positive, while g has been taken negative because its direction (downward) is opposite to u and h_1.   It should be mentioned that the same results would be obtained by taking u and h_1 negative and g positive.

$$v' = u + at_1$$
$$0 = 80 \frac{\text{ft}}{\text{sec}} + \left(-32 \frac{\text{ft}}{\text{sec}^2}\right) t_1$$
$$80 \frac{\text{ft}}{\text{sec}} = 32 t_1 \frac{\text{ft}}{\text{sec}^2}$$

therefore
$$t_1 = 2.5 \frac{\text{sec}^2}{\text{ft}} \times \frac{\text{ft}}{\text{sec}} = 2.5 \text{ sec}$$
$$(v')^2 = u^2 + 2as$$
$$0 = 80 \frac{\text{ft}}{\text{sec}} \times 80 \frac{\text{ft}}{\text{sec}} + 2\left(-32 \frac{\text{ft}}{\text{sec}^2}\right) h_1$$
$$80 \times 80 \frac{\text{ft}^2}{\text{sec}^2} = 2 \times 32 h_1 \frac{\text{ft}}{\text{sec}^2}$$
$$h_1 = 100 \frac{\text{ft}^2}{\text{sec}^2} \times \frac{\text{sec}^2}{\text{ft}} = 100 \text{ ft}$$

Solution (c): The ball starts and finishes at the same point on the ground; thus the over-all displacement is zero.   Let T equal the total time the ball is in the air in seconds.   By substitution in

$$s = ut + \tfrac{1}{2}at^2$$

we obtain
$$0 = 80 \frac{\text{ft}}{\text{sec}} \times T + \tfrac{1}{2}\left(-32 \frac{\text{ft}}{\text{sec}^2}\right) T^2$$
$$80T \text{ sec} = 16T^2$$

We can divide both sides of this equation by T since $T \neq 0$.   Therefore

$$T = 5 \text{ sec}$$

Solution (d):

$$v = u + at$$

For $T = 5$ sec,

$$v = 80 \,\frac{\text{ft}}{\text{sec}} + \left(-32 \,\frac{\text{ft}}{\text{sec}^2}\right) \times 5 \text{ sec}$$

$$= 80 \,\frac{\text{ft}}{\text{sec}} - 160 \,\frac{\text{ft}}{\text{sec}}$$

$$= -80 \,\frac{\text{ft}}{\text{sec}}$$

That is, the final velocity of the ball on returning to the ground is the same as the velocity on leaving, but with the sign reversed.   This is a general result in problems of this type where there is no net change in height and air resistance is neglected.

Note:

$t_1 =$ the time to reach the highest point $= 2.5$ sec
$T =$ the total time in the air $= 5.0$ sec
$t_2 =$ the time to fall to the ground from the highest point
$\quad = T - t_1 = 2.5$ sec

that is,   TIME UP = TIME DOWN

This is also a general result for this type of problem.

Example III.   A man stands on top of a building which is 100 ft high. He throws a stone vertically upward with a velocity of 40 ft sec^{-1}.   What time elapses before the stone strikes the ground at the foot of the building?

Solution 1: The stone starts at O and ends at B, therefore its displacement is **OB**, or 100 ft.

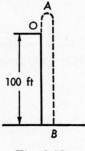

100 ft

Fig. 2.08.

$u =$ initial velocity $= 40$ ft sec^{-1}
$s =$ displacement $= -100$ ft
$g =$ acceleration $= -32$ ft sec^{-2}
$$s = ut + \tfrac{1}{2}at^2$$
$$-100 \text{ ft} = 40 \,\frac{\text{ft}}{\text{sec}} t + \tfrac{1}{2}\left(-32 \,\frac{\text{ft}}{\text{sec}^2}\right) t^2$$

For the units to balance in this equation, t must be in seconds.

$$-100 = 40t - 16t^2$$
$$4t^2 - 10t - 25 = 0$$
$$t = \frac{+10 \pm \sqrt{500}}{8}$$
$$= +4.04 \text{ sec} \qquad \text{or} \qquad -1.58 \text{ sec}$$

A negative time has no physical meaning in this problem, so that the time taken to reach the ground is 4.04 sec. (Mathematically, if at time $t = -1.585$ sec the stone had been thrown vertically upward from B with a speed of 89.44 ft sec^{-1}, at time $t = 0$ it would have been at O with a vertical speed of 40.00 ft sec^{-1}.)

Solution 2: First, find the time to reach the point $A = t_1$ sec.

$$u = \text{initial velocity} = 40 \text{ ft sec}^{-1}$$
$$g = \text{acceleration} = -32 \text{ ft sec}^{-2}$$
$$v' = \text{velocity at } A = 0$$
$$v' = u + at_1$$
$$0 = 40 \text{ ft sec}^{-1} + (-32 \text{ ft sec}^{-2})t_1$$
$$40 = 32t_1$$
$$t_1 = 1.25 \text{ sec}$$

Next, find height of A above $O = h$ ft.

$$u = \text{initial velocity} = 40 \text{ ft sec}^{-1}$$
$$g = \text{acceleration} = -32 \text{ ft sec}^{-2}$$
$$v' = \text{velocity at } A = 0$$
$$(v')^2 = u^2 + 2ah$$
$$0 = 40 \frac{\text{ft}}{\text{sec}} \times 40 \frac{\text{ft}}{\text{sec}} + 2\left(-32 \frac{\text{ft}}{\text{sec}^2}\right)h$$
$$40 \times 40 = 2 \times 32h$$
$$h = \frac{40 \times 40}{2 \times 32} = 25 \text{ ft}$$

Finally, find the time to fall from A to $B = t_2$ sec.

$$v' = \text{new initial velocity} = 0$$
$$g = \text{acceleration} = 32 \text{ ft sec}^{-2}$$
$$s' = \text{new displacement} = 100 \text{ ft} + 25 \text{ ft} = 125 \text{ ft}$$
$$s' = v't_2 + \tfrac{1}{2}at_2^2$$
$$125 \text{ ft} = 0 + \tfrac{1}{2}\left(32 \frac{\text{ft}}{\text{sec}^2}\right)t_2^2$$
$$125 \text{ sec}^2 = 16t_2^2$$
$$t_2^2 = \tfrac{125}{16} \text{ sec}^2$$
$$t_2 = \frac{11.16}{4} = 2.79 \text{ sec}$$

Therefore

$$\text{Total time} = t_1 + t_2 = 1.25 \text{ sec} + 2.79 \text{ sec} = 4.04 \text{ sec}$$

Thus, the result is the same as before except that Solution 1 finds the answer in one step as opposed to three steps for Solution 2.

Example IV.   A train starts from rest at a station and accelerates at 1.00 ft/sec² until it reaches a speed of 60.0 mph.   It runs at this speed until it nears the next station, which is 15.0 miles from the last stop, when it is decelerated uniformly to rest in the last quarter-mile of the run. Find

(a) the distance required to reach maximum speed
(b) the negative acceleration while slowing down
(c) the time for the trip

Solution (a):

u = initial velocity = 0
a = acceleration = 1.00 ft sec⁻²
v = maximum velocity = 60.0 mph = 88.0 ft sec⁻¹

(The student should check this equality.   It is a useful conversion figure to keep in mind.)

s = distance (ft)
t_1 = time for this stage of trip (sec)

$$v^2 = u^2 + 2as$$

$$88 \frac{\text{ft}}{\text{sec}} \times 88 \frac{\text{ft}}{\text{sec}} = 0 + 2 \times 1 \frac{\text{ft}}{\text{sec}^2} \times s$$

$$88 \times 88 \text{ ft} = 2s$$

$$s = 44 \times 88 \text{ ft} = \frac{44 \times 88}{5280} \text{ miles} = \tfrac{11}{15} \text{ mile}$$

$$v = u + at$$

$$88 \frac{\text{ft}}{\text{sec}} = 0 + 1 \frac{\text{ft}}{\text{sec}^2} \times t_1$$

$$88 \frac{\text{ft}}{\text{sec}} = t_1 \frac{\text{ft}}{\text{sec}^2}$$

$$t_1 = 88 \text{ sec}$$

Solution (b):

u = initial velocity = 88 ft sec⁻¹
s = distance = $\tfrac{1}{4}$ mile = 1320 ft
v = final velocity = 0
a = acceleration (ft sec⁻²)
t_2 = time for this stage of the trip (sec)

$$v^2 = u^2 + 2as$$

$$0 = 88 \frac{ft}{sec} \times 88 \frac{ft}{sec} + 2a \times 1320 \text{ ft}$$

$$2 \times 1320 \times a = -88 \times 88 \frac{ft}{sec^2}$$

$$a = -\frac{88 \times 88}{2 \times 1320} \frac{ft}{sec^2} = -\tfrac{44}{15} \text{ ft sec}^{-2}$$

$$v = u + at$$

$$0 = 88 \frac{ft}{sec} + \left(-\tfrac{44}{15} \frac{ft}{sec^2}\right) t_2$$

$$88 \text{ sec} = \tfrac{44}{15} t_2$$

$$t_2 = \frac{15 \times 88}{44} = 30 \text{ sec}$$

Solution (c): The intermediate portion of the trip is carried out at a constant speed of 60 mph = 88 ft sec^{-1}.

$$s = \text{distance} = (15 - \tfrac{11}{15} - \tfrac{1}{4}) \text{ miles}$$
$$= 14\tfrac{1}{60} \text{ miles} = 74,008 \text{ ft}$$
$$v = \text{velocity} = 88 \text{ ft sec}^{-1}$$
$$t_3 = \text{time for this stage of trip (sec)}$$

$$v = \frac{s}{t}$$

$$88 \frac{ft}{sec} = \frac{74,008}{t_3} \text{ ft}$$

$$t_3 = \tfrac{74008}{88} = 841 \text{ sec}$$

Total time for trip $= t_1 + t_2 + t_3$
$$= (88 + 30 + 841) \text{ sec} = 959 \text{ sec}$$
$$= 16 \text{ min (approx.)}$$

2.07 INITIAL VELOCITY NOT PARALLEL TO ACCELERATION—GRAPHICAL SOLUTION

We derived the equations of motion for constant acceleration in section 2.06 and stated that equations (2.03) and (2.04) were vector equations and in general must be solved by geometrical addition, which may be done by a graphical method. This method is shown in Figure 2.09, which is a velocity diagram. Lines representing **u** and various values of **a**t are plotted and added by the parallelogram theorem to give **v**.

Draw *OX* in the direction of the acceleration and mark off, to some convenient scale, lengths *OA*, *OB*, *OC*, *OD*, etc., proportional respectively to a, $2a$, $3a$, $4a$, etc. Let $a = 2.25$ m/sec^2. Then if the scale is

1 cm = 1 m/sec, $OA = 2.25$ cm represents a velocity of 2.25 m/sec since $OA = 1 \times a = 1$ sec $\times 2.25$ m/sec^2 = 2.25 m/sec. Next draw OK to represent u to the same scale. Draw KY parallel to OX. Draw AL, BM, CN, etc., parallel to OK to cut KY. Join OL, OM, ON, OP, etc. Then OL is velocity after 1 sec, OM that after 2 sec, etc., for

$$v = ON = OC + CN = 3a + OK = 3a + u$$
$$= u + 3a$$

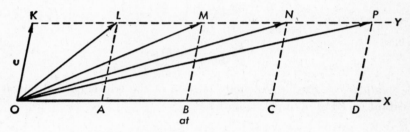

Fig. 2.09. $v = u + at.$

A similar process can be used to solve the equation $s = ut + \frac{1}{2}at^2$, only in this case it is a displacement diagram that is being drawn rather than a velocity diagram. Choose scale as (say) 1 cm = 2 m. Draw $O'X'$ in direction of acceleration and $O'K'$ in direction of **u**. Calculate magnitudes of **ut** and $\frac{1}{2}$**at**^{2} for various values of t and plot these values to scale along $O'X'$ and $O'K'$. The calculations are shown in Table 2.03 with **u** = 2.20 m/sec, and the graphical work is shown in Figure 2.10.

TABLE 2.03   **Magnitudes of ut and $\frac{1}{2}$at².**

t (sec)	ut (m)	ut to Scale (cm)	$\frac{1}{2}at^2$ (m)	$\frac{1}{2}at^2$ to Scale (cm)
1.00	2.20	$O'L' = 1.10$	1.13	$O'A' = 0.57$
2.00	4.40	$O'M' = 2.20$	4.50	$O'B' = 2.25$
3.00	6.60	$O'N' = 3.30$	10.13	$O'C' = 5.07$
4.00	8.80	$O'P' = 4.40$	18.00	$O'D' = 9.00$

To find the displacement at any of these times, we add the two components by the parallelogram law as indicated by the dotted lines. If the ends of the displacement vectors are joined by a smooth curve, we get a picture of the path followed by the body. This curve looks like, and is, a parabola, and we shall prove in section 2.09 that this is the type of path which always results from a constant acceleration acting at an angle to the initial velocity.

We have discussed this graphical solution in some detail because we feel it illustrates well how vectors work, but it is not a very practical method because anything involving accurate drawing requires special equipment and tends to be laborious. Most simple problems like this one can be solved more quickly and easily by the methods of algebra.

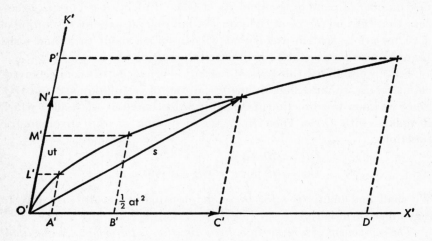

Fig. 2.10. $s = ut + \frac{1}{2}at^2$.

Before showing this solution we must develop one more concept relating to vectors.

2.08 RESOLUTION OF VECTORS

We have seen in section 2.03 that two vectors can be combined into or replaced by a single unique vector. The reverse process is called **resolving** a vector into components. In Figure 2.11 **OR** is a given vector which is difficult to deal with algebraically. (It may be an acceleration at an angle to the original velocity as in section 2.07). If it were in the direction OX it would be much easier, so we draw a line OY perpendicular to OX and find two vectors, **OP** along OX and **OQ** along OY, which will

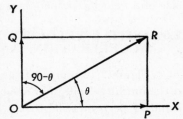

Fig. 2.11. Resolution of a vector.

have the same effect as **OR**.   That is,

$$\textbf{OR} = \textbf{OP} + \textbf{OQ}$$

The method of finding **OP** and **OQ** is simple.   We draw the rectangle with sides parallel to OX and OY which has OR as its diagonal.   Then **OP** and **OQ** are called the **components** of **OR**.   There is nothing unique about this process since OX may be in any direction and hence there are any number of pairs of components of **OR**.   In fact, it isn't even necessary that OX and OY be at right angles, but oblique axes for resolution of a vector are so seldom useful that we can forget about them and insist that the axes for resolution be mutually perpendicular.

Since we shall use this trick of resolution primarily to avoid geometrical methods, we must find an analytical way of calculating **OP** and **OQ**. Since we know the direction of OR, let it be measured by the angle θ which it makes with OX.   Then from the definition of the trigonometric functions,

$$OP = OR \cos \theta$$
$$OQ = OR \sin \theta = OR \cos (90 - \theta)$$

We shall find many uses for these simple equations.   An easy way to remember them is this:

The component of a vector in a given direction is the original vector times the cosine of the angle between the vector and the direction.

A particular but very important case occurs when we try to find a component of a vector along a direction perpendicular to itself.   From our equation,

$$OP = OR \cos 90° \qquad \text{but} \qquad \cos 90° = 0$$

so there is no such component.   As an example, an acceleration can have no component at right angles to itself and therefore cannot change the size of a velocity perpendicular to itself.

2.09 INITIAL VELOCITY NOT PARALLEL TO ACCELERATION—ANALYTICAL SOLUTION

Figure 2.12 represents again the same problem as Figure 2.09, with **u** the initial velocity and **a** the acceleration.   Choose axes OX parallel to **a** and OY perpendicular to it.   Resolve **u** along these axes into components u_X and u_Y.   Then replace **u** by u_X and u_Y.   The motion along the Y direction is one of constant speed, as discussed above, since there is no acceleration in that direction.   The accelerated motion in the X direction

can be worked out by equations (2.03), (2.04), and (2.05). The two
motions can thus be treated quite independ-
ently of each other and can be recombined
later. Let x and y be the displacements.

$$y = u_Y t$$
$$x = u_X t + \tfrac{1}{2}at^2$$

or

$$y = (u \sin \theta)t$$
$$x = (u \cos \theta)t + \tfrac{1}{2}at^2$$

If we eliminate t, we get a relation between x
and y giving the equation of the path followed
by the body. This is

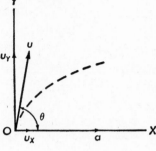

Fig. 2.12.

$$x = u \cos \theta \, \frac{y}{u \sin \theta} + \tfrac{1}{2}a \, \frac{y^2}{u^2 \sin^2 \theta} = y \cot \theta + y^2 \frac{a \, \text{cosec} \, \theta^2}{2u^2}$$

which is an equation in x to the first power and y to the second. It is
proved in analytical geometry that this is the equation of a parabola.

2.10 PROJECTILES

The ideas we have been developing in the last few paragraphs have
an interesting and mildly practical application in the problem of projectiles. A projectile is any body which is given an initial velocity and
then is subject *only* to air resistance and the acceleration of gravity.
Bombs, bullets, and baseballs are projectiles; birds and rockets are not,
according to this definition. The air resistance is the factor which makes
our analysis somewhat academic because we haven't yet seen how to
allow for its effect. Air resistance, in fact, turns out to be a very
difficult problem, too much so for this book. So we take the easy way
out and say "Let us neglect air resistance". The results we get are
thus not precise, but they give a good indication of how projectiles
move, particularly at low velocities.

Consider a projectile which is fired with an initial velocity **u** in a
direction making an angle θ with the horizontal. Resolve **u** into vertical
and horizontal components. The horizontal motion is thus a case of
constant speed $u \cos \theta$ with displacement $ut \cos \theta$. The vertical motion
has an initial velocity $u \sin \theta$ with acceleration $-g$, if height is measured
as positive upward. This type of motion has been discussed in section
2.06, particularly in Examples II and III. Figure 2.13 illustrates the

problem.   The maximum height above the starting point is marked in the diagram as h and can be found as follows:

Initial vertical velocity $= u \sin \theta$

Vertical velocity at time $t = u \sin \theta - gt$

Vertical velocity at point $A = 0$

hence   Time to rise to A $= t_1 = \dfrac{u \sin \theta}{g}$

Average vertical velocity $= \dfrac{u \sin \theta + 0}{2}$

$$h = \frac{u \sin \theta}{2} \frac{u \sin \theta}{g}$$

$$h = \frac{u^2 \sin^2 \theta}{2g} \qquad (2.06)$$

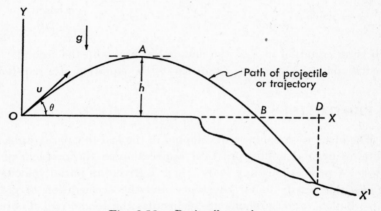

Fig. 2.13.   Projectile motion.

The horizontal distance traveled is called the range, R. If the projectile moves over a horizontal plane so that the end point of the flight is at the same level as the firing point, the time to fall from A to the ground is the same as the time to rise from O to A.   The projectile is in the air a total time $(2u \sin \theta)/g$ and during this time moves in the direction OX with constant speed.   Hence

$$OB = R = \frac{2u \sin \theta}{g} u \cos \theta$$

$$= 2 \frac{u^2}{g} \sin \theta \cos \theta$$

or using the trigonometrical identity $2 \sin \theta \cos \theta = \sin 2\theta$

$$R = \frac{u^2}{g} \sin 2\theta \qquad (2.07)$$

A word of warning to the student is in order here. Equations (2.06) and (2.07) are typical of most of the equations we shall derive in this book. They are useful for solving problems of a certain restricted type, that is, problems in which the conditions are exactly those on which the derivations are based. If the actual conditions are different, a blind application of the equations will give a completely wrong result. Suppose, for example, the actual profile of the ground were that shown by the solid line OX' rather than OX. Clearly the projectile would hit the ground at C, not B, and the horizontal range would be OD, not OB as given by equation (2.07). This illustrates the danger of the process of memorizing formulas, which is the approach to physics of far too many students. It also shows the necessity of *understanding* the derivation of equations. The student who has followed the logic used in obtaining (2.07) should see how to calculate OD; the student who has memorized (2.07) will merely wonder why his instructor marks his answer wrong when he tries to apply this equation to this (modified) problem.

Equations have another use. Equation (2.07) shows in simple form that R depends on three factors u, g, and θ, and shows how R changes as each of these is changed. If u and θ are constant, $R \propto 1/g$, but since g is virtually constant on the earth, this is of little interest except in speculations regarding other planets, where g is different. Evidently $R \propto u^2$ if θ is constant; double the initial speed of a bullet and it will go four times as far. Finally, if u is constant, $R \propto \sin 2\theta$, and since $\sin 2\theta$ has a maximum value of 1 for $2\theta = 90°$, i.e., $\theta = 45°$, we see that a projectile has a maximum range when it is fired at an angle of $45°$. This is not surprising but would be difficult to prove without the intermediate step of deriving (2.07).

We could now derive the equation of the trajectory as we did in section 2.09, but we know it must be a parabola and we shall not need the actual equation.

In dealing with real projectiles, air resistance cannot be neglected, so the height reached will be less than h of equation (2.06) and the range will be less than R of equation (2.07). This qualitative modification is easy enough to see but, as stated earlier, the quantitative solution is beyond the scope of this book.

2.11 VARIABLE ACCELERATION

All the work of this chapter is concerned with bodies which have constant or zero acceleration. Clearly, acceleration may vary with time, and the simple equations of section 2.06 will not then be valid.

Such cases are much more difficult than our work so far, and in fact we shall take up only one case of variable acceleration, the type known as simple harmonic motion, which is discussed in Chapter 8.

PROBLEMS

1. Small boys rarely move in straight lines for long. David's mother takes him to a playground and releases him. His subsequent movements (reasons not relevant to this problem, if indeed they are known even to him) can be summarized as follows: 40/030°, 20/090°, 16/120°, 8/270°, 10/235°, where the first number in each displacement is the distance covered in feet. Find graphically his distance and direction from his starting point.

2. A canoe is paddled at 4.00 mph straight across a river which is 0.500 miles wide and which is flowing at a speed of 3.00 mph. If the canoe is kept pointing at right angles to the river, how far will it be carried downstream and how long does it take to get across the river?

3. An aircraft carrier travels through the water at 20 mph. Its aircraft have a take-off and landing speed of 100 mph relative to the air. If the carrier is traveling straight into a wind of 25 mph, how fast do the aircraft take off and land relative to the flight deck? What would these speeds be if the carrier's velocity were reversed? Which arrangement would the pilots prefer?

4. The long dimensions of a certain football field lie east and west. On a passing play the quarterback runs due north at 20 ft sec^{-1} and while running throws the ball with a speed of 40 ft sec^{-1} in a direction due east. The wind is blowing from the southwest at 15 mph. Find graphically the speed and direction of the football relative to the field.

5. An airplane sets out to fly to a point due north and 600 miles distant. The speed of the plane is 275 mph, and the wind blows to the west at 20 mph. If the pilot maintains the nose of the plane in a northerly direction, by how many miles will he miss his destination? In what direction must the pilot point the plane in order to reach his destination?

6. A body starts from rest and is accelerated at 2.00 m sec^{-2}. Find the velocity and the distance traveled at the end of 20.0 sec.

7. A body has an initial velocity of 4.00 m sec^{-1} and is accelerated at 2.00 m sec^{-2}. Find the velocity and the distance traveled at the end of 20.0 sec.

8. A ball has an initial velocity of 3.00 m sec^{-1} and after moving a distance of 90.0 m has a velocity of 15.0 m sec^{-1}. Find the acceleration and the time taken to travel this distance.

9. A ball rolling along the ground with a velocity of 20.0 ft sec^{-1} is subject to a negative acceleration of 2.00 ft sec^{-2}. Find the distance it rolls before coming to rest and the time taken.

10. The driver of a car moving at 40.0 mph sees a stop sign and comes to a stop opposite the sign in 15.0 sec. Find how far away the stop sign was when first seen and the acceleration of the car.

11. The driver of a car moving at 40.0 mph sees a stop sign 50.0 ft away and comes to a stop opposite it. How long does it take and what is the car's acceleration?

12. An airplane must be moving with a velocity of 100 mph before it can take off. If its engines give it an acceleration of 4.00 ft sec^{-2}, find the minimum length of runway it requires and the time taken for a take-off.

13. An airplane traveling at a uniform speed approaches to within 5.00 miles of a landing strip, at which time the pilot reduces speed at 5.00 ft sec^{-2}. Landing speed is 100 mph. How long does the airplane take to touch down on the runway, and what was the speed of the airplane before the reduction in speed was applied?

14. An airplane starts at rest on the runway and accelerates at 4.00 ft sec^{-2} until its speed is 90.0 mph, at which point it takes off and then accelerates at 6.00 ft sec^{-2} until its speed is 375 mph. It then flies at this speed for 40.0 min, at which time it is 10.0 miles from a second runway. It then reduces speed at 6.00 ft sec^{-2} until it touches down on the runway, moving with a speed of 100 mph. It continues to slow down on the runway at 4.00 ft sec^{-2} until it comes to rest. Find the time taken for the trip and the distance covered.

15. A ball is thrown vertically into the air with a velocity of 30.0 m sec^{-1}. How high does it rise, and how long does it take to reach this height? Find the velocity of the ball on returning to the ground and the total time in the air.

16. A bullet is fired vertically up into the air with a velocity of 1000 m sec^{-1}. How long does it take to rise 500 m, and what is its velocity then?

17. A man stands on top of an 80.0-ft building and throws an object vertically upward with a velocity of 20.0 ft sec^{-1}. How long does it take to reach the ground at the foot of the building, and what is its velocity then?

18. A boy stands on a cliff overlooking a lake and throws a stone almost straight up into the air. If the cliff is 30.0 ft above the surface of the lake and if the stone strikes the surface with a velocity of 75.0 ft sec^{-1}, find the initial velocity of the stone and the total time of flight.

19. It is proposed to use rockets to obtain meteorological data on the upper atmosphere. A rocket is constructed capable of producing a net upward acceleration of $10g$ (320 ft sec^{-2}) for 10.0 sec if fired vertically. After this 10.0 sec the charge is spent and the rocket becomes an ordinary projectile. Neglecting air resistance and variation of g with height,
    (a) What height could the rocket reach?
    (b) What is the time of flight to maximum height?
    (c) What is the total time in the air?

20. A body is projected up a smooth plane, inclined at an angle of 45° to the horizontal, with a velocity of 25.0 m sec^{-1}.

    (a) How long will it take the body to return to its starting point?

    (b) How far up the plane did it go?

21. A runner is traveling at a steady speed of 15 mph. At the instant he passes a boy on a bicycle the boy starts from rest, accelerating at 11 ft sec^{-2}. How soon does the boy catch up to the runner, and how far have they both gone since the boy started?

22. A man is running along a road at a steady speed of 15 ft sec^{-1} and passes a boy standing beside a bicycle. After the runner has a head start of 50 ft the boy starts from rest and accelerates at 4.0 ft sec^{-2}. When and where does he catch up to the runner? If they both continue in the same manner, how far ahead will the bicycle rider be 1 sec after he passes the runner?

23. A baseball player throws a ball from the outfield to home plate, a distance of 330 ft. If he throws the ball at an angle of elevation of 45°, find the initial velocity of the ball and its maximum height.

24. A quarterback throws a pass to a player 60.0 ft away. If he throws the ball at an angle of 30° to the ground, with what velocity must the ball be thrown? Find the velocity if the angle is 60° and again for an angle of 45°.

25. A boy throws a stone with a velocity of 60.0 ft sec^{-1}. Find the maximum range of the stone.

26. A quarterback throws a pass at an angle of 45° to the horizontal to a player 45.0 ft away. Find the time taken for the pass.

27. A boy stands on the ground 20.0 m from a building and throws a snowball into a window 15.0 m above the ground so that the ball enters the window horizontally. Find the initial velocity of the ball and the angle of projection.

28. Two men stand on a cliff 120 ft high overlooking a lake. They each throw a stone horizontally, one with a velocity of 75.0 ft sec^{-1} and the other with a velocity of 60.0 ft sec^{-1}. Find how much farther one goes than the other.

29. A shell is fired at an angle of 30° with a velocity of 2000 ft sec^{-1}. Find the height it has reached in 5 sec, the maximum height it reaches, and the velocity it has acquired at its maximum height.

30. A shell is fired from a gun with a velocity of 1200 ft sec^{-1} at an angle of 30° to the horizontal. Find the maximum height and the range of the shell on a horizontal plane passing through the gun.

31. A shell is fired with an initial speed of 1000 ft sec^{-1} at a target 24,000 ft away and at the same height as the gun. Find (a) the possible angles of elevation to hit the target; (b) the shorter time of flight of the projectile.

32. A toboggan moves down a toboggan slide 100 ft long with an acceleration just one-fourth that of free fall. It strikes the frozen surface of a lake and

travels over the ice for 10 sec before it comes to rest. Assuming constant negative acceleration, how far does the toboggan slide on the ice?

33. The top of a hill is 1100 ft above a level plain. What will be the horizontal range of a shell fired at an angle of elevation of 30° with a muzzle velocity of 800 ft sec^{-1} from a gun on top of the hill?

34. The last part of the runway on a ski jump is horizontal and the hill below slopes down at 60° below the horizontal. If a jumper lands 166.3 ($= 288/\sqrt{3}$) ft from the take-off, what was his initial velocity?

35. An aircraft is to patrol along a line running due east from its base. Its speed through the air is 300 mph, and there is a wind of 60 mph from the west. If the safe flying time of the aircraft is 4.00 hr, how far may it go and return to its base? After what time should it turn around?

36. A steamer takes 4.5 hr to travel a distance of 63 miles up a river and 3.5 hr to return. Assuming the speed of the current in the river to be constant, find the speed of the steamer relative to the water and the speed of the current.

37. A ship is steaming due east at 24 knots. (One knot is a speed of 1 nautical mile per hour and 1 nautical mile = 6080 ft.) There is a wind of 12 knots blowing from the north. In what direction will the free end of a flag (flying from the bow) point?

38. A ship is steaming due west at 10 knots, and the free end of a pennant on the masthead points $22\frac{1}{2}$ degrees south of east. The ship alters direction (but not speed) to due south, and the pennant now points $22\frac{1}{2}$ degrees north of east. From what direction does the wind blow and at what speed?

39. A boy stands on a hillside sloping down at an angle of 30.0° below the horizontal. He throws a stone with a speed u at an angle of elevation of 30.0° above the horizontal. Prove that the maximum horizontal distance the stone can travel before striking the hillside is $\sqrt{3}\, u^2/g$.

40. Prove the old nautical rule "constant bearing means collision". That is, if two ships are moving along intersecting lines toward each other and the direction of one ship from the other remains unchanging, they will collide.

3

Force

3.01 FORCE AS A PUSH OR PULL

Most of the terms used in mechanics are used in ordinary speech, frequently with a somewhat different meaning from the scientific one. In science the attempt is made to give a single, precise definition for each term used, and so when the term is a common word, it is especially important to understand the scientific use of it. The word force is a good example. The phrases "a forceful speaker", "the force of experience", and "the force of public opinion", are perfectly good English, but in none of them does "force" have the meaning used in physics.

Definition. We define **force** as that which causes or attempts to cause a change in the state of motion of a body. Force is a vector quantity.

The most familiar forces are those pushes and pulls exerted by the human body or a machine. They may or may not produce a change of motion, depending on what other forces are present—if we kick a football, it moves, but if we push against a building wall, it does not. In either case we exert a force. Forces like these, in which there is physical contact between the body exerting the force and the body on which the force acts, are, or seem at first to be, quite straightforward. Another very common force is **weight,** the pull of the earth on a body which causes it to fall if it is free to move. In this case there may be no contact between the two bodies, and we say this force is a case of "action at a distance". Other types of forces which act at a distance will arise in the study of electricity and magnetism, and these forces will include both forces pulling two bodies together (attraction) and forces pushing them apart (repulsion). Fortunately, the treatment of such forces in mechanics can almost always be the same as that for "contact" forces, so that the distinction does not have to be stressed here.

3.02 INERTIA. FIRST LAW OF MOTION

The motion of most bodies is quite complicated, being due to several forces acting at the same time. The essence of scientific method in physics is to try to analyze the various causes of a phenomenon and separate them so that a single cause produces a single effect which can be related numerically (or algebraically) to the cause responsible for it. In the case of motion, we should start with a single body acted on by a single force and compare this with the case of the same body with no force acting on it. Since we must carry out our experiment on the earth where every body is pulled downward by the earth, i.e., has weight, we cannot achieve this simplicity but must deduce what would probably happen from the most simple practical case.

Consider a small body of mass m moving on a slope. Figure 3.01 illustrates the forces acting on it.

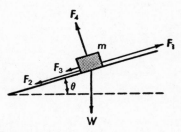

Fig. 3.01. Forces acting on a body.

F_1 is an applied force.
F_2 is a force due to the roughness of the slope.
F_3 is a force due to air resistance.
F_4 is a push on the body by the slope.
W is the weight of the body.

It was mentioned in section 2.05 that the effect of air resistance increases with velocity. Conversely, F_3 becomes smaller and smaller as the velocity decreases, being zero for a stationary body. Mathematically this is written

$$F_3 \to 0 \text{ as } v \to 0 \qquad \text{or} \qquad \lim_{v \to 0} F_3 = 0$$

which in words is "F_3 tends to zero as v tends to zero, or the limit of F_3 as v tends to zero is zero". For very low velocities we shall ignore F_3, with negligible errors in our results, but we must expect the error to increase with velocity. The force F_2 is called friction and will be discussed fully in Chapter 6. The smoother the surfaces of the body and the slope, the smaller F_2 will be, but it will never vanish for any real surfaces. Let us, however, introduce an idealization called a *smooth surface* for which F_2 is by definition zero. Next, experience tells us that the weight W seems to have least effect when the surface is horizontal, so we make $\theta = 0°$. Thus our system reduces in principle to Figure 3.02, and the only effect of the surface on the body is the force F_4. Now if the surface were not there, the body would fall, so that F_4 counteracts

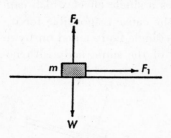

W. It is plausible to assume that they are equal and opposite and have no effect on the motion of the body over the level surface, that is, in a plane at right angles to their directions. Ignoring the F_4, W combina-

Fig. 3.02. Forces acting on a body on a smooth, level surface.

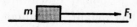

Fig. 3.03. Single force on a body.

tion, we now consider Figure 3.03, which is the simple system we wanted to study first. Since this system cannot be set up in practice, we must attempt to generalize from the best approximations available, which are probably a cart moving over a level floor or a body sliding on smooth ice. (We assume that the cart wheels are mounted on the axles with well-lubricated ball-bearing races.)

Case 1: $F_1 = 0$. There are two possibilities. When we first look at the object m it is at rest. We observe that it remains at rest indefinitely. If it is moving in some direction, we see that it keeps on moving in that direction but with very gradually decreasing speed. Galileo was the first to assume that this decrease must be due to friction and that if a perfectly smooth surface could be found (as we have assumed above), the object would continue to move at constant speed.

Case 2: $F_1 = \text{constant} \neq 0$. When a force is exerted on the object m, which is initially at rest, it starts to move in the direction of the force and accelerates. Careful measurement shows that the acceleration is approximately constant and presumably would be exactly so if the frictional effects were completely absent. If m has an initial velocity, the experiment is harder to perform, but the result is the same—a constant acceleration in the direction of the force, if friction is negligible.

The results of similar experiments were studied by Galileo and Sir Isaac Newton (1642) and stated by the latter as the three laws of motion which are the basis of mechanics.

Newton's First Law of Motion. *Every body remains in a state of rest or of uniform motion in a straight line unless it is compelled to change that state by an applied force.*

This is sometimes called the law of inertia, inertia being that property of matter of keeping on doing whatever it is doing unless forced to change. In section 1.04 the property of matter called mass was introduced without a definition being attempted. Experimentally, the greater the mass the greater the inertia and vice versa, and no experiment is known which distinguishes between these two properties of matter. Thus inertia is another name for mass, but by custom is not used in a numerical context. Note that we have still failed to define mass (or inertia). Force is that which gives an acceleration to mass and this serves to define force, but it is poor logic then to say that mass is that which accelerates when acted upon by force. It seems that we must accept mass as an intuitive concept.

It is important to realize that the above argument does not constitute a proof of the First Law of Motion, it merely attempts to make it plausible. In the next few sections we shall consider the other two laws in the same way and try to show that they are reasonable extensions of experiment. The final test of their validity must be the success or failure of the science of mechanics which rests on them.

3.03 NEWTON'S SECOND LAW OF MOTION

Returning to Figure 3.03, let us consider the effect of changing the size of F_1 or m. Without worrying at the moment about units of force or details of the mechanisms, we shall assume we have a spring balance to compare forces and some kind of beam balance to compare masses. (A spring balance is based on the assumption that the stretch of a spring is proportional to the force applied; a beam balance on the fact that if a uniform rod is pivoted at its center, unequal masses attached to its ends will cause it to move, equal masses will leave it at rest.) The diagram is redrawn as Figure 3.04 with m as the total mass of the cart and F_1 the applied force as measured on the spring balance.

Suppose in each test the force F_1 is applied for a definite time, say 5 sec, and the increase in velocity in that time is measured. Qualitative tests show immediately that if the force is about the same in several tests, the smaller the mass the greater the increase in velocity, while if the mass is constant, the greater the force the greater the increase in velocity. Quantitative tests can be done by making allowance for the small frictional forces. If for each mass the force F_1 is increased slowly from zero, F_1 will have a small value, say F_r, just before the cart starts to move. This can be taken to be the force necessary to counteract the

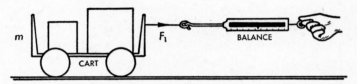

Fig. 3.04. Experiment to demonstrate Second Law of Motion.

friction, and if it is subtracted from other values of F_1 for the given m, the results can be stated algebraically as

$$m(v - u) \propto (F_1 - F_r)$$

where u and v are initial and final velocities. Note again that this result applies when the time to gain velocity from u to v is fixed. The product of mass times velocity occurs so frequently in mechanics that it is given a special name, **momentum.**

Definition. *The momentum of a body is the product of its mass times its velocity. Momentum is a vector quantity having the same direction as the velocity.*

It remains to test the effect of applying the same force for different lengths of time. Suppose the velocity is u at time t_1. The force is then applied and by time t_2 the velocity has increased to v. It is found that

$$(F_1 - F_r)(t_2 - t_1) \propto (mv - mu)$$

or since $F_1 - F_r = F$ is the net force available to produce motion,

$$F \propto \frac{mv - mu}{t_2 - t_1}$$

$$F = k\frac{mv - mu}{t_2 - t_1} \tag{3.01}$$

where k is a constant whose size depends on the units in which the various quantities are measured. This equation is one form of Newton's Second Law.

Newton's Second Law of Motion. *Rate of change of momentum is proportional to the applied force and takes place in the direction of that force.*

It is convenient to use the symbol Δx to represent the change in x. Thus $\Delta(mv)$ represents the change in momentum. Equation (3.01) can be written in this notation as

$$F = k \frac{\Delta(mv)}{\Delta t} \tag{3.02}$$

In most problems m is a constant and hence is a common factor of both initial and final momenta. In such problems

$$F = km \frac{\Delta v}{\Delta t} = kma \tag{3.03}$$

since $\Delta v/\Delta t$ is the change in velocity per unit time, or acceleration. (Note that v is rate of change of displacement or $\Delta s/\Delta t$, a is rate of change of velocity or $\Delta v/\Delta t$.) Equation (3.03) is the form in which the Second Law is usually applied, but experience has shown that (3.02) is more fundamental and must be used if the mass is variable, as it is, for example, in problems dealing with rockets or aircraft which burn up part of their total mass as fuel.

3.04 UNITS OF FORCE

The equation $F = kma$ is used to define the units in which force is measured. The process used here to assign units is repeated over and over again in physics and should be studied closely. Units of mass and acceleration have already been discussed. There are left therefore two arbitrary quantities in the equation, k and F. We may pick any numerical value and units we like for k, but once they are chosen the value of F is automatically assigned if the equation is to be valid; that is, picking k determines the number for F and the unit in which F is to be measured. The quantity k may be chosen to be dimensionless, i.e., as a pure number having no units. This is the simplest choice and is the one used in the so-called absolute systems which are based on the fundamental units of mass, length, and time.

Example I. A certain force acting on a mass of 40.0 kgm produces an acceleration of 6.60 m sec^{-2}. How big is the force? Let us take $k = 1$. Then

$$F = 1 \times 40.0 \text{ kgm} \times 6.60 \text{ m sec}^{-2}$$
$$= 264 \text{ kgm m sec}^{-2} = 264 \text{ newtons}$$

where the name of the unit of force, the newton, is a shorter equivalent to the kilogram-meter per second per second.

An alternative is to choose the unit of force arbitrarily which automatically determines the numerical value and units of k. Thus, a convenient unit of force is the pull of the earth on a one-pound mass. This unit is called the *pound-weight (lb-wt)*. Suppose the only force acting on a one-pound mass is its own weight. Then we know it will fall with the acceleration of gravity g. Substituting in the equation $F = kma$, we have

$$1 \text{ lb-wt} = k \times 1 \text{ lb} \times g \text{ ft sec}^{-2}$$
$$k = \frac{1}{g} \frac{\text{lb-wt}}{\text{lb}} \frac{\text{sec}^2}{\text{ft}}$$

Since the numerical value of g varies slightly over the surface of the earth, as discussed in 2.05, the unit of force called the pound-weight is not the same at all places, although the variation is quite small.

There are a number of different units of force in use which we shall now summarize.

(1) METRIC ABSOLUTE

An absolute unit is one derived from the fundamental units of mass, length, and time. All absolute units of force are defined from the equation

$$F = ma \tag{3.04}$$

obtained by choosing $k = 1$. In the mks system, unit force is that which acting on one kilogram produces an acceleration of one meter per second per second. As stated above, it is called a *newton*. We shall use the abbreviation N for this unit.

A newton is that force which acting on one kilogram of mass produces an acceleration of one meter per second per second.

$$F \text{ (N)} = m \text{ (kgm)} \times a \text{ (m sec}^{-2}) \tag{3.04a}$$

In the cgs system the unit of force is called the *dyne*, and

$$F \text{ (dynes)} = m \text{ (gm)} \times a \text{ (cm sec}^{-2})$$

Since $1 \text{ kgm} = 10^3 \text{ gm}$ and $1 \text{ m} = 10^2 \text{ cm}$
$$1 \text{ newton} = 10^5 \text{ dynes}$$

Notice that, unlike the pound-weight, the size of the newton (or the dyne) is independent of the location on the earth. This is the reason for the name "absolute".

(2) BRITISH GRAVITATIONAL (ENGINEERING)

Engineering practice in the United States, Canada, and the United Kingdom is to use British or fps units. Since the commonest forces in engineering are the weights of the objects in question, gravitational units are used very extensively. The pound-weight is the basic unit of force, the ton-weight (ton-wt) being used as a multiple of this for large forces. (In this book a "ton" is always the so-called short ton of 2000 lb.) Three things should be noted about gravitational units:

(a) Although widely used because of the importance of weight, which acts downward, the pound-weight is a unit of force which may be and is used to measure the size of any force acting in any direction.

(b) The variation in the size of the pound-weight from point to point on the earth's surface is almost never of importance in engineering but may be significant in scientific work. For this reason absolute units are always used in science.

(c) The word "weight" is almost always dropped from the name of the gravitational units in practice, and one speaks of a force of 40 lb. Some engineers go a step farther than this and *define* the pound as a unit of force and then introduce a derived unit of mass called the *slug* so that equation (3.04) may be used directly if force is measured in pounds, mass in slugs, and acceleration in feet per second per second.

A force of 1 lb-wt (or 1 lb) acting on a mass of 1 lb produces an acceleration of g ft sec^{-2}. If the force is kept the same, the mass-acceleration product is the same, thus it follows that a force of 1 lb acting on a mass of g lb produces an acceleration of 1 ft sec^{-2}, and

$$1 \text{ slug} = g \text{ pounds}$$

The basic equation can therefore be written in two ways with gravitational units:

$$F \text{ (lb-wt)} = \frac{m \text{ (lb)} \times a \text{ (ft sec}^{-2})}{g} \tag{3.04b}$$

or
$$F \text{ (lb)} = m \text{ (slugs)} \times a \text{ (ft sec}^{-2}) \tag{3.04c}$$

In this equation k has not been shown explicitly because its numerical value is unity, but it does have units; namely,

$$k = 1 \frac{\text{lb}}{\text{slug}} \frac{\text{sec}^2}{\text{ft}}$$

(3) BRITISH ABSOLUTE

Using mass in pounds and acceleration in feet per second per second, if we set k in $F = kma$ equal to unity, we have defined a unit of force called the *poundal*, and

$$F \text{ (poundals)} = m \text{ (lb)} \times a \text{ (ft sec}^{-2})$$

The poundal is the absolute unit of force in the fps system, and a little thought will show that

$$1 \text{ lb-wt} = g \text{ poundals} = 32.0 \text{ poundals}$$

The poundal is as valid a unit as the newton or the dyne and has some advantages over the pound-weight, but for some reason it is not as widely used in engineering as the gravitational units.

(4) METRIC GRAVITATIONAL

Just as in the fps system, we can introduce forces of 1 gm-wt or 1 kgm-wt and use them as gravitational units, the conversion factor from gravitational to absolute units again being g.

$$1 \text{ gm-wt} = g \text{ dynes} = 980 \text{ dynes}$$
$$1 \text{ kgm-wt} = g \text{ newtons} = 9.80 \text{ N}$$

The whole question of force units is one which frequently presents a problem to students. There is a real difficulty here which will disappear only after careful study and the solution of many numerical problems. The root of the difficulty is the confusion of mass and weight, which are used synonymously in everyday life and which are numerically equal in many systems of units but which are dimensionally quite different. Mass is a scalar property of a body completely independent of its position in space, while weight is a force and hence a vector, and its value depends not only on the mass of the body but *also* on where the body is in space. It is an experimental fact that weight is always proportional to mass, but the proportionality constant contains the acceleration of gravity, implicitly if not explicitly and may thus vary from point to point in space. Weight has been defined as the pull of the *earth* on a body, but this definition can be extended to speak of the weight of a body on the planet Mars, say, meaning in this case the pull of Mars on the body.

For purposes of comparison let us use the average value of the weight of one pound on the surface of the earth as a unit. Then in terms of this unit a body of mass 10 lb has a weight of about 10 lb-wt on the earth, but would have a mass of 10 lb and a weight of about 4 lb-wt if somehow transported to the surface of Mars.

Units are arbitrary, man-made things, and choice of units cannot alter the physics of a problem. The force needed to produce a certain acceleration in a certain body must be the same whether measured in newtons, kilograms-weight, or pounds-weight. If all or most of the data are given in mks units, it will increase the work of solution of a problem, however, to find the result in fps units. The various systems of force units are listed again in Table 3.01 in their approximate order of importance.

TABLE 3.01   Force Units.

System	Force Unit	k	Second-Law Equation
mks abs.	Newton (N)	1	$F \text{ (N)} = m \text{ (kgm)} \times a \text{ } (m \text{ sec}^{-2})$
ENG fps grav.	Pound (lb)	1	$F \text{ (lb)} = m \text{ (slugs)} \times a \text{ (ft sec}^{-2})$
ENG fps grav.	Pound-weight (lb-wt)	g^{-1}	$F \text{ (lb-wt)} = \frac{1}{g} m \text{ (lb)} \times a \text{ (ft sec}^{-2})$
ENG fps abs.	Poundal	1	$F \text{ (poundals)} = m \text{ (lb)} \times a \text{ (ft sec}^{-2})$
mks grav.	Kilogram-weight (kgm-wt)	g^{-1}	$F \text{ (kgm-wt)} = \frac{1}{g} m \text{ (kgm)} \times a \text{ } (m \text{ sec}^{-2})$
cgs abs.	Dyne	1	$F \text{ (dynes)} = m \text{ (gm)} \times a \text{ (cm sec}^{-2})$
cgs grav.	Gram-weight (gm-wt)	g^{-1}	$F \text{ (gm-wt)} = \frac{1}{g} m \text{ (gm)} \times a \text{ (cm sec}^{-2})$

Conversion Factors.   Based on
$$g = 9.80 \text{ m sec}^{-2} = 980 \text{ cm sec}^{-2}$$
$$= 32.0 \text{ ft sec}^{-2}$$
$$1 \text{ N} = 10^5 \text{ dyne} = 0.102 \text{ kgm-wt} = 102 \text{ gm-wt}$$
$$1 \text{ lb-wt} = 32.0 \text{ poundals}$$
$$1 \text{ N} = 0.225 \text{ lb-wt}$$
$$1 \text{ slug} = 32.0 \text{ lb}$$

Example II.   Consider a body of mass m resting on a smooth, level surface with a force F acting parallel to the surface. This is illustrated at the left of Figure 3.05. The greatest single aid to clear thinking in mechanics is the *free body diagram*, that is, a diagram in which the body whose motion we are investigating is considered by itself, and all the reactions of its surroundings on it are represented by the forces they exert on the body. Note that the forces exerted by the body on its surroundings are **not** shown in such a diagram. The free body diagram of this problem is drawn at the right of Figure 3.05.

The weight of the body is **W**. In absolute units **W** = **mg**, for if it were the only force, it would produce an acceleration of g downward, and force equals mass times acceleration in absolute units. The presence

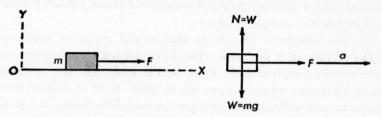

Fig. 3.05. Free body diagram of a mass on a smooth, level surface.

of other forces does not alter the weight, which is the force exerted by the earth on the body. The force exerted by the surface on the body is **N**. Since experience tells us that in this case there is no acceleration in the Y direction, there can be no net force in that direction.

$$\mathbf{N} = -\mathbf{W}, \qquad N = W = mg$$

where N is the magnitude of **N**. In the X direction the only force is F. Hence

$$F = ma$$

If F = 40.0 newtons and m = 8.00 kgm, then

$$a = \frac{40.0}{8.00} = 5.00 \text{ m sec}^{-2}$$

in the direction shown. If gravitational units are used,

$$F = 9.00 \text{ lb-wt}, \, m = 17.6 \text{ lb} = 0.550 \text{ slug}$$

By (3.04b), $F = \dfrac{1}{g} ma$

$$9.00 \text{ lb-wt} = \frac{1}{32.0} \frac{\text{lb-wt sec}^2}{\text{lb ft}} \times 17.6 \text{ lb} \times a$$

$$a = \frac{9.00 \times 32.0}{17.6} \text{ ft sec}^{-2}$$

$$= 16.4 \text{ ft sec}^{-2}$$

Alternatively, by (3.04c),

$$F = ma$$

$$9.00 \text{ lb} = 0.550 \text{ slug} \times a \times 1 \frac{\text{lb sec}^2}{\text{slug ft}}$$

$$a = \frac{9.00}{0.550} \text{ ft sec}^{-2}$$

$$= 16.4 \text{ ft sec}^{-2}$$

Since   16.4 ft sec^{-2} = 16.4 ft sec^{-2} × 0.3048 m ft^{-1} = 5.00 m sec^{-2}

the result for the acceleration is the same in both systems of units, as it must be.

3.05 NEWTON'S THIRD LAW OF MOTION

In the last three sections we have been considering the effect of a force, or forces, applied to a single body, and for this purpose the first two laws of motion are entirely adequate.   Actually, however, force arises only when *two* bodies are interacting (either because they are in contact or through action at a distance) and we must now consider the effect or reaction of the body in question on the agency producing the force.   In other words, we must study both aspects of the interaction. Newton clarified the ideas of Galileo and others in stating the first two laws of motion, but the third law was an original contribution of his own.

Newton's Third Law of Motion.   *When two bodies interact, the force exerted by body B on body A is exactly equal in size and opposite in direction to the force exerted by A on B, and the two forces must act for exactly the same interval of time.*

In Figure 3.05 the body presses down on the surface with a force equal to its weight.   The law says that the surface must push up on the body with an equal force.   Figure 3.06(a) illustrates a slightly more compli-

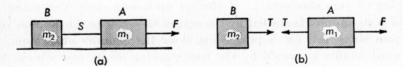

Fig. 3.06.

cated case, with two bodies A and B connected by a string S and both resting on a smooth table top.   If a force F is exerted on A, as shown, this body will start to move to the right, pulling the string S and so exerting a force T on the body B.   The law asserts that in consequence B must exert a force T on A in the opposite direction.   Free body diagrams are shown in (b) with the horizontal forces indicated but not the vertical since there will be no motion in the latter direction.   Note that nothing in the third law asserts that the forces T and F on A will be equal.   The equal and opposite pairs of forces always act on *different* bodies.   In fact, F must be greater than T since *any* force F will cause the system to move to the right if the table is perfectly smooth.   The two bodies must have the same acceleration since they are tied together by the string, and applying the second law to each of them, we have

$$F - T = m_1 a \tag{3.05}$$
$$T = m_2 a \tag{3.06}$$

Adding these equations gives

$$F = (m_1 + m_2)a \tag{3.07}$$

which is just the equation obtained by applying the second law to the system $A + B$ treated as one body.

No direct, experimental proof of the third law is known, but any other assumption about the forces involved in an interaction leads to contradictions with the other two laws. If in equations (3.05) and (3.06), for example, the interaction forces were T_1 and T_2 (with $T_1 \neq T_2$), then (3.07) would not follow from them, but this must be the correct equation for the whole system since F is the only external force acting horizontally. Another argument for this law is based on gravitational pull. Consider a mountain and the rest of the earth. The earth attracts the mountain and the mountain attracts the rest of the earth with an equal and opposite force; otherwise there would be a net force acting on the combination (i.e., the whole earth) resulting in a steady acceleration with effects which would ultimately be observable.

The implications of this law are a little startling. An object moves because of the force acting *on* it, not because of the force exerted *by* it— which is the physics of the old saying, "You can't raise yourself by pulling on your shoelaces". If you get up from a chair, the motion of your body upward is started by the seat of the chair pushing up on you. If your shiny new car is proceeding along the highway at 60 mph, its forward motion is caused by the road pushing on its rear wheels, not (directly) by the 200-horsepower motor under the hood. This seems at first a topsy-turvy way of looking at motion, but it is the only way which gives consistently correct results. Its validity may be more apparent if we think of that same car trying to start on wet ice. The motor is just as powerful, the wheels can turn just as fast, but because the wet ice can't push very hard on the wheels in the forward direction, the acceleration of the car is small or even zero.

This completes the set of Newton's Laws of Motion. It is important to realize that they do form a set and that all the laws are needed to understand any physical interaction. Their use is best studied by working out some simple examples, which will be done in the next section. In order to make the examples simpler than most practical problems that arise, a number of idealizations are introduced. Thus the principles of mechanics will be clear before too many complications are added. It may be worth listing a few of these idealizations which are frequently used.

Point Masses. We assume that the moving bodies are very small, in fact, theoretically, geometrical points with the added property of mass. This avoids the consideration of rotation. A body of negligible size is often called a mass-point.

Smooth Surfaces. If a body A is in contact with a surface S, the surface will exert a force **R** on A. The direction of **R** will not in general be perpendicular to S. Since **R** is a vector, it can be resolved into components perpendicular to S and parallel to S. The former is called the normal force **N** and the latter the frictional force **F**. The rougher the surface the larger **F** will be relative to **N**. Friction is a rather complicated force which will be discussed in detail in Chapter 6, but for the present it is simpler to deal with imaginary, perfectly smooth surfaces for which **R** is always normal to S, i.e., $\mathbf{R} = \mathbf{N}$, $\mathbf{F} = 0$.

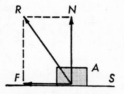

Fig. 3.07. Reaction force.

Light, Inextensible Strings. No string, rope, cable, or chain has zero mass, and no body exists which will not stretch, at least minutely, if two ends of it are pulled. However, it is a simplification and frequently an entirely satisfactory approximation to imagine that we can connect two bodies by such an ideal string which is infinitely strong but has zero mass. It is also assumed to be perfectly flexible.

Light Rods. A string can exert only pull or *tension*. If we want to transmit a push or thrust, we postulate a light (zero mass) rod which is infinitely strong and rigid. If we pull with a string or a rod, it is said to be under *tension*. If we push with a rod, it is said to be under *compression*.

Light, Frictionless Pulleys. Our ideal pulley is a wheel which has no mass and cannot exert any force along the length of a string passing over it.

All these various simplifications will be removed in due course, but to do so will require the study of rotational motion, friction, and elasticity. "Simple" mechanics presents enough difficulties at the start without these added complications. As mentioned earlier, air resistance will always be ignored in this book.

3.06 WORKED EXAMPLES

EXAMPLE I

In Figure 3.06, $m_1 = 12.0$ kgm, $m_2 = 8.0$ kgm, and $F = 40.0$ N. Find the acceleration and the tension in the string.

By (3.05), $40.0 - T = 12.0a$
By (3.06), $T = 8.0a$

There are thus two simultaneous equations and two unknowns. Adding, we have

$$40.0 \text{ N} = 20.0 \text{ kgm} \times a$$

or since $1 \text{N} = 1 \text{ kgm m sec}^{-2}$

$$40.0 \, \frac{\text{kgm m}}{\text{sec}^2} = 20.0 \text{ kgm} \times a$$

$$a = 2.00 \text{ m sec}^{-2}$$

To find T, we may substitute this value of a in either equation; the second is chosen as slightly simpler.

$$T = 8.0 \times 2.00$$
$$= 16.0 \text{ N}$$

EXAMPLE II

Atwood's Machine. Because of the numerical size of g, freely falling bodies rapidly acquire high velocities, and it is difficult to time their

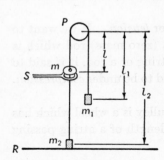

Fig. 3.08. Atwood's machine.

motions accurately. A device called Atwood's machine uses two masses hanging at the ends of a cord passing over a pulley to study a system with a smaller acceleration. Figure 3.08 illustrates one arrangement. A light, frictionless pulley is located at P, and m_1 and m_2 are masses suspended by a light, inextensible cord passing over P. At S is a ring stand through which m_2 can pass but, if desired, a disk of mass m can be placed on S. If the cord is passed through the hole in the disk, when m_2 rises through S it lifts m off the stand. Mass m_2

rests originally on the surface R. For accurate work a simple electrical timing system can be connected to S and R. The initial distances of the centers of m, m_1, and m_2 below the pulley are shown as l, l_1, and l_2. Figure 3.09 shows the free body diagrams of the forces on m_1 and m_2 at any time after m_2 has risen off R. It is assumed that $m_1 > m_2$.

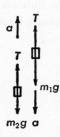

The effect of the cord is to exert an upward pull on each of the two masses. This is the force T, which is the same on each of them because the string is of zero mass and the pulley can exert no force along the length of the string. The acceleration of each mass is a because the string cannot stretch, so if m_1 goes down 10 cm, m_2 goes up 10 cm, and their velocities and accelerations must be the same in magnitude but opposite in direction. Let us find the tension T and acceleration a. Applying the second law to each mass in turn, and counting a force positive if it is in the direction of the acceleration, we have

Fig. 3.09. Free body diagrams.

$$T - m_2g = m_2a$$
$$m_1g - T = m_1a$$

If m_1 and m_2 are known, this gives two equations for two unknowns. They could be solved to give explicit, algebraic relations for T and a, but the important thing here is the method, not two "formulas" which someone might be tempted to memorize. If $m_1 = 0.600$ kgm and $m_2 = 0.400$ kgm,

$$T - 0.400g = 0.400a$$

and
$$0.600g - T = 0.600a$$

Adding gives
$$0.200g = 1.000a$$

whence
$$a = 0.200g = \frac{g}{5.00} = \frac{9.80}{5.00}$$
$$= 1.96 \text{ m sec}^{-2}$$

Then
$$T = 0.400g + 0.400a = 0.400\left(g + \frac{g}{5}\right)$$
$$= 0.400(1 + \tfrac{1}{5})g$$
$$= 0.480 \times 9.80$$
$$= 4.70 \text{ N} = 0.480 \text{ kgm-wt}$$

The disk of mass m has not been used here but will appear in problems at the end of the chapter.

EXAMPLE III

In Figure 3.10(a) a body of mass m rests on a smooth plane S inclined at an angle θ to the horizontal H. A horizontal force F acts as shown. Figure 3.10(b) is the free body diagram showing the three forces acting on m. The forces act at various angles to each other, so resolution of forces is indicated. The only possible direction of motion is up or down the plane, so we resolve all forces into components parallel or perpendicular to

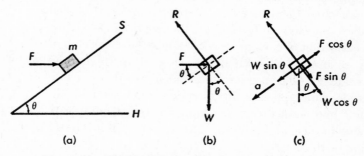

(a)   (b)   (c)

Fig. 3.10.   Inclined plane and free body diagrams.

S: R is already perpendicular; F makes an angle θ with S and thus has a parallel component $F \cos \theta$ and a perpendicular component $F \sin \theta$; W makes an angle θ with the *normal* to S and thus has a component $W \cos \theta$ perpendicular to S and a component $W \sin \theta$ parallel. These components are shown in (c) where, for convenience, they are all drawn away from the body.

The direction of the acceleration depends on which of $F \cos \theta$ or $W \sin \theta$ is the larger. Assuming the latter, as shown in (c), we can now write down the equations of motion:

$$R - F \sin \theta - W \cos \theta = 0$$

since there is no acceleration in this direction; and

$$W \sin \theta - F \cos \theta = ma$$

Numerically, let $m = 32.0 \text{ lb} = 1.00 \text{ slug}$
$$\theta = 36°52', \sin \theta = 0.600, \cos \theta = 0.800$$
$$W = 32.0 \text{ lb}$$
$$F = 20.0 \text{ lb}$$

Then by substitution,

$$R - 20.0 \times 0.600 - 32.0 \times 0.800 = 0$$
$$32.0 \times 0.600 - 20.0 \times 0.800 = 1.00a$$
$$a = 2.20 \text{ ft sec}^{-2}, \qquad R = 37.6 \text{ lb}$$

EXAMPLE IV

In Figure 3.11(a), a mass m_1 slides on a smooth inclined plane, being connected by a string passing over a pulley P with a second mass m_2 which hangs vertically downward. Figure 3.11(b) is the free body diagram for m_1 and (c) that for m_2. The first matter to decide is the direction of

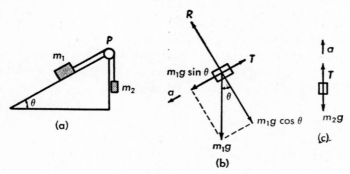

Fig. 3.11. Inclined plane problem.

motion. This depends on the relative size of $m_1g \sin \theta$ and m_2g. The former is taken here as the larger. Then

$$R = m_1g \cos \theta$$
$$T - m_2g = m_2a$$
$$m_1g \sin \theta - T = m_1a$$

Numerically, if $m_1 = 2.40$ kgm
$m_2 = 0.800$ kgm

$$\theta = 30.0°, \sin \theta = \tfrac{1}{2}, \cos \theta = \frac{\sqrt{3}}{2} = 0.866$$

$$R = 2.40 \times 9.80 \times 0.866 = 20.4 \text{ N}$$
$$T - 0.800 \times g = 0.800a$$
$$2.40g \times 0.500 - T = 2.40a$$

Adding the last two equations, we obtain,

$$(1.20 - 0.80)g = 3.20a$$

$$a = \frac{g}{8.00} = \frac{9.80}{8.00} = 1.22 \text{ m sec}^{-2}$$

Substituting this value of a in either equation gives

$$T = 8.82 \text{ N}$$

3.07 IMPULSE.   CONSERVATION OF MOMENTUM

Many of the forces of common occurrence act for a very short time and vary greatly in size during that time.   Examples are the forces involved in driving a nail, striking a golf ball, or catching a baseball.   It is often convenient to use the product of force and time to find the effect of such a brief force, and this product is called **impulse.**   The unit of impulse is a unit of force times a unit of time (e.g., a newton-second) and no special, shorter names are used for impulse units.

We use a bar over a symbol to represent its average value over a time interval t.   Let a force F act on a mass m producing an acceleration a.   Then F and a are both variables.   At any time

$$F = ma$$

and hence

$$\bar{F} = \overline{ma} = m\bar{a}$$

if the mass remains constant.   The average acceleration $\bar{a}$ is

$$\bar{a} = \frac{v - u}{t}$$

where u and v are the velocities before and after the impulse.   Then

$$\text{Impulse} = \bar{F}t = m\bar{a}t = m\,\frac{v - u}{t}\,t = mv - mu$$

Since mu is the initial momentum,

$$\text{Impulse} = \text{change of momentum} \tag{3.08}$$

Consider two bodies sliding over a smooth, level surface and colliding. Since the surface has no effect other than to counteract the weight of the two bodies, this is a very simple system in which any changes in motion are due to the interactions of the two bodies, which we can call A and B. Bodies A and B are said to form an isolated system.   When they collide A exerts a force F on B and, according to the third law, B exerts a force $-F$ on A.   The size of F may vary during the collision, but the two forces are equal and opposite at any instant.   Hence if the impulse during the collision is calculated,

$$\text{Impulse on } A = -(\text{Impulse on } B)$$

By (3.08)

$$\text{Change of momentum of } A = -(\text{Change of momentum of } B)$$

i.e., the decrease in momentum of one body is exactly equal to the increase in momentum of the other, or in other words, the total momentum of the system is unchanged by the collision.   This important result is by no means limited to two bodies but applies to any isolated or closed system, i.e., to any system on which no external force acts.   It is called the conservation of momentum.

Conservation of Momentum.   *The total momentum of any closed system is a constant, regardless of any interactions between parts of it.*

An algebraic discussion of a simple case may clarify this principle.   In Figure 3.12 the bodies A and B are sliding over the smooth surface in the

Fig. 3.12.   Conservation of momentum in a collision.

same straight line.   Let u and v stand for the initial and final velocities, with subscript A or B indicating the body in question.   Initially, $u_A > u_B$, so that a collision takes place and as a result the velocity of A is decreased while that of B becomes larger and B draws away from A as shown at the right of the figure.

$$\text{Impulse on } A = -(\text{Impulse on } B)$$
$$m_A v_A - m_A u_A = -(m_B v_B - m_B u_B)$$
Transposing gives $m_A v_A + m_B v_B = m_A u_A + m_B u_B$

and the left-hand side is the momentum after the collision while the right-hand side is that before.

One classic example of conservation of momentum is the recoil of a rifle or shotgun.   When the hammer strikes the cartridge the powder burns rapidly, producing a very high gas pressure.   This expels the bullet or shot rapidly.   Now the bullet and gun were initially at rest, i.e., had zero momentum.   Hence, since the total momentum must still be zero, the gun must move backward in such a way that

$$mv = -MV$$

where m, v are the mass and velocity of the bullet, V is the velocity of recoil, and M is the total mass moved backward.   (The signs can be confusing here—since velocities are vectors, the equation is based on measuring velocities positive in the direction of motion of the bullet, so that V is a negative quantity.   If only magnitudes are used, the equation is

$mv = MV$.) The trick of firing a high-powered gun is in keeping M large by holding the stock of the gun firmly against the shoulder. In this way the mass of the body is combined with the mass of the gun to make M large and V small. Many a man has bruised his pride and his shoulder, not to mention other parts of his anatomy, by not understanding this bit of physics.

3.08 REACTION MOTORS

Until recently all means of propulsion invented by man have involved a direct physical contact with the surroundings of the vehicle. Thus the driving wheels of a locomotive push on the railroad tracks (which push back on the locomotive, causing it to move), a ship's propeller pushes on the water, an aircraft's propeller pulls the air toward it, and so on. Within the last decade engines using a direct application of the principle of conservation of momentum have become important, chiefly as a result of developments during the Second World War. These engines are called reaction motors, and the two main types are jet aircraft engines and rocket motors. They operate in a similar manner. Fuel is burned to produce gas at a very high temperature; the gas is expelled rapidly in one direction, causing the engine and the framework on which the engine is mounted to move in the reverse direction. The difference between the two is that jet engines draw the oxygen for burning the fuel from the surrounding air, whereas rockets carry the oxygen within their own tanks. The first jet aircraft appeared about 1944 and could reach speeds of about 600 mph. By 1953 manned aircraft had attained speeds of the order of 1200 mph, and unmanned rockets about 3600 mph.

This is not the place for a detailed discussion of jet aircraft engine design. It is sufficient to say that air is sucked into the nose of the engine, compressed greatly in a supercharger, mixed with fuel (usually vaporized kerosene), and ignited. The resulting blast of hot gas is directed backward by a system of baffles. Figure 3.13 is a photograph of a recent type of jet fighter aircraft.

Jet aircraft work better at high speeds and burn huge quantities of fuel very rapidly. This limits their use as transport aircraft, and much interest is being shown in a compromise between a propeller drive and pure jet propulsion. This type of aircraft uses what is called a "turbo-prop" motor. It is a jet type up to the stage of the production of very hot gases. Instead of sending the hot gases directly out of the rear of the motor, however, the stream of gas strikes the blades of a turbine, causing it to rotate at the expense of a loss of most of the momentum of the gas. The turbine is geared to a conventional propeller. The forward thrust of the motor is thus obtained mainly by a propeller pulling on the surrounding air and partly by the reaction from the discharge of the gas, which is moving quite slowly compared with the gas ejected from a jet engine. Aircraft using "turboprop" motors are now in service and are proving to be both speedy and economical. It seems probable that, for

Fig. 3.13. CF-100 all-weather jet fighter. (Photograph courtesy of Royal Canadian Air Force.)

fast transport service, they will soon replace aircraft with propellers driven by conventional internal-combustion engines.

Jet engines derive their oxygen from the air and are thus limited to flying in the lower levels of the atmosphere. The altitude record for this type of plane in 1953 was about 64,000 ft, i.e., a little more than 12 miles above the surface of the earth. Rockets are not limited for this reason and would work better in empty space because air resistance is a very serious factor at the high speeds involved. Rockets came to prominence when the Germans bombarded England during the war with the V-2 rockets, and military research into rocket design has been continuing since, mostly under conditions of great secrecy at White Sands, New Mexico, and other experimental stations. The emphasis has, of necessity, been mainly on military applications, but there are few rocket men who do not occasionally speculate on the use of rockets to cross the millions of miles of empty space separating us from the other planets.

Figure 3.14 is a sketch of the essential parts of a rocket: A is the fuel tank (one fuel often used is ethyl alcohol), B the tank for liquid oxygen, and P the pumps to carry the fuel and oxygen to C, the combustion chamber, where the mixture is burned. The exhaust gases go out through the jet or nozzle N, the design of which has much to do with the efficiency of

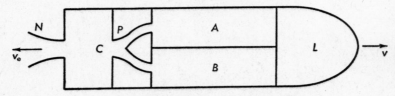

Fig. 3.14. Essential parts of a rocket.

the motor. The pay load L is the useful load which the rocket is to carry. It may consist of an explosive war head or a cargo of meteorological instruments and radio equipment. No attempt is made in the sketch to indicate the elaborate control mechanisms necessary in a successful design.

The initial mass of the rocket before firing is called M_0 and is made up of three parts:

$$M_0 = M_R + M_F + M_L \qquad (3.09)$$

where M_R is the mass of the permanent structure of the rocket, M_F the mass of the fuel and oxygen, and M_L is the mass of the pay load.

When the rocket is fired the fuel is burned up with the oxygen and goes out through N with an exhaust velocity v_E, so that M_F decreases rapidly. It is shown in section 3.09 that if v is the velocity of the rocket when its total mass is M then, under ideal conditions,

$$M = M_0 e^{-\frac{v}{v_E}} \qquad (3.10)$$

where e is the number $2.718 \cdots$, the base of natural logarithms. The minimum value of M is $M = M_R + M_L$ when the fuel is all gone, and this permits us to calculate the (theoretical) maximum velocity v_m. We define the *mass ratio*, m, of the rocket as

$$m = \frac{M_0}{M_R + M_L}$$

Substituting in (3.09) and (3.10) gives

$$M_R + M_L = M_0 e^{-\frac{v_m}{v_E}}$$

$$m = e^{\frac{v_m}{v_E}}$$

$$\ln m = \frac{v_m}{v_E}$$

where $\ln m$ is the logarithm of m to base e, whence

$$v_m = v_E \ln m \tag{3.11}$$

The numerical details of the V-2 will be used to illustrate this equation. The fuel used was ethyl alcohol, which was burned with oxygen at a temperature of about 3000C and gave an exhaust velocity of 6600 ft sec^{-1}. The initial mass M_0 was 14 tons and M_F was 9 tons, giving $m = 2.8$. Since $\ln 2.8 = 1.03$, equation (3.11) gives

$$v_m = 6600 \times 1.03 = 6800 \text{ ft sec}^{-1}$$

This theoretical maximum was not achieved in the V-2, which reached a maximum speed of about 5600 ft sec^{-1}. V-2's fired in Holland traveled a horizontal distance of about 200 miles to England, taking about 6 min for the trip, during which they reached an altitude of over 60 miles. The 9 tons of fuel and oxygen were burned in the first 68 sec of the flight.

Escape Velocity. In 1949 a rocket reached a height of about 250 miles above the surface of the earth. This is really beyond the atmosphere, so that the rocket was in space but it still fell back to earth. The pull of the earth on a body decreases with height, however, so that if a rocket were fired with a sufficiently high velocity, it would keep on going and leave the earth. The minimum velocity for this to happen is called the **escape velocity** and is shown in section 10.06 to be about 7 miles sec^{-1}. Since the present rocket speeds are about 1 mile sec^{-1}, interplanetary travel is not "just around the corner" but the problems are understood and will probably be solved in the next fifty years, or even sooner.

3.09 CALCULUS METHODS

Most of the science of mechanics was put into its present form by Newton, who found that the mathematics of his time was inadequate for the job. This led him to invent suitable mathematical tools which, with certain additions, constitute the subject now known as calculus. Since it was invented for this purpose, it is not surprising that calculus is the language of physics. Because we realize that most students using this book will have little or no facility with calculus notation or methods, our aim is to develop physical theories using only algebra, geometry, and trigonometry, as far as this is possible. It should be realized, though, that the concepts of calculus always lie just below the surface of our discussions, and occasionally calculus notation must be introduced. For this reason, and largely for the benefit of those who have had some training in this branch of mathematics or are now studying it, we intend occasionally to review the work already covered, expressing it in calculus notation to show the greater power and elegance obtained in that way.

Fundamental to calculus and physics is the notion of an instantaneous rate of change. If a body moves from A to B, its velocity is rarely constant. If the displacement AB $(=s)$ is made in time t,

$$\frac{s}{t} = \bar{v}$$

the average velocity. If we measure the difference in displacement between two positions of the body at slightly different times, then $\Delta s/\Delta t$ is the average velocity in that time interval. If we imagine Δs to become smaller and smaller, the time interval Δt also decreases and the limit of their ratio as both quantities tend to zero is written as ds/dt and called the instantaneous velocity. Thus

$$v = \frac{ds}{dt} \tag{3.12}$$

Similarly, acceleration

$$a = \frac{dv}{dt} = \frac{d}{dt}\left(\frac{ds}{dt}\right)$$

which is written $$a = \frac{d^2s}{dt^2} \tag{3.13}$$

The inverse of differentiation is called integration and, if a is constant, integration of (3.13) gives

$$\frac{d^2s}{dt^2} = a, \qquad \int d\left(\frac{ds}{dt}\right) = \int a\, dt$$

$$\frac{ds}{dt} = v = at + \text{constant}$$

If $v = u$ at time $t = 0$, this determines the constant and

$$v = u + at$$

which is equation (2.03). A second integration gives

$$s = ut + \tfrac{1}{2}at^2 + \text{constant}$$

and if the origin of displacement measurements is chosen so that $s = 0$ for $t = 0$, the constant vanishes, giving equation (2.04).

Newton's Second Law of Motion in absolute units is

$$F = \frac{\Delta(mv)}{\Delta t}$$

Let $\Delta t \to 0$. Then, if m is constant,

$$F = \frac{d(mv)}{dt} = m\frac{dv}{dt} = ma \qquad (3.14)$$

If F varies during the time when it is applied,

$$\text{Impulse} = \int F\, dt \qquad (3.15)$$

$$= \int \frac{d(mv)}{dt}\, dt = \int d(mv)$$

$$= mv + \text{constant}$$

Initially, before the force is applied, impulse $= 0$ and $v = u$, so that

$$0 = mu + \text{constant}, \qquad \text{constant} = -mu$$

i.e., $\qquad\qquad\qquad \text{Impulse} = mv - mu$

The power of calculus methods is indicated in the derivation of equation (3.10). The mass of the rocket decreases continuously, and the

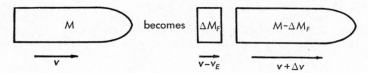

Fig. 3.15. Acceleration of a rocket.

acceleration is not a constant. Suppose the rocket at time t has a mass M and a velocity v. In the next time interval Δt a mass ΔM_F is ejected with a velocity $-v_E$ with respect to the rocket, increasing the velocity of the remaining mass by Δv. The magnitude of the exhaust velocity is v_E. The system can be represented schematically as in Figure 3.15. The total momentum must be conserved, so that

$$Mv = \Delta M_F(v - v_E) + (M - \Delta M_F)(v + \Delta v)$$

$$= v\,\Delta M_F - v_E\,\Delta M_F + Mv - v\,\Delta M_F + M\,\Delta v - \Delta M_F\,\Delta v$$

or $\quad v_E\,\Delta M_F = M\,\Delta v - \Delta M_F\,\Delta v \qquad (3.16)$

Now if Δt becomes very small, ΔM_F and Δv become smaller and smaller and the term $\Delta M_F \, \Delta v$, which is the product of *two* very small quantities, becomes negligible compared to $M \, \Delta v$, giving, as $\Delta t \to 0$,

$$v_E \, dM_F = M \, dv$$

Also, the rate at which fuel and oxygen are consumed is the rate at which the total mass decreases, or

$$\frac{dM_F}{dt} = -\frac{dM}{dt}$$

(negative because dM/dt is the rate of *increase* of M).   Therefore

$$-v_E \, dM = M \, dv$$
$$\frac{dM}{M} = -\frac{dv}{v_E}$$

Integrating gives, $\ln M = -\dfrac{v}{v_E} + \text{constant}$

When the rocket first starts, $t = 0$, $v = 0$, and $M = M_0$; therefore

$$\ln M_0 = 0 + \text{constant}, \qquad \text{constant} = \ln M_0$$

or $\ln M - \ln M_0 = -\dfrac{v}{v_E}$

$$M = M_0 e^{-\frac{v}{v_E}} \tag{3.17}$$

PROBLEMS

1. A body of mass 3.00 kgm rests on a smooth, level table.   What force is required to give it an acceleration of 4.00 m sec^{-2}?

2. A hand-truck of mass 30.0 lb rolls over a level floor.   Neglecting friction, what steady horizontal force is needed to raise its speed from 2.00 ft sec^{-1} to 26.0 ft sec^{-1} in 3.00 sec?

3. If the frictional force on the hand-truck of problem 2 is exactly one-tenth of the total weight of the truck and contents, (a) what acceleration would result from a steady force of 18.0 lb-wt acting horizontally on the unloaded truck? (b) what steady force would raise its velocity to 8.00 ft sec^{-1} in 10.0 sec if the truck carried a mass of 410 lb?

4. A man of mass 180 lb is falling through the air and reaches a terminal velocity of 120 mph.   What is the maximum force of air resistance on his body? When he opens his parachute he slows down to a terminal velocity of 15.0 mph in 2.80 sec.   What is the average upward force exerted on the man and the parachute during this slowing-down period?

5. A bullet of mass 40.0 gm is accelerated from rest to a speed of 350 m sec^{-1} as it travels along the barrel of the gun, a distance of 98.0 cm. What average force is exerted on it?

6. A golf ball of mass 60.0 gm is struck by a golf club and during the impact, which lasts for 1.00×10^{-4} sec, the ball gains a speed of 70.0 m sec^{-1}. What average force is exerted? Give the answer in both newtons and kilograms-weight.

7. A cable on a crane has a maximum allowable tension of 20,000 lb. What is the shortest time in which it can raise a mass of 18,000 lb through a height of 16.0 ft starting from rest?

8. An elevator has a mass of 2000 lb and is designed to operate with a maximum acceleration of 4.00 ft sec^{-2}. If the safe tension in the cable is 4400 lb-wt, what is the maximum number of passengers (average mass 150 lb each)?

9. If a 200-lb passenger is riding in an elevator, what is his apparent weight when the elevator's acceleration is 4.00 ft sec^{-2} upward? Downward?

10. An automobile of mass 2500 lb is traveling at 60 mph and is brought to rest in 1000 ft by braking. What is the average force exerted on the car by the pavement?

11. An automobile of mass 2500 lb is traveling at 60 mph and crashes into a truck, being brought to rest in a distance of 15.0 ft. What is the average force exerted on the car?

12. The chamber of a pump contains 37.5 lb of water. The piston exerts a force of 1.50×10^4 poundals on this water for a period of 0.200 sec. To what height could the ejected jet of water rise?

13. A body of mass 9.00 kgm rests on a smooth, level table. It is connected by a light string, which passes over a pulley at the edge of the table to a 3.00-kgm mass which is hanging freely. Find the acceleration of the system and the tension in the string.

14. Two rectangular blocks of masses 500 and 300 gm are connected by a light, rigid rod. The blocks rest on a smooth, horizontal table. If a force of 40.0 newtons is exerted on the heavier block, as in Figure 3.16, find the compression force in the rod and the acceleration of the system.

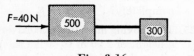

Fig. 3.16.

15. In an Atwood's machine (Figure 3.08) $m_1 = 4.000$ lb, $m_2 = 3.750$ lb, $l = 0.50$ ft, $l_2 = 4.50$ ft. The time interval between m_2 leaving R and reaching S is 2.78 sec. Find the acceleration of gravity.

16. A body of mass 10.0 kgm rests on a smooth plane inclined at an angle of 30.0° to the horizontal. If a force of 99.0 N acting parallel to the plane is applied to the body, find the time taken to raise it through a vertical height of 20.0 m.

17. In Figure 3.11(a) if $m_1 = 10.0$ lb, $m_2 = 22.0$ lb, $\theta = 36°52'$, find the acceleration of the system and the tension in the cord.   What is the force exerted
on the inclined plane?

18. A ramp for loading a freight car is inclined at an angle of 15.0°.   Loads are
placed on a light, frictionless cart and pushed up the ramp.   If the force
which can be exerted by a man is 120 lb, what maximum load can be placed
in the freight car per trip?   If the actual load on the cart were 250 lb, what
acceleration could he give it up the ramp?

19. An elevator and operator have a mass of 2000 lb and the counterweight has a
mass of 2500 lb.   If the elevator were allowed to rise freely, how long would
it take it to go up 225 ft from rest, neglecting friction?

20. In Figure 3.08, $m = 0.500$, $m_1 = 0.400$, $m_2 = 0.350$, all in kilograms, and
$l = 0.200$, $l_1 = 0.250$, $l_2 = 1.700$, all in meters.   Mass m_2 is released at T.
Find (a) the time for m_2 to reach S; (b) the velocity of the system at that
time; (c) the velocity of the system an instant later; (d) the distance m rises;
(e) the time when the system first comes to rest.

21. In problem 6, if the mass of the head of the golf club is 400 gm and its speed
was 15 m sec^{-1} at the beginning of the impact, what was its speed just after
the ball left the club face?

22. A gun on a battleship has a mass of 3000 lb.   It fires a shell of mass 200 lb
with a velocity of 1000 ft sec^{-1}.   What is the recoil velocity of the gun?

23. A young man of mass 120 lb takes out a canoe (mass 50 lb) together with
25 lb of ballast in the form of 5 equal stones.   A short distance from shore
he breaks his paddle and decides to return by throwing the stones astern as
fast as he can.   If the speed with which he throws each stone is 40 ft sec^{-1}
relative to the canoe, find the maximum speed attained, neglecting the
resistance of the water.

24. A 1.00-lb hammer is used to drive a 4.00-in. nail (mass 0.0400 lb) into a
plank.   The plank exerts an average force of 1000 lb-wt against the motion
of the nail.   If the hammer hits the nail with a speed of 10.0 ft sec^{-1} and
is stopped without rebound, how many blows are needed to drive the nail in
completely?

25. The moving mass in a pile driver is 125 kgm and is dropped from rest through
a height of 2.50 m to strike the pile.   If the mass is brought to rest without
rebound in driving the pile down 7.00 cm, what is the average force exerted on
the pile during the impact?   Give answer in both newtons and kilograms-
weight.

26. A certain jet engine can deliver a thrust of 8000 lb-wt.   If the exhaust
velocity of the hot gases is 4000 ft sec^{-1}, what mass of material must be
exhausted per second to deliver this thrust?   If 10% of the ejected mass is
derived from the fuel carried by the aircraft and the other 90% from the air
drawn into the engine, what mass of fuel is used if the motor delivers its full
thrust for one hour?

27. If the air resistance to the high-speed motion of a jet aircraft increases as the cube of the speed and the motor of problem 26 can drive a certain aircraft at 600 mph, what thrust would be needed to drive this aircraft at 650 mph?

28. If a rocket fuel gives an exhaust velocity of 8000 ft sec^{-1}, what mass ratio is necessary to attain a rocket speed of 7.00 miles sec^{-1}? Compare with the mass ratio of the V-2.

29. The mass ratio found in problem 14 could not be obtained with present engineering methods. An alternative method of obtaining high velocities is the "step" rocket in which the pay load of the main rocket is a smaller one which is fired when the first one reaches maximum velocity and leaves the spent "shell" behind. The altitude of 250 miles referred to in section 3.08 was achieved with a two-step rocket. Prove that the effective mass ratio of a multistage rocket is the product of the mass ratios of the individual stages.

30. A three-step rocket consists of parts A, B, and C, which are fired in turn. Each rocket motor has an exhaust velocity of 8000 ft sec^{-1}. Other data are, in the notation of section 3.08, with all masses in pounds:

	M_R	M_F	M_L
A	15,000	70,000	3,750
B	600	3,000	150
C	20.0	125	5.00

Find the final velocity of the C rocket. (Needless to say this rocket is hypothetical, but the figures are of the right order of magnitude for a rocket designed to be sent to the moon and to produce a flash, visible in a telescope, when it hits there.)

4

Statics

4.01 BALANCED FORCES

According to Newton's Second Law of Motion, if all the forces on a body balance each other so that there is no net or resultant force, the body has zero acceleration and is said to be in **equilibrium.** Statics deals with bodies in equilibrium. It is a special case of dynamics but is of such great practical importance that it needs separate attention. Problems in statics can be solved graphically, using carefully made scale drawings, or analytically, i.e., using the methods of algebra, trigonometry, and higher branches of mathematics. Engineers tend to use graphical methods somewhat more frequently, but both methods are important, and sometimes a judicious combination of the two helps reduce the time required for the solution of a complex problem. The physical principles used in both types of solution are identical.

Statics of a Particle. Frequently a problem can be solved by treating the body in question as a particle. In this case the basic graphical tool is the polygon of forces (section 2.03). A free body diagram is sketched, and the forces acting on it are added by the polygon method. If the polygon is closed, the resultant force is zero. If the body is known to be in equilibrium, the polygon must be closed, which permits the determination of unknown forces.

Analytically, one chooses a convenient direction and sets up OX, OY axes through the body along the chosen direction and the perpendicular to it. Each force is then resolved into components along OX and OY, and the algebraic sums are found. If X is the resultant force in the OX direction and Y the resultant along OY, and if X is not equal to zero, the body cannot be in equilibrium since it will have an acceleration along OX regardless of the size of Y. Note that since the resultant Y is perpendicular to OX it cannot produce any acceleration along OX. Hence, for equilibrium, $X = 0$. Similarly $Y = 0$ for equilibrium.

$$X = \Sigma F_x = 0 \ \\ Y = \Sigma F_y = 0 \ \right\}$$ (4.01)

where F_x, F_y are the components of an individual force.

The above discussion has tacitly assumed that all the forces act in the same plane, which is frequently not true in practice. The extension to problems in three dimensions adds greatly to the complexity, although the method, at least in analytical solutions, is simple enough in theory. Thus, instead of OX, OY axes we choose three mutually perpendicular directions called OX, OY, OZ; resolve each force into three components along these axes; and require that $\Sigma F_x = \Sigma F_y = \Sigma F_z = 0$ for equilibrium. We shall restrict ourselves to statics problems in two dimensions in this book.

Example. A cable car is used to lower heavy material into an excavation, a drag line preventing the car from running down the cable

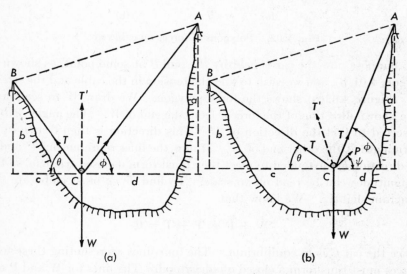

Fig. 4.01. Forces on a cable car.

too fast. The cable is suspended from pylons at A and B. The cable car C is assumed to be frictionless, so that the tension in the cable does not change in passing around the car. The weights of the cable and drag line are assumed to be negligible.

Let us first consider the equilibrium reached if the pull of the drag line P is zero. A schematic picture of the system is shown in Figure 4.01(a). The only forces acting on the car are the weight W, the tension T toward B, and the tension T toward A. Since the two forces T are equal, they can be replaced by a single force T' whose direction must bisect the angle ACB. For equilibrium $T' = W$ and T' must be in the same straight line as W, i.e., it must act vertically upward. The force polygon is shown in Figure 4.02(a). Evidently $\theta = \phi$ in this simple case, i.e., $a/d = b/c$.

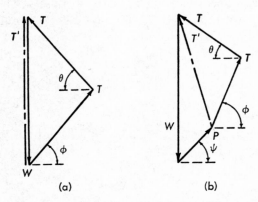

(a)   (b)

Fig. 4.02. Polygons of forces on cable car.

Suppose now the car is held by the pull P at some point, as shown in Figure 4.01(b), and we wish to find the tension in the cable and the size of P. Figure 4.02(b) shows the force polygon. We draw W to scale and the known direction of the force P from the end of W. The angle ACB is bisected to find the direction of T'. This direction is then drawn in to terminate at the other end of W. If now the lines representing T' and P in direction are extended to meet they must form a closed triangle, so the magnitudes can be read off to scale. To find T we must elaborate the diagram slightly. We know that

$$\mathbf{W} + \mathbf{P} + \mathbf{T} + \mathbf{T} = 0$$

since the car C is in equilibrium. The four lines representing these four forces must thus form a closed quadrilateral. The lines for $\mathbf{W}$ and $\mathbf{P}$ are already drawn in the correct directions and to proper scale lengths. We know the directions of $\mathbf{T}$ in CA and in CB. From the end of $\mathbf{P}$ we draw a line making an angle ϕ with the direction chosen to represent the horizontal. From the top end of the $\mathbf{W}$ vector we draw back a line giving the direction of $\mathbf{T}$ in CB. These two lines meet to close the figure, and the length of either gives the size of T. Note that T, T must form an isosceles triangle on the line T' as base.

Numerically, if $W = 650$ lb, $\theta = 36.0°$, $\phi = 67.5°$, and $\psi = 47.0°$, measurement of a large-scale drawing of Figure 4.02(b) gives $T = 330$ lb, $P = 205$ lb.

Analytical Solution. Resolving all the forces acting on the car horizontally and vertically, and applying equations (4.01) to the point C in Figure 4.01, we have

$$T \cos \phi + P \cos \psi - T \cos \theta = 0 \qquad (4.02)$$
$$T \sin \phi + T \sin \theta + P \sin \psi - W = 0 \qquad (4.03)$$

whence

$$0.383T + 0.682P - 0.809T = 0$$
$$0.924T + 0.588T + 0.731P - W = 0$$

giving

$$P = \frac{0.426}{0.682} T$$

$$T \left(0.924 + 0.588 + 0.731 \times \frac{0.426}{0.682} \right) = 650$$

Solving these equations gives $T = 330$ lb, $P = 206$ lb.

This problem has been solved using pounds (or actually pounds-weight) as the unit of force. Note that all equations in statics are balanced equations, so that the choice of units is immaterial provided it is consistent. Note also that equations (4.02) and (4.03), which were obtained from Figure 4.01, could also be obtained by resolving the forces in Figure 4.02(b) horizontally and vertically. The equations then state that the sums of the horizontal and vertical projections of the force vectors of the figure are separately zero, which is just the condition for a closed polygon. This illustrates the statement above that the graphical and analytical methods are physically identical. The choice of method to use is purely one of convenience.

4.02 EQUILIBRIUM OF A RIGID BODY

When we come to deal with bodies of finite size it is convenient to introduce another idealization, the rigid body, which is one that maintains its size and shape unchanged regardless of the forces applied to it. No such body exists, but most solid objects acted on by forces of ordinary size come sufficiently close to this property for the results we shall obtain to be valid. The study of the small changes in size and shape which actually result is usually not classed as a part of ordinary mechanics but

as a separate branch of physics called **elasticity**.   This rather artificial
separation makes the work simpler and causes very little trouble.

Restricting ourselves then to rigid bodies, let us look more closely at
the point of application of a force and its line of action.   Figure 4.03
represents a two-dimensional body (a thin, heavy plate of the shape
shown) with a force F acting at the point A.   If the direction in which F
acts is extended both ways, the resulting line LM is called the line of action

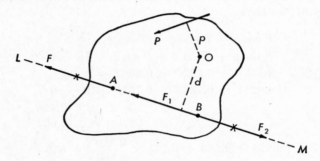

Fig. 4.03.   Transmissibility of force.

of the force.   Choose any point B in LM and introduce forces F_1, F_2 at B
acting in the directions shown.   The sizes of F, F_1, F_2 are the same.   Thus
F_1 and F_2 are equal and opposite and have no effect on the body.   Since
the body is rigid we can now cancel F and F_2, which are equal and opposite,
leaving F_1 only.   The result is that the point of application of F has been
shifted from A to B.   Thus a force can be moved anywhere along its line
of action.   This is called the Principle of Transmissibility of Force.

Suppose the body in Figure 4.03 has a fixed axis, passing through O
perpendicular to the plane of the diagram, and is free to turn about this
axis.   What will be the effect of the force F?   It will cause the body to
rotate clockwise.   We say that F exerts a turning effect or **torque** (Γ) on
the body, and we wish to find out how to measure torque.   One of the
commonest cases of rotation occurs when we open a door.   From experience, the door handle is always placed near the edge away from the hinges,
because the closer to the hinges the push is applied the larger the force
needed to open the door.   In the extreme case no force, however large,
pushing on the hinge pins will open the door (omitting the drastic possibility of ripping the hinges out of the wall).   Evidently turning effect
depends on the distance from the line of action of the force as well as on
the latter's size.   A simple experiment can be performed with the system
of Figure 4.03.   We mount the body horizontally so that the axis through

O is vertical. (This permits us to ignore the weight of the body because weight acts vertically and cannot produce any motion about a fixed vertical axis.) A second force P is applied as shown, and this force tries to rotate the body counterclockwise so that its turning effect is opposite to that of the force F. The experiment consists of varying the size of P until no rotation takes place. It is found that the necessary condition for equilibrium is

$$P \times p = F \times d = M \qquad (4.04)$$

where p and d are the perpendicular distances from the axis through O to the lines of action of P and F, respectively. The distance p is called the **lever-arm** of the force P, and $M = P \times p$ is called the **moment of the force** P about O, or more simply the moment of P about O.

Suppose next that the force P is applied in the same direction but closer to O so that the lever-arm p is only half as great as in the first test. It is found that the applied force must be doubled to maintain equilibrium, that is, the moment of the force must be kept the same. Apparently the moment of a force measures its turning effect because if two forces have equal moments in opposite directions (one clockwise and the other counterclockwise), their torques cancel and no rotation takes place. We shall use the words torque and moment as exactly equivalent, with symbols Γ or M. By convention a counterclockwise moment is called positive and a clockwise one negative.

General Conditions of Equilibrium. If the forces F and P in Figure 4.03 satisfy equation (4.04), the body is in equilibrium with regard to rotation about an axis through O, but it would not be in equilibrium if the possible axis of rotation passed through the point B. To ensure that a body will not rotate about *any* axis, we require that the algebraic sum of the moments about every possible axis vanishes or, in algebraic form,

$$\Sigma M \text{ about any axis} = 0 \qquad (4.05)$$

For equilibrium of a rigid body this is a third condition to be added to the conditions of equation (4.01), giving

$$\left. \begin{array}{l} \Sigma F_X = 0 \\ \Sigma F_Y = 0 \\ \Sigma M \text{ about any axis} = 0 \end{array} \right\} \qquad (4.06)$$

Equations (4.06) are the *necessary and sufficient conditions for the equilibrium of a rigid body acted on by a set of coplanar forces*, and all two-dimensional statics problems can be solved by them, if a solution exists. Some statics problems cannot be solved without allowance for the elastic properties of matter, that is, the assumption of completely rigid bodies is unworkable. We shall not deal with any of these so-called statically indeterminate problems. In most applications of (4.05) it is known that the body is in equilibrium, so that this equation must hold. The choice of the axis for calculating ΣM is then made in such a way as to simplify the mathematics of the solution. It is usually chosen to pass through the intersection of the lines of action of two or more unknown forces.

4.03 PARALLEL FORCES AND COUPLES

The resultant of any two forces in a plane which are not parallel can be found by moving them along their lines of action to a common point, and then using the parallelogram law. Since parallel forces do not have a common point, a different method is used.

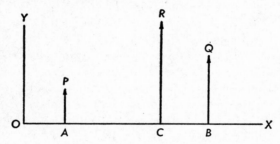

Fig. 4.04. Resultant of like parallel forces.

Consider a body (outline not shown) acted on by two like (same direction), parallel forces P and Q, as in Figure 4.04. The line OX is any line at right angles to their lines of action. We want to find a resultant force R which will replace P and Q completely, that is, will have the same effect in moving the body as a whole in the OY direction and will also have the same turning effect. The size of R presents no problem;

$$R = P + Q \tag{4.07}$$

To ensure the same turning effect, we require that R shall have the same torque about *any* perpendicular axis as the resultant torque of P and Q about the axis. Let R act at C. Then, calculating moments about an axis through the arbitrary point O, we require that

$$R \cdot OC = P \cdot OA + Q \cdot OB$$

That is,
$$R \cdot OC = P \cdot (OC - AC) + Q \cdot (OC + CB)$$
$$R \cdot OC = (P + Q) \cdot OC - P \cdot AC + Q \cdot CB$$

and using (4.07),
$$0 = -P \cdot AC + Q \cdot CB$$
$$P \cdot AC = Q \cdot CB \tag{4.08}$$

Equation (4.08) determines the location of the point C and hence of the line of action of the resultant R. Also, since the equation does not involve the location of O, it holds for *any* choice of axis of rotation, as required above.

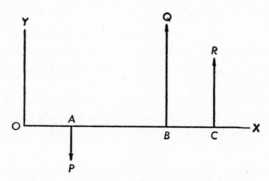

Fig. 4.05.   Resultant of unlike parallel forces.

Figure 4.05 shows the difference if the parallel forces are unlike (opposite directions).

$$R = Q - P$$
$$R \cdot OC = Q \cdot OB - P \cdot OA$$
$$= Q \cdot (OC - CB) - P \cdot (OC - AC)$$
$$= (Q - P) \cdot OC - Q \cdot CB + P \cdot AC$$
$$P \cdot AC = Q \cdot CB \qquad\qquad (4.09)$$

This is formally the same as (4.08), but in this case the point C is outside the line AB. Equations (4.08) and (4.09) can be stated in geometrical language as follows.

The line of action of the resultant of two parallel forces divides the distance between them inversely in the ratio of the forces, internally if the forces are like and externally if they are unlike.

If $P = Q$ in size and they act in op-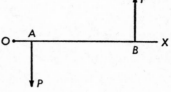posite directions (but not in the same straight line), this method breaks down also, and we conclude that no single force can replace a pair of equal, unlike, parallel forces whose lines of action do not coin-

Fig. 4.06.   Torque of a couple.

cide. Such a combination is called a **couple.** The torque exerted by a couple is important and is seen from Figure 4.06 to be

$$\Gamma = P \cdot OB - P \cdot OA = P \cdot AB \qquad\qquad (4.10)$$

The torque of a couple is thus the same for all axes of rotation and is equal to the magnitude of either force times their perpendicular distance apart (which is called the arm of the couple).

4.04 CENTER OF GRAVITY AND CENTER OF MASS

In dealing with rigid bodies great simplification is introduced by the concept of the **center of gravity.** This concept is that all the weight of the body can be considered to be concentrated at a single, unique point and to act downward through this point.

This is illustrated for a simple body in Figure 4.07, where A and B are heavy particles of masses m_1 and m_2 connected by a light, rigid rod. The weights act as shown. The forces m_1g and m_2g are like, parallel

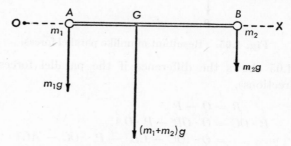

Fig. 4.07. Center of gravity of two particles.

forces and thus can be replaced by a single force $(m_1 + m_2)g$, acting at G where, by equation (4.08),

$$m_1g \times AG = m_2g \times GB$$

If we introduce a coordinate system as shown and write $OA = x_1$, $OB = x_2$, $OG = \bar{x}$, then

$$m_1g(\bar{x} - x_1) = m_2g(x_2 - \bar{x})$$

$$\bar{x} = \frac{m_1x_1 + m_2x_2}{m_1 + m_2} \tag{4.11}$$

The center of gravity of this body is G, and equation (4.11) can be used to find its location. If $m_1 = m_2$, G is at the mid-point or geometrical center of the bar. A *uniform* rod can be considered to consist of large numbers of pairs of particles symmetrically located with respect to the center. The center of gravity of each pair of particles is at their mid-point, that is, at the center of the rod, and so the center of gravity of the entire rod is at its center. Similarly, using symmetry considerations, it can be shown that the center of gravity of a uniform circular plate is at

EXAMPLE **83**

its center, of a uniform rectangular plate at the intersection of its diagonals, and so on. The center of gravity of *any* uniform body will be at its geometrical center, if that point can be defined.

If the body is irregular in shape or nonuniform in density, the calculation of its center of gravity is difficult and frequently impossible. The methods used are extensions of equation (4.11) to systems of massive particles on a line, on a plane, and in three dimensions and then to continuous bodies. Calculus is usually necessary.

Center of Mass. The discussion of the center of gravity of bodies has assumed that the weights of the various parts are parallel. This is not strictly true since weight acts vertically downward and the surface of the earth is curved. This error is completely negligible for all but the largest bodies, but in theoretical work it is convenient to define the center of mass of a body without reference to gravitational forces. The center of mass is defined by equations similar to (4.11). Thus if a number of masses m_1, m_2, m_3, etc., have x coordinates x_1, x_2, etc., the x coordinate of the center of mass, $\bar{x}$, is given by

$$\bar{x} = \frac{m_1x_1 + m_2x_2 + m_3x_3 + \cdots}{m_1 + m_2 + m_3 + \cdots} \tag{4.12}$$

with similar equations for $\bar{y}$ and $\bar{z}$. For a body of reasonable size the center of gravity and the center of mass coincide.

Both terms can be applied to nonrigid bodies as well, but the location of the "center" will then change as the shape of the body changes. The center of mass of a system of moving particles is a very useful concept in many calculations.

4.05 EXAMPLE

A uniform ladder 25.0 ft long rests against a smooth wall with its base on a smooth floor. It is prevented from slipping by a light rope 7.00 ft long tied to the base of the ladder and the intersection of the wall and the floor. If a man of mass 180 lb stands on the ladder at a vertical height of 16.0 ft above the floor, find the tension in the rope and the reactions of the wall and floor, the mass of the ladder being 96.0 lb.

Figure 4.08(a) illustrates the problem and 4.08(b) is the diagram of the forces on the ladder AB. The weight of the man acts at C, where $CD = 16.0$ ft, and OB is the rope. Then

$$AO = \sqrt{AB^2 - OB^2} = (25^2 - 7^2)^{\frac{1}{2}} = 24.0 \text{ ft}$$

The weight of the ladder acts at G, where $AG = GB$. The reaction of the smooth wall to the ladder leaning against it is an outward push perpendicular to the surface. Thus in (b) R and S have been drawn perpendicular to the surfaces.

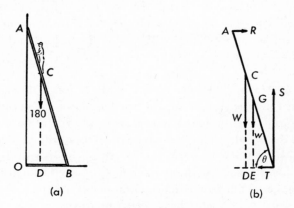

(a) (b)

Fig. 4.08. Ladder problem.

Applying the first two equilibrium conditions, we have

$$R - T = 0 \qquad (4.13)$$
$$S - W - w = 0 \qquad (4.14)$$

Before applying the third condition we must select a suitable axis for the calculation of moments. There are many possibilities, but a horizontal axis through B is a good one because the moments of the unknown forces S and T about this axis are zero since their lever-arms are zero.

$$\Sigma M \text{ about } B = 0$$
$$W \cdot DB + w \cdot EB - R \cdot AO = 0 \qquad (4.15)$$

The next step is to find DB and EB from the geometry of the figure.

$$DB = CD \cot \theta = CD \cdot \frac{OB}{AO} = 16 \times \tfrac{7}{24} = \frac{2 \times 7}{3}$$

$$EB = GB \cos \theta = GB \cdot \frac{OB}{AB} = 12.5 \times \tfrac{7}{25} = \tfrac{7}{2}$$

Substituting in equations (4.13)–(4.15) gives

$$R - T = 0$$
$$S = 180 + 96.0$$
$$180 \times \frac{2 \times 7}{3} + 96 \times \tfrac{7}{2} = R \times 24$$
$$R = 49.0 \text{ lb}, \qquad T = 49.0 \text{ lb}, \qquad S = 276 \text{ lb}$$

PROBLEMS

1. In Figure 4.09, OA is a uniform ladder of mass 120 lb. Two men carry it horizontally, supporting it on their shoulders at A and B. Find the weight carried by each of the men if $OA = 20.0$ ft, $AB = 15.0$ ft.

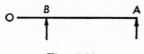

Fig. 4.09.

2. A cable is stretched tightly between two points A and B, 30.0 ft apart and on the same horizontal level. A tightrope walker stands in the middle of the cable. The combined mass of the man and his balancing pole is 200 lb, and this weight causes the cable to sag 0.500 ft. Neglecting the weight of the cable, find its tension.

3. A mass of 10.0 kgm is suspended from a point in the ceiling by a light string 3.00 m long. What horizontal force acting on the body will cause the string to be inclined 30.0° to the vertical? What is the tension in the string under this condition?

4. In Figure 4.01, $a = 200$, $b = 120$, $c = 140$, $d = 170$, all in feet. If the drag line is along the cable AC, what force P is needed to hold a 1.00-ton mass at C in equilibrium in this position? What is the tension in the cable ACB?

5. A uniform beam 20.0 ft long has a mass of 400 lb. At one end a flange of mass 20.0 lb is attached, and a man of mass 208 lb sits 3.00 ft from the other end. How far from the flange should a crane cable be attached in order that the beam may remain horizontal while being lifted?

6. The center of gravity of a 15.0-ft ladder is 5.00 ft from its base. The foot of the ladder rests on a rough floor and the top against a smooth, vertical wall, making an angle of 36°52′ with the wall. The mass of the ladder is 120 lb. Find the direction and size of the forces exerted on the ladder by the wall and the floor.

7. The forces acting on an aircraft in flight can be reduced to four: weight (W), forward pull (P) which acts along fore and aft line, air resistance or drag (D) also along fore and aft line, and lift (L) acting approximately normal to the wings. Sketch this system for an aircraft in level flight and write down the conditions for constant speed.

8. For a certain aircraft of mass 8000 lb the drag at a speed of 400 mph is 275 lb-wt. If the forward thrust of the motor is 1875 lb-wt, at what angle above the horizontal can it climb at this speed? What is its rate of climb?

9. Find the center of gravity of a uniform triangular plate. Show that the position of the center of gravity is unchanged if three equal masses are attached to the vertices of the triangle.

10. A square board is 2.000 ft to the side. A smaller square piece, 1.000 ft to the side, is cut from one corner. Find the distance of the center of gravity of the remainder of the board from the vertex opposite the corner cut away.

11. In Figure 4.10, M is the mast of a sailboat and AB the boom, which is uniform, hinged at A, and of weight W. The boom is supported in any desired vertical position by a light cord BCD which passes over a pulley at C and is tied to a cleat on the mast at D. If $AB = AC$, prove that the tension in the cord is $W \cos \theta$, θ being the angle between the boom and the cord.

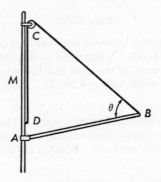

Fig. 4.10.

12. A uniform chain of length 20.0 ft and mass 20.0 lb hangs in equilibrium over a smooth pulley with masses of 10.0 and 6.0 lb attached to its ends. Find the length of the chain on each side of the pulley.

13. Figure 4.11 shows a framework or truss ABC which rests on two piers; AB, BC, and CA are light rods. If a load $W = 1000$ lb is applied to A as shown, find the compressional stresses on AB and AC and the tension in BC. $AB = AC = 7.07$ ft and $BC = 10.0$ ft.

14. If in Figure 4.11 $AB = 6.00$, $AC = 8.00$, $BC = 10.00$, all in feet, find the stresses in the three rods for $W = 1000$ lb.

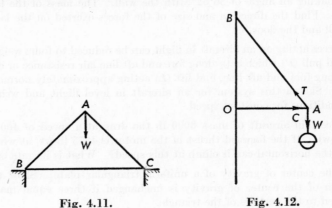

Fig. 4.11.   Fig. 4.12.

15. Figure 4.12 represents a street lamp supported on a pole by the rod OA and the rope AB. If the weight of the lamp is 20.0 lb and $OA = 3.00$ ft, $AB = 5.00$ ft, find the tension in the rope and the thrust on the rod.

16. Figure 4.13 illustrates a method of raising an elevator E. A cable supporting E goes around two pulleys A, B to a counterweight C. Pulley B is free running, but A is rigidly attached to a drum D and a second cable is wound around the drum. An electric motor exerts a pull P on this second cable. Neglecting the masses of the pulleys, drum, and cables, find the size of P to raise the elevator, at a steady rate, if its mass is 2600 lb and that of the counterweight is 2000 lb. Assume no slipping of the cable around A. The radii of A and D are 4.00 in. and 2.00 ft.

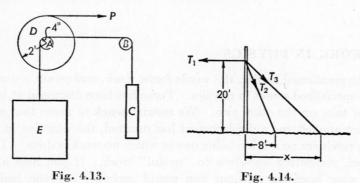

Fig. 4.13.   Fig. 4.14.

17. A telephone cable is supported by a steel strand attached to a line of poles at a height of 20 ft above the ground. At the last pole two guy cables are attached to anchors in the ground, as shown in Figure 4.14. The tensions in the cable are $T_1 = 4000$, $T_2 = 4000$, $T_3 = 5000$, all in pounds-weight. Find the required distance to the second anchor in order that there shall be no sideways thrust on the pole. What is the compressional force on the pole?

18. A cylindrical roller has a radius of 1.50 ft and a mass of 400 lb. What horizontal force must be exerted on its center in order that it may just surmount a 3.00-in. curb?

19. A body is in equilibrium under the action of three forces, no two of which are parallel. Prove that the forces lie in one plane and that their lines of action meet in a point.

20. A uniform beam 10.0 ft long has a mass of 50.0 lb. It is suspended from a fixed point by light ropes 8.00 and 6.00 ft long attached to its ends. Find the tension in each rope.

5

Energy and Power

5.01 WORK IN PHYSICS

As mentioned earlier, the words force, work, and power are used in highly specialized senses in physics. Force has been discussed at length; we now take up the other two. We restrict **work** to mean that a force has been applied *and* a displacement has resulted, the situation in which a force produces no motion being one in which no work is done. This is, in effect, restricting ourselves to "useful" work. If you held a brick above your head for an hour you would probably say you had been "working" hard. There is no doubt of your fatigue, but you would have difficulty finding anyone to pay you for this "work".

The displacement caused by a force may not be exactly along the line of action of the force, owing to some constraint on the motion of the body. An example would be the case of a handcar moving on railroad tracks as the result of a horizontal force acting at an angle θ to the tracks, as shown in Figure 5.01. In this case, the force F can be resolved into

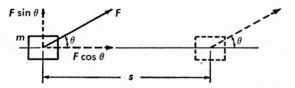

Fig. 5.01. Definition of work.

components along and perpendicular to the tracks. The component $F \sin \theta$ can do no work since the rails prevent any motion in that direction. Thus in the displacement s shown, the work W done is

$$W = (F \cos \theta) \times s \tag{5.01}$$

Evidently (5.01) can be rewritten as

$$W = F \times (s \cos \theta) \tag{5.02}$$

which means that the work done is the product of the force times the component of the displacement in the direction of the force. The quantities F and s are vectors, but no direction can be given to work, so that we have the result that the product of two vectors times the cosine of the angle included is a scalar. This type of product occurs sufficiently often for a special notation to have been invented, and we write

$$W = \mathbf{F} \cdot \mathbf{s} \tag{5.03}$$

which is an abbreviation for (5.01) or (5.02). Here W is called the **"dot"** or **"scalar" product** of the vectors **F** and **s**.

Units. Any unit of force times a unit of distance is a unit of work. The commonest are:

> *mks system:* 1 newton-meter, called 1 *joule*
> *fps grav. system:* 1 lb-wt ft, called 1 *foot-pound* (ft-lb)

Others which we shall rarely use are the cgs unit, the *erg*, which is 1 dyne-cm, and the *fps abs. unit*, the *foot-poundal*. Conversion factors are

$$1 \text{ joule} = 10^7 \text{ ergs} = 0.7373 \text{ ft-lb} \tag{5.04}$$
$$1 \text{ ft-lb} \doteq 32.0 \text{ foot-poundals}$$

5.02 ENERGY. SOURCES OF ENERGY

The ability to do work is called **energy.** In English usage energy, in the physical sense of the word, is a slightly more general term than work. Thus the gasoline in the tank of your car contains energy and can do work, but only if you turn the ignition key and operate the starter, clutch, and gear shift. However, work and energy measure the same thing, have the same units, and are virtually synonymous, although in advanced studies it is sometimes advantageous to distinguish between them.

The industrial revolution, which started in the eighteenth century, has consisted largely of the discovery of new sources of energy and the invention of machines to use this energy to perform tasks originally done by man power or beyond man's unaided capacity. The standard of living of a nation or group of people increases rapidly as the supply of energy available per person per year increases.

SOURCES OF ENERGY

Almost all our energy comes directly or indirectly from the sun, but it is convenient to classify the immediate sources of the energy used as follows.

1. Direct Solar Energy.   The sun is a large, very hot body which gives off enormous quantities of energy.   The source of this energy and the method by which it travels will be discussed later.   A very small fraction of this energy is absorbed by the earth, but it is enough to make our world habitable for us.   All the artificial lighting and heating produced by man can only modify slightly, in restricted localities, the conditions due to the balance between the energy received from the sun and that lost by the earth.   It is possible to collect and store energy from sunlight, but no simple system for doing this is known, with the result that energy storage from direct solar energy is of trivial importance at present.

2. Indirect Solar Energy.   Winds are caused when the sun heats different parts of the atmosphere to different temperatures.   Wind power has been used for centuries to drive windmills and sailing ships, but it is hard to get much energy this way, so that little use is now made of wind power.   Far more important is the fact that the sun's energy evaporates water from the oceans and elsewhere.   Evaporation consists of raising water (in invisibly minute particles called molecules) above the surface of the earth.   This requires work.   The evaporated water forms clouds which are blown about by the wind, and under suitable conditions the water falls back to earth as rain or snow.   Ultimately it runs "downhill" back to the ocean, giving up some of the energy it stored when lifted by the sun.   The running streams of water can be made to do work for us by turning water wheels or turbines.   Hydroelectric power is generated in this way.

3. Chemical Fuels.   Many substances combine with oxygen to give off energy.   The most important energy sources of this type are wood, coal, and oil—all of which are complex organic substances, built up by living organisms using energy derived from sunlight.   This process is called photosynthesis.   They are thus storage mechanisms which can be used to release solar energy received some time ago—from twenty years ago in the case of wood, to two hundred million years ago for coal.

Food is the source of the energy we need to live, and the energy in our food all ultimately comes from solar energy stored by plants.

4. Atomic Energy. Certain rearrangements of the internal structure of atoms cause large amounts of energy to be released. This process occurs spontaneously among certain heavier atoms and is called radioactivity. Control of the release of atomic energy by man has been achieved only within the last twenty years, and its commercial applications are under development. It is believed that the sun derives its energy from atomic processes.

5.03 POTENTIAL ENERGY

Consider an object of mass m near the surface of the earth. The weight of this mass is mg. If a force F, very slightly larger than mg, is applied upward on the body, it will be raised, moving with a very small acceleration. The work done in raising it a height h is

$$W = Fh$$

The larger F is, the more rapidly the body will be raised, so that if we take $F \doteq mg$, the time will be very long and the body will gain virtually no velocity. In the limit of $F = mg$ we say (for purposes of calculation) that the body is being raised infinitely slowly and reaches the height h with zero velocity. In this case

$$W = mgh \tag{5.05}$$

and the body is motionless in its new position. The work done on it has apparently disappeared, but we know that if F is removed, the body will fall and can be made to do work in falling. The body thus has greater energy at height h than it had originally. Such energy due to position is called **potential energy (P.E.)**.

Another example of potential energy is a clockwork motor. It takes a certain amount of work to increase the tension in the spring of a clock. The clock is a mechanism for releasing this stored energy slowly and at a uniform rate to turn the hands. Thus a spring has greater potential energy when wound up. So has a stretched rubber band or a bent bow. Such objects are in a state of strain.

Definition. *Mechanical potential energy is the energy possessed by a system because of its position or state of strain.*

This definition is limited to mechanical potential energy because the general term, potential energy, has been extended to cover any system which has latent or stored energy. Thus a lump of coal or a charged storage battery can reasonably be said to possess (chemical) potential energy.

5.04 KINETIC ENERGY

In contrast to the stored or hidden, potential energy is the obvious energy possessed by a moving body because of its motion. This is called **kinetic energy (K.E.)**. It takes work to set a body in motion and that work is returned when the body stops, although it may not be returned in the form of mechanical energy. For example, a moving car can exert great force if it is brought to rest by running into another object. The damage to the second object is the result of the mechanical work done by the car. If, however, the same car is brought to rest by a smooth application of the brakes, we cannot see any work being done. But if we touch the tires and brake drums, we find they are hot, and this heat is another form of energy, the kinetic energy having been converted into heat energy. Most mechanical energy ultimately ends up as heat energy.

To find a useful formula for kinetic energy, consider a body of mass m at rest and let an unbalanced force F act on it through a distance s.

$$\text{Work done} = Fs$$
$$W = mas$$

Now since $u = 0$, by equation (2.05)

$$v^2 = 2as$$

therefore

$$W = m\left(\frac{v^2}{2}\right)$$

That is,

$$\text{K.E.} = \tfrac{1}{2}mv^2 \tag{5.06}$$

This derivation assumes F and hence a constant, but this restriction is quite unnecessary. Any body of mass m and velocity v has kinetic energy as given by (5.06), regardless of how it was accelerated to reach this velocity.

Units. Equations (5.05) and (5.06) were derived assuming $F = ma$. Thus the results will be valid only in absolute units (or in the fps grav. system if force is measured in pounds and mass in slugs). If m is in kilograms, g in meters per second per second, h in meters, and v in meters per second, either equation gives the energy in joules. If the same quantities are measured in slugs, feet per second per second, feet, and feet per second, respectively, the energy will be in foot-pounds.

Zeros of Energy. As pointed out in Chapter 2, all measurements of displacement must be made from some origin, all measurements of velocity presume some stationary reference line. The origin and the coordinate lines are called a frame of reference, and this frame may be moving or not—usually we don't know. In fact, modern physical theories claim that there is no such thing as a frame of reference absolutely at rest. This is one of the conclusions of the theory of relativity (see section 10.05). The importance of this argument here is that we can only measure differences in kinetic energy and potential energy—that is, the difference between the kinetic energy of a body in motion with respect to a given frame of reference and its kinetic energy when at rest in that frame, the difference in the potential energy of a body in some position in a frame and its potential energy when at the origin of that frame. Normally our frame of reference is with respect to a fixed origin in the surface of the earth.

The discussion leading to equation (5.05) may have seemed artificial because of its specification of infinitely slow motion. That was to avoid for the moment any kinetic energy of the body raised. We now consider both in an example.

Example. Consider a body of mass m resting on a level plane OA, as in Figure 5.02. Let a force $F = 3mg$ act vertically upward on the body. The net force of $2mg$ will cause an acceleration

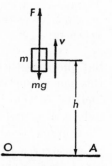

$$a = 2g \qquad \text{(upward)}$$

After the body has risen through a height h the work done is

$$W = 3mgh$$

Fig. 5.02. Kinetic energy and potential energy.

The velocity attained is given by $v^2 = 2as$, i.e.,

$$v^2 = 2 \cdot 2gh$$
$$\text{K.E.} = \tfrac{1}{2}mv^2 = \tfrac{1}{2}m \cdot 4gh = 2mgh$$
$$\text{P.E.} = mgh$$

so that the work done is the sum of the kinetic energy and the potential energy.

5.05 CONSERVATION OF ENERGY. CONSERVATION LAWS

In Figure 5.03 a mass m rests on a surface a distance h above the ground. Its potential energy is mgh. Suppose it is pushed over the edge. It will fall with an acceleration g, and since its initial velocity is zero,

$$v^2 = u^2 + 2as$$

becomes

$$v^2 = 0 + 2gh$$

Therefore its kinetic energy on hitting the ground is

$$\text{K.E.} = \tfrac{1}{2}mv^2 = \tfrac{1}{2}m \cdot 2gh = mgh \qquad (5.07)$$

i.e., its kinetic energy on hitting the ground is the same as its potential energy at the top. If we write E for the total mechanical energy.

At top: $E = \text{K.E.} + \text{P.E.} = 0 + mgh = mgh$

At bottom: $E = \text{K.E.} + \text{P.E.} = mgh + 0 = mgh$

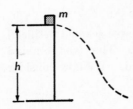

Fig. 5.03. Conservation of mechanical energy.

Thus the total energy is the same at both top and bottom, and a simple calculation would give the same result for any intermediate position of the body. In this simple system mechanical energy is conserved.

Suppose that, instead of falling vertically from the top, the body m slid down the smooth surface shown by the dashed line in Figure 5.03. Would the velocity at the bottom be given by (5.07)? Experimentally, the velocity at the bottom in this case is always less than for free fall, but the smoother the surface the more closely the velocity appoaches this maximum value. Presumably for a perfectly smooth surface the increase of velocity of the mass would depend on the decrease of height only, and would thus be independent of the path followed by the body.

Conservation of mechanical energy does not apply when a body moves over a rough surface because friction produces heat (hence the classic phrase about "rubbing two Boy Scouts together to start a fire"), and heat represents a loss of mechanical energy. The equivalence of heat and mechanical energy is a relatively new idea introduced by Rumford (1753) about 1800. Careful experiments by Joule (1818) showed that when mechanical work disappeared heat was produced and that in all cases the heat produced was proportional to the work done. Many other forms of energy besides mechanical work and heat are known, notably chemical and electrical energy. A little over a hundred years ago the idea grew among a number of scientists that all the forms of energy are equivalent, in the sense that one form can be converted into another, and that energy is indestructible. The first formal statement of this principle seems to have been made by Mayer (1814), with Helmholtz (1821) soon after giving very convincing arguments for its truth. The credit for this great principle should probably be shared equally by the four men whose names are given in this paragraph—two Germans, an American, and an Englishman. In modern language the principle may be stated as follows.

Conservation of Energy. *In any closed system the total amount of energy, in all forms, is a constant.* Here, a closed system means one with no transfer of energy to or from its surroundings.

The first principle of science is the existence of natural law in the universe, what we may call the assumption of predictability: that if effect B follows on cause A today, it will tomorrow and at any future time, other things being equal. Without this assumption it is difficult to conceive of the existence of science.

Next to this, the greatest generalization in science is the Conservation of Energy. It cannot be proved, but in all cases where it can be studied the total energy is constant within experimental error, and the principle is universally accepted.

CONSERVATION LAWS

The law of the conservation of energy has been slightly modified during the present century. Einstein showed that a rapidly moving body appears to have more mass than a stationary one, the extra mass being the kinetic energy divided by the square of the velocity of light, c. From this it is a short step to the speculation that mass and energy are equivalent quantities, and experiments in nuclear physics have shown that it *is* possible to convert mass into energy and vice versa. The quantitative connection is the Einstein equation

$$E = mc^2$$

and the conversion of mass in this manner is the source of atomic energy. This is contrary to the basic assumption of chemistry that matter is indestructible, but the reason that chemical experiments always show that mass is conserved is that the fraction of the mass converted in any chemical reaction is too small to measure. Measurable changes occur only in nuclear physics, and in all other applications we can treat mass and energy as being conserved separately, although it is now clear that it is the total of mass plus energy which is conserved or is indestructible. With this reservation we list the conservation laws.

1. Conservation of Mass.

2. Conservation of Energy.

3. Conservation of Momentum.   This has been discussed in section 3.07.

4. Conservation of Angular Momentum.   This will be taken up in section 7.07.   Angular momentum is similar to linear momentum and is a measure of turning or rotational effects.

5. Conservation of Electric Charge.   It is a fundamental assumption of electricity that the algebraic sum of electric charge in any closed system is a constant.   No exceptions to this law are known.

These five conservation laws are the most fundamental principles of physics.   Their importance lies in their universality, and they form very powerful tools in the investigation of any system.   It is important to realize that they apply just as well to *living* objects as to inanimate matter.

5.06 POWER

For many purposes the rate at which energy is delivered is just as important as the total quantity.   An automobile engine, given time, can deliver as much energy as is used by an aircraft in flying the Atlantic, but the automobile engine could not supply energy fast enough to get the aircraft off the ground.

Power is defined as the rate of doing work.   In symbols,

$$P = \frac{W}{t} \quad \text{or} \quad W = Pt \tag{5.08}$$

If P is a variable quantity, (5.08) defines the average power.

Units.   The mks unit is the joule per second or *watt*.   The basic fps unit is the foot-pound per second, but a larger unit is more commonly used, the *horsepower* (*hp*), which is defined arbitrarily as

$$1 \text{ horsepower} = 550 \text{ ft-lb sec}^{-1}$$

The name arose when James Watt (1736) invented the steam engine. He sold his engines to mine owners as guaranteed to replace so many horses and for safety chose to define the horsepower of his engines rather conservatively. Few horses can work at this rate for long. Conversion factors are

$$1 \text{ hp} = 746 \text{ watts}$$
$$1 \text{ kw} = 1.34 \text{ hp}$$

Another useful relation for power is derived from (5.08) and the definition of work

$$P = \frac{W}{t} = \frac{1}{t} \mathbf{F} \cdot \mathbf{s} = \frac{\mathbf{F} \cdot \mathbf{s}}{t} = \mathbf{F} \cdot \mathbf{v} \tag{5.09}$$

Efficiency. Machines are devices for the transmission and modification of force. The force is exerted on the machine by an external agent. The machine transmits the force to a different point and exerts a force (usually different in size from the original one) on an external object. Thus work is done on a machine by the external agent, and the machine delivers work to the external object. All machines waste some energy in frictional work and other ways, so that the output work is always smaller than the input.

Efficiency of a machine is defined as the ratio of output to input. In symbols

$$\text{Eff.} = \frac{W_{\text{out}}}{W_{\text{in}}} = \frac{W_{\text{out}}}{t} \frac{t}{W_{\text{in}}} = \frac{P_{\text{out}}}{P_{\text{in}}} \tag{5.10}$$

From (5.10), efficiency is always a decimal number less than 1. Frequently it is multiplied by 100 to express it as a percentage.

5.07 A POWER SYSTEM

The ideas of this chapter are well illustrated by considering Figure 5.04, which is a schematic diagram of a hydroelectric power system.

Sunlight S falling on the ocean O evaporates water which rises to form a cloud. Wind blows the cloud inland, and when the cloud is deflected upward, say by a mountain, rain falls. The rain collects in a lake or reservoir. A large pipe, or penstock P, drains off water from the lake and allows it to fall through a height h to the turbines in the powerhouse.

The turbines turn generators which produce electrical power. The water coming out of the turbines is discharged into a river R and flows back to the ocean. The electrical power is transmitted over wires to the users in a city which may be as much as three hundred miles away. There it is converted into heat energy in toasters, etc., or into light in electric lamps, or may be supplied to a motor (M) which converts it back to mechanical power to operate the machines in a factory.

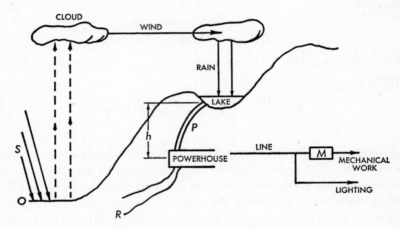

Fig. 5.04. A hydroelectric power system.

If m is the maximum mass of water which can flow through P per second, mgh is the maximum mechanical power available at the power-house. The electrical power output is reduced below this figure because the turbines and generators do not have an efficiency of 100%, and the power delivered to the city is further reduced by losses in the line. The power requirements of the city change throughout the day, and the flow of water is adjusted by partially closing gates in P so that the power-house continually supplies the right amount of power.

5.08 COLLISIONS AND COEFFICIENT OF RESTITUTION

In section 3.07 the collision of two objects was considered, and it was seen that momentum was conserved. To find out what happens to energy, we must consider more carefully what actually takes place in a collision. If you hold a soft rubber ball in your hand and squeeze it, your fingers push the surface in, but when you let go the ball returns rapidly to its original shape. You certainly did some work in deforming the ball. What has happened to it? As the surface of the ball moves out it pushes air in front of it, and the kinetic energy of the air represents part of the work done originally. The rest of the work done seems to disappear but, as is usually the case when mechanical energy is lost, this is because heat has been generated. Any deformation of a solid object generates heat, as may be seen readily by bending a wire back and forth rapidly at one point to break it. The wire may become too hot to touch at the point where it is being bent.

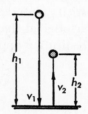

Because the ball returns to its original shape we say it is elastic. Almost all substances possess this ability to some extent, putty markedly less so than rubber. A convenient measure of the elasticity is the rebound when a ball of the material is dropped on a hard, fixed surface such as a concrete floor. Figure 5.05 shows such a test.

Fig. 5.05. Coefficient of restitution.

An object, such as a golf ball, is dropped through a height h_1 onto a hard floor. It rebounds owing to its elasticity but only rises through a height h_2 before coming to rest. If v_1 is the velocity just before the impact and v_2 that just after,

$$v_1^2 = 2gh_1, \qquad v_2^2 = 2gh_2, \qquad \frac{v_2^2}{v_1^2} = \frac{h_2}{h_1} \tag{5.11}$$

Experimentally, if h_1 is varied, it is found that the ratio of h_2/h_1 remains constant for a given ball. Hence from (5.11) the ratio of impact velocities is a constant, called the **coefficient of restitution**, and denoted by the symbol e.

$$e = \frac{v_2}{v_1} = \left(\frac{h_2}{h_1}\right)^{\frac{1}{2}} \tag{5.12}$$

Strictly speaking, e depends on the material of the floor as well as on that of the ball, but it is assumed, and justified experimentally, that if e is measured as above, the numerical value obtained is usually applicable to collisions between two bodies of the material of the ball.

Figure 5.06 illustrates a collision in one-dimensional motion, the u's

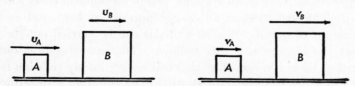

Fig. 5.06. Collision of two bodies.

being initial velocities and the v's final, and the bodies sliding on a smooth, level surface.

$$u_A > u_B, \qquad v_B > v_A$$

From section 3.07, $m_A u_A + m_B u_B = m_A v_A + m_B v_B$ \hfill (5.13)

During the impact both A and B are deformed and, as a result of their elasticity, internal forces are developed which tend to restore them to their original shape as the bodies separate again.   If e is the coefficient of restitution applicable to the two bodies, then from (5.12)

$$e = \frac{v_B - v_A}{u_A - u_B} \tag{5.14}$$

since in (5.12) v_1 is the relative velocity of approach of the ball and the floor and v_2 the relative velocity of separation.   Equations (5.13) and (5.14) are two independent relations which can be solved to find v_A and v_B in terms of u_A and u_B.   Figure 5.06 has been drawn for the case in which the four velocities are all directed to the right.   If we treat the velocity symbols as algebraic quantities, so that a positive value of u_B (say) means a velocity to the right while a negative value means one to the left, equations (5.13) and (5.14) can be applied to any collision in one dimension.

In Figure 5.05 all the mechanical energy of the ball is kinetic immediately before and after impact with the floor.   The change in kinetic energy is

$$\Delta \text{ (K.E.)} = \tfrac{1}{2}mv_2{}^2 - \tfrac{1}{2}mv_1{}^2$$

$$= \frac{m}{2}\, 2g(h_2 - h_1) = mgh_1\left(\frac{h_2}{h_1} - 1\right)$$

$$= mgh_1(e^2 - 1) \qquad [\text{by (5.12)}]$$

By (5.07), \qquad\qquad $mgh_1 = \text{K.E. just before impact}$

therefore \qquad\qquad\qquad $\dfrac{\Delta \text{ (K.E.)}}{\text{K.E.}} = e^2 - 1$ \hfill (5.15)

Now $e \leq 1$ in all cases, so unless $e = 1$, in which case we say the ball is perfectly elastic, there is always some loss of mechanical energy in such a collision.   The lost mechanical energy appears as heat and as a very small amount of sound.   Similar analysis can be carried out for Figure 5.06, but the algebra is rather tedious.   The same result is obtained, namely that there is a loss of mechanical energy in any collision between objects which are not perfectly elastic.   The equation connecting e and Δ (K.E.) in this case is not as simple as (5.15).   It can be used in place of (5.14) as the second equation needed, in addition to (5.13), to solve a problem in which the loss of kinetic energy as a result of the collision is known.

In Figure 5.05 it appears that momentum is not conserved. This is because we assumed the floor to be fixed, which is equivalent to assuming it to have infinite mass. The change in momentum of the ball is

Final momentum − initial momentum

$$= (-mv_2) - (mv_1) = -m(v_1 + v_2)$$

if we take momentum directed downward as positive. The floor and anything to which the floor is attached (which ultimately includes the whole earth) must therefore acquire a momentum equal and opposite to this, namely $m(v_1 + v_2)$. However, the mass being moved is so great that the velocity it attains is far too small to be observed.

5.09 CALCULUS METHODS

In calculus notation the general definition of the work done by a force F in moving a body from s_1 to s_2 is

$$W = \int_{s_1}^{s_2} \mathbf{F} \cdot \mathbf{ds} \tag{5.16}$$

$$= \int_{s_1}^{s_2} F \cos \theta \, ds$$

$$= F \cos \theta \int_{s_1}^{s_2} ds \qquad \text{(if } F \text{ and } \theta \text{ are constants)}$$

$$= F \cos \theta (s_2 - s_1)$$

$$= Fs \cos \theta \qquad \text{(if } s_2 - s_1 = s)$$

$$= \mathbf{F} \cdot \mathbf{s}$$

This is in agreement with (5.03) but (5.16) is more general.

This definition permits a general derivation of the formula for kinetic energy of a body of mass m and velocity v. If initial velocity is u, the gain in kinetic energy is given by

$$\Delta \text{ (K.E.)} = W = \int_{s_1}^{s_2} \mathbf{F} \cdot \mathbf{ds} = \int_{s_1}^{s_2} m\mathbf{a} \cdot \mathbf{ds}$$

$$= m \int_{s_1}^{s_2} \frac{dv}{dt} \, ds$$

where ds is the component of $\mathbf{ds}$ in the direction of the acceleration.

$$\Delta \text{ (K.E.)} = m \int_{u}^{v} dv \frac{ds}{dt} = m \int_{u}^{v} v \, dv = m \left[\tfrac{1}{2}v^2 \right]_{u}^{v}$$

$$= \tfrac{1}{2}mv^2 - \tfrac{1}{2}mu^2 \tag{5.17}$$

This equation is more general than (5.06) since it shows the effect of an initial velocity and does *not* assume a constant value of **F**. The force may be a function of position.

If power is a variable quantity,

$$P = \frac{dW}{dt} \tag{5.18}$$

replaces equation (5.08) as the definition of instantaneous power.

PROBLEMS

1. What energy is gained by a body of mass 10.0 lb in falling freely through a height of 40 ft? by a body of mass 6.00 kgm in 4.00 m?

2. A shell weighing 25.0 lb has a speed of 2000 ft sec⁻¹. Find its kinetic energy.

3. What is the speed of a ball of mass 1.60 kgm if its kinetic energy is 720 joules?

4. A man drives a golf ball (mass 0.125 lb) 300 yd, the initial velocity of the ball being at an angle of 45.0° to the horizontal. What amount of energy did the man transmit to the ball?

5. If the same energy as in problem 4 had been used to hit a baseball (mass 0.625 lb), how far could it have gone?

6. A 2000-lb automobile is accelerated from a speed of 30.0 mph to 60.0 mph in a distance of 242 ft. How much work was done on the car? At what average rate was the motor developing power, neglecting losses?

7. A man drags a load along the ground by means of a rope passing over his shoulder. The rope makes an angle with the ground of 25°50′. If the man pulls on the rope with a force of 150 newtons, how much work does he do in walking 200 m?

8. If the man in problem 7 is working at the rate of 0.100 hp, how long does it take him to walk the 200 m?

9. A road is inclined at an angle of 21°06′ to the horizontal. A car of mass 2000 lb starts from rest on the slope and rolls 100 ft downhill. Find its velocity, assuming friction negligible.

10. A 180-hp motor drives a pump of 80% efficiency. How many imperial gallons of water (mass 10.0 lb each) can the pump raise through a height of 11.0 ft each second? (Note: 1 imperial gallon = 1.200 U.S. gallons.)

11. The average flow of water into a reservoir is 100,000 imperial gallons per second. If the head available is 110 ft and the over-all efficiency is 50%, what power output is available from a hydroelectric plant built below this reservoir? (Head is the vertical height from the intake end of the penstocks to the turbines.)

12. A bullet of mass 30.0 gm and velocity 400 m sec^{-1} strikes a board and penetrates 15.0 cm before coming to rest.   Find the average force it exerts on the board.

13. A small heavy mass (or bob) suspended on the end of a light string is called a simple pendulum.   If the mass is drawn to one side so that the taut string makes an angle of 60.0° with the vertical and is then released, find the maximum speed of the bob if the string is 8.00 ft long.

14. A body of mass 20.0 kgm slides down a rough plane inclined at an angle of 30.0° to the horizontal.   It starts from rest and in descending a vertical distance of 5.00 m it reaches a speed of 7.00 m sec^{-1}.   What amount of heat (in joules) is generated?   What average retarding force must the plane exert on the body?

15. Figure 5.07 illustrates a device for measuring bullet speeds called the ballistic pendulum.   A block of wood of mass M hangs by a light string.   The bullet of mass m and velocity v is fired into the block and remains imbedded in it. The momentum given to the block causes it to swing upward, and the maximum height of rise h is measured.   Prove that

$$v = \frac{m + M}{m} \sqrt{2gh}$$

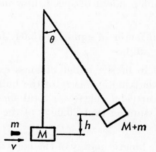

Fig. 5.07.   Ballistic pendulum.

16. A bullet of mass 5.00 gm is fired into a block of mass 5.00 kgm suspended from a string 100 cm long.   The string is observed to deflect through an angle of 10.0°.   Find the speed of the bullet.

17. A ping-pong ball, a golf ball, and a tennis ball are dropped on a hard floor from a height of 10.0 ft.   They rebound to heights of 8.10, 5.63, and 3.60 ft, respectively.   Find the coefficient of restitution in each case.

18. A ball of mass 1.00 kgm is moving westward at a speed of 16.0 m sec^{-1} while another of mass 1.00 kgm is moving eastward at a speed of 40.0 m sec^{-1} along the same straight line.   If the balls are perfectly elastic, find their velocities after collision.

19. If in problem 18 the coefficient of restitution had been 0.5, what would the recoil velocities have been?   Calculate the loss in energy in the collision.

20. If two bodies collide with a glancing impact, both their speeds and directions of motion will change.   This two-dimensional problem can be solved if it can be assumed that the surfaces are smooth so that the impulses are normal to the surfaces in contact.   The components of velocity parallel to the surfaces will then be unaltered while the changes in the normal components can be found from the coefficient of restitution.   In Figure 5.08 a small object traveling along the line AO with speed 50.0 m sec^{-1} strikes a hard, fixed surface at O.   Find the speed of recoil and the angle θ for (a) $e = 1.00$, (b) $e = 0.500$.

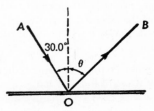

Fig. 5.08.

21. A 3000-lb automobile is traveling at 60.0 mph on a level road.   When the clutch is pushed in, it comes to rest in a distance of 1936 ft.   Assuming the retarding force was independent of speed, how much power was being used to drive it at 60 mph?

22. Derive the conversion factor of equation (5.04) from the relations between the basic mks and fps units.

23. A rifle of mass 3.000 lb fires a bullet of mass exactly $\frac{1}{2}$ ounce ($= \frac{1}{32}$ lb). What is the ratio of the kinetic energy of the bullet to that of the gun?   If the explosion of the cartridge releases a total energy of 900.0 ft-lb, find the speed of the bullet, assuming that 20.00% of the energy is lost as heat and sound.

24. In Figure 5.03 find the kinetic energy of the mass after it has fallen through a height of $h/4$.   What is the total energy of the body at this time?

25. A shell of mass 60.0 lb is traveling at a speed of 2000 ft sec^{-1} in a horizontal direction when it explodes.   Because of a defective casing it breaks into two parts rather than many pieces.   The masses of the two fragments are 14.0 and 42.0 lb, the remainder of the original mass being the explosive material consumed.   Both fragments move initially on the original horizontal path, the heavier fragment gaining speed.   The energy released in the explosion is 420,000 ft-lb.   Assuming all of it appears as kinetic energy of the fragments, find their speeds.

26. A rocket (initial mass 2000 lb) is fired vertically upward.   It ejects mass at the rate of 20.0 lb sec^{-1} with an exhaust velocity of 4000 ft sec^{-1}.   What is the net upward thrust initially? after 10.0 sec?   Using the average thrust and neglecting air resistance, calculate the velocity reached after 10.0 sec and the height at that time.   What is the energy of the rocket?   Now find the velocity, using equation (3.11), and the work done by the rocket motor. Discuss the discrepancies in your results.

6

Friction and Machines

6.01 EXAMPLES OF FRICTION

Numerous references have already been made to frictional effects —this was unavoidable because friction is present in almost every practical problem in mechanics. Friction is needed to make most methods of propulsion on the surface of the earth possible—cars and trains would not move, nor could one walk, if the surface were frictionless. On the other hand, whenever one surface slides or rolls over another, friction causes a loss of mechanical energy and the production of heat, both of which may be undesirable.

6.02 EXPERIMENTAL LAWS OF FRICTION

Figure 6.01(a) illustrates a simple method for investigating friction. A body of mass M rests on a level surface, being connected by a string

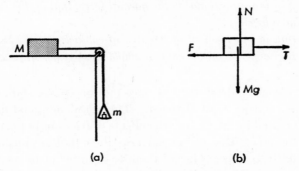

(a)   (b)

Fig. 6.01. Experiment on friction.

over a light, well-oiled pulley (which we can treat as being approximately frictionless) to a scale pan to which masses can be added. Let m be the total mass at this end of the string. Figure 6.01(b) is the diagram of the forces on M, the reaction of the surface on the mass being resolved into a normal force N and a frictional force F as described in section 3.05. The forces F and N must act on the lower surface of M while the weight Mg acts through the center of gravity.

As mg is increased gradually from zero, there is no motion of the system for some range of values of mg. Hence the rules of statics apply and

$$N = Mg$$
$$F = T = mg$$

Since mg is a variable, it follows that friction has the peculiar property of being variable also and of just the right size to prevent motion. By increasing mg sufficiently, however, motion eventually starts, so that F is limited in size. The value of $F = T = mg$ at which motion just starts is called **limiting friction**. Once M starts to move, it is usually observed that the system has a slight acceleration, so that F decreases slightly below limiting friction when the body is in motion. The change is small and is usually disregarded in problems.

Several experiments can be done, including altering N by placing additional loads on the sliding body, altering the area of contact without altering M (by using different faces of a brick, say), and increasing the smoothness of the surfaces by sandpapering or buffing. In each case the value of the limiting friction is measured by increasing mg until M just starts to move. The results of these experiments form the *Empirical Laws of Sliding Friction*, which are:

(1) *Friction is proportional to the normal force, that is, the force pressing the two surfaces together.*

(2) *Friction is independent of the area of contact.*

(3) *Friction depends on the state of smoothness of the surfaces in contact.*

Further experiments show that once motion starts, sliding friction is approximately independent of speed. These laws are good first approximations to be used in calculating the effects of friction, but certain limitations must be recognized. The surfaces must not be pushed together sufficiently hard to cause either of them to crumble or break up. If this happens, the laws fail entirely. If the surfaces are lubricated, as with oil, graphite, talc, etc., the frictional force F is greatly decreased, but the ratio of F to the normal force N is no longer a constant and depends on the size of N, the thickness of the lubricating film, and the area of contact.

In equation form the first law of friction is

$$\frac{F}{N} = \text{a constant, } \mu; \qquad F = \mu N \tag{6.01}$$

This constant μ is called the **coefficient of friction.** Strictly speaking, we should distinguish between two coefficients: μ_s, the coefficient of *static* friction ($= F_s/N$), and μ_K, the coefficient of *kinetic* friction ($= F_K/N$), where F_s is the smallest tangential force to start motion and F_K is the smallest tangential force to maintain uniform motion. Their relation is $\mu_s > \mu_K$. The value of μ_K remains approximately independent of speed for moderate speeds but usually starts to decrease slightly above speeds of the order of 30 to 40 ft/sec. Both this decrease and the difference $\mu_s - \mu_K$ are small, rarely amounting to 10% of μ_s, and we shall ignore the distinctions and speak of *the* coefficient of friction.

By the third law of friction μ depends on the nature and state of both surfaces in contact. It has been measured for many combinations of different substances, but the values found depend so critically on the state of the surfaces that it is not worth giving a list of values here. For sliding friction, typical values of μ range between 0.1 and 0.8.

A simple method of measuring μ is shown in Figure 6.02. A body of mass m rests on a plane inclined at an angle θ to the horizontal. As θ is increased from zero, the normal force, which is the component of weight perpendicular to the plane, decreases and hence possible limiting friction decreases. At the same time the component of weight available to accelerate the body down the plane increases. Initially $W \sin \theta \ll$ the

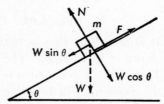

Fig. 6.02. Forces on an inclined plane.

possible value of limiting friction, and since frictional forces *always* oppose motion and *never* initiate it, the body remains at rest. When θ increases to some value λ such that

$$\text{Limiting friction, } F = W \sin \lambda \tag{6.02}$$

then the slightest increase in θ beyond this angle will cause the body to start to slide. Thus λ can be measured by slowly increasing θ until the body just starts to slide and taking this value of θ as λ. Since F in (6.02) is limiting friction,

$$F = \mu N = \mu W \cos \lambda \tag{6.03}$$

Dividing (6.02) by (6.03) gives

$$\mu = \tan \lambda \tag{6.04}$$

The angle λ is called the **angle of friction** or the angle of repose. This latter term comes from the observation that if a finely divided material (such as sand, coal, or grain) is piled in a heap, it will slide until the sides form a cone. The angle each side makes with the horizontal is the angle of repose and is related to the coefficient of static friction between two pieces of the material by (6.04).

6.03 EXPLANATION OF FRICTION

Friction between two surfaces is certainly due to their roughness, but the details of the mechanism are still imperfectly understood. Any surface, however smooth it may appear to the eye or the hand, will be seen to be quite irregular in a high-power microscope. Figure 6.03 represents the appearance in such a microscope of two surfaces in contact.

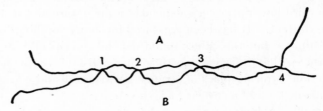

Fig. 6.03. Enlargement of surfaces in contact.

It is seen that they actually touch at very few points, only four being shown in the sketch. The actual area in contact is thus extremely small. The ratio of force to area is called **pressure,** and in this case it is seen that the pressure will be large, even though the normal force is relatively small. Now on a large scale, if two substances are forced together under very great pressure, high temperatures are developed and the two parts tend to fuse and weld to each other. Presumably the same thing happens at the microscopic points of contact 1, 2, 3, etc. If now one tries to slide A over B, it is necessary to exert a force to break these fused points apart. The normal force soon causes other welds to form, so that there is an uneven but continued resistance to sliding motion which we call friction. Recent experiments have confirmed this qualitative explanation but have shown that the phenomenon of friction is quite complex. The coefficient of friction of two metal surfaces, for instance, is critically dependent on the degree of oxidization of the metals.

6.04 EXAMPLES

In examples in this book we shall assume that the laws of friction given in section 6.02 are exactly correct.

EXAMPLE I

Inclined Plane. Figure 6.04(a) shows an inclined plane problem similar to that solved in Example IV, section 3.06, but with the added complication that the mass m_1 slides on a rough plane, the coefficient of friction between the plane and the mass being μ. Figure 6.04 (b) shows a partial free body diagram for the mass m_1. The forces shown are the tension of the cord, the normal component of the reaction of the plane,

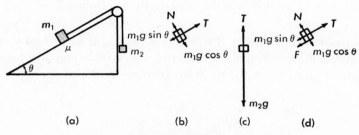

(a)   (b)   (c)   (d)

Fig. 6.04. Rough inclined plane problem.

and the components of weight parallel and perpendicular to the plane. Frictional force is not shown because we don't know which way it will act. To determine the direction of F, the frictional force, we must find the direction in which the system will try to move. Figure 6.04(c) is the free body diagram of forces on m_2. If $m_2g > m_1g \sin \theta$, the system will try to move to the right (clockwise rotation of the frictionless pulley). If $m_2g < m_1g \sin \theta$, the system will try to move to the left. We assume the former to be the case here. Then F, which always opposes motion, must act down the plane and can now be added to the force diagram which is shown completed for m_1 in (d). We can now write down the force equations.

$$m_2g - T = m_2a \tag{6.05}$$
$$T - m_1g \sin \theta - F = m_1a \tag{6.06}$$
$$N - m_1g \cos \theta = 0 \tag{6.07}$$
$$F = \mu N = \mu m_1g \cos \theta \tag{6.08}$$

The right-hand side of (6.07) is zero because there is no possibility of motion of m_1 perpendicular to the plane and hence the acceleration in this direction is zero. Equation (6.08) must be used with caution since it gives the limiting value of friction and there is no certainty that F in (6.06) is limiting friction. If

$$T - m_1g \sin \theta < \mu m_1g \cos \theta \tag{6.09}$$

F will be just large enough to make the left-hand side of (6.06) zero, so that a is zero and the system is stationary. (It was because of this possibility that in connection with determining the possible direction of motion we spoke of the system *trying* to move to the left or right.) If the solution of equations (6.05) to (6.08) should give a negative acceleration, this will always mean that the system will remain at rest and that we were wrong in assuming that limiting friction acted. It will *never* mean that the system will accelerate in the opposite direction—the possible direction of motion was the first result determined.

Numerical Example. If $\theta = 30°$, $\mu = 1/\sqrt{3}$, $m_1 = 1.00$ kgm, and $m_2 = 4.00$ kgm, find the acceleration of the system and the tension in the cord. Equations (6.05) to (6.08) become

$$4.00g - T = 4.00a$$
$$T - 1.00g \times \tfrac{1}{2} - F = 1.00a$$
$$N - 1.00g \times \frac{\sqrt{3}}{2} = 0$$
$$F = \frac{1}{\sqrt{3}} 1.00g \frac{\sqrt{3}}{2} = 0.500g$$

Substituting for F gives

$$4.00g - T = 4.00a$$
$$T - 0.500g - 0.500g = 1.00a$$
$$a = \frac{3g}{5} = 5.88 \text{ m sec}^{-2}, \qquad T = 15.7 \text{ N}$$

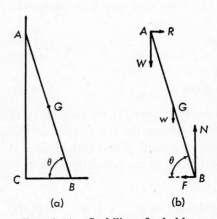

(a)   (b)

Fig. 6.05. Stability of a ladder.

EXAMPLE II

Ladder. A uniform ladder of mass 75 lb rests against a smooth wall with its base on a rough floor, the coefficient of friction between floor and ladder being 0.250. What is the smallest angle between the ladder and the floor which will allow a man of 150 lb to climb to the top of the ladder?

The problem is illustrated in Figure 6.05(a) and the free body diagram of forces on the ladder is shown in (b). It is assumed that the man's weight W acts through the top point of the ladder. We assume limiting friction to act on the foot of the ladder, just keeping it in equilibrium.

$$R = F = \mu N$$
$$N = W + w$$

Taking moments about B, we have

$$w \times GB \cos \theta + W \times AB \cos \theta = R \times AB \sin \theta$$

$$75 \frac{AB}{2} \cos \theta + 150AB \cos \theta = F \times AB \sin \theta$$

$$\cos \theta(\tfrac{7.5}{2} + 150) = \sin \theta \times \mu N = \sin \theta \times 0.250(150 + 75)$$

$$\tan \theta = \frac{187.5}{0.250 \times 225} = 3.33$$

$$\theta = 73.3°$$

Note that the length of the ladder cancels out of the equation.

6.05 ROLLING FRICTION. STARTING WHEELED VEHICLES

The wheel is one of the greatest of man's inventions and serves to reduce friction to a very small force but does not eliminate it completely. A wheeled vehicle rolling, without sliding, over a level surface will still slow down unless a driving force is applied to it. This force counteracts the small amount of friction remaining. This so-called **rolling friction** seems to be due principally to the slight deformation of the surfaces in contact caused by the normal force. The same "laws" of friction apply to rolling friction as to sliding, but the coefficient of rolling friction is much smaller, as low as 0.01 or 0.001. In a wheeled vehicle the wheels are attached to axles which support the body of the vehicle. The contact between wheel and axle may be a sliding one, as in a bushing, but in better quality vehicles ball or roller bearings are used. Figure 6.06 illustrates a ball-bearing suspension for a wheel, C being a cylindrical groove or race in the center of the wheel, A the fixed axle of the vehicle, and B the balls which turn as shown when the wheel rotates. To keep the balls in their relative positions in the race, they are held loosely in the framework F, which makes no contact with either A or C. The suspension is well lubricated,

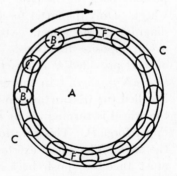

Fig. 6.06. Ball bearing connection between wheel and axle.

of course.   Roller-bearing suspensions are similar to ball-bearing ones but use cylinders of hard steel in place of balls.

The starting of an automobile (or train engine) depends on the sliding friction between the driving wheels and the surface on which they rest. Rolling friction plays a negligible part.

In Figure 6.07(a) the forces acting on one of the driving wheels are shown.   The wheel supports some fraction mg of the total weight of the vehicle.   This downward force is balanced by the upward push of the roadway, shown as N.   Numerically, $N = mg$ since there is no motion

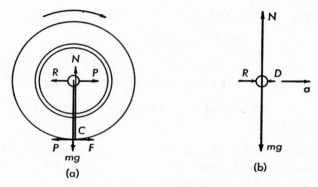

(a)   (b)

Fig. 6.07.   Forces on a wheel and axle.

perpendicular to the road.   The motor supplies the energy to turn the wheel and thus set the whole mass in motion, and drive shafts and other linkages transmit a torque (represented by the forces P, P) from the motor to the wheel.   The normal force N gives rise to a pair of equal and opposite frictional forces F between the wheel and the fixed surface, the wheel pushing back on the road (or rail) and the road pushing forward on the wheel.   Only the latter force is shown in the figure since it is a free body diagram of the wheel.   At the point of contact C the forces P and F act in opposite directions.   The force F will be just large enough to balance P provided P is less than the limiting value of friction (limiting $F = \mu N = \mu mg$).   In this case C is at rest with respect to the road and is called the **instantaneous center of rotation** because at this instant the wheel is turning about the momentarily fixed point C, owing to the upper force P.   This rotation causes the wheel to press forward against the axle.   The wheel exerts some horizontal force R on the axle, which must therefore push backward against the wheel with a numerically equal force R.   Thus six components of forces act *on* the wheel.   The vertical forces are in equilibrium and the net forward force is $P + F -$

$R - P = F - R$, from which it is seen that $F > R$ if the wheel has a forward acceleration.

Suppose that in an attempt to get faster acceleration we increase the torque exerted by the motor, that is, increase P.   As soon as $P > \mu N$ the wheel will slip, and the result is that the maximum value of F is reduced because the appropriate coefficient of friction is now the smaller, kinetic coefficient.

From this discussion we see that the force producing acceleration of the car is R, and $R \not> F \not> \mu N$, so that increasing P beyond the value μN does not accelerate the car any more rapidly.   In fact, spinning the wheels actually reduces the acceleration (and also wears out the tires rapidly).   (*Note:* the inequality $R \not> F$ is mathematical shorthand for the sentence "R is not greater than F".   Remember that the inequality sign points toward the smaller quantity: $x > y$ and $y < x$ both mean that x is larger than y.)

Figure 6.07(b) is the free body diagram of the axle.   The weight of the wheel has been neglected, and the weight pressing on the axle is again balanced by the upward push N transmitted by the wheel.   The net force available for accelerating the car is $R - D$, where D represents part of the drag on the car (compounded of air resistance, internal friction in the motor, etc.).

The mechanics of the motion of a car is complicated but interesting. The student should try his hand at redrawing Figure 6.07 for a car traveling at a steady speed and for a car being slowed down by application of the brakes.

Example I.   A car of mass 3000 lb is driven by its rear wheels, which support 40% of the car's weight.   The coefficient of friction between tires and road is 0.60.   What is the maximum acceleration which can be given to the car?

The maximum force which can be exerted on the car is

$$F = \mu N = 0.60(0.40 \times 3000)$$
$$= 720 \text{ lb-wt}$$
$$F = \frac{1}{g} ma$$
$$720 = \frac{3000}{32}a$$
$$a = 7.7 \text{ ft sec}^{-2}$$

Example II.   If the car of example I is moving at 60 mph, how fast can it be brought to rest, if equipped with four-wheeled brakes?

Since all four wheels have brakes the normal force on the tires is the full weight.

$$N = 3000 \text{ lb-wt}$$
$$F = \mu N = -0.60 \times 3000 = -1800 \text{ lb-wt}$$
$$F = \frac{1}{g} ma$$
$$-1800 = \tfrac{1}{32} 3000a$$
$$a = -19.2 \text{ ft sec}^{-2}$$
$$v^2 = u^2 + 2as$$
$$0 = 88 \times 88 - 2 \times 19.2s$$
$$s = 202 \text{ ft}$$

Example III. A shunting engine (of mass 200 tons) is pushing a string of boxcars (total mass 1000 tons) up an inclined track in a freight yard. The track makes an angle of 1.00° with the horizontal. The coefficient of sliding friction between the driving wheels of the engine and the rails is 0.200, and the coefficient of rolling friction for the entire train is 0.0050. Find the maximum acceleration of the train and the minimum time and distance to reach a speed of 15.0 mph, starting from rest.

Since the train is on an incline there is a component of weight along the track. If W is the total weight of the train, this component is $W \sin 1°$ and the normal force is $W \cos 1°$. Only the normal component of the weight of the engine is useful in establishing the maximum thrust of the engine, which is thus

$$P = \mu_s 200 \cos 1°$$
$$= 0.200 \times 200 \times 0.9998 = 40.0 \text{ tons-wt}$$

The retarding forces are the component of weight along the track and the rolling friction. The second law of motion gives the equation

$$P - W \sin 1° - \mu_R W \cos 1° = \frac{1200}{g} a$$

since the total mass is 1200 tons. Note the use of units. Forces are in tons-weight and masses in tons. The equation balances dimensionally, and it is not necessary to convert to the ordinary fps units since to do this would only mean multiplying each term in the equation by 2000.

$$40.0 - 1200 \times 0.0175 - 0.0050 \times 1200 \times 0.9998 = \tfrac{1200}{32}a$$
$$a = 0.347 \text{ ft sec}^{-2}$$

$$\text{Time to reach speed of 15.0 mph} = \frac{22.0 \text{ ft sec}^{-1}}{0.347 \text{ ft sec}^{-2}} = 63.4 \text{ sec}$$

$$\text{Distance to reach this speed} = \frac{22.0 \times 22.0}{2 \times 0.347} = 697 \text{ ft}$$

6.06 SIMPLE MACHINES. MECHANICAL ADVANTAGE

A machine is any device which alters the point of application, line of action, or size of a force. A motor (or engine, the two words being practically synonymous) is a source of mechanical energy. A machine and a motor are frequently combined in one permanent unit, such as an automobile or a machine tool with a built-in motor.

Almost all machines alter the size of the force applied to them, and the ratio of the output to input force is an important property called the **mechanical advantage** of the machine.

$$\text{Mech. adv.} = \frac{\text{force out}}{\text{force in}} \tag{6.10}$$

Mechanical advantages of several thousand are developed by some machines, but it is important to realize that the gain in force *must* be paid for by a loss in the distance the force moves. Would-be inventors of perpetual-motion machines—that is, machines which will continue to deliver work indefinitely without work being done on them—waste their time through failure to accept the law of conservation of energy.

If the input force F_{in} moves through a distance s_1, causing the output force F_{out} to move a distance s_2, then

$$F_{in} \times s_1 = F_{out} \times s_2 \tag{6.11}$$

for a machine in which there are no energy losses. Any actual machine involves some loss in its operation, so that the right-hand side of (6.11) is invariably somewhat less than the left-hand side. Hence for an actual machine

$$\frac{F_{out}}{F_{in}} < \frac{s_1}{s_2}$$

The left-hand ratio is the *actual* mechanical advantage achieved, while the ratio s_1/s_2 may be called the *theoretical* mechanical advantage since, by (6.11), it is equal to the mechanical advantage obtained in a machine without losses. By definition, efficiency is the ratio of output work to input. Therefore

$$\text{Eff.} = \frac{F_{\text{out}} \times s_2}{F_{\text{in}} \times s_1}$$

$$= \frac{F_{\text{out}}}{F_{\text{in}}} \times \frac{s_2}{s_1}$$

or

$$\text{Eff.} = \frac{\text{actual mech. adv.}}{\text{theoretical mech. adv.}} \tag{6.12}$$

A feature of our mechanical age is the development of more and more elaborate automatic machines. In fact, quite serious discussion is going on concerning the design of automatic factories in which it is expected that raw materials will be delivered at one end and finished goods turned out at the other with no need of human work or supervision of the machines in the process. Machines of great complexity are found on analysis to be built up of combinations of a few simple machines, the more important of which are discussed below.

(1) LEVERS

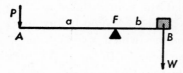

Fig. 6.08. The lever.

Figure 6.08 illustrates the principle of the lever, which was probably the first machine discovered by primitive man. A stiff rod AB, of negligible mass in the simplest case, turns about a fixed point, or **fulcrum**, F. What force P must be applied at one end to raise a mass of weight W at the other? We calculate the size of P for equilibrium; any larger force will raise W. If a, b are the distances from the fulcrum to P and to the center of gravity of the mass, then the equality of moments about F gives

$$P \cdot a = W \cdot b$$

$$\text{Mech. adv.} = \frac{W}{P} = \frac{a}{b} \tag{6.13}$$

If a is $10 \times b$, a force of 20 lb-wt will serve to raise a mass of 200 lb, but if W is to be raised 1 in., the point A must be pushed 10 in. down. Everyone has used a lever of this type, but it is not so generally recognized that the human forearm is a lever in which mechanical advantage is sacrificed to gain large displacement. Figure 6.09 is a sketch of the arrangement. The biceps muscles are attached to the forearm 2 in. or so from the elbow E, which acts as the fulcrum. Since the forearm is, say, 14 in. long from the elbow to the palm of the hand, the pull P of the biceps must be about seven times as great as the weight W. A consequence is that a small contraction of the length of these powerful muscles causes a move- ment of the hand seven times as great, thus permitting very rapid motion.

Fig. 6.09. Schematic drawing of human forearm.

(2) PULLEYS

For simplicity we still consider pulleys at this stage as light, friction- less wheels. The essential function of a single pulley is to change the direction of a force, as illustrated in Figure 6.10(a). The mechanical

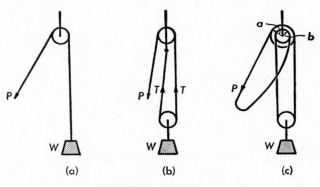

(a) (b) (c)

Fig. 6.10. Pulleys.

advantage is unity. By combining two or more pulleys, increased mechanical advantage can be obtained. In Figure 6.10(b), if the weight of the lower pulley is neglected and T is the tension in the rope,

$$P = T = \frac{W}{2}$$

so that Mech. adv. $= 2$

The familiar block and tackle replaces each of the pulleys of (b) by a set of three pulleys side by side on an axle. A continuous rope is threaded around the six pulleys. Hence W is lifted by six ropes and the mechanical advantage is six, neglecting friction and the weight of the rope and the lower set of pulleys.

Various special pulley systems have been designed for the rigging of sailing ships and other purposes, but no new principle is involved. An important variant is the **differential pulley,** which is shown in Figure 6.10(c). The upper wheel consists of two pulleys of slightly different diameters ($2a$ for the larger, $2b$ for the smaller) which are rigidly attached together. A continuous chain is threaded through the pulley system as shown. Suppose the force P acting on the chain pulls a length of chain $2\pi a$ over the upper wheel. Work done by P is then $2\pi aP$ and the upper wheel rotates once. The right-hand side of the loop of chain supporting W is thus raised a distance $2\pi a$, but because the smaller pulley on the upper wheel has also rotated once, a length of chain $2\pi b$ is let down by it. Thus the loop supporting W is now shorter by a length

$$2\pi a - 2\pi b$$

so that W must have risen a distance

$$\frac{2\pi a - 2\pi b}{2}$$

requiring work of amount

$$W(\pi a - \pi b)$$

to be done. Assuming 100% efficiency,

$$W(\pi a - \pi b) = P2\pi a$$

$$\text{Mech. adv.} = \frac{2a}{a - b} \tag{6.14}$$

As seen in the diagram, part of the chain is always slack and yet it must not slide on the smaller upper pulley. It is for this reason that toothed pulley wheels and a chain are used. The efficiency of this machine is always much less than 100% because of friction, etc., so the result of (6.14) is higher than the mechanical advantage actually found, but a very large multiplication of force can be obtained by making the difference $a - b$ small. A chain hoist capable of lifting one ton with an applied force of 30 lb is quite a commonplace piece of equipment for a machine shop.

(3) INCLINED PLANE AND SCREWS

One of the simplest of machines is the inclined plane or ramp. In Figure 6.11, if friction can be neglected, a force P is sufficient to raise a weight W if

$$P = W \sin \theta$$

so that

$$\text{Mech. adv.} = \frac{1}{\sin \theta}$$

Friction can rarely be neglected, but a ramp and a wheeled cart, or dolly, are very helpful in raising heavy loads. A machine screw (Figure 6.12) is an inclined plane wrapped around a cylinder. The distance between threads, d, is sometimes called the **pitch** of the screw. If the screw engages a threaded hole, one complete turn of the screw causes it to move

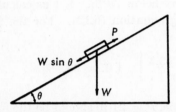

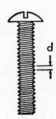

Fig. 6.11. Inclined plane.   **Fig. 6.12.** Machine screw.

a distance d parallel to its length. If the opposition to motion is W and the applied force P has a lever arm a, theoretical mechanical advantage is

$$\frac{W}{P} = \frac{2\pi a}{d}$$

Machine screws are used to fasten pieces of metal together. Similar threaded cylinders are important components of machine tools, and one form of automobile jack uses this principle. Wood screws differ only in having a conical shape in order to penetrate wood more easily.

6.07 EFFECT OF FRICTION ON MACHINES

In the preceding section the theoretical mechanical advantages of several machines were calculated, neglecting friction. The effect of friction is to reduce the efficiency of a machine and to give a mechanical advantage which is often considerably less than the theoretical one. Two points are worth noting.

Self-Locking Machines. In many machines, if the force P is removed, the friction is large enough to prevent W from causing the machine to run backward. If the differential pulley of Figure 6.10(c) has a theoretical mechanical advantage of 100 and W is 1000 lb, a force P of 10 lb should be enough to lift the weight. In practice it may be found necessary to pull with a force of 30 lb, so friction amounts to a 20-lb force. If P is removed, this frictional force reverses and opposes W instead of P, and since it is more than enough to hold W, the machine is self-locking. This can be a great convenience.

Effect of Load on Efficiency.   Frictional forces in a machine tend to be independent of the size of the load.   Thus in the differential pulley cited above, if the load were reduced to 100 lb, it would probably be found that the friction was reduced little if any below 20 lb.   Let us calculate the efficiency for these two loads, using equation (6.12).   For the first load,

$$\left. \begin{array}{l} \text{Actual mech. adv.} = \tfrac{1000}{30} = 33.3 \\ \text{Theoretical mech. adv.} = 100 \end{array} \right\} \quad \text{Eff.} = 33.3\%$$

For the second load, if friction is the same, $P = 21$ lb should be the force required to lift $W = 100$ lb.   Hence

$$\left. \begin{array}{l} \text{Actual mech. adv.} = \tfrac{100}{21} = 4.8 \\ \text{Theoretical mech. adv.} = 100 \end{array} \right\} \quad \text{Eff.} = 4.8\%$$

Thus the efficiency of a machine decreases as the load gets smaller. Using a pile driver to crack a peanut is silly from every point of view.

PROBLEMS

1. A mass of 10.0 kgm rests on a level table, the coefficient of friction being 0.400.   What force is needed to cause it to move?

2. A mass rests on a level surface which is gradually tilted.   When the surface makes an angle of 19.8° with the horizontal the mass starts to move.   What is the coefficient of friction?

3. A body is released at the top of a plane inclined at an angle of 40.0° to the horizontal.   If the angle of friction is 30.0°, how long does it take to reach the bottom of the plane, a distance of 12.0 ft?

4. A box of mass 500 lb is dragged 20.0 ft up a slope of 15.0°, the coefficient of friction being 0.200.   Find the work done.   What is the mechanical advantage of the slope?

5. In Figure 6.04, $m_1 = 8.00$ kgm, $m_2 = 2.00$ kgm, $\theta = 30.0°$, $\mu = 1/(4\sqrt{3})$. Find the acceleration of the system and the tension in the cord.   How long does it take for m_2 to rise 1.00 m, starting from rest?

6. A ladder of mass 75.0 lb is 25.0 ft long.   Its center of gravity is 10.0 ft from its base.   The ladder rests on a rough floor ($\mu = 0.300$) and leans against a smooth wall, the angle between ladder and wall being 30.0°.   How high can a man of mass 150 lb climb the ladder safely?

7. A pulley system is constructed using two blocks of three pulleys each, the top one being attached to a fixed beam. If the block and tackle is used to raise a 300-lb mass and each of the blocks has a mass of 6.00 lb, what is the force needed to raise the mass and what is the mechanical advantage?

8. The upper wheel of a differential pulley consists of two pulleys of diameters 12.0 and 10.0 in. Find the theoretical mechanical advantage. It is found that pulls of 60.0 lb and 120 lb are needed to raise masses of 480 and 1200 lb, respectively. Calculate the efficiency in each case.

9. The coefficient of rolling friction between a train and the rails is 0.0100. At a steady speed of 60.0 mph the force of air resistance is 90.0 tons-wt. What horsepower is the engine developing at this speed if the mass of the train is 1000 tons?

10. Two masses A and B slide on slopes of 30.0° and 60.0° as shown in Figure 6.13. The coefficients of friction for A and B are, respectively, 0.289 and 0.200. The mass of A is 100 lb. Find the acceleration of the system and the tension in the cord for (a) mass of B = 10.0 lb, (b) mass of B = 30.0 lb.

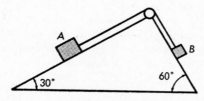

Fig. 6.13.

11. A car of mass 3000 lb is parked facing upward, on a hill of slope 10.0°. In this attitude 50.0% of the weight of the car rests on the rear wheels. If the coefficient of friction is 0.600, what is the maximum acceleration with which the car can be started? What power is needed to maintain this acceleration when the car reaches a speed of 20.0 mph?

12. A 4000-lb car is traveling at 40.0 mph. If the coefficient of friction is 0.600, in what distance can it be stopped (a) on a level road, (b) on a 20.0° downgrade?

13. What is the maximum efficiency of a "self-locking" machine, such as a differential pulley?

14. A body of mass 6.00 lb rests on a rough, inclined plane. A force of 2.40 lb-wt parallel to the plane is just sufficient to prevent the mass slipping, and the parallel force must be increased to 3.60 lb-wt to just start the body sliding up the plane. Find the coefficient of friction and the inclination of the plane to the horizontal.

15. A uniform ladder rests against a smooth wall with its base on a rough floor, the angle of friction being λ. If the inclination of the ladder to the vertical

is θ, show that if the ladder is not to slip, the maximum value of θ is given by $\tan \theta = 2 \tan \lambda$.

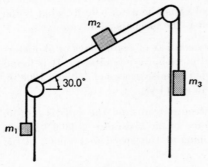

16. In Figure 6.14 three masses are connected by light cords passing over light, frictionless pulleys. The coefficient of friction between m_2 and the slope is $1/(2\sqrt{3})$. If $m_1 = 4.00$, $m_2 = 12.00$, $m_3 = 16.00$, all in pounds, find the acceleration of the system, the tensions in the cords, and the velocity of m_3 after moving 6.00 ft from rest.

Fig. 6.14.

17. A uniform ladder is on the point of slipping when it rests with one end on a rough, horizontal floor ($\mu = 0.300$) and the other on a rough, vertical wall ($\mu = 0.200$). Find the angle between the ladder and the floor.

18. A small object is to be dragged along a rough surface (angle of friction equal to λ) by a rope making an angle θ with the horizontal (Figure 6.15). For what value of θ will the required force be a minimum? (Problems concerning maxima and minima are best handled by calculus methods.)

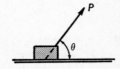

Fig. 6.15.

19. A uniform chain 10.0 ft long rests on a horizontal table with one end hanging over the edge. If the coefficient of friction between the table and the chain is 0.200, what is the greatest length of chain which can hang freely without slipping occurring?

20. Two bodies of masses 10.0 and 20.0 lb are connected by a light string and placed on an inclined plane so that the string lies along a line of greatest slope. The coefficients of friction between the bodies and the plane are respectively 0.300 and 0.600, and the smoother body is below the other. Find the inclination of the plane with the horizontal when both bodies start to slide.

21. A uniform rectangular block rests with its square base on a horizontal surface. The coefficient of friction between the block and the surface is 0.400. If the side of the base is 2.00 ft, find the lowest point of application at which a horizontal force will cause the block to overturn rather than slide.

22. A uniform board of weight W and negligible thickness rests horizontally across a fixed circular cylinder. The length of the board is twice the diameter of the cylinder, and the angle of friction between the two surfaces is λ. Prove that the greatest weight which can be applied at one end without causing the plank to slip is $\lambda W/(2 - \lambda)$.

7

Angular Motion

7.01 ROTATION OF RIGID BODIES

Any body of finite size is capable of two different types of motion, called **translation** and **rotation.** So far we have been discussing the first of these, in which the center of mass of the body moves in such a way that its displacement increases with time. In section 4.02 we saw that the condition for no rotation was that the net torque about any axis should vanish. We now proceed to investigate the dynamics of rotational motion. If a body such as a stick is thrown, in general it will have both types of motion simultaneously, and this general case will be discussed in section 7.08, but it is simpler to start with pure rotation about a fixed axis. The axis may pass through the center of mass, in which case this point is stationary, or the axis may be elsewhere, in which case the center of mass describes a circle. It is still convenient to classify the latter case as pure rotation since the average dis-placement of the center of mass is zero over any number of complete turns of the body.

A body is in rotation when every part of it describes a circle, with the circles centered on a given line. The outer parts move more rapidly than the inner ones, and this gives rise to internal stresses in the body, that is, to forces exerted between different parts of it.

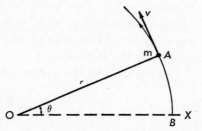

Fig. 7.01. Angular motion.

We avoid discussion of these frequently important forces by assuming that we are dealing with rigid bodies only. Internal stresses are considered under the headings of **elasticity** and **strength of materials** (see Chapter 9.)

Figure 7.01 illustrates the simplest type of extended body, undergoing

123

rotation about an axis through O perpendicular to the plane of the diagram. A light rod OA has a particle of mass m attached at A. At $t = 0$ the rod OA lay along some direction OX, and at $t = t_1$ it is in the position shown, with $<XOA = \theta$; θ is called the **angular displacement** of the body. The distance moved by the mass m is the arc BA. We represent the distance BA measured along the arc by s, and the distance of A from the axis by r. Then from the definition of radian measure,

$$\theta \text{ (in radians)} = \frac{s}{r} \quad \text{or} \quad s = r\theta \qquad (7.01)$$

It is clear from equation (7.01) that an angle does not have dimensions since it is a ratio of two lengths. The only reason for introducing a "name" for the unit angle (the radian) is that the system of measuring angles in degrees, minutes, and seconds was invented first. The convenience of (7.01) is so great that in all theoretical work in physics angles are always measured in radians.

For a body of any shape, angular displacement is measured in a similar fashion. Draw a plane through the body perpendicular to the axis of rotation. In this plane draw a line in the body through the axis (and perpendicular to it) in some reference direction which is fixed in space. As the body rotates the angle between the reference direction and the line in the body is the angular displacement.

7.02 ANGULAR VELOCITY AND ANGULAR ACCELERATION

The similarities between angular motion and linear motion, i.e., translation, are very great, and most of our earlier definitions can be applied to rotation with only slight modifications. Thus **angular velocity** is the time rate of change of angular displacement. It is represented by the symbol ω.

In Figure 7.01 the average angular velocity $\bar{\omega}$ is

$$\bar{\omega} = \frac{\theta}{t_1} = \frac{\theta - 0}{t_1 - 0} = \frac{\Delta\theta}{\Delta t} \qquad (7.02)$$

If the angular velocity changes with time, we speak of the *instantaneous* angular velocity as the limit to which the ratio $\Delta\theta/\Delta t$ tends as both $\Delta\theta$ and Δt become very small. The displacement of the point A in time t_1 is the chord BA. The linear velocity of the point A is found as follows:

$$\bar{v} = \frac{BA}{t_1} \doteq \frac{\text{arc } BA}{t_1 - 0} = \frac{s - 0}{t_1 - 0} = \frac{\Delta s}{\Delta t} \qquad (7.03)$$

From (7.01), since r is a constant,

$$\Delta s = r \, \Delta \theta$$

$$\frac{\Delta s}{\Delta t} = r \frac{\Delta \theta}{\Delta t}$$

therefore,
$$\bar{v} \doteq r\bar{\omega}$$

The difference between the chord and arc from B to A becomes less as $\Delta \theta$ and Δt become smaller, and in the limit (7.03) becomes exact. The average signs can then be dropped, giving

$$v = r\omega \qquad (7.04)$$

for the instantaneous linear velocity. The direction of v is the limiting direction of Δs, that is, the direction of the tangent to the path of A. Thus v is perpendicular to r, and hence it is constantly changing in direction.

The time rate of change of angular velocity is called the **angular acceleration** and will be denoted by α. A similar argument to that above shows that

$$\alpha = \lim_{\Delta t \to 0} \frac{\Delta \omega}{\Delta t} \qquad (7.05)$$

and the linear acceleration a is given by

$$a = r\alpha \qquad (7.06)$$

and is also tangential to the path of A. But a is not the only linear acceleration of m. We see that if $\alpha = 0$ then $a = 0$ also, so that the size of v, or the linear speed, is constant. Since the direction of v is constantly changing toward the center of rotation, the particle experiences an acceleration toward the center. This important acceleration is called **centripetal** (or center-seeking) and will be studied in detail in section 7.04. In general, the total linear acceleration is the resultant of the centripetal acceleration and a of equation (7.06).

7.03 ANGULAR EQUATIONS OF MOTION

We shall have little occasion to consider rotational motions more complicated than those in which α is constant (the value of α frequently being zero). If the angular velocity at $t = 0$ is ω_0 then after 1 sec it is $\omega_0 + \alpha$, and at any time, if α is constant,

$$\omega = \omega_0 + \alpha t \qquad (7.07)$$

This is closely parallel to equation (2.03), and we see that equations of motion for constant angular acceleration can be written down by inspection from the linear case, as follows:

Linear Motion	**Angular Motion**	
$v = u + at$	$\omega = \omega_0 + \alpha t$	(7.07)
$s = ut + \frac{1}{2}at^2$	$\theta = \omega_0 t + \frac{1}{2}\alpha t^2$	(7.08)
$v^2 = u^2 + 2as$	$\omega^2 = \omega_0{}^2 + 2\alpha\theta$	(7.09)

Units. The basic units for angular displacement, velocity, and acceleration are radians, radians per second, and radians per second per second, respectively. Angular velocities are also frequently given in revolutions per minute (rpm) or revolutions per second (rps). Before substituting in equations, angular velocities in revolution per minute or per second must be converted into radians per second.

Example. An electric motor spins at 1800 rpm. What is its angular velocity?

$$1800 \text{ rpm} = \tfrac{1800}{60} \text{ rps} = 30 \text{ rps}$$
$$1 \text{ revolution} = 2\pi \text{ radians}$$

therefore
$$\omega = 60\pi \text{ radians/sec}$$

7.04 CENTRIPETAL ACCELERATION

Let us next calculate the centripetal acceleration. The simplest case is that of a body rotating with constant angular velocity ω and hence constant linear speed v. Figure 7.02(a) shows two positions of the body

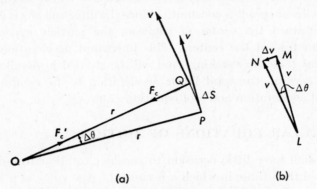

(a)   (b)

Fig. 7.02. Centripetal acceleration.

of Figure 7.01, with angular displacements differing by a small angle $\Delta\theta$. Figure 7.02(b) is the vector diagram of the linear velocities in the two positions. Since each of the velocities **v** is perpendicular to the corresponding radius, the angle between **v**, **v** is the same as that between **r**, **r**. Thus the two isosceles triangles *OPQ*, *LMN* are similar and

$$\frac{MN}{LM} = \frac{PQ}{OP} \qquad (7.10)$$

If $\Delta\theta$ is small, we can substitute the arc *PQ* for the chord *PQ* in (7.10). This enables us to calculate the magnitude of **Δv**, the change in velocity, which is the third side of the vector triangle; *LM* is the speed v, the arc *PQ* is Δs, and so on. Hence

$$\Delta v \doteq v\,\frac{\Delta s}{r}$$

and in the limit, as $\Delta\theta$ and Δt tend to zero, this equation becomes exact.

$$\frac{\Delta v}{\Delta t} = \frac{v}{r}\frac{\Delta s}{\Delta t} = \frac{v}{r}\,v = \frac{v^2}{r}$$

Now $\Delta v/\Delta t$ is the acceleration toward the center of rotation, since $MN \perp LM$ in the limit of small Δt, and is thus parallel to **r**. If we use the symbol $\mathbf{a}_c$ for the centripetal acceleration,

$$\mathbf{a}_c = \frac{v^2}{\mathbf{r}} = \mathbf{r}\omega^2 \qquad (7.11)$$

The derivation of (7.11) was based on a constant angular velocity, which is the case of main interest to us, but a more general derivation shows that this equation is always valid. If v is variable, $\mathbf{a}_c$ is variable also, and in the general case of a body following a curved path, **r** is the instantaneous radius of curvature of the path and v the instantaneous speed.

If in Figure 7.02 the body moving from P to Q has a mass m, force is required to produce the centripetal acceleration. This force is called the **centripetal force** and is

$$\mathbf{F}_c = \frac{mv^2}{\mathbf{r}} = m\omega^2\mathbf{r} \qquad (7.12)$$

In this case, the centripetal force is supplied by the pull of the rod connecting the mass to the axis. This light, rigid rod transmits the inward force exerted on the mass by the axis. By the Third Law of Motion the body must exert an equal and opposite force on the rod, which it in turn transmits as a pull on the axis. This outward force on the axis is called the **centrifugal force,** $\mathbf{F}_c'$. The two forces are often confused, and free body diagrams are important in avoiding this confusion.

The acceleration $\mathbf{a}_c$ is always perpendicular to **v**, and $\mathbf{F}_c$ is always perpendicular to the linear distance element **Δs**. Thus centripetal force has no component along the displacement and does no work.   A particle can follow a circular path at constant speed for any length of time, the size of the centripetal acceleration, the linear velocity, and the angular velocity all remaining constant and no change occurring in the energy of the particle.

Example I.   Figure 7.03 shows an automatic speed control known as

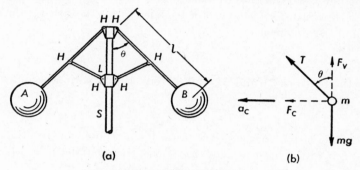

(a)   **(b)**

Fig. 7.03.   Watt's Governor.

Watt's governor.   In (a), A and B are heavy spheres, each of mass m, attached by light rods of length l to a shaft S.   A sleeve L sliding on the shaft is attached as shown.   The points marked H represent hinges. Parts A, B, and L, and the various rods must remain in one plane which rotates with the shaft.   Suppose the shaft is rotating with a constant angular velocity ω.   The forces on one of the balls are shown in (b). Resolve the tension of the rod, T, into a vertical component F_v and a horizontal one F_c; then the ball will remain at a constant height if

$$F_v = T \cos \theta = mg \tag{7.13}$$

If it is to remain at a constant height, it must describe a horizontal circle of radius $l \sin \theta$, and there must be a centripetal force to keep it moving in this circular path.   This force is supplied by the component F_c and, using (7.12), we have

$$F_c = T \sin \theta = m\omega^2 r = m\omega^2 l \sin \theta \tag{7.14}$$

Dividing (7.14) by (7.13) gives

$$\tan \theta = \frac{\omega^2 r}{g} = \frac{\omega^2}{g} l \sin \theta$$

$$\frac{\sin \theta}{\tan \theta} = \frac{g}{l\omega^2}$$

or

$$\cos \theta = \frac{g}{l\omega^2} \tag{7.15}$$

Equation (7.15) determines the steady-state value of θ. The tension can be found, if needed, from (7.13).

From (7.15), if ω increases, so does θ, and the sleeve L rises. If L is connected by a linkage (not shown) to the power source turning the shaft, this rise in L can be made to reduce the power supplied to the shaft, in turn reducing ω. Conversely, a decrease in ω lowers L, increases power, and corrects the angular velocity upward. The governor uses virtually no power itself but keeps the angular velocity of the shaft constant, within reasonably narrow limits.

This governor was invented to regulate the speed of a steam engine but can readily be adapted to any form of rotating machinery. It is one of the first of a group of remarkable devices now called **servomechanisms** or closed-loop controls, which are becoming increasingly important. The ordinary or open-end control is a control whose action is arbitrary and independent of changes in the volume or rate of whatever it is controlling. A good example is the ordinary traffic-light system at an intersection of two streets. The police adjust it to some time cycle, such as "green, 45 sec east-west; red, 30 sec east-west", and the lights continue to change according to this cycle regardless of the flow of traffic. In more elaborate traffic-light controls the numbers of cars approaching the intersection from each of the four directions are counted automatically, and the time cycle of the lights is adjusted by the control system itself in accordance with the differing rates of traffic. This is a closed-loop control. Another familiar one is the thermostat on a house furnace. The thermostat is set for 72F and turns the furnace on when the temperature at the location of the control thermometer falls to 71F, and then turns it off when the temperature rises to 73F.

Example II. Banking of a Roadway. If a car goes around a curve on a road, its velocity is changing, in direction at least, and it has a centripetal acceleration. The force required to produce this acceleration is perpendicular to the forward motion of the car. If the road is level, the force must be supplied by friction between the tires and the road surface, and as the size of the frictional force is limited, the car must travel slowly around sharp curves. On high-speed highways it is the practice to "bank", or tilt, the roadway on curves so that the thrust of the road on the car may remain normal to the surface, a component of this normal reaction supplying the centripetal force. This condition will hold exactly for one speed only; at lower speeds a frictional component is needed to prevent the car from sliding down the "bank" and at higher speeds friction is needed to prevent the car from sliding up the slope. For a fair range of speeds above and below the designed speed for the curve the frictional force needed will be small.

Figure 7.04 shows a curve of radius r, centered at C, the roadway being tilted at an angle θ to the horizontal. In the diagram it is assumed that

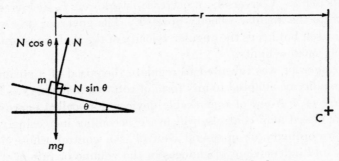

Fig. 7.04.   Car traveling around a banked curve.

the reaction of the surface is normal, so that N and mg are the only forces acting on the car in the plane of the figure.   Resolving N into components,

$$N \cos \theta = mg$$

and $N \sin \theta$ supplies the centripetal force.   If the car has a linear speed v,

$$N \sin \theta = \frac{mv^2}{r}$$

i.e.,
$$\frac{mg}{\cos \theta} \sin \theta = \frac{mv^2}{r}$$

$$\tan \theta = \frac{v^2}{rg} \qquad (7.16)$$

Equation (7.16) can be used to calculate θ for a given speed and conversely.

In this discussion the car has been treated as a point mass.   Actually the weight acts through the center of gravity, and N is made up of forces of reaction at all four contacts between tires and road.   For stability the sum of the moments of the various forces must vanish, and this will result in different sizes of reaction forces on inner and outer wheels.   Details are left for a problem.

7.05 SUITABLE FORM OF NEWTON'S SECOND LAW OF MOTION

Sections 7.01 to 7.04 dealt with the kinematics of rotation.   To discuss the effect of forces and torques acting on extended bodies, we need an appropriate form of Newton's Second Law.   Suppose a force P acts on the point mass A of the simple body whose motion was considered in section 7.01. If P (Figure 7.05) is resolved into components G and F parallel and perpendicular to r, the force G has no effect on the body because the axis through O is fixed. The force F produces acceleration.

$$F = ma \tag{7.17}$$

By (7.06), $$F = mr\alpha$$

and multiplying by r gives

$$Fr = (mr^2)\alpha$$

where Fr is the torque Γ due to F and equally the torque due to P. Therefore

$$\Gamma = (mr^2)\alpha \tag{7.18}$$

We have seen that α is the rotational analogue of a and Γ was shown in Chapter 4 to be the analogue of force, as far as rotational motion was concerned. It is plausible therefore to compare (7.17) and (7.18) and assume

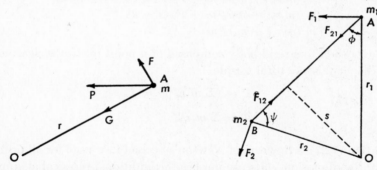

Fig. 7.05. Effect of torque.   **Fig. 7.06.** A rigid body composed of two point masses.

that (7.18) is the appropriate form of the Second Law of Motion to apply to bodies in rotation.

Consider now the rigid body of Figure 7.06 consisting of two point masses connected with the axis of rotation and with each other by rigid rods of negligible mass. External forces act on the two bodies, and the components of these forces which are perpendicular to the radius vectors r_1 and r_2 are shown as F_1 and F_2 (forces along r_1 and r_2 are ignored since they cannot produce motion). The two masses will exert forces on each other via the rod connecting them. These forces must act along the rod and are shown as F_{12} and F_{21}. By the Third Law of Motion,

$$\mathbf{F}_{12} = -\mathbf{F}_{21}$$

so that their numerical values are equal. If s is the perpendicular distance from the origin to the line of action of this pair of forces, the total torque on the body is

$$\Gamma = F_1 r_1 + F_{21} s - F_{12} s + F_2 r_2$$
$$= F_1 r_1 + F_2 r_2 \qquad (7.19)$$

Now the net force on A producing motion is the resultant of both the external force and the internal force exerted by B on A. Thus

$$F_1 + F_{21} \sin \phi = m_1 a_1 = m_1 r_1 \alpha_1 \qquad (7.20)$$

Similarly, $\qquad F_2 - F_{12} \sin \psi = m_2 a_2 = m_2 r_2 \alpha_2 \qquad (7.21)$

The usual notation is used in these equations, with a's and α's standing for linear and angular accelerations, respectively. Since the body is rigid, $\alpha_1 = \alpha_2 = \alpha$, say. Solving (7.20) and (7.21) for F_1 and F_2 and substituting in (7.19) gives

$$\begin{aligned} \Gamma &= (m_1 r_1 \alpha - F_{21} \sin \phi) r_1 + (m_2 r_2 \alpha + F_{12} \sin \psi) r_2 \\ &= (m_1 r_1^2 + m_2 r_2^2)\alpha + F_{12}(r_2 \sin \psi - r_1 \sin \phi) \\ &= (m_1 r_1^2 + m_2 r_2^2)\alpha + F_{12}(s - s) \\ &= (m_1 r_1^2 + m_2 r_2^2)\alpha \qquad (7.22) \end{aligned}$$

The extension to a rigid body composed of n point masses is clear, and in this case if Γ is the total torque,

$$\Gamma = (\sum_n m_n r_n^2)\alpha = I\alpha \qquad (7.23)$$

where $\qquad I = \sum_n m_n r_n^2 \qquad (7.24)$

Equation (7.23) is the form of Newton's Second Law used for all problems of rotational motion. Its use implies the additional physical assumption that any solid body is equivalent to an assemblage of point masses, any two of which interact only along the line joining them.

No specific unit of torque has been introduced as yet. In the mks system the unit will be the *newton-meter* (Nm). This is *not* equated to the joule in this case, because torque is the product of force and a distance *perpendicular* to the direction of force whereas energy is the product of force and the component of distance *parallel* to the force. Energy and torque are not equivalent concepts, and the distinction is emphasized by using the joule and the newton-meter as their respective mks units.

In the case of a rigid body made up of point masses, equation (7.23) can be shown to be consistent with the law of the conservation of energy. Suppose a force F acts on a rigid body initially at rest and causes it to rotate once, the direction of F remaining perpendicular to its lever arm r

throughout the rotation.   Force F is then removed, leaving the body with zero angular acceleration and hence constant angular velocity ω.   The work done is

$$W = F \cdot 2\pi r = 2\pi Fr = 2\pi \Gamma \qquad (7.25)$$

If v_n is the linear velocity of the nth particle,

$$v_n = r_n \omega$$

and $\qquad$ K.E. $= \sum_n \frac{1}{2} m_n v_n{}^2 = \frac{1}{2} \sum_n m_n (r_n \omega)^2 = \frac{1}{2} (\sum_n m_n r_n{}^2) \omega^2$

$$= \frac{1}{2} I \omega^2 \qquad (7.26)$$

By (7.23), $\qquad\qquad\qquad \alpha = \dfrac{\Gamma}{I}$

and by (7.09), $\qquad\qquad \omega^2 = 0 + 2\alpha \cdot 2\pi$

since the angular acceleration acted through an angle of 2π radians or one revolution.   Therefore

$$\omega^2 = 4\alpha\pi = 4\,\frac{\Gamma\pi}{I}$$

or $\qquad\qquad$ K.E. $= \frac{1}{2} I \omega^2 = 2\pi \Gamma = W \qquad (7.27)$

as we set out to show.   Note the similarity of form between kinetic energy of rotation and kinetic energy of linear motion.

7.06 MOMENTS OF INERTIA

The quantity $I = \sum\limits_n m_n r_n{}^2$ is called the **moment of inertia**.   It measures the inertia of a body as regards rotation about a given axis just as the total mass measures the inertial effect in linear motion.   The perpendicular distance r_n from the nth mass to the axis of rotation must not be confused with the distance to any central point.   For a given body, I depends on the position of the axis of rotation.   The calculation of I is straightforward for a body composed of a limited number of point masses, but for a continuous body calculus methods must be used (see section 7.12) and for a body of any irregularity of shape I must be found experimentally.

A few moments of inertia which will be used in problems are given below.   In each case M is the total mass.

I. Flywheel.   A wheel in which all or virtually all the mass is concentrated in a rim of radius a has a moment of inertia about a perpendicular axis through its center of

$$I = \sum_n m_n a^2 = a^2 \sum_n m_n = Ma^2 \qquad (7.28)$$

since each particle is the same distance a from the axis.

II. Uniform Rod. A rod of length l has a moment of inertia about a perpendicular axis through its center of

$$I = \frac{Ml^2}{12} \tag{7.29}$$

III. Uniform Disk. For a disk of radius a,

$$I = \tfrac{1}{2}Ma^2 \tag{7.30}$$

about a central, perpendicular axis.

IV. Uniform Sphere. For a sphere of radius a,

$$I = \tfrac{2}{5}Ma^2 \tag{7.31}$$

about an axis through the center.

7.07 CONSERVATION OF ANGULAR MOMENTUM

In Figure 7.01 the momentum of the point mass is mv. We define the **moment of momentum** or **angular momentum** of m about O as the product of momentum times the perpendicular distance to the center of rotation. This is quite analogous to the moment of a force. Using the symbol p for angular momentum

$$p = mvr = mr\omega r = (mr^2)\omega$$

The total angular momentum of a rigid body of many particles is

$$p = (\Sigma mr^2)\omega$$

since ω is a constant for all the particles; that is

$$p = I\omega \tag{7.32}$$

Equation (7.23) was derived from $F = ma$, but in section 3.03 we saw that $F = ma$ is a special case of the more general equation

$$F = \frac{\Delta(mv)}{\Delta t}$$

Similarly, $\Gamma = I\alpha$ is a special case of the more general equation

$$\Gamma = \frac{\Delta p}{\Delta t} = \frac{\Delta(I\omega)}{\Delta t} \tag{7.33}$$

which must be used if I varies with t.

If $\Gamma = 0$, $\Delta p/\Delta t = 0$, i.e., p does not change with time, or

$$I\omega = \text{constant} \tag{7.34}$$

Equation (7.34) is a mathematical statement that the angular momentum is constant or conserved. It is not restricted to rigid bodies but applies to any system on which no *external* torques act. Any internal reactions between two parts of the system consist of pairs of equal and opposite forces and hence produce no net torque.

Conservation of Angular Momentum.   *The total angular momentum of any closed system is a constant, regardless of any interactions between parts of it.*

From this law we see that if a body is set in rotation, it continues to spin as long as there is no external torque. Since $I\omega$ is constant, if I decreases, ω must increase. A very simple experiment confirms this. Sit on a piano stool, or other seat which can be rotated, holding heavy weights in your outstretched hands, and get someone to set the stool turning slowly. Pull your hands and the weights in close to your body, thereby reducing your moment of inertia. A word of caution is in order. Don't do this too rapidly—the increase in angular velocity is surprising. Divers use this principle in executing somersaults by going into a crouch, or tuck, after pushing themselves off the board with a slight spin. Similarly, figure skaters can achieve a very rapid spinning motion in this way.

7.08 COMBINED LINEAR AND ROTATIONAL MOTION

Figure 7.07 shows a rigid body of mass m acted on by a single force F_1. The center of mass of the body is at G, and the perpendicular distance from G to the line of action of F_1 is d. At G introduce two forces, F_2 and F_3, parallel to F_1 and equal to it in size. Then

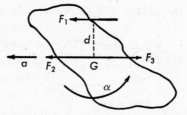

$$\mathbf{F_1} = \mathbf{F_2} = -\mathbf{F_3}$$

These forces do not alter the system in any way but permit us to separate translational and rotational effects. Force

Fig. 7.07. Combined effects of force on a free body.

F_2 causes the whole body to move with a linear acceleration a given by

$$F_2 = F_1 = ma \tag{7.35}$$

This is exactly the same as if the mass were concentrated at the point G. Forces F_1 and F_3 constitute a couple, of torque

$$\Gamma = F_1 d \tag{7.36}$$

which causes the body to rotate about its center of mass with an angular acceleration α given by

$$\Gamma = F_1 d = I\alpha \tag{7.37}$$

where I is the moment of inertia of the body about an axis through G perpendicular to the plane of the diagram.   The motion of the body through space will be quite complicated in appearance, but by this device we have reduced it for purposes of calculation to a linear motion of G with an acceleration a given by (7.35), together with a rotation about G with an angular acceleration α given by (7.37).

If several coplanar forces act on the body, they can be combined by the methods of section 4.03 into a single force or a single couple.   If it is a single force, we proceed as above; if a single couple, the motion reduces to pure rotation if there is a fixed axis.   If the forces are not all coplanar or if rotation can take place about more than one axis, the problem becomes difficult.   This general case will be discussed briefly in sections 7.09 to 7.11 on gyroscopic motion, but a complete solution would be out of place in this introduction to mechanics.

Example I.   An electric motor is delivering 2.00 hp when the current to the motor is cut off without disconnecting the load.   If the moment of inertia of the rotor of the motor is 25.0 lb ft², how many revolutions does the motor make before coming to rest if it was originally turning at 1800 rpm?

We shall suppose there is a pulley of radius r on the end of the shaft of the motor and that the pulley is connected to the load by a belt, with sufficient friction between the pulley and the belt to prevent any slipping.   In the steady state, when the motor is running at constant speed, the motor and the belt exert equal and opposite torques on the pulley.   When the driving force of the motor stops, the load continues to exert the same torque, the belt exerting a force F on the pulley as shown in Figure 7.08.

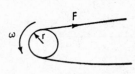

Fig. 7.08.

Thus the original output torque of the motor was $\Gamma = Fr$.

$$\text{Power} = \text{force} \times \text{velocity}$$
$$P = Fv = Fr\omega \qquad [\text{by (7.04)}]$$
$$= \Gamma\omega \tag{7.38}$$

Equation (7.38) is a useful connection between power and torque.

$$\text{Output torque } \Gamma = \frac{P}{\omega} = \frac{2 \times 550}{60\pi} \frac{\text{ft-lb}}{\text{sec}} \frac{\text{sec}}{\text{radian}}$$

$$= \frac{55}{3\pi} \text{ lb-wt} \times \text{ft}$$

Hence $\text{Retarding torque } = -\dfrac{55}{3\pi} \text{ lb-wt ft}$

To use equation (7.23) with a torque in fps grav. units, we must put the moment of inertia in a suitable unit. Since $F = ma$ can be used with fps grav. units if the mass is in slugs, $\Gamma = I\omega$ can be used with these units if I is in slug ft².

$$I = \frac{25.0}{32.0} \text{ lb ft}^2 \times \frac{\text{slugs}}{\text{lb}}$$

Therefore $\alpha = \dfrac{\Gamma}{I} = -\dfrac{55}{3\pi} \times \dfrac{32.0}{25.0} = -7.54 \text{ radians sec}^{-2}$

By (7.09), $\omega^2 = \omega_0^2 + 2\alpha\theta$

$$0 = (60\pi)^2 - 2 \times 7.54 \times \theta$$

$$\theta = 2380 \text{ radians} = \frac{2380}{2\pi} \text{ revolutions}$$

$$= 379 \text{ revolutions}$$

Example II.   A pulley of mass 150 gm and radius 2.00 cm turns on a frictionless support. Masses of 2.00 and 2.50 kgm are suspended by a light cord passing over the pulley. Find the acceleration of the system and the tension in each side of the cord. The problem is illustrated in Figure 7.09. We assume that the friction between the cord and the pulley is sufficient to prevent slipping. Then if α is the angular acceleration of the pulley and a the linear acceleration of the system,

$$a = r\alpha$$

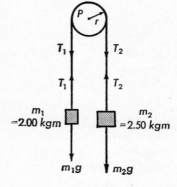

Fig. 7.09.

The tensions on the two sides of the pulley must be different in order to provide the torque needed to accelerate the pulley. Applying Newton's Second Law, in the appropriate linear or rotational form, to the mass m_2, the pulley, and the mass m_1, we have

$$m_2g - T_2 = m_2a \qquad (7.39)$$

$$(T_2 - T_1)r = I\alpha = I\frac{a}{r} \qquad (7.40)$$

$$T_1 - m_1g = m_1a \qquad (7.41)$$

where I is the moment of inertia of the pulley. We assume the pulley can be treated as a uniform disk, so that by (7.30)

$$I = \tfrac{1}{2}Mr^2$$

In equation (7.40), the right-hand side is thus

$$\frac{Ia}{r} = \tfrac{1}{2}Mr^2\frac{a}{r} = \tfrac{1}{2}Mar$$

Hence we can cancel a factor r from both sides of the equation. Substituting numerical values gives

$$2.50g - T_2 = 2.50a$$
$$T_2 - T_1 = \tfrac{1}{2} \times 0.150a$$
$$T_1 - 2.00g = 2.00a$$

Adding the three equations, we obtain

$$0.50g = 4.575a$$
$$a = 1.07 \text{ m sec}^{-2}$$

The tensions can now be found from (7.39) and (7.41) and the angular acceleration from $\alpha = a/r$.

$$T_1 = 21.74 \text{ N}, \qquad T_2 = 21.82 \text{ N}, \qquad \alpha = 53.5 \text{ radians sec}^{-2}$$

Example III. A uniform sphere is allowed to roll down a rough, inclined plane. Find the acceleration if no slipping occurs, and the maximum angle of elevation of the plane if the sphere is not to slip.

Figure 7.10(a) illustrates the problem. Only two forces act on the sphere, its weight and the thrust of the plane. Since the plane is rough, this thrust P will not be normal to the surface but will act at some such angle as shown in (b). In (c), P has been replaced by its components normal to the plane (N) and parallel to the plane (F), and the weight has been resolved in a similar manner. The component F is the frictional force on the ball, and $F \leq \mu N$ where μ is the coefficient of friction. Since there can be no acceleration normal to the inclined plane,

$$N = mg \cos \theta$$

and $$F \leq \mu mg \cos \theta$$

The moment of inertia of a sphere of radius r and mass m is given by (7.31):

$$I = \tfrac{2}{5}mr^2$$

The net force on the center of mass G gives the linear acceleration a,

$$mg \sin \theta - F = ma \tag{7.42}$$

and the torque about G gives the angular acceleration α,

$$Fr = I\alpha = \tfrac{2}{5}mr^2\alpha$$

That is,

$$F = \tfrac{2}{5}mr\alpha \tag{7.43}$$

If slipping does not occur, C is the instantaneous center of rotation and

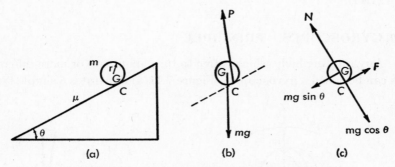

Fig. 7.10. Sphere rolling down inclined plane.

$a = \alpha r$. Combining this with (7.48) and substituting in (7.42), we obtain

$$mg \sin \theta - \tfrac{2}{5}ma = ma$$
$$a = \tfrac{5}{7}g \sin \theta \tag{7.44}$$
$$F = \tfrac{2}{5}ma = \tfrac{2}{7}mg \sin \theta$$

Let ϕ be the value of θ at which slipping just starts. Then the value of F for this angle is limiting friction and

$$F = \tfrac{2}{7}mg \sin \phi = \mu mg \cos \phi$$
$$\tan \phi = \frac{7\mu}{2} \tag{7.45}$$

An alternative solution may be found by noting that if $\theta < \phi$, the point C is at rest at any instant. Thus since the force P always acts through a point which is at rest, it does no work. In other words, if no slipping occurs, the body does no work against friction and the conservation of energy must apply. Suppose the sphere starts from rest and descends a vertical distance h. Then the loss of potential energy is mgh and the gain of kinetic energy is

$$\text{K.E.} = \tfrac{1}{2}I\omega^2 + \tfrac{1}{2}mv^2$$
$$= \tfrac{1}{2} \cdot \tfrac{2}{5}\, mr^2\omega^2 + \tfrac{1}{2}mv^2$$
$$= \tfrac{1}{5}mv^2 + \tfrac{1}{2}mv^2 = \tfrac{7}{10}mv^2$$

since $r\omega = v$. Now $v^2 = 2as$, where s is the distance through which the acceleration a acted.

$$s = h \text{ cosec } \theta; \qquad v^2 = 2ah \text{ cosec } \theta$$
$$\text{K.E.} = \tfrac{7}{10}m \times 2ah \text{ cosec } \theta = mgh$$

Therefore $$a = \tfrac{5}{7}g \sin \theta$$
as in (7.44).

7.09 GYROSCOPES. PRINCIPLE

Any rotating body which is free to turn about two or more different axes can be called a **gyroscope**. Figure 7.11(a) illustrates a simple type.

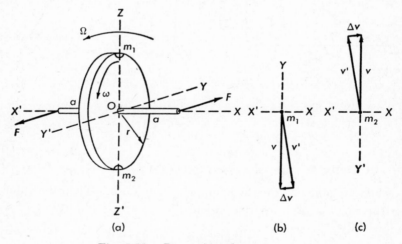

Fig. 7.11. Precession of a gyroscope.

A heavy wheel is spinning about an axle with a high angular velocity ω. The axis of rotation in the figure is taken as the $X'OX$ axis, and the other two coordinate axes are shown. Suppose now a couple F, F is applied, as shown, to the axle. If the wheel were stationary, the result would be rotation about the ZOZ' axis. For a spinning gyroscope the result is a counterclockwise rotation about the $Y'OY$ axis, that is, the right-hand or X end of the axle turns toward Z and the X' end turns toward Z'. This motion is called **precession.**

The origin of this peculiar effect can be seen qualitatively by considering the velocity diagrams of the particles m_1 and m_2, which are the particles in the rim of the gyro farthest in the Z and Z' directions, respectively. These diagrams are Figure 7.11(b) and (c). In the absence of the torque $\Gamma = 2Fa$, m_1 has a velocity $v = \omega r$ in the direction YOY'. If the torque is applied, it produces a slight rotation about the ZOZ' axis, changing the direction of v. The new velocity vector is shown as v'. There is no net force acting on m_1, so momentum must be conserved. This means the particle must now have a second velocity component Δv in the direction shown. Vectorially,

$$v = v' + \Delta v$$
or
$$mv = mv' + m\,\Delta v$$

Since the angle of rotation about ZOZ' is very small, Δv is virtually perpendicular to v, that is, m_1 has been given a velocity component in the direction XOX'. A similar argument applied to the particle m_2 shows that it has been given a velocity component Δv in the direction $X'OX$. In this manner every particle in the wheel above the XY plane has a velocity component to the left, and every particle in the lower half of the wheel has a velocity component to the right, resulting in an angular velocity Ω as shown. This angular velocity is caused by the torque Γ, will be constant if Γ is constant, and will cease if Γ is removed. For a rapidly spinning gyro of high moment of inertia, the angular velocity of precession Ω is so much greater than the rate of rotation about the ZOZ' axis that the latter will probably not be observed.

7.10 VECTOR THEORY OF GYROSCOPES

In linear motion in one dimension velocity, acceleration, and force have only two possible directions, which can be labeled positive and negative, and the quantities can be treated as algebraic. As soon as motion is possible in two or three dimensions, however, these quantities must be treated as vectors. The situation is analogous in rotational motion. When there is a fixed axis, angular velocity, angular acceleration, and torque may be treated algebraically. Thus in section 4.02 a sign convention was defined for torque, but its vector nature was not otherwise mentioned. If the axis of rotation can change or if there are simultaneous rotations about different axes, we must treat most angular quantities as vectors.

The magnitude of an angular velocity being known, what shall we take as its direction? The simplest choice is the axis of rotation, and the sense of the angular velocity vector is chosen so that if one looks along the axis in the direction of the angular velocity vector, the body rotates clockwise. Angular acceleration and angular momentum vectors are set up in the same way. Figure 7.12(a) represents a rotating body

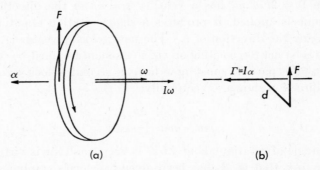

Fig. 7.12. Vector representation of angular quantities.

which is slowing down, the vector α being oppositely directed to the angular velocity. Torque must have the same direction as the angular acceleration which it produces, just as force and resulting linear acceleration have the same direction. Figure 7.12(b) shows a force F acting through a lever-arm d and producing a torque Γ. The direction of a torque is thus perpendicular to the plane containing the force and the lever-arm and is directed so that the torque vector points the way a right-hand screw would advance if the force were applied to turn it. Let us apply these vector concepts to find the effect of torque on a gyroscope.

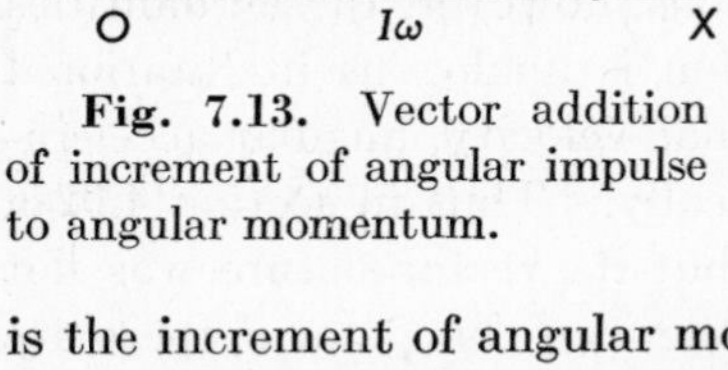

Returning to Figure 7.11, we see that by (7.33)

$$\Gamma = \frac{\Delta(I\omega)}{\Delta t}$$

Fig. 7.13. Vector addition of increment of angular impulse to angular momentum.

where Γ is the torque applied, I is the moment of inertia, and ω is the original angular velocity of the gyro. Thus

$$\Gamma\,\Delta t = \Delta(I\omega)$$

is the increment of angular momentum. These quantities are shown in the vector diagram in Figure 7.13. All the vectors lie in the XZ plane. Just as Ft is called impulse, Γt is called angular impulse. Adding $\Delta(I\omega)$

to $I\omega$ shows that the angular momentum of the gyro changes direction owing to the torque Γ acting for a time Δt. It does not change in size since each tiny increment of angular momentum is at right angles to the $I\omega$ vector at that instant.

The direction of $I\omega$ thus rotates or precesses about the $Y'OY$ axis through an angle $\Delta\phi$ in time Δt. Therefore

$$\Omega = \frac{\Delta\phi}{\Delta t} \doteq \frac{1}{\Delta t}\frac{\Gamma\,\Delta t}{I\omega} \tag{7.46}$$

since $\tan(\Delta\phi) \doteq \Delta\phi$, as $\Delta\phi$ is a very small angle. In the limit as $\Delta t \to 0$, equation (7.46) becomes exact and can be written

$$\Omega = \frac{\Gamma}{I\omega} \tag{7.47}$$

This equation allows us to calculate precessional angular velocities. A convenient rule for remembering the direction of precession is that "precession goes from spin axis to torque axis".

Anyone who has played with a toy gyroscope or a top will realize that this brief discussion has by no means exhausted the peculiar motions possible to gyroscopes, but further analysis of gyroscopic behavior would take us beyond the scope of an introduction to mechanics.

7.11 GYROSCOPES. APPLICATIONS

Gyroscopes find an ever-increasing number of uses, particularly in aircraft instruments and controls. A few of these applications follow. The gyroscope must rotate rapidly, and one method commonly used to drive it is by a stream of air blown against small notches in the rim.

Figure 7.14(a) illustrates a gyroscope G mounted in three rings or gimbals so that it can turn about three mutually perpendicular axes. Each gimbal is mounted in the next with jeweled bearings. The detail of such a bearing is shown in Figure 7.14(b). The shaft S ends in a pointed tip T of very hard material such as agate or sapphire and bears against a hollow cup H of the same material in the frame B. The friction between A and B is extremely small with this construction. The outer frame C is attached rigidly to the rest of the equipment.

A gyroscope in this type of mount is called a free gyro because, assuming it to be perfectly balanced and free of friction, there is no way of applying an external torque to it through the frame C. Thus it will maintain the same axis of spin as long as it is kept turning. A free gyro *appears* to alter its direction slowly, returning to its original reading in twenty-four hours, because it keeps the same direction in space while the earth turns under it. Free gyroscopes are used in aircraft to give a continual indication of the aircraft's direction. They are called **directional gyros** in this application, and because of friction and the effect of the earth's rotation they have to be reset periodically by comparison with some other directional indicator such as a magnetic compass.

If a fixed mass is suspended below the gimbal A, it can be shown that a precessional torque is developed which keeps the gyro pointing toward true north. This **gyrocompass** is an elaborate, heavy instrument if it is to be accurate, and for this reason is useful in ships but has had little application in aircraft.

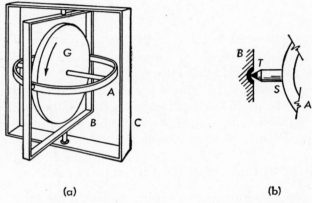

(a)   (b)

Fig. 7.14. (a) Gyroscope mounted in gimbal rings. (b) Detail of jeweled bearing.

It has been found that when flying in cloud or on a dark night a pilot's senses do not give a reliable indication of the aircraft's attitude, or orientation, with respect to the horizontal. The reason for this is that, if the pilot is unable to see the earth, his only indication of the directions "up" and "down" is the sensation of weight. The accelerations to which the pilot's body are subjected in flight are comparable to the acceleration of gravity, so that the resultant force on him which he interprets as weight may point in almost any direction. A gyro instrument called an **artificial horizon** is used as an aid to flying under these conditions. It is an almost-free gyro in gimbal rings like those in Figure 7.14 but spins with its axis normally vertical. If it changes from this position, a weight suspended under it develops a restoring torque to bring it back to the vertical. An indicator attached to the gyro shows the attitude of the aircraft with respect to the horizon at any time.

If, in Figure 7.14, we dispense with the outer gimbal so that torque may be applied by turning the frame B, we no longer have a free gyro but are back to an arrangement like Figure 7.11. The **turn indicator** is an aircraft instrument which works on this principle. The frame B is connected to the structure of the aircraft with the bearings of A fore-and-aft. If the aircraft turns, the torque causes G and A to precess, and this motion is recorded by a needle on a scale to show the rate at which the aircraft is turning.

Fig. 7.15. Aircraft instrument flying panel. (Photograph courtesy of Sperry Gyroscope Company of Canada Ltd.)

Two of the instruments just described (artificial horizon and turn indicator), together with other nongyro ones, form the **instrument flying panel** which is mounted directly in front of the pilot. This panel is his principal aid in flying the aircraft. A photograph of the panel is shown in Figure 7.15 with most of the instruments identified. The heading selector is a type of magnetic compass. The other three (not identified) are indicators for electronic navigation instruments.

The directional gyro indicates any change from a chosen direction of motion of the aircraft, and the artificial horizon shows any bank, climb, or descent. If changes of direction and attitude are measured automatically, any change, or error, from pre-set values can be used to control servomechanisms which operate the control surfaces of the aircraft (rudder, elevators, and ailerons) in such a way as to correct the error. This combination of instruments and servomechanisms is called an **automatic pilot.** It is limited to fairly simple maneuvers such as straight and level flying or gentle climbs, descents, or turns, but within these limits a well-adjusted automatic pilot can fly an aircraft more smoothly and accurately than a human pilot.

7.12 CALCULUS METHODS

Angular displacement, velocity, and acceleration are connected by the equations

$$\alpha = \frac{d\omega}{dt} = \frac{d^2\theta}{dt^2}; \qquad \omega = \frac{d\theta}{dt} \qquad (7.48)$$

Moments of inertia were defined in 7.05 by the equation

$$I = \sum_n m_n r_n{}^2$$

For continuous bodies this is generalized to

$$I = \int r^2 \, dm = \int_{\text{vol.}} r^2 \, \rho \, dv \qquad (7.49)$$

where ρ is the density and dv the volume element. We use (7.49) to calculate the four moments of inertia quoted in 7.05.

I. Flywheel: $I = Ma^2$. This requires no further proof since it assumes that all the mass of the flywheel is at the same distance a from the central axis.

II. Uniform Rod. An element of rod of length dx at a distance x from the origin is taken as shown in Figure 7.16. If the cross-sectional area is A,

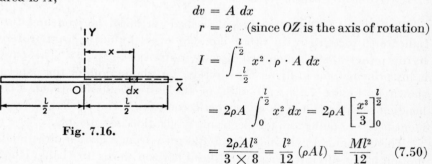

Fig. 7.16.

$$dv = A \, dx$$

$$r = x \quad \text{(since } OZ \text{ is the axis of rotation)}$$

$$I = \int_{-\frac{l}{2}}^{\frac{l}{2}} x^2 \cdot \rho \cdot A \, dx$$

$$= 2\rho A \int_0^{\frac{l}{2}} x^2 \, dx = 2\rho A \left[\frac{x^3}{3} \right]_0^{\frac{l}{2}}$$

$$= \frac{2\rho A l^3}{3 \times 8} = \frac{l^2}{12} (\rho A l) = \frac{M l^2}{12} \qquad (7.50)$$

III. Uniform Disk.   We choose as the element of volume an annular ring of radius r and width dr (Figure 7.17).   Let σ be the mass per unit area of the disk, so that $M = \sigma\pi a^2$.   This permits us to replace a volume integral by a surface one.

$$dA = 2\pi r \, dr$$

$$I = \int_0^a r^2 \cdot \sigma \cdot 2\pi r \, dr = 2\pi\sigma \int_0^a r^3 \, dr$$

$$= 2\,\frac{\pi\sigma a^4}{4} = \frac{a^2}{2}\,(\sigma\pi a^2) = \frac{Ma^2}{2} \tag{7.51}$$

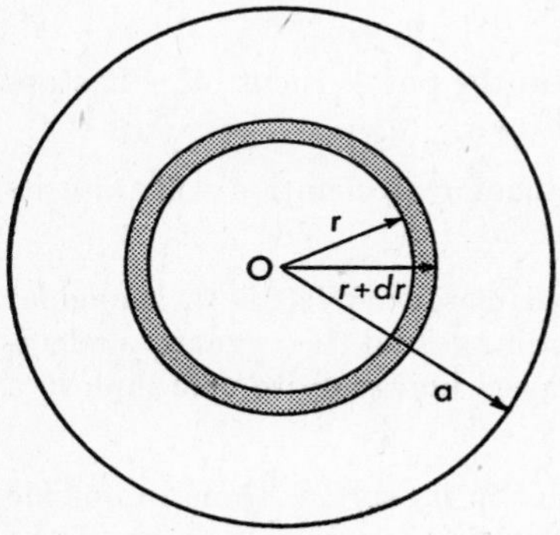

Fig. 7.17. 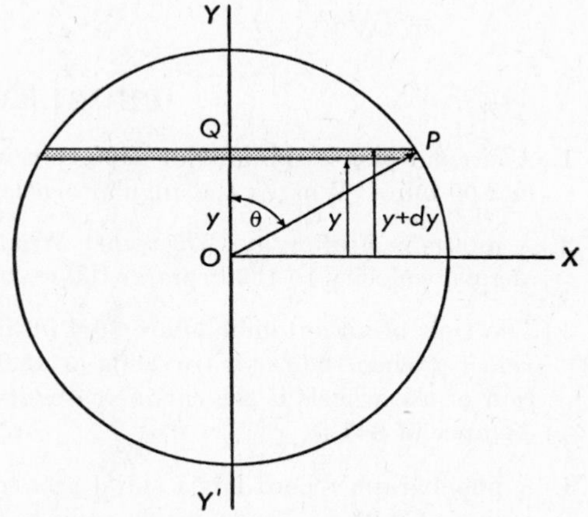   Fig. 7.18.

IV. Uniform Sphere.   Let YOY' in Figure 7.18 be the axis of rotation.   The figure shows the XY plane through the center of the sphere.   Take a thin disk parallel to the XZ plane as the element of volume.   From symmetry, total I will be twice the moment of inertia of the hemisphere above the XZ plane.

$$\text{Radius of disk} \;=\; PQ$$
$$\text{Volume of disk} \;=\; \pi(PQ)^2\,dy$$
$$\text{Mass of disk} \;\;\;\;=\; \rho\pi(PQ)^2\,dy$$

Therefore, by (7.51),

$$\text{Moment of inertia of disk} \;=\; \frac{\rho\pi(PQ)^2\,dy \times (PQ)^2}{2}$$

that is,

$$I = 2\int_0^a \frac{\rho\pi(PQ)^4}{2}\,dy$$

Now $PQ = a \sin \theta$

$$y = a \cos \theta \qquad (\cos\theta = 0 \text{ when } y = 0, \; \cos\theta = 1 \text{ when } y = a)$$
$$dy = a\, d(\cos\theta)$$

$$I = \rho\pi \int_0^1 a^4 \sin^4 \theta \cdot a \cdot d(\cos \theta)$$

$$= \rho\pi a^5 \int_0^1 (1 - \cos^2 \theta)^2 \, d(\cos \theta)$$

$$= \rho\pi a^5 \int_0^1 (1 - 2\cos^2 \theta + \cos^4 \theta) \, d(\cos \theta)$$

$$= \rho\pi a^5 \left[\cos \theta - \tfrac{2}{3} \cos^3 \theta + \tfrac{1}{5} \cos^5 \theta \right]_0^1$$

$$= \tfrac{8}{15} \rho\pi a^5 = \tfrac{2}{5} a^2 (\rho \tfrac{4}{3}\pi a^3)$$

$$= \tfrac{2}{5} M a^2 \qquad\qquad\qquad (7.52)$$

PROBLEMS

1. A circular saw is spinning at 2400 rpm when the power is cut off. It stops in 2.00 min. What is the angular acceleration?

2. A motor is turning at 1200 rpm. What angular acceleration will raise its angular velocity to 1800 rpm in 100 revolutions?

3. The tires of an automobile are 30.0 in. in diameter. What is their angular velocity when the car is traveling at 45.0 mph? Find the angular acceleration of the wheels if the car increases its speed uniformly to 60.0 mph in a distance of 847 ft.

4. A phonograph record has a spiral groove cut in its surface from an outside radius of 6.00 in. to an inside radius of 2.00 in. Successive turns of the spiral are 5.00×10^{-3} in. apart. If the record is turned at $33\tfrac{1}{3}$ rpm, how long does it take to play it? How far does the needle travel with respect to the groove?

5. An airplane propeller has blades 3.00 ft long. If the velocity of the propeller tips reaches the speed of sound (about 1100 ft/sec at sea level), there is a marked loss of power. What is the maximum rotational speed of the propeller if the linear velocity of any part of the blade is limited to 1000 ft/sec?

6. A piece of mud sticks to the tread of a car wheel which is 30.0 in. in diameter. If the mass of the mud is 0.200 lb and the tread holds it with a force of 4.50 lb-wt, at what linear speed of the car will the mud be thrown off?

7. A boy swings a pail containing water in a vertical plane. If the distance from his shoulder to the center of gravity of the water is 1.00 m, what is the maximum time for a complete swing if the water is not to spill? (Assume constant angular velocity.)

8. A fighter plane is in a dive and the pilot pulls it out of the dive, describing a circle of radius 4000 ft. At the bottom of the circle what is the total acceleration to which the pilot is subjected if the speed of the plane is 480 mph at that point?

9. One of the "rides" at an amusement park is a flat, horizontal turntable which rotates at 8.00 rpm. If the coefficient of friction between the surface and a man's clothes is 0.300, how close to the center must he sit in order not to be thrown off?

10. A Watt's governor (Figure 7.03) has two balls, each of mass 2.00 lb, on the ends of rods 0.500 ft long. What is the angular velocity of the shaft if θ is 60.0°?

11. A road curves with a radius of 1000 ft. At what angle should the road be banked for cars traveling at 50 mph?

12. A curve of 1000-ft radius is banked at an angle of 10.0° to the horizontal. At what speed may a car travel on this curve and experience no sideways thrust on the tires? If a 3200-lb car goes around the curve at 60.0 mph, calculate the normal force on each tire, assuming the front and rear tires share the load equally. The wheels are 5.00 ft apart and the center of gravity of the car is 4.00 ft above the road. What is the total frictional force on the tires?

13. If the coefficient of friction between tires and road is 0.600, how fast may a car travel around a 500-ft radius, unbanked curve without skidding? If the distance between the wheels is 5.00 ft, what is the maximum height of the center of gravity of the car in order that it shall skid rather than overturn if this speed is exceeded?

14. A force of 400 N acts tangentially on the rim of a wheel of diameter 0.200 m for 20.0 sec. The moment of inertia of the wheel is 200 kgm m². Find the final angular velocity if the wheel was initially at rest, neglecting friction. How many revolutions does the wheel make in this time?

15. Find the moment of inertia about its center of a propeller blade 6.00 ft long if its mass is 40 lb. Assume it can be treated as a uniform rod.

16. What is the moment of inertia about its central axis of a cylinder 3.00 cm in radius, 0.500 m long, and of density 8900 kgm m⁻³?

17. A cylinder of mass 2.00 kgm and radius 0.400 m is rotating about its central axis at 40.0 rps. What torque is required to bring it to rest in 20.0 sec?

18. A flywheel, the moment of inertia of which is 90.0 kgm m², is free to turn about its axle, which is 5.00 cm in radius. A light rope is wound around the axle and supports a mass of 80.0 kgm which is allowed to descend under its own weight. Find the acceleration of the 80-kgm mass, the tension in the rope, and the time taken to descend from rest through a distance of 2.00 m.

19. A man sits on a turntable holding a 10-lb mass in each hand at a distance of 2.5 ft from the axis of rotation. The turntable is set spinning at 20 rpm and the man then pulls the masses in to positions 0.50 ft from the axis. Calculate the new angular velocity, taking the moment of inertia of the man to be 25 lb ft² and neglecting any changes in this moment due to the movement of his arms. Calculate the kinetic energy of the system in both cases.

The difference is the work done by the man in pulling the masses in toward him.

20. Figure 7.19 represents a rod 4.00 ft long and of mass 12.0 lb spinning about a vertical axis through its center O. At C and D are the centers of two small spheres, each of mass 10.0 lb, which can slide on the rod but which are held in place by setscrews so that $CO = OD = 0.500$ ft. Calculate the moment

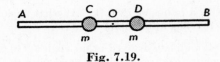

Fig. 7.19.

of inertia of the system. The rod is spinning at 300 rpm when the setscrew at D loosens and the right-hand sphere slides out until its center is at B. Find the new angular velocity and the unbalanced force on the axis at O under the changed conditions.

21. Let Figure 7.09 represent an elevator of mass $m_1 = 3000$ lb and its counterweight of mass $m_2 = 3500$ lb. The moment of inertia of the pulley is 100 lb ft^2, and the weight of the cable is negligible. Find the time for the elevator to rise 30.0 ft from rest and the tension in each side of the cable. The radius of the pulley is 0.800 ft.

22. The elevator of problem 21 is stationary at an upper floor. Three passengers (total mass 400 lb) get on.

  (a) What counterclockwise torque must the motor exert on the pulley for the elevator to descend at a constant speed?
  (b) If the motor exerts a counterclockwise torque of 800 lb-wt $\times$ ft, what is the downward acceleration of the elevator?

23. Two cylinders have the same mass and dimensions, but one is solid and uniform and the other is hollow, with almost all its weight in the surface. They are released together to roll without slipping down an inclined plane which is 30° to the horizontal. Which will roll the faster? How far apart will they be after 6.0 sec?

24. A boy rolls a circular hoop of diameter 3.00 ft along a level road at a speed of 15.0 ft/sec. The hoop then rolls up an incline. How far does its center of gravity rise before coming to rest?

25. An electric motor has a pulley of 3.00-in. diameter. A belt passing over the pulley transmits power to a machine. If the tension in the slack side of the belt is 40 lb while that in the taut side is 150 lb when the motor is turning at 1800 rpm, what is the power of the motor?

26. A gyroscope has a moment of inertia of 0.150 kgm m^2 and is spinning at 2000 rpm. A torque of 5.00 newton-meters is applied about an axis perpendicular to the spin axis. Find the rate of precession.

27. A rapidly moving motorcycle is turned to the right. Draw a sketch showing the direction in which the precession tends to turn the motorcycle.

28. A body of mass M has a moment of inertia of I_G about an axis through its center of gravity G. Let a second axis parallel to the first be drawn through a point P. If $PG = d$, show that the moment of inertia about the axis through P is

$$I_P = I_G + Md^2 \tag{7.53}$$

This useful result is known as **Steiner's Parallel Axes Theorem.** It shows that for any set of parallel axes the moment of inertia about the axis through G is a minimum. [Suggestions for proof: Consider any element of mass and let its distances from the two axes be r_1 (to G axis) and r_2. Use the cosine law of trigonometry to relate r_2 to r_1 and d. Substitute in definition of I and remember equation (4.12).]

29. Show that the moment of inertia of a uniform rod about an axis through one end perpendicular to its length is $Ml^2/3$ in the notation of Figure 7.16.

30. Show that the moment of inertia of a uniform cylinder about a line in its surface parallel to its central axis is $3Ma^2/2$ in the notation of Figure 7.17.

8

Simple Harmonic Motion

8.01 VARIABLE ACCELERATION

Except for free fall through short distances, constant accelerations such as we have been discussing are exceptional, and acceleration is variable in most motion. Consider the starting of a car. In problems, we have talked about a car moving from rest with constant acceleration until it reaches a certain speed which is then kept constant. That isn't at all the way a driver starts a car. He lets the clutch in slowly to avoid "spinning" the wheels and starts with a small acceleration which he then increases rapidly until a speed of about 10 mph is reached. Then he depresses the clutch (negative acceleration for a moment due to air resistance and friction) and shifts to second gear and accelerates again but less rapidly. Another shift to third gear or "high", and the car must then move with a decreasing acceleration since the power is limited. By (5.09), $P = Fv = mav$, so if the full power of the motor is used, or any constant fraction of it, the product av is constant, and acceleration must decrease as velocity increases. Mathematical analysis of this sort of motion is difficult, but useful results can often be found from energy considerations.

Figure 8.01 shows a track curving in a vertical plane, such as a roller coaster. If we can neglect friction, the curve, besides being a picture of the track, is also a graph (to a different scale) of the potential energy of a body moving on the track. The energy scale is drawn at the right. If a body of mass m is at rest at A, it has a potential energy of mgh_1. If released, it will slide or roll down the track, gaining kinetic energy, and this energy will cause it to climb the next hill, coming to rest eventually at B. It will then return to A and, in the absence of friction, move back and forth from A to B indefinitely. This is called **oscillatory motion.** The velocity of the mass at any point C (x, h) can be found from the energy relation

$$E_1 = mgh_1 = mgh + \tfrac{1}{2}mv^2$$

We see that the body will never get outside the horizontal range (x_1, x_2). In contrast, if a body is released from rest at D with energy E_2, it will keep on moving to the right. In many types of motion it is possible to

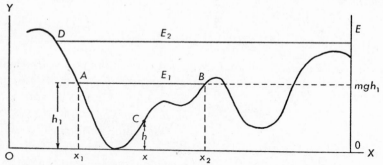

Fig. 8.01. Qualitative analysis of motion using potential energy curve.

draw a potential-energy curve similar to the one above and deduce the possible limits of motion and speeds at various points in this manner.

Another interesting case of variable acceleration is the motion of the earth about the sun. The earth follows an elliptical path, with the sun at one of the foci of the ellipse. Figure 8.02 shows a sketch of the system with the eccentricity of the ellipse greatly exaggerated. The eccentricity is actually so small that if the orbit were drawn accurately to this scale, it would be impossible for one to distinguish it from a circle. Point S is the sun, F the other focal point, and E is the earth, a distance r from S. Since r varies throughout the year, the centripetal acceleration $a_c = v^2/r$ varies also. We shall see in section 11.02 that the force

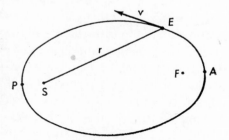

Fig. 8.02. Motion of the earth in its orbit.

which provides this centripetal acceleration is always along the line joining S and E and hence can exert no torque on E. Thus the angular momentum is a constant, which permits a complete solution. The value of v turns out to be variable also, and both v and a_c are maxima when the earth is at its point of closest approach to the sun. This point P is called **perihelion** and occurs each year about January 1. The point of greatest separation, A, is called **aphelion**.

Most problems of motion with variable acceleration are too difficult to solve by the methods of this book, but the rest of this chapter is devoted to a discussion of one very important case, simple harmonic motion.

8.02 SIMPLE HARMONIC MOTION

(1) DEFINITION

When a body moves in oscillatory motion along a line so that its accelera-tion is directed toward a fixed center and is proportional to its distance from that center, it is said to have simple harmonic motion (S.H.M.).

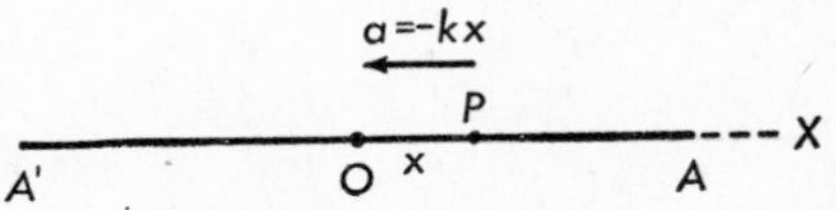

$$a = -kx$$

A'   O   x   P   A   X

Fig. 8.03. Period and amplitude of a simple harmonic motion.

The name harmonic comes from the close relation between simple harmonic motion and the harmonic (sine and cosine) functions. Most harmonic motion is due to the effect of several motions superimposed, and the word "simple" is restricted to motions which can be represented by a single sine or cosine function and which therefore have only one period. In Figure 8.03 a body is moving in simple harmonic motion about a central point O. Suppose at some instant the body is moving to the right, passing O. The accele-ration a is zero at this point, but as the body continues to the right the acceleration builds up, being $-kx$ when the body is at P. The accel-eration brings the body to rest at A and then causes it to move back toward O with increasing velocity. It then slows down again, coming to rest at A', and then repeats the cycle over and over again. The time for a complete oscillation or circuit $OAOA'O$ is called the **period** of the motion. The distance OA ($= OA'$) is called the **amplitude**.

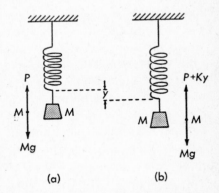

Fig. 8.04. Oscillations of a mass suspended by a spring.

A physical system which experiences simple harmonic motion is shown in Figure 8.04. In (a) a mass M hangs at rest at the end of a light spring. If the mass is pulled down slightly, the spring is stretched and exerts a restoring force on the mass which is proportional to the stretch of the spring. This is an example of Hooke's Law, which will be discussed in section 9.01.

In (a) the pull of the spring is P and equals the weight of the mass. In (b) the pull increases to $P + Ky$, where K is a constant of the spring. If now the mass is released, the unbalanced force is Ky in a direction to decrease y. Thus

$$Ma = -Ky$$

$$a = -\frac{K}{M}y = -ky$$

and the mass will oscillate up and down with simple harmonic motion.

(2) CIRCLE OF REFERENCE

Simple harmonic motion is closely related to uniform circular motion, and the period can be calculated from this connection. In Figure 8.05

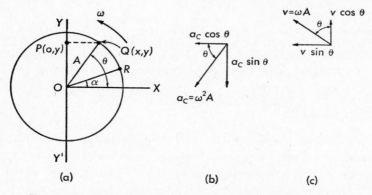

(a)   (b)   (c)

Fig. 8.05. Circle of reference of simple harmonic motion.

a point Q is moving with uniform angular velocity ω around a circular path of radius A. Point P is the projection of Q on a diameter, chosen in this diagram to be the Y axis. Point Q must have a centripetal acceleration $\mathbf{a}_c = v^2/r = \omega^2 r$, which is resolved in (b) into components parallel to the X and Y axes. Point P must have the same acceleration in the Y direction as Q. Hence

$$a_P = -a_c \sin \theta$$

$$= -\omega^2 A \frac{y}{A}$$

$$= -\omega^2 y \qquad\qquad (8.01)$$

Thus P has an acceleration directed toward O and proportional to its distance from O, i.e., it describes simple harmonic motion with $\omega^2 = k$. The negative sign shows that the acceleration is in the opposite sense to the displacement. The period of P is the same as the period of Q, and if it is represented by T,

$$T = \frac{2\pi}{\omega} \tag{8.02}$$

since P describes a complete cycle when Q rotates once. If a simple-harmonic-motion equation is in the general form

$$\text{Acceleration} = -k \times \text{displacement} \tag{8.03}$$

Then since $\omega^2 = k$,

$$T = \frac{2\pi}{\sqrt{k}} \tag{8.04}$$

If we choose $t = 0$ to be the instant when Q lies on the OX axis, we can obtain explicit equations for y and t.

$$y = A \sin \theta \quad \text{and} \quad \theta = \omega t$$

therefore

$$y = A \sin \omega t \tag{8.05}$$

or in general

$$y = A \sin \sqrt{k}\, t \tag{8.06}$$

where A is the amplitude. If we choose an arbitrary time origin such as $t = 0$ when Q is at R, with $\angle XOR = \alpha$, then

$$\theta = \omega t + \alpha$$

and (8.05) becomes

$$y = A \sin (\omega t + \alpha) \tag{8.07}$$

The expression $\omega t + \alpha$ is called the **phase** of the motion and α the **phase constant.** In dealing with a single motion it is usually most convenient to take $\alpha = 0$, which is always possible by a particular choice of the time origin. Since

$$\sin \theta = \cos (\theta - 90)$$

(8.05) can be written

$$y = A \cos (\omega t - 90)$$

so that a change from a sine form of equation to a cosine form can always be made by changing the phase constant by 90° or $\pi/2$ radians.

Another term often used in discussing oscillations is **frequency,** the number of times a second that an event or cycle takes place. If the period is one-tenth of a second, the frequency is ten events or cycles per second. In general, if f is the frequency,

$$f = \frac{1}{T} = \frac{\omega}{2\pi} \tag{8.08}$$

Frequencies are measured in cycles per second, kilocycles per second, or megacycles per second. The standard abbreviations for these units are cycles sec^{-1}, kc, Mc, respectively. It will be noted that the last two of these abbreviations should logically have "sec^{-1}" at the end, but by convention this is omitted in the abbreviations and also frequently in speaking, as when a radio announcer says "This is station WXYZ operating on a frequency of 1010 kilocycles". A "cycle" is a pure number, so that in checking the dimensions of an equation in which f appears, its dimensions are per second. A somewhat rarely used unit for f is the *hertz*. One hertz $\equiv$ 1 cycle/sec.

(3) DISPLACEMENT-TIME GRAPH

Figure 8.06 shows a graph of the displacement y of the point P against time, plotted for the two different choices of zero time on which equations (8.05) and (8.07) are based. The two curves are of course identical in shape, but (8.07) is displaced a constant amount $BC = DE = FG = \alpha/\omega$ to the left of (8.05). The period T is the time interval between any two identical points on either curve, such as J and K, and

$$T = t_2 - t_1$$

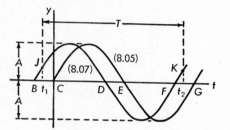

Fig. 8.06. Displacement-time curves for simple harmonic motion.

In Figure 8.06 y is plotted against a time axis with t measured in seconds. Sometimes it is convenient to plot y against ωt. The shape of the curve is unaltered in this new graph, but the axis of abscissas is now measured in radians, and a period is the time interval in which ωt changes by 2π radians.

(4) VELOCITY AND ENERGY

The velocity and hence the kinetic energy of a particle in simple harmonic motion can be found from the circle of reference. In Figure 8.05(c) the velocity v of the point Q is resolved, and we see that

$$v_P = v \cos \theta = \omega A \cos \theta \tag{8.09}$$

whence v_P is a maximum for $\theta = 0$ or π and vanishes for $\theta = \pi/2$ or $3\pi/2$, that is, at the ends of the path of the body. The kinetic energy has a maximum value of

$$\text{K.E.} = \tfrac{1}{2}m\omega^2 A^2 \tag{8.10}$$

when the body is at the center of its motion.   If we choose this point to be the zero of potential energy, (8.10) is the total energy E.   All the energy must be potential when the body is at rest at a distance A from the center.

The last few pages have shown the convenience of discussing simple harmonic motion in terms of an associated circular motion at constant angular velocity.   This convenience is so great that even if the simple harmonic motion has no circular motion associated with it, as in Figure 8.04 for example, we supply a phantom one and use the symbol ω freely. In this usage ω is often called the **angular frequency** rather than the angular velocity.   See equation (8.08).   The identity of simple harmonic motion and the projection on a straight line of uniform circular motion cannot be stressed too strongly.

8.03 EXAMPLES OF SIMPLE HARMONIC MOTION

Cases of simple harmonic motion will be discussed from time to time throughout the rest of the book, but a few examples are listed here to illustrate the importance of this type of motion.

I. THE SIMPLE PENDULUM

This is an idealized body in which a point mass, suspended by an inextensible, light cord, swings in a vertical plane under the influence of gravity.   It is closely approximated by a small lead sphere or "bob" on the end of a light string, and this form is used as simple laboratory equipment for finding the acceleration of gravity.

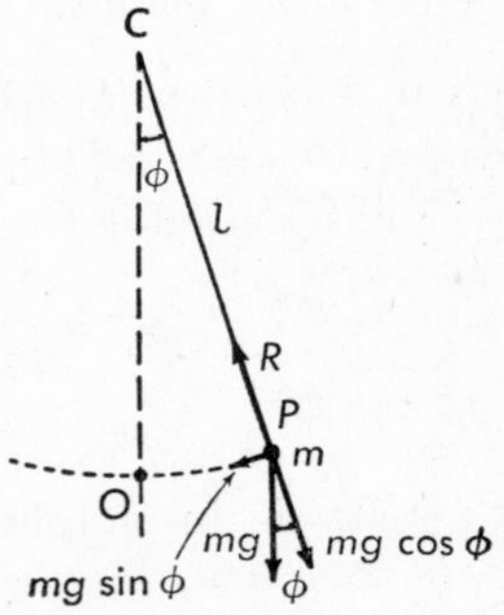

Figure 8.07 illustrates a simple pendulum. A small body P of mass m is suspended from C by a light cord.   If it is pulled aside so that the cord makes an angle ϕ with the vertical and then released, it will swing back and forth along the curved path shown.   The only forces on the bob are the tension R of the cord and the weight mg. Resolving mg perpendicular and parallel to the path of the bob, we have

$$mg \cos \phi = R$$

and the unbalanced force $mg \sin \phi$ produces an acceleration a along the arc OP.

Fig. 8.07.

$$ma = mg \sin \phi$$
$$a = g \sin \phi \tag{8.11}$$

If the angle ϕ is small ($<5°$),

$$\sin \phi \doteq \phi$$

in radians, with a maximum error of about 0.1%. Also

$$\phi = \frac{OP}{l} \tag{8.12}$$

where l is the distance CP.   Acceleration a is directed along OP and always in such a direction as to reduce OP.   Combining (8.11) and (8.12) and calling the acceleration negative, since it acts in a direction to reduce the displacement, gives

$$a \doteq -\frac{g}{l} OP$$

i.e.,
$$\text{Acceleration} = -\frac{g}{l} \times \text{displacement} \tag{8.13}$$

Thus the bob describes simple harmonic motion, for a small initial displacement, with a period T given by (8.04) as 2π divided by the square root of the constant in (8.13).

$$T = \frac{2\pi}{\sqrt{g/l}}$$
$$= 2\pi \sqrt{\frac{l}{g}} \tag{8.14}$$

or
$$g = \frac{4\pi^2 l^2}{T^2} \tag{8.15}$$

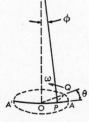

Fig. 8.08.

Figure 8.08 shows how a phantom uniform circular motion can be associated with the simple harmonic motion of the pendulum bob. Let the arc through which the bob swings be AOA'.   On AOA' as diameter, construct a circle in the plane perpendicular to CO.   Let a point Q describe this circle with uniform angular velocity ω chosen so that the projection of Q on AA' coincides with the position of the bob.   At A, Q and P coincide and the centripetal acceleration, $-\omega^2 \times OA$, of Q must equal the acceleration of P, which is $-g/l \times OA$ by (8.13).   Then

$$\omega^2 \times OA = \frac{g}{l} \times OA; \quad \omega = \sqrt{\frac{g}{l}}$$

This construction assumes that AOA' is a straight line, which is not entirely accurate even for a small initial angular displacement, ϕ_0. The inaccuracy here, as in equation (8.13), disappears only in the limit as $\phi_0 \to 0$.

Equation (8.15) gives g in terms of measurements of l and T. The accuracy of the method depends on using a small value of ϕ_0. Figure 8.09 is a graph showing the ratio of the actual period and the period calculated from (8.14), as a function of ϕ_0.

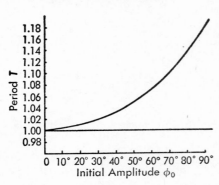

Fig. 8.09. Effect of amplitude on period of a simple pendulum.

II. THE COMPOUND PENDULUM

The exact length l of a simple pendulum is difficult to measure, and the weight of the cord, though small, introduces some error. These factors limit the accuracy of the determination of g using the simple apparatus described above. Accurate measurements are usually made with some form of compound pendulum. This is *any* rigid body mounted so that it can swing in a vertical plane about some axis passing through it.

Figure 8.10 is a sketch of a compound pendulum which can rotate about a horizontal axis through C. The center of gravity of the body is G. Let I be its moment of inertia about the axis through C. If m is the total mass of the body and

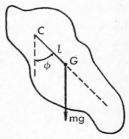

Fig. 8.10. A compound pendulum.

$CG = l$, the weight in absolute units is mg and the torque due to weight is

$$\Gamma = -mgl \sin \phi$$

therefore

$$-mgl \sin \phi = I\alpha$$

or if we again restrict the initial angular displacement ϕ_0 to be a small angle,

$$\alpha \doteqdot \frac{-mgl}{I} \phi$$

i.e.,   Angular acceleration $= \dfrac{-mgl}{I} \times$ angular displacement

This relation between angular quantities gives simple harmonic motion, just as it does between linear ones. Hence the pendulum has simple harmonic motion with period equal to 2π divided by the square root of the constant of proportionality.

$$T = 2\pi \sqrt{\frac{I}{mgl}} \qquad (8.16)$$

The simple pendulum is a special case of a compound pendulum, and we note that (8.16) reduces to (8.14) if all the mass is concentrated at G, for in that case I about C is ml^2.

A compound pendulum for the accurate determination of g is very carefully mounted so that the friction of the support at C is small. The pendulum may be of regular shape so that both the distance from the support to the center of gravity and the moment of inertia can be calculated accurately. In this case the period is measured and (8.16) used directly. Even more accurate results are obtained with so-called reversible pendulums, the theory of which is an extension of the analysis just completed.

III. WAVES

One of the principal reasons for our interest in simple harmonic motion lies in its connection with wave motion. The simplest type of wave is one in which every particle in the medium through which the wave travels describes simple harmonic motion. More complex waves can be considered as the result of the superposition of simple harmonic waves.

8.04 DAMPED OSCILLATORY MOTION

So far, the discussion of simple harmonic motion has assumed that once a body is set in motion it continues to oscillate indefinitely. That is, we have neglected dissipative forces such as friction which cause a decrease in the mechanical energy of the system, usually by transforming it into heat. The simple pendulum, for example, if drawn aside and released, will swing for half an hour or more, but the amplitude gradually decreases because of air resistance. This decrease in amplitude is called **damping,** and the pendulum is said to have damped simple harmonic motion.

Mathematical analysis of damped simple harmonic motion is difficult or impossible, depending on the nature of the dissipative force involved. A common case, and one which lends itself to mathematical treatment, is the case of a damping force which is proportional to the velocity of the body. For such a force it can be shown that the oscillations have a constant period but that the amplitude decreases exponentially with time.

(An exponential decay is one in which a quantity diminishes by a constant percentage in any one of a set of equal time intervals. For example, if the initial amplitude is 100 units and after 5 sec the amplitude has fallen to 50 units, then if the decay is exponential, the amplitude 10 sec after the start will be 50% of 50, or 25 units. After 15 sec it will be down to 50% of 25, or 12.5 units, and so on.) The period is sightly different from that which the body would have in the absence of damping, but in many cases of interest the difference is so small as to be negligible. Thus equation (8.14), derived neglecting damping, is perfectly valid for a simple pendulum swinging in air.

For a damping force proportional to the velocity, equation (8.07) becomes

$$y = A_0 e^{-bt} \sin(\omega t + \alpha) \tag{8.17}$$

which is illustrated in Fig. 8.11. In equation (8.17) b is a numerical factor having the dimensions of a frequency, and its size depends on the

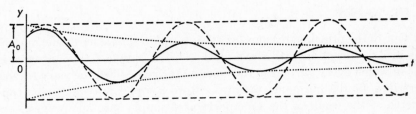

Fig. 8.11. Damped simple harmonic motion.

size of the damping force. The dashed lines shown in the figure give the amplitude A_0 (and the displacement-time graph) of the undamped oscillation, and the dotted lines are the graphs of $y = \pm A_0 e^{-bt}$. The solid line is the graph of equation (8.17). It is assumed in the diagram that the difference in periods between damped and undamped motions is negligible.

The same general considerations apply to any damped oscillatory motion. Referring to Figure 8.01, a particle with an initial energy E_1 will oscillate indefinitely between the points A and B if there is no friction. If there is friction, the motion will be damped, and each time the particle comes to rest its height and energy will be lower. After a few oscillations it will not have enough energy to get over the hump between A and B, and its subsequent motion will be confined to the left-hand hollow. It will eventually come to rest permanently at the lowest point between A and B.

Let us consider an alternative graphical representation of the equation

$$y = A_0 e^{-bt} \tag{8.18}$$

If we take logarithms to base e of both sides of this equation,

$$\ln y = \ln A_0 - bt \tag{8.19}$$

and if we plot $\ln y$ against t, the result will be a straight line with an intercept on the axis of ordinates of $\ln A_0$ and a slope of $-b$. Suppose we have a set of experimental values of y and t and suspect that the relation between them is of the form of (8.18). How can we confirm or reject this surmise? If we plot y against t, we may get points falling close to a smooth curve, but it is difficult to draw the best-fitting curve through the points and when it is drawn it is hard to be sure that it is an exponential curve. On the other hand, if we plot $\ln y$ against t, it is a simple matter of using a straightedge to see how close the points come to a straight line. Because of this advantage logarithmic plots of one kind or another are widely used in physics.

Logarithms to base 10 are more convenient arithmetically than the so-called natural logarithms to base e. We shall adopt the convention that

$$\log y \equiv \log_{10} y \qquad \text{and} \qquad \ln y \equiv \log_e y \tag{8.20}$$

Using logarithms to base 10, equation (8.18) becomes

$$\begin{aligned}
\log y &= \log A_0 + \log (e^{-bt}) \\
&= \log A_0 - bt \log e \\
&= \log A_0 - 0.4343bt \tag{8.21}
\end{aligned}$$

which again is a straight-line relation between $\log y$ and t. The slope in this form is $-0.4343b$.

To save the effort of looking up the values of $\log y$ for all our experimental points, we may use semilogarithmic graph paper, which is illustrated in Fig. 8.12. This figure includes a graph of equation (8.21). The axis of abscissas is divided into a normal linear scale but, the axis of ordinates presents an unusual appearance. Equal vertical increments represent equal increments in $\log y$, but the horizontal lines are drawn for, and labeled with, convenient values of y just as is done in the construction of a slide rule. Thus the vertical separation of the lines $y = 2$ and $y = 1$ is the same as that between $y = 10$ and $y = 5$ since

$$\log 2 - \log 1 = 0.3010 - 0 = 0.3010$$
and
$$\log 10 - \log 5 = 1.0000 - 0.6990 = 0.3010$$

Plotting a sequence of (y, t) points on this graph paper is equivalent to plotting $(\log y, t)$ points on ordinary linear graph paper.

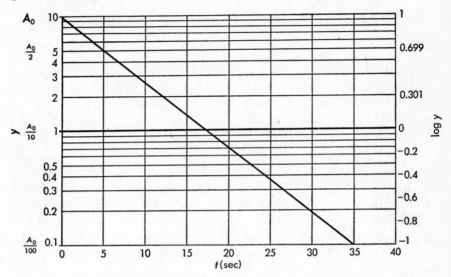

Fig. 8.12. Semilogarithmic plot of an exponential decay.

8.05 CALCULUS NOTATION

If the only force acting on a body is a restoring force proportional to the displacement y,

$$F = ma$$

becomes

$$-Ky = m\frac{dv}{dt} = m\frac{d}{dt}\frac{dy}{dt}$$

$$= m\frac{d^2y}{dt^2}$$

or

$$\frac{d^2y}{dt^2} = -ky \tag{8.22}$$

where $k = K/m$. This is a differential equation and must be integrated twice to find an explicit relation between y and t. The solution of a differential equation is usually a matter of guessing the form of the answer and verifying that it satisfies the equation. The use of the circle of reference in 8.02 led to harmonic functions, so we try

$$y = A\sin(\omega_0 t + \alpha) \tag{8.23}$$

where A and α are the two arbitrary constants needed because there are two integrations. Differentiating twice gives

$$\frac{dy}{dt} = \omega_0 A \cos (\omega_0 t + \alpha)$$

$$\frac{d^2y}{dt^2} = -\omega_0^2 A \sin (\omega_0 t + \alpha) = -\omega_0^2 y \qquad (8.24)$$

Comparison of (8.22) and (8.24) shows that (8.23) is the solution of (8.22) if $\omega_0^2 = k$. We thus arrive at the same results as already obtained using the circle of reference, which was, in effect, a device for solving the differential equation without formally using calculus notation.

For damped simple harmonic motion, if the retarding force due to friction or air resistance is proportional to velocity,

$$F = -Ky - Cv = -Ky - C\frac{dy}{dt}$$

and the differential equation of motion is

$$m\frac{d^2y}{dt^2} + C\frac{dy}{dt} + Ky = 0 \qquad (8.25)$$

Substitution of (8.17) in (8.25) shows it to be the solution if

$$b = \frac{C}{2m} \quad \text{and} \quad \omega = \sqrt{k - \frac{C^2}{4m^2}} \qquad (8.26)$$

If the damping is small, C is small and $[C^2/(4m^2)] \ll k$, so that $\omega \doteq \omega_0$.

PROBLEMS

1. A simple pendulum of length 48.0 in. is found to have a period of $\pi/\sqrt{2}$ sec. Find the acceleration of gravity.

2. What will be the length of a simple pendulum whose period is 1.00 sec?

3. A uniform meterstick is suspended at one end. Find its period of oscillation. (The moment of inertia of a uniform rod of mass M and length l about a perpendicular axis through one end is $Ml^2/3$.) What is the length of a simple pendulum having the same period?

4. A body moves on a straight line with simple harmonic motion. If the size of the acceleration is 4.00 times the displacement from the center of motion, find the period. The amplitude is 2.00 ft. Find the maximum velocity of the body.

5. A body moves in simple harmonic motion with an amplitude of 10.0 ft and a period of 2.000 sec. At zero time the displacement is zero and the velocity positive. Find the displacement and velocity at times 0.500, 1.200, and 4.800 sec later.

6. The earth's mean distance from the sun is 92.9×10^6 miles. Perihelion distance is 1.5×10^6 miles less, and aphelion distance is the same amount

greater than the mean distance. Find the maximum and minimum linear velocities of the earth in its orbit relative to the sun.

7. A 3000-lb automobile has a 60.0-hp motor. Neglecting all losses, what is the minimum time in which it can increase its speed from zero to 60.0 mph? What is the maximum acceleration when the car's speed is 20.0 mph? 30.0 mph?

8. A thin, long board is clamped at one end so that it rests horizontally. If the free end is displaced from rest, the whole board vibrates in simple harmonic motion with a period of 0.600 sec. If a pebble rests on the end of the board, what is the maximum amplitude of that point in order that the pebble may remain in contact with the board at all times?

9. A succession of waves travels over the surface of a lake and sets a log of mass 40.0 lb moving up and down with simple harmonic motion of amplitude 1.00 ft and period 9.00 sec. What energy has been transferred from the waves to the log?

10. In Figure 8.04 the restoring constant K of the spring is 12.0 ft-lb per ft and $M = 20.0$ lb. What is the period of vertical oscillations of the mass? If the amplitude of the oscillation is 6.00 in., what are the maximum acceleration and velocity of the mass?

11. A pendulum clock keeps accurate time at a point on the earth's surface where $g = 980.6$ cm sec^{-2}. If it is moved to a different latitude where $g = 979.3$ cm sec^{-2}, what amount will it gain or lose in a day?

12. A particle is oscillating in simple harmonic motion with amplitude 10.0 cm and frequency 100 cycles sec^{-1}. At $t = 0$ its displacement is 5.00 cm and its velocity is positive. What is the phase constant? Write the displacement-time equation.

13. Two particles execute simple harmonic motion of frequency 100 cycles sec^{-1} and amplitude 10.0 cm on the same straight line. At $t = 0$ the first has a displacement of 5.00 cm and the second is at the center of motion. Both have positive velocities. When and where will they first coincide?

14. A particle of mass m is free to move on a plane surface. It is acted on by forces $F_x = -Kx$, $F_y = -Ky$ and starts from rest at the point whose coordinates are (3, 4). Prove that it executes simple harmonic motion along the line whose equation is $4x = 3y$. What is the amplitude of the motion?

15. The particle of mass m of the previous problem is acted on by forces $F_x = -Kx$, $F_y = -Ky$ with $K = m$. At time $t = 0$ the particle has a velocity in the x-direction of 5 units/sec and zero velocity in the y-direction, and its position is (0, 5). Find the equation of the path followed by the particle.

16. A simple pendulum is drawn aside so that the angle the cord makes with the vertical is 45°, and then it is released. Calculate from Figure 8.09 the

approximate error involved in a determination of g from the period of this pendulum.

17. The amplitude of a certain oscillatory motion decreases with time. The amplitude is 10.0 cm at $t = 0$ and 0.100 cm at $t = 100$ sec. A plot of amplitude against time on semilogarithmic paper yields a straight line. Find the equation relating amplitude y and time.

18. The period of the oscillatory motion of problem 17 is measured as 15.71 sec. Calculate the period it would have in the absence of damping.

19. A uniform meterstick is pivoted so that it can rotate freely about a horizontal axis through the 25.00-cm mark. Find the period of small oscillations. Use equation (7.53).

20. Find a second location on the meterstick (between 75.0 cm and 100.0 cm) for a horizontal axis about which the meterstick will oscillate with the same period as found in the previous problem. Find the distance between these two axes and show that a simple pendulum of this length has the same period.

21. The results of the two previous problems illustrate the principle of the reversible pendulum. This is a compound pendulum with two supports at different distances on either side of the center of gravity. It can be suspended at either of these supporting points and allowed to oscillate in a vertical plane. The pendulum must be reversed in changing supports. If the two periods are identical, prove that the period is equal to that of a simple pendulum of length $h_1 + h_2$ where h_1 and h_2 are the distances from the center of gravity to the axes of rotation. The advantage of a reversible pendulum is that the only measurements required are the distance between the supports (usually knife edges) and the period. These can both be measured very accurately, and then equation (8.15) may be used to find g.

22. A circular metal hoop is hung over a horizontal nail and given a push so that it executes small oscillations in its own plane. Prove that its period is equal to that of a simple pendulum of length equal to the diameter of the hoop.

23. A thin, uniform disk of mass 10.0 kgm and radius 30.0 cm is suspended horizontally by a fine wire attached to its center. If the disk and wire are twisted through an angle θ, the wire exerts a restoring torque proportional to θ. Prove that if the disk is released after the initial twist it executes simple harmonic oscillations and find its period if the restoring constant of the wire is 5.00 newton-meters per radian. A system undergoing motion of this type is called a torsional pendulum.

24. A three-bladed propeller is clamped symmetrically to the disk of problem 23, and the period of oscillation is found to increase to 8.46 sec. Find the moment of inertia of the propeller about its central axis.

9

Elasticity

9.01 STRETCHING A WIRE

Perhaps the simplest deformation of a body to study is the effect due to tension forces applied to a wire or rod. Figure 9.01 shows a suitable apparatus. A wire AB, supported from the ceiling by a clamp C, has a scalepan attached at B to which weights can be added. A light

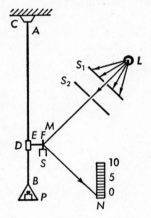

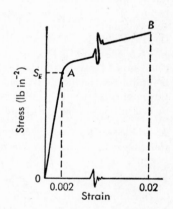

Fig. 9.01. Extensometer with optical lever.

Fig. 9.02. Stress-strain graph.

collar D is mounted on the wire, and a rod EF is hinged to D at E. A mirror M is mounted rigidly on the end of the rod and rests on a fixed support S so that any movement of D will cause the mirror to rotate. The light from a lamp L is collimated (restricted to a fine pencil beam) by holes in screens S_1 and S_2. The beam of light reflects off M to a scale N. This arrangement of lamp, mirror, and scale is called an optical lever and is used to magnify the movement of the collar D, which will be very slight. The geometry of the optical lever is known, so that

168

scale readings on N can be changed back into extensions of the length AD of the wire, using the fact that the incident and reflected beams of light will make equal angles with M.

The experiment consists of placing various weights on P and observing the increase Δl in the length AD, which was originally l. Let us consider the forces acting at any interior point in the wire. Mentally we draw a horizontal plane through the wire at any point between A and D and consider the free body diagram of the forces on the lower part of the wire. The downward force is the weight of the scalepan and the masses on it, plus the weight of the lower section of wire. This is balanced by the upward force exerted by the remainder of the wire. This is the force we call the tension T. Its numerical value will depend on where we draw the horizontal plane and will increase at points progressively higher up the wire since a greater weight of wire must be supported. In a practical experiment, however, the weight of the wire is usually negligible compared to the weight of the masses on P, and we can ignore the variation in tension and take its value throughout the length of the wire as equal to the weight or load applied at the lower end.

The tension force in wires, cables, and ropes has been used repeatedly in our analysis of problems in mechanics, but so far we have attempted no explanation of its origin. It can be considered as a measure of the property of a solid to resist any increase in length, that is, to resist any attempt to separate the particles of which the solid is composed. It has its seat in the forces between atoms. In a solid these interatomic forces result in matter having a stable condition when there is a certain definite spacing between atoms (this spacing varying from substance to substance). If external forces attempt to change this spacing, the interatomic forces oppose the external ones, resulting in tension throughout the solid if the load acts to stretch the body or compression if it attempts to make the body more compact. Interatomic forces also resist attempts to change the shape of a body without alteration in size, the reaction force being called a shear force in this case.

In previous work solid bodies were treated as rigid, that is, it was assumed that the reaction force was always big enough to prevent any deformation. Actually, a slight deformation must take place for the reaction force to develop. As will be seen below, greater generality is obtained in discussions of deformation by using the ratio of reaction force to area, which we shall call the **stress**. At the surface of a body the stress must be equal (and opposite) to the load applied per unit area, but the stress may and usually does vary throughout the interior of the body. Stress is somewhat analogous to friction. The stress is zero for zero applied load, increases just sufficiently to balance the load as the latter increases, but has a definite maximum value. If the load applied per unit area exceeds the maximum stress, the body breaks.

Returning to the experiment of Figure 9.01, the observed quantities are the load applied and the resulting increase in length Δl. If the weight of the wire is neglected, the tension in the wire equals the load. We could plot T against Δl, but the resulting graph would apply only to this wire with its particular cross-sectional area A and length l. More general results, applicable to any wire or rod of the material tested, are obtained by plotting stress against **strain**. Stress, in this case, is the tension divided by A and can be taken as the applied load divided by the area of the wire. We represent stress by S. The strain, in this case, is the increase in length divided by the original length or the *fractional deformation* corresponding to the stress. Strain is represented by the symbol ϵ. We use ϵ_1 for the strain along the length of the wire. Then

$$S = \frac{T}{A}, \qquad \epsilon_1 = \frac{\Delta l}{l} \tag{9.01}$$

If the S, ϵ_1 graph is plotted, we get Figure 9.02. In the region OA the graph is straight. That is,

$$\text{Stress} \propto \text{strain} \tag{9.02}$$

Equation (9.02) is called **Hooke's Law** and is the basic law of elasticity. In the region OA, furthermore, the extension of the wire is a reversible process—if the load is reduced, the strain decreases accordingly, following the same line on the graph, and if the load is removed entirely, the wire reverts to its original length.

If the stress S_E, corresponding to the point A, is exceeded, something happens to the material of the wire. The stress now increases less rapidly with increasing strain, and if the load is removed, the wire shrinks in length but does *not* go back to the original l—we say that a permanent **set** has occurred in the wire. The stress S_E at which this irreversible change just starts is known as the **elastic limit**, OA is the elastic region for the material, and AB is the region of plastic flow. It is present engineering practice to design so that materials are stressed only within the elastic region. The theory of the region of plastic flow is called plasticity and not much is known about it; but there are indications that it may become important in the future. If stress is increased too far, we reach the breaking point B and have two pieces of wire instead of one. The **ultimate tensile strength** of a material is the stress at the breaking point. The word ultimate is usually dropped from the name. Tensile strengths are listed in Table 9.01. Clearly no material can be safely subjected to such a stress but must be used in such a way that the maximum stress which will be developed is less than this. The ratio of tensile strength to maximum stress is called the safety factor.

The graph of Figure 9.02 is typical of the results obtained with wires of most of the more common metals—steel, copper, brass, etc. It will be noted that the plastic region is very much longer on the strain axis than the elastic one and that elastic deformations must be very minute. The strains shown at A and B give the orders of magnitude of these regions for metals. With other materials similar tests show a wide variety of properties. Although the stress-strain graph can usually be analyzed into elastic and plastic regions, either of these may be very small. The plastic region often shows strange effects such as a section with a negative slope corresponding to a sudden jump in the strain when the stress is increased gradually.

9.02 YOUNG'S MODULUS. COMPRESSION. POISSON'S RATIO

Hooke (1635) announced his law in 1676, and his work was repeated and extended by Young (1773). Writing (9.02) as an equation, we have

$$S = Y\epsilon \tag{9.03}$$

or

$$Y = \frac{Tl}{(\Delta l)A} \tag{9.04}$$

where Y is a constant of the material known as **Young's Modulus.** Values of Y are listed, along with other elastic properties, for several materials in Table 9.01. The advantage of defining stress and strain as in section 9.01 is that Y is independent of the geometry of a particular sample of the material.

If the material to be tested is in the form of a rod of sufficient stiffness, the length of the rod can be measured under increasing compressional forces applied along its length. Now Δl is negative, and if T is replaced by $-C$, the compressional force, it is found that (9.04) applies equally to tension and compression, with Y remaining the same. Young's Modulus is thus a very important property of any material. It determines the elongation or compression of a structural member subjected to forces acting along its length, and it can also be shown to control the bending of a beam by a transverse force.

Returning to Figure 9.01, let us suppose the diameter d of the wire is measured before the load is applied and each time the weight is increased. It is found that the diameter decreases as the length increases, so that the wire is experiencing a deformation in its cross section as well as its length.   Putting

$$\epsilon_2 = \frac{\Delta d}{d} \qquad (9.05)$$

where Δd is the decrease in diameter, we find that the ratio of ϵ_2/ϵ_1 is a constant for a particular material for all values of stress within the elastic limit.   This ratio is called **Poisson's Ratio** after S. D. Poisson (1781), the French mathematical physicist who introduced it.   Representing the ratio by σ, we have

$$\sigma = \frac{\epsilon_2}{\epsilon_1}$$

9.03 EXTENSION OF A VERTICAL CABLE

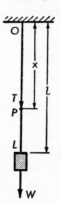

Fig. 9.03. Vertical cable with load.

The equations of the preceding section enable us to calculate extension for a definite tension.   Consider, however, a cable hanging freely, as in Figure 9.03, supporting a weight W.   Let the density of the material of the cable be ρ, its length OL be l, and its cross-sectional area be A.   At a point P in the cable the tension T exerted must equal the weight supported below P, that is, the weight of the load and the weight of the length of cable PL.   Then

$$T = W + \rho A(l - x) \qquad (9.06)$$

The tension at L is thus a minimum and increases steadily as we consider points higher up on the cable.   The cable will stretch at any point in accordance with the tension there.   To calculate the total stretch, we note from (9.06) that the tension varies *linearly** with x, with an average value of

$$T_{\text{avg.}} = W + \frac{\rho A l}{2} \qquad (9.07)$$

---

* Linear relations are *very* important in physics, first because they occur frequently and second because if the relation is more complex than linear, it is usually impossible to derive an exact mathematical solution and we have to rely on a linear approximation, aided sometimes by graphical methods.   Note that if T varies linearly with x, it does not necessarily mean that T is proportional to x but only that ΔT is proportional to Δx.

We assume that if this average tension is considered to apply to the total length, we can use it in (9.04) to find the total extension. Thus,

$$\Delta l = \frac{T_{\text{avg.}} l}{YA}$$

$$= \left(W + \frac{\rho A l}{2} \right) \frac{l}{YA}$$

$$= \frac{Wl}{YA} + \frac{\rho l^2}{2Y} \tag{9.08}$$

This assumption, that average values can be used when the effect is in a linear relation with the cause, is found experimentally to give accurate results. Note that if $W = 0$ the extension is independent of the cross-sectional area.

9.04 STRETCHING OF A SPRING

The stretching of a spring involves the elastic constants of the material of the spring in a rather complex manner since the metal of the spring is both stretched, involving Young's Modulus, and twisted, which involves the shear modulus n (section 9.06). Nevertheless, Hooke's Law applies to a stretched spring—in fact, the law was first discovered from a study of this problem. If l_0 is the unstretched length of a spring and a tension T is applied to it, the spring increases in length by an amount Δl (Figure 9.04). Experimentally,

$$\frac{\Delta l}{l_0} \propto T$$

or

$$T = \lambda \frac{\Delta l}{l_0} \tag{9.09}$$

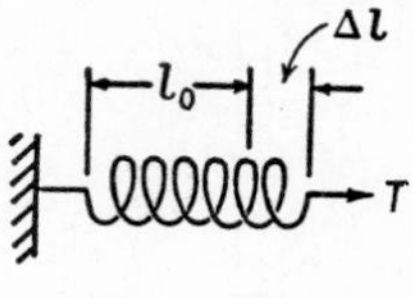

Fig. 9.04. Extension of a spring.

where λ is a constant for a particular spring. It would be useful to be able to express λ in terms of Y and n and the dimensions of the spring, but no simple formula is available. The constant λ is sometimes called the coefficient of stiffness. Suppose the total increase in length of the spring is ξ. The restoring force is zero when the spring's length is l_0 and increases linearly to $\lambda \xi / l_0$ when the spring is fully extended. The average force exerted by the spring is $(0 + \lambda \xi / l_0)/2$, and the work W done in stretching the spring is the average force exerted times the distance the force moves. Therefore

$$W = \frac{\lambda \xi^2}{2 l_0} \tag{9.10}$$

In part (1) of section 8.02 we discussed briefly the simple harmonic oscillations which result when a mass hanging on the end of a spring is displaced vertically. Figure 9.05 illustrates this problem again, using the notation of this section. Let l_0 be the unstretched length of the spring. When M is attached, the length increases by Δl. By (9.09),

$$T = Mg = \lambda \frac{\Delta l}{l_0} \tag{9.11}$$

which enables us to find λ.

If now the mass is pulled down and released, it will oscillate. Let the increase in length of the spring beyond $l_0 + \Delta l$ be called y as shown. The restoring force is

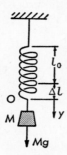

$$- \frac{\lambda}{l_0} (\Delta l + y) = - \frac{\lambda \Delta l}{l_0} - \frac{\lambda y}{l_0} = - Mg - \frac{\lambda y}{l_0}$$

The net force is thus $-\lambda y/l_0$. If the mass of the spring is negligible compared to M,

$$- \frac{\lambda y}{l_0} = Ma \tag{9.12}$$

$$a = - \frac{\lambda}{Ml_0} y$$

$$T = \frac{2\pi}{\sqrt{\dfrac{\lambda}{Ml_0}}}$$

Fig. 9.05.
Oscillations
of a mass
suspended
by a spring.

Substituting for λ from (9.11) gives

$$T = 2\pi \sqrt{\frac{Ml_0 \, \Delta l}{Mgl_0}} = 2\pi \sqrt{\frac{\Delta l}{g}} \tag{9.13}$$

If the mass of the spring is not negligible, we note that the bottom coil of the spring will have an amplitude almost as great as that of M while the top coil will hardly move at all. The effective mass of the spring will not be its total mass, and a further analysis shows that only one-third of the mass of the spring, M_S, enters into the mass-acceleration equation. Equation (9.12) becomes

$$- \frac{\lambda y}{l_0} = \left(M + \frac{M_S}{3} \right) a$$

giving in place of (9.13)

$$T = 2\pi \sqrt{\frac{\Delta l}{g} \left(1 + \frac{M_S}{3M} \right)} \tag{9.14}$$

This experiment can be used as another method of measuring g from the observed period of oscillation and equation (9.14).

9.05 BULK MODULUS AND COMPRESSION

In section 9.02 we discussed the compression resulting in a rod due to a force along its length. This involves a decrease in length and an increase in cross-sectional area. Another type of compression results when force is applied normally to all surfaces of a body and the volume is decreased in consequence. This happens to any body submerged in a liquid. Stress is again force per unit area, or pressure P, and strain is fractional deformation, which in this case is change in volume, ΔV, divided by the original volume V.

$$S = \frac{F}{A} = P, \qquad \epsilon = \frac{\Delta V}{V}$$

The basic assumption is that in all cases of elastic deformations stress and strain are proportional. Hence

$$\frac{\text{Stress}}{\text{Strain}} = \text{a constant, } K$$

and K is called the **bulk modulus.**

$$K = \frac{P}{\dfrac{\Delta V}{V}} = \frac{PV}{\Delta V} \tag{9.15}$$

Values of K are listed in Table 9.01. The reciprocal of K is called the **compressibility,** c.

$$c = \frac{1}{K}$$

TABLE 9.01   Elastic Properties of Various Materials.

Material	Young's Modulus, Y	Bulk Modulus, K	Shear Modulus, n	Tensile Strength
Aluminum	10×10^6	11×10^6	3.7×10^6	16×10^3
Brass	13×10^6	12×10^6	4.9×10^6	67×10^3
Copper	15×10^6	16×10^6	5.6×10^6	40×10^3
Iron, cast	17×10^6	13×10^6	6.7×10^6	17×10^3
Iron, wrought	27×10^6	21×10^6	11×10^6	47×10^3
Magnesium	6.1×10^6	4.5×10^6	2.4×10^6	28×10^3
Steel, annealed	29×10^6	21×10^6	11.4×10^6	100×10^3
Acetone	0	1.8×10^5	0	0
Ethyl alcohol	0	1.5×10^5	0	0
Water	0	2.8×10^5	0	0
Sea water	0	2.3×10^5	0	0
Air	0	14.7	0	0
Hydrogen	0	14.7	0	0

All figures in Table 9.01 are in pounds per square inch and are only to be taken as representative since these properties depend critically on the exact composition of an alloy or the purity of an element, and also on the heat treatment used in preparing the samples of metals. The bulk moduli of the gases are quoted at atmospheric pressure, and on the assumption that any compression of the gas takes place at constant temperature. Metric values of the moduli can be calculated readily, but the elastic properties are usually given by engineers in the fps units shown.

9.06 RIGIDITY AND SHEAR MODULUS

There is a third type of deformation known as **shear**, which is illustrated in Figure 9.06. The solid lines show an undeformed rectangular parallelepiped. If the base

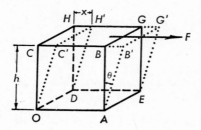

Fig. 9.06. Shear of a rectangular parallelepiped.

$OAED$ is fixed and a force F acts on the top $CBGH$ in a direction parallel to CB, the prism will be sheared or skewed to the right as shown. The name comes from the action of a pair of scissors or shears. The blades of these tools do not quite meet edge on, but have a slight gap between them so that when closed on a piece of paper (or tin) they cause such a large shear strain that the paper tears or cuts along the line of the blades.

Let area $OAED$ = area $CBGH = A$. Then stress $= F/A$ and the shear strain is defined as the ratio of the sideways movement x to the height h through which the shear occurs. Since x is a very small quantity, if θ is the angle of shear, the strain is

$$\epsilon = \frac{x}{h} = \tan \theta \doteq \theta \qquad (9.16)$$

The ratio of stress to strain is called the **modulus of rigidity** or **shear modulus, n.**

$$n = \frac{\dfrac{F}{A}}{\dfrac{x}{h}} = \frac{Fh}{Ax} = \frac{F}{A\theta} \qquad (9.17)$$

Any wire or rod which is twisted is undergoing a shear strain as may be seen by drawing a line along its length before twisting. Figure 9.07

illustrates the effect. A line AB is drawn on the cylinder. The lower end is clamped, and a torque Γ applied to the top. The line is now found in the position AC, showing that successive layers of the cylinder have rotated by larger and larger angles as one goes to the top. The angle θ through which the top end has rotated can be shown to be

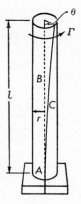

$$\theta = \frac{2\Gamma l}{\pi n r^4} \qquad (9.18)$$

where l and r are the length and radius of the cylinder.

Fig. 9.07. Shear of a cylinder.

Torsion Suspensions. Delicate instruments, such as accurate electrical meters, often use a fine wire or fiber clamped at one end to support the moving parts. Figure 9.08 is a sketch of a moving coil meter of this type. A light framework C, on which a coil of wire is wound, is suspended by a fiber AO. When an electric current goes through the coil it reacts with a magnetic field to produce a torque Γ_e on the coil. The coil turns, winding up the fiber and producing a restoring torque given by (9.18). For equilibrium,

$$\Gamma_e = \Gamma = \frac{\pi r^4 n}{2l} \theta = k\theta \qquad (9.19)$$

where k is written for the factor $\pi r^4 n/(2l)$, which is a constant of the fiber. Thus the steady deflection which results is proportional to the mechanical torque caused by the electromagnetic interaction.

If I is the moment of inertia of the coil, then if the electric current is stopped, Γ_e disappears and there is an unbalanced torque acting which will produce an angular acceleration α.

$$-k\theta = I\alpha \qquad (9.20)$$

Fig. 9.08. Moving - coil meter.

This is seen to be the equation of a simple harmonic motion of period

$$T = 2\pi \sqrt{\frac{I}{k}} \qquad (9.21)$$

A body oscillating in rotational motion in this way is called a **torsional pendulum.** It is interesting to note that the period of a torsional pendulum depends on the elastic properties of the suspension but is independent of g. This is just the reverse of the simple pendulum, whose period depends on g but is independent of the nature of the material of which it is made.

Transmission of Power by a Shaft. Many machines transmit power from one point to another by means of a cylinder which transmits torque—the drive shaft of an automobile is an example. Equation (9.18) is useful in relating the angle of twist of the shaft to its dimensions and the torque transmitted. Power and torque are connected by equation (7.38),

$$P = \Gamma\omega$$

9.07 RELATIONS BETWEEN ELASTIC CONSTANTS

In this chapter we have introduced and defined the four basic elastic moduli or parameters of a material. These are:

Young's Modulus, Y
Bulk Modulus, K
Shear Modulus, n
Poisson's Ratio, σ

It is worth noting, although we shall not be able to give the proofs, that these four are not independent since two relations exist between them.

$$K = \frac{Y}{3(1 - 2\sigma)} \tag{9.22}$$

$$n = \frac{Y}{2(1 + \sigma)} \tag{9.23}$$

Thus, if any two can be measured, the others can be deduced. A method of measuring Y was discussed in section 9.01, and equation (9.18) can be used to find n by measuring the angular deflection of a rod twisted by a known torque. The moduli usually measured are Y and n.

PROBLEMS

1. A copper wire 4.00 ft long has a cross-sectional area of 0.250 in.². It is subjected to a tension of 1000 lb-wt. Find the increase in length.

2. A roof which weighs 160.0 tons is supported by six equal steel posts each 12.0 ft long. If the maximum strain permitted is 1.00×10^{-3}, find the cross-sectional area required for each post. What was the decrease in length of each post when the roof was installed?

3. A straight copper telephone wire is lowered down a mine shaft. Before it is attached to insulators on the wall of the shaft, it is hanging freely from a support at the top. If the total length is 2000 ft, how much does the wire

stretch owing to its own weight? Density of copper wire is 555 lb ft^{-3}. What is the greatest length of copper wire which could be installed by this method if a safety factor of 1.50 is required?

4. An unstretched spring is 2.00 ft long. One end is fastened, and a force of 100 lb-wt exerted on the other stretches the spring to 2.40 ft. What force would be required to stretch it to a total length of 3.00 ft, and how much work would be done in this elongation of 1.00 ft?

5. One end of a light spring is attached to the ceiling. The length of the unstretched spring is 3.000 ft, and when a 10.00-lb mass is hung on it the length increases to 3.850 ft. Find the period of oscillation if the mass is given an initial vertical displacement.

6. A spring is suspended from the ceiling. Its unstretched length of 3.000 ft increases to 4.100 ft when a 50.00-lb mass is hung on it. The period of oscillation with this weight is 1.200 sec. When the suspended mass is increased to 100.00 lb, the period becomes 1.670 sec. Find the acceleration of gravity at the place. What is the mass of the spring?

7. The density of sea water at the surface is about 1.03 gm cm^{-3}. At a depth of two miles the pressure is 4720 lb in.$^{-2}$. Calculate the density at that depth.

8. A steel wire is 16.0 in. long and 0.400 in. in diameter. It is held rigidly at one end, and a light clamp with a socket is mounted on the other end. A rod 2.000 ft long is fitted into the socket so that it is perpendicular to the wire. A force of 6.40 lb-wt exerted on the end of the rod twists the end of the wire through an angle of 5.00°. Find the modulus of rigidity of the steel.

9. A steel shaft 2.00 m long must transmit 10.0 kw at an angular speed of 200 rpm. If it is not to twist more than 0.100 radians under operating conditions, what should its diameter be?

10. A light wire, 2.00 ft long and 0.100 in. in diameter, is made of a material with a modulus of rigidity of 2.00×10^6 lb in.$^{-2}$. The wire is clamped at the top and hangs vertically, supporting centrally a cylinder of mass 100 lb and diameter 48.0 in. If the cylinder is given an initial angular displacement and released, calculate the period of the motion.

11. Calculate Poisson's ratio for steel, copper, and aluminum.

12. A steel wire 0.200 in.^{2} in area and 4.00 ft long and an aluminum wire 0.350 in.^{2} and 5.00 ft long are joined end to end. If a force of tension is applied between the free ends, what percentage of the total stretch will occur in the steel wire?

13. A steel rod 4.000 ft long has a cross-sectional area of 0.5000 in.^{2}. It is clamped longitudinally between two fixed blocks and heated to a temperature of about 500C, so that its length would have expanded by 0.260 in. had the blocks not prevented this expansion. Calculate the force exerted by the rod on each block.

14. An elevator and its maximum passenger load have a mass of 4000 lb. It is designed to operate with a maximum acceleration of 4.00 ft sec^{-2}. Find the required cross-sectional area of the steel cable supporting it if a safety factor of 5.00 is demanded.

15. Show that $\sigma = \frac{1}{2}$ if matter is considered to be a continuum whose density is unaltered by tensional stresses.

10

Gravitation

10.01 STRUCTURE OF THE SOLAR SYSTEM

The close relationship between physics and astronomy is a long-standing one which has been fruitful for both sciences. Astronomy is probably the oldest of the sciences, and throughout most of recorded history its central problem has been the explanation of the nature of the members of the solar system and of their curious motions through the sky. The members of the solar system visible to the naked eye are the sun, the moon, and five bright **planets**—Venus, Jupiter, Mars, Saturn, and Mercury. The other objects in the sky are stars, similar to the sun but at distances too great to be visualized by the human mind, the nearest, Alpha Centauri, being 1.4×10^{13} miles away, so far away that light traveling at 186,000 miles sec^{-1} takes 4.4 years to travel from that star to us. (The distances in astronomy are so vast that the distance light travels in a year, the *light-year*, forms a convenient unit. Thus Alpha Centauri is 4.4 light-years away, the distance of Rigel is 540 light-years, and so on.) There are about 9000 stars visible (to the naked eye) from the earth, about 2500 of these being visible at any location on a clear night, and maps of the relative locations of these stars have been made for thousands of years. The maps made today differ so slightly from those made by the Greeks three thousand years ago, that the stars are called fixed.

The fixed stars appear to rotate once in twenty-four hours about the north point in the heavens which is marked approximately by Polaris, the Pole Star, and for most of them this means that they rise in the east and set in the west just as the sun does. Each night a particular star rises just a little earlier, so that the section of the starry sky visible each night changes with the seasons, repeating itself exactly after a year has passed. Against this regular apparent motion of the stars the moon and the planets have rather irregular motions. It is interesting to make a

181

sketch of the appearance of the fixed stars and plot the position of one of the planets, such as Jupiter, night by night. It will be found to move generally eastward with respect to the stars, but once a year it will appear to stop, reverse direction, move westward for two months or so, and then stop and resume its eastward movement. The westward movement is called *retrograde* as opposed to the normal *direct* motion eastward. The movement of the planets against the background of the fixed stars is responsible for the name since planet means wanderer in Greek.

The first scientific attempts to explain the solar system were made by the Greeks, who had many distinguished and capable astronomers including Aristotle (384 B.C.), Hipparchus (second century B.C.), and Ptolemy (second century A.D.). The most detailed description of the conclusions of Greek astronomy was written by Ptolemy, and the system is known as Ptolemaic astronomy. It assumes the earth to be stationary and at the center of the universe, with the sun, moon, planets, and stars revolving about the earth in complex eccentric curves and epicycles. The system broke down of its own complexity, being unable to account quantitatively for the observed motions of the heavenly bodies. Nevertheless, it was the accepted theory for two thousand years and exerted a profound influence on literature, philosophy, and mathematics.

Ptolemaic astronomy was unquestioned until the sixteenth century when Copernicus (1473) suggested that a simpler description of the motion of the heavenly bodies could be given in terms of a sun-centered system. He proposed that the earth was a planet which rotated on its axis and revolved about the sun, and that the other planets had similar motions. No experimenter himself, Copernicus realized that more accurate observational data were needed to settle the controversy. These data were accumulated by Tycho Brahe (1546), who leaned to the Ptolemaic theory but was really responsible for its ultimate downfall. He built an observatory on an island in the Baltic and using very carefully made instruments recorded the position of the planet Mars (and other heavenly bodies) over a period of years. The interpretation of the data was the work of Kepler (1571), who was Brahe's assistant for a time and spent twenty-five years analyzing his observations. The result was **Kepler's Laws of Planetary Motion:**

(I) *Each planet moves in an ellipse, the sun being at one of the foci.*

(II) *The radius vector from sun to planet sweeps out equal areas in equal units of time.*

(III) *The squares of the periods of revolution of the planets are proportional to the cubes of their mean distances from the sun.*

Another vigorous proponent of Copernican astronomy was Galileo, who built one of the first telescopes and with it discovered the moons of Jupiter and the phases of Venus.   The satellites or moons of Jupiter form a miniature solar system, and Galileo used the fact that Venus shows phases like those of the moon to develop an ingenious proof that Venus revolves about the sun and not the earth.

This is not a textbook on astronomy, and students wishing to learn more about this fascinating subject must read one of the numerous books available.   A good one is *Astronomy*, by R. H. Baker, published by Van Nostrand.   However, it may be worth taking time to show how the Copernican theory and Kepler's Laws give a simple explanation of the peculiar motion of the heavenly bodies described at the beginning of this section.

The apparent daily rotation of the heavenly bodies about the north point in the sky, called the North Celestial Pole, is a consequence of the earth's rotation about its axis.   This axis if produced indefinitely would pass through the North Celestial Pole.   The shift in the celestial scenery with the seasons is illustrated in Figure 10.01.   (It should be emphasized

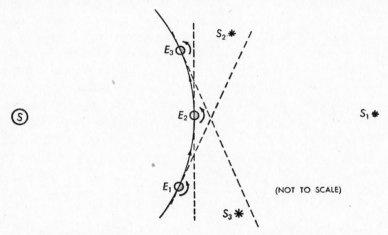

Fig. 10.01.   Seasonal changes in the aspect of the heavens.

that the drawing is not to scale—the sun is vastly bigger than the earth, and if the distance from the sun to the earth is scaled as shown, the nearest star would be six miles away, to the same scale.)   The sun is represented by S, and E_1, E_2, E_3 are successive positions of the earth at about one-month intervals.   The shaded portions of each representation of the earth are the night sides.   Since stars cannot be seen in the daytime, the star S_2 cannot be seen when the earth is at E_1, the star S_3 cannot be seen when the earth is at E_3, and the star S_1 is visible from all three positions. However, at midnight S_1 appears in the east from E_1, directly south from E_2, and in the west from E_3.

Figure 10.02 shows the cause of retrograde motion of a planet farther away from the sun than the earth is; a similar explanation holds for the

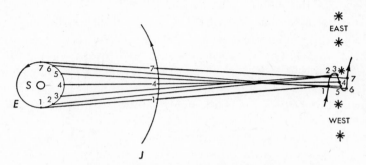

Fig. 10.02. Retrograde motion of the planet Jupiter.

two planets Mercury and Venus, which are inside the orbit of the earth. By Kepler's Third Law, Jupiter, which is five times as far from the sun as the earth is, must have a smaller angular velocity than the earth, Jupiter's period of revolution actually being about twelve years. Again S is the sun, and E and J are the orbits of the earth and Jupiter respectively. The points numbered 1 to 7 on the earth's orbit represent successive positions of the earth at monthly intervals for six months. Corresponding positions of Jupiter are marked on its orbit. The apparent position of the planet with respect to the fixed stars is found by joining corresponding points and extending the line. A background of stars is shown, and the ends of each of the lines are numbered and joined. The resulting curve shows the apparent path of Jupiter.

10.02 NEWTON'S THEORY OF GRAVITATION

Kepler's Laws describe the kinematics of planetary motion, but Kepler had no concept of the force responsible for the regularities; in fact, the concept of force was not clearly formulated during his lifetime. This was the work of Newton, as described in Chapter 3. After this clarification in thought the idea of a single type of force responsible for the motions of all the heavenly bodies became possible. One of the greatest of Newton's many great contributions to science was the discovery of the force law involved.

The falling of bodies released above the earth's surface is familiar to everyone.   Newton realized that it must be due to a force exerted by the earth on each body and speculated that the same force exerted by the earth on the moon was responsible for the latter describing an orbit around the earth.   If this was true, Kepler's Laws suggested that the sun exerted a similar pull on the planets.   Newton deduced the nature of the force from Kepler's Third Law.   A simplified version of his argument follows, based on the discussion of circular motion in Chapter 7.

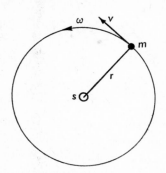

Fig. 10.03. Planet moving in a circular orbit.

It has been mentioned earlier that the eccentricity of the earth's orbit is so small that it is virtually circular.   The same holds approximately true for most of the planets, and the mathematics is simplified by considering a circular orbit.   Figure 10.03 shows a planet of mass m, period T, angular velocity ω, and linear velocity v describing an orbit of radius r about the sun.   It is assumed that ω is constant.   The centripetal force acting on the planet is

$$F_c = \frac{mv^2}{r} \tag{10.01}$$

and the period

$$T = \frac{2\pi}{\omega} = \frac{2\pi r}{v} \tag{10.02}$$

By Kepler's Third Law,

$$\frac{T^2}{r^3} = \text{a constant, } K$$

i.e.,

$$\frac{4\pi^2 r^2}{v^2}\frac{1}{r^3} = K; \qquad \frac{v^2}{r} = \left(\frac{4\pi^2}{K}\right)\frac{1}{r^2}$$

Substituting in (10.01) gives

$$F_c = \left(\frac{4\pi^2}{K}\right)\frac{m}{r^2} \tag{10.03}$$

Now if the sun exerts a centripetal force given by (10.03) on the planet, by the Third Law of Motion the planet exerts an equal centrifugal force on the sun.   Because of the reciprocal nature of these forces it is highly probable that the mass of the sun, M, is involved as well as the mass of the planet.   Equation (10.03) can be rewritten as

$$F = \left(\frac{4\pi^2}{KM}\right)\frac{mM}{r^2} \tag{10.04}$$

Newton then made his great assumption, that the force exerted by one body on the other is an example of a universal property of mass, and that the quantity in the bracket is a universal constant which we shall write in future as G, the constant of gravitation.

The Law of Universal Gravitation. *Any two particles of masses* m_1 *and* m_2 *separated by a distance* r *exert forces of attraction on each other that act along the line joining them and are equal in size to*

$$F = G \frac{m_1 m_2}{r^2} \tag{10.05}$$

The law is stated in terms of mass-points, and Newton's next step was to show that if a spherical body has a density which is a function only of distance from its center (spherical symmetry), the force of attraction it will exert at a point outside itself is exactly the same as if its mass were concentrated at its center. This permits us to treat the sun, planets, etc., as mass-points, to a very good approximation.

Newton then applied the theory to the motion of the moon about the earth and obtained excellent agreement with the observed data on its motion. The details are discussed in a problem. Bodies moving under the influence of an inverse square law, such as (10.05), can have only a few types of orbits. These are elliptical (with circular as a special case), hyperbolic, and parabolic. All the planets follow elliptical orbits, and when equation (10.05) is applied to an orbit of this type it can be shown that Kepler's Second and Third Laws are necessary consequences. The mathematics is rather involved, which is why we deduced the law of gravitation from consideration of a circular orbit. Examples of hyperbolic orbits are found in the study of comets.

10.03 CAVENDISH'S EXPERIMENT

The constant G is one of the most important numbers in physics. It was first measured by Henry Cavendish (1731), who devised an instrument called a torsion balance. It is illustrated in Figure 10.04, where M, M are two large, fixed, uniform, lead spheres, and m, m two small gold spheres on the ends of a light, rigid rod. The centers of the four spheres lie on a horizontal plane. The rod and small spheres are supported by a vertical fiber S whose modulus of rigidity has been measured accurately. The size of the apparatus is such that, because of the inverse square law, the force of attraction of the right-hand M on the left-hand m is negligible compared to the force of attraction between adjacent spheres. Initially, the spheres M, M are removed, and the rod hangs in an equilibrium position, the fiber having zero twist. The heavy spheres are then replaced, and the small gravitational forces cause the rod and small spheres to rotate slightly toward the attracting masses. A knob K on the end of the suspension is now turned until the fiber returns spheres m, m to their initial positions. From a knowledge of the angle through which K has been turned and of the geometry of the system, G can be calculated when the masses M, m are known.

This experiment of Cavendish has been repeated a number of times since he first performed it in 1798, and the presently accepted value of G is

$$G = 6.67 \times 10^{-11} \text{ Nm}^2 \text{ kgm}^{-2}$$

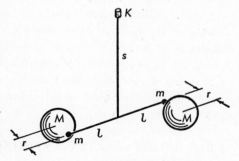

Fig. 10.04. Principle of Cavendish's Torsion Balance.

(The unit in which G is measured is sufficiently lengthy for it to be customary to say that $G = 6.67 \times 10^{-11}$ mks units. This terminology will be used frequently and always indicates that the numerical size of the quantity in question is adjusted so that it will give correct results in an equation if all the other quantities are measured in the appropriate mks units.) Since G is a very small number, forces of gravitation between ordinary bodies are small. For example, if two uniform spheres of mass 1000 kgm each are placed with their centers 1.00 m apart, the force on either of them is

$$F = \frac{6.67 \times 10^{-11} \times (1000)^2}{(1.00)^2} = 6.67 \times 10^{-5} \text{ N}$$

It is readily seen why the measurement of G requires delicate apparatus.

The Mass of the Earth. Care must be taken to avoid confusing G and g, the former being a universal constant and the latter a number which varies from point to point on the earth's surface. Knowledge of both of them, at a location where the distance to the center of the earth is known, is sufficient to find the mass of the earth. Treating the earth as a spherically symmetrical body of radius r, the weight W of a body of mass m is given by

$$W = G\frac{mE}{r^2}$$

where E is the mass of the earth.   But $W = mg$, therefore

$$\frac{GE}{r^2} = g \qquad\qquad (10.06)$$

The radius r can be found from a survey using purely geometrical methods.   Its value is approximately 6.37×10^6 m.   This gives E as 5.97×10^{24} kgm.   This number is too large to grasp, but converting to the mean density of the earth we get about 5.5 gm cm^{-3}, or about 5.5 times the density of water.   The surface crust of the earth has a density of about 2.5 gm cm^{-3}, so we conclude that the interior of the earth must be made of a much denser material than soil, rock, or water.   It is probably mainly metal since only metals have densities of the order of 7 to 10 gm cm^{-3}.

10.04 IMPORTANCE IN ASTRONOMY.   PRECESSION OF THE EARTH'S AXIS

Newton's Law of Gravitation started astronomy on an entirely new level.   Formerly a subject restricted to the measurement of positions and distances of the heavenly bodies, astronomy was now able to find their masses and sometimes their densities.   Other developments in physics, notably the analysis of light in spectrographs, enable us to tell the temperatures of stars and much about the types of matter of which they are composed.   Thus astronomers have found that the red star Betelgeuse in the constellation Orion is distant 300 light-years and has a surface temperature of about 3000C, a diameter about 500 times that of the sun, but a density so low that it would be classed as a quite respectable vacuum in a laboratory on earth.   On the other hand, the companion star to Procyon has a density of about 65,000 gm cm^{-3}.   A cubic inch of this star has a mass of over a ton.   Physics has done much for astronomy, but astronomy has contributed much to physics with information about what happens to matter at temperatures, pressures, and densities impossible to produce in the laboratory.

A problem in astronomy satisfactorily explained by the law of gravitation is that of the **precession of the equinoxes.**   The so-called fixed stars are actually in motion.   Their velocities relative to the solar system can be measured with some precision for the nearer ones and with less accuracy for stars up to distances of a few hundred light-years, and it is found that most of them move at speeds of the order of 15 miles per sec. Their directions of motion seem to be almost as completely random as those of the molecules in a gas.   Because of these movements the **relative** positions of the stars undergo gradual changes, but owing to the vast distances involved, hundreds or thousands of years must elapse for the changes to be observable by the comparison of star maps. The apparent motion of a star as seen from the earth is known technically as its **proper motion.**

The coordinate system used to describe the position (i.e., the direction) of any star is based on the directions of north and south established by the earth's axis. Relative to this system the entire heavens seem to be shifting slightly from year to year. This is an over-all movement in which the positions of the stars relative to each other remain unchanged and is thus *not* a consequence of proper motion. The shift is sufficient to be appreciable in astronomical tables in a matter of five years or so. When it is a case of "everybody out of step but our Johnny" you begin to suspect Johnny, and here the suspicion is correct—it's the direction of the earth's axis which is slowly changing. This effect was probably first detected by Hipparchus, but the explanation is comparatively recent. ◀

The earth is not a perfect sphere but an oblate (or flattened) spheroid with a bulge at the equator. It is shown in Figure 10.05, with the flatten-

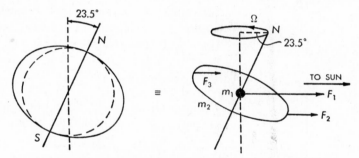

Fig. 10.05. Gyroscopic torque producing precession of the earth's axis.

ing greatly exaggerated. Actually the polar diameter is 7900 miles while the equatorial diameter is 7926 miles. Within the spheroid is drawn the largest possible sphere, leaving a ring of matter outside it. The sphere is equivalent to a point mass at the center for gravitation purposes. On the right-hand side of the diagram the earth has been replaced by a point mass m_1 and a ring of mass m_2. The axis of the earth is not perpendicular to the plane of the earth's orbit but is inclined at an angle of 23.5° to the normal to the orbital plane. The forces exerted by the sun on the earth have been shown as F_1 acting on m_1, F_2 acting on the half of the ring nearer the sun, and F_3 on the farther half of the ring. The resultant of F_1, F_2, and

F_3 is the centripetal force keeping the earth in its orbit. Force F_1 is enormously larger than the other forces, but the important thing is that F_2 is slightly larger than F_3 because it is slightly nearer the sun. Hence there is a small torque trying to right the axis of the earth and make it perpendicular to the plane of the orbit. Since the spinning earth is a huge gyroscope this torque produces precession about the normal. The precessional angular velocity Ω is very slow, so that the period is about 26,000 years. The observable effect is that the north point in the sky describes a circle of angular radius 23.5° among the constellations. At present the earth's axis points within a degree of the star Polaris. In the year 14000 A.D. it will point within four degrees of the bright star Vega. For simplicity the above explanation has been given in terms of the righting torque exerted by the sun. Actually the effect is due to torques exerted both by the sun and the moon. These torques are additive because the moon's orbit is practically in the plane of the earth's orbit.

The Shape of the Earth. It is believed that at one stage in its history the earth was a molten mass rotating about its axis and held

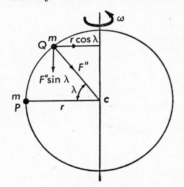

together by gravitational forces. In Figure 10.06, if E is the mass of the earth, the force of gravity on a particle of mass m at a point P on the equator is

$$F = G \frac{mE}{r^2}$$

This gravitational pull supplies the centripetal force $m\omega^2 r$, the difference

$$\mathbf{F'} = \mathbf{F} - m\omega^2 \mathbf{r}$$

being the apparent weight of m. This weight "packs" the sphere and holds it together.

Fig. 10.06. Effect of rotation on a molten sphere.

Consider a particle of mass m at Q, where the angle $PCQ = \lambda$ is called the *latitude* of Q. The gravitational force on m is the same as at P, if the earth is a sphere. This pull $\mathbf{F}$ can be broken up into two terms.

$$\mathbf{F} = \mathbf{F'} + \mathbf{F''}$$

where $\mathbf{F'}$ is the "packing" force as before. Force $\mathbf{F'}$ can be disregarded since a uniform force acting on every particle and directed toward the center will not change the spherical shape. The other force $\mathbf{F''}$ is the important one.

$$\mathbf{F''} = \mathbf{F} - \mathbf{F'} = m\omega^2 \mathbf{r}$$

It can be resolved into two components parallel and perpendicular to the axis as shown in the figure. The perpendicular component

$$F'' \cos \lambda = m\omega^2 r \cos \lambda$$

is exactly the centripetal force needed for the particle to move in a circle of radius $r \cos \lambda$. The unbalanced component $F'' \sin \lambda$ will cause a movement of m toward the equatorial plane. The result is a flattening at the poles and a bulge at the equator. As the earth's crust solidified it kept this shape and remains today an oblate spheroid.

10.05 THE THEORY OF RELATIVITY

Probably the best publicized development of the twentieth century in physics, at least until the atomic bomb, has been the theory of relativity, first announced by Einstein in 1905. This is a theory of considerable mathematical complexity and is mentioned here principally because of a rather widespread impression that it supersedes Newtonian mechanics and Newton's Law of Gravitation. Strictly speaking this is true, but if it leads to the attitude that Newton's ideas are unimportant, no conclusion could be more incorrect. Relativity is a minor modification of Newtonian mechanics which is normally *completely* insignificant. It becomes important only when dealing with very great masses, as in astronomy, or with very high velocities, as in electronics or nuclear physics. For example, Mercury is the planet closest to the sun and thus is acted on most strongly by the gravitational force of the sun. For a variety of causes the major axis of its orbit rotates about the sun slowly— at the rate of some ten degrees per hundred years. This effect took many years of careful observation to detect. When Newtonian gravitational theory is applied to the problem it predicts that the rate should be nine degrees per century. This difference is completely unimportant for practical purposes, *but* Einstein's theory predicts the ten-degree figure which agrees with observation.

Newtonian mechanics assumes that somewhere a stationary frame of reference exists. If it could be found, absolute position and absolute velocity could be measured. This frame has never been discovered. A famous test, the Michelson-Morley experiment, was made in 1887 to attempt to measure the velocity of light with reference to this fixed frame. It was a failure, and the conclusion was drawn by Einstein that the fixed frame did not exist, in other words, that no frame of reference was intrinsically better than any other. The theory of relativity grows out of this abstract conclusion. The reader may well wonder what conceivable connection this has with gravitation. We have neither time nor mathematical equipment to trace the development, but it leads to a different point of view regarding gravitation which gives results very slightly different from Newton's law in extreme cases.

As a matter of interest some of the conclusions of the theory of relativity are stated.

(1) The velocity of light in free space is an absolute constant. All observers, regardless of how their local frames of reference may be moving, will find the same value for c, this velocity.

(2) If any object whose mass and length are m_0, l_0 when it is at rest, moves with a velocity v relative to you, you will find that its mass and length have changed, being now given by the equations

$$m = \frac{m_0}{\sqrt{1 - \dfrac{v^2}{c^2}}} \qquad (10.07)$$

$$l = l_0 \sqrt{1 - \frac{v^2}{c^2}} \qquad (10.08)$$

(3) Time is also relative. If the object above carries a clock, its rate of timekeeping will not agree with a clock you hold. If t_0 is the time interval between two events as read on your "stationary" clock and t is the time interval between the same two events as measured on the "moving" clock, then

$$t = \frac{t_0}{\sqrt{1 - \dfrac{v^2}{c^2}}} \qquad (10.09)$$

(4) Newton's Second Law of Motion is still applicable in the form

$$F = \frac{\Delta(mv)}{\Delta t}$$

but *not* in the form $F = ma$ since m is likely to be a function of time.

(5) Energy and mass are two manifestations of the same thing. If mass m is changed into energy E,

$$E = mc^2 \qquad (10.10)$$

These results seemed strange and in contradiction to experience when they were first announced. Now, physicists take them for granted, particularly nuclear physicists who use (and verify) these equations every day. For most practical matters they are of no importance because of the arithmetic of the equations. Equation (10.07) says that a baseball on its way to the plate has a greater mass than when it rests in the catcher's mitt. Let us see just how much the increase is. The baseball has a mass at rest of 200 gm. The pitcher throws it with a speed of 40 m sec^{-1}. Velocity $c = 3 \times 10^8$ m sec^{-1}. Neglecting significant figures for a moment, (10.07) gives

$$m = \frac{200}{\sqrt{1 - \dfrac{1600}{9 \times 10^{16}}}}$$
$$= 200.000,000,000,000,1 \text{ gm}$$

Let's play out the ball game in Newtonian mechanics.

10.06 ESCAPE VELOCITY

Because of the inverse square law, the acceleration of gravity decreases as an object rises from the surface of the earth. We wish to find what initial velocity a body fired vertically must have to *just* keep going up indefinitely. If distance r is measured from the center of the earth and r_0 is the radius of the earth,

$$F = ma$$
$$-G\,\frac{mE}{r^2} = m\,\frac{d^2r}{dt^2}$$

where E is the mass of the earth. By (10.06),

$$\frac{GE}{r_0^2} = g$$

where g is the acceleration of gravity at the surface. Substituting gives

$$\frac{-r_0^2}{r^2}\,g = \frac{d^2r}{dt^2} = \frac{d}{dt}\left(\frac{dr}{dt}\right) = \frac{d}{dr}\left(\frac{dr}{dt}\right)\frac{dr}{dt}$$

But
$$\frac{dr}{dt} = v$$

the velocity at time t and distance r from the center. Therefore

$$\frac{-r_0^2}{r^2}\,g = v\,\frac{dv}{dr}$$
$$v\,dv = -r_0^2 g\,\frac{dr}{r^2}$$

Integrating,
$$\tfrac{1}{2}v^2 = \frac{r_0^2 g}{r} + C$$

We want v to vanish as $r \to \infty$. Therefore $C = 0$ and

$$v^2 = \frac{2r_0^2 g}{r}$$

To find the initial velocity we set $r = r_0$. Then, if v_0 is the escape velocity,

$$v_0^2 = 2r_0 g \tag{10.11}$$

Taking $r_0 = 6.37 \times 10^6$ m and $g = 9.80$ m sec^{-2}, we have

$$v_0 = 11.2 \times 10^3 \text{ m sec}^{-1} = 6.96 \text{ miles sec}^{-1}$$

PROBLEMS

1. Calculate the mass of the sun. (The mean distance from the earth to the sun is 1.49×10^{11} m.)

2. If the diameter of the sun is 1.39×10^9 m, how many times greater than that of the earth is the acceleration of gravity at its surface?

3. What would be the escape velocity from the sun in miles per second? No body moving with a speed greater than this can remain a permanent part of the solar system.

4. The moon is 2160 miles in diameter, has a mass of 8.10×10^{19} tons, and revolves about the earth once in 27.3 days at a mean distance of 2.39×10^5 miles from the center of the earth. Calculate the surface gravity and escape velocity for the moon.

5. The period of revolution of the planets Mercury, Venus, Mars, and Jupiter are respectively 0.241, 0.617, 1.88, and 11.9 years. Find their mean distances from the sun in astronomical units. (The astronomical unit is the mean distance from the sun to the earth.)

6. The mass of the planet Mars is about 0.106 times that of the earth and its diameter is 0.538 times as great. Compare their surface gravities.

7. There has been some discussion of an artificial satellite of the earth which would be a rocket fired beyond the atmosphere and directed into a stable orbit a fixed distance above the surface of the earth. If it were placed 1000 miles above the surface, what would be its period of revolution about the earth? How high would it have to be to remain apparently stationary over a point on the earth's equator?

8. In Figure 10.04, the restoring constant of the fiber is 2.29×10^{-7} newton-meters per radian, $m = 0.500$ kgm, $M = 10.00$ kgm, $l = 56.24$ cm, $r = 8.00$ cm. The apparatus is designed so that r is perpendicular to l. With the masses M removed the small spheres rest in position with the fiber untwisted. When M, M are replaced the knob K has to be turned through 14.7° to

bring the small spheres back to their original positions. Find the gravitational constant.

9. Using a diagram similar to Figure 10.02, show that the planet Venus will also have retrograde motion. Explain why it is difficult to observe this retrograde effect.

10. Newton's confirmation of the law of gravitation by lunar observations was based on the fact that the moon's distance can be measured directly by surveying methods and can also be predicted by comparing the acceleration of gravity at the earth's surface and at the distance of the moon. If $g = 32.2$ ft sec^{-2}, the radius of the earth is 2.09×10^7 ft, and the period of revolution of the moon about the earth is 27.3 days, find the distance of the moon, assuming its orbit to be circular. Compare with the distance given in problem 4.

11. In the fission of uranium in an atomic reactor or "pile", about $\frac{1}{10}$ of 1% of the mass of the uranium is converted into energy. Calculate the energy released in the fission of one gram of uranium.

11

Fluid Mechanics

11.01 THE THREE STATES OF MATTER

The previous chapters have been discussions of the mechanics of mass-points and solid bodies. In this chapter we extend the subject to deal with fluids. All the principles already introduced apply to fluids as well as solids, but a number of new points arise because of the differences in the three states of matter. To summarize the properties of the three states, let us define them.

Solid State. Matter in the form of a solid has a definite volume and shape, both of which can be altered only by the application of large forces.

Liquid State. A liquid has a definite volume, which can be altered only by the application of large forces; it has no definite shape and will take on the shape of its container, but forms a free surface at the top. A free surface of the liquid means a boundary with the liquid on one side and a gas or a vacuum on the other. In general, the atmosphere or some other gas exerts pressure on a liquid surface.

Gaseous State. A gas has neither definite volume nor definite shape but will fill completely any container. Force is necessary to reduce the volume of a gas, but gases are very much more easily compressed than liquids. Compare the bulk moduli of examples of matter in the three states given in Table 9.01.

Liquids and gases have so many properties in common that it is convenient to group them as **fluids,** that is, substances which flow readily. A substance in one state can be changed to another by altering the temperature and pressure suitably. In general, any substance can exist in any one of the three states, although the temperatures involved in liquefying some solids or vaporizing some liquids may alter their chemical composition. Change of state and the molecular theory of matter which

196

helps explain the various states are discussed at length in the part of this book on "heat".

The main physical properties which distinguish fluids from solids are that fluids will sustain no permanent shear stress and no appreciable tension.   If a fluid flows through a pipe, the walls of the pipe are found to exert a shearing force on the liquid.   In terms of friction, the fluid-solid surface is not perfectly smooth.   Similarly, one layer of fluid flowing over another exerts a slight drag.   This friction between layers of fluid is called **viscosity.**   Although this is important in practical work, it is difficult to deal with theoretically, so we introduce another idealization, the **perfect fluid,** which is one that exerts only normal forces or has zero viscosity. The theory is developed for perfect fluids and then modified where necessary to allow for viscosity.

Fluid mechanics is divided into **hydrostatics** and **hydrodynamics,** dealing respectively with fluids at rest and in motion.   The name "hydro" is illogical but convenient since the commonest and most important fluid is water.   Viscosity plays no part in hydrostatics, which is a relatively simple subject, but is important in hydrodynamics, which cannot be so described.

11.02 HYDROSTATICS.   PRESSURE

In dealing with fluids, pressure is a more useful concept than force. As already defined, pressure is the ratio of force to the area over which the force acts.

$$P = \frac{F}{A} \tag{11.01}$$

Pressure is the ratio of two vector quantities but is itself a scalar.

Consider a body of liquid at rest, as shown in Figure 11.01(a), where C is a cylinder of the liquid of area A and depth h below the surface.   The liquid below the bottom of this cylinder must be supporting its weight, since if it were not, there would be an unbalanced force on the cylinder and it would move down, contrary to the assumption that the liquid is at rest.   Note that the rest of the liquid can exert no tangential or shear force on the curved part of the cylinder to aid in supporting its weight. The force exerted on the area A at the bottom of the cylinder is

$$W = mg = \rho Ahg$$

where ρ is the density of the liquid.   Therefore

$$P = \frac{F}{A} = \rho gh \tag{11.02}$$

It is tacitly assumed here that ρ is a constant regardless of depth. This is not strictly true since any liquid has some compressibility, but problem 7, Chapter 9, shows how insignificant is the error of this assumption.

Consider the liquid contained in a small prism of triangular cross section at some point S. The base of the prism is horizontal, one side and two ends are vertical, and the fifth side makes an angle θ with the horizontal. Let the vertical height of the prism be Δz and the horizontal sides be of lengths Δx, Δy. Figure 11.01(b) shows a vertical section through the

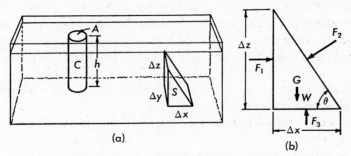

(a)

(b)

Fig. 11.01. Hydrostatic pressure.

prism perpendicular to the y axis. The liquid surrounding the prism exerts forces on its five faces. The force on each area must be normal to that face, because if it were not its tangential component would cause motion of the liquid parallel to the face. Since this does not happen in a liquid at rest the force exerted on any surface by a liquid at rest must be perpendicular to that surface. Let forces $F_1, F_2,$ and F_3 act on three of the faces as shown. If P_1, P_2, P_3 are the average pressures over these faces,

$$F_1 = P_1 \, \Delta y \, \Delta z \qquad \left. \begin{aligned} F_2 &= P_2 \, \Delta y (\Delta z \text{ cosec } \theta) \\ F_2 &= P_2 \, \Delta y (\Delta x \text{ sec } \theta) \end{aligned} \right\} \qquad F_3 = P_3 \, \Delta x \, \Delta y$$

The weight of the prism is $W = \frac{1}{2}\rho g \, \Delta x \, \Delta y \, \Delta z$, where ρ is the density of the liquid, and acts downward through G. Since the prism is in equilibrium

$$F_1 = F_2 \sin \theta$$
$$P_1 \, \Delta y \, \Delta z = P_2 \, \Delta y \, \Delta z \text{ cosec } \theta \sin \theta = P_2 \, \Delta y \, \Delta z$$

Therefore $P_1 = P_2$

Also $F_3 = F_2 \cos \theta + W$
$$P_3 \, \Delta x \, \Delta y = P_2 \, \Delta y \, \Delta x \sec \theta \cos \theta + \frac{1}{2}\rho g \, \Delta x \, \Delta y \, \Delta z$$
$$P_3 = P_2 + \frac{1}{2}\rho g \, \Delta z$$

If we now imagine the prism to shrink in size, as $\Delta z \to 0$, $P_3 \to P_2$. Hence for an infinitesimally small prism

$$P_1 = P_2 = P_3$$

that is, the pressure at a point is independent of the direction of the surface on which it acts (since θ is an arbitrary angle in this argument). This is the justification for calling it a scalar quantity. The conclusion reached in this paragraph applies equally to gases, although (11.02) does not because of their compressibility.

Nothing in the derivation of (11.02) assigned any unique position to the cylinder C, and since from this equation P is a function of depth only, the pressure is uniform on a horizontal plane. This conclusion can be verified another way by considering any horizontal cylinder of fluid. Suppose in Figure 11.02 LM is taken as the axis of a cylinder of small cross-sectional area A. Since the fluid is at rest

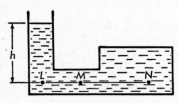

Fig. 11.02.

there can be no net force on it in any direction, including the direction LM. If P_L and P_M are the pressures at L and M, the net force in the direction LM is

$$P_L A - P_M A = 0$$

That is, $P_L = P_M$ or, in general, the pressure at any point on the line LN is given by (11.02), h being the depth indicated.

Units. Since in the derivation of (11.02) the weight is in absolute units, the equation will give P in newtons per square meter in the mks system. If gravitational units are preferred, the g drops out of (11.02) and $P = \rho h$ will give pressure in kilograms per square meter (kgm m^{-2}) or pounds per square foot (lb ft^{-2}). Pressure is frequently measured by balancing a column of liquid against the pressure and quoting the height of the column. The most widely used liquid is mercury because it has the greatest density of any substance which is a liquid at room temperature, and thus permits measuring pressure with columns of minimum height. (Another advantage of mercury is that it has a low vapor pressure at room temperature. Vapor pressure will be discussed later in connection with heat, but its low value for mercury reduces errors in pressure measurements and helps avoid certain other experimental troubles.) Thus a pressure may be given as so many *inches of mercury* (abbreviated *in. Hg*). The absolute pressure can be calculated from (11.02). The normal pressure of the earth's atmosphere is about 30 in. Hg or about 76 cm Hg. Meteorologists prefer an absolute unit of pressure called the *bar*. It is defined by the relation

$$1 \text{ bar} = 10^5 \text{Nm}^{-2}$$

Although atmospheric pressure is usually close to 1 bar, it is often quoted in millibars (abbreviated mb). The *atmosphere* is another pressure unit. It is understood to mean the so-called standard (or average) atmosphere of 76.0 cm Hg.

$$1 \text{ atmosphere} = 760.0 \text{ mm Hg} = 1.0132 \text{ bars} = 1013.2 \text{ mb}$$

11.03 ARCHIMEDES' PRINCIPLE

A very simple but useful theorem in hydrostatics was discovered by the Greek, Archimedes (287 B.C.). A probably apocryphal story is that he discovered it by observing the buoyancy of his bath water and in his excitement rose from his bath, and neglecting to dress, ran through the streets shouting "I have found it". The Principle is

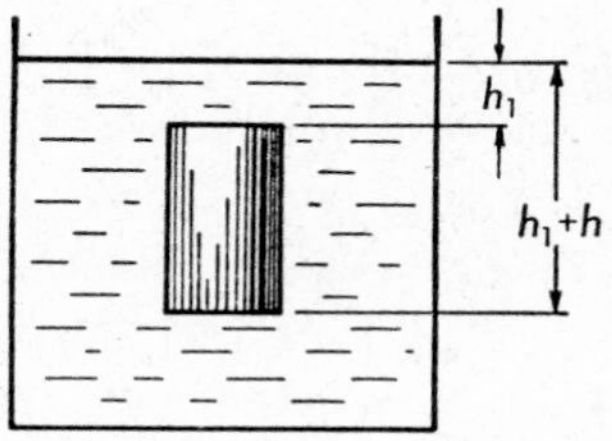

Any body partially or totally immersed in a fluid is buoyed up by a force equal to the weight of the fluid its volume displaces.

It is illustrated in Figure 11.03, which shows a cylinder of height h and area A immersed with its axis vertical in a liquid of density ρ. Since the force exerted by a liquid is everywhere normal to the surface, the forces on the curved side of the cylinder are horizontal and can be disregarded here. (The resultant of these forces must be zero in any case since the cylinder may rise or fall but will not be moved sideways by a liquid at rest.)

Fig. 11.03. Archimedes' Principle.

The downward force on the upper horizontal surface is

$$F_1 = P_1 A = \rho h_1 g A$$

and on the lower surface the force acting upward is

$$F_2 = P_2 A = \rho(h_1 + h)g A$$

The net force is thus upward and is called the force of **buoyancy** B.

$$B = F_2 - F_1 = \rho g h A = \rho g V$$

where V is the volume of the cylinder. The right-hand side of the equation is the weight of a volume of the liquid equal to the volume of the cylinder, which proves the Principle in this case. A general proof extended to fluids and to bodies of any shape follows. Consider the volume of fluid contained in an imaginary closed surface and let us treat this volume as a free body. Acting downward on it is its weight. Since it remains at rest, the resultant force exerted on it by the surrounding fluid must be equal to the weight but directed upward. This buoyant force is a property of the remainder of the fluid, and thus will be unaltered if the original volume of fluid is replaced by any other body of the same shape and volume. The buoyant force must act through the center of gravity of the original volume of fluid, or through the center of gravity of the immersed part of the body, this center being calculated as for a body of uniform density. This point is called the **center of buoyancy** and will not usually coincide with the actual center of gravity of the body being buoyed up. This is an important factor in the stability of ships.

11.04 DENSITY AND SPECIFIC GRAVITY

The **density** of a body was defined early in the book as mass per unit volume, and the term has been used freely. A discussion of density and methods used in its measurement has been deferred to this section because most of the methods use hydrostatics.

In symbols,

$$\rho = \frac{M}{V} \tag{11.03}$$

where M and V are the mass and volume of the body whose density is ρ. The units of density favored in this book are grams per cubic centimeter (gm cm^{-3}), kilograms per cubic meter (kgm m^{-3}), and pounds per cubic foot (lb ft^{-3}). The second of these is the mks unit and will be of an unfamiliar size to those not used to this system. The cgs unit (gm cm^{-3}) is more familiar. In dealing with fluids, particularly gases, the cubic centimeter (abbreviated as cu cm or cm^3 or cc) is rather small, and another derived unit of volume called the *liter* is often used.

As mentioned in 1.05, when the metric system was first set up it was intended that the density of pure water, at normal pressure and at the temperature of maximum density (4C), should be precisely 1 gm cm^{-3}. More exact measurements have changed it from this figure, but the change is small. The *liter* is *defined* as the volume of exactly one kilogram of pure water at 4C and 760 mm Hg. The experimental conversion factor is

$$1 \text{ liter} = 1000.027 \text{ cc}$$

or the density of water at this temperature and pressure is

$$\rho = 0.999\ 973 \text{ gm cm}^{-1}$$

The difference between 1 liter and 1000 cc and the difference of the maximum density of water from unity in the cgs system will both be ignored from here on.

Other conversion factors are

$$1 \text{ kgm m}^{-3} = 1 \text{ gm liter}^{-1}$$
$$1 \text{ kgm m}^{-3} = 10^{-3} \text{ gm cm}^{-3}$$
$$1 \text{ gm cm}^{-3} = 1000 \text{ kgm m}^{-3}$$
$$1 \text{ gm cm}^{-3} = 62.43 \text{ lb ft}^{-3}$$

(The student should verify the last of these equalities from the relations between the basic units of mass and length.)

Specific Gravity. Of frequent use is the ratio of the mass of a given volume of a substance to the mass of an equal volume of pure water at its densest. This is called the **specific gravity** of the substance. Since it is a ratio of two masses it is a pure number independent of the system of units being used. In the various systems:

$$\text{cgs density} = \text{specific gravity} \times 1 \text{ gm cm}^{-3}$$
$$\text{mks density} = \text{specific gravity} \times 1000 \text{ kgm m}^{-3}$$
$$\text{fps density} = \text{specific gravity} \times 62.43 \text{ lb ft}^{-3}$$

11.05 METHODS OF MEASURING SPECIFIC GRAVITY

(1) MEASUREMENT OF MASS AND VOLUME

The simplest method of finding density and specific gravity (s) is to find the mass with a balance, measure the dimensions of the body with rules or calipers, and calculate the volume and hence ρ and s. This method will only work if the sample is regular in shape. When this is not the case the volume is usually found by adding the sample to a liquid in a graduated vessel and noting the volume of liquid displaced. The sample should not be soluble in the liquid or react chemically with it.

(2) ARCHIMEDES' PRINCIPLE

Specific gravity can be found in two weighings for a solid object whose specific gravity is greater than unity. Let the body be weighed in air, the result being $W_1 = Mg$.   (In accurate work a correction must be made for the buoyant force exerted on the body by air.   This correction rarely amounts to more than $\frac{1}{10}$ of 1%.)   Next it is suspended by a light thread from one end of a beam balance, and then a vessel of water is raised about it until the body is submerged in water but does not touch the wall of the vessel.   It is then reweighed, giving W_2.   By Archimedes' Principle,

$$W_2 = W_1 - V \times g \times \rho_W$$

where ρ_W is density of water, since $Vg\rho_W$ is the weight of water displaced by a body of volume V.   Then

$$\frac{W_1}{W_1 - W_2} = \frac{Mg}{Vg\rho_W} = \frac{Vg\rho}{Vg\rho_W} = \frac{\rho}{\rho_W} = s$$

(3) SPECIFIC GRAVITY BOTTLE

This method uses a small glass jar with a ground-glass neck into which can be fitted a ground-glass stopper with a capillary tube bored through it.   The purpose of the stopper is that, when the bottle is filled with liquid and the stopper is inserted, a bit of the liquid can escape through the capillary, leaving a very closely reproducible volume.   This type of bottle is illustrated in Figure 11.04.   It is useful in measuring the specific gravities of liquids or of solid samples which can be broken up into smaller pieces.   Details are left for a problem.

Fig. 11.04. Specific gravity bottle.

(4) HYDROMETERS

The hydrometer is a direct reading instrument for finding the specific gravity of a liquid.   Avoid confusion between this name and a similar one (hygrometer) applied to a device for measuring humidity.   A typical hydrometer is shown in Figure 11.05.   It consists of a long, sealed tube (usually hollow glass) of constant cross section.   The graduations are on the upper part of the tube, and the bottom is usually blown out into a bubble of greater cross section to reduce the length of the instrument. The bubble is weighted with lead shot (held in place by a packing) so that the tube will float upright.   It is calibrated by allowing it to float in water and marking the level of the water on the stem.   Since the weight is constant, when it is placed in a liquid denser than water more of the stem will be above the surface. If the specific gravities of several liquids are known, it can be placed in each of them, and the appropriate level can be marked. Alternatively, if the weight and volume of the instrument are measured, together with the area of cross section of the stem, the calibration can be worked out from the theory of hydrostatics, and the stem can be engraved. It should be noted from the figure that the intervals of constant increment of specific gravity are represented by progressively shorter lengths on the stem as the specific gravity increases.

The instrument illustrated is a general-purpose one with a wide range of specific gravities. Most hydrometers are designed for a particular purpose, and being restricted to a narrow range of s, have an expanded scale giving greater accuracy. Two familiar types of hydrometers are used in service stations to measure the specific gravity of the water-antifreeze mixture in the radiator and of the sulphuric acid solution in batteries. From the readings it is possible to tell the temperature at which the coolant will freeze and the state of charge of the battery. The range of specific gravities of battery solution is considerable, so that the use of a hydrometer for this purpose is quite straightforward, but in the case of antifreeze solution the range is small and the specific gravity depends on the actual temperature of the solution as well. The interpretation thus requires careful reading of both the temperature and the specific gravity.

Fig. 11.05. Constant weight hydrometer.

(5) GASES

The method used for gases is essentially that of paragraph (1) above, but extra care is needed because of the small mass involved. Two containers A and B of closely similar external volume (of the order of one or two liters) are needed. One of them, A, must be strong enough to sustain atmospheric pressure; the other need not be. The internal volume of A is measured carefully by weighing the mass of water required to fill it. Then after being evacuated, A is weighed, using B as one of the counterweights in order that the buoyant effect of the surrounding air may be ignored as acting equally on the two vessels. The gas whose density is to be measured is then admitted to A, and the extra mass needed to rebalance the scale is the mass of the known volume of the gas.

Table 11.01 lists a number of specific gravities and densities.

TABLE 11.01 Specific Gravities and Densities.

Substance	Specific Gravity	Density (kgm m^{-3})	(lb ft^{-3})
Solids			
Aluminum	2.67	2670	168
Brass	8.44	8440	527
Copper	8.89	8890	555
Glass	2.4–2.8	2400–2800	150–175
Granite	2.64–2.76	2640–2760	165–172
Ice (0C)	0.917	917	57.2
Iron, cast	7.03–7.73	7030–7730	439–482
Lead	11.35	11350	708
Limestone	2.68–2.76	2680–2760	167–171
Magnesium	1.74	1740	109
Platinum	21.37	21370	1334
Steel	7.83	7830	489
Wood	0.11–1.33	110–1330	7–83
Liquids			
Acetone	0.792	792	49.4
Ethyl alcohol	0.791	791	49.4
Gasoline	0.66–0.69	660–690	41–43
Mercury	13.59	13590	849
Sea water	1.025	1025	64.0
Gases (0C, 76 cm Hg)			
Air	1.293 × 10^{-3}	1.293	0.0807
Hydrogen	0.0899 × 10^{-3}	0.0899	0.00561
Oxygen	1.429 × 10^{-3}	1.429	0.0897

11.06 PASCAL'S PRINCIPLE

Another basic theorem of hydrostatics is the principle first stated by Pascal (1623).

If a fluid completely fills a closed container, a pressure increment applied at one point on the fluid is transmitted undiminished to every other point in the fluid.

This is a necessary consequence of the fact that pressure acts equally in all directions at any point. Consider Figure 11.02 again. In section 11.02 the upper left-hand surface of the liquid was treated as if no pressure was exerted on it from above, that is, as if it was open to a vacuum. Suppose instead that the vessel was open to the air. Then atmospheric pressure Π is exerted on the liquid. Since the surface layer remains stationary, the downward force ($\Pi \times$ area) must be balanced by an upward force from the rest of the liquid. Thus an infinitesimal distance below the surface the pressure in the liquid has increased to an amount Π owing to the pressure of the atmosphere. This argument can be repeated again and again until any level in the liquid is reached. Thus the pressure at A is really

$$P = \Pi + h\rho g \qquad (11.04)$$

This is called the **absolute pressure** at A while (11.02) gives the excess pressure above atmospheric, or **gauge pressure.** Frequently gauge pressure is all we are interested in, and many instruments (e.g., a tire pressure gauge) measure this excess pressure only.

The transmission of pressure by a fluid is the basis of hydraulic machinery such as jacks, presses, and automobile brakes. A hydraulic press is illustrated in Figure 11.06. A force F is exerted on the smaller piston and produces an excess pressure F/A in the liquid, A being the area of the piston. This pressure causes a force equal to $(F/A)B$ to act on the larger piston of area B. If this force just balances a load W,

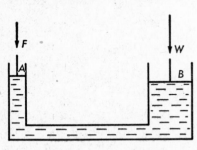

$$W = \frac{F}{A} \times B$$

$$\text{Mech. adv. } = \frac{W}{F} = \frac{B}{A} \quad (11.05)$$

Fig. 11.06. A hydraulic press.

Equation (11.05) gives the theoretical mechanical advantage. The actual mechanical advantage will be slightly smaller, owing to leakage of the liquid around the seals of the pistons, but the efficiency of hydraulic machinery is usually high, 90% or more. From (11.05) it can be seen that the mechanical advantage can be made as large as desired, but of course the travel of the left-hand piston is correspondingly increased. For this reason the left-hand piston is usually operated as a pump drawing additional fluid from a reservoir. This requires a check valve in the pipe leading to the large piston to prevent the liquid flowing back. Hydraulic presses of enormous size and mechanical advantage are used in the automobile industry to form fenders and other body sections by pressing sheet metal against steel forms or dies.

Pascal's Principle applies to all fluids, but because of their great compressibility gases are rarely used in hydraulic equipment. The normal working fluid is a nonvolatile oil.

11.07 SIPHONS AND PUMPS

The transport of large quantities of liquids and gases from one point to another is an essential feature of modern industries, particularly those based on chemical engineering. An extreme example is the way in which petroleum products and natural gas are now pumped for hundreds or even thousands of miles from their sources to the locations

where they are used.   Pumps of many varieties and sizes are in use, but
they operate on a few simple principles.

The simplest pump is the siphon, a form of which is shown in Figure
11.07.   Two containers A and B are partly filled with a liquid, the surfaces being at different levels.   It is desired to transfer some liquid from
A to B.   A tube bent in an approximate U-shape is filled with the liquid,
frequently by putting one end in A and sucking on the other, and its
ends are placed in the two containers as shown.   It will be found that
liquid will flow from A to B until the levels are at the same height or
until the level in A falls to the end of the U-tube.   The explanation is
simple.   The pressure at both C and
E is atmospheric.   The absolute hydrostatic pressure at D is

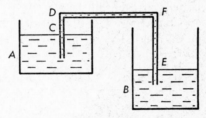

$$P_D = \Pi - \rho g \times CD$$

where ρ is the density of the liquid.
Similarly,

$$P_F = \Pi - \rho g \times EF$$

Fig. 11.07.   A simple siphon.

As long as $EF > CD$, $P_D > P_F$ and liquid will flow to the right along DF.
This tends to reduce the pressure at D, and atmospheric pressure on the
surface of A causes the liquid to flow up CD.   The absolute pressure at
D must be equal to or greater than zero.
Therefore

$$\rho g \times CD \not> \Pi$$

This places a limit on the height atmospheric
pressure can raise a liquid.   This limit depends
on the density of the liquid, being about 32 ft
for water or 30 in. for mercury.   It should
also be noted that there is no necessity for the
end of the pipe to be immersed in liquid in B.

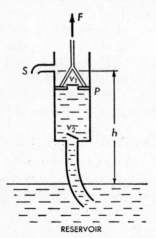

Fig. 11.08.   A suction
pump.

Suction Pumps.   Figure 11.08 illustrates
a simple suction pump suitable for raising
water from a well or lake.   A piston P can
slide up and down in a cylinder.   It has a hole
in the center with a valve V_1.   The bottom
of the cylinder is connected through a valve
V_2 to a pipe leading to the reservoir of liquid.   The system is pictured on
an up stroke.   The valve V_1 is closed and V_2 is open.   The force F pulls

the piston up, tending to reduce the pressure below it. Atmospheric pressure on the reservoir forces liquid up the pipe. On the down stroke V_1 opens and V_2 closes, permitting the piston to descend through the stationary liquid to raise an additional volume on the next up stroke. As with the siphon, the height h, through which liquid is to be raised, cannot be greater than 32 ft for water, and in practice h must be rather less because of leakages around the piston rings and valves.

Vacuum Pumps. In handling gases rotary pumps are used. Figure 11.09 shows a common design. A solid block B has a cylindrical hole bored in it, in which an eccentrically mounted cylindrical rotor R turns about an axle A in the direction shown. A spring-loaded plate C rides on the rotor, separating the space inside the pump into two compartments, one connected to the intake pipe I and the other to the output O. The

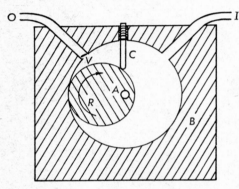

clearance between R and B is so small that the lubricating film of oil forms an effective seal at the line of contact. During each rotation, as the line of contact moves over the intake a volume of gas is trapped between R and B and then compressed until the pressure forces open the valve V in O. Further rotation discharges this gas through O and the check valve V closes. In the meantime, as

Fig. 11.09.   A rotary gas pump.

the space between R and B connected to I increases, the pressure is lowered, drawing more gas from I to repeat the cycle. Usually the block B is completely submerged in oil.

This type of pump can be used to create a steady flow in a pipe line, to compress gas in a tank connected to O, or to evacuate a tank connected to I. The last use is the most interesting to physicists since so much experimental work needs high vacua. A rotary pump of this nature can reduce the gas pressure to about 10^{-3} mm Hg. If lower pressures are needed, a mercury or oil **diffusion pump** is connected in series between the rotary pump intake I and the chamber to be evacuated. In a diffusion pump the mercury (or oil) is vaporized by heating the pump at one point and condensed by refrigerating it at another. In this way mercury vapor is caused to circulate in the pump owing to an appreciable pressure gradient. This pressure gradient also causes the gas to drift from the vacuum chamber to the line I. The mechanical pump is called a **fore pump** in this use and is necessary because diffusion pumps will only work at pressures below about 100 microns of mercury. (A micron Hg is a unit of pressure equal to one-millionth of 1 m Hg. Thus

$$1 \text{ micron Hg} = 10^{-6} \text{ m Hg} = 10^{-3} \text{ mm Hg}$$

A micron (μ) is strictly a unit of length, but it is common practice to refer to a pressure of so many microns, the qualifying "of mercury" being understood.) A good diffusion pump can reduce pressure to 0.01 μ, and pressures as low as 10^{-4} μ can be achieved.

Besides their research uses, high-vacuum systems are important in industry in the manufacture of radio tubes, fluorescent lights and incandescent lamps, thermos bottles, etc.

11.08 GASES AND THE EARTH'S ATMOSPHERE

(1) BOYLE'S LAW

The compressibility of gases was first described mathematically in 1662 by the English physicist Robert Boyle (1627). His law states that

For a given amount of gas at constant temperature, the volume varies inversely as the pressure.

Figure 11.10 shows a simple experiment to verify this law. A meterstick M is mounted in an upright position, and two glass tubes A and B are attached to it with clamps so that their heights can be varied. Tubes A and B are connected by a long rubber tube R. Some mercury is poured into B so that the level of mercury in A is just above the rubber tube. A cork C is driven into the end of A, enclosing a definite mass of gas. Some additional mercury can now be added to B. The tube B is now raised a few centimeters at a time, compressing the air in A.

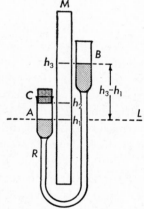

Fig. 11.10. Boyle's Law apparatus.

The figure shows one of the positions with the relevant heights marked. The volume V of gas is $(h_2 - h_1)A$, where A is the internal cross-sectional area of the tube A. The absolute pressure P of the gas can be found as follows. Because of the low density of gases the hydrostatic pressure difference in a small height such as the length of the tube A is completely negligible, and the pressure of the gas in A can be taken to be equal to the pressure in the mercury at the level marked L. Since the pressure in the mercury must be equal at the same level in both arms, we need to know the pressure at L in the right-hand arm, which is the atmospheric pressure Π acting on the open surface of the mercury plus the hydrostatic pressure due to the mercury column of height $h_3 - h_1$. Therefore

$$P = \Pi + h_3 - h_1 \text{ cm Hg}$$

A number of readings of P and V are taken and V is plotted against $1/P$. A straight line, which on being extrapolated will pass through the origin, is found. Hence

$$V \propto \frac{1}{P}$$

or
$$PV = \text{a constant, } C$$

which is Boyle's Law. A similar result will be obtained with a gas other than air.

Boyle's Law is not exact, failing if the temperature is near the point where the gas will liquefy or if very high pressures are used, but for most purposes it gives sufficiently accurate results.

(2) THE EARTH'S ATMOSPHERE

The earth is surrounded by a blanket of gas several hundred miles thick which is held by the gravitational pull of the earth. The atmosphere is a mixture of several gases, the composition varying with height. At the surface it is approximately 78% nitrogen, 21% oxygen, and 1% argon, with traces of carbon dioxide, hydrogen, neon, and helium together with varying amounts of water vapor. As height above the earth increases, the pressure drops rapidly, the oxygen content diminishes, and the hydrogen percentage increases.

Variations in pressure, temperature, and moisture content of the atmosphere near the surface are taking place continually and are responsible for our weather. The physics of these atmospheric changes is complex and imperfectly understood, as witness the uncertainties of weather forecasting. Meteorology is a branch of applied physics but too large a subject to be more than touched on in this book.

(3) BAROMETERS AND PRESSURE GAUGES

The pressure of the atmosphere was first measured by Toricelli (1608), who was the inventor of the barometer. He took a long glass tube, sealed it at one end, filled it with mercury, and inverted it in an open dish of mercury with his finger over the open end. On removing his finger the level of mercury in the tube fell until its vertical height above the free surface was about 76 cm. This was the first barometer, and present ones differ only in greater refinements in the accuracy of measurement of the height of the column.

The mercury barometer is of necessity a large instrument, about a meter long, and not readily portable. A secondary type called an **aneroid barometer** is widely used. The essential feature of this instrument is a sealed, flexible capsule, illustrated in Figure 11.11. The capsule C is made of corrugated metal for flexibility, partially evacuated, and then permanently sealed. The center of its base is rigidly connected to the case of the instrument. Any change of external pressure will cause this capsule to expand or contract like a bellows, raising or lowering a button B welded to the center of the top. The motion of B is small and

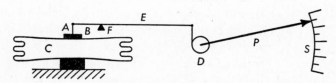

Fig. 11.11. Sealed pressure capsule.

is magnified by a delicate linkage which is shown in a rather schematic form in the figure—actual linkages used are often more elaborate. A rod A welded to B is hinged to a second rod E which rocks about a fixed fulcrum F. The other end of E is attached to a light cable or chain which is wound around a spring-loaded drum D. The drum carries a long pointer P which moves over the scale S to show variations in pressure. Aneroid barometers need to be calibrated against a standard mercury barometer at fairly frequent intervals because the characteristics of the capsule tend to change with age and use.

Manometers. An instrument frequently used in laboratories to measure pressure is the manometer, which is a simple adaption of the mercury barometer principle. A glass tube is bent in a U-shape and mounted vertically beside a scale S. One end A is connected to the vessel where the pressure is to be measured. The other end B may be open to the atmosphere or sealed. In Figure 11.12 an open type is shown. If the liquid in the manometer tube has a density ρ, pressure in the vessel is

$$P = \Pi + (h_2 - h_1)\rho g$$

in absolute units. The liquid used may be mercury, or a nonvolatile oil of low density if it is desired to measure smaller pressure changes. Figure 11.10 is another example of an open manometer.

If the end B is sealed, and if the liquid is inserted in the manometer tube so that the space between B and h_2 is a vacuum, the manometer measures absolute pressure instead of pressure relative to the atmosphere.

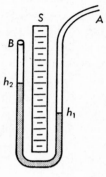

Fig. 11.12.
Open manometer.

High-Pressure Gauges. Pressures considerably above atmospheric may be measured with an instrument similar to an aneroid barometer in which the case of the instrument is sealed except for an outlet which is connected to the high-pressure region. A similar instrument of cheaper construction is the Bourdon gauge. It is made of a flattened metal tube sealed at one end and wound in a spiral. If the open end is connected to a high-pressure region, the gas entering the gauge will cause it to expand slightly, partially unrolling the spiral. (Paper spirals which do the same thing when blown, and also emit a raucous noise, are often seen at parties.) The movement of the sealed end can be amplified by a linkage and used to indicate pressure when suitably calibrated.

(4) AIRCRAFT INSTRUMENTS

Figure 7.15 shows the flying instrument panel of an aircraft. The gyroscopic instruments were described in Chapter 7. The others are pressure instruments, or indicators for electronic equipment.

Altimeter. The pressure altimeter is an aneroid barometer and thus measures pressure, *not* height above the ground. At any given height the pressure is no more constant than it is at ground level, but it fluctuates about an average value. The proportional, or percentage, decrease of pressure per kilometer is approximately constant. If a convention is adopted giving the approximate average pressure dependence on height, the pressure scale on the barometer can be marked to show height above sea level. Most altimeters have a setting knob which permits the current ground-level pressure to be set on the instrument, adjusting the height scale accordingly, but despite this correction some computation is needed to deduce true height from the height indicated by the altimeter.

Air-Speed Indicator. The pressure exerted by stationary air is called *static.* If the air is moving against a fixed surface, or alternatively if the surface is moving through the air, the force on the surface is greater and we call the pressure exerted *dynamic.* The difference between dynamic and static pressures increases with speed and thus serves as a means of measuring speed. Aircraft carry a small tube called the **pitot head,** which is shown in Figure 11.13. It is mounted rigidly on the airframe pointing forward and in a position chosen so that the air striking it is undisturbed by the wings or propellers.

The pitot head consists of two tubes, one within the other for convenience but sealed off from each other. The inner one P is called the pitot line, and the pressure in it is dynamic. The outer one S is called the static line. It has a number of small holes drilled in it to permit its pressure to be the same as the static pressure of the outside air. The pitot line leads to the inside of a capsule similar to that in the aneroid barometer. This capsule is in a sealed case connected to the static line. An aircraft at rest with respect to the air would have equal pressures in both lines, and the position of the needle on the scale would be marked as zero air speed. As the speed increases the pitot line

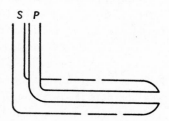

Fig. 11.13. Pitot head operating air-speed indicator.

pressure builds up, expanding the capsule and moving the pointer on the scale, which can be calibrated in miles per hour. Two points should be noted. The reading of the instrument depends on the dynamic-static pressure difference, which depends on height and temperature as well as speed. The true air speed (T.A.S.) must be calculated from the indicated air speed (I.A.S.), making allowance for these factors. Secondly, the instrument measures speed with reference to the surrounding air. The speed and direction with reference to the ground must be found by compounding the velocity through the air with the velocity of the air over the ground, using vector addition.

Rate-of-Climb Indicator. The correct name for this instrument is the vertical-speed indicator. It measures both rate of climb and rate of descent but is usually called rate-of-climb by illogical custom. Once again it is a capsule instrument in a sealed case, but this time the static line is connected to both the inside of the capsule (through a large tube) and the inside of the case (through a capillary tube). In level flight the static pressure is steady and the pressure on both inside and outside of the capsule is the same, giving zero reading. If the aircraft starts to climb, the static pressure drops. The decrease inside the capsule is instantaneous, but because of the capillary connection the pressure in the case does not drop as fast, leading to a pressure difference and a reading showing rate of climb.

(5) VARIATION OF PRESSURE WITH HEIGHT

In section 11.02 the variation of pressure with depth was found for an incompressible liquid. This relation will certainly not hold for a gas like the atmosphere. The pressure at any height will be the weight of the gas above unit area at that height. The pressure will be great near the surface, and because of the compressibility of gas the density will be much greater near the surface than higher up. Thus the major part of the mass of the atmosphere will be near the surface. In fact, although traces of atmosphere are found at heights of 400 miles, over half its mass is below a height of 4 miles.

The actual variation of pressure with height is complicated by temperature changes, variations of composition, etc., and no exact formula is known. If the temperature is assumed to be constant, it can be shown that

$$P = P_0 e^{\frac{-gh}{k}} \tag{11.06}$$

where g is the acceleration of gravity, k is the ratio of pressure to density, and P and P_0 are the pressures at levels a height h apart. Equation (11.06) does fit the actual atmosphere fairly well except that the coefficient of h in the index has to be adjusted arbitrarily by a numerical factor. By this equation we see that the atmosphere never actually "stops" but gets more and more tenuous with increasing height.

11.09 SURFACE TENSION

A steel razor blade or needle lowered very carefully onto water will float. If a capillary tube is placed in water, the water will rise up in the tube above the level of the free surface. A drop of water will "stick" to the bottom of a glass rod without falling. These and similar phenomena, contrary to the laws of hydrostatics applicable to fluids in bulk, are examples of surface tension. For an explanation of surface tension we turn to the microscopic (or ultramicroscopic) nature of a fluid. The molecules exert attractive forces on each other which are not gravitational in nature. They decrease far more rapidly than by an inverse square law and are called short-range forces. They arise from a complicated electrical phenomenon. The attractive force between molecules within a homogeneous volume is called **cohesion,** and that across a boundary between two different substances or different states of one substance is called **adhesion.** (It doesn't "explain" the forces to give them names; it merely makes them easier to discuss.)

So far it has been possible to ignore forces of cohesion and adhesion, but they are frequently relevant to a deeper understanding of the phenomena we have been discussing. Consider, for example, the curious fact that a siphon will work in a vacuum provided the fluid has to be lifted through a small height only. The explanation of the action of a siphon offered in 11.07 was based on the effect of atmospheric pressure. It is a perfectly valid explanation but is evidently not the whole story. The net action of a siphon is to reduce the potential energy of the liquid, to lower its center of gravity. Any system *tends* to move in such a way as to reduce its energy to a minimum, but if there is any opposition, the system needs a force to start it moving. In the case of the siphon cohesion

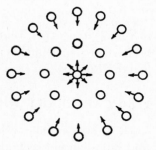

Fig. 11.14. Surface tension forming a spherical drop.

supplies this force, either with or without the aid of atmospheric pressure. This aspect is usually ignored because of the difficulty of describing cohesion quantitatively.

Figure 11.14 shows a number of molecules of liquid in a drop. The inner molecules are pulled equally in all directions by their immediate neighbors and thus experience no net force. The surface ones, however, have unbalanced forces directed inward as shown. Since the liquid is incompressible, these forces cannot alter the volume of the drop, but they can make it as compact as possible by rearranging the liquid to have the minimum possible surface area for the given volume. The figure of this shape is a sphere, and small raindrops or drops of water on a flat surface do take on this spherical shape. The effect of cohesive forces is thus to make a liquid behave as though its surface were under tension. This **surface tension** may be *defined* as the force acting on one side of a straight line of unit length in the surface. It acts parallel to the surface and perpendicular to the line.

Figure 11.15 illustrates a simple method of measuring surface tension.

A wire W is bent into an open rectangle, and a second wire L is laid across it at right angles. The wires are held together and dipped in a soap solution which forms a film over the rectangle (shown shaded).

If L is released, the film will shrink, pulling L with it. If the wire L is held in some position by a force F, the surface tension T is given by

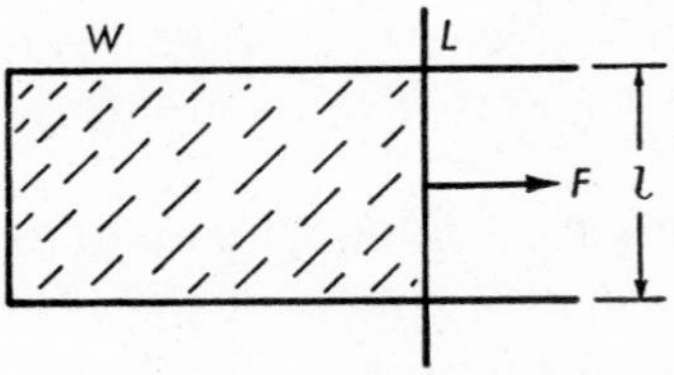

$$T = \frac{F}{2l} \qquad (11.07)$$

Fig. 11.15. Tension in a film.

Since T is the force exerted per unit length of the film, it is in units of newtons per meter or dynes per centimeter (cgs). The factor 2 in (11.07) arises because the soap film has a top and a bottom surface and thus a total length $2l$ pulling on L.

11.10 CAPILLARY RISE. PRESSURE IN A DROP

If a clean glass rod is dipped in water, it comes out wet, showing that adhesion between glass and water is greater than cohesion between water and water. The reverse is true for mercury and glass—mercury will not "wet" glass.

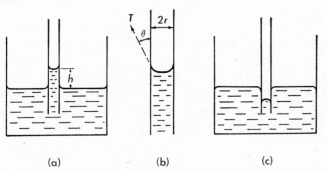

(a)   (b)   (c)

Fig. 11.16. Capillarity in water and mercury.

Figure 11.16 shows the resulting capillary action in a glass tube. Part (a) shows the rise of water level, (b) the detail of the shape of the surface, and (c) the depression of mercury.

The cause of the rise of water can be thought of in this way. The inner surface of the glass tube is wet with water, and there is thus a layer of water firmly anchored to the glass. This water exerts a tension

T per unit length on the surface of the water in the tube, or a total force

$$T \times 2\pi r \tag{11.08}$$

This force is not vertical but is inclined at an angle θ. Its vertical component holds up the weight of water raised. Therefore

$$2\pi rT \cos \theta = \pi r^2 h\rho g$$

$$h = \frac{2T \cos \theta}{r\rho g} \tag{11.09}$$

Equation (11.09) shows why capillary rise is noticeable only in tubes of small bore. It also suggests a simple method of measuring T which is more accurate and more convenient than that of Figure 11.15. The angle of contact, θ, is a function of the magnitudes of cohesion and adhesion and cannot be predicted by theory. This angle is approximately zero degrees for a water-glass contact but is about 140° for a mercury-glass contact. Thus in the latter case the surface tension has a large component downward and lowers the level in the tube. Equation (11.09) is still valid.

Example. A vessel contains a liquid of specific gravity 0.750. A capillary tube of internal diameter 2.00×10^{-4} m is inserted vertically into the liquid, which rises 6.00 cm in the tube. The angle of contact is observed to be 30.0°. Find the surface tension of the liquid.

$$T = \frac{rh\rho g}{2 \cos \theta}$$

$$= \frac{1.00 \times 10^{-4} \times 0.0600 \times (0.750 \times 1000) \times 9.80}{2 \times 0.500} \text{ Nm}^{-1}$$

$$= 0.0441 \text{ Nm}^{-1}$$

$$= 44.1 \text{ dyne cm}^{-1}$$

Pressure in a Drop. As discussed in section 11.09, a spherical drop of liquid acts as if it were enclosed in a membrane under tension. Thus the pressure in the drop must be greater than atmospheric. Figure 11.17 shows the forces acting on half of a drop. The *excess* pressure P in the drop causes forces of $F = P \Delta A$ on each element of the surface area. Force F acts normally to the area and has a component $F \cos \phi$ perpendicular to the base of the hemisphere.

$$F \cos \phi = P \Delta A \cos \phi = P(\Delta A \cos \phi)$$

Since $\Delta A \cos \phi$ is the projection of the element of area ΔA on the base of the hemisphere, if $F \cos \phi$ is summed over the entire hemispherical surface, the upward force is

$$\Sigma F \cos \phi = P\Sigma \, \Delta A \cos \phi = P\pi r^2$$

because the projection of the curved surface on its base is the base itself. The downward force is the total pull on the circumference of the base by

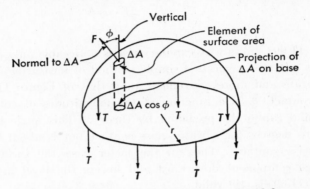

Fig. 11.17. Forces on a hemisphere of a liquid drop.

the lower half of the drop, i.e., the surface tension T acting along a length $2\pi r$. Equating forces gives

$$2\pi r T = P\pi r^2$$
$$P = \frac{2T}{r} \tag{11.10}$$

In the case of a bubble there are two surfaces, each of radius r since the wall of a bubble is extremely thin. Thus the force due to surface tension is twice as great, and the excess pressure in a bubble is

$$P = \frac{4T}{r} \tag{11.11}$$

Equations (11.10) and (11.11) show that the pressure is greater in a small drop or bubble than in a large one. This has important consequences in studying the formation of clouds.

Surface tension plays an important part in the life of plants which must lift water from the soil, in the action of blotting paper, in accurate measurements with manometers, and in a number of other physical applications. Industrially, surface tension is important in the "flotation" process for extracting useful ore particles from a finely ground specimen of rock. The liquid used has a surface tension big enough to "float" off the lighter rock particles but insufficient to support the heavier ore particles.

Table 11.02 gives the surface tensions of a few common liquids.

TABLE 11.02   Surface Tensions.

Liquid	T (Nm^{-1})	Temperature (C)
Water	0.0728	20
Water	0.0589	100
Mercury	0.487	15
Acetone	0.0237	20
Ethyl alcohol	0.0223	20

11.11 VISCOSITY

Viscosity has already been defined as the internal friction in a fluid. To put this in quantitative form, consider the case of a fluid moving slowly over a horizontal solid surface S_1 (Figure 11.18), owing to

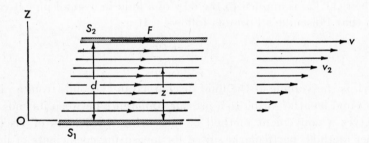

Fig. 11.18.   Effect of a shear stress applied to a real liquid.

a tangential force F applied by the upper surface S_2. Suppose S_1 is at rest and S_2 has a constant velocity v to the right. For small enough values of v a steady-state condition exists in which each particle of the fluid moves parallel to the surface with a velocity which depends only on z, the perpendicular distance from S_1. It is usually assumed that the boundary layers of the liquid have the same velocities as the adjacent solids, and that the velocity at any height z is given by

$$\frac{v_z}{z} = \frac{v}{d} = \text{the velocity gradient}$$

The shear stress applied is F/A, where A is the area of S_2. Newton assumed that for fluids moving in layers, as in this case, the stress varies as the velocity gradient. That is,

$$\frac{F}{A} \propto \frac{v}{d}$$

$$\frac{F}{A} = \eta \, \frac{v}{d} \tag{11.12}$$

where the constant of proportionality η is called the **coefficient of viscosity**. The assumptions on which this definition is based are difficult to check directly, but theory based on them agrees well with experiment, provided v is not too large. Some consideration will be given in the next section to the effects occurring at high velocities in fluids. The coefficient is a function of temperature θ, increasing with θ for gases but decreasing with θ for liquids.

The mks unit of viscosity can be seen from (11.12) to be the newton-second per square meter. The cgs unit is the dyne-second per square centimeter, or *poise*, named after Poiseuille (1799). Both the poise and the mks unit (which is equal to 10 poises) are rather large, and viscosities are often quoted in centipoises (1 centipoise = 10^{-2} poise).

When (11.12) is applied to the flow of a fluid in a small pipe it can be shown that Poiseuille's Formula follows. It is

$$V = \frac{\pi r^4 P t}{8 l \eta} \tag{11.13}$$

where V is the volume of the fluid discharged in t seconds from a pipe of radius r and length l owing to a pressure difference between its ends of P. This gives a convenient method of measuring coefficients of viscosity. Another method, particularly suited for measuring coefficients of liquids of large viscosity, is based on the connection between terminal velocity and viscosity. Stokes (1819) proved that if a sphere of radius r falls through a medium of viscosity η, its terminal velocity is given by

$$v = \tfrac{2}{9} \, \frac{r^2 g}{\eta} \, (\rho - \rho_M) \tag{11.14}$$

where ρ and ρ_M are the densities of the sphere and the medium. This relation, combined with other, electrical ones, was used by R. A. Millikan (1868) in finding the charge of the electron (see section 43.03).

Viscosity has an important bearing on the efficiency of lubricating oils, and the Society of Automotive Engineers (SAE) has set up standards of viscosity for motor oils. The higher the number of the oil the greater is its viscosity. Thus changing from SAE 30 oil in summer to SAE 20 in winter means using a thinner oil. The main reason for the change is to make the car easier to start. SAE 30 is rather thick at the low temperatures experienced in winter and would make it difficult for the starter motor to turn over the engine rapidly enough.

TABLE 11.03   Viscosities Measured in Centipoises.

Substance	Temperature (C)	Viscosity
Water	0	1.793
Water	20	1.006
Ethyl alcohol	20	1.2
Glycerin	20	830
Mercury	20	1.55
SAE 20 oil	40	280
SAE 30 oil	40	400
Air	0	0.0171
Air	20	0.0184

11.12 HYDRODYNAMICS

Hydrodynamics, which includes aerodynamics, is an extremely important subject. The theoretical aspect is difficult and incomplete. It serves as a useful guide to experiment, but practical designs of aircraft, ships, propellers, turbines, etc., are the result of trial and error with models tested in wind tunnels and hydraulics laboratories.

The motion of fluids is of two distinct types. If a fluid moves slowly past a smooth surface of small curvature, the individual particles of the fluid themselves move in smooth curves called **streamlines.** This type of flow is called **laminar flow** because the fluid moves in approximately parallel layers or lamina. If the velocity is increased gradually, at some critical velocity the character of the flow changes rather abruptly to one containing whirls or eddies. This is called **turbulent flow.** These two types show clearly in the smoke rising from a lighted cigarette resting on an ash tray in a still room. For some distance the smoke rises in almost straight columns or filaments. These filaments may twist a bit about each other, but their identities are evident in this laminar flow. At some height a clearly distinguishable change to turbulent flow occurs, and the column of smoke breaks up into confused eddies.

In the preceding section Poiseuille's Formula and Stoke's Law were quoted. Both of these are valid only for laminar flow and the question arises, Can we predict in advance which type of flow will occur in a particular problem? This was studied by Reynolds (1842), and his answer was a qualified Yes. He found that a certain dimensionless ratio kept recurring frequently in the theory of hydrodynamics. This ratio is now called **Reynolds Number** (R) and is defined as

$$R = \frac{\rho v d}{\eta} \qquad (11.15)$$

where ρ, η, and v are the density, viscosity, and velocity of the fluid, and d is the maximum transverse dimension of the channel in which the fluid moves. In the case of a pipe, d is its diameter. Small values of R are always associated with laminar flow and large values of R with turbulence. For any particular system the critical value of R usually must be found by experiment, but its order of magnitude can often be inferred from knowledge of a similar system. In the case of a straight pipe, if $R < 2000$, the flow is laminar; if $R > 3000$, the flow is turbulent. For intermediate values of R the flow may be either. The pressure required to deliver fluid through a pipe increases abruptly and rapidly as the flow changes from laminar to turbulent.

Another example of the two types of motion is the flow of air over an

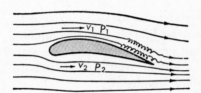

Fig. 11.19. Air flow over an aircraft wing.

aircraft wing. Figure 11.19 shows a section parallel to the flow of air. The shaded portion is the section of the wing, and the lines represent the paths of the particles of air. It will be noticed that laminar flow is replaced by turbulence about two-thirds of the way along the upper surface of the wing. It is found that the lift of the wing comes almost entirely from the forward part where the air moves over it in laminar motion.

Sharp edges usually produce turbulence and provide increased resistance to motion. For this reason, objects which are to move rapidly through air or water are made as smooth as possible and shaped to avoid large curvatures—in the popular usage of the word, they are "streamlined". The ideal shape is the teardrop as seen in a falling drop of rain. At still higher speeds through air the conditions change again, and aircraft designed to travel faster than sound (in technical language, at Mach numbers greater than unity, where Mach one is the speed of sound) are built with needle-pointed noses and thin, almost knife-edged wings.

Bernoulli's Theorem. One of the first results in hydrodynamics is a theorem attributed to a Swiss mathematician, Daniel Bernoulli (1700). One form of the theorem is stated as follows:

In a streamline flow, the pressure is greatest where the velocity is least and vice versa. We shall not attempt to prove this theorem, but a few applica-

tions are discussed.   Figure 11.20 shows a Venturi or filter pump.   A
pipe P is attached to a tap, and water is turned on.   A constriction or
nozzle N in the pipe forces the water to flow more rapidly through N than
elsewhere in the pipe.   This follows because water is incompressible, and
the volume of water passing a point per second is

$$V = Av$$

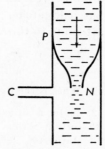

where A is the cross-sectional area and v the velocity
of the water.   The greater velocity at N thus means
lower pressure, and a side tube C can be connected to
a space to be pumped out.   A good filter pump will
reduce gas pressure to about 5 cm Hg.

The lift of an aircraft wing is due to a pressure
difference.   In Figure 11.19 the air passing over the
wing has farther to go than the air passing under it.

Fig. 11.20.
Venturi pump.

Hence $v_1 > v_2$ and $P_2 > P_1$.   The lift L will be the product of $(P_2 - P_1)$ times the effective area of the wing, that is, the area back
to the point where turbulence starts.

Figure 11.21 shows a golf ball traveling through the air with a forward
velocity v, and spinning about a vertical axis with an angular velocity ω.
It will be seen to veer off in the direction the front of the ball is turning.
The golfer behind the ball calls it a "slice" or a "hook", depending on

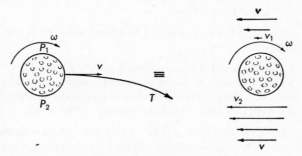

Fig. 11.21.   "Slice" of a golf ball.

which side he swings from, and wonders what he did to *that* stroke to start
the ball spinning.   The trajectory T can be quite sharply curved.
Bernoulli's theorem provides the explanation.   The right-hand side of
the figure shows the equivalent problem of a ball with spin but no linear
velocity, with air streaming past it in the opposite direction with velocity
v.   The surface of the ball is rough, and because of the viscosity of air,
tends to carry a surface layer of air with it as it spins.   The resultant

velocity of the layer of air next the ball is thus smaller than v on one side and larger on the other. The way in which the velocities of successive layers of air change is indicated by the velocity arrows in the right-hand picture. Since $v_1 < v_2$, $P_1 > P_2$ and the ball follows T. Similar effects are observed with any spinning ball if the surface is rough enough. A baseball pitcher likes to roughen the surface of a new ball before he attempts to throw a curve.

PROBLEMS

1. What is the hydrostatic pressure due to a column of acetone 40.0 cm high?

2. Water is stored in a reservoir, the level of the surface being 12.0 ft above a certain water main. Find the pressure in the main when the water is stationary.

3. A submarine is designed to withstand safely a pressure of 200 lb in^{-2}. How far may it descend in the ocean?

4. A dam stretches 300 ft across a river. The average depth of water is 120 ft. Calculate the force on the dam.

5. The atmospheric pressure is 29.02 in. Hg. Convert to millibars.

6. An iceberg (frozen fresh water) floats in the sea. What fraction of its volume is above the surface?

7. A man of mass 160 lb just floats, with virtually all his body below the surface of a lake. What is his volume?

8. A stone weighs 27.0 lb in air and 15.9 lb when immersed in water. Find its specific gravity.

9. A block of wood is weighed in air, giving a result of 0.690 kgm. It floats on water, so a strip of lead is fastened to the bottom of the block, whose weight in air is now 0.924 kgm. The extra mass is enough to sink the block, which weighs 0.106 kgm in water. Find the density of the wood.

10. A block of balsa wood is $10.0 \times 4.00 \times 20.0$ cm^3. It is weighed in air on a beam balance using counterweights of brass. Calculate the true mass if the apparent weight is 155.0 gm. Find the density of the balsa and the percentage error in neglecting the correction for the buoyancy of air.

11. A specific gravity bottle has a mass of 90.26 gm. When filled with water and a few small pieces of an alloy, the mass is 258.48 gm. The metal pieces are dumped out, and the bottle is refilled with water. The mass is now 189.71 gm. Find the specific gravity of the alloy if the dry weight of the metal pieces is 78.16 gm.

12. The stem of a hydrometer is a cylinder of external diameter 1.00 cm, and the total volume of the instrument is 31.50 cc. When floating in water,

5.63 cm of the stem is above the surface. Calculate the length of stem corresponding to specific gravities of 0.90, 1.10, 1.20, 1.30, and 1.40. Sketch the calibration.

13. A hydraulic lift is operated by the water from the city mains which have a pressure of 75 lb in.$^{-2}$. If the piston on the lift has an area of 1.50 ft^2, what weight can the lift raise if its efficiency is 90%? What is the actual mechanical advantage?

14. A hydraulic jack is used in a garage to lift the rear end of an automobile. The weight lifted is 1400 lb. The large piston of the jack has an area of 4.00 in.^{2}, and the small one has an area of 1.00 in.^{2}. The small piston is operated as a pump by a lever of mechanical advantage 14.0. The travel of the small piston per stroke is 3.00 in., and the efficiency of the hydraulic system is 80%. Find the force which must be exerted on the end of the lever and the number of strokes to raise the rear end of the car 1.00 ft off the ground.

15. A large, tall tank of gasoline (of specific gravity 0.670) contains a siphon pipe to discharge the liquid. The top of the siphon is 15.0 ft above the level of the gasoline, and the pipe is connected to the air outside. The siphoning action is started by temporarily raising the pressure in the tank. The pressure is allowed to revert to atmospheric when the liquid flows through the siphon. Find the starting pressure (excess over atmospheric) and the depth of gasoline which will be discharged if atmospheric pressure is 30.1 in. Hg.

16. An oxygen tank has an internal volume of 3.00 ft^3, and the excess pressure inside it is 175 lb/in.^{2}. It is connected to an oxyacetylene torch which uses oxygen at a pressure of 6.00 lb/in.^{2} at a rate of 0.40 ft^3 per minute. How long will the tank last?

17. The pumping speed of a vacuum pump is the volume of gas which it will extract from a container per unit time. This volume is virtually independent of pressure over a wide range of pressures. If the pumping speed of a pump is 10 liters per minute and it is connected to a closed system containing air at an original pressure of 76.0 cm Hg, calculate the approximate time to reduce the pressure to 0.100 mm Hg if the pressure drops to 38.0 cm Hg in 8.00 sec. (Suggestion: Note that in any short time interval mass of gas removed is proportional to pressure of gas remaining. But decrease of pressure is proportional to decrease of mass, i.e., $\Delta P/P$ is the same for all equal intervals of time.)

18. The gas containers of a dirigible have a volume of 1.00×10^6 ft^3. They are filled with hydrogen at atmospheric pressure. What is the total lifting capacity of the dirigible? If helium (density 0.0100 lb ft^{-3}) had been used as the gas, what would the total lifting capacity of the airship have been?

19. Figure 11.22 illustrates an ingenious toy called a Cartesian diver. A cylindrical test tube A containing some air floats inverted in the water. The

tank has a sheet of rubber stretched over the top and tied tightly. If R is pushed down, the driver A sinks to the bottom. If R is released, it rises to the top. Explain this action, in particular the fact that there is no stable

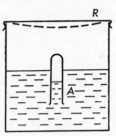

Fig. 11.22.
A cartesian diver.

position other than these two regardless of the air pressure. If the top of the test tube is 1.00 cm out of the water, the air column in A is 4.00 cm long, and the air pressure in the container is 76.0 cm Hg, by how much must the air pressure be increased to cause the diver to sink?

20. A barometer tube is only partially filled with mercury so that an air space 0.50 cm long and at atmospheric pressure is left at the top of the tube, which is 80.0 cm long. When inverted in a bowl of mercury, the mercury column is 71.8 cm long and the space above the mercury in the tube is 8.10 cm long. Find the atmospheric pressure.

21. If pressure in the atmosphere decreases exponentially with height so that it falls to half the surface level (76 cm) at 19,000 ft, what is the pressure at 45,000 ft? How high would one have to go to reach a pressure of 1.0 cm Hg?

22. A glass tube of internal diameter 1.00 cm is used as the tube for a mercury barometer. Find the correction needed to allow for surface tension. (Angle of contact of mercury on glass is 140°.)

23. A glass capillary tube of internal diameter 0.200 mm is placed upright in water at 20C. Calculate the capillary rise. The tube is lowered into the water until only 10 cm of it is above the surface. Describe what happens to the water in the capillary tube. (Be careful you don't invent a perpetual motion machine.)

24. What is the excess pressure in millibars in a drop of acetone of diameter 4.00 mm?

25. A bubble is blown in a soap solution of surface tension 30 dynes cm^{-1}. The excess pressure in the bubble is 1.00 cm Hg. Find its radius.

26. For water, η, the coefficient of viscosity, is 1.00×10^{-3} mks units. If water is to be delivered through a pipe at the rate of 0.400 liter sec^{-1}, what is the minimum diameter of the pipe to ensure laminar flow?

27. A cylindrical tank has a flat bottom and an inside diameter of 50.0 cm. A hollow cylinder of iron of external diameter 40.0 cm and internal diameter 39.0 cm rests on the bottom of the tank. The cylinder is open at the top and is closed at the bottom with a circular plate of iron 40.0 cm in diameter and 1.00 cm thick. The over-all length of the cylinder is 20.0 cm. The density of the iron is 7500 kgm m^{-3}. Find the mass of the iron cylinder. Water is added around the cylinder until the depth of water in the tank is 22.0 cm. What is the distance between the bottom of the tank and the bottom of the cylinder? What mass of water is floating the iron? What depth of mercury must be added to the inside of the cylinder to sink it?

28. A long glass capillary tube is closed at one end, and some air is sealed in it by a thread of mercury 2.0 cm long. When the tube is held vertically, closed end down, the length of the column of air is 18.0 cm when the barometric pressure is 76.0 cm Hg. If the top of the tube were connected to a volume at one-half atmospheric pressure, what would be the length of the air column?

29. A liquid is forced through a pipe 1.00 m long with an internal diameter of 0.600 cm by a pressure difference of 1.20×10^4 newtons m^{-2}. The volume of liquid collected from the pipe in 5.00 minutes is 0.570 liter. Find the viscosity of the liquid in centipoises.

30. An oil pipe line has an internal diameter of 8.00 in. If the pumps maintain a pressure gradient of 5.56×10^{-5} lb per square inch per lineal foot, find the volume in gallons which the pipe line can deliver per 24-hr day. The oil has a viscosity of 300 centipoises = 6.27×10^{-3} fps grav. units and 1 ft^3 = 6.23 imperial gallons = 7.48 U.S. gallons.

31. Small steel balls of diameter 0.200 cm are timed as they fall through a tall jar of glycerin of specific gravity 1.32. The average terminal velocity is 1.72 cm sec^{-1}. Find the coefficient of viscosity of the glycerin.

32. Hailstones of diameter 0.0240 in. and of specific gravity 0.500 are falling. If the air near the ground is at a temperature of 20.0C, with what velocity do the hailstones strike the ground?

HEAT

12

Relative Temperature

12.01 DEDUCTIONS FROM EVERYDAY EXPERIENCE

Heat has been correctly described as a mode of motion, and we wish to make that our basic concept of it in this book. This can be made to fit with the notions of heat that all of us acquire in our everyday experience, but the relationship is not obvious in that experience. As a preamble, then, let us first summarize those notions, which for most of us have been somewhat sharpened and clarified by physics courses in the schools.

Consider a kettle of water on a stove, say an electric stove. If it has been there overnight, with the stove turned off, then water, kettle, and stove are all at room temperature, whatever that means. Now when an electric switch is closed an electric current flows. There is then a flow of electrical energy into the heating element. The heating element gets hot. Somewhat more gradually, the kettle and its water, because they are resting on the element, get hot too. What do we infer from these observations? The increasing hotness is associated with the flow of energy, electrical in this case, into the stove. The stove converts the energy into a form that makes substances hot, and energy is transferable in this form from the hot element to the less-hot kettle and water. We call energy in this form heat, so that *heat is a form of energy* and *heat flows from a hot region to a less-hot, or relatively cold, region.*

With a thermometer, i.e., a temperature meter, in the kettle, we could observe its readings as an alternative to relying on our sense of hot and cold. Temperature is a measure of hotness, or of hotness and coldness, with a change in the direction from cold to hot corresponding to an increase in temperature. But we may fairly suspect, even from everyday experience, that we have this statement backward: *hotness is our sensory perception of temperature*, and not a consistently accurate measure. Thus, by this sense we can detect small differences in temperature between two bodies which are otherwise similar. Particular temperatures, such as that of our bathwater, can be reproduced from day to day with reasonable accuracy. But more often than not, we find our subjective impression to be based not on temperature alone, but on a complex product of the temperature and other factors. Thus a hot day becomes apparently less hot when there is a breeze stirring, and a cold seat is chillier if it is made of metal. Physiological measurement of temperature is very good in its place, which is in the thermostatting of our body's metabolism. It is too complex, too elaborate, for general use, for use in sundry processes that do not involve that metabolism at all.

Let us assume that there is a thermometer in the water of the kettle. A series of readings of the thermometer show the temperature to be increasing steadily with time. The rate of increase may fall off gradually, but this can be attributed to heat flowing out of the water, now that it is hotter than its surroundings, into the room. In a kettle designed so that this heat loss was negligible, we would find the temperature rising at a constant rate all the while heat was added from the stove at a constant rate. This fits with the notion that *the temperature increase of a sample of substance is proportional to the quantity of heat added.*

12.02 SPECIFIC AND LATENT HEATS

If the kettle had contained half as much water, we would have anticipated twice as great an increase in temperature in the same time: *The temperature increase of a sample is inversely proportional to the mass of the sample.* Summing up, then,

$$\Delta t \propto \frac{\Delta Q}{m}$$

where ΔQ is the amount of heat added, Δt the temperature increase, and m the mass of the sample. Or introducing a constant of proportionality s, we have

$$\Delta Q = ms \, \Delta t \tag{12.01}$$

A finding that we are not likely to make on a kitchen stove, but can readily establish in the laboratory, is that the constant of proportionality differs from one substance to another. We can define this constant as *the amount of heat required to raise the temperature of unit mass of a substance by one degree.* We call this quantity the **specific heat** of a substance. In order to give water a specific heat of unity, we take as our unit of heat *the quantity of heat required to raise the temperature of one gram* *of water by one Centigrade degree.* This unit of heat is called the **calorie** (abbreviated cal). *The specific heat of any substance can then be given in calories per gram per degree change in temperature.*

Let us turn back to the kettle of water again. As heat continues to flow into the water, the temperature of the water continues to rise until boiling commences. At that stage we observe a cloud issuing from the kettle. If we look inside, we see the boiling, i.e., the formation and rapid expansion of bubbles in the water. Closer inspection indicates that the bubbles are not cloud but gas, and that it is this gas that issues from the spout of the kettle and changes to cloud a little way out from the spout. Collection of this cloud would reveal it to consist of tiny drops of water. At the onset of boiling, the temperature stops rising, and remains constant. From then on, heat flows into the kettle, water cloud flows away from the spout of the kettle, and, to judge from the constant temperature, the heat content of the water in the kettle remains unchanged. What is happening? When water boils, water substance is converted from the liquid phase to the gas phase. (In the latter phase it is referred to as water vapor.) The conversion of substance from liquid to vapor uses heat. When vapor is cooled it changes back to liquid, frequently in the form of a cloud, and releases heat. *The heat used in converting liquid to vapor and released in condensing the vapor to liquid is proportional to the amount of substance converted:*

$$\Delta Q \propto \Delta m$$

or introducing a constant of proportionality gives

$$\Delta Q = L \, \Delta m \tag{12.02}$$

where ΔQ is the heat used (or released), and Δm is the mass converted from one phase to another. The quantity L is *the amount of heat required to convert unit mass of liquid to vapor* and is called the **latent heat of vaporization.** Its value for water, if the pressure is one atmosphere, is 540 cal gm^{-1}.

If we had filled the kettle with ice cubes straight from the freezing trays, instead of water, the flow of heat from stove to ice would have raised the temperature of the ice until a certain temperature was reached, at which the ice cubes would have commenced to melt. That certain temperature would have been maintained as long as there were both ice and water present. As for the case of water changing to vapor, the heat used in converting solid (ice) to liquid (water) and released in freezing the liquid to solid is proportional to the amount of substance converted:

$$\Delta Q = L \, \Delta m$$

The quantity denoted by L in this case is called the **latent heat of fusion.** Its value for water is 80 cal gm^{-1}.

12.03 SCALES OF RELATIVE TEMPERATURE

A thermometer provides us with a scale reading that changes with the temperature. In the most common sort of thermometer, a small amount of liquid occupies a glass bulb and extends some distance out into a tube of small bore. An increase in temperature increases the volume of the liquid more than it does that of the containing bulb, so that the liquid extends further into the capillary tube. With continuously increasing temperature, the liquid extends continually further into the tube. Other thermometers and temperature-measuring devices involve other observable changes, the change being always a continuous function of temperature. Many physical quantities change continuously with temperature:

    The volume of a solid, or a liquid, or a gas
    The pressure, most usefully of a gas at constant volume
    Electrical resistance
    Thermal electromotive forces (voltages developed in thermocouples)
    The quantity and quality of radiant heat

Any one, sometimes two together, of the above quantities or of several other quantities varying with temperature, may serve as the **thermometric property** of a thermometer, a device which will give a reading that varies when the temperature varies.

The simplest everyday notion of temperature is a relative one. A thermometer will readily tell us which of two beakers of water is hotter than the other. But to answer the question, "How hot is this beaker of water?" we must have a standard of reference. Then we can say that the sample is hotter or colder than the standard. The answer then is definite, but far from complete. We are much better off if we can say how much hotter. The answer is still relative, but it is quantitative. We can achieve it by having two standards of reference instead of just one.

We have already mentioned two possible standards of reference. When ice is heated, its temperature rises steadily, or at least continually, until the ice begins to change to water. The temperature of the mixture of ice and water remains constant until all the ice is melted. Then, if heat is added continually, the temperature of the water rises steadily until it begins to boil. The temperature of the boiling water remains constant as long as there is water left to boil. Solid, liquid, and gas are called three different states or phases of matter. Melting and boiling are changes of phase and might be added to the thermometric properties listed above. They differ notably from the items already listed, though, in that they occur discontinuously with changing temperature: Water substance has a specific melting temperature, below which it is solid and above which it is liquid. To the extent that they occur at specific, reproducible temperatures, melting and boiling temperatures may be used as standards of reference.

We exaggerated in saying that the temperature of a mixture of melting ice and water remained constant as long as there was ice left to be melted. For instance, if heat is added rapidly, some of the water may be considerably warmer than the ice. Again, the temperature at which water boils varies considerably with the air pressure and appreciably with other factors. By care in definition, though, we can make the temperature of these phenomena specific and reproducible. The established definitions are as follows:

The ice point *is by definition* the temperature at which ice is in equilibrium with air-saturated water (not pure water) under atmospheric pressure.

The steam point *is by definition* the temperature at which steam is in equilibrium with pure water under atmospheric pressure.

These are called **the standard fixed points.** With two fixed points decided upon, a scale of temperature can be established.

The simplest and generally most convenient is the Celsius (1701) or **Centigrade** scale, which sets its zero (0C) at one of the two standard fixed points (the ice point) and sets 100C at the other standard fixed point (the steam point). This scale was first used in Sweden, by Celsius among others, in the first half of the eighteenth century. A thermometer calibrated in the Centigrade scale will be found to read 0 if its bulb is placed in a bath at the ice point, 100 at the steam point. The distance along the scale between 0 and 100 will be marked into 100 equal divisions, and divisions of the same size may be found beyond the 100 (marked in numbers greater than 100) and below the zero (marked in negative numbers). If the room temperature is read on this thermometer at 20, we know not only that it is higher than the ice point, but how much higher: one-fifth as much above the ice point as is the steam point.

The **Fahrenheit** scale (Gabriel Fahrenheit, 1686), as now used, is based on the same two fixed points: the scale is now defined by saying that 32F is the temperature of the ice point, and 212F the temperature of the steam point. Fahrenheit had based his scale on less precise fixed points. Cork* quotes from Fahrenheit's paper in the Philosophical Transactions of the Royal Society of London in 1724: " · · · placing the thermometer in a mixture of sal ammoniac or sea salt, ice and water, a point on the scale will be found which is denoted as zero. A second point is obtained if the same mixture is used without salt. Denote this position as 30. A third point, designated as 96, is obtained if the thermometer is placed in the mouth so as to acquire the heat of a healthy man".

The unit of temperature is always referred to as a degree, the size of one degree depending on the scale used. When we write 20C (which is read as "twenty degrees Centigrade"), we refer to a temperature twenty Centigrade degrees above the zero of the Centigrade scale, i.e., above the ice point. (This may be written more fully 20°C, but we will omit the degree sign as being redundant.) Thus the Centigrade and Fahrenheit scales can be related by the statements

$$0C = 32F, \qquad 100C = 212F$$

Sometimes we want to refer to a temperature interval that does not commence at the zero of the scale, however. For instance, normal body temperature is 98.6F, and normal room temperature may be taken as 68F. What difference in temperature is there between the two? It is not correct to write

$$98.6F - 68F = 30.6F$$

A correct form of expression is

$$98.6F - 68F = 30.6 \text{ Fahrenheit degrees}$$

The corresponding statement in the Centigrade scale would be

$$37C - 20C = 17 \text{ Centigrade degrees}$$

Since the degrees used in this book will almost always be Centigrade degrees, we will usually let the abbreviation "deg" stand for Centigrade degrees, and write this statement more briefly as

$$37C - 20C = 17 \text{ deg}$$

We can see from the interval between the ice and steam points the relative size of the two sorts of degree:

$$212F - 32F = 100C - 0C$$
$$180 \text{ Fahrenheit degrees} = 100 \text{ Centigrade degrees}$$
$$9 \text{ Fahrenheit degrees} = 5 \text{ Centigrade degrees} \qquad (12.03)$$

---

* James M. Cork, *Heat*, 2nd Ed., Copyright 1942 by James M. Cork (John Wiley & Sons, Inc.).

If x denotes any number

$$xC = 0C + x \text{ Centigrade degrees}$$
$$= 32F + \tfrac{9}{5}x \text{ Fahrenheit degrees}$$
$$= (32 + \tfrac{9}{5}x)F \qquad (12.04)$$

Similarly, this time taking y to represent any number,

$$yF = 32F + (y - 32) \text{ Fahrenheit degrees}$$
$$= 0C + \tfrac{5}{9}(y - 32) \text{ Centigrade degrees}$$
$$= [\tfrac{5}{9}(y - 32)]C \qquad (12.05)$$

12.04 THE METHOD OF MIXTURES

In elementary experiments on specific and latent heats, the problems of heat transfer are simplified by the techniques of mixing and immersion. Consider some examples:

(A) If 100 gm water at 10C is mixed with 100 gm water at 30C, what is the resulting temperature?

Let the resulting temperature of the mixture be xC.

$$\text{Heat gained by cold water} = 100(x - 10) \text{ cal}$$
$$\text{Heat lost by hot water} = 100(30 - x) \text{ cal}$$

Therefore $x = 20$; resulting temperature $= 20$C

(B) A sample of metal of mass 200 gm and temperature 50C is immersed in 100 gm water at 10C. The resulting temperature is 17C. What is the specific heat of the metal?

Let the specific heat of the metal be x.

$$\text{Heat gained by water} = 100 \times 7 = 700 \text{ cal}$$
$$\text{Heat lost by metal} = 200x \times 33 = 6600x \text{ cal}$$

Therefore $$x = \frac{700}{6600} = 0.106 \text{ cal gm}^{-1}$$

In these examples one significant point has been neglected: The water must have been in a container, and the container must have risen in temperature along with the water. This can be taken into account readily, as follows:

(C) A copper ($s = 0.093$ cal gm^{-1}) vessel of mass 150 gm contains 200 gm water at 15C. We add 100 gm of another liquid at 60C, and the resulting temperature of the mixture is 20C. What is the specific heat of the second liquid?

Let the specific heat of the second liquid be x.

Heat gained by water and calorimeter $= (200 + 150 \times 0.093)5$ cal

Heat lost by second liquid $= 100x \times 40$ cal

Therefore $x = 0.268$ cal gm^{-1} deg^{-1}

A similar technique can be used in experiments on latent heats, as in the final example:

(D) A copper vessel of mass 200 gm contains 300 gm of a mixture of water and ice. Water at 90C is added to bring the total mass of water and ice to 500 gm. Some of the ice remains. How much ice is melted?

Heat lost by added water $= 200 \times 90 = 18000$ cal

Therefore   Heat released by melting ice $= 18000$ cal

Hence   Mass of ice melted $= \dfrac{18000 \text{ cal}}{80 \text{ cal gm}^{-1}}$

$= 225$ gm

In working out the above examples, no mention has been made of the details of laboratory procedure involved. In the performance of the experiments in such a manner as to yield results of useful accuracy, much greater care would be required than one would infer from the simplicity of the arithmetic.

12.05 ELASTIC AND INELASTIC COLLISIONS

To introduce the topic of heat, we considered an electric stove, a device for converting electrical energy into thermal energy, i.e., into heat. We might have used instead a gas or coal stove, converting the chemical energy of the fuel and the oxygen of the air into heat. Our aim in this book, however, is to relate heat to mechanical energy. Let us turn, then, to a consideration of systems involving mechanical energy.

When two elastic balls collide—two billiard balls, say—their behavior is much as we would calculate it on the two mechanical principles of the conservation of momentum and the conservation of energy, assuming all the energy to be either kinetic or potential. Bouncing an elastic ball on a hard floor is a special case of elastic collision, for the amount of energy transferred to the massive earth is negligible, and the kinetic energy of the up-bouncing ball just after the collision is the same as that of the falling ball just before the collision. If the ball is dropped from a given height, the principle of conservation of energy indicates that it will bounce back up to that same height. In practice, the ball never does bounce quite back to the height from which it was dropped, although if it is a good elastic ball, of rubber or ivory or steel, it may come within a few per cent of that height.   But a nonelastic ball, say one of putty, won't rise at all.   Why not?   Is the law of conservation of energy only approximately applicable to steel, and ivory, and rubber, and not applicable to such materials as lead and putty?

The law of conservation of energy is perfectly general, but there is a difference in the ways that elastic and inelastic substances are put together, and a resulting difference in the way that the law of conservation of energy may be applied.   Solids are built up of atoms which, while they are locked together into the pattern of the solid, are still free to vibrate each about its central position.   Such atomic vibration is going on continually, whether the substance is elastic or inelastic.   But when an elastic body bounces, its pattern as a solid resists the shock, and the movement of the body as a whole remains independent of the vibratory motion of the atoms.   In that case the mechanical theory by which the principle of conservation of energy is applied is simple.   When an inelastic solid suffers an impact, when it fails to bounce, its pattern as a solid gives way under the shock, and proper motion of the body, motion of the body as a whole, is transferred to the independent vibratory motions of the separate atoms.   In this case, the application of the mechanical theory, to follow the individual vibrations of millions of millions of millions of millions of atoms, is impossibly complex.   A certain calculable amount of energy, formerly belonging to the organized motion of the body as a whole, has been transferred to the independent, random or disorganized, motions of the individual atoms.   That much can be said.   The motions of the individual atoms cannot be observed. Neither can the fact that many individual motions exist; not directly, that is, as the presence of motion.   Indirectly, though, an increase in the random motions of the individual atoms is readily detectable, and measurable by a "thermometer", which indicates a corresponding increase in "temperature".   We call the random motion of independent vibration of the individual atoms heat, as it has been called since long before its true nature was recognized.

We do not have to bounce an inelastic ball to convert mechanical energy (i.e., energy of organized motion) into heat.   This conversion is going on all around us all the time.   All the mechanical energy developed by the engine of an automobile, as the automobile travels along a level road, goes rapidly into heat.   Some of the mechanical energy goes directly to heat through friction in the engine and in the transmission. Some goes to stir up a wind in the air through which the car moves.

The energy of the wind is mechanical energy, but it rapidly degenerates through progressively less-well-organized turbulence into the completely disorganized thermal motion whose energy we call heat. It so happens that an automobile engine is a "heat engine", converting heat into mechanical energy, the heat coming in turn from the combustion of gasoline. The laws of conversion of heat into mechanical energy are a most important and revealing part of the study of heat.

The conversion of mechanical energy into heat is a most common occurrence, but it almost always happens because we cannot avoid it, rather than because we want it to happen. If we *want* heat, we obtain it from a region where it exists already, or from chemical energy by combustion, or on occasion from electrical energy, but hardly ever from mechanical energy.

12.06 MICROSCOPIC AND MACROSCOPIC POINTS OF VIEW

The individual particles that move independently in heat motion are too small for us to observe singly. The number of such particles (atoms or molecules), in even a small sample, is much too great for us to hope to keep track of them, even if they could be observed singly. On the other hand, the effects of changes in this thermal motion are readily apparent indirectly; most of the physical quantities around us vary with the temperature, with the degree of the thermal motion. Thus, our thinking about heat tends to take two forms. First, there is the **microscopic** view, in which we develop a mental picture, a theoretical picture, of the sort of thing we would see if microscopes could let us look at single atoms. Secondly, there is the **macroscopic** view, wherein we develop a concept of heat that is related to what it does in the world of ordinary-sized things around us. Thus, heat is a form of energy, into which other forms of energy can be converted. Three million joules of energy, for instance, can be transformed into enough heat to convert one kilogram of ice into steam. That is a fact of macroscopic physics. A whole science of heat can be built up, based on observations of heat phenomena, to give a well-rounded-out fundamental theory of heat, without recourse to the microscopic view. Sometimes, for the sake of logical development, it is best to stick to one view or the other. Sometimes thermodynamic theory, by avoiding the microscopic view, can be made more general, made applicable to any problem of many individuals, whether the precise peculiarities of those individuals have been established or not.

Turning away from physics, the distinction between microscopic and macroscopic approaches might reasonably be applied to the consideration of people and peoples. The characteristics of a nation are the summed-up characteristics of the members of that nation. One may study and discuss the characteristics of the French nation. One may do this by observing the behavior of that nation, in war and peace, in commerce and in politics, without ever singling out individual Frenchmen, typical or otherwise, for a study of their characteristics as individuals. That would be the macroscopic approach. Or one may study primarily the characteristics of French individuals, and develop from that one's picture of the nation as a whole. That would be the microscopic approach. Both points of view should agree in the end, should come to the same conclusions about the French nation.

In studying the heat motion of matter, our "systems", our samples, will always include millions of millions as many individuals as there are Frenchmen in France. Our laws of averages should work well. Unless we have reached the stage of specialists in the study of heat, we may fairly use every opportunity offered by either point of view, in endeavoring to build up the clearest and most intelligible concepts possible of matter and the heat motion of matter.

PROBLEMS

1. Calculate the heat required to raise 1.000 cm³ through 1.000 deg (C) for the following substances. (The data are for temperature 20C.)

Substance	Specific Heat (cal gm⁻¹)	Density (gm cm⁻³)
Aluminum	0.214	2.70
Copper	0.092	8.89
Iron	0.107	7.90
Lead	0.0306	11.34
Mercury	0.0333	13.55
Acetone	0.528	0.792
Carbon tetrachloride	0.201	1.595
Glycol	0.571	1.116
Methyl alcohol	0.600	0.796
Crown glass	0.160	2.50

2. Given that 0C = 32F and 100C = 212F, what is the normal temperature of the mouth of a healthy human (98.6F) on the Centigrade scale?

3. The British "normal" body temperature is 0.20 Fahrenheit degrees lower than the accepted "normal" in the United States. Express this difference in Centigrade degrees.

4. One liter of water at 60.0C is poured into a copper beaker, weighing 500 gm, at 20.0C. What is the resulting common temperature of water and beaker?

5. A 500-gm copper weight is heated to 100.0C in a bath of boiling water, then immersed in 600 gm water in a 400-gm copper beaker, water and beaker being initially at 20.0C. What is the resulting temperature of weight, water, and beaker?

6. A covered beaker of water (sp. gr. about 0.975) cools from 80.0C to 60.0C in 7.00 min. A duplicate beaker containing the same volume of glycol ($C_2H_6O_2$), sp. gr. 1.100, cools through the same temperature interval in 4.00 min. Assuming that the rate of heat flow is the same in both cases, what is the specific heat of the glycol?

7. A vessel of water at exactly 0C has 40 gm ice floating in it, also at exactly 0C. The addition of 120 gm water at room temperature reduces the amount of ice to 10 gm. What is room temperature?

8. An elastic mass m_1, traveling at speed v_1, collides head-on with a second elastic mass m_2, which until the impact was stationary. What are the speeds of m_1 and m_2 after the collision? What are these speeds if $m_1 = m_2$?

9. A bullet of mass m is fired into a ballistic pendulum of mass M in which it becomes embedded, so that both have the same final velocity. Momentum is conserved. The initial velocities were u and zero. What fraction of the bullet's energy goes into heat?

10. A ball of mass 0.500 kgm is dropped from a height of 1.500 m onto a hard flat surface. It bounces to a height of 1.100 m. From a comparison of its kinetic energy arriving at and departing from the surface, how much energy (in joules) is transformed from organized energy into heat? (Ignore the bit of energy that is radiated away as sound.)

11. A ship of mass 5.00×10^7 kgm (about 50,000 tons) is traveling at a speed of 54.0 km hr^{-1} (about 29 knots) when its engines are stopped. One minute later its speed is 45.0 km hr^{-1}. At what rate is energy being transformed from energy of organized motion into heat?

12. How much energy is converted into heat when 1.000 kgm water is brought to rest after falling freely for 160 ft, i.e., after passing over Niagara Falls? If this heat goes to heating the water, and if 4.186×10^3 joules raise the temperature of 1.000 kgm of water by 1 Centigrade degree, by how much does the temperature of the water rise?

13. Suppose that the energy released by the water in falling 160 ft (problem 12) is all converted into electrical energy, and then used at a point some distance away to heat a kettle containing 1.000 kgm of water. How much water must fall through 160 ft on this basis (i.e., through penstocks and turbines rather than freely over the Falls) to raise the temperature of the water in the kettle by 100.0 Centigrade degrees?

14. What kinetic energy is converted into heat when a lead bullet of mass 15.0 gm traveling 300 m sec^{-1} is suddenly stopped by a sheet of armor plate? If all the heat stays with the lead, will it raise the bullet from its initial temperature of 27C to its melting point of 327C? (The amount of heat required to raise the temperature of lead by one degree is 0.134 joules gm^{-1}.)

13

Gas Thermometers and the
Molecular Theory of Gases

13.01 WHICH THERMOMETRIC PROPERTY IS RIGHT?

Having defined 0C as the ice point and 100C as the steam point, just what is 50C, or any other temperature? For a start, we made a mercury-in-glass thermometer, and marked on it 0C (when it was in a bath of slowly melting ice) and 100C (when it was in a steam bath over boiling water). We divided the distance along the glass tube between 0C and 100C into one hundred equal parts. Thus, provided everyone following this procedure used tubing of uniform bore and the same sort of glass, all mercury thermometers would be in agreement. It should be noted, however, that any statement of temperature on this basis involves the behavior of mercury and glass, behavior which is more or less peculiar to those substances.

Just how much difference does it make if we go to some other substance, some other thermometric property, for our interpolation between the standard fixed points and for extrapolation beyond them? It makes some difference, although usually a slight one. Imagine a series of tests in which the temperature is measured simultaneously with each of five different sorts of thermometer, each working to the Centigrade scale, but each interpolating linearly to its own thermometric property. Some of the results of such tests are given in Figure 13.01.

Which of the thermometers is right? Or are they all wrong? We have used mercury-in-glass for the basis of our comparison because it is the most familiar sort. We could argue that it is the most likely to be right because it is a sort of average case, with gas thermometers departing from it in one direction and electrical thermometers in the other. There is a more promising feature, however, about the gas thermometers. They are all, both constant-volume and constant-pressure types, in good agreement among themselves. A still more hopeful indication is found in that the variations among the gas thermometers decrease as the pressure of the gases is lowered. (It must be recognized, of course, that difficulties of measurement and inaccuracies due to experimental error are increased by lowering the pressure; this must be allowed for.) Exhaustive experiments show that all gases in both constant-volume and constant-pressure thermometers approach the same temperature indication as the pressure is lowered and made to approach zero. They are considered in that limit as approaching the behavior of an **ideal gas**. We study the behavior of an ideal gas experimentally in this way, by observing the behavior approached by real gases as their pressure approaches zero.

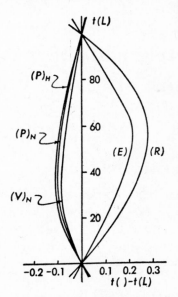

Fig. 13.01. Departure of Centigrade temperature, as indicated by various thermometers, from that indicated by mercury in glass, $t(L)$.

R, platinum resistance
E, thermocouple, $Pt/(Pt + Rh)$
V_N, constant-pressure nitrogen
P_N, constant-volume nitrogen
P_H, constant-volume hydrogen

13.02 CONSTANT-PRESSURE GAS THERMOMETER

The factor by which the volume of a confined mass of gas increases at constant pressure, when the temperature rises from the ice point to the steam point, is greater than for the corresponding expansions of liquids, much greater than for those of solids. The factor is very nearly the same at low or moderate pressure, atmospheric for instance, for all gases: a little over 1.366.

This approximate equality of the volume coefficients of different gases is known as Charles' Law or Gay-Lussac's Law. (Dates of publication were 1787 and 1802, respectively.) The approximation becomes steadily better as the pressure of the gas under consideration is reduced. The factor for every gas approaches the same value of 1.36608 as the pressure approaches zero.

In Figure 13.02(a), the two crosses represent Charles' Law: The relative increase of volume as the temperature increases from the ice point

to the steam point (0C to 100C) is the same for all gases, 0.36608 times
the volume at the ice point.   If we accept as our principle of interpolation the linear increase of temperature with the volume of gas in a constant-pressure gas thermometer, we can draw in the solid line joining the
two crosses, to give us a relation between volume and temperature.   The
equation of this straight line is

$$\frac{t}{100} = \frac{\dfrac{V}{V_i} - 1}{\dfrac{V_s}{V_i} - 1}$$

where V_i and V_s are the values of V at the ice point and at the steam
point, respectively, so that

$$t = \frac{100}{0.3661}\left(\frac{V}{V_i} - 1\right) = 273.165\,\frac{V}{V_i} - 273.165$$

Transposing and rounding off the constant to an integral number gives

$$t + 273 = 273\,\frac{V}{V_i} \quad (13.01)$$

(The rounding-off corresponds to
raising the volume ratio from
1.36608 to 1.3663.)

A relation simpler than
(13.01) can be obtained by absorbing the numerical constant
into the temperature. Take as
the temperature a new variable
T defined by

$$T = t + 273 \quad (13.02)$$

and denote temperatures in the
new scale by a suffixed K.   Then

$$T_i = 273K$$

and (13.01) becomes

$$T = T_i\,\frac{V}{V_i}$$

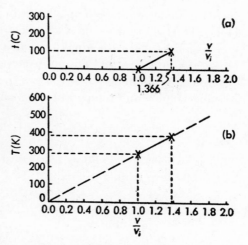

Fig. 13.02. Centigrade (a), and
absolute (Kelvin) temperature (b), related to volume of a sample of gas at
constant pressure.

or, adding an indication that the pressure remains constant, we have

$$\frac{T}{T_i} = \left[\frac{V}{V_i}\right]_P \quad (13.03)$$

The transposed axis is shown in Figure 13.02(b).   This new variable T is called the **absolute temperature,** and the scale of absolute temperature using Centigrade-sized degrees, denoted above by K, is called the **Kelvin scale.**

The ratio T_s/T_i equals 1.36608 or about 373/273 regardless of the size of degree used; its value is based on experiments on gases at the steam and ice points.   The further specification (for the *Kelvin* scale of absolute temperature) that there shall be 100 degrees between the ice and steam points then establishes that $T_i = 273\mathrm{K}$.

13.03 CONSTANT-VOLUME GAS THERMOMETER

If an enclosed mass of gas is heated without any increase in the size of its container, thus without any increase in the volume of the gas, then the pressure of the gas increases.   The fraction by which the pressure increases as the gas is taken from the ice point to the steam point is very nearly the same for all gases.   Quite strikingly, it is a little over 1.366, or very nearly the same fraction as that by which the volume increases under similar circumstances in a constant-pressure gas thermometer.   Thus, all that we have said about constant-pressure gas thermometers could be said with equal force about constant-volume gas thermometers; absolute zero and absolute temperature could be deduced in just the same way from either sort of gas thermometer.   To equation (13.03) relating volume and temperature we can add

$$\frac{T}{T_i} = \left[\frac{P}{P_i}\right]_V \tag{13.04}$$

That is, when the volume is held constant, the pressure is proportional to the absolute temperature.

13.04 VARIATION OF BOTH P AND V

If a sample of gas goes from T_1 to T_2 with V constant, then

$$\frac{P_2}{P_1} = \frac{T_2}{T_1}$$

If the sample goes from T_1 to T_2 with P constant, then

$$\frac{V_2}{V_1} = \frac{T_2}{T_1}$$

What if both P and V vary?   Supposing we start with

$$P_1,\ V_1,\ T_1$$

and end with
$$P_2,\ V_2,\ T_2$$

then what relation will exist among the variables? Let us make the change in two steps, holding one variable constant in each step. First, increase the temperature at constant pressure:
$$P_1,\ V_1,\ T_1 \rightarrow P_1,\ V_2,\ T_{1a}$$

Then increase the temperature further to its final value at constant volume:
$$P_1,\ V_2,\ T_{1a} \rightarrow P_2,\ V_2,\ T_2$$

Now we know that for the constant-pressure step,
$$\frac{V_2}{V_1} = \frac{T_{1a}}{T_1}$$

and further, for the constant-volume step,
$$\frac{P_2}{P_1} = \frac{T_2}{T_{1a}}$$

Eliminating the intermediate temperature T_{1a} gives
$$\frac{V_2 T_1}{V_1} = \frac{P_1 T_2}{P_2}$$

or
$$\frac{P_1 V_1}{T_1} = \frac{P_2 V_2}{T_2}$$

Since we were quite free in our choice of P_2, V_2, T_2, we can say that therefore
$$\frac{PV}{T} = \text{constant} = \frac{P_i V_i}{T_i} \qquad (13.05)$$

or
$$PV \propto T$$

where P, V, and T are the pressure, volume, and absolute temperature of a given mass of gas.

13.05 BOYLE'S LAW

If T is held constant, equation (13.05) reduces to
$$[PV]_T = \text{constant} \qquad (13.06)$$

This is Boyle's Law, discovered experimentally in the seventeenth century, more than one hundred years before the work of Charles and Gay-Lussac on gas thermometers. In the preceding section, we combined the two gas-thermometer relations to provide the general relation $PV \propto T$, of which Boyle's Law is a particular case. Historically, Boyle's Law having preceded both the gas thermometer relationships, it was possible to combine the relationship for the constant-pressure thermometer with Boyle's Law to provide the general relationship $PV \propto T$, and to predict the behavior of the constant-volume thermometer. The latter, however, proved to be the much more practicable instrument for use in precise thermometry.

There is no real gas that obeys Boyle's Law perfectly, but over a wide range of pressures and temperatures the agreement is very good.

13.06 AVOGADRO'S NUMBER

All matter as we know it is built up of atoms; the atomic physics of today concerns itself with the internal structure of atoms and more particularly with that of the central dense nuclei that are the cores of the atoms. To the chemist there are about a hundred different sorts of atom; to the atomic physicist there are several times more, for several isotopic forms that reveal distinct differences to the atomic physicist behave identically or almost identically in chemical processes.

Very strong evidence for the *existence* of atoms was obtained by chemists quite a long time before physicists began intensive study of their structure. (Indeed, much information about atomic structure has been achieved in the study of chemical reactions.) The chemists' experiments were not of a microscopic sort, wherein the behavior of individual atoms was studied. They were simple, macroscopic experiments on chemical reactions, such as combining sulphur and oxygen to form compounds of the two. The experiments did involve weighing, but it was a matter of weighing the few grams of this substance and the few grams of that substance that went into a reaction, and the few grams of the substances that resulted. They never involved weighing an atom.

These experiments revealed first the existence of **elements,** substances that could not be analyzed further by chemical means. Then they revealed that when the various elements combine they do so in predictable proportions, as though each element entered into the reaction in a standard size of package. Samples of the relative masses of the packages of a few of the elements follow, the numbers being only approximate:

Hydrogen,   1 unit of mass
Carbon,   12 units of mass
Oxygen,   16 units of mass
Sulphur,   32 units of mass
(and so forth)

The experiments suggested that the package-size for oxygen was about 16 times that for hydrogen, and that for sulphur twice that for oxygen. It did not matter whether one pictured the oxygen package as 16 gm or 16 oz or 16 lb, provided that at the same time the size of the sulphur package (say) was kept in the same porportion to it of 32/16.

These findings become intelligible when it is assumed that each element consists of indivisible units or **atoms,** the atomic masses being small compared with the mass of any element that might be involved in a chemical reaction, and the atomic masses of the various elements being in the same proportion to one another as the package-masses of those same elements. Chemical reactions, on this assumption, are atomic combinations, or atomic dissociations and recombinations. The chemical reaction of one package of carbon combining with two packages of oxygen thus becomes the combining of many carbon atoms each with two oxygen atoms.

Now comes the question of particular interest to us here. If chemical reactions are atomic combinations and dissociations, then every package presumably contains the same number of atoms. If we arbitrarily specify the package-size, say 16 gm in the case of oxygen, then just how many atoms are there in every package? Let

$$A_0 = N_0 a \tag{13.07}$$

where a is the mass of an atom of any element, A_0 is the package-mass of the same element, and N_0 is the number of atoms in a package, the same for all elements. The number of atoms involved in any macroscopic observation is very large; therein lies the convenience of dealing in packages of many atoms. Just how large the packages should be is an arbitrary matter, although naturally the A_0's for hydrogen, carbon, oxygen, and sulphur will be in the approximate ratio $1:12:16:32$, and so forth. The established convention takes the smallest package-mass, that for hydrogen, as approximately 1 gm. The package-masses denoted by A_0 are then known as the **gram-atomic weights.** Thus the gram-atomic weights of carbon, oxygen, and sulphur are approximately 12 gm, 16 gm, and 32 gm.

The equation $A_0 = N_0 a$ suggests that the value of a is the same for every atom of a given element. Actually, this is not the case. For instance, the atoms of chlorine are of two different sorts, varying somewhat in mass but practically identical in chemical behavior. Chlorine is said therefore to have two different "isotopes" (see section 44.01). These are separable in small amounts by difficult physical processes, but not by normal chemical procedures. The proportions of these isotopes is almost exactly the same regardless of the source of the chlorine. So with greater precision, we can say

$$A_0 = N_0 \bar{a}$$

where $\bar{a}$ is the average weight of the atoms.

In its present form, the convention with regard to atomic weights, rather than taking $A_0 = 1$ gm exactly for hydrogen, takes $A_0 = 16$ gm exactly for oxygen. Because the proportions of the various isotopes vary (only very slightly) with the source of the sample examined, a new modification of the convention, permitting greater precision, is to take $A_0 = 16$ gm exactly for the principal isotope of oxygen, rather than for the standard mixture of oxygen atoms. It is atomic weights based on this "physical" form of the convention that will be used here. On this scale, the atomic weight of oxygen, the "standard mixture", is about 16.0044.

The number of atoms in a gram-atomic weight, denoted by the symbol N_0, is called **Avogadro's Number** (after Amadeo Avogadro, 1776) and is a very important atomic constant. In crystals, atoms are regularly spaced, and the spacing can be measured by X-ray diffraction. Comparing the number-density of atoms in crystals with the density of the crystals, N_0 has been determined with considerable accuracy. Based principally on this "direct" method of determination, but paying attention also to the relationship of the value of N_0 to the values of the other atomic constants, a "most probable" value for N_0 was reached in 1952 of

$$N_0 = 6.02544 \times 10^{23} \tag{13.08}$$

atoms per gram-atomic weight. This is on the basis of $A_0 = 16$ for the principal isotope of oxygen. The random experimental errors in this determination are estimated as $\pm 0.00011 \times 10^{23}$. There may be a somewhat larger systematic error that will be revealed in later years, but it is highly probable that the number falls between 6.025 and 6.026×10^{23}.

On the basis of $A_0 = 16$ exactly for the standard mixture of oxygen, this value of N_0 becomes 6.0238×10^{23}. So the rounded number 6.02×10^{23} is below both chemical and physical values, and the rounded number 6.03×10^{23} is above them both. We will undertake to use 6.025×10^{23}, but the difference between the two rounded numbers is too small to affect the work that we are setting out to do.

13.07 AVOGADRO'S HYPOTHESIS

Although the previous mention of Boyle's Law was made under the heading of temperature, all that the law specifies about the temperature is that it shall remain constant. For any sample of any gas, provided that the amount and the sort of gas remain constant throughout the experiment,

$$[PV]_T = \text{constant} \qquad [\text{equation (13.06)}]$$

The variation in the constant in going from one gas to another has been studied extensively. It has been found that, with the same specification that was applied in the case of gas thermometers (i.e., the equation holds approximately at moderate pressures, approaching perfection apart from experimental error as the pressure is reduced),

$$P_i V_i = \frac{M}{M_0} \times 22.42 \text{ liter atmospheres} \qquad (13.09)$$

(subsequently abbreviated lit. atm.) where P_i and V_i are the pressure and volume at the ice point of a sample of gas of mass M. The mass M_0 varies from one gas to another, but is always a simple combination of the gram-atomic weights involved. Thus its values for a few gases are as follows:

	A_0	M_0
Oxygen	16	$32 = 2 \times 16$
Nitrogen	14	$28 = 2 \times 14$
Carbon dioxide	12, 16	$44 = 1 \times 12 + 2 \times 16$
Argon	40	$40 = 1 \times 40$

In general, M_0 can be described by the relation

$$M_0 = b_1 A_{01} + b_2 A_{02} + \cdots$$

to a small number of terms (usually one or two or three), where the A_0's are the gram-atomic weights of the elements involved and the b's are small integers.

This quantity M_0, defined macroscopically by equation (13.09), is called the **gram-molecular weight** of a gas. One gram-molecular weight of any gas is called a **mole**. Using the symbol n to denote the number of moles in the sample of gas considered in equation (13.09), that equation becomes

$$P_i V_i = n \times 22.42 \text{ lit. atm.} \qquad (13.10)$$

Since $A_0 = N_0a$, where a is the mass of a single atom,

$$M_0 = N_0(b_1a_1 + b_2a_2 + \cdots)$$

or $$M_0 = N_0m \tag{13.11}$$

where m is the total mass of b_1 atoms of type 1, b_2 of type 2, and so forth. For oxygen and nitrogen, then, $m = 2a$, while for argon $m = a$, and for carbon dioxide $m = a_1 + 2a_2$, the subscripts 1 and 2 denoting carbon and oxygen. Letting the symbol N denote the number of m's in the sample of mass M, we have

$$M = Nm \tag{13.12}$$

Then $$n = \frac{M}{M_0} = \frac{Nm}{N_0m} = \frac{N}{N_0} \tag{13.13}$$

so that (13.10) can be written

$$P_iV_i = \frac{N}{N_0} \times 22.42 \text{ lit. atm.} \tag{13.14}$$

This general relationship has a simple explanation if we make two simple assumptions:

(a) In the gaseous state the atoms combine in small groups of mass m, to be called **molecules,**

(b) P_iV_i is proportional to the number of molecules N in the sample, and independent of the mass of a molecule (m), which varies from one substance to another.

In the words of **Avogadro's Hypothesis:** *Equal volumes of all gases at the same pressure and temperature have the same numbers of molecules.*

13.08 INCONCEIVABLY LARGE SIZE OF AVOGADRO'S NUMBER

The number of molecules in a sample is usually very large. In equation (13.09), let us set $P = 1$ atm., $M = M_0$. Then $V_i = 22.42$ lit. That is to say, 32 gm oxygen (or mass M_0 of any gas) at a pressure of 1 atm. and temperature at the ice point occupies 22.42 lit. But that 32 gm consists of

$$602\ 544\ 000\ 000\ 000\ 000\ 000\ 000$$

molecules. If, instead of picturing 22.4 lit. we limit ourselves to one ten-thousandth of that volume, i.e., 2.24 cm^3 (to be precise, 2.24 milliliters) or just a thimbleful, we can shrink that number a bit:

$$60\ 254\ 400\ 000\ 000\ 000\ 000$$

Reducing the pressure from 1 atm. to 10^{-10} atm. which is about the best that present-day methods can achieve, the number of molecules in that thimbleful will be reduced a good deal further, to only

$$6\ 025\ 440\ 000$$

That is still a considerable population.

Sir James Jeans,* goes at the matter more picturesquely:

A man is known to breathe out about 400 cc of air at each breath, so that a single breath of air must contain about 10^{22} molecules. The whole atmosphere of the earth consists of about 10^{44} molecules. Thus one molecule bears the same relation to a breath of air as the latter does to the whole atmosphere of the earth. If we assume that the last breath of, say, Julius Caesar has by now become thoroughly scattered through the atmosphere, then the chances are that each of us inhales one molecule of it with every breath we take. A man's lungs hold about 2000 cc of air, so that the chances are that in the lungs of each of us there are about five molecules from the last breath of Julius Caesar.

13.09 DALTON'S LAW OF PARTIAL PRESSURES

Consider the situation when a number of gases, a number of different sorts of molecule, are present, as in air. With molecules of various sorts present, the number of molecules is given by

$$N = N_a + N_b + N_c + \cdots \qquad (13.15)$$

where the different subscripts represent the different gases, as for instance nitrogen, oxygen, and so forth in the atmosphere. Then from equation (13.14),

$$P_i V_i = \frac{22.42 \text{ lit. atm.}}{N_0} N = \frac{22.42 \text{ lit. atm.}}{N_0} (N_a + N_b + N_c + \cdots)$$
$$= P_a V + P_b V + P_c V \cdots$$

where $P_a, P_b, P_c, \cdots$ are the pressures that the individual gases would exert if each gas in turn had the volume V to itself. Thus

$$P = P_a + P_b + P_c \cdots \qquad (13.16)$$

where P is the pressure of a mixture of gases and $P_a, P_b, P_c \cdots$ are the **partial pressures,** the pressures that the individual gases would have in sole occupancy of the same volume at the same temperature. This is Dalton's Law, arrived at experimentally by Dalton in 1802. Chemical interaction between the gases would of course alter the N's and so nullify the law.

* Sir James Jeans, *An Introduction to the Kinetic Theory of Gases*, Cambridge University Press, 1940.

13.10 EQUATION OF STATE OF AN IDEAL GAS

Equations (13.09) and (13.14), relevant to Avogadro's hypothesis, deal with the product of pressure times volume for various samples of gas, all at the same temperature, the ice point. For any given sample, taken at the low-pressure limit, equation (13.05) relates the product of pressure times volume at any temperature to the value of that product at the ice point:

$$\frac{PV}{T} = \text{constant} = \frac{P_i V_i}{T_i}$$

Combining this relation between PV and T for any fixed amount of gas with equation (13.10), which takes us from one sample to another at fixed temperature, we obtain the general relation

$$\frac{PV}{T} = \frac{P_i V_i}{T_i} = n \times \frac{22.42 \text{ lit. atm.}}{273 \text{ deg}}$$
$$= n \times 0.0821 \text{ lit. atm. deg}^{-1}$$

The product "liters $\times$ atmospheres" has the dimensions of energy, and a straightforward transformation gives

$$0.0821 \text{ lit. atm.} = 8.31 \text{ joules}$$

The above equation can then be written

$$PV = nRT \tag{13.17}$$

where
$$R = 0.0821 \text{ lit. atm. deg}^{-1} \text{ mole}^{-1}$$
$$= 8.31 \text{ joules deg}^{-1} \text{ mole}^{-1}$$
$$= 8.31 \times 10^7 \text{ ergs deg}^{-1} \text{ mole}^{-1}$$

and n is the quantity of gas in moles. The quantity R is known as the **universal gas constant.** The equation states that the product PV is proportional to the Kelvin temperature and to the quantity of gas in moles.

For an alternative form of this statement, we recall that the n moles in the sample contain $N = nN_0$ molecules, so that

$$nR = \frac{NR}{N_0}$$

and introducing a new symbol, we have

$$k = \frac{R}{N_0} = \frac{8.31 \text{ joules deg}^{-1} \text{ mole}^{-1}}{6.025 \times 10^{23} \text{ molecules mole}^{-1}}$$
$$= 1.38 \times 10^{-23} \text{ joule molecule}^{-1} \text{ deg}^{-1}$$

and we can write

$$PV = NkT \qquad (13.18)$$

i.e., the product PV is proportional to the Kelvin temperature and to N, the quantity of gas in molecules. Thus k bears the same relationship to one molecule that R bears to one mole. It is known as **Boltzmann's Constant.**

Useful alternative forms of these relations may be evolved by introducing density, the mass per unit volume, defined in symbols by

$$\rho = \frac{M}{V} = \frac{nM_0}{V}$$

and number-density, the number of molecules per unit volume,

$$\nu = \frac{N}{V}$$

Combining these defining relations with (13.17) and (13.18), respectively, gives

$$\rho = \frac{M}{V} = \frac{PM_0}{RT} \qquad (13.19)$$

and

$$\nu = \frac{N}{V} = \frac{P}{kT} \qquad (13.20)$$

It should be noted that these relations are dimensionally balanced; the units in which ρ and ν are obtained depend on the units used for P, R, and k. The gram-molecular weight will almost surely (but not necessarily) be in grams. If P is in newtons per square meter and R in joules per degree (= newton-meters per degree), ρ will be in grams per cubic meter. If P is in dynes per square centimeter, then, for simplicity, R should be in ergs per degree (= dyne-centimeters per degree; 1 joule = 10^7 ergs), and ρ will be in grams per cubic centimeter. If P is in atmospheres and R is taken in liter atmospheres, ρ will be in grams per liter.

13.11 EQUATION OF STATE OF MIXTURES

For a mixture, as for a single gas,

$$PV = NkT$$

but in the case of a mixture the number of molecules is the sum of the number of each sort, or

$$N = \Sigma N_a = \sum \frac{M_a}{M_{0a}} N_0$$

so

$$PV = \left(\sum \frac{M_a}{M_{0a}} \right) RT \qquad (13.21)$$

For a mixture, the density is the sum of the individual densities,

$$\rho = \Sigma\rho_a = \sum \frac{P_a M_{0a}}{RT}$$

Thus we can write

$$\rho = \frac{P\overline{M}_0}{RT} \tag{13.22}$$

if we set

$$P\overline{M}_0 = \Sigma P_a M_{0a}$$

that is, if we take

$$\overline{M}_0 = \sum \frac{P_a}{P} M_{0a} \tag{13.23}$$

13.12 A SUMMARY OF THE GAS LAWS AND MOLECULAR THEORY

Summarizing,

A_0 is the mass of N_0 atoms, and
M_0 is the mass of N_0 molecules, where
A_0 is called the gram-atomic weight, and
= 1.008 gm for hydrogen (H)
=   16 gm for oxygen (O)
= 39.94 gm for argon (A)
(etc.)
M_0 is called the gram-molecular weight, and
= 2.016 gm for hydrogen (H$_2$)
=   32 gm for oxygen (O$_2$)
= 39.94 gm for argon (A)
(etc.)
One gram-molecular weight is called a mole.
N_0 is called Avogadro's number, and
= 6.025×10^{23}, approximately. The exact
value depends on whether the physical or
chemical scale of atomic weights is used.

For any gas, holding approximately at moderate pressures, approaching perfection apart from increasing experimental errors as the pressure is reduced,

$$PV = nRT \qquad \text{[equation (13.17)]}$$

and so

$$PV = NkT \qquad \text{[equation (13.18)]}$$

This may alternatively be stated

$$\rho = \frac{PM_0}{RT} \qquad \text{[equation (13.19)]}$$

and
$$\nu = \frac{P}{kT} \qquad \text{[equation (13.20)]}$$

In these relations,

P is the pressure.
V is the volume of a sample of mass M.
M_0 is the gram-molecular weight, the mass of one mole.
n is the number of moles in the sample.
N is the number of molecules in the sample.
ρ is the density, $= M/V$.
ν is the number-density, $= N/V$.
T is the absolute temperature, using an ideal gas scale, i.e., $T \propto PV$.
R is the universal gas constant, the constant of proportionality
      between PV and T when $M = M_0$, and
      $= 0.0821$ lit. atm. per Centigrade degree per mole
      $= 8.31$ joules per Centigrade degree per mole.
k is Boltzmann's Constant, $= R/N_0$, i.e., the constant of propor-
      tionality between PV/N and T, and
      $= 1.3803 \times 10^{-23}$ joules per Centigrade degree per molecule.

In the opening sections of this chapter, we defined T as proportional to PV, which has the dimensions of energy, for any sample of gas, in the "ideal gas" limit. We lacked information as to the variation of the constant of proportionality as we went from one gas to another. Now we have found that, with the same constant k for all gases, T is proportional to PV/N, which has the dimensions of energy per molecule. The constant k has the dimensions of energy per unit of temperature and so would become a dimensionless constant if the unit of temperature, i.e., the degree of temperature, were looked on as having the dimensions of energy per molecule. In the following chapter we will proceed to a theory of the mechanical nature of gases, called the "kinetic theory of gases", and see how temperature comes to have these dimensions.

PROBLEMS

1. Absolute temperatures are decreased by 0.16 Centigrade degrees when the temperature of the ice point is rounded off to the integral value 273K. Express this error of approximation in Fahrenheit degrees.

2. Convert the temperatures of the following fixed points (given on the Centigrade scale) to the Fahrenheit scale:

Oxygen point (equilibrium between liquid and vapor)	-182.97
Ice point (equilibrium between ice and air-saturated water; fundamental fixed point)	0.00
Steam point (equilibrium between liquid and vapor; fundamental fixed point)	100.00
Sulphur point (equilibrium between liquid and vapor)	444.60
Silver point (equilibrium between solid and liquid)	960.80
Gold point (equilibrium between solid and liquid)	1063.00

3. Convert the temperatures of problem 2 to the Kelvin scale, on the basis $0.000C = 273.165K$.

4. Two glass bottles each of 1-lit. volume sit in an oven, one (a) open and the other (b) stoppered. The temperature of the oven is raised from the ice point to the steam point, while the atmospheric pressure remains constant at 760 mm Hg. How much air leaves (a), and by how much (in mm Hg) does the pressure increase inside (b)?

5. Design as simply as you can, using a 1-lit. flask, glass and (if necessary) rubber tubing and a nonvolatile liquid, (a) a constant-pressure air thermometer (the requirement being that the pressure remains very nearly constant while the volume change can be observed) and (b) a constant-volume air thermometer (the requirement being that the volume remains constant while the pressure change can be observed).

6. A certain mass of gas at the ice point has pressure and volume P_i and V_i. With the volume held constant, to what (Centigrade) temperature must the gas be taken to double its pressure?

7. A certain mass of gas at the steam point has pressure and volume P_s and V_s. With the pressure held constant, to what Centigrade temperature must the gas be taken to halve the volume?

8. The pressure of the gas inside a 1-lit. flask would increase by a factor 1.3663 for a temperature increase from the ice point to the steam point, if the volume remained constant. The flask is made of glass, however, and its volume increases by 8 parts in 10,000 during this temperature rise. By what factor will the pressure actually rise?

9. The gauge pressure in an automobile tire is 1.50 atm., that is to say the pressure inside the tire is that much above the pressure outside, which is exactly 1 atm. What will be the percentage increase in this gauge pressure due to a rise in temperature from 20.0C to 30.0C?

10. When V remains constant, $P \propto T$. When P remains constant, $V \propto T$. Show that in general $PV \propto T$.

11. A meteorological pilot balloon has a diameter of 20.0 in. at ground level, where the pressure is 1 atm. and the temperature 14.0C. What will be its diameter at 18,000 ft, with pressure 0.500 atm. and temperature −20.0C?

12. For a certain mass of oxygen, $PV = 0.0821T$, where T is temperature on the Kelvin scale, P is pressure in atmospheres, and V is volume in liters. For $T = 273$ and for $T = 373$, plot (a) P against V, (b) P against $1/V$, (c) PV against P, (d) PV against V. The plots should cover the range of pressures 1 to 30 atm.

13. When the volume of a sample of gas was decreased by 1 lit. at constant temperature, its pressure rose from 760 mm Hg to 800 mm Hg. What was the initial volume of the sample?

14. A sample of gas has volume 22.4 lit. at pressure 760 mm Hg, temperature 0.0C = 273.0K. Suppose that its temperature is increased 27.3 Centigrade degrees at constant pressure, then decreased the same amount at constant volume, and that nine more pairs of steps of this sort are taken. Tabulate the pressures, volumes, and temperatures. Mark all the points on a plot of P against V, and on a plot of P against $1/V$. Draw a smooth curve through all points having temperature 0C, and another through all points having temperature 27.3C.

15. How many atoms are there in 1 gm aluminum (atomic weight 26.97)? What mass of copper (atomic weight 63.59) will contain this same number of atoms?

16. One helium atom in 100,000 is an isotope differing markedly from the rest in mass. How many such atoms will there be in exactly 1 micromicrogram (i.e., 10^{-12} gm) of helium (atomic weight 4.004)?

17. In oxygen as normally found,

$$99.784\% \text{ of the atoms are } O^{16} \text{ (i.e., } M_0 = 16\text{)}$$
$$0.038\% \text{ of the atoms are } O^{17} \text{ (i.e., } M_0 = 17\text{)}$$
$$0.178\% \text{ of the atoms are } O^{18} \text{ (i.e., } M_0 = 18\text{)}$$

What is the mass of an individual atom of each sort? What is the number of each sort in exactly one gram-atomic weight of the mixture, where the total number of atoms is $N_0 = 6.02544 \times 10^{23}$? What is the mass of each sort in one gram-atomic weight? Adding these, what is the gram-atomic weight (on the physical scale) of oxygen?

18. What is the pressure of 10.0 gm nitrogen ($M_0 = 28.0$ gm) contained within a volume of 10.0 lit. at 0C? At 100C?

19. In a gas at normal temperature and pressure, what is the available space per molecule?

20. The work done on the piston when the volume of gas in a cylinder is increased by 1.00 lit. at a pressure of 10.0 atm. is 10.0 lit.-atm. Express this quantity in joules.

21. Given that the density of dry air at N.T.P. (Normal Temperature and Pressure, exactly 0C and 1 atm.) is 1.293 gm lit.$^{-1}$, and that 1.30% by mass of this air is argon, what mass of argon does a man inhale in one breath (i.e., in 400 cm^3)? Given that 0.060% of this mass of argon is in the form of atoms having gram-atomic weight 38.0 gm, how many atoms of this sort are acquired in one breath? What is the square root of this number (the mean fluctuation in this number from one breath to the next)?

22. How many molecules are there in 1.00 cm^3 of oxygen at pressure 38.0 cm Hg, temperature -23C?

23. At a pressure of 10.0 atm., temperature 100C, how many molecules are there in 1.00 lit. of gas?

24. Plot pressure against temperature, 100K to 1000K, for 10^{20} molecules contained in a volume of 400 cm^3. What is the density, if the molecular weight of the gas is 40?

25. In order to compare theory with observation, calculate the part per cent by which the density calculated from the chemical formula differs from the observed density for the following gases:

Gas	Observed Density (gm liter^{-1} at 0C, pressure 760 mm Hg)	Formula	Molecular Weight
Argon	1.7837	A	39.955
Carbon dioxide	1.9769	CO_2	$12.01 + 2 \times 16.00$
Chlorine	3.214	Cl_2	2×35.467
Helium	0.17847	He	4.004
Hydrogen	0.08988	H_2	2×1.0083
Neon	0.90035	Ne	20.188
Oxygen	1.42904	O_2	32.008
Xenon	5.851	Xe	131.33

26. Dry air at a pressure of exactly 1 atm. contains, at 0C, 760 mm Hg, the following:

Gas	Partial Pressure (atm.)	Gram-molecular Weight (gm)
N_2	0.7803	28.02
O_2	0.2099	32.01
A	0.0094	40.00
CO_2	0.0003	44.02
H_2	0.0001	2.016

There are also traces of neon (0.000012 atm.) and helium (0.000004 atm.) that can be neglected for our purpose. Calculate the density of dry air, and the molecular weight of a single gas that would have the same density.

14

The Kinetic Theory of Gases

14.01 KINETICS OF A SINGLE MASS-POINT IN A BOX

Macroscopic observations suggest that when a substance is in the form of a gas its atoms may be found combined in small groups, called molecules. These observations provide the relation

$$[PV]_T \propto N$$

and, with some reservations about the nature of temperature,

$$PV = NkT \qquad \text{[equation (13.18)]}$$

For values of P, V, T that we are likely to encounter, N is always a very large number. Now we will devise a simple mechanism that obeys $PV \propto N$, and from it discover the mechanical significance of k and T.

Let us take X, Y, and Z axes at right angles to one another, the X

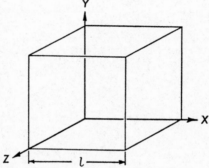

Fig. 14.01. The basic relation of the kinetic theory is derived by considering the behavior of a point mass bouncing against the rigid walls of a cubical box.

axis pointing eastward, the Y vertically upward, and Z southward. Picture a cubical container, each edge of length l, built into this system of axes so that its edges are parallel to the axes (Figure 14.01). The inside surfaces of this container are perfectly smooth and hard.

First, let there be inside this container one particle, of mass m, diameter zero, and perfectly elastic. (It is rather unrealistic to say "diameter zero", but we want to neglect the energy of rotation of the particle, and so to consider the limiting case when the mass is concentrated at a single point.)   Let this particle be moving at a particular instant with a velocity c, the components of which parallel to the X, Y, and Z axes are u, v, and w, respectively, so that the scalar value of c is given, as in Figure 14.02(a), by

$$c^2 = u^2 + v^2 + w^2 \qquad (14.01)$$

This moving particle will suffer successive collisions with the walls. Suppose that the next such collision after the instant referred to above is with the east wall.   Then at the collision the velocity component u will become $-u$, but the components v and w will not be affected.   See Figure 14.02(b).

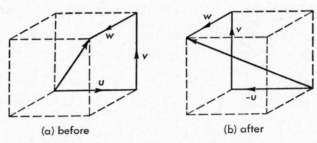

(a) before   (b) after

Fig. 14.02.   Velocity and its components before (a) and after (b) collision with east wall.

Next, if there is a collision with the top of the box, the component v will be reversed, but the components u and v will not be affected.   So, since the velocity has been stated as having, at one particular instant, components u, v, w, its components will continue to be $\pm u$, $\pm v$, $\pm w$, there being repeated interchanges (one at a time) of the algebraic signs. The speed c, related to the components by equation (14.01), will remain constant.

Assuming that the box is small, we will neglect slight changes in the vertical component v due to gravity.   During those intervals occupying half the total time when v is negative, it will be (negatively) increasing steadily with time according to the relation $v = v_0 - gt$.   During the equal intervening intervals when v is positive, it will be (positively) decreasing according to the same relation.   The small variations of the equal and alternating time intervals will keep canceling each other out.

Now consider the change in momentum when the particle suffers a collision, say with the east wall.   We can take components of momentum just as we took components of velocity.   Thus,

Momentum approaching east wall, normal to face $= +mu$

Momentum leaving east wall, normal to face $= -mu$

Change in momentum $= -2mu$

Time between strikes on east wall $= \dfrac{2l}{u}$

Average force exerted on particle by east wall

$$= \frac{\text{change in momentum}}{\text{time in which change occurs}} = \frac{-2mu}{\dfrac{2l}{u}} = -\frac{mu^2}{l}$$

Average force exerted on east wall by particle $= \dfrac{mu^2}{l}$ \qquad (14.02)

The concept of the force, instant by instant, is in this case a bit tricky. If the particle were sizable, and although perfectly elastic not perfectly hard, it would spend a finite time in contact with the wall at each collision, and a plot of force against time would look like Figure 14.03(a). With the postulated particle of zero diameter, and with perfectly hard walls, the time spent in contact becomes zero. But this is only approached as a limiting case, and it can be assumed that in the limit, with time-in-contact zero and instantaneous force infinitely great, the average force remains the same. See Figure 14.03(b).

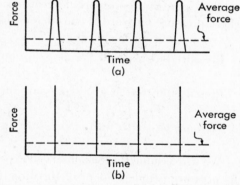

14.02 MANY PARTICLES AND BOYLE'S LAW

Now let us increase the number of particles in the container from one to a large number, N. Let us assume that the particles

Fig. 14.03. (a) Force exerted against wall by a compressible ball. (b) Force exerted against wall by an incompressible mass-point.

may differ from one another in mass, and that the velocity of motion varies from particle to particle, both in magnitude and direction, particle number one having velocity components u_1, v_1, w_1, and so forth. We will neglect the collisions between particles. This can be justified by assuming that because of their zero diameters they would not get in each other's way. The important justification, though, is the indication given by further development of the theory that the effect on the walls is independent of collisions between particles.

With N particles,

$$\text{Force exerted on east wall} = \frac{1}{l}\,(m_1u_1{}^2 + m_2u_2{}^2 + \cdots + m_Nu_N{}^2)$$

Let $\overline{mu^2}$ denote the average value of the mu^2's; that is,

$$\overline{mu^2} = \frac{1}{N}\,(m_1u_1{}^2 + m_2u_2{}^2 + \cdots + m_Nu_N{}^2) \qquad (14.03)$$

Then, $\text{Force exerted on east wall by } N \text{ molecules} = \dfrac{N\overline{mu^2}}{l} \qquad (14.04)$

To obtain the pressure on the east wall, we must divide the force by the area against which it is exerted:

$$\text{Pressure on east wall} = \frac{N\overline{mu^2}}{l \times l^2} = \frac{N\overline{mu^2}}{V}$$

where V is the volume of the container.

The same reasoning would lead to all the following relationships, where pressure outward is considered positive in every case:

$$\text{Pressure on east wall} \quad = \text{pressure on west wall} \quad = \frac{N\overline{mu^2}}{V} \qquad (14.05a)$$

$$\text{Pressure on top} \quad\quad = \text{pressure on bottom} \quad = \frac{N\overline{mv^2}}{V} \qquad (14.05b)$$

$$\text{Pressure on south wall} = \text{pressure on north wall} = \frac{N\overline{mw^2}}{V} \qquad (14.05c)$$

We will assume that, as observed experimentally for gases and liquids, the pressure is independent of the direction.   Then

$$P = \frac{N\overline{mu^2}}{V} = \frac{N\overline{mv^2}}{V} = \frac{N\overline{mw^2}}{V}$$

i.e., $PV = N\overline{mu^2} = N\overline{mv^2} = N\overline{mw^2}$

or, rewriting to make kinetic energies appear, we have

$$PV = 2N\overline{\tfrac{1}{2}mu^2} = 2N\overline{\tfrac{1}{2}mv^2} = 2N\overline{\tfrac{1}{2}mw^2} \qquad (14.06)$$

14.03 KINETIC ENERGY

It might be argued that $\tfrac{1}{2}mu^2$, $\tfrac{1}{2}mv^2$, and $\tfrac{1}{2}mw^2$ are not kinetic energies because u, v, and w are not velocities but velocity components.

For a single particle it is easily shown, referring to equation (14.01), that

$$\tfrac{1}{2}mu^2 + \tfrac{1}{2}mv^2 + \tfrac{1}{2}mw^2 = \tfrac{1}{2}mc^2$$

A similar relationship holds for the related averages over many particles, even when m varies from one particle to another.

Let subscript 1 denote particle number 1, and so forth. Then, from equation (14.01),

$$u_1{}^2 + v_1{}^2 + w_1{}^2 = c_1{}^2$$

and so forth. Then

$$\overline{\tfrac{1}{2}mu^2} + \overline{\tfrac{1}{2}mv^2} + \overline{\tfrac{1}{2}mw^2}$$

$$= \frac{\tfrac{1}{2}m_1u_1{}^2 + \tfrac{1}{2}m_2u_2{}^2 + \cdots + \tfrac{1}{2}m_1v_1{}^2 + \tfrac{1}{2}m_2v_2{}^2 + \cdots + \tfrac{1}{2}m_1w_1{}^2 + \tfrac{1}{2}m_2w_2{}^2 + \cdots}{N}$$

$$= \frac{\tfrac{1}{2}m_1(u_1{}^2 + v_1{}^2 + w_1{}^2) + \tfrac{1}{2}m_2(u_2{}^2 + v_2{}^2 + w_2{}^2) + \cdots}{N}$$

$$= \frac{\tfrac{1}{2}m_1c_1{}^2 + \tfrac{1}{2}m_2c_2{}^2 + \cdots}{N} = \overline{\tfrac{1}{2}mc^2}$$

That is, omitting the intermediate steps, we have

$$\overline{\tfrac{1}{2}mu^2} + \overline{\tfrac{1}{2}mv^2} + \overline{\tfrac{1}{2}mw^2} = \overline{\tfrac{1}{2}mc^2} \tag{14.07}$$

But from (14.06),

$$\overline{\tfrac{1}{2}mu^2} = \overline{\tfrac{1}{2}mv^2} = \overline{\tfrac{1}{2}mw^2}$$

Therefore, $\qquad \overline{\tfrac{1}{2}mu^2} = \overline{\tfrac{1}{2}mv^2} = \overline{\tfrac{1}{2}mw^2} = \tfrac{1}{3}\overline{\tfrac{1}{2}mc^2} \tag{14.08}$

and (14.06) can be extended to read

$$PV = 2N\overline{\tfrac{1}{2}mu^2} = 2N\overline{\tfrac{1}{2}mv^2} = 2N\overline{\tfrac{1}{2}mw^2} = \tfrac{2}{3}N\overline{\tfrac{1}{2}mc^2} \tag{14.09}$$

Throughout the discussion, since (14.06) was stated, the number 2 has been carried outside the averaging sign and the fraction $\tfrac{1}{2}$ inside. This is not necessary, but enables us to recognize the quantity averaged as kinetic energy, in the case of $\overline{\tfrac{1}{2}mc^2}$, and as having the form of kinetic energy in every other case ($\tfrac{1}{2}mu^2$, $\tfrac{1}{2}mv^2$, $\tfrac{1}{2}mw^2$), although velocity components appear in place of velocities.

If we consider the equality of PV to any of the other equated members of (14.09), we have an equation very much resembling $PV = NkT$ (equation 13.18). A careful comparison of the theoretical forms with the empirical $PV = NkT$ will be made, but it will be helpful to give further consideration to the theory first.

14.04 DEGREES OF FREEDOM

In deriving equation (14.06), we assumed pressure independent of direction.   With this assumption we were able to equate $\overline{\frac{1}{2}mu^2} = \overline{\frac{1}{2}mv^2} = \overline{\frac{1}{2}mw^2}$, where the u's, v's, and w's were components in three different directions.   The number three seems to have come in because we considered a cubical box, which of course had three pairs of parallel sides. The assumption, made in section 14.02, of pressure independent of direction, permits us to equate any number of terms,

$$\overline{\tfrac{1}{2}mu_a{}^2} = \overline{\tfrac{1}{2}mu_b{}^2} = \cdots = \overline{\tfrac{1}{2}mu_n{}^2} = \cdots$$

where u_a, u_b, etc., are velocity components in any and as many directions as we may care to consider.   But the number three occurs again in equation (14.08), and the reason for its presence there is not at all arbitrary.   The equation says that

$$\overline{\tfrac{1}{2}mc^2} = 3\overline{\tfrac{1}{2}mu^2}$$

where the u's are velocity components in any direction whatsoever.   Why three?   Because it takes components along three directions at right angles to each other to describe a velocity, as indicated in equation (14.01). The directions being at right angles to each other makes the components independent of each other; if the directions along which u and v were taken were not at right angles, then a change in u would involve a change in v.   So we can say that it takes three *independent* components to describe a velocity, and it is for that reason that $\overline{\frac{1}{2}mc^2}$, the average kinetic energy of a particle, is equal to three times $\overline{\frac{1}{2}mu^2}$, a quantity of the same form, but involving a *velocity component* in any direction.   We say that, because the velocity of a single particle has three independent components, the system of many particles has three **degrees of freedom** per particle. Then we can describe equation (14.08) by the following statement: *The average energy is uniformly divided among all the degrees of freedom.*   To develop the notion of degrees of freedom further, an assembly including more complicated particles will be considered.

14.05 THE DIATOMIC MODEL

So far we have considered mass-points, masses so concentrated that energy of rotation would be negligible.   Now consider mass-points traveling in pairs.   Let the members of each pair be rigidly connected, the connecting member having finite and fixed length but no mass.   This model is sometimes compared to a dumbbell; remember that it is the limiting case of a dumbbell, as the diameter of the balls and the mass (but not the length) of the handle approach zero (Figure 14.04). These more complex "molecules" can contain energy in a way not available to the single mass-points: They can have energy of rotation.

Picture a plane in which a model "diatomic molecule" lies; see Figure 14.05(a). The molecule can rotate in this plane. Picture another plane, at right angles to the first, in which the molecule also lies, Figure 14.05(b). The molecule can rotate in this plane too. Finally, picture a plane

Fig. 14.04. A random array of diatomic models.

through the center of gravity of the molecule and at right angles to the other two planes, Figure 14.05(c). The molecule can also rotate "in" this plane, or at least the rotation is said to be in or parallel to this plane, when the molecule rotates about its own axis.

Any rotation of the molecule can be treated as a vector and broken down into three components in planes at right angles to each other, as in

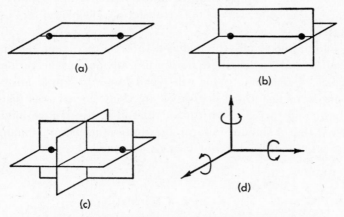

Fig. 14.05. The rotation of a diatomic model related to axes fixed to the model.

Figure 14.05(c), or about axes at right angles to each other as in Figure 14.05(d). Just as motion of translation could be considered in terms of three independent degrees of freedom, so can motion of rotation, with the components of the rotation about three axes mutually at right angles, be considered in terms of three independent degrees of freedom. In the case of the model diatomic molecule, however, there is one rotational "degree of freedom" that cannot contain energy.   This is rotation about the molecule's own axis.   The mass is concentrated at two points, both on the axis of rotation.   Where the distance of the mass from the axis is zero, the energy of rotation must be zero.   So, if we think of "degree of freedom" as denoting "degree of freedom capable of containing energy", our model contains just two rotational degrees of freedom.   It has the same three translational degrees of freedom as the single mass-point.

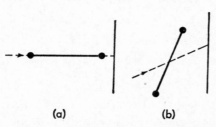

(a)   (b)

Fig. 14.06. Except for the particular end-on case (a), any collision (b) of the diatomic model will involve a change in energy of rotation.

Collisions with a wall are more complex affairs for the diatomic model.   In the special case of a normal and end-on approach, the collision remains a simple reversal of momentum, as in Figure 14.06(a), but in any other case, Figure 14.06(b) for example, the collision will involve some transfer of energy between rotation and translation, with the molecule coming away spinning more or less rapidly than it approached, and the energy of translation decreased or increased accordingly.

It is found, and it may be deduced theoretically, that the energy of the molecules tends to distribute itself uniformly among the various available degrees of freedom.   You will recall how for simple mass-points, when there were just three degrees of freedom, energy was distributed uniformly among these.   Now for our diatomic, five-degree model, it is being stated that a similar uniform distribution of energy is maintained. Equation (14.09) still holds, but may be extended:

$$
\left.
\begin{aligned}
\frac{PV}{2N} &= \overline{\tfrac{1}{2}mu^2} \\[4pt]
&= \overline{\tfrac{1}{2}mv^2} \\[4pt]
&= \overline{\tfrac{1}{2}mw^2} \\[4pt]
&= \tfrac{1}{3}\overline{\tfrac{1}{2}mc^2}
\end{aligned}
\right\}
\begin{array}{c}
\text{Energy of translation} \\
\text{per degree of freedom}
\end{array}
\left.
\begin{array}{c}
\\ \\
\text{Energy} \\
\text{per degree} \\
\text{of} \\
\text{freedom}
\end{array}
\right.
$$

$$
\left.
\begin{aligned}
&= \tfrac{1}{8}md^2\omega^{2}* \\[4pt]
&= \tfrac{1}{8}md^2\omega^2
\end{aligned}
\right\}
\begin{array}{c}
\text{Energy of rotation per} \\
\text{(rotational) degree of} \\
\text{freedom}
\end{array}
$$

(14.10)

* The form of this relation is not necessary for the present discussion. A straightforward mechanical derivation gives this value for the energy of rotation about their center of gravity of two particles, each of mass $m/2$, separated by a fixed distance d, and rotating with angular speed ω.

The diatomic model differs from the monatomic or mass-point model in that it has five degrees of freedom per molecule capable of containing energy instead of just three. Diatomic and monatomic models are the same in two respects:

(a) They have the same average energy per degree of freedom.

(b) They have the same number (3) of *translational* degrees of freedom, and so the same average energy of translation ($\frac{1}{2}mc^2$).

So the general statement that can be made regarding both models can have two alternative forms,

$$PV = 2N \times \text{(energy per degree of freedom)} \tag{14.11}$$

and
$$PV = 2N \times (\tfrac{1}{3} \text{ the energy of translation}) \tag{14.12}$$

In solids, there is not the same freedom of translation, but we can reasonably hope that the concept of degrees of freedom is applicable to the behavior of all matter, presumably in more complex form in some cases. As a relation to compare with the empirical $PV = NkT$, therefore, (14.11) would appear the more likely to be generally applicable.

To avoid adopting a new symbol for "energy per degree of freedom", we will use the expression $\frac{1}{2}mu^2$ in place of those words, trusting that the reader will recognize this as equal to the average energy for any degree of freedom. Equation (14.11) then takes the form

$$PV = 2N\overline{\tfrac{1}{2}mu^2} \tag{14.13}$$

where $\overline{\frac{1}{2}mu^2}$ represents the energy per degree of freedom. It is worth noting that N is the number of molecules, not the number of degrees of freedom. Thus it is $Nf\,\overline{\frac{1}{2}mu^2}$, where f is the number of degrees of freedom per molecule, that gives us the total energy of random motion in a sample of gas.

14.06 POLYATOMIC AND NONRIGID MODELS

Any further complexity of a rigid system leads to three degrees of freedom for rotation; that is the maximum number of modes of rotation that there can be. If the bonds, rather than being rigid, are free to vibrate, then a diatomic model can have one vibrational degree of freedom. The number of possible modes of vibration goes up rapidly with increasing complexity of the model. Further, where degrees of freedom of rotation and translation are inherent in the geometry of the molecule, those of vibration depend on a departure from rigidity. Such departures becomes increasingly likely with increased rapidity of motion, and so the number of degrees of vibrational freedom increases in complex fashion with the temperature.

14.07 TEMPERATURE

Now let us compare equation (13.18), containing our macroscopically defined temperature,

$$PV = NkT$$

with the result of the microscopic considerations of kinetic theory, equation (14.13),

$$PV = 2N \overline{\tfrac{1}{2}mu^2}$$

Combining these relations to eliminate P, V, and N, we have

$$kT = 2 \overline{\tfrac{1}{2}mu^2} \tag{14.14a}$$

or

$$T = \frac{2}{k} \overline{\tfrac{1}{2}mu^2} \tag{14.14b}$$

The temperature on the Kelvin scale, in the macroscopic units already given for it (Centigrade degrees), is proportional to the energy of random motion per degree of freedom. If we look on $2/k$ as the constant of proportionality between units of temperature (Centigrade degrees) and units of energy, we can base a definition of temperature on this equation:

Temperature is the average energy of random motion per degree of freedom.

It will be useful to make a summary list of the macroscopic products and the kinetic-theory products that may be equated to PV:

$$
\left.
\begin{aligned}
PV &= nRT & \text{[equation (13.17)]} \\
&= NkT & \text{[equation (13.18)]} \\
&= 2N\overline{\tfrac{1}{2}mu^2} & \text{[equation (14.13)]} \\
&= \tfrac{2}{3}N\overline{\tfrac{1}{2}mc^2} & \text{[equation (14.09)]}
\end{aligned}
\right\} \tag{14.15}
$$

14.08 SPECIFIC HEAT OF A GAS AT CONSTANT VOLUME

For a sample of gas,

Energy of random motion $= \tfrac{1}{2}mu^2$ per degree of freedom

$\qquad\qquad\qquad\qquad = f\tfrac{1}{2}mu^2$ per molecule

$\qquad\qquad\qquad\qquad = N_0 f\tfrac{1}{2}mu^2$ per mole

where f is the number of degrees of freedom per molecule. Since from (14.14)

$$\overline{\tfrac{1}{2}mu^2} = \tfrac{1}{2}kT$$

Energy of random motion $= \frac{1}{2}kT$ per degree of freedom

$\left.\begin{array}{l} = \frac{1}{2}fkT \text{ per molecule} \\ = \frac{1}{2}N_0 fkT \text{ or } \frac{1}{2}fRT \text{ per mole} \end{array}\right\}$ (14.16)

The energy that must be invested in the random motion of a gas to raise the temperature of the gas by one degree is thus

$\frac{1}{2}k$ per degree of freedom

$\frac{1}{2}fk$ per molecule

$\frac{1}{2}fR$ per mole, and so

$\frac{1}{2}f \dfrac{R}{M_0}$ per unit mass

where M_0 is the gram-molecular weight, the mass of one mole.

Now, if the volume of the sample of gas is held constant during the heating, this investment of energy is all that is required to raise the temperature. So

$$c_v = \frac{1}{2}f \frac{R}{M_0} \tag{14.17}$$

where c_v is the **specific heat at constant volume**, i.e., *the energy required to raise the temperature of unit mass of gas* (usually one gram) *one degree* (usually one Centigrade degree) *at constant volume.* Even for gases of the same f, it varies from gas to gas, since it is inversely proportional to M_0. It is usually more convenient to deal in moles of gas, for

$$C_v = \frac{1}{2}fR \tag{14.18}$$

where C_v, is the **molar heat at constant volume**, i.e., *the energy required to raise the temperature of one mole of gas one degree at constant volume.* It varies from gas to gas only as f, and there are only a few likely values for f.

14.09 CHANGES IN VOLUME

In our consideration of kinetic theory, the volume of the container was kept constant. The particles were bouncing against fixed walls and did no work on them. They exerted a force, but did no work, for the force did not act "through a distance". If one wall were gradually withdrawn, like a piston moving out of a cylinder, the force would act through a distance, and work would be done. Or in terms of the particles, they would be bouncing off a receding wall, and each impact would reduce their speed by twice the speed of the wall. Their kinetic energy would be reduced. If our array of randomly moving particles finds itself in an expanding container, then it is losing some of its energy of random motion in doing work, in exerting a force through a distance on the receding walls.

Thus its temperature is dropping, for temperature is the amount of that energy of random motion per degree of freedom.

In our consideration of kinetic theory, because the particles were bouncing against rigid walls, we assumed zero energy transfer on impact. The velocity component changed from $+mu$ to $-mu$. But even if the volume of the container is kept constant, the walls will not really be rigid, not on a microscopic, molecular or atomic scale. The walls will actually consist of arrays of atoms just as agitated by thermal motion as the gas. If molecules bounce off these atomic arrays without loss of energy, it will be because an individual molecule is as likely to gain as to lose energy in colliding with a similarly agitated atom. That is to say, if there is no net energy transfer between the gas and the stationary wall, it is because they are both at the same temperature.

If the container enclosing a gas expands, the gas does work on it and so, having given up some energy, the gas cools, or tends to cool. If the expansion is very slow, the molecules of the gas may remain in thermal equilibrium with the atoms of the solid walls. That is, the molecules may draw from the store of energy of random motion of the atoms of which the wall is built as rapidly as they give up energy to the macroscopic motion of the wall. That would constitute an "isothermal" or constant-temperature expansion. If the expansion is rapid, there is not time for the molecules to collect from the atoms of the walls the energy that they give up in doing work. When the thermal transfer to the gas is in this way negligible, that constitutes an "adiabatic" or zero-heat-transfer expansion. If the expansion is extremely rapid, so that the walls recede at speeds great compared with those of the molecules, no work is done, there is no temperature drop, but the process, as we shall consider later, is "irreversible".

The next section will consider the effect of expansion on the specific heat. It will consider expansion, not in terms of bouncing particles, but rather in terms of a fluid obeying the equation of state $PV = nRT$, with specifications regarding heat and energy transfers. That is, the treatment will be macroscopic. The next chapter, in turn, will develop the notions of "isothermal" and "adiabatic" expansions, not from kinetic theory, but from the specific heats.

14.10 SPECIFIC HEAT OF A GAS AT CONSTANT PRESSURE

If the volume of a gas increases, work must be done by the gas in expanding its container. Heat transferred to a gas may be converted into this sort of work by the gas, or it may go to increasing the energy of random motion. In considering the amount of heat or other form of energy that must be transferred to a gas to raise its temperature one degree, we must take into account both uses to which this energy may be put. The simplest case of zero expansion has been considered. Of those cases where the volume changes, the simplest, from which all others may be deduced, is the case of expansion at constant pressure.

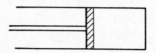

Fig. 14.07. Work done by gas on piston

= pressure × area of piston × increase in length

= pressure × increase in volume

Suppose a piston of area A is moved a distance Δl along a cylinder (Figure 14.07), and that all the while the pressure of the gas in the cylinder remains constant at P. Recalling that pressure is force per unit area, the force exerted by the gas on the piston is PA. When the piston moves a distance Δl, the force is exerted through that distance.

$$\text{Work done by gas} = \text{force} \times \text{distance} = PA\ \Delta l$$

Let ΔV denote the increase in the volume of the cylinder. Then

$$\Delta V = A\ \Delta l$$

and so
$$\text{Work done by gas} = P\ \Delta V \tag{14.19}$$

It is not necessary to have a parallel-sided cylinder for this result to hold. It would hold as well for gas in a balloon expanding in all directions. For any expansion at constant pressure,

Work done by gas on container = pressure of gas × increase in volume

Now for n moles of any gas, we have equation (13.17):

$$PV = nRT$$

If the temperature is increased by unity at constant pressure, the volume will increase to a new value, which we will call $(V + \Delta V)$. Then

$$P(V + \Delta V) = nR(T + 1)$$

Subtracting the former equation from the latter, we have

$$P\ \Delta V = nR \tag{14.20}$$

But $P\ \Delta V$ is the work done by the gas on the container. So when n moles of gas are heated one degree at constant pressure, they do work nR in expanding the container. More simply, when one mole (mass M_0) of any gas is heated one degree at constant pressure, it does work R in expanding the container. Again, when unit mass (usually one gram), is heated one degree at constant pressure, it does work R/M_0 in expanding the container.

To heat a mole of gas through one degree, one must in any case increase the average energy per degree of freedom. If the volume is kept constant, that is all the energy that is required, and we have equation (14.18),

$$C_v = \frac{fR}{2}$$

If the volume is allowed to increase and the pressure is kept constant, it is still necessary to make this addition to the energy of random motion. But also in this case there is the work R to be done in expanding the container, so the total energy required is

$$C_p = C_v + R \tag{14.21}$$

where C_p is the **molar heat at constant pressure.** And, of course, just as the specific heat at constant volume was related to the molecular heat at constant volume, Equations (14.17) and (14.18), by

$$c_v = \frac{C_v}{M_0} \tag{14.22}$$

we will have for the **specific heat at constant pressure**

$$c_p = \frac{C_p}{M_0} \tag{14.23}$$

The macroscopic item of expanding the container hardly seems like an item of temperature-raising. If we expanded the container from outside,

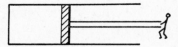

Fig. 14.08. As long as the piston moves gradually outward, the gas must do work $P\,\Delta V$ on it.

by hand, would that not relieve the gas of the task (Figure 14.08)? No; it would not, unless the piston were pulled out with extreme rapidity. As the piston moves outward, the gas follows it, pressing against it, exerting a force. And as the force is exerted through a distance, work is done by the gas. Molecules striking the receding piston bounce back more slowly: The work is coming from the supply of energy contained in the random motion of the molecules, and it is that supply that must be replenished.

14.11 THE RATIO OF THE SPECIFIC HEATS

Summarizing the findings of sections 14.08 and 14.10, we have

$$C_v = \tfrac{1}{2}fR \qquad \text{[equation (14.18)]}$$

from kinetic theory, and

$$C_p = C_v + R \qquad \text{[equation (14.21)]}$$

from the equation of state $PV = nRT$; and by definition,

$$c_v = \frac{C_v}{M_0} \qquad \text{[equation (14.22)]}$$

$$c_p = \frac{C_p}{M_0} \qquad \text{[equation (14.23)]}$$

where C and c denote molar and specific heats, and subscripts v and p denote constant volume and pressure, respectively.

A useful quantity of frequent occurrence in the theory of heat is the ratio of the specific heat at constant pressure to the specific heat at constant volume. It is denoted by the Greek letter γ, and

$$\gamma = \frac{c_p}{c_v} = \frac{C_p}{C_v} = \frac{C_v + R}{C_v} \qquad (14.24)$$

and so from kinetic theory,

$$\gamma = \frac{\dfrac{fR}{2} + R}{\dfrac{fR}{2}} = \frac{f + 2}{f} = 1 + \frac{2}{f} \qquad (14.25)$$

Knowing γ, we can determine f; knowing R, we can determine C_v and C_p, for any gas for which $PV = nRT$. Since f is always positive with a minimum value of 3, and increases with increasing complexity of the molecule, $\gamma = \frac{5}{3}$ for the simplest molecule and approaches unity for very complex molecules.

14.12 MOLECULAR SPEEDS

From equation (14.15), the average kinetic energy of translation is proportional to the absolute temperature:

$$\overline{\tfrac{1}{2}mc^2} = \tfrac{3}{2}kT$$

For any group of molecules having the same molecular mass m, the averaging can be limited to c^2:

$$\tfrac{1}{2}m\overline{c^2} = \tfrac{3}{2}kT$$

and recalling that $m = M_0/N_0$ and $k = R/N_0$, we see that

$$\tfrac{1}{2}M_0\overline{c^2} = \tfrac{3}{2}RT$$

$$\overline{c^2} = 3\,\frac{RT}{M_0}$$

The left-hand term is the average or mean of the squares of the molecular speeds.

The square root of $\overline{c^2}$ is a *sort* of average speed, where the averaging has been done over the squares. (It is not *the* average speed; that is what you get by averaging the speeds themselves.) This square root of $\overline{c^2}$ is called the **root-mean-square speed** or "rms speed" (or call it rms velocity, for no trouble will ensue) of the molecules. It is useful as an "effective" speed, and we will denote it by c_e. Then

$$c_e = \sqrt{\overline{c^2}} = \sqrt{3\,\frac{RT}{M_0}} \qquad (14.26)$$

This speed is seen to increase as the square root of the absolute temperature. Substitution (and conversion of the unit of speed) will reveal that molecules at room temperature have speeds of a few thousand feet per second, the same sort of speeds that bullets have. When values are substituted in this equation, the value of R in liter atmospheres would lead to an awkward unit for speed, and should be avoided. If R is in joules per degree and M_0 in kilograms, the speed is in meters per second; if R is in ergs per degree and M_0 in grams, the speed is in centimeters per second.

In the kinetic theory we implied that the molecules in a sample of gas would not all have the same speed. More advanced kinetic theory shows that the molecules definitely do not all have the same speeds. Figure 14.09 shows the distribution with speed of molecules. Speed is given as a fraction of rms speed, so that the same diagram is applicable to any gas at any temperature. Figure 14.09 has as ordinate the fraction of the molecules having speeds greater (and for the second curve less) than the speed specified on the scale of the abscissas. The curves cross at the "median" speed, than which half of the molecules are slower, half faster. There is no specific upper limit; this is revealed more clearly when a logarithmic scale is used for the ordinate, as in Figure 14.09(b). In Figure 14.09(c), the area of the column extending upward above any interval of speeds c_1/c_e to c_2/c_e is proportional to the number of molecules having speeds in that interval. The "modal" or most probable speed (value of c for maximum of curve) is

$$\sqrt{\tfrac{2}{3}}\,c_e = 0.816c_e$$

Figure 14.09(d) is similar to 14.09(c), but refers to the component of the velocity, u, in any specified direction. It is $|u|$, the magnitude of u, that has been used, so that all the curve is to the right of the axis of ordi-

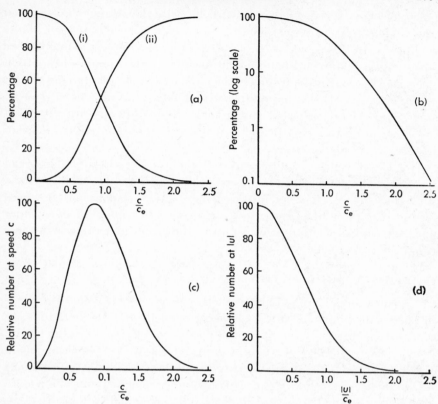

Fig. 14.09. (a) Fraction of molecules (i) of speed greater than c, (ii) of speed less than c. (b) Fraction of molecules of speed greater than c, plotted against a logarithmic scale. (c) Distribution of molecules with speed. (d) Distribution of molecules with velocity component in any specified direction. For u instead of $|u|$, a mirror image of this curve would be required to the left of the ordinate axis.

nates. Since components in opposite directions are equally likely, $\bar{u} = 0$. If magnitude only is considered, a simple relation exists between average velocity component and average speed:

$$\overline{|u|} = \tfrac{1}{2}\bar{c}$$

The average speed, in turn, is found to be not so very different from the rms speed:

$$\bar{c} = \frac{8}{3\pi}\,c_e = 0.921c_e$$

These distributions are a statistical business, of course, and must be considered as such. For instance, Figure 14.09(b) reveals that 1% of the molecules have speeds greater than about twice the mean. Suppose that the sample of gas we are considering is one mole. Then that 1% includes 6.02544×10^{21} molecules. Because it is statistical, that 1% has an uncertainty, in any particular instance, equal to the square root of itself. That is to say, our statement as to the number of molecules having greater than two times the rms speed at some specific instant may be in error by something like ten thousand million molecules. But why worry? That is still accurate to 1 part in 10^{10}. What's ten thousand million more or less, *under the circumstances*?

Instead of being looked on as the statistics of a very large number of molecules, the curves may be looked on as giving the probabilities for a single molecule. Then, for instance, the fraction of molecules at speeds greater than three times the rms speed becomes the chance of a particular molecule having at a specified instant in time a speed greater than three times the rms speed.

14.13 MEAN FREE PATH

It was important to our kinetic-theory development that the particles be small compared with the space around them. We found it convenient to go to the extreme of considering "mass-points" having no size at all. One result of this extreme assumption was that in our theory there would never be any collisions between molecules, at least between monatomic molecules. If the mass-points are replaced somewhat more realistically by small spheres, similar results are found to those that we have obtained already, but in addition information is revealed about other physical properties of the gas, and collisions between molecules are found to be very frequent.

Suppose that molecules are spheres of diameter σ. Then two molecules collide whenever their centers come within distance σ of each other. Let an array of molecules be distributed randomly (as they are), but let them all be stationary (as they surely are not)—all but one molecule, which moves through the stationary array. Consider the path followed by the center of the moving molecule as being the center line of a tube of radius σ. The molecules involved in collisions will be those whose centers lie within that tube.

The number of collisions in unit distance equals the volume of the tube per unit length of path, $\pi\sigma^2$, times the number of molecules per unit volume, ν (section 13.10). The average distance that the traveling molecule will go between collisions is just the reciprocal of this, or $(\pi\nu\sigma^2)^{-1}$. When, more realistically, it is recognized that all the molecules are in motion, rather than just one, this mean free path becomes less by $\sqrt{2}$; thus

$$\lambda = (2^{\frac{1}{2}}\pi\nu\sigma^2)^{-1} \tag{14.27}$$

where λ is the **mean free path.**

Now the macroscopic quantity called viscosity is related to the mean free path. Taking axes X, Y, Z, suppose that gas is flowing in the direction of the X axis, but that the rate of flow is proportional to z, so that all gas above the XY plane is flowing forward, all gas below that plane flowing backward, relative to the gas in that plane (Figure 14.10). Then

$$v_s = sz \tag{14.28}$$

where v_s is the rate of flow (super-imposed on the random motion of the molecules), and s is the rate of increase of flow velocity with distance across the flow, or rate of shear.

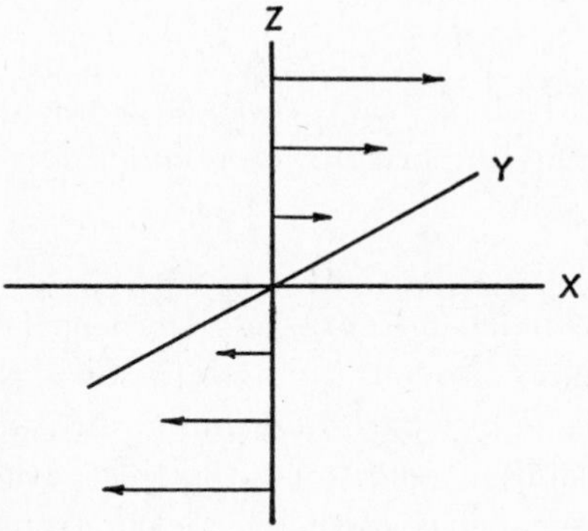

Now along the XY plane in the direction X, or along any other surface to which the direction of flow is parallel, there is a force resembling friction, the force per unit area being

$$F = \eta s \tag{14.29}$$

Fig. 14.10. Gas flows in the direction of the X axis, its velocity increasing with z. Arrows indicate velocity relative to the gas in the X–Y plane.

where η, defined by this equation, is the **coefficient of viscosity.** It is a number that can be determined experimentally. The derivation of this force from kinetic theory involves the mean free path λ. The exact theory is difficult, but a crude approximate theory gives a relationship of the right dimensions and close (as it happens) to the right numbers.

First consider the rate of transfer of molecules across the XY plane. The average magnitude of the velocity component normal to the XY plane (some going down, some up) is $\overline{|w|} = \overline{|u|} = \frac{1}{2}\bar{c}$ (section 14.12). The number crossing unit area in unit time (some down, some up) is then $\frac{1}{2}\bar{c}\nu$.

Now consider the momentum transferred by each molecule. The average z-component of the mean free path is $\lambda/2$, just as that of the velocity is $\bar{c}/2$. A molecule changing its level or z-value by $\frac{1}{2}\lambda$ between collisions will find itself among new neighbors, with an average motion along the X axis differing from that of its old neighbors by $s\lambda/2$, and thus will differ in momentum from the average of those new neighbors by $ms\lambda/2$.

Combining the statements of the above two paragraphs, we have

Momentum transferred across unit area in unit time
$$= \tfrac{1}{2}\bar{c}\nu \times \tfrac{1}{2}ms\lambda = \tfrac{1}{4}\rho\bar{c}\lambda s \qquad (14.30)$$

But this rate of momentum transfer is just the force F of equation (14.29). Combining the two equations to eliminate F gives

$$\eta s = \tfrac{1}{4}\rho\bar{c}\lambda s$$
$$\eta = \tfrac{1}{4}\rho\bar{c}\lambda$$

More precise theories disagree among themselves as to the exact value of the numerical factor, but a fair average is 0.35, and we can fairly state that

$$\eta \simeq 0.35\rho\bar{c}\lambda \qquad (14.31)^*$$

The coefficient η can be measured experimentally; ρ, $\bar{c}$, and ν we already know something about. So λ can be determined from η, and σ from λ. The free path in ordinary air is about 6×10^{-6} cm. In hydrogen, under similar conditions, the free path is about twice as great. The length of mean free path, as is clear from equation (14.27), is independent of the temperature or speed of molecular motion, and for any given gas depends only on the density. If we double the number of molecules in the gas, keeping its volume unaltered, each molecule has twice as many molecules to collide with, so that the mean free path is halved. In general, the length of the mean free path is inversely proportional to the number of molecules per cubic centimeter of gas.

The free path of air, given above as 6×10^{-6} cm, will increase to 6 cm if the pressure is reduced from atmospheric by a factor of 10^6. This is just about what a good mechanical pump will do, and so in laboratory and industrial vacuum systems the free path is liable to be great in comparison with the dimensions of the apparatus, the diameters of the tubes, and so forth. This effects a change in the nature of the flow of gases through the equipment and must be taken into account.

Having estimated the free path from an experimental determination of the coefficient of viscosity, we may proceed to estimate the molecular diameter from relation (14.27). We find that the diameter of a molecule of air is about 3.75×10^{-8} cm, and that of a molecule of hydrogen is a little less: about 2.72×10^{-8} cm. Thus in gas at atmospheric pressure, the mean free path of a molecule is some hundreds of times its diameter

---

* Approximate equality of two quantities is indicated by $\simeq$ or $\doteqdot$.

(160 times for air, 400 times for hydrogen). When the pressure is reduced to half a millimeter of mercury, the free path is hundreds of thousands of times the diameter. It is generally legitimate to suppose, as a first approximation, that the linear dimensions of molecules are small in comparison with their free paths.

Quoting now from Sir James Jeans,*

It is no easy matter to discuss [the size of a molecule] with any precision; we cannot even define [it]. The difficulty arises primarily from our ignorance of the shape and other properties of the molecule. If molecules were in actual fact elastic spheres, the question would be simple enough; the size of the molecule would be measured simply by the diameter of the sphere. The molecules are not, however, elastic spheres; if they are *assumed* to be elastic spheres, experiment leads to discordant results for the diameters of these spheres, showing that the original assumption is unjustifiable. Not only are the molecules not spherical in shape, but also they are surrounded by fields of force, and most experiments measure the extension of this field of force, rather than that of the molecules themselves.

PROBLEMS

1. An elastic ball of mass 100 gm continues to bounce vertically on a rigid horizontal platform, rising against gravity after each bounce to a height of 10.0 m. What is the time between bounces? What is the average force exerted by the ball on the platform? Repeat the calculation, giving the ball less energy, so that it rises to only 1.00 m.

2. Derive the relation between pressure on the walls and kinetic energy that is basic to kinetic theory as presented in equation (14.05), but in place of a cubical box use a rectangular one with width, length and height all different.

3. *A* leans against a wall with force 2.50 lb. *B* volleys a 4.00-ounce ball to and fro between himself and the wall with a speed of 80 ft/sec. How far back from the wall must *B* stand to exert the same average force on the wall as *A*?

4. A perfectly elastic ball of mass 100 gm is released in a room 4.00 m long, 4.00 m wide, 3.00 m high, having perfectly rigid walls. It is released with horizontal velocity 30.0 m sec^{-1} toward one wall. What is the average force that it will exert on this wall? On the opposite wall?

5. What pressure would be exerted by exactly 10^{22} molecules in a cylindrical bottle having an internal diameter of 4.00 in. and height of 12.00 in., at temperature 127C?

6. By how much does the pressure drop in a one-liter flask when exactly 10^{22} gas molecules leak out of it, provided that the temperature is kept constant at 27C?

* Sir James Jeans, *An Introduction to the Kinetic Theory of Gases*, Cambridge University Press, 1940.

7. What is the average kinetic energy per molecule of a gas at temperature 200K? at 400K?

8. Exactly ten grams of nitrogen initially at 17C are heated at constant volume until the pressure is twice the original value. How much heat is required?

9. A gastight bag is filled with 6.000 m³ of air at atmospheric pressure (inside and out) in 10.00 sec. What is the rate of work, in watts?

10. What is the specific heat at constant pressure (in joules per gram per degree) of a diatomic gas, $M_0 = 28.0$ gm?

11. What is the ratio of the specific heat at constant pressure, of oxygen ($M_0 = 32.0$ gm, diatomic) to that of argon ($M_0 = 40.0$ gm, monatomic)?

12. What is the volume of 10.0 gm argon (a monatomic gas, take $M_0 = 40.0$ gm) at normal temperature and pressure? What power is required (watts) to raise its temperature 1.00 deg (C) per second at constant volume? With the same power, how fast would the temperature rise at constant pressure?

13. (a) How much heat is required to raise the pressure of 1.00 mole of monatomic gas from 1.00 atm. (300K) to 2.00 atm. at constant volume, then to expand the gas to twice its initial volume at constant pressure? What is the final temperature?

   (b) How much heat is required to expand 1.00 mole of monatomic gas, initially at 1.00 atm. and 300K, to double its initial volume at constant pressure, then to double the pressure at constant volume? What is the final temperature? (Note that the gas does more work when it expands at high pressure than when it expands at low pressure.)

14. What is the specific heat at constant pressure of a mixture of 28 parts (by mass) of nitrogen and 4 parts (by mass) of helium?

15. Take air as a gas of molecular weight 29.0 gm, $\gamma = 1.40$. What heat is required to raise the temperature of sufficient air from outdoors (0.0C) to fill a room 10.0 m by 20.0 m by 7.0 m at 20.0C? (The heating will be at constant pressure.)

16. The following is a list* of values, determined experimentally at or near room temperature, of C_p/R and γ. From these calculate C_v/R, first by dividing C_p/R by γ and second by subtracting 1 from C_p/R. Calculate the percentage by which the latter exceeds the former. Calculate $2/(\gamma - 1)$, which on simple theory should give the number of degrees of freedom per molecule.

Gas	C_p/R	γ
H_2	3.42	1.410
He	2.52	1.659
N_2	3.50	1.404
O_2	3.52	1.401
A	2.52	1.67
Cl_2	4.12	1.36
CO_2	4.40	1.304

* From Table 12-3, *Thermodynamics*, by F. W. Sears, Addison-Wesley Publishing Company, 2nd Ed., 1953.

17. Draw curves of c_e against M_0 for temperatures 200K and 400K, over the range $M_0 = 2$ gm to $M_0 = 40$ gm, marking points on the curve for hydrogen, helium, nitrogen, oxygen, and argon.

18. What is the rms speed at temperature 0C of an oxygen molecule consisting of two O^{16} atoms (i.e., $M_0 = 32.0$ gm)? of a molecule consisting of two O^{18} atoms (i.e., $M_0 = 36.0$ gm)?

19. What is the rms speed at temperature 300K of a hydrogen molecule consisting of two H^1 atoms (i.e., $M_0 = 2.016$ gm)? of a molecule consisting of two H^2 atoms (i.e., $M_0 = 4.029$ gm)?

20. Give (a) the mass of one molecule, (b) the number of molecules per unit volume, (c) the density of the gas, and (d) the root-mean-square speed of the molecules, all in terms of Boltzmann's constant, Avogadro's number, molecular weight, pressure, and temperature.

21. Take the coefficient of viscosity of nitrogen at 20.0C and 1.00 atm. as 175 micropoises. One poise equals one dyne-second per square centimeter. What is the mean free path? Use equation (14.31). What is the "diameter" of a nitrogen molecule? Use equation (14.27).

22. Express effective molecular speed as a function of pressure and density.

15

The Expansion of Gases

15.01 DEFINITIONS OF ISOTHERMAL AND ADIABATIC EXPANSIONS

An expanding gas, as we have noted in considering specific heats, exerts a force against its surroundings, against its expanding container, and so does work. The energy to do that work comes from the energy of random motion of the molecules. If this energy is replaced as fast as it is removed, by a flow of heat into the gas, the temperature can be maintained constant. If, on the other hand, there is no flow of heat energy into the gas, the average energy per degree of freedom will be reduced, that is, the temperature of the gas will drop.

A gradual expansion without change in temperature is termed **isothermal**. A gradual expansion without transfer of heat to or from the gas is termed **adiabatic**. An isothermal expansion must be gradual, for it takes time for heat to flow into the gas; a sudden expansion must involve a drop in temperature and therefore cannot be isothermal. An adiabatic expansion must be gradual, in order that the pressure shall be uniform throughout the gas at every instant, and thus so that there shall be no energy in the form of wind.

In general, we may expect some heat transfer to a gas during expansion. An adiabatic is the limiting case where there is none; an isothermal is the particular case, and a most useful one, where there is just enough to maintain the temperature constant. In considering specific heats, we have already discussed the case of constant pressure, the "isobaric" case if you like, where there is just enough heat transfer to maintain the pressure at a constant value. The word "expansion" will be used; findings with regard to it will apply also, with appropriate changes in sign, to contraction or "compression".

15.02 ISOTHERMAL EXPANSION

Suppose that the quantity of gas whose expansion we wish to consider is exactly one gram-molecular weight. Then, whatever happens by way of an expansion, we know that the relation

$$PV = RT$$

will hold.

Suppose we want to consider an expansion without change in temperature. Mathematically, the statement "the temperature shall remain constant" is

$$T = T_0$$

where the subscript zero denotes some particular value of temperature. Combining this with $PV = RT$, we have an equation for the isothermal expansion of one mole of gas:

$$PV = RT_0 \tag{15.01}$$

This is a statement of Boyle's Law, that with the temperature constant, the product of pressure times volume must remain constant. The locus on a rectangular chart of P against V is an hyperbola. By taking a series of values for the temperature, say 100K, 200K, 300K, etc., a family of rectangular hyperbolas is produced (Figure 15.01). Each of these can be looked on as the path followed by the point indicating the condition of the sample of gas as the sample expands isothermally. Alternatively, each curve can be looked on simply as a locus of constant temperature. Every point on the P/V diagram for a specified sample of gas (in this

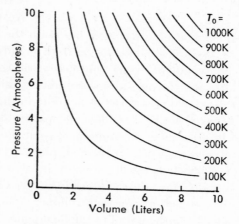

Fig. 15.01. Loci of $PV = RT_0$ for a series of values of T_0.

case one mole of any gas), has a specific temperature associated with it, and along each of the hyperbolic loci all points have the same value of T. If instead of plotting P against V we plot P against V^{-1}, the isothermal loci become straight lines through the origin. On a plot of PV against P or V they are horizontal straight lines.

15.03 INCREMENTAL CHANGES

Suppose that, commencing at specified values (P, V, T), some small change is made in the environment of the gas: a change say in the size of its container. If sufficient heat is transferred to the gas (say by raising the temperature of the container), the pressure can be maintained constant. A smaller transfer of heat (achieved by maintaining the temperature of the container constant and proceeding slowly enough to maintain thermal equilibrium) can maintain the temperature constant. The pressure will then drop (Figure 15.02). Zero transfer of heat will cause the same volume increase to produce a still greater pressure drop: The slope of an adiabatic step from a given point on the P/V diagram will be greater (i.e., the slope more negative, the curve steeper) than the slope of the isothermal step from the same point. We will now set up differential equations relating the change in P with the change in V and the change in T.

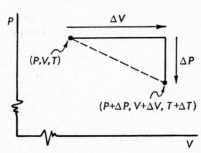

Fig. 15.02. Incremental change on a P/V diagram. ΔV and ΔP should be small in comparison with V and P; they may be either positive or negative.

We want to take the gas from an initial volume V to a slightly different final volume $V + \Delta V$ (not necessarily greater, since ΔV may be negative, although the one in the diagram is positive) and from an initial pressure P to a final pressure $P + \Delta P$ (and in the diagram we have actually taken ΔP as negative). Unless we specify otherwise, we must assume that T will also change to some new value $T + \Delta T$; the magnitude of ΔT does not show as such on the P/V plot.

This change will probably involve a transfer of heat ΔQ to the gas. We only know the relationship between ΔQ and ΔT for changes at constant pressure and at constant volume. The best that we can do, then, is to move from the initial to the final point in two steps, one at constant pressure and one at constant volume.

15.04 THE STEP AT CONSTANT PRESSURE

Quite arbitrarily, let us make the constant-pressure move first. With the volume increasing at constant pressure, we have in effect a gas thermometer, and volume proportional to temperature. That is, since

$[V]_P \propto T,$

$$\frac{V + \Delta V}{V} = \frac{T + \Delta T_p}{T}$$

where the subscript p on the term ΔT_p indicates that we are referring to the temperature increment during a change at constant pressure. From this,

$$\frac{\Delta V}{V} = \frac{\Delta T_p}{T} \tag{15.02}$$

Regarding heat transfer, we can say

$$\Delta Q_p = C_p \, \Delta T_p \tag{15.03}$$

where ΔQ_p denotes the heat transferred to the gas during this expansion at constant pressure.

15.05 THE STEP AT CONSTANT VOLUME

Having obtained these two relationships for the move at constant pressure, let us turn to the second move, at constant volume. This time again we have a gas thermometer, but a constant-volume one. Since $[P]_V \propto T,$

$$\frac{P + \Delta P}{P} = \frac{T + \Delta T_p + \Delta T_v}{T + \Delta T_p}$$

from which
$$\frac{\Delta P}{P} = \frac{\Delta T_v}{T + \Delta T_p} \tag{15.04}$$

If ΔT_p is small, it may be neglected as a term added to T, without serious inaccuracy. Consider, for instance, the case $T = 300$, $\Delta T_p = 0.3$, $\Delta T_v = 0.3$. Then $\Delta T_v/(T + \Delta T_p)$ and $\Delta T_v/T$ differ by only 1 part in 1000. As progressively smaller increments are taken, the approximation becomes progressively better, to become perfect in the limit used in infinitesimal calculus. So, assuming ΔT_p to be negligible as a term added to T,

$$\frac{\Delta P}{P} \simeq \frac{\Delta T_v}{T} \tag{15.05}$$

If the constant-volume step were taken first, the approximation would disappear from equation (15.05) and appear in (15.02). So it really did not matter which step was taken first.

For the constant-volume step, the relation between heat transfer and temperature change is

$$\Delta Q_v = C_v \, \Delta T_v \tag{15.06}$$

15.06 COMBINING THE STEPS

Equations (15.02), (15.03), (15.05), and (15.06) are four statements about the general case, i.e., about any and every case, of motion on a P/V diagram, statements relating incremental changes in P, V, T, and Q. They involve the arbitrary breakdown of the general step into one at constant volume and one at constant pressure. This may be removed by combining the equations to eliminate ΔT_p and ΔT_v as such and introduce $\Delta T = \Delta T_p + \Delta T_v$, similarly to eliminate ΔQ_p and ΔQ_v as such and introduce $\Delta Q = \Delta Q_p + \Delta Q_v$, as follows:

$$\frac{\Delta T}{T} = \frac{\Delta T_p}{T} + \frac{\Delta T_v}{T} \simeq \frac{\Delta V}{V} + \frac{\Delta P}{P}$$

Hence, as a good approximation when the increments are small and approaching perfection as the steps approach zero,

$$\frac{\Delta T}{T} = \frac{\Delta V}{V} + \frac{\Delta P}{P} \tag{15.07}$$

Also,

$$\frac{\Delta Q}{T} = \frac{\Delta Q_p}{T} + \frac{\Delta Q_v}{T} = C_p \frac{\Delta T_p}{T} + C_v \frac{\Delta T_v}{T} \simeq C_p \frac{\Delta V}{V} + C_v \frac{\Delta P}{P}$$

Hence, as an approximation of the same sort as equation (15.07),

$$\frac{\Delta Q}{T} = C_p \frac{\Delta V}{V} + C_v \frac{\Delta P}{P} \tag{15.08}$$

We now have in equations (15.07) and (15.08) just two statements about the general case, relating P, V, T, ΔP, ΔV, ΔT, and ΔQ.

15.07 DIFFERENTIAL EQUATION OF AN ISOTHERMAL CHANGE

In deriving equation (15.01), we described an isothermal expansion as one in which "the temperature shall remain constant", i.e., $T = T_0$. To put the same thing in slightly different words and slightly different symbols, an isothermal step is one in which there is no change in temperature, i.e.,

$$\Delta T = 0 \tag{15.09}$$

Combining this statement with the general statement of 15.07, we have

$$\frac{\Delta V}{V} + \frac{\Delta P}{P} = 0 \tag{15.10}$$

This is the differential equation of isothermal expansion. It gives us the slope of the isothermal curve through any point (P, V) on a P/V diagram:

$$\frac{\Delta P}{\Delta V} = -\frac{P}{V} \qquad (15.11)$$

The slope is always negative, large where P is large and small where P is small (Figure 15.03). Now, for comparison, the algebraic equation of an isothermal $PV = RT_0$ gives us explicitly the value of P for any value of V, when we have first selected a value for the constant temperature T_0. If we plot this information as a series of points on a P/V plot, and draw a continuous locus through these points, we can measure the slope at any point on the locus. To obtain the slopes from the algebraic equation without

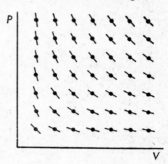

Fig. 15.03. The slope of isothermal expansion through an array of points on a P/V plot according to equation (15.11).

such graphical development, it is necessary to differentiate through the equation; the result of such differentiation would be effectively equation (15.11).

15.08 DIFFERENTIAL EQUATION OF AN ADIABATIC CHANGE

The definition of an adiabatic change, "no transfer of heat to or from the gas", may be stated

$$\Delta Q = 0 \qquad (15.12)$$

Combining this with (15.08), we have

$$C_p \frac{\Delta V}{V} + C_v \frac{\Delta P}{P} = 0$$

or dividing through by C_v gives

$$\frac{\Delta P}{P} + \gamma \frac{\Delta V}{V} = 0 \qquad (15.13)$$

where γ is the ratio of the specific heats. This gives us the slope of the adiabatic curve through any point on a P/V diagram:

$$\frac{\Delta P}{\Delta V} = -\gamma \frac{P}{V} \qquad (15.14)$$

The slope is always negative, large where P is large and small where P is small (Figure 15.04), as for an isothermal change. The slope of an adiabat through any point is greater than the slope of the isotherm through the same point, as anticipated. Further, comparing (15.14) with (15.11), we see that

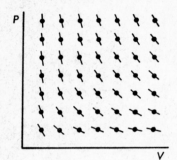

$$\frac{\left(\dfrac{\Delta P}{\Delta V}\right)_{\text{adi.}}}{\left(\dfrac{\Delta P}{\Delta V}\right)_{\text{iso.}}} = \gamma \qquad (15.15)$$

Fig. 15.04. The slope of adiabatic expansion through an array of points on a P/V plot according to equation (15.14).

the ratio of the slope of an adiabat through any point to the slope of the isotherm through the same point is equal to the ratio of the specific heats. This finding can be reached more quickly with reference to Figure 15.05, where a common volume increment at constant pressure is followed by one size of pressure increment for the isothermal change, by an increment larger by factor γ for the adiabatic change.

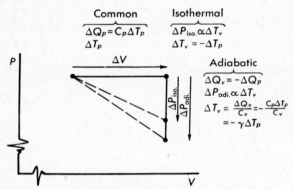

Fig. 15.05. Comparison of incremental isothermal and adiabatic changes.

15.09 THE EXPERIMENT OF CLÉMENT AND DÉSORMES

The foregoing theory is applied in the classical experiment of Clément and Désormes to determine γ, the ratio of the specific heats. In this experiment, a large glass bottle contains air at atmospheric pressure. Its mouth is stopped by a flat glass plate pressed against it and sealed by

a gasket or by grease (Figure 15.06).   A little more air is added, a small
water or mercury manometer showing the resultant pressure increase over
atmospheric.   This compression may raise the temperature of the air in
the bottle as well as its pressure, but in the course of several seconds,
transfer of heat to the walls of the bottle
removes the temperature excess, and we have
a bottle full of air at room temperature and
slightly more than room pressure.   Now the
flat stopper is removed, just for a second or
two, which permits the escape of enough air
to reduce the pressure in the bottle to that of
the atmosphere.   The contained air expands,
and so it does work and is cooled.   Some of
the air is forced out of the bottle, mixes with
the room air, and is lost.   Most of the air,
though, remains in the bottle, at room pressure and less than room temperature.   In

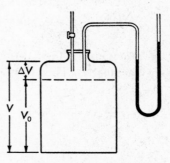

Fig. 15.06.   Apparatus
for the experiment of Clément and Désormes.

the course of several seconds, transfer of heat from the walls of the bottle
returns this gas to room temperature.   Before such heat transfer has
properly started, before there has been any appreciable expansion of the
gas, the stopper is replaced, and the return of the enclosed gas to room
temperature occurs at constant volume.   During this heating at constant
volume, the pressure rises.   The initial and final pressures are read from
the manometer.   These are "gauge" pressures, i.e., pressure excess of the
inside of the bottle above the atmosphere.   Call them h_0 and h_1.

Consider the air that did not escape.   It had volume V_0 before the
expansion, volume V (the whole of the bottle) afterward.   Denoting the
atmospheric pressure by Π, and room temperature by T_0, the pressure,
volume, and temperature values for this sample are given in Table 15.01
and Figure 15.07.

TABLE 15.01.

	Pressure	Vol.	Temp.
(a) Before the adiabatic	$\Pi + h_0$	V_0	T_0
(b) After the adiabatic, before warming-up	Π	V	T
(c) After return at constant volume to room temperature	$\Pi + h_1$	V	T_0

The initial and final conditions of the air lie on the same isothermal
line, i.e., the air has the same initial and final temperatures, although the
air *never did expand isothermally:* It expanded adiabatically, then warmed

up at constant volume to reach its final position on the isotherm from which it started. From the figure,

$$\text{Slope of adiabatic} = \frac{h_0}{\Delta V}$$

$$\text{Slope of isothermal} = \frac{h_0 - h_1}{\Delta V}$$

From equation (15.15), the ratio of these slopes equals the ratio of the specific heats. Therefore,

$$\gamma = \frac{\dfrac{h_0}{\Delta V}}{\dfrac{h_0 - h_1}{\Delta V}} = \frac{h_0}{h_0 - h_1} \tag{15.16}$$

Here is a very simple way indeed of determining the ratio of the specific heats and so of determining the specific heats themselves.

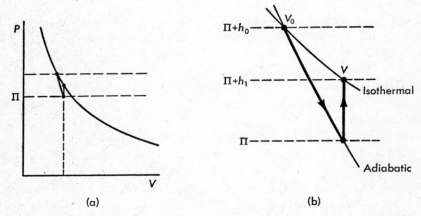

(a) (b)

Fig. 15.07. Path followed by gas in experiment of Clément and Désormes.

It is worth comparing Figure 15.07(b) with Figure 15.05 so that the actual processes of 15.07(b) will not be confused with the hypothetical processes of 15.05.

15.10 LOGARITHMIC SCALES

There are many occasions in physics when it is convenient to plot and consider the logarithm of a quantity rather than the value of the quantity itself. Frequently a scale is used which, while progressing linearly in log x as in Figure 15.08(a) is subdivided nonlinearly in the function x itself as in Figure 15.08(b). The most familiar case is the slide rule. Equal lengths along the scale represent equal factorial increases in x, wherever they are taken. Algebraically,

$$\Delta \log x = \log (x + \Delta x) - \log x = \log \frac{x + \Delta x}{x}$$

$$= \log \left(1 + \frac{\Delta x}{x}\right) \qquad (15.17)$$

The quantities Δx and x enter the right-hand side of the equation only in the ratio $\Delta x/x$. Thus for a given value of $\Delta x/x$, there is a specific value of $\Delta \log x$, no matter what the value of x. For instance, if $\Delta x/x = 0.5$, then $\Delta \log_{10} x = 0.1761$, regardless of whether $x = 2$ and $\Delta x = 1$ or $x = 50$ and $\Delta x = 25$. This is true for any value of $\Delta x/x$, however large.

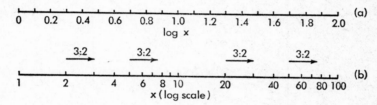

Fig. 15.08. Equal distances on a logarithmic scale represent equal ratios regardless of their starting points.

Further, if Δx is small in comparison with x, the increment of the logarithm varies *proportionately* with $\Delta x/x$:

$$\Delta \log x \propto \frac{\Delta x}{x} \qquad \text{(approx.)} \qquad (15.18)$$

The approximation approaches exactitude as Δx approaches zero. This is an important relationship, because functions of the form $\Delta x/x$ arise frequently in physics. In Figure 15.09(a), $\Delta \log x$ is plotted against $\Delta x/x$, using 10 as the base of the logarithms, and the goodness of the approximation can be seen. The constant of proportionality depends on the base used. For base 10 it is 0.4343:

$$\Delta \log_{10} x \simeq 0.4343 \frac{\Delta x}{x} \qquad (15.19)$$

It is possible to find a base for which the constant of proportionality is unity. That base is denoted by e, and so

$$\Delta \log_e x \simeq \frac{\Delta x}{x} \qquad (15.20)$$

Equation (15.20) can serve to define e, and can be developed without much trouble into the usual definition of e.   The numerical value of e is, to six figures, 2.71828.   Figure 15.09(b) is a repetition of Figure 15.09(a), but using the base e, so that the slope of the curve as it passes through the origin is unity.

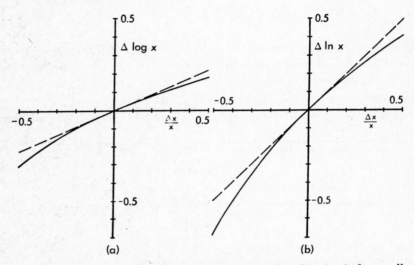

(a)   (b)

Fig. 15.09. $\Delta \log x$ is approximately proportional to $\Delta x / x$ for small values of $\Delta x / x$.   In part (a) of the figure, with logarithms to the base 10, the constant of proportionality is 0.4343.   In the (b) part, the constant of proportionality has been made unity by taking $e = 2.71828$ as the base of the logarithms.

In this book, the convenient usage is followed of denoting a logarithm to the base 10 by the abbreviation "log", and any logarithm to the base e by the abbreviation "ln".

15.11 LOGARITHMIC PLOTS OF ISOTHERMALS AND ADIABATICS

Terms of the form $\Delta x / x$ in equations (15.10) and (15.13) can be changed to terms of the form $\Delta \log x$ or $\Delta \ln x$ by introducing equations (15.19) or (15.20).   We then obtain for the isothermal equation

$$\left. \begin{array}{c} \Delta \log V + \Delta \log P = 0 \\ \dfrac{\Delta \log P}{\Delta \log V} = -1 \end{array} \right\} \tag{15.21}$$

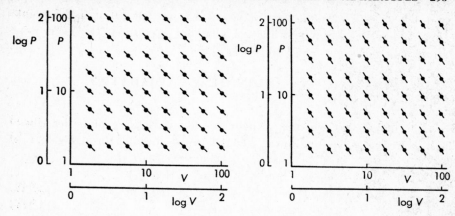

Fig. 15.10. The slope of isothermal expansion through an array of points on a $(\log P)/(\log V)$ plot is everywhere -1.

Fig. 15.11. The slope of adiabatic expansion through an array of points on a $(\log P)/(\log V)$ plot is everywhere $-\gamma$.

and for the adiabatic equation

$$\Delta \log P + \gamma \Delta \log V = 0 \\ \left.\frac{\Delta \log P}{\Delta \log V} = -\gamma \right\} \qquad (15.22)$$

Now, in Figures 15.03 and 15.04 we drew short line elements through an array of points on a P/V plot to indicate the slope of isothermal and adiabatic expansions. If we do the same thing on a $(\log P)/(\log V)$ plot, the slope $(\Delta \log P)/(\Delta \log V)$ is everywhere -1 for the isothermal case shown by equation (15.21) and everywhere $-\gamma$ for the adiabatic case shown by (15.22). The resulting diagrams are shown in Figures 15.10 and 15.11.

The constancy of the slope makes it a simple matter to draw the complete locus of an isothermal expansion. If the expansion commences at (or at any stage passes through) the condition $P = P_0$,

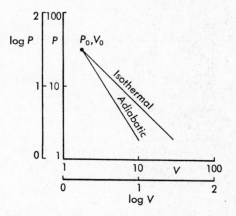

Fig. 15.12. Isothermal and adiabatic loci on a $(\log P)/(\log V)$ plot are straight lines of slope -1 and $-\gamma$ respectively.

$V = V_0$, then the locus drawn against rectangular coordinates of $\log P$

and $\log V$ is a straight line of slope -1 passing through the point $(\log P_0, \log V_0)$. Similarly for an adiabatic expansion, the locus is a straight line of slope $-\gamma$ (Figure 15.12).

15.12 ALGEBRAIC EQUATION OF AN ADIABATIC EXPANSION

The equations of the straight-line loci on log/log plots described above are easily written down. That of an isothermal through (P_0, V_0) is

$$\log P = \log P_0 - (\log V - \log V_0)$$

that is,
$$\log P + \log V = \log P_0 + \log V_0 \qquad (15.23)$$

or
$$PV = P_0V_0 \qquad (15.24)$$

If it is known that $P_0V_0 = RT_0$, then the equation is

$$PV = RT_0 \qquad (15.25)$$

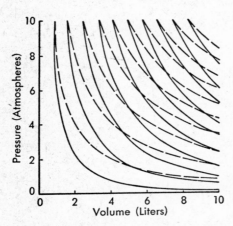

By considering the log/log plot, we have "solved" differential equation (15.10) to give the algebraic equation of an isothermal expansion. It so happens that we were able to obtain that equation much more easily by combining $PV = RT$ and $T = T_0$. It also happens, though, that there is no such easy way of obtaining the algebraic equation of an adiabatic expansion, so that a similar solution of differential equation (15.13) will be very useful. The locus of successive applications of (15.13) on a log/log plot is a straight line of slope $-\gamma$, that is,

Fig. 15.13. The solid lines are loci of adiabatic expansions for which the temperatures *at pressure 10 atmospheres* are 100K, 200K, 300K, etc. The broken lines are isothermals at these temperatures. At every intersection the adiabat has slope greater by a factor γ than the intersecting isothermal.

$$\log P = \log P_0 - \gamma(\log V - \log V_0) \qquad (15.26)$$

or
$$\log P + \gamma \log V = \log P_0 + \gamma \log V_0$$

or
$$PV^\gamma = P_0V_0{}^\gamma \qquad (15.27)$$

This, then, is the equation in P and V of an adiabatic expansion through (P_0, V_0): it is drawn against P and V scales in Figure 15.13.

15.13 THE CALCULUS OF ISOTHERMAL AND ADIABATIC EXPANSIONS

The correct representation of equation (15.10) in calculus notation is

$$\frac{dV}{V} + \frac{dP}{P} = 0 \tag{15.28}$$

Use of d's rather than Δ's indicates that the relation holds accurately in the limit as dV and dP approach zero. Rewriting it, we have

$$\frac{dV}{V} = -\frac{dP}{P}$$

and integrating gives

$$\int \frac{dV}{V} = -\int \frac{dP}{P} + \text{constant}$$

From lists of integrals it may be found that

$$\int \frac{dx}{x} = \ln x + \text{constant}$$

and so $\qquad \ln V = -\ln P + \text{constant}$

and $\qquad \log V = -\log P + \text{constant}$

from which, as we have seen, equation (15.24) may be derived. Thus equation (15.28) is "solved", to give its algebraic form, by integration. Conversely, the algebraic form $PV = RT_0$ may be differentiated to give the differential equation

$$P \, dV + V \, dP = 0$$

that is, $\qquad \dfrac{dV}{V} + \dfrac{dP}{P} = 0$

Similarly, in correct calculus notation, equation (15.13) becomes

$$\frac{dP}{P} + \gamma \frac{dV}{V} = 0 \tag{15.29}$$

This may be solved by integration to give equation (15.27), which conversely may be differentiated to yield (15.29). The setting-up of (15.13), pretty much in the way that we did it, is necessary in order to arrive at (15.29) and so at (15.27).

15.14 ADIABATIC EQUATIONS INVOLVING TEMPERATURE

The adiabatic equation

$$PV^\gamma = P_0 V_0^\gamma$$

may be combined with the equation of state

$$PV = RT$$

to define an adiabatic expansion in terms of P and T, or of V and T. The equation of state implies of course that $P_0 V_0 = RT_0$.

Eliminating P and P_0 from the above equations, we obtain

$$\frac{RT}{V} V^\gamma = \frac{RT_0}{V_0} V_0^\gamma$$

$$V^{\gamma-1} T = V_0^{\gamma-1} T_0 \qquad (15.30)$$

Similarly, eliminating V gives

$$P \left(\frac{RT}{P}\right)^\gamma = P_0 \left(\frac{RT_0}{P_0}\right)^\gamma$$

that is,

$$P^{1-\gamma} T^\gamma = P_0^{1-\gamma} T_0^\gamma$$

or, avoiding negative indices, we have

$$\frac{T^\gamma}{P^{\gamma-1}} = \frac{T_0^\gamma}{P_0^{\gamma-1}} \qquad (15.31)$$

15.15 HEAT TRANSFERRED AND WORK DONE

The heat transferred to a gas during an adiabatic expansion is by definition zero. The heat transferred to a gas during an isothermal expansion is equal to the work done by the gas, for the energy of random motion remains constant. In considering specific heats, it was noted (section 14.10) that the work done during an increase in volume ΔV at constant pressure is $P \Delta V$. This is perfectly true for any increase in volume, however large. If the pressure varies, it is still approximately true, provided the percentage change in pressure is small. So for any *small* step, the incremental amount of work is given approximately by

$$\Delta W = P \Delta V$$

For the isothermal expansion of one mole of gas, $PV = RT_0$, so we can eliminate P and say

$$\Delta W = P \Delta V = RT_0 \frac{\Delta V}{V} \qquad (15.32)$$

Recalling that $\Delta V/V = \Delta \ln V$, this can be written

$$\Delta W = RT_0 \Delta \ln V$$

This tells us that if we plot W against $\ln V$, the slope has the constant value RT_0. If at the start $V = V_0$, the plot of W against $\ln V$ is a straight line, through ($W = 0$, $\ln V = \ln V_0$), of slope RT_0 (Figure 15.14). Its equation is

$$W = RT_0(\ln V - \ln V_0) = RT_0 \ln \frac{V}{V_0}$$
$$(15.33)$$

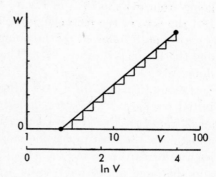

Fig. 15.14. Relation between work done and volume for one mole of gas expanding at constant temperature. Slope anywhere on plot equals RT_0.

This, then, is the equation relating work done, during the isothermal expansion of one mole of gas, to the increase in volume. For any sample of gas containing n moles, the work done is of course $nRT_0 \ln (V/V_0)$. If we want to know the amount of heat transferred, we need only recall that this equals, in the isothermal case, the work done.

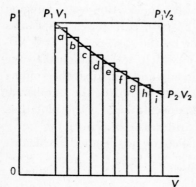

Fig. 15.15. Work done by an expanding gas equals area under path-curve on a plot of P against V.

15.16 WORK ON AN INDICATOR DIAGRAM

A single point on a plot of P against V (such as P_1V_1, Figure 15.15) can be used to represent the condition of a sample of gas. If the number of moles in the sample of gas is known, then the value of T can be determined from P and V. Most simply, as in Figures 15.01 and 15.13, a sample of one mole is considered. A line on a plot of P against V can be used to represent the continuously changing condition of the sample as two or all of the quantities P, V, and T change. The line does not show the rate of change of any of these quantities with time.

For a change at constant pressure, the work done by the gas in expanding its container is $P \Delta V$, where ΔV is the change in volume. Thus, in going from $P_1 V_1$ to $P_1 V_2$ in Figure 15.15, the work done is $P_1(V_2 - V_1)$. But the area of the rectangle lying between the line joining $P_1 V_1$ to $P_1 V_2$ (i.e., the path followed by the point indicating the condition of the gas) and the V axis is $P_1(V_2 - V_1)$. The area under the path equals the work done.

Let us turn now to a case where the final pressure differs from the initial pressure. The work done in moving in small constant-pressure steps from $P_1 V_1$ to $P_2 V_2$ is exactly $P_a(\Delta V)_a + P_b(\Delta V)_b + \cdots + P_i(\Delta V)_i$, and this is the area under the stepped line. But the stepped line has been drawn to resemble the smooth curve joining the same two points, and this area approximates the area under the smooth curve. If the ΔV's were made smaller and the number of steps greater, the stepped curve would approximate better the smooth curve. The exact amount of work done in following the smooth curve is the limit as the number of steps increases, and the size of steps decreases, of $\Sigma(P \Delta V)$ where Σ indicates the sum of many terms. This is exactly the area under the smooth curve.

In summary, then, a point on a plot of P against V indicates the condition of a sample of gas, provided we know the size of the sample in moles. The point can be referred to as an **indicator point.** The **path** followed by this point can be used to represent the continuously changing condition of the gas. The area under the path and above the V axis (i.e., the line $P = 0$) equals the work done by the gas.

A heat-engine indicator is a mechanism which, when attached to the engine, automatically plots pressure within a cylinder against the volume of the cylinder. (In practical engines, it may be noted, the number of moles of gas in the cylinder does not remain constant.) The plot thus obtained of P against V is then called an **indicator diagram.**

The work done, and the area under the curve, are denoted in calculus symbols by

$$\int_{V_0}^{V} P \, dV$$

In the preceding section, we found that for the particular case of an isothermal expansion the work done is

$$\int_{V_0}^{V} RT_0 \frac{dV}{V} = RT_0 \ln \frac{V}{V_0}$$

15.17 VARIATION OF PRESSURE WITH HEIGHT IN THE ATMOSPHERE

Before considering expansions further with especial reference to engines, some consideration will be given to the atmosphere. We will consider the atmosphere pretty much as a static thing, although in fact it is in itself an intricate and most interesting heat engine.

Pressure varies with height. The force exerted on the bottom of a box by the air within it exceeds the force exerted on the top of the box by the weight of the air in the box. This variation was neglected in our kinetic theory.

Let h be distance above the earth's surface, or more specifically above mean sea level. The pressure P at any height h is greater than the pressure $P + \Delta P$ at height $h + \Delta h$ by the weight of gas in a vertical column of unit cross-sectional area. This weight is $\rho \, \Delta h \times g$, where ρ is the density of air. Thus,

$$\Delta P = -\rho g \, \Delta h \qquad (15.34)$$

For a mixture of gases,

$$\rho = \frac{P \overline{M}_0}{RT}$$

(section 13.11). In the lowest 10 miles of the atmosphere, including nearly all the air, there is continued mixing, and $\overline{M}_0 = 29$ gm. Then equation (15.34) becomes, dropping the bar on $\overline{M}_0$,

$$\frac{\Delta P}{P} = - \frac{M_0 g}{RT} \Delta h \qquad (15.35)$$

For temperature 15C and $g = 981$, this works out to a proportional change in pressure of -0.012% per meter, or -0.39% per 100 ft. Since the pressure at sea level is about one standard atmosphere, which is 1013.25 mb (millibars) or 760 mm Hg or 29.92 in. Hg, the decrease in pressure in rising 100 ft at about sea level will be about 4.4 mb or 3.0 mm Hg or 0.12 in. Hg.

Barometer readings at various weather stations can be compared for meteorological purposes only when they have been corrected to a common level, and of course mean sea level is used. Altimeters determine height from pressure; for the height of the aircraft above the ground to be determined, the height of that ground above sea level must be known, obviously. So must the prevailing surface pressure, which varies by tens of millibars with the weather.

If in equation (15.35) the temperature is taken as being constant, the form of the differential equation is the same as that of (15.32). Thus in the same way that (15.32) was solved to give algebraic (15.33), equation (15.35) can be solved to give, as an algebraic relation between pressure and height in an atmosphere of constant temperature,

$$h = -\frac{RT}{M_0 g} \ln \frac{P}{P_0} \quad (15.36)$$

The locus of this equation is plotted in Figure 15.16. The temperature of the atmosphere decreases with height over most of the region shown in the figure, but comparison of the locus of the equation with that of a "Standard Atmosphere", taking the mean temperature variation into account, shows that we have achieved a reasonable approximation.

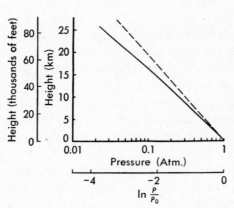

Fig. 15.16. Pressure in the atmosphere.

Broken line: $h = -\dfrac{RT}{M_0 g} \ln \dfrac{P}{P_0}$

where $T = 288$ (Kelvin, constant)

$M_0 = 29$ gm

$g = 981$ cm sec^{-2}

$P_0 = 1$ atm $= 1013.25$ millibars

Solid line: NACA "Standard Atmosphere"

15.18 VARIATION OF TEMPERATURE WITH HEIGHT IN THE ATMOSPHERE

If a parcel of air rises up through the surrounding atmosphere, it expands adiabatically, doing work by pushing outward against its environment as surely as if it were driving a piston along a cylinder. And parcels of air, particularly cloud-laden ones, certainly do rise up through the surrounding atmosphere. Let us consider a rising parcel of dry air. The differential equation of an adiabatic change (15.13) states that

$$\frac{\Delta P}{P} + \gamma \frac{\Delta V}{V} = 0$$

We want a relationship between pressure and temperature. We can get this by combining the above equation with the generally applicable differential equation (15.07) relating pressure, volume, and temperature changes,

$$\frac{\Delta P}{P} + \frac{\Delta V}{V} = \frac{\Delta T}{T}$$

to eliminate $\Delta V/V$:

$$\gamma \frac{\Delta T}{T} + (1 - \gamma) \frac{\Delta P}{P} = 0 \tag{15.37}$$

Combining this in turn with equation (15.35) relating pressure and height, to eliminate $\Delta P/P$, we obtain

$$\gamma \frac{\Delta T}{T} + (\gamma - 1) \frac{M_0 g}{RT} \Delta h = 0$$

or

$$\Delta T = - \frac{M_0 g}{R} \frac{\gamma - 1}{\gamma} \Delta h$$

But

$$\frac{\gamma - 1}{\gamma} = \frac{C_p - C_v}{C_p} = \frac{R}{C_p}$$

Therefore

$$\Delta T = - \frac{M_0 g}{C_p} \Delta h = - \frac{g}{c_p} \Delta h \tag{15.38}$$

Calculating c_p for a diatomic gas of gram-molecular weight 29 gm and substituting, it is found that the temperature of a rising parcel of dry air drops off at a rate of about 10 deg km^{-1}.

Suppose that a parcel of air is heated, and so becomes warmer than the air around it. It expands on heating, and so becomes buoyant and starts to rise. The same would apply to a parcel of water heated at the bottom of a pool, but with different consequences. If all the water in the pool, other than the heated parcel, were at the same temperature, the parcel of water would rise to the top of the pool, expanding only very slightly as it rose, owing to the reduction in pressure. The parcel of air, on the other hand, will expand as it rises, and so will cool according to equation (15.38), unless there is a continuing addition of heat. If all the atmosphere, other than the heated parcel, is at the same temperature, the parcel will soon find itself back at the temperature and density of its surroundings, and so without buoyancy. The parcel will continue to rise indefinitely (like the water parcel rising to the top of the pool) only if the temperature of the atmosphere decreases with height at the same rate of 10 deg km^{-1} at which the rising parcel cools.

The atmosphere is heated from the bottom: The sun's radiation passes through a largely transparent atmosphere and heats the earth's surface, and the atmosphere receives most of its heat in turn from the heated surface at its base. If we start with an "isothermal" atmosphere, one having the same temperature at all heights, the air near the ground will expand upward somewhat, but will not rise up in parcels to the top of the atmosphere. Instead, the isothermal atmosphere will change gradually to one having temperature decreasing with height. Suppose, however, that this process were to proceed until the temperature dropped off with height as rapidly as the 10 deg km⁻¹ given by equation (15.38). Then any heated parcel of dry air that started to rise would continually find itself surrounded by air slightly colder and so denser than itself, and hence would retain its buoyancy and continue to rise, like a heated parcel of water in a pool at a uniform lower temperature. A dropping-off in temperature with height appreciably more rapid than this 10 deg km⁻¹ would not be possible, then, for vertical currents would be set up that would reduce it to this rate.

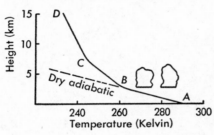

Fig. 15.17. An example of temperature against height in the atmosphere, indicating regions of stability (C–D), instability for cloud (B–C), and instability for clear air (A–B).

The rate at which temperature decreases with increasing height in the atmosphere is known as the **lapse rate.** The rate established by equation (15.38) is known as the **dry adiabatic** lapse rate. If the lapse rate through dry air is any less than this, the air is stable: Slight heating of any part of it will lead to only a slight lifting. If the lapse rate is as great as given by the equation, dry air is unstable: Slight heating of any part of it will lead to extended lifting of that part.

The lapse rate is not often as great as this, except close to the ground. But the atmosphere is seldom dry, and cloud-filled air becomes unstable for a smaller lapse rate, the **saturated adiabatic lapse rate,** owing to release of latent heat as further water vapor condenses. This lapse rate increases with temperature (because vapor content increases with temperature) and at −15C is 5 deg km⁻¹. The average lapse rate used in describing a "standard atmosphere" is 6 deg km⁻¹, up to 11 km. In Figure 15.17, a hypothetical line of temperature against height has been drawn. There will be updrafts from the earth's surface at A to the point B. If cumulus cloud has formed in these updrafts by the time B is reached, the updrafts will continue to C assuming that BC is as steep as the "saturated adiabat". Beyond C the lapse rate is too modest, and the cloud will stop rising.

15.19 ENTROPY

In considering expansions, we have kept the amount of gas constant (1 mole) and introduced increments of P, V, T, and Q. Now P, V, and T reveal the state of the gas; values of any two of them reveal its state completely; substitution of values for two of them in the equation of state $PV = RT$ gives the value of the third. Thus the state of the gas can be shown by a point on a P/V plot, or on a P/T plot, or on a V/T plot.

The quantity Q is less specific. If we add an incremental amount of heat ΔQ, it goes in part to increasing the energy of random motion, in part to expanding the container. The successive addition of several increments ΔQ will take the gas from condition (1) $(P_1V_1T_1)$ to condition (2) $(P_2V_2T_2)$ (Figure 15.18). But the sum of those increments $\overset{2}{\underset{1}{\Sigma}}\,\Delta Q$ will vary with the path followed from (1) to (2), being greatest for the high-temperature path a and least (among the paths shown) for the low-temperature path d. Thus if we start from point (1) and know any two of $\overset{2}{\underset{1}{\Sigma}}\,\Delta P\ (= P_2 - P_1),\ \overset{2}{\underset{1}{\Sigma}}\,\Delta V\ (= V_2 - V_1),$ and $\overset{2}{\underset{1}{\Sigma}}\,\Delta T\ (= T_2 - T_1)$, we can locate point (2), i.e., we can evaluate $P_2,\ V_2,\ T_2$. But because $\overset{2}{\underset{1}{\Sigma}}\,\Delta Q$ may have any value, it does not help us to locate the point (2). The increment ΔQ, the mathematicians say, is not a perfect differential.

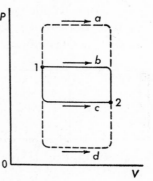

Fig. 15.18. The work done in expanding from $P_1V_1T_1$ to $P_2V_2T_2$, denoted by the area under the curve on a P/V plot, depends on the route followed.

Equation (15.08), however, introduced us to a perfect differential that involves ΔQ. If we treat the whole of $(\Delta Q)/T$ as an increment, rather than breaking it down into an increment divided by temperature, we find that we have (in the limit) a perfect differential. The sum $\overset{2}{\underset{1}{\Sigma}}\,(\Delta Q/T)$ does have a definite value, like $\overset{2}{\underset{1}{\Sigma}}\,\Delta P,\ \overset{2}{\underset{1}{\Sigma}}\,\Delta V,$ and $\overset{2}{\underset{1}{\Sigma}}\,\Delta T$, and can do its part in locating point (2), in specifying the state of the gas. The sum $\Sigma\,(\Delta Q/T)$ is called entropy, denoted by the symbol ϕ, so that we may define entropy by a statement about its increment:

$$\Delta\phi = \frac{\Delta Q}{T} \tag{15.39}$$

This gives us four properties of the gas, $P,\ V,\ T$, and ϕ, any two of which will specify the state of the gas. A very convenient alternative to a P/V plot is a T/ϕ plot (known in some circles as a "tephigram"). During an adiabatic expansion ΔQ is always zero, and so $\Delta\phi$ is always zero.

During an isothermal expansion, ΔT is always zero, of course. So on a tephigram adiabats are straight lines parallel to the T axis, and isotherms are straight lines parallel to the ϕ axis. At the same time, the straight lines of a P/V plot, P constant and V constant, become curved lines.

15.20 JOULE'S EXPERIMENT (SIMPLEST HYPOTHETICAL FORM)

An expanding gas does work in pressing against its expanding container. Is there not some way in which it can expand without pressing against an expanding container? Yes. Take, for instance, the somewhat oversimplified diagram of Figure 15.19. Suppose that there is gas in the left compartment, vacuum in the right. If the dividing partition is suddenly broken, the gas will redistribute itself uniformly throughout the total volume. But nowhere, if the breaking is done expertly enough, will the gas molecules bounce off a receding wall. None of the supply of energy of random motion is used up; the average kinetic energy per molecule, or per degree of freedom, remains the same. The temperature, then, remains the same, in spite of the expansion.

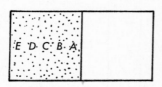

Fig. 15.19. Hypothetical apparatus for sudden release of gas into a vacuum.

There is no transfer of heat involved, the transfer that we would expect in an isothermal expansion. There is no temperature drop involved, the temperature drop that we would expect in an adiabatic expansion. By putting the word "gradual" into our definitions of isothermal and adiabatic, we keep this unusual sort of expansion from qualifying as either one. In that way, we avoid having to refer to it either as "isothermal but with no heat transfer" or as "adiabatic but with no temperature drop". Instead, we say that the expansion is sudden, and so does not qualify as either isothermal or adiabatic.

If one compares this rather idealized form of "Joule's Experiment" with the similar rapid release of gas in the experiment of Clément and Désormes, one may wonder why there was any drop of temperature in the latter case. Admittedly there was no pressing of the gas, no bouncing of molecules, against a retreating piston. But the gas was pressing everywhere against other gas, was in that way exerting a force through a distance.

With this comparison between the two experiments in mind, we will do well to look at Joule's experiment again, in more detail. Suppose that by some clever arrangement, the partition is made to vanish in an instant.

in no time at all. Then, even though the gas at A (Figure 15.19) is rushing freely into a vacuum, the gas at B is pushing against the gas ahead of it. So is the gas at C, D, and E. This gas farther back has no way of realizing, so to speak, that there is a vacuum ahead. Most of the gas has other gas ahead of it, and must be doing work, must be losing energy, must be dropping in temperature.

Suppose that, as the gas from A reaches the far wall, the gas from C has reached the original location of the partition. Just at that stage in the proceedings, imagine that a still more clever device permits the partition to reappear in its original position. Then surely all the gas remaining to the left of the partition has done work, and is all at a temperature lower than the original. Does this not make Joule's experiment, or our idealized version of it, look a bit unsound? Yes, but we are all right in our argument, really. For the gas on the right of the partition should now be at a higher temperature than it was originally. When the partition vanished, the gas accelerated into the vacuum, achieved a kinetic energy as a whole mass. It had energy as a wind. It would not be long before that organized motion as a wind had died down, had been converted into the disorganized, each-for-himself motion of the individual molecules. If we insert the partition back in place, the right-hand compartment will have more than its share of wind; when the wind dies down, it will have more than its share of energy, will be at a higher temperature. But if we remove the partition once more, or if we never reinsert it, the final energy of random motion will be the same as the original. So will the final temperature.

One further point: The above argument assumes that there is no attractive force between one molecule and another. If there were, then the spreading out of the molecules, the increase in the average intermolecular distance, would involve the exerting of force through a distance, would involve the doing of work. It would involve a drop in temperature. Now in fact molecules do attract one another, and when the density of molecules is high, just such a temperature drop may be noted. We will have cause, therefore, to discuss Joule's experiment again, in a somewhat different form, for the case of attractive molecules, and the result will be quite different.

15.21 JOULE'S EXPERIMENT (THROTTLING) COMPARED WITH THE IMPACT TURBINE

Phenomena similar to those of the preceding section will arise when gas is forced continuously through a nozzle as a high-speed jet. Let us consider first the case of an impact turbine, as in Figure 15.20(a). To the left of the nozzle there is gas at high pressure moving slowly along a tube. To the right of the nozzle is a region of much lower pressure. Gas passing through the nozzle has high pressure behind it and low pressure ahead of it, and so it accelerates. A strong wind is set up.

Kinetic energy is proportional to the square of the velocity. The motion of the air to the left of the nozzle was slow, and the kinetic energy was negligible. The motion of the air in the jet is fast, and the kinetic energy of that fast-moving air is considerable. That energy came from what was previously energy of random motion. The added kinetic energy is balanced by a loss of thermal energy, energy of random motion,

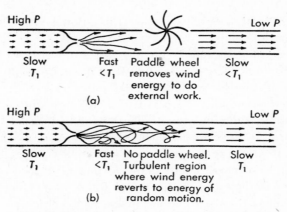

Fig. 15.20. Impact turbine (a) and throttling device (b).

and so the fast-moving air is slightly cooler than it was before its acceleration. If the fast-moving air strikes the blades of a rotating paddle wheel, it will be slowed down. If the paddle wheel is rotating at just the right speed, the air will be slowed down almost to zero speed. It will continue along the pipe slowly and still at a reduced temperature. The speed of the air beyond the paddle wheel must be greater than the speed before the nozzle, because it is at a lower pressure, but the motion will still be slow enough for its kinetic energy to be negligible. What happens is that some energy is converted from random to organized motion at the nozzle. The energy of organized motion is removed by the paddle wheel to do work somewhere outside the pipe. The air proceeds along the pipe with most of its energy of organized motion gone and with its energy of random motion slightly reduced.

Now suppose that the paddle wheel is removed from the system, as in Figure 15.20(b). The jet of high-speed air emerging into the low-pressure region to the right of the nozzle fails to maintain its organization. Its motion becomes turbulent. Eddies are set up, so that while the air is still moving rapidly, it is not all moving in the same direction. The motion becomes more and more confused until it is reduced to the every-molecule-on-its-own disorganization that we know as thermal motion. The only remaining organized motion is the steady flow that carries the air down the tube at a rate appropriate to the pressure existing in this part of the tube. Most of the energy that went from random to organized motion at the nozzle has reverted to random motion again. The temperature, which was lower while the air was moving fast, returns to practically its initial value.

The process just described, without any paddle wheel, as illustrated in Figure 15.20(b), is known as **throttling**. The remarks of the last paragraph of section 15.20 are again applicable. For gas with no attractive force between the molecules, the process is quite pointless. With real gases, however, where such forces do exist, the throttling process becomes one of great value. It is discussed at length in a later chapter. In practice, the single small orifice or nozzle is replaced by a many-orificed plug.

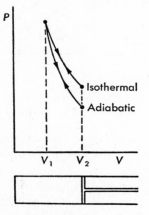

Fig. 15.21. Isotherms and adiabats are exactly reversible.

15.22 REVERSIBLE AND IRREVERSIBLE PROCESSES

The processes described in the preceding two sections are irreversible: one cannot arrange to have them proceed backward through exactly the same steps. On the other hand, the isothermal and adiabatic processes, for which we have set up equations, are exactly reversible. Suppose that a sample of gas is contained in a cylinder, one end of which is a movable piston. Suppose there is no heat transfer through the walls. If the piston is gradually withdrawn, the gas will expand adiabatically. If the piston is gradually moved into the cylinder the gas will contract, be compressed, adiabatically, and will go through all the same stages as during expansion, but in the reverse order (Figure 15.21). The amount of work done by the gas in expanding from V_1 to V_2 will exactly equal the amount of work done on the gas in compressing it from V_2 to V_1.

Or suppose that the walls of the cylinder are maintained at a temperature T_0 and there is good heat transfer from the walls to the gas. If the piston is gradually withdrawn, thermal energy will continually be lost by conversion to mechanical energy as work is done by the gas on the piston, but this loss will continually be compensated by a flow of heat from the walls, to maintain the temperature of the gas equal to that of the walls. If after withdrawal through some distance the motion is reversed and the piston begins to move into the cylinder, the work done on the gas appears as thermal energy, and as quickly as it appears flows to the walls, so that again the gas remains at the temperature of the walls.   The gas goes through exactly the same steps during compression as during expansion,

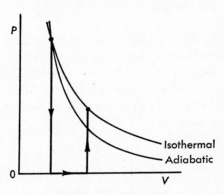

Fig. 15.22.   The bold line shows pressure *on the piston* during and after an instantaneous expansion.

but in the reverse order (again in Figure 15.21).   Exactly as much work is converted *into* heat at T_0 as was converted *from* heat at T_0. Both isothermal and adiabatic processes are exactly reversible.

Both isothermal and adiabatic processes are exactly reversible, but they are both impossible.   We can come close to achieving them, and the more effort we make and the more care we take the closer we can come.   But they are limiting cases, that can be approached and cannot be achieved, or to use other words, that can be achieved only in the limit.

What happens when an adiabatic expansion is attempted?   Usually in practice when one wants the expansion to be near adiabatic, the piston is pulled out rapidly, to minimize heat transfer by minimizing the time available for heat transfer.   Suppose that, going far beyond this, the piston were pulled out at a speed greater than that of most of the molecules.   Then, as in section 15.19, the gas would expand into a vacuum. A plot of the pressure *on the piston* against the volume of the container is shown in Figure 15.22.   Although the temperature of the gas will drop somewhat as thermal energy goes into energy of organized motion of the gas, or wind, the wind will die down in a few seconds, and its energy will revert to energy of random motion of the molecules.   Thus the final point will lie, not on the adiabatic curve through the initial point, but on the isothermal that passes through the initial point.   Note that the path drawn is that for the volume of the container, and the pressure on the piston. The curve for the gas cannot be drawn, because the pressure and temperature will not be the same in all parts of the container.

Now, we have been discussing an extreme case, but something of this effect will be felt for any speed of withdrawal of the piston. So in any case the path will tend to lie somewhat below the adiabatic curve, and then end at a final point slightly above the adiabatic (Figure 15.23). Although the path refers to the pressure on the piston, the final point is true also for the gas after the expansion has been completed and the wind that was set up has died down.

Suppose now that this attempted adiabatic expansion be followed by a similar effort at adiabatic compression. The pressure will tend to be higher against the piston than elsewhere. Even a perfectly adiabatic return would miss the initial point, for two adiabatics cannot intersect. But the practical approach will fall still wider of the mark. If the return stroke is ended a bit before the initial volume is reached, the end point can be made to fall on the isothermal passing through the initial point. The gas can then be brought to the initial point by compressing it isothermally, i.e., by converting mechanical work into heat at the initial temperature (Figure 15.23). Alternatively, the "adiabatic" compres-

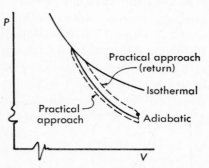

Fig. 15.23. Nature of practical attempts at adiabatic expansion, followed by compression.

sion could have been carried to the initial volume, and the return to the initial point achieved by cooling the gas at constant volume. Another alternative would be to carry the compression to the initial *pressure* and return to the initial point by cooling at constant volume. In any case, return to the initial point cannot be achieved by a practical approach to adiabatic processes alone, but requires in addition either some heat transfer or the conversion of some mechanical work into heat.

The practical process is irreversible, meaning not exactly reversible. It does not and cannot be made to carry the gas through the same points coming and going. The practical process involves an increase in entropy, for the final point of the practical expansion lies to the right of the adiabatic through the initial point. The same is true of the practical compression. Practical approaches to adiabatic expansions involve increases in entropy.   To bring the entropy of the gas back to its original value involves heat transfer or the conversion of mechanical work into heat, and this would increase the entropy of something else.

When an isothermal expansion is attempted, the same difficulties arise as with an attempted adiabatic expansion.   Consideration of these difficulties is more complicated because we lack the simplifying specification of zero heat flow.   Another form or facet of irreversibility now appears, however.   The concept of an exactly reversible isothermal involves a heat reservoir from which the gas receives heat during expansion and to which the gas gives heat during compression.   If the system is to be exactly reversible for a fixed temperature of the reservoir, heat must flow between two bodies at the same temperature.   Now in fact heat flows only from a hotter to a colder region, and so for this reason the practical approach to an isothermal expansion must fall below the line $T = T_0$, where T_0 is the temperature of the reservoir.   Similarly, the practical compression must fall above the line $T = T_0$, and so the practical approach to an isothermal cannot be exactly reversible.   In the case of an isothermal, one cannot comment on the increase in entropy during expansion alone, or during compression alone, for entropy changes along an isothermal.   But consider a cycle consisting of an expansion followed by a compression.   The heat transferred from the reservoir equals the work done, equals the area under the expansion curve, taking both terminal points on the line $T = T_0$ (Figure 15.24).   Let the compression proceed only until the work reconverted to heat equals the amount of work done by the gas during expansion, that is, until the area under the compression curve equals the area under the expansion curve.   Then the end of the cycle will be a point on the curve $T = T_0$ below the initial point, i.e., with the final volume greater than the initial volume.   The gas at this point has greater entropy than it had initially, and mechanical energy must be converted into heat to return the gas to its initial state.   The gas can be restored to its initial entropy value either by converting mechanical energy into heat or by cooling the gas until it reaches a point on the adiabatic through the initial point.

The temperature difference that must exist between reservoir and gas

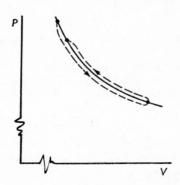

Fig. 15.24.   Nature of practical attempts at isothermal expansion, followed by compression.

is not the only relevant temperature difference. Unless the process is carried out infinitely slowly, or the conductivity or other heat transfer coefficient of the gas is infinitely high, there will be temperature gradients within the gas itself. This applies not only to the isothermal, but to any expansion or compression, and is related to the pressure differences and "wind" discussed in connection with the adiabatic case.

The situation during any change in the condition of the gas is complex, and there is danger of error through oversimplification in discussing it in detail as has been done here. It is safe to conclude, however, that any real expansion is irreversible. Any expansion cycle will return the gas to a state of greater entropy. The cycle can be completed to its starting point only by transferring heat across a temperature drop or by converting mechanical work into heat, and so increasing the entropy of some other region. The complexities of real expansions justify the consideration of the simpler exactly reversible processes, recognizing at the time that we are dealing with a limiting case that can be approached, closely if need be, but cannot be achieved.

PROBLEMS

1. Plot isothermal curves of P against $1/V$ for 1.00 gm nitrogen at temperatures 200, 400, 600, 800K, to a maximum pressure of 10 atm. and a minimum volume of 0.1 lit.

2. State the slope $(\Delta P/\Delta V)$ of an isothermal at temperature T_0 as a function of V, i.e., eliminate P from equations (15.11) and (15.01).

3. State the slope of the adiabatic locus through (P_0, V_0) as a function of V, i.e., eliminate P from equations (15.14) and (15.27).

4. Commencing at pressure 1.00 atm., temperature 0C, on a P/V plot for 1.00 mole of monatomic gas, you can approximate to an adiabatic step by increasing the volume 10% at constant pressure, then decreasing the pressure $\gamma \times 10\%$ at constant volume. Take ten such approximately adiabatic steps, and compare the final pressure with that obtained by substituting the final volume into the adiabatic relationship between P and V.

5. What is the condition (in terms of P and V) that the slope of an isothermal be exactly -1? Draw on a P/V plot the locus of all points meeting this condition. State the condition and draw the locus similarly for an adiabatic slope of exactly -1, taking $\gamma = \frac{5}{3}$.

6. Describe, with particular reference to a P/V diagram, the thermal processes of the experiment of Clément and Désormes. How does it make possible the determination of gamma? and how the number of degrees of freedom of the molecules involved?

7. If the initial gauge pressure in the experiment of Clément and Désormes is 10.0 cm water, what final pressure should be anticipated (a) for a monatomic gas, (b) for a diatomic gas?

8. A bottle of argon at 20C and gauge pressure 5.00 cm Hg is opened briefly to bring the pressure to 1.00 atm. It is closed again before the gas begins to warm. What final pressure will the gas reach when it returns to its initial temperature? What was the intermediate temperature?

9. A diatomic gas at 300K is heated 5.00 deg at constant volume V_0, then expanded adiabatically to its original pressure. What is its volume then?

10. A sample of diatomic gas has pressure 1000 mb, volume 5.000 liters. The volume is increased adiabatically by 50 cm³. By how much does the pressure drop, (a) according to equation (15.14) (which is accurate only in the limit when increments are very small), (b) according to (15.27)? Repeat for an increase in volume of 1.000 lit.

11. A sample of monatomic gas has volume 1.000 lit., pressure 1.000 atm., temperature 20C. By how much must the volume be increased to drop the temperature by 30 Centigrade degrees according to equation (15.30), in logarithmic form? By how much must the pressure be dropped for this same temperature change (15.31)? To check your work, substitute from your volume calculations into (15.26); you should obtain the same result regarding pressure.

12. Exactly one liter of monatomic gas is suddenly expanded to twice its volume and kept there. What is the pressure (a) immediately after the expansion, (b) after the gas has warmed again to its original temperature?

13. An aircraft was flying at an altitude of about 9 km (where the atmospheric pressure was 300 mb), with its cabin pressure maintained at 700 mb, temperature 20C. A window blew out, dropping the pressure adiabatically to 300 mb. Neglecting the effect of condensing vapor, to what value did the temperature drop? To what value would the pressure have returned when the temperature was restored to 20C if the window had been closed again before the temperature had recovered appreciably?

14. Given the general equation of state $PV = RT$, and the relation between P and V for an adiabatic expansion, derive relations between P and T, and between V and T, for an adiabatic expansion.

15. From what initial pressure must air at 20C be expanded so that adiabatic expansion to pressure 1.00 atm. reduces the temperature to 0C?

16. What work (in joules) is done by exactly one mole of gas expanding isothermally at temperature 27C from 5.00 lit. to 10.00 lit.? Plot the path of this expansion and measure the area under the curve to show, converting units if necessary, that this area equals the work done.

17. At a time when the atmospheric pressure at ground level is 1011.00 mb, that at the top of a building is 1003.00 mb. The temperature is 27C. What is

the height of the building? Take M_0 for air as 29.0 gm, and of course use equation (15.35).

18. A building is 100.0 m high. The doors at ground level are kept open, so that pressure at this level, inside and out, is 1.000 atm. Windows at all other levels are closed. The temperature is $-20C$ outdoors, $+20C$ indoors. What is the pressure at the top of the building (a) outside, (b) inside? What is the force on a window 1.000 m² at the top of the building, resulting from this pressure differential?

19. In an atmosphere all at temperature 0C, at what height is the pressure just half that at ground level according to equation (15.36)? What further height would effect a further reduction in pressure of factor two?

20. If at some height in the atmosphere the pressure decreases 1.40 % per hundred meters, what is the temperature? (Take M_0 for air = 29.0 gm.)

21. Calculate the dry adiabatic lapse rate, taking $\gamma = 1.40$ and $M_0 = 29.0$ gm for air.

16

Heat Engines and the
Laws of Thermodynamics

16.01 MUTUAL CONVERTIBILITY

The first law of thermodynamics states that *mechanical energy and heat are mutually convertible, the total energy remaining constant.* Now, we have been developing a picture of heat as a form of mechanical energy, as that form in which the energy is shared among a great many independently moving particles, indeed among the independent "degrees of freedom" of those particles. It seems reasonable, therefore, that when energy is transformed from the energy of organized mechanical motion (normally referred to by us as "mechanical energy") to the energy of disorganized motion that we call heat, the transformation should be on the basis of an erg for an erg (or one calorie for 4.18×10^7 ergs, where the calorie is a unit based on the properties of water). If one erg of mechanical energy is transformed to heat, it should become one erg of heat. If one erg of heat energy is transformed to mechanical energy, it should become one erg of mechanical energy.

The fact that mechanical energy *can* be converted into heat energy is common knowledge. Such conversion goes on all around us. Whenever we try to maintain mechanical motion, we find it gradually degenerating into the random motion whose energy we call heat. The energy of rotation of a rotating flywheel is gradually lost as heat is generated in the bearings. The kinetic energy of a bullet is gradually spent in heating the bullet and the air around it. When the bullet strikes armor plate, there is a sudden conversion into heat of the remaining kinetic energy.

Heat energy can be converted into mechanical energy, too. We have noted how gas molecules bouncing against a receding piston lose some of their heat energy, and of course the motion of the piston can be accelerated thereby.

16.02 LIMITED CONVERTIBILITY

Unfortunately, we cannot take a certain mass of gas and transform *all* of its heat into mechanical energy. The energy of random motion of the air around us is considerable. The energy of the air passing through the radiator of a car is more than enough to propel the car. Why buy gasoline? Because *the transformation of heat energy into mechanical energy is only possible when temperature differences exist, and to the extent that the absolute temperatures differ.* The demonstration of this statement is the major aim of this chapter.

Fig. 16.01. Velocity vectors for a random array of particles.

Before entering into our logical development, let us just glance at a kinetic picture of what we are about. If you have an unlimited supply of randomly moving particles, with everywhere the same average energy per particle (Figure 16.01), there is no device for converting the energy of those particles into organized energy: the energy of a piston or a wheel. (No self-acting device, that is.) If, however, you have one isolated region where the average energy is higher (Figure 16.02) or lower (Figure 16.03),

Fig. 16.02. Velocity vectors for a random array of particles containing a region where average energy is *higher* than elsewhere.

Fig. 16.03. Velocity vectors for a random array of particles containing a region where average energy is *lower* than elsewhere.

then in the process of bringing the average energy of the particles in the isolated region to the same value as the average energy over-all, one can produce mechanical energy equal to the change in energy of random motion. The device by which we accomplish this conversion is called a **heat engine.**

This limitation to temperature differences in extracting organized mechanical motion from heat has a profound effect on the engineering design of heat engines. Usually, when an engineer designs a machine, he aims at an efficiency of 100%, at getting work out of the machine at the same rate at which it goes in. When he designs an electric motor, he aims at an output in mechanical power approaching the input in electrical power. The efficiency of 100% will never be reached, but it is the limit which, by paring down the various losses, he may approach. The difference between the work in and out appears as heat energy, evolved by friction or in the case of the electric motor by electrical resistance. One can keep whittling away at these losses almost indefinitely, especially if expensive construction can be justified. There will always be such losses, but the limit approached, asymptotically if you like, is 100% efficiency.

Now when an engineer designs a heat engine, i.e., any device for converting heat energy into organized mechanical motion, he no longer aims at 100%, even as an upper limit. Instead, he has a quite definite theoretically imposed upper limit, $(T_1 - T_2)/T_1$, where T_1 and T_2 are the highest and lowest temperatures available to him. As the engineer goes about his normal pursuit of efficiency, reducing friction and waste, it is this limit of $(T_2 - T_1)/T_1$ that he approaches, in the case of heat engines, and not 100%.

The aim of this chapter is to establish the existence of this upper limit. The heat engine that will be discussed is quite "out of this world" so far as practice is concerned, but it is a most convenient one for theoretical discussion. Its working substance, too, is chosen for ease of discussion rather than practicability: a gas obeying the relation $PV = RT$.

16.03 THEORETICALLY SIMPLE HEAT ENGINE

The expansion of a gas against a receding piston or turbine blade is the usual device for converting heat, the energy of random motion, into organized mechanical energy. The expansion converts the heat energy of the gas into mechanical energy of the engine and any machine attached to it. The heat energy of the gas is replenished by the transfer of heat, as heat, to the gas from a source of heat, or by the transformation of chemical energy into heat energy by burning in the gas itself.

For the derivation of general theorems about heat engines, one wants the design of engine most conveniently treated on paper, not the design best adapted for practical operation. The *Carnot engine* (Sadi Carnot, 1796) meets this requirement. So we take a cylinder containing, as "working substance", one mole of gas obeying the relation $PV = RT$. The side walls of the cylinder and the piston sliding freely in it are of a material that does not conduct heat at all (Figure **16.04**). The thin end wall conducts heat readily. This end wall may be pressed against the "source": a body which is a good conductor and is maintained somehow at a temperature T_1. Heat will then flow between the source and the working substance until the latter is also at temperature T_1. Alternatively the end wall may be pressed against the "sink": a body which is a good conductor and is maintained at a temperature T_2, where T_2 is less than T_1. As a third choice, the end wall may be pressed against a nonconducting block, so that the working substance is completely surrounded by nonconducting walls.

There must be more to the engine than is described above, although it is found convenient not to describe it, nor even to work it out. There must be machinery to the right of the cylinder, connected to the piston rod, to accept the work done by the expanding gas, and to effect whatever force on the piston we may require in order that the gas shall pass through a specified cycle.

Just for convenience, let us impose two further conditions on our model of the Carnot engine: a maximum permissible pressure and a maximum available volume. All this is represented in Figure 16.04.

16.04 THE CARNOT CYCLE

Let us start at the point A, Figure 16.04, i.e., at maximum temperature and pressure. On the assumption that it is desirable to have a minimum drop in temperature, let us expand the gas along the isotherm $T = T_1$, recognizing as we do that we are taking the limiting case, which can be approached but never actually achieved. If we follow the isotherm to maximum volume at B', the gas will do mechanical work equal to the area under the line AB', or $RT_1 \ln (V_{B'}/V_A)$, according to equation (15.33), and in so doing will remove just this much energy as heat from the source.

So far, all the heat that has been removed from the source has been converted into work, without any waste. But what can we do now? We have reached our arbitrarily specified maximum volume. Even without that limitation, the volume cannot go on increasing forever. We want our engine to keep on with the job of conversion, and it can keep on indefinitely only if we plan a cycle of operations that can be repeated indefinitely. We must judge our engine by what it can do in a complete cycle, and to complete the cycle the gas must be returned to A. The path along which the gas expanded is an isotherm at the temperature of the source, an exactly reversible cycle, and so we could return to A by the very same path. But the amount of work done on the gas during this return trip, and so restored to the source as heat, would be exactly equal to the amount done by the gas from A' to B. We would end up at A with no waste, but with no work done.

The purpose of the sink at temperature T_2 is to permit a return path requiring less work. We should drop down to C, then, and return with less work at the lower temperature T_2. If with the gas at B' we put it in contact with the sink, the gas will follow the line $B'C$, doing no work but giving up a considerable fraction of its heat, across a considerable temperature drop, until its temperature is equal to that of the sink. But we can do better. Suppose that when the expansion has reached the point B we replace the source by the nonconducting block. Then the expansion proceeds adiabatically to C, cooling it to do work (area under BC). The flow of heat across a temperature drop is thus avoided.

Now we must reduce the volume, proceeding along a path lower down than CBA, so that less work will be reinvested than has been brought out. Again assuming that heat flow across a temperature drop is to be avoided, let us put the gas in direct contact with the sink and follow the isotherm $T = T_2$, again recognizing that this is the limiting case that can be approached but never exactly realized.

All the time that we are compressing along the line $T = T_2$, we are not only doing work on the gas but also discharging that work as heat from the gas into the sink. To keep the loss of heat to a minimum, let us turn off the isotherm $T = T_2$ as soon as we reach an adiabat (line of zero heat transfer) that will carry the gas back to A. That is to say, when we reach D, let us replace the sink by the nonconducting end-block and continue the compression. This route does not involve the minimum of work done on the gas, but once we turn onto the adiabatic, all the work that is done on the gas stays with the gas as heat.

The route $ABCD$ is known as the Carnot heat-engine cycle. It is an exactly reversible cycle, made up of exactly reversible processes. In those parts of the cycle where heat is transferred, it is transferred across zero temperature drop. The work done by the gas during expansion is equal to the area under the line ABC; the work done on the gas during compression is equal to the area under the line ADC; the net work done by the gas is the difference of these, or the area enclosed by the line $ABCDA$.

16.05 EQUATIONS OF THE CARNOT CYCLE

From A to B, during isothermal expansion, the amount of heat transferred to the gas equals the work done by the gas, given by the area

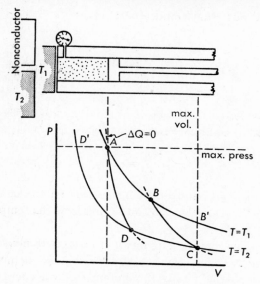

Fig. 16.04. Carnot engine. *ABCDA* is Carnot cycle.

under the curve or by equation (15.33) as

$$Q_1 = RT_1 \ln \frac{V_B}{V_A} \qquad (16.01)$$

From B to C the amount of heat transferred to the gas is zero. The adiabatic relation between volume and temperature, equation (15.30), relates V_B and V_C to T_1 and T_2:

$$V_B{}^{\gamma-1}T_1 = V_C{}^{\gamma-1}T_2 \qquad (16.02)$$

From C to D, during isothermal compression, the amount of heat transferred to the sink equals the work done on the gas, given by the area under the curve. Using relation (15.33) again, we would obtain a negative quantity, the work done *by* the gas. Inserting a factor -1 to change this to work done *on* the gas, we have

$$Q_2 = -RT_2 \ln \frac{V_D}{V_C} = RT_2 \ln \frac{V_C}{V_D} \qquad (16.03)$$

From D to A the amount of heat transferred is zero, and the adiabatic relation is

$$V_D{}^{\gamma-1}T_2 = V_A{}^{\gamma-1}T_1 \qquad (16.04)$$

Combining relations (16.02) and (16.04) gives

$$\frac{V_B}{V_C} = \left(\frac{T_2}{T_1}\right)^{\frac{1}{\gamma-1}} = \frac{V_A}{V_D}$$

$$\frac{V_B}{V_A} = \frac{V_C}{V_D} \tag{16.05}$$

Therefore the logarithmic factors in (16.01) and (16.03) are equal, and (16.01) and (16.03) combined become

$$\frac{Q_1}{T_1} = \frac{Q_2}{T_2} \tag{16.06}$$

That is to say, the heat removed from the source is to the temperature of the source as the heat transferred to the sink is to the temperature of the sink.

Let a heat engine remove a quantity of heat Q_1 from a source (at temperature T_1) and transfer quantity Q_2 to a sink (at a temperature T_2). Then Q_2 will be less than Q_1 by the amount of heat energy transformed into mechanical energy, or in equation form,

$$\text{Heat transformed to mechanical energy} = Q_1 - Q_2$$

The **efficiency** of any heat engine is defined as

$$\frac{\text{Heat transformed}}{\text{Heat removed from source}} = \frac{Q_1 - Q_2}{Q_1} \tag{16.07}$$

Now for the case of the Carnot cycle, the Q's are related to the T's by equation (16.06). Combining (16.06) and (16.07), we obtain for *the efficiency of the Carnot cycle*

$$\left[\frac{Q_1 - Q_2}{Q_1}\right]_{\text{Carnot}} = \frac{T_1 - T_2}{T_1} \tag{16.08}$$

16.06 HEAT PUMPS

To achieve a Carnot cycle (or any other cycle) from T_1 to T_2, it is not necessary that T_2 be less than T_1. If T_2 is greater than T_1, then on reaching the point B the process along the adiabatic must be compression rather than expansion, with subsequent processes similarly reversed (Figure 16.05). The derivation of equation (16.06) does not require $T_2 < T_1$, and still holds if $T_2 > T_1$. The counterclockwise cycle, achieved when the region to which heat is transferred is hotter than the region from which it is withdrawn, is known as a "heat-pump" cycle: $ABCDA$ is a heat-engine cycle, converting some heat into work and transferring some heat to a region of lower temperature; ABC_rD_rA is a heat-pump cycle, converting some work into heat and transferring some heat to a region of higher temperature. The cycle $ADCBA$, taken in that direction, is another heat-pump cycle. It is the exact reverse of $ABCDA$. If one trip around $ABCDA$ were followed by one in the reverse direction $ADCBA$, the over-all change would be zero: no work done, no heat transferred.

We will let Q_1 denote heat withdrawn from a region at temperature T_1, and Q_2 heat transferred to a region at T_2, no matter which temperature is higher. Then the net amount of heat converted into work during a cycle will be $W = Q_1 - Q_2$. If $T_1 > T_2$, then $Q_1 > Q_2$, and W is positive; if $T_1 < T_2$, then W is negative.

Every electrical refrigerator is a heat pump, in which mechanical energy provided by an electrical motor, in being transformed to heat, carries with it heat out of a low-temperature region into a high-temperature region. The **coefficient of performance** of a refrigerator is the ratio of the heat removed from the cooler region to the work done in removing it,

$$\text{C.O.P.} = \frac{Q_1}{-W} = \frac{Q_1}{Q_2 - Q_1} \quad (16.09)$$

and for a Carnot cycle,

$$\text{C.O.P.} = \frac{T_1}{T_2 - T_1} \quad (16.10)$$

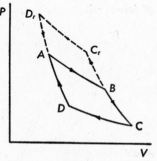

Fig. 16.05. Carnot engine and pump cycles.

$ABCDA$: engine cycle
ABC_rD_rA: pump cycle
$ADCBA$: pump cycle

If the requirements are $T_1 = 273$ and $T_2 = 300$, the coefficient of performance is about ten. Practical cycles, especially of the small size of home refrigerators, have considerably lower coefficients of performance.

Increasing attention is now being paid to the use of heat pumps for heating, so that only part of the heat released in a house or other building is bought and paid for, and the rest is pumped out of the large less-hot reservoir out of doors. The relevant coefficient for a heat pump used for heating is of course the ratio of the heat obtained (at high temperature) to the mechanical energy put in, sometimes called the **heating energy ratio:**

$$\text{H.E.R.} = \frac{Q_2}{Q_2 - Q_1} \quad (16.11)$$

For a Carnot cycle,

$$\text{H.E.R.} = \frac{T_2}{T_2 - T_1} \qquad (16.12)$$

Again factors of about ten are theoretically possible. Figures quoted from actual installations are more like three. Even so, the electrical energy that must be fed into a heat pump to deliver a unit of heat to a heating system is just one-third as much as must be fed into an immersion heater, say, to produce the same effect.

16.07 IRREVERSIBLE APPROACHES TO THE CARNOT CYCLE

Having drawn a Carnot cycle on a P/V plot, let us sketch the sort of irreversible cycle that would be achieved if the Carnot cycle were

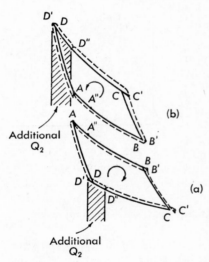

attempted. Starting at A in Figure 16.06(a), let us transfer to the gas as much heat (Q_1) as was transferred in the true isothermal. In line with previous discussion of possible approaches to isothermal expansions (section 15.22), the path will fall somewhat below the locus $T = T_1$, and so must be carried further to have the same area under it and therefore the same Q_1; thus B' will be at greater volume than B. Similarly, C' will be at greater volume than C, the volume difference in this case being greater.

Now if in the isothermal compression the same Q_2 were used as in the reversible cycle, the path would reach some point D'' short of D, from which A'' would be reached at considerably greater volume than the initial A.

Fig. 16.06. The nature of practical approaches to Carnot heat-engine (a) and heat-pump (b) cycles.

Return to A would then involve conversion of work into heat at temperature T_1. Instead, let us use a larger Q_2, large enough for the subsequent approach to an adiabatic to complete the cycle to the initial point A. The cycle has been completed by making the amount of heat discharged into the sink (Q_2) greater, and so the amount converted into work ($Q_1 - Q_2$) less. So, for the possible approach to the Carnot cycle, in the direction of a heat engine,

$$\frac{Q_2}{T_2} > \frac{Q_1}{T_1} \tag{16.13}$$

and the efficiency

$$\frac{Q_1 - Q_2}{Q_1} < \frac{T_1 - T_2}{T_1} \tag{16.14}$$

Similarly, for a possible approach in the direction of a heat pump, Figure 16.06 (b), if we put into the gas the same heat Q_1 from the cold region as for the reversible cycle, Q_2 must be made larger to complete the cycle counterclockwise to A. And so again, for the possible heat-pump cycle as for the possible heat-engine cycle,

$$\frac{Q_1}{T_1} < \frac{Q_2}{T_2} \tag{16.15}$$

The coefficient of performance for a possible refrigerator will be

$$\frac{Q_1}{Q_2 - Q_1} < \frac{T_1}{T_2 - T_1} = \left[\frac{Q_1}{Q_2 - Q_1}\right]_{\text{Carnot}} \tag{16.16}$$

and the heating energy ratio

$$\frac{Q_2}{Q_2 - Q_1} < \frac{T_2}{T_2 - T_1} = \left[\frac{Q_2}{Q_2 - Q_1}\right]_{\text{Carnot}} \tag{16.17}$$

At the end of a cycle, the entropy of the gas is the same as in the beginning. But during one cycle, the source loses entropy Q_1/T_1, the sink gains Q_2/T_2, and so

$$\text{Increase in entropy, whole system} = \frac{Q_2}{T_2} - \frac{Q_1}{T_1} \tag{16.18}$$

Here the "whole system" includes source, working substance, and sink. So any possible approach to a Carnot cycle, either as a heat engine or as a heat pump, involves an increase in the entropy of the system, whereas in the limiting case of the exactly reversible cycle there is no change in the entropy of the system.

16.08 GREATEST POSSIBLE HEAT-ENGINE EFFICIENCY

An insight into the behavior of exactly reversible cycles may be obtained from the hypothetical apparatus pictured in Figure 16.07.

A heat engine (Carnot cycle) working between a hot reservoir a at temperature T_a and a cold reservoir b at temperature T_b is mechanically coupled to a heat pump with the same cycle in reverse. Then unit heat flowing from a into the engine leads to a flow of heat T_b/T_a into b and work $(T_a - T_b)/T_a$ into the pump. This is just enough work, applied to the reverse Carnot cycle, to remove heat T_b/T_a from b and add unit heat to a. So we have a sort of perpetual motion. No fuel is used, there is no net loss of heat from a or b, yet the machine keeps going.

We obtain this result only because we neglected in our theoretical engines all friction and all heat leakage. Even then, we obtain this result only in the limit: This is only the result that we approach more and more closely as the rate of working is reduced, as the actual paths of Figure 16.06 (the broken lines) approach more and more closely to true

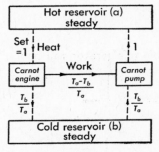

Fig. 16.07. Carnot engine driving Carnot pump results in no *output* of work and no net heat transfer.

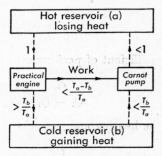

Fig. 16.08. Practical engine driving Carnot pump results in no output of work but transfers heat from hot to cold.

isothermals and adiabats (the solid lines). In Figure 16.08 the Carnot engine is replaced by a practical engine, while the Carnot pump remains as it was. With this arrangement b receives more heat. The pump, receiving less work, removes less heat from b, and adds less heat to a. We no longer have perpetual motion, even if the mechanical parts are friction-free, for the continued motion is at the expense of a continuing transfer of heat from the hot reservoir a to the cold reservoir b.

Now suppose that there were such a thing as a heat engine working between temperatures T_a and T_b with efficiency greater than that of the Carnot cycle. If this were used in place of the Carnot-cycle heat engine, the situation would be as shown in Figure 16.09. Whenever unit heat is removed from a, less than T_b/T_a is transferred to b and more than $(T_a - T_b)/T_a$ is transferred as work to the heat pump. Now work $(T_a - T_b)/T_a$ applied to the heat pump will extract T_b/T_a from b and deliver unit heat to a. Therefore work more than $(T_a - T_b)/T_a$ will remove more than T_b/T_a from the sink and deliver more to the source. So we would have a machine without any outside source of power conveying heat from one body to another at a higher temperature.

An alternative form of the machine would deliver just enough mechanical energy to the heat pump to maintain zero net flow of heat from a. That would provide mechanical power, available for doing outside work, without any transfer of heat from a to b. That is to say,

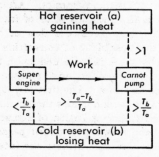

Fig. 16.09. Better-than-Carnot "super" engine driving Carnot pump results here in no output of work but transfers heat from cold to hot without any *input* of work.

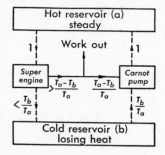

Fig. 16.10. Better-than-Carnot "super" engine driving Carnot pump can alternatively transform heat from the cold reservoir into mechanical work without any net transfer of heat from the hot reservoir.

the only transfer of heat would be from the cold reservoir, and it would all be going into mechanical energy (Figure 16.10).

Now, such things do not happen. You know that from experience. The second law of thermodynamics says that such things don't happen. Regarding that law, we will quote Zemansky:*

No engine has ever been developed that converts the heat extracted from one reservoir into work without rejecting some heat to a reservoir at a lower temperature. This negative statement, which is the result of everyday experience, constitutes the second law of thermodynamics and has been formulated in several ways. The original statement of Kelvin is "It is impossible by means of an inanimate material agency to derive mechanical effect from any portion of matter by cooling it below the temperature of the coldest of the surrounding objects". In the words of Planck, "It is impossible to construct an engine

* Mark W. Zemansky, *Heat and Thermodynamics*, 3rd Ed., Copyright 1951 McGraw-Hill Book Company, Inc.

which, working in a complete cycle, will produce no effect other than the raising of a weight and the cooling of a heat reservoir". We may combine these statements into one equivalent statement, to which we shall refer hereafter as the Kelvin-Planck statement of the second law, thus: *It is impossible to construct an engine that, operating in a cycle, will produce no effect other than the extraction of heat from a reservoir and the performance of an equivalent amount of work.*

If the second law were not true, it would be possible to drive a steamship across the ocean by extracting heat from the ocean or to run a power plant by extracting heat from the surrounding air. The student should notice that neither of these "impossibilities" violates the first law of thermodynamics. After all, both the ocean and the surrounding air contain an enormous store of internal energy, which, in principle, may be extracted in the form of a flow of heat. There is nothing in the first law to preclude the possibility of converting this heat completely into work. The second law, therefore, is not a deduction from the first but stands by itself as a separate law of nature, referring to an aspect of nature different from that contemplated by the first law. The first law denies the possibility of creating or destroying energy; the second denies the possibility of utilizing energy in a particular way. The continual operation of a machine that creates its own energy and thus violates the first law is called *perpetual motion of the first kind.* The operation of a machine that utilizes the internal energy of only one heat reservoir, thus violating the second law, is called *perpetual motion of the second kind.*

Our argument about a heat engine driving a heat pump operating around exactly the same cycle applies, not just to the Carnot cycle, but to any exactly reversible cycle. If no cycle can be more efficient than an exactly reversible cycle, then no particular exactly reversible cycle can be any more efficient than any other exactly reversible cycle operating between the same temperatures. Thus all exactly reversible cycles must have the same efficiency in terms of temperature. We know that one exactly reversible cycle, the Carnot cycle, has efficiency

$$\left[\frac{Q_1 - Q_2}{Q_1} \right]_{Carnot} = \frac{T_1 - T_2}{T_1} \qquad \text{[equation (16.08)]}$$

Apparently, then, this is the efficiency of any exactly reversible cycle working between temperatures T_1 and T_2. This efficiency,

$$\left[\frac{Q_1 - Q_2}{Q_1} \right]_{reversible} = \frac{T_1 - T_2}{T_1}$$

is an upper limit to the efficiency that can be achieved in practice, an upper limit that may be approached as closely as we are prepared to make the effort, but that cannot be exactly achieved.

To revert to the form used in the introductory portion of this chapter, the heat energy of a quantity of matter at T_1 can be converted into mechanical work only to the extent that will reduce the temperature of that matter to the temperature of its surroundings.

If equation (16.08) is applicable to any exactly reversible cycle, then so is (16.06). For any exactly reversible cycle, the quantities of heat transferred are related to the temperature by

$$\frac{Q_1}{T_1} = \frac{Q_2}{T_2} \qquad \text{[equation (16.06)]}$$

This is the relation that can be approached only in the limit; for any practical cycle, as stated previously,

$$\frac{Q_1}{T_1} < \frac{Q_2}{T_2} \qquad \text{[equation (16.15)]}$$

16.09 THE TEMPERATURES AND EFFICIENCIES OF PRACTICAL ENGINES

Reciprocating steam engines tend to work from input temperatures less than 200C. If the exhaust steam is discharged at atmospheric pressure, the discharge temperature is about 100C. Use of cooling water in a condenser reduces the discharge temperature to between 30C and 50C. In compound engines, the total temperature drop is shared among two or three or four separate expansions. Large steam turbines can accept heat at as high a temperature as 600C, but the pressure of steam is then inconveniently high, and other desirable attributes of steam as a working substance have diminished. In discussing temperatures it should be noted that, by heat exchange within a practical heat engine, it is possible to make heat available during parts of the cycle at temperatures other than the input temperature.

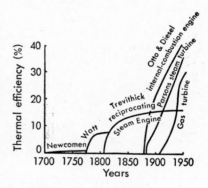

Fig. 16.11. Heat-engine efficiency over the years. (After M. W. Thring, "Revolution in Fuel Technology", *Journal of the Institute of Fuel*, Vol. XXVII, No. 163, August 1954. Liberties have been taken with Professor Thring's curve for the gas turbine.)

In internal-combustion engines, the heat is produced by burning within the working substance (air) itself; the metal of the engine does not have to withstand continually the full temperature of the working substance, and so higher temperatures can be used. The exhaust temperature is also higher, however. Thus, for a large diesel engine, T_1 and T_2 might be 1800K and 800K. Gas turbines have until recently been limited to an input temperature of about 1000K, the limit imposed by the temperature that the turbine blades can endure. Cooling the blades permits an input temperature a few hundred degrees higher. The output temperature is somewhat above atmospheric. Figure 16.11 shows the development in thermal efficiency over the years.

PROBLEMS

1. Assume that the radiator, area 0.200 m², of an automobile traveling 100 km hr⁻¹, scoops up all the air in its path. If all the energy of random motion of this air ($\frac{5}{2}RT$ per 22.42 lit., $T = 273$K) could be converted to energy of organized motion, what is the rate at which such energy would be obtained?

2. How much energy is transformed from thermal to mechanical when 1000 joules of heat enter a Carnot engine cycle working between temperatures 500K and 300K?

3. How much heat is transferred to the sink at 50C when 1000 joules of heat enter a Carnot engine cycle at 200C?

4. A Carnot engine cycle operates between 400C and 30C. Heat enters the cycle at a rate of 100,000 joules per minute. At what rate, in kilowatts, is mechanical energy produced?

5. It requires 418,000 joules to raise the temperature of 1 lit. of water in an electric kettle from 0C to 100C. Assume that the transformation of mechanical energy to electrical, the transmission of the electrical energy, and its transfer to the water are all perfectly efficient. Then how much heat must enter a Carnot engine cycle at the generating plant to achieve this heating, if the cycle operates between 400C and 30C?

6. For a Carnot pump cycle operating between 0.0C and 30.0C, how much mechanical energy is required to produce 1.00 joule of heat at 30.0C? How much mechanical energy is required to remove 1.00 joule of heat from the region at 0C? What is the "coefficient of performance" of the cycle considered as a refrigerator? What is the "heating energy ratio" of the cycle considered as a heating plant?

7. Explain with the help of a plot of P against V the Carnot cycle, indicating in words and on the diagram the manner in which practical cycles depart from the limiting case. Indicate this departure both for the engine cycle and the reverse or heat-pump cycle.

8. A house is heated by hot-water radiators at 70.0C. The power required to maintain these radiators at this temperature by immersion heaters is 5.00 kw.

What power would be required if a heat pump were used, working to a Carnot cycle and drawing its heat from water at 0.0C?

9. The conversion of 1.000 m³ of water at 0.00C to ice at 0.00C requires the removal of 333,600 joules of heat. What work must be done on a heat pump working to a Carnot cycle, if the lowest naturally occurring temperature at which heat can be disposed of is 20.00C? if it is 5.00C?

10. One U.S. gallon of fuel oil weighs 3.50 kgm and on combustion provides 45,000 joules of heat per gram. How much mechanical energy must be invested in a Carnot heat-pump cycle operating between 0.0C and 40.0C to provide as much heat at the latter temperature as 1 gallon of fuel oil? How much heat would this remove from the 0.0C region? If this heat came from the freezing of water (334 joules per gram), how much water would be frozen, in kilograms? in gallons?

11. Heat obtained by burning fuel enters a Carnot engine cycle operating between 300C and 50C. The mechanical energy produced drives a Carnot heat-pump cycle operating between 0.0C and 40.0C. How many joules of heat are provided at 40.0C for every one invested at 300C?

17

Sizable and Attractive Molecules

17.01 DEPARTURE FROM BOYLE'S LAW

The kinetic-theory "explanation" of the relation found experimentally, PV = constant, was derived for particles of negligible size and having no intermolecular forces. Careful experimental study over a wide range of pressures and temperatures reveals departures from Boyle's Law, departures that can be explained by taking account of the appreciable sizes of the molecules and of attractive forces among them.

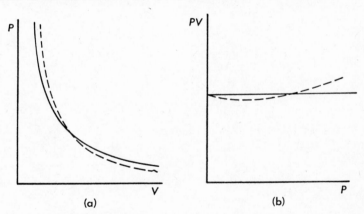

Fig. 17.01. Nature of departures of actual gases (broken lines) from $PV = RT$ (solid lines).

The departures of a gas from Boyle's Law can be studied on a graph of P/V, as shown in Figure 17.01(a). On this graph, Boyle's Law will give a rectangular hyperbola, and the curve for a real gas will depart somewhat from this. The departures from Boyle's Law are most readily seen, however, on a graph of PV/P, Figure 17.01(b). On this graph, Boyle's Law gives a straight horizontal line (a different straight line for every temperature); departures from this straight line are readily observed.

A PV/P graph for hydrogen is shown in Figure 17.02. It is typical of most gases in that at low temperatures PV drops at first with increasing P, then rises, but at high temperatures it increases with P right from the start at zero pressure. There is an intermediate temperature where the gas comes very close to obeying Boyle's Law. The temperature at which PV is most constant may be referred to as the "Boyle Temperature". Similar changes occur in the behavior of other gases as we go from low to high temperatures. But whereas hydrogen displays its low-temperature characteristics at $-200C$ and below, carbon dioxide displays them at

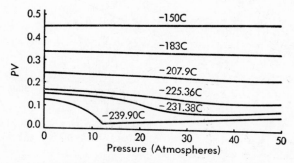

Fig. 17.02. The behavior of hydrogen. (From Mark W. Zemansky, *Heat and Thermodynamics*, 3rd Ed., Copyright 1951, McGraw-Hill Book Company, Inc.)

$+200C$, and for most gases room temperature qualifies as a "low temperature" in that as the pressure rises, the product PV first drops, then rises. In Figure 17.03 we compare the behavior of different gases, all at the same temperature. At low pressures all the gases are seen to approach the value of PV per mole of an ideal gas.

Now, to connect the departures from Boyle's Law with the size of molecules and their intermolecular attractions, consider the lowest curve of Figure 17.02. The effect of intermolecular attractions should be to make the gas *more* compressible than a perfect gas. This effect predominates in the left-hand part of the curve. But as the pressure increases, the volume of the gas decreases, and the volume occupied by the molecules themselves becomes relatively more significant. Its effect should be to make the gas *less* compressible than a perfect gas, and it evidently predominates in the right-hand part of the curve. The two effects counteract each other at the minimum. The equation of state, $PV = RT$, has been modified by van der Waals (1837) to account for the two effects. He replaced V by $(V - b)$ where b, the "co-volume", represented the reduction in accessible volume due to the presence of the molecules. The intermolecular forces are considered to increase as the square of the

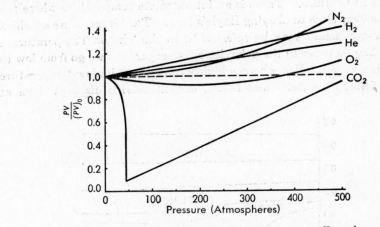

Fig. 17.03. The behavior of various gases all at the same temperature. (From A. G. Worthing and D. Halliday, *Heat*, John Wiley & Sons, Inc., New York, 1948. A broken line has been added to show the behavior that a gas would have if it remained "ideal" at all pressures.)

density, and density is inversely proportional to volume, so he replaced P by $P + (a/V^2)$ and so obtained the relation:

$$\left(P + \frac{a}{V^2}\right)(V - b) = RT$$

in which a and b are (positive) constants for any particular gas. If we take $b = 0$ to study the effect of the term a/V^2, we find that PV *decreases* with increasing pressure (decreasing volume) for all values of P. If we take $a = 0$ to study the effect of the term b, we find that PV *increases* with increasing pressure for all values of P. Kinetic-theory explanations of these terms are possible, and interesting, but tend to be confusing. Van der Waals' equation does represent fairly well the chief phenomena of gases (and liquids). More exact results can be obtained by treating a and b, assumed by van der Waals to be constants, as parameters varying gradually with the temperature.

17.02 THE THROTTLING PROCESS

The effect of forcing air through a small orifice was discussed in section 15.21. The same comments could be made about the passage of air through a many-orificed plug, a procedure known as **throttling**. In dealing now with the throttling of gases consisting of sizable and attractive molecules, a new approach will be convenient. Rather than considering in detail the behavior of the gas as it accelerates and then becomes turbulent, we will consider the process in terms of the pressure, density, and temperature, before and after throttling. Imagine a cylinder closed by a piston at each end, and somewhere between the pistons a porous plug (Figure 17.04). A large pressure difference can be maintained across the plug as gas is forced gradually through it. For a start, let us imagine the walls of the cylinder to be good conductors of heat, and the whole device to be surrounded by a constant-temperature bath. (This is a point of difference between the imaginary device and actual throttling experiments, but a considerable convenience to our argument.)

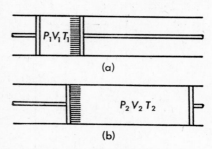

Fig. 17.04. A sample of gas passes through a porous plug. The regions to left and right of the plug are maintained at constant high and low pressures by appropriate motion of the pistons.

Now suppose that a certain mass of gas to the left of the plug has a high pressure P_1 and volume V_1, as shown by Figure 17.04 (a), and that by manipulating the pistons it is forced through the plug to the region to the right of the piston, where its pressure P_2 is several times less than P_1 and its volume is greater than V_1, Figure 17.04(b). What transfers and transformations of energy have occurred?

(a) The left piston, advancing on the gas, has done work P_1V_1 on the gas. (That is, this much energy has been transferred from the piston to the gas and has been transformed from organized mechanical energy of the machine to heat energy of the gas.)

(b) The right piston, retreating before the gas, has had work P_2V_2 done on it. (This is just the reverse sort of interchange to that above.)

(c) The molecules of the gas have been spaced more widely from each other; if any attractive forces exist between them, then work has been done against those forces.   The expanded gas can, as a result, be looked on as having potential energy like that of a stretched spring.

(d) In case there has been any tendency for the mean energy per degree of freedom of the molecules to increase or decrease, i.e., any tendency for the temperature to rise or fall, there will have been a flow of heat energy through the walls to or from the constant-temperature bath, preventing any change in the temperature of the gas.

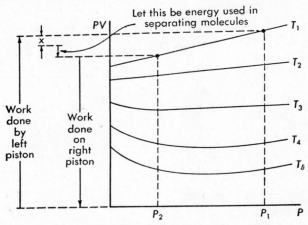

Fig. 17.05. The throttling process, when surrounded by a constant-temperature bath.   The amount of energy that must have been released as heat and that flowed out of the gas into the bath is represented as x.   If a greater amount of energy had been required to separate the molecules, x might have been negative.

In Figure 17.05, typical isothermal plots of PV against P are given for five different temperatures.   Along the left side of the figure, the energy transfers for our throttling experiment are indicated for the isothermal $T = T_1$.   Since PV drops along this isothermal with decreasing pressure, the work done by the gas on the low-pressure (right) piston is considerably less than the work done on the gas by the high-pressure (left) piston. The "profit" may be sufficient to do the "internal" work of separating the molecules against intermolecular forces, and still have some heat energy (x in Figure 17.05) to spare.   In our hypothetical isothermal experiment, this excess will be transferred to the surrounding bath.

If the experiment had been performed at temperature $T = T_3$ or thereabouts, the final value of PV would have been equal to the initial value.   (Here, then, is the Boyle Temperature.)   None of the energy transferred from the high-pressure piston would have been available for use in separating the molecules against intermolecular forces. Energy for this purpose would then have been drawn through the walls as heat *from* the bath.

At temperatures lower than T_3, the final PV is greater than the initial PV. Heat must flow in from the bath sufficient to separate the molecules, and also to provide that portion of the work on the right piston not provided by the piston on the left. Both these items, it may be noted, are due to the attractive forces between the molecules of the gas, for it is those forces that make the gas "more compressible" than an ideal gas, and so give PV decreasing with increasing P.

What is the trend, then, as we perform the throttling experiment at lower and lower temperatures? At the highest temperatures, there is a surplus of heat, which in our design of the experiment flows out to the surrounding bath. At the Boyle Temperature, this has changed to a heat deficit, which in our design is made up from the bath. At still lower temperatures, this deficit becomes greater. Somewhere *above* the Boyle Temperature there is an **inversion temperature**: Above this temperature throttling leads to a surplus of heat, below it to a deficit. This inversion temperature will depend on the pressures used, but there is for a given gas a maximum inversion temperature, above which all pressure ratios lead to a heat surplus.

With a constant-temperature bath around the device, we have been able to follow the throttling process along the isothermal plots of a PV-against-P diagram. In practice, one finds the throttling process used without the surrounding bath. Any *surplus heat* then remains in the throttled gas, to send its temperature above the temperature before throttling. Any *deficit of heat* is made up by the throttled gas, leaving its temperature below the temperature before throttling. At temperatures above the maximum inversion temperature of a given gas, then, throttling leads to a rise in the temperature of the gas. At temperatures below the maximum inversion temperature, throttling may lead to a drop in the temperature of the gas. As the initial temperature of the gas is lowered, this temperature drop on throttling becomes greater.

17.03 THE JOULE-THOMSON EXPERIMENT*

We have already (section 15.20) considered an idealized form of "Joule's Experiment", wherein a gas having expanded into a previously

---

* Sections 17.03 and 17.04 are drawn largely, including Figures 17.06, 17.07, and 17.08, from James M. Cork, *Heat*, 2nd Ed., Copyright 1942 by James M. Cork (John Wiley & Sons, Inc.).

evacuated space is found to have the same temperature as before its expansion. Now, if there are attractive forces between molecules, work must be done against them in such an expansion, and our conclusion of zero temperature drop will no longer hold. In 1850 Joule (James Prescott Joule, 1818) performed such an experiment, using apparatus as shown in Figure 17.06. The chamber A was filled with a compressed gas while chamber B was evacuated. The turning of the stopcock S allowed the free expansion of the gas into the evacuated chamber. The complete assembly was immersed in a water bath. No change in the temperature of the bath being observed, it was concluded that "the internal energy of the gas was a function of the temperature only", i.e., that energy was stored in the gas only as kinetic energy of the molecules, not as the potential energy of holding attractive molecules apart; see item (c), section 17.02. The statement in quotation marks is known as Joule's Law.

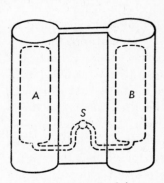

Fig. 17.06. Joule's experiment, in which the heat capacity of the bath and container was much too great in comparison with that of the gas.

Professor W. Thomson (1824, later Lord Kelvin) suggested that the small mass of gas used in the expansion should not be expected to produce a measurable change in the temperature of the large amount of water used as the bath. He went to Manchester and cooperated with Joule in carrying out the throttling experiments now famous as the "porous plug" experiments.

In these experiments the gas was allowed to pass continuously from a region of high pressure to one of lower value. The expansion nozzle consisted of a plug of either cotton wool or unspun silk, held in place by a boxwood tube. This loose material prevented the formation of violent eddies, whose energy would come out of the heat energy of the gas. The inlet and outlet tubes were well insulated, and in the steady state the pressures and temperatures on either side of the nozzle or plug were observed. The schematic arrangement of the apparatus is shown in Figure 17.07.

To follow the process, imagine pistons inserted in the inflow and outflow tubes, not far from the plug, moving in such a way that the gas flows in the presence of the pistons just as it does flow in fact without the pistons. Then the arrangement is just the one in terms of which throttling has already been discussed.   In the absence of pistons, the gas can be pictured in slices, each one being pushed by the one behind and pushing on the one ahead.   At any stage in its progress along the tube, each slice is pushed just as much as it pushes, i.e., has as much work done on it as it does in its turn.   If $P_1V_1 = P_2V_2$, this statement applies even to a "slice" making its way through the plug: The slice (of cross-sectional area A) is pushed into the plug by a strong push P_1A for a short distance, it forces its way out by exerting a less strong push P_2A for a long distance and with $P_1V_1 = P_2V_2$ the net work done by the slice is still zero.

In their first published report on air in 1852, Joule and Thomson stated that on expanding from a pressure P_1 of 34.4 lb in.$^{-2}$ and a temperature of 15C to a pressure P_2 of one atmosphere, the temperature fell 0.3 deg (C).   It was thus shown that Thomson's contention was correct, that there was a form of potential energy in the gas which increased when the gas expanded.   Expansion with zero temperature drop would obtain in Joule's experiment for a hypothetical gas with zero attraction between molecules.   Any real gas

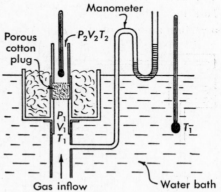

Fig. 17.07. The Joule-Thomson Experiment utilized continuous flow and revealed the temperature changes that occur when a gas is throttled.

has some attraction of this sort, however, and when Joule performed his experiment there must have been a temperature drop, but one too small for him to detect.

Many more exact throttling experiments, using higher pressure ratios, have been performed since Joule and Thomson's original one, and much useful information on the extent to which various gases depart from the ideal gas in their behavior has been obtained in this way.

17.04 USE OF THROTTLING FOR LIQUEFACTION OF GASES

Substances which can exist only as gases at room temperature can exist as liquids if cooled below their "critical temperatures": 154K for oxygen, 126K for nitrogen, 33K for hydrogen, and 5K for helium. The cooling effect produced by most gases when they are allowed to expand through a jet to a region of reduced pressure serves as a possible method of producing low temperatures such as these. The suggestion of this possibility is attributed to various investigators, but it was first successfully applied by Linde in 1896. A modification of this apparatus was used almost at the same time by Hampson. The apparatus as usually employed is shown diagrammatically in Figure 17.08. The method as used for air is as follows: Air at a pressure of 1 atm., with all water vapor and carbon dioxide removed, is compressed by C_1 to a pressure of about 16 atm. The compressor C_2, besides receiving the output of C_1, receives a certain amount of air rejected by the liquefier at the same pressure, and compresses the whole to about 200 atm. The output of C_2, hot because of a partially adiabatic compression, is cooled by an ice bath and thence conducted to the liquefier. Here it expands through the nozzle N_1 to a pressure of 16 atm. After this expansion, about four-fifths of the gas travels back along the outside of the inlet pipe so as to cool progressively the incoming air at a high pressure. The remaining one-fifth of the air expands through the nozzle N_2 to a pressure of 1 atm. This gas passes back through an outer

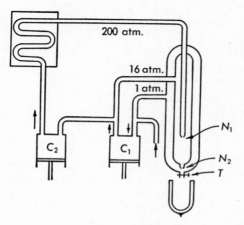

Fig. 17.08. Liquefaction by the Linde process. C_1, C_2, compressors; N_1, N_2, nozzles; T, tap.

concentric pipe so as to cool still further the incoming gas. After a steady state is reached, it will be found that about one-fourth of the gas upon this final expansion is liquefied and may be drawn off at T.

If hydrogen is subjected to these same pressures and allowed to expand, it will show a progressive warming rather than cooling. However, if it be precooled below about $-80C$, it behaves upon throttling in a manner similar to air. Kamerlingh Onnes successfully employed the method to liquefy helium in 1908. In this investigation the compressed helium before throttling was supercooled by passing it through a chamber containing liquid hydrogen boiling at a reduced pressure so that its temperature was 15K.

17.05 OTHER METHODS OF GAS LIQUEFACTION*

The use of the Joule-Kelvin effect to produce liquefaction of gases has two advantages. (1) There are no moving parts at low temperatures that it would be difficult to lubricate. (2) The lower the temperature, the larger the drop in temperature for a given pressure drop. For the purpose of liquefying hydrogen and helium, however, it has a serious disadvantage, namely, the large amount of precooling that is necessary. The hydrogen must be precooled with liquid nitrogen, and the helium must be precooled with liquid hydrogen, which makes the liquefaction of these gases very expensive.

An approximately reversible adiabatic expansion against a piston or a turbine blade always produces a decrease in temperature, no matter what the original temperature. If, therefore, a gas like helium could be made to do external work adiabatically through the medium of an engine or a turbine, then, with the aid of a heat exchanger, the helium could be liquefied without precooling. But this method has the disadvantage that the temperature drop on adiabatic expansion decreases as the temperature decreases.

A combination of both methods has been used successfully. Thus, adiabatic reversible expansion is used to achieve a temperature within the inversion curve [i.e., a temperature and pressure from which throttling leads to a temperature decrease], and then the Joule-Kelvin effect completes the liquefaction. Kapitza was the first to liquefy helium in this way, with the aid of a small expansion engine that was lubricated by the helium itself. Later he liquefied air with the aid of a small centrifugal turbine a trifle larger than a watch.

The latest development in the field of gas liquefaction is the Collins helium liquefier, in which helium undergoes adiabatic expansion in a reciprocating engine. The expanded gas is then used to cool the incoming gas in the usual counter-current heat exchanger. When the temperature is low enough, the gas passes through a throttling valve and Joule-Kelvin cooling is used to complete the liquefaction. The unit consists of a three-stage compressor, a gas-holder, a purifier, and a cryostat containing the engines, heat exchangers, Dewar flasks, vacuum pumps, and all switches and gauges.

Precooling with liquid nitrogen may be used but is not essential. Starting with helium at room temperature, it takes only two or three hours for liquid helium to be produced, and when a few liters have collected, the liquid may be transferred to an external Dewar. Installation of Collins helium liquefiers in many laboratories throughout the world has expedited low-temperature physics to a great extent.

PROBLEM

1. On a plot of PV against P draw a typical family of five isothermal curves, the range of pressure covered being such that departures from $PV = RT$ are evident. Indicate the region where throttling might be expected to result in a cooling of the gas.

* This section is quoted from Mark W. Zemansky, *Heat and Thermodynamics*, 3rd Ed., McGraw-Hill Book Company, Inc., 1951.

18

The Solid and Liquid States

18.01 MOLECULES BOUNCING AGAINST A WALL

In the development of the kinetic theory of gases that was used in an earlier chapter, molecules were pictured as rebounding from a solid surface with their energy unchanged. Monatomic molecules were pictured for the purpose as elastic mass-points, and the solid surface was pictured as a smooth, rigid surface. This served our purpose, and the molecules of a gas do rebound from a solid surface, on the average, without any change in their energy. They do so, that is, if the temperature of the surface is the same as that of the gas. Viewed on the scale of molecular dimensions, however, a solid surface is not smooth and continuous. The closest approach to smooth and continuous is the surface of a simple cubic crystal. That surface is made up of an orderly array of atoms. There is a fixed separation, say l, between the locations of neighboring atoms in a row. There is the same separation l between adjacent rows (Figure 18.01). This orderly array is not limited to the surface; it is a three-dimensional array, with a second plane of atom-locations spaced behind the surface array by the same modular distance l. The distance l separating the atoms is about the same as that already noted as the "diameter" of a molecule, to the extent that a molecule has a diameter, i.e., it is a few times 10^{-8} cm.

These atom-locations that are so precisely arrayed in an orderly lat-

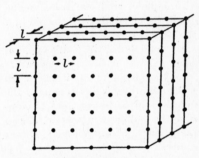

Fig. 18.01. Atom-locations in a simple cubic lattice. The atoms move to and fro, randomly as to direction and amplitude, about these locations as their mean positions.

tice are just the average positions of the atoms, averaged over considerable time. If we could watch the individual atoms, we would see each one vibrating rapidly to and fro about its mean position. The amount of vibration of any one atom keeps changing, but its average amount of vibration is the same as that for every other atom in the crystal. The direction of its vibration keeps changing, too, and bears no fixed relation to that of its neighbors. Both the direction and the amount of vibration of any one atom at any moment are matters of chance, for this vibration is heat motion, or thermal motion, as it occurs in the solid state.

It is with this sort of array of vibrating atoms, then, that a gas molecule collides when it strikes a "solid" wall. The collision may be looked on as a collision between a freely traveling gas molecule and an atom locked into a crystal lattice. The atom is vibrating; if it is moving rapidly outward at the instant of the collision, it will transfer energy to the molecule, which will depart faster than it approached. If the atom is moving inward, into the crystal lattice, it will take energy from the molecule, and the molecule will depart more slowly than it approached. But if on the average the energy of random vibration, per degree of freedom, of the atom, is the same as that of the molecule, then on the average the collisions between molecules of the gas and atoms of the solid will result in no change in the energy of the molecule. That is to say, if the *temperature* of the solid is the same as the *temperature* of the gas, the sum of many collisions, and so the average collision, will result in no transfer of energy from gas to wall or from wall to gas.

18.02 THE NATURE OF CRYSTALS

The predominant characteristic of the gaseous state is empty space. A single atom is a complex affair. But in a gas, space is so sparsely populated by "molecules" of one or two or a few atoms each that we can achieve a simple picture in which the details of the atoms are omitted, in which the atoms become mass-points, with no more by way of individual characteristics than so many black dots. When there is less open space, when the molecules spend a considerable portion of their time close enough to feel each other's attractive forces, then our simple picture must be amended.

The predominant characteristic of the solid state is order, the orderliness of crystalline aggregation. In a crystal, the atoms arrange themselves according to a precise plan, and interatomic forces hold them to that plan. Apparently interatomic forces change from forces of attraction to forces of repulsion as the interatomic distances become small, and so when the atoms or molecules are crowded very close together they lock into a balanced system or lattice. Figure 18.02(a) shows the basic elements of a simple cubic lattice. A body-centered lattice is similar but has one additional atom in the center of each such cube. Again, a face-centered cubic lattice is similar to the simple lattice except for an additional atom in the center of each *face* of the cube. In these cases all the atoms are of the same sort. The basic pattern is repeated

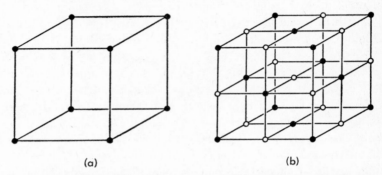

(a)   (b)

Fig. 18.02. (a) Simple cubic lattice. (b) Crystal lattice of rock salt.

over and over again indefinitely to form a sizable crystal. Figure 18.02(b) shows a crystal lattice involving two types of atom, sodium and chlorine.

18.03 X-RAY CRYSTALLOGRAPHY

When crystals are placed in the path of a beam of X-rays, the crystals with their regular arrangement scatter the X-rays in certain specific directions relative to that plan, just as a regularly ruled diffraction grating scatters light in certain specific directions (section 32.08). Since the crystal is more complicated than the diffraction grating, however, the pattern of scattered radiation is also more complicated. Diffraction gratings are used to analyze light; if the spacings in the grating are known and the scattering angles measured, the wavelengths of the light can be determined. If the wavelengths of the X-rays scattered by a crystal are known and the angles measured, the spacings within the crystal can be determined. Or if the spacings are known, the wavelengths can be determined.

To evaluate Avogadro's number, the wavelength of a beam of X-rays is determined, using a diffraction grating of known spacing. Then from the scattering of these X-rays by a crystal, the spacings within that crystal are determined, and so the number-density of the crystal is derived.

18.04 THE CRYSTALLINE NATURE OF SOLIDS

Crystals can be grown from solutions or from the substance in its liquid state, the crystal extending outward to increasing size as more and more atoms attach themselves into the lattice pattern. The growth must be gradual if perfect crystalline structure is to be obtained, but there is no limit to the size of crystal that can be achieved if the necessary conditions are maintained for a long enough time.

Most solids are crystalline, but the individual crystals are seldom large. Suppose that a large crystal were pulverized and packed into a mold. The result would be a crystalline aggregate, typical of the structure of most ordinary crystalline substances. The finer the pulverization of the crystal before packing, the more *amorphous* the resulting substance. Some substances, such as glass and plastics, appear to be perfectly amorphous, with no evidence of crystal structure. We like to refer to such substances as resembling liquids in their lack of structure. It is found, however, that liquids themselves show some evidence of orderly arrangement. It is probably more helpful to note the resemblance of amorphous substances to liquids, than it is to postulate any solid completely lacking in orderly arrangement of its atoms.

18.05 SPECIFIC HEATS OF SOLIDS

A very simple theory of the specific heats of solids can be developed if one assumes that the atoms vibrate according to the laws of classical mechanics and vibrate quite independently of one another. Each atom can vibrate in any direction, and (as for the translational energy of a gas molecule) there are three independent direction-components; on this basis each atom has three degrees of freedom in which it can vibrate. Because vibration involves a continual interchange between kinetic energy and a potential energy of the same average value, each degree of freedom can be looked on as effectively doubled. That gives each atom *six* degrees of freedom. Taking the energy per degree of freedom the same for solids as for liquids, then,

Energy per degree of freedom $= \frac{1}{2}kT$
Energy per atom $= \frac{6}{2}kT = 3kT$
Energy per gram-atomic weight $= N_0 \times 3kT = 3RT$

That is to say,

Atomic or atomic-specific heat of a solid $= 3R$
$$= 24.93 \text{ joules per gram-atomic weight per degree}$$

As long ago as 1819, Dulong and Petit observed that the experimental values of the specific heats of some twenty common elements when multiplied by their gram-atomic weights gave approximately a constant value of 6.4 cal or 26.75 joules. (This was, of course, the atomic heat at constant pressure, C_p. For solids and liquids, the small amount by which C_p exceeds C_v is better calculated than measured.)   They concluded that

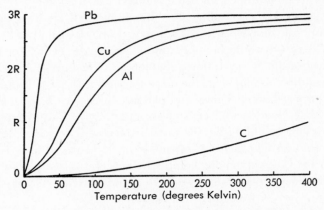

Fig. 18.03.   Atomic heats of elements in solid state as functions of temperature.

"the product of the atomic weight and the specific heat is the same for all elementary substances".   Actually, the atomic heats of solid elements increase with temperature, rapidly at first and then slowly, very gradually approaching the Dulong and Petit value as they approach their melting points.   Those elements having high atomic weights come close to this limiting value sooner than those which have low atomic weights (Figure 18.03).

For pure chemical compounds, the logical extension of Dulong and Petit's Law holds to some extent.   Better theories of the specific heats of solids, showing approximately the observed dependence on temperature, have been obtained by going beyond classical mechanics to apply quantum-theory considerations.

Empirically, it may be worth noting that for solids generally (excluding substances containing liquid water) the product of specific heat times density, i.e., the heat capacity per unit *volume*, is approximately half that for water.

18.06 CHANGES OF STATE BETWEEN SOLID AND LIQUID

If heat were added at a constant rate to a crystalline solid, a plot of temperature against time might look something like Figure 18.04. The temperature at first increases steadily, neglecting any change of specific heat with temperature in this region. Then at some specific temperature, the solid begins to melt, and there is no further increase in temperature until the substance is all melted. Then the temperature rises again, usually somewhat less rapidly for the liquid than for the solid.

During the heating of the solid, very little of the energy supplied goes to expanding the solid. Most of the energy goes to increasing the energy of vibration of the atoms, i.e., to raising the temperature. At about the time the mean amplitude of the vibrations equals the spacing between adjacent atom-locations in the crystal lattice, the atoms begin to break loose from their moorings. A good deal of energy goes into the work of breaking loose,

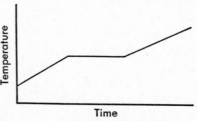

Fig. 18.04. Temperature against time as heat is added at a constant rate to a substance initially crystalline solid, then melting, then all liquid.

and the average kinetic energy per degree of freedom does not increase further, the temperature does not rise higher, until all the atoms have broken loose, that is, until all the solid substance has been transformed to liquid. When all the substance has been transformed, the incoming heat is again available for speeding up the thermal motions; the energy per degree of freedom and the temperature of the liquid proceed to rise.

The heat required to transform unit mass of substance (usually one gram) at its melting-point temperature to liquid at the same temperature is known as the **latent heat of fusion** of the substance. Melting, like changing the temperature of a solid or liquid, does not involve much change in the density of the substance. The density usually decreases on melting (ice is an exception, and in a way this is fortunate), but the change is not great. Most of the energy goes to breaking the atoms loose from their moorings, relatively little to increasing the spacing between them.

If heat is steadily *removed* from the substance in its liquid phase, a similar path to that of Figure 18.04 is followed in the reverse direction, with the same value of latent heat of fusion. One notable difference may arise. A liquid may be cooled below its freezing point (the same point as the melting point referred to above, approached from the opposite direction) without any solidification taking place, unless there is some nucleus present, such as a tiny bit of the crystalline solid, from whose surface the crystalline growth may proceed. The liquid is then said to be "supercooled". If a nucleus is introduced into a supercooled liquid, the liquid is transformed rapidly from a liquid below its freezing point to part solid, part liquid, all at the temperature of the freezing point.

Glass has been referred to as an amorphous solid. It may be looked on more reasonably as a supercooled liquid, whose viscosity has so increased with falling temperature that its state is quite stable. It is not perfectly stable, for the process of "devitrification" consists of the very slow building up of a crystalline structure in some regions of the glass.

In a single crystal, every part of the crystal is under essentially the same condition as every other part, except for the exposed surface. Melting sets in therefore at a specific temperature, either at the surface or throughout the crystal. In the case of a crystalline aggregate, however, all sorts of internal surfaces exist between adjacent bits of crystal. Atoms on these surfaces are in different fields of force than those within the crystalline structure and removed from such surfaces. This results in a melting "point" that is not sharply defined but instead extends over a range in temperature of several degrees. The extent of this temperature range over which there is evidence of melting can be used as a measure of the degree to which a substance is amorphous.

18.07 NATURE OF THE LIQUID STATE

It has been suggested in the preceding section that a substance goes from the solid state to the liquid when the kinetic energy of individual atoms or of very small portions of the crystal lattice overcomes the restraint of the interatomic forces that have been holding the crystal together rigidly. There is little change in volume when the substance melts; the average spacing remains small, and the forces between molecules of the liquid must be comparable with those which at a temperature only slightly lower held the solid rigidly together. These forces are enough to prevent the molecules from traveling away from one another indefinitely, as in a gas. The volume of a gas is determined only by the limits imposed by its container. A liquid holds itself together, in that the molecules cannot escape from one another's field of attraction, and so a liquid possesses a definitive volume. If this volume is less than that of any container in which the liquid finds itself, a "free surface" exists between the liquid and the remaining space in the container.

X-ray studies of liquids suggest that they have something of the structure of solids. The orderly structure probably extends over a region of ten or twenty atoms, instead of over much larger numbers as in a crystal. Because of the close spacing there is a tendency toward crystal-building, but because of the more energetic random motions the process never gets very far. The atoms are more likely to join and break away from the transient bits of crystal pattern as groups forming molecules than as single atoms. The atoms of a crystal are held in fetters all the time. The molecules of a liquid are held in fetters nearly all the time, and are free only in the very brief intervals between one term of imprisonment and the next. This is not a proved description, but rather a likely picture on the basis of present knowledge.

18.08 SPECIFIC HEATS OF LIQUIDS

One of the few comments on the state of knowledge of the specific heats of liquids is to be found in Roberts'* *Heat and Thermodynamics*:

The theory of the specific heats of liquids has not been developed to any considerable extent on account of the meagreness of our knowledge of the liquid state. It is, however, interesting to compare the specific heat of a liquid just above the melting point with that of the solid just below the melting point. It is found in general that, if the specific heat of the solid has reached the Dulong-Petit value, the difference between the values for the liquid and for the solid is small. If it has not, there is in general a large difference.

18.09 THERMAL EXPANSION OF SOLIDS

As solids and liquids get hotter, there is a gradual increase with temperature in the mean spacing between atoms or molecules and so a gradual increase in the volume occupied by a given sample. The effect of pressure is much less marked with these relatively incompressible states than it is with gases, but the pressures developed if a constant volume is maintained tend to be great.

Since solids have shape, the change in any linear dimension of a

* J. K. Roberts, *Heat and Thermodynamics*, 3rd Ed., Blackie & Son Ltd., 1940.

sample can be considered independently. Figure 18.05(a) relates length to temperature for rods of metal whose lengths at 0C were all 1 m. An increase in temperature of 500 Centigrade degrees increases the lengths

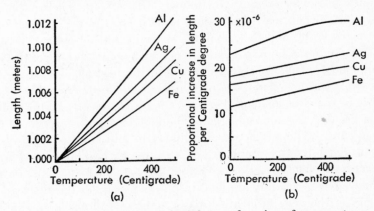

Fig. 18.05. (a) Length of solids as a function of temperature. (b) Coefficient of linear expansion as a function of temperature.

by the order of 1 cm. If the lines of Figure 18.05(a) were straight, they could be described by equations of the form

$$L = L_0(1 + at) \qquad (18.01)$$

where L is the length at temperature t and L_0 the length at 0C. Being almost straight, they can be described with satisfactory precision by equations containing an additional term:

$$L = L_0(1 + at + bt^2) \qquad (18.02)$$

Any additional precision that may be required can be obtained by increasing the number of terms. The coefficients a, b, etc., are known as "virial coefficients".

18.10 COEFFICIENTS OF EXPANSION

The most useful quantity in connection with expansion is the rate of expansion at any given temperature. The increase in length depends not only on the increase in temperature, but also on the initial length, to which the increment of length is proportional. (Thus the temperature rise that lengthens a 1-m rod by 1 mm will lengthen a 10-m rod by 10 mm.) The **coefficient of linear expansion** is defined as the *proportional* increase in length per degree rise in temperature:

$$\alpha = \frac{\Delta L}{L} \times \frac{1}{\Delta T} \tag{18.03a}$$

or precisely, to define the coefficient at any specified temperature,

$$\alpha = \lim_{\Delta T \to 0} \frac{\Delta L}{L} \times \frac{1}{\Delta T} \tag{18.03b}$$

The coefficient of linear expansion varies more nearly linearly with temperature than does the length itself; see Figure 18.05(b). It may be of interest to note that the linear coefficient increases with temperature at about the same rate as the specific heat at constant pressure, so that the ratio of the two is approximately invariant with temperature.

When a solid body expands, its surface area increases. The **coefficient of surface expansion** is defined, quite analogously to the linear coefficient, by

$$\gamma = \frac{\Delta S}{S} \times \frac{1}{\Delta T} \tag{18.04}$$

Analogously again, the **coefficient of volume expansion** is

$$\beta = \frac{\Delta V}{V} \times \frac{1}{\Delta T} \tag{18.05}$$

If ΔT is taken large instead of small in equations (18.03), (18.04), and (18.05), the resulting coefficients are average coefficients over the temperature interval considered. Thus, denoting the now-large ΔV and ΔT by $V_2 - V_1$ and $T_2 - T_1$, we have

$$\beta_{\text{avg.}} = \frac{V_2 - V_1}{V_1} \times \frac{1}{T_2 - T_1}$$

This may be written alternatively as

$$\frac{V_2 - V_1}{V_1} = \beta_{\text{avg.}}(T_2 - T_1)$$

or
$$\frac{V_2}{V_1} = 1 + \beta_{\text{avg.}}(T_2 - T_1) \tag{18.06}$$

The virial coefficient a of equation (18.01) is called the "zero coefficient", and is the same as $\alpha_{\text{avg.}}$ for the temperature interval 0 to t.

18.11 RELATIONSHIP AMONG THE COEFFICIENTS FOR SOLIDS

When the length and width of a rectangular surface increase from L and W to $(L + \Delta L)$ and $(W + \Delta W)$, its surface area increases from

$$S = LW$$

to
$$(S + \Delta S) = (L + \Delta L)(W + \Delta W)$$
$$= LW + L\,\Delta W + W\,\Delta L + \Delta L\,\Delta W$$

Thus
$$\Delta S = L\,\Delta W + W\,\Delta L + \Delta L\,\Delta W \tag{18.07}$$

Equation (18.07) is illustrated in Figure 18.06 where the small shaded portion in the corner represents the term $\Delta L\,\Delta W$.

Dividing the left-hand side of (18.07) by $S\,\Delta T$ and the right by $LW\,\Delta T$, which is the same thing, gives

$$\frac{\Delta S}{S} \times \frac{1}{\Delta T} = \frac{\Delta W}{W} \times \frac{1}{\Delta T} + \frac{\Delta L}{L} \times \frac{1}{\Delta T} + \frac{\Delta L\,\Delta W}{LW} \times \frac{1}{\Delta T} \tag{18.08}$$

The last term on the right-hand side of equation (18.08) is negligible by comparison with the others, so we can say approximately that

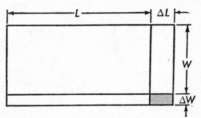

$$\gamma = \alpha + \alpha = 2\alpha \tag{18.09}$$

This is more than an approximation, however. As ΔT, ΔL, and ΔW become vanishingly small, the ratios $\Delta W/\Delta T$ and $\Delta L/\Delta T$ remain finite, but the last term with its two Δ's disappears. So if we adopt more precise in-the-limit definitions of γ and β, as we did for

Fig. 18.06. Change in length, width, and area of a plate with temperature.

α in equation (18.03b), equation (18.09) becomes perfectly true.

It can be shown similarly that

$$\beta = 3\alpha \tag{18.10}$$

An exception to (18.09) and (18.10) is found in the case of crystals and some other substances, including wood, that have a different structural form in different directions. The expansion of such substances can be described by three different α's in directions at right angles to one another. Equation (18.10) is then replaced by

$$\beta = \alpha_1 + \alpha_2 + \alpha_3 \tag{18.11}$$

18.12 EXPANSION AND DENSITY

The coefficient of volume expansion can be used not only in connection with volume but also in connection with density. We can develop the relation between density and the coefficient more briefly for the average coefficient. Let any mass m of a substance have volume V. Then its density is given by

$$\rho = \frac{m}{V}$$

If the mass is heated, its volume will change, and also its density, but its mass will remain constant. Thus if it goes from $T_1 V_1 \rho_1$ to $T_2 V_2 \rho_2$, we will have

$$V_1 \rho_1 = m = V_2 \rho_2$$

Combining this relation with equation (18.06), we obtain

$$\frac{\rho_1}{\rho_2} = \frac{V_2}{V_1} = 1 + \beta_{\text{avg.}}(T_2 - T_1) \tag{18.12}$$

18.13 THERMAL EXPANSION OF LIQUIDS

Since a sample of liquid lacks any shape of its own, the only relevant coefficient is the volume coefficient β. Liquids in general expand more than solids, less than gases at constant pressure (Figure 18.07). The expansion of liquids is conveniently measured by the method

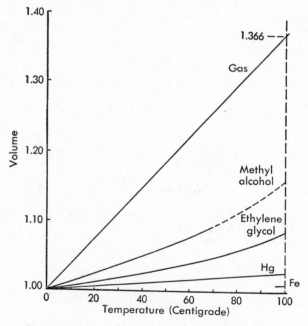

Fig. 18.07. Variation of volume with temperature for gases, liquids, and a solid.

of balanced columns, wherein columns of liquid of different temperatures are balanced one against the other. The relative heights of the two columns gives the ratio of the densities and so gives $\beta_{\text{avg.}}$ for the temperature interval between the two. In Figure 18.08, let the liquid of the right-hand column, and in the U of the tube up to height a in the left-hand column, be at temperature T_1. Let the liquid above a in the left-hand column be at a somewhat higher temperature T_2. Since the two columns are identical up to the level a, the pressure is the same at that level in both columns. Therefore, denoting the atmospheric pressure by Π,

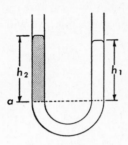

Fig. 18.08. A column of warm liquid is slightly taller (h_2) than a column of equal weight of cooler liquid (h_1).

$$h_1\rho_1 g + \Pi = h_2\rho_2 g + \Pi$$
$$= \text{pressure at level } a$$

Therefore $\qquad h_1\rho_1 = h_2\rho_2$

Therefore, from (18.12),

$$\frac{h_2}{h_1} = \frac{\rho_1}{\rho_2} = 1 + \beta_{\text{avg.}}(T_2 - T_1) \qquad (18.13)$$

This is a good way of determining β for a liquid. There is an unfortunate possibility for confusion, however, in this relationship between the *linear* quantity h and the *volume* coefficient β. This point must be watched.

Another case worth considering is that of a mercury barometer. The pressure at the base of the column of mercury equals atmospheric pressure, thus:

$$\Pi = h\rho g$$

If the temperature increases without change in the atmospheric pressure, then the height of the mercury column increases to compensate for the decrease in ρ. Thus

$$h_2\rho_2 = \frac{\Pi}{g} = h_1\rho_1 \qquad (18.14)$$

Combining (18.14) with (18.12), we again obtain (18.13). The mercury column "expands", but with the volume coefficient rather than the linear coefficient of expansion. It is that same point, which must be watched so carefully, of a relation between *length* and a *volume* coefficient.

18.14 EXPANSION OF A LIQUID IN A VESSEL

If there is a hole in a brass plate, and the brass plate expands, what happens to the hole? It expands too, with the same coefficient of expansion as the brass. The linear coefficient is applicable not only to the outside edges of the plate, but also to the edges of the hole.

Similarly, the capacity of a glass bottle—the volume of the cavity inside the glass container—expands with the coefficient of volume expansion of glass. Now the coefficients of solids are much smaller than those of liquids, but not so much smaller that they can be neglected. So the observed expansion of liquids in vessels is not what it appears to be. An "apparent coefficient of expansion" is sometimes used, equal to the difference between the coefficient of the liquid and that of the vessel. The safest thing to do in any problem involving the expansion of a liquid in a vessel is to develop a solution from first principles, calculating the expansion of the cavity and that of the liquid independently.

18.15 STRESSES RESULTING FROM TEMPERATURE CHANGE

If a solid is heated or cooled while its volume or any one of its linear dimensions is held constant, considerable forces are set up, which can be related to the Young's Modulus of the solid.

A metal rod of length L can be extended to $L + \Delta L$ by pulling on it with a tension P. Just how great the tension must be depends on the cross-sectional area of the rod, A, and on the sort of material, as described by its Young's Modulus Y, where

$$Y = \frac{\text{stress}}{\text{strain}} = \frac{\text{force per unit cross section}}{\text{proportional extension}}$$

$$= \frac{\dfrac{P}{A}}{\dfrac{\Delta L}{L}} = \frac{PL}{A\,\Delta L}$$

That is,

$$P = YA\,\frac{\Delta L}{L} \tag{18.15}$$

An alternative method of increasing the length of the rod by the same amount is to raise its temperature by ΔT, where ΔT is related to ΔL by

$$\alpha_{\text{avg.}} = \frac{\Delta L}{L}\,\frac{1}{\Delta T} \tag{18.16}$$

Suppose that the rod while at temperature $T + \Delta T$ is clamped, then cooled to its original temperature T, the clamps being strong enough to keep the rod extended to length $L + \Delta L$. Then, when the rod has resumed its original temperature, the tension will be just that given by equation (18.15), and can be related to $\alpha_{\text{avg.}}$ and ΔT by combining (18.15) and (18.16):

$$\frac{P}{YA} = \alpha_{\text{avg.}}\Delta T$$

$$P = YA\alpha_{\text{avg.}}\Delta T \tag{18.17}$$

If the case of a compression of the rod had been considered, the similar result

$$P = \frac{YA\alpha_{\text{avg.}}\Delta T}{1 + \alpha\,\Delta T}$$

would have been obtained. The difference between the two forms is always negligible and disappears in the limit as ΔT approaches zero.

18.16 TENSILE STRENGTH OF LIQUIDS

It is easy for us to picture a metal bar, perhaps stretched in a testing machine, exhibiting its tensile strength by existing in a state of tension. The corresponding behavior of liquids is less simply pictured, but is important, particularly in connection with the process of boiling.

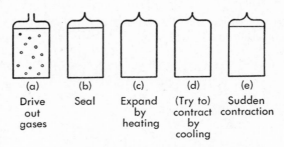

| (a) | (b) | (c) | (d) | (e) |
| Drive out gases | Seal | Expand by heating | (Try to) contract by cooling | Sudden contraction |

Fig. 18.09. Development of liquid under tension.

Suppose that a glass tube, one end closed and the other necked ready for sealing off, be filled with water, and the whole carefully heated until all dissolved gases are driven off; see Figure 18.09(a). Then let the tube be sealed off, with no air in it, but only water, plus perhaps a small region containing water vapor; Figure 18.09(b). In case there is a vapor region, let the tube be heated now, until the water has expanded and filled the whole of the glass tube; Figure 18.09(c). (A little too much heating at this stage would develop high enough pressure to break the glass tube.) Now if the vessel is cooled, any pressure developed in the liquid should first drop off, then the contracting liquid (contracting much more rapidly than the glass) should pull away from the glass, reforming a vapor space. But this does not happen readily. Rather than break open and form a vapor space, the liquid clings to the walls (adhesion) and holds together itself (cohesion) even although it is being stretched—it is in a state of tension or negative pressure; Figure 18.09(d). If the cooling is carried far enough, contraction will finally come suddenly, and the state of tension will be terminated; either the water or the water-to-glass seal has been broken; see Figure 18.09(e).

PROBLEMS

1. In a crystal of sodium chloride, the atoms are arrayed in a simple cubic lattice containing equal numbers of sodium ($A_0 = 23.0$ gm) and chlorine ($A_0 = 35.5$ gm) atoms; see Figure 18.02(b). The density is 2.16 gm cm^{-3}. What is the distance between adjacent atoms?

2. A lead bullet has speed x and temperature 27C when it strikes a steel target. Assume that all its kinetic energy is converted to heat, and all this heat stays with the bullet to heat it to its melting point and melt it. (Melting point 327C, average specific heat 0.03 cal gm^{-1} deg^{-1}, heat of fusion 5.86 cal gm^{-1}.) What speed must the bullet have for this conversion to melt the whole of the bullet?

3. In order to use heat from the sun to heat a house, a large supply of sodium sulphate is maintained at its melting point of 31C. During hours of sunshine this substance is melted by the sun's heat; throughout the rest of the 24-hr cycle it freezes and releases its heat of fusion (51.3 cal gm^{-1}). If the heat required for a 24-hr period is that provided by 50.0 kgm of coal with a heat of combustion of 6.00×10^6 cal kgm^{-1}, what quantity of sodium sulphate will be needed to last through the same period?

4. If steel rails are laid on ties, free to expand, in lengths of 20.0 m, what gaps must be left between lengths at 0.0C so that the rails will just touch at 50.0C? ($\alpha = 12.0 \times 10^{-6}$ deg^{-1}.)

5. A wire is stretched between two points A and B, both at the same height and 1.00 m apart. A small weight hung halfway between the supports pulls the center point of the wire down 6.9 cm below A and B, at room temperature. At 500C, the center point has dropped to 10.9 cm below A and B. What is the average coefficient of expansion of the material of which the wire is made, in the region between room temperature (20C) and 500C?

6. Recalling that the period of a pendulum varies as the square root of its length, what coefficient of expansion in the material of a simple pendulum will lead to a clock, correct at 0C, losing 1.00 sec day^{-1} deg^{-1}?

7. What must be the clearance at 20C of an aluminum piston ($\alpha = 25.0 \times 10^{-6}$ deg^{-1}) in an iron cylinder ($\alpha = 12.0 \times 10^{-6}$ deg^{-1}) of diameter 10.0 cm

so that a clearance of 0.10 mm (i.e. a difference in radius of this amount) remains when the cylinder reaches 120C and the piston 220C?

8. At 0C, a piston fits in a cylinder of diameter 10.0 cm with clearance all around of 0.20 mm. The metals used for cylinder and piston both have $\alpha = 12.0 \times 10^{-6}$ deg^{-1}. What is the clearance when the cylinder is heated to 100C and the piston with its less-effective cooling to 200C?

9. An aluminum sphere has diameter 10.00 cm at 0C. What is its diameter at 200C, taking $\alpha = 25.0 \times 10^{-6}$ deg^{-1}? What is its increase in volume (a) accurately, from initial and final diameters, (b) approximately, from $\beta = 3\alpha$?

10. A mercurial barometer reads 775 mm while the attached thermometer reads 80.0F. The brass scale on which this reading is made, however, was calibrated at 20.0C. What is the true height of the column of mercury? What is the atmospheric pressure, in millimeters of mercury at 0C? The linear coefficient for brass is 18.9×10^{-6} deg^{-1}(C), and the volume coefficient for mercury is 0.181×10^{-3} deg^{-1}(C).

11. A glass bottle of volume 100 cm^3 with a volume coefficient of 0.036×10^{-4} deg^{-1}(C) is full to the brim at 0C with carbon tetrachloride, which has a volume coefficient of 1.24×10^{-3} deg^{-1}(C). If bottle and liquid are heated to 40C, what volume of liquid will be outside the bottle?

12. A steel wire of diameter 1.00 mm is stretched between two fixed points at a temperature of 20.0C. Neglecting the initial tension, determine its tension when the temperature falls to 10.0C, taking $\alpha = 11.0 \times 10^{-6}$ deg^{-1}, Young's Modulus $= 2.10 \times 10^{12}$ dyne cm^{-2}.

13. A steel rod of cross section 1.00 cm^2 is prevented from expanding as it is heated from 0C to 200C. What force does it exert at 200C? ($\alpha = 12.0 \times 10^{-6}$ deg^{-1}, Young's Modulus $= 2.00 \times 10^{12}$ dyne cm^{-2}). Repeat for aluminum, with $\alpha = 25.0 \times 10^{-6}$ deg^{-1}, modulus 9.0×10^{11} dyne cm^{-2}.

14. If steel rails are so laid that expansion is not permitted, what compressive force results from an increase in temperature of 20.0 deg, starting at 0C? ($\alpha = 12.0 \times 10^{-6}$ deg^{-1}, Young's Modulus 20.0×10^{11} dyne cm^{-2}).

19

Evaporation

19.01 EVAPORATION IN A CLOSED VESSEL

Suppose that a vessel has been partly filled with a liquid, the remainder of its space being left full of gas (Figure 19.01). The "free surface" of the liquid, between the liquid and the gas, exists because the molecules of the liquid lack the energy necessary to fly away from each other against the intermolecular forces, and so the liquid has a definite volume other than that of its container.

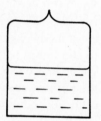

Fig. 19.01. Evaporation into a constant volume.

The condition that the molecules lack the energy necessary to fly apart applies to most of the molecules of the liquid, but not to all of them. In Chapter 14, the variation in energy among the molecules of a gas was discussed. Figure 14.09(b) indicated that one per cent of the molecules would have speeds greater than twice the root-mean-square value, and so (for a monatomic gas) energies greater than four times the mean energy value. Whatever energy is considered, we can expect to find some small fraction of the molecules having higher energy values. Similarly, for a liquid or a solid, there will always be some fraction of the molecules or atoms having abnormally high energies. Thus among those molecules at the free surface of a liquid, there will always be some achieving great enough energy to break away from their fellows, and so gaining freedom to roam about the gas-filled region along with the rest of the gas molecules. Just how many molecules of the liquid break away from the liquid surface in unit time depends on the temperature, the number increasing more and more rapidly with increasing temperature. This breaking-away of molecules from the liquid at its free surface, i.e., at a boundary between liquid and gas, is called **evaporation.**

Suppose, to give them names, that the liquid we are considering is water and the gas above it is nitrogen. As a result of evaporation, the gas space above the liquid will acquire a continually increasing number of water molecules that have achieved the freedom of motion of gas molecules. The gas space can truly be said to contain two gases: nitrogen and water. We will find it convenient, however, to refer to the nitrogen as a gas and to the water molecules in the gas phase as a vapor.

The energy of a vapor molecule will vary with successive collisions with the gas molecules. From time to time, a vapor molecule will find itself back at the free surface, and with sufficiently small energy for it to become attached once more to the liquid. Just what *proportion* of the vapor molecules arriving back at the free surface become reattached to the liquid depends again on the temperature. Just how *many* become reattached in unit time depends also on how many vapor molecules there are, mixed with the gas.

We commenced with no vapor molecules at all in the gas, so that all flow of molecules through the free surface was upward from the liquid to the gas. This condition will lead to an increasing number of vapor molecules in the gas, and so to an increasing rate of return of vapor molecules to the liquid. Gradually, a condition is reached wherein the number of vapor molecules becoming reattached to the liquid per second is equal to the number emerging upward per second into the gas. Once reached, this condition is maintained as an equilibrium condition, wherein there is a considerable interchange of molecules between the liquid and the gas-and-vapor space, but no net change. The pressure in the gas space will then be $P_0 + P_e$, where P_0 is the initial pressure of the dry gas and P_e is the pressure due to the equilibrium number of vapor molecules mixed with the gas. This term P_e is known as the **equilibrium vapor pressure** of the liquid. It depends on the rate at which molecules break free from the liquid and so, in turn, on the temperature of the liquid.

The equilibrium vapor pressure of a substance increases at an ever-increasing rate with increasing temperature until the critical temperature of the substance is reached. At any lower temperature the substance can exist as a gas or as a liquid, and the two phases can exist in equilibrium. The two phases have distinct physical properties, and a clearly defined boundary, the free surface of the liquid, can be observed between them. With any further small rise in temperature, the boundary surface that until that time had been observed between liquid and gas would disappear. Below its **critical temperature** (374C for water) a substance can exist as a liquid or as a vapor, and these two phases can exist beside one another in equilibrium. Above its critical temperature, a substance can exist as a gas. If the pressure of this gas is increased to high values, the gas will become continually more like a liquid in its properties, but the coexistence of two distinct phases at the same temperature and pressure will not be observed.

We can now distinguish properly between the terms "vapor" and "gas". A **vapor** is a substance in the gaseous state or phase at less than its critical temperature, whereas a gas is a substance in the gaseous state or phase at more than its critical temperature. We were thus correct in referring to those water molecules in the gas-space as a vapor, and to the nitrogen (for which the critical temperature is $-147C$) as a gas.

It has been implied that although the molecules that broke away from the liquid to become vapor molecules are likely to reattach themselves to the liquid, the gas molecules do not attach themselves similarly to the liquid when they find themselves at the free surface and with low energy. This is not perfectly true; the extent to which the gas molecules attach themselves to the liquid depends on the solubility of the particular gas in the particular liquid.

Evaporation occurs not only from the free surface of a liquid; it occurs also from the surface of a solid. Every substance, whether solid or liquid, has its equilibrium vapor pressure, varying widely from substance to substance, and always a function of the temperature. The equilibrium vapor pressures of most solids are very small. In designing vacuum pumps, it is desirable to use liquids whose vapor pressures are very small. Such liquids are rare, but they can be found.

If the temperature of a vessel, containing a liquid (or solid) and its vapor in equilibrium, is reduced, the existing vapor pressure will exceed the new equilibrium value. Then the rate of return of molecules to the liquid will exceed the rate of release until the new equilibrium has been achieved. This reverse process is known as **condensation.** When a solid is involved, rather than a liquid, both processes, evaporation and condensation, are referred to as **sublimation.**

19.02 CONTINUED EVAPORATION

Suppose that the liquid (or solid), instead of being in a closed vessel, had been in the open, with a stream of dry gas passing over it rapidly enough to carry away the evaporating molecules before they had had any appreciable opportunity to become reattached to the liquid. Then evaporation would have continued until all the liquid had evaporated.

Evaporation is a selective process. It removes from the liquid the fastest molecules—leaves behind all but the fastest molecules. The average kinetic energy of the molecules left behind is obviously not as great as the average kinetic energy over all of them before evaporation. That is to say, the temperature of the residue is less: The liquid has been cooled by evaporation. If the temperature of an evaporating liquid is to be kept constant, heat must continually be transferred from some source to the liquid, to compensate for the heat used in evaporation.

Usually, continued evaporation will cool the liquid. As a result of the temperature dropping, two things happen: The rate of evaporation drops, and heat begins to flow into the liquid from its surroundings. An equilibrium temperature is reached at which the inflow of heat just equals the expenditure of heat by evaporation.

In any case of evaporation in a closed vessel, one might think that the vapor molecules would have a higher kinetic energy, a higher energy per degree of freedom, than those in the liquid. Certainly the molecules that find themselves in the vapor phase had, before leaving the liquid, a higher-than-average energy. The process of leaving the liquid involved work against intermolecular forces, however, and on the average this was just enough to bring the escaping molecules back to the same average value of energy per degree of freedom as existed in the liquid. If, as in the closed-vessel case, vapor molecules return from the gas space to the liquid, they will during that process have work done on them, and so will revert to their status of faster-than-average molecules in the liquid.

In the closed-vessel case, there is a net evaporation (more molecules leaving the liquid than returning to it) until equilibrium is achieved. This initial evaporation removes heat from the liquid, and effects a drop in the temperature of the liquid unless an equal amount of heat is transferred to the liquid from outside. Once equilibrium has been established, there is no further cause for a change in temperature.

19.03 LATENT HEAT OF VAPORIZATION AND SUBLIMATION

The latent heat of vaporization of a substance at a given temperature is the heat required to convert one gram of the substance from its liquid state at that temperature to the vapor state at the same temperature. Like latent heat of fusion, it is generally very large by comparison with specific heat. The latent heat varies with temperature, decreasing as the temperature increases. This fits in with something else: the fact that at a given temperature the specific heat of a given substance as a liquid is greater than its specific heat as a vapor. Thus to proceed from the liquid state at one temperature to the vapor state at a higher temperature, one may first vaporize at a relatively high latent heat and then raise the temperature at the relatively low specific heat of the vapor state, or else raise the temperature of the liquid with its relatively high specific heat and then vaporize at a relatively low latent heat. Both routes must require the same total amount of heat in taking the substance from the same initial to the same final condition.

The latent heat of sublimation is the heat required to convert one gram of the substance from its solid state at that temperature to the vapor state at the same temperature. Like heat of vaporization, it varies with temperature.

19.04 THE VARIATION OF THE EQUILIBRIUM VAPOR PRESSURE WITH TEMPERATURE

An increase in temperature increases the proportion of molecules energetic enough to escape from the liquid, and thus increases the rate of evaporation; this in turn increases the equilibrium vapor pressure. The simplest approximation to the observed relationship is:

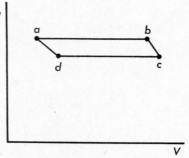

$$\log P_e = -\frac{A}{T} + B \quad (19.01)$$

where A and B are constants varying from substance to substance and T is the absolute temperature. This equation represents satisfactorily the observations for many substances, as may be discovered by plotting $\log P$ against $1/T$ and noting the constancy of the slope of the resulting curve. The logarithmic relationship is in

Fig. 19.02. Reversible cycle, vapor in equilibrium with its liquid phase.

keeping with the form of the Maxwellian distribution of molecular velocities (Figure 14.09).

Equation (19.01) is one form of the "Clausius-Clapeyron Equation". (R. J. E. Clausius, 1822, B. P. E. Clapeyron, 1799.) One simple thermodynamic derivation of it can be based on our consideration of engine cycles in Chapter 16. Consider a reversible cycle (Figure 19.02) in which rather than a gas we have a vapor in equilibrium with its liquid (or for that matter, solid) phase. Let the volume be increased a considerable amount at constant temperature, and so at constant equilibrium vapor pressure, from V_a to V_b. Then let the volume increase just a little more, adiabatically, to V_c. Then let there be isothermal compression to such a point d that a small further adiabatic compression will carry the cycle to a.

Because the cycle is reversible,

$$\frac{Q_1}{T_1} = \frac{Q_2}{T_2} \quad \text{and} \quad \frac{Q_1 - Q_2}{Q_1} = \frac{T_1 - T_2}{T_1}$$

Since the temperature drop is being kept small, we will write this as

$$\frac{\Delta Q}{Q} = \frac{\Delta T}{T} \tag{19.02}$$

where
$$\Delta Q = \text{work done} = \text{enclosed area}$$
$$\simeq \Delta P(V_b - V_a)$$

This is an approximation because the two adiabatics are not parallel.

We can also relate Q to the latent heat of vaporization, L:

$$Q = LM \tag{19.03}$$

where M is the mass of substance vaporized.

If for the vapor $\rho \simeq P_e M_0/(RT)$, then

$$M = \rho(V_b - V_a) \simeq \frac{P_e M_0}{RT}(V_b - V_a)$$

$$Q \simeq \frac{L P_e M_0}{RT}(V_b - V_a) \tag{19.04}$$

and
$$\frac{\Delta T}{T} = \frac{\Delta Q}{Q} \simeq \frac{RT}{L P_e M_0(V_b - V_a)} \times \Delta P_e(V_b - V_a)$$
$$\simeq \frac{RT\, \Delta P_e}{L P_e M_0}$$

That is,
$$\frac{\Delta P_e}{P_e} = \frac{L M_0}{R}\frac{\Delta T}{T^2} \tag{19.05a}$$

or
$$\frac{\Delta P_e}{\Delta T} = \frac{L M_0}{R}\frac{P_e}{T^2} \tag{19.05b}$$

The differential equation (19.05) can be solved to give an algebraic equation of the form of (19.01). As it stands, (19.05a) differs from any of the differential equations of the preceding chapters. Let us change the temperature variable from T to T^{-1}, however. When T increases to $T + \Delta T$, $1/T$ increases or at any rate changes to $(1/T) + \Delta(1/T)$, and we can state that

$$\frac{1}{T} + \Delta\left(\frac{1}{T}\right) = \frac{1}{T + \Delta T} \tag{19.06}$$

Multiplying the right side of the equation, top and bottom, by $(T - \Delta T)$, we have

$$\frac{1}{T + \Delta T} = \frac{T - \Delta T}{T^2 - (\Delta T)^2} \simeq \frac{T - \Delta T}{T^2} = \frac{1}{T} - \frac{\Delta T}{T^2}$$

The approximation is valid if ΔT is small compared with T, and approaches perfect validity as ΔT approaches zero. So (19.06) can be extended to read

$$\frac{1}{T} + \Delta\left(\frac{1}{T}\right) \simeq \frac{1}{T} - \frac{\Delta T}{T^2}$$

$$\Delta\left(\frac{1}{T}\right) \simeq -\frac{\Delta T}{T^2} \tag{19.07}$$

Substituting from (19.07) in (19.05a) gives

$$\frac{\Delta P_e}{P_e} \simeq -\frac{LM_0}{R}\Delta\left(\frac{1}{T}\right) \tag{19.08}$$

Equation (19.08) has the same form as (15.32) and (15.35); comparing it with them, its solution as an algebraic equation can be seen to be

$$\ln\frac{P_e}{P_{e0}} = -\frac{LM_0}{R} \times \frac{1}{T}$$

or

$$\ln P_e = -\frac{LM_0}{R} \times \frac{1}{T} + \ln P_{e0} \tag{19.09}$$

Thus we not only find an equation of the same form as (19.01), but we also find the constant A to be proportional to the product of the latent heat of vaporization times gram-molecular weight.

19.05 EVAPORATION AT CONSTANT PRESSURE

Evaporation in a closed vessel has been discussed with reference to a vessel in which the volume of the gas space was practically constant. Suppose we repeat our consideration with a cylindrical vessel closed by a weighted piston as in Figure 19.03, so that the volume of the gas space can change and the pressure remain unaltered. Evaporation into the gas space will proceed until the pressure of vapor reaches the equilibrium value P_e. The total pressure remains constant at P_0, so that

$$P_0 = P_g + P_e \tag{19.10}$$

where P_g is the partial pressure of the gas. Regardless of the presence of vapor, the continuing relationship between gas pressure, volume, and temperature is

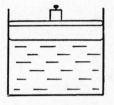

$$\frac{P_g V}{T} = \text{constant} = \frac{P_0 V_0}{T_0} \qquad (19.11)$$

where P_0 is the initial value of the gas pressure (and the continuing value of total pressure), and V_0 and T_0 are the initial values of volume and temperature. Combining (19.10) and (19.11) to eliminate P_g, we obtain

Fig. 19.03. Evaporation at constant pressure.

$$\frac{V}{V_0} = \frac{P_0}{P_0 - P_e} \times \frac{T}{T_0} \qquad (19.12)$$

The ratio V/V_0 is plotted against temperature in Figure 19.04, for water

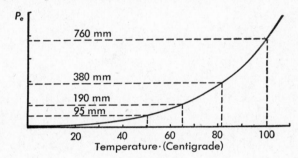

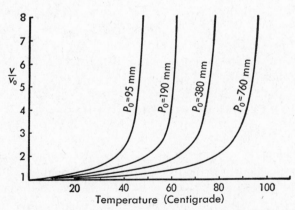

Fig. 19.04. V is the volume, at the specified pressure, of a bubble containing air plus vapor in equilibrium with water. V_0 is volume of dry-air content alone, at the specified pressure.

and for various values of total pressure. When the temperature is increased until $P_e = P_0$, there is no "final volume": The volume can go on increasing at constant pressure until all the liquid has evaporated. If P_e should become greater than P_0, equation (19.12) would cease to hold; the volume would increase at an increasing rate, for the piston would move with an accelerating motion.

The constant-pressure experiment with increasing temperature can be pictured without any gas at all. We start with the piston of Figure 19.03 pressing on the liquid with pressure greater than the equilibrium vapor pressure of water at the existing water temperature, i.e., $P_0 > P_e$. As the temperature is raised steadily by the transfer of heat from an external source, nothing happens until the temperature is reached at which $P_e = P_0$; that is, the equilibrium vapor pressure equals the pressure under the piston. At that stage vapor should begin to form, increasing the volume under the piston. This formation of vapor should proceed until the liquid is all transformed, utilizing all the incoming heat, so that the temperature rises no further until all the liquid has been transformed.

In practice, as we shall discuss next under "Boiling", it is very likely that some air would come out of solution before the temperature giving $P_e = P_0$ has been reached, and so provide an air space above the liquid. If the liquid were quite free of dissolved gases, then vaporization would have to create its own free surface through which evaporation could occur. Because of the cohesion of the water and its adhesion to the walls, this breaking apart of the water to form a free surface requires effort and may not occur until further increasing temperature has brought P_e to a considerably higher value than P_0.

19.06 BOILING

Liquid in an open vessel gradually evaporates. The rate of evaporation increases rapidly with temperature; the curve of rate of evaporation against temperature is similar to that of equilibrium vapor pressure against temperature. Thus, if we take a beaker of tap water at room temperature and put it on a hot stove, the rate of evaporation from its free surface will increase, and increase more and more rapidly, as the temperature rises. The evaporation will not be visible, although wisps of condensed vapor in the cooler air a few inches away from the beaker may be observed.

Another phenomenon important to our study is visible, though, and that is the formation of air bubbles in the liquid on the floor or walls of the beaker. The solubility of gases in liquids decreases with rising temperature, and air or any other gas coming out of solution apparently is able to "break open" the liquid, against its forces of cohesion or tensile strength, and form these little air spaces.

Evaporation will occur through the surfaces of the bubbles as well as through the principal free surface of the liquid. Under the preceding heading "Evaporation at Constant Pressure", the relation between final volume (gas plus vapor) and initial volume (dry gas) was derived, equation (19.12). In the case of these gas bubbles, P_0 is approximately atmospheric pressure. As long as P_e is small compared with P_0, the vapor content of the bubbles will be small. As P_e approaches P_0 with increasing temperature, however, vapor will form a larger and larger part of each bubble. Thus for water at atmospheric pressure (Figure 19.04), the bubbles at 80C will be almost half vapor, but at 97C they will contain almost ten times as much vapor as gas.

The little gas bubbles left to themselves tend to adhere to the walls of the vessel. At temperatures above 90C, however, the enlargement of the bubbles by the addition of vapor makes them too buoyant for this, and they rise to the surface. By the time they reach the surface they contain several times as much water vapor as gas.

Now it was noted under "Evaporation at Constant Pressure" that when $P_e = P_0$ there is no final value for the volume to approach, but instead there should be expansion of the volume indefinitely. In the case of water (containing dissolved air) heating in a beaker, the air spaces into which evaporation is proceeding are air bubbles at the bottom of the beaker. The pressure there is atmospheric plus the head of water in the beaker itself, this latter a relatively small term. The temperature at the bottom of a beaker, right next to the stove, is usually higher than that anywhere else in the beaker. Convection currents should reverse this situation, but usually the rate at which heat comes in from the stove is greater than the modest convection currents can take care of.

When the temperature of the water at the bottom of a beaker reaches a value close to 100C (the exact value depending on the existing atmospheric pressure and the depth of water in the beaker), the equilibrium vapor pressure becomes equal to the pressure on the air bubbles. There is then no limit to the volume that the bubbles can achieve by evaporation into them. They can expand without limit and they expand rapidly. On rising from the bottom of the beaker, the bubbles travel into a region where the pressure is a trifle less, so that their gas content tends to expand slightly. But they may find this a region where the temperature is also somewhat less, and so the equilibrium vapor pressure is very considerably less, so that $P_e < P_0$. This can lead to condensation of the vapor in the bubbles, and to the rapid shrinking of the bubbles to their appropriate volume. Under the conditions of this paragraph, the top surface of the water is almost undisturbed, but the rapid formation of bubbles, followed by their still more rapid shrinkage after they have left the bottom, may set up the sound effect known as "singing".

The rising bubbles act as heat-transfer agents themselves, transferring heat to the cooler upper levels. They also tend to stir the liquid.

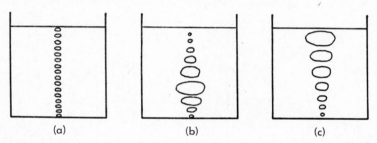

(a)   (b)   (c)

Fig. 19.05. Onset of boiling in a vessel of water. (a) Release of gas when $P_e < P_0$. Small bubbles of gas and vapor form and rise. (b) Singing. The temperature being greater at bottom of vessel during heating, $(P_e)_{bottom} > (P_0)_{bottom}$, while $(P_e)_{top} < (P_0)_{top}$. Rising bubbles expand, then collapse. (c) Boiling. $P_e > P_0$ throughout. Bubbles continue to expand, greatly increasing the surface area available for evaporation.

Between these two effects, they rapidly reduce the temperature gradient required for "singing", and the bubbles from then on reach the top surface, breaking there to release their content, by this time almost entirely vapor, to the atmosphere. All the water is then at such a temperature that P_e equals P_0, or P_e slightly exceeds P_0, and the water is said to be **boiling** (Figure 19.05).

Until boiling begins, most of the heat transferred from the stove to the water has gone to raise the temperature of the water, with a smaller share going to provide the energy of "latent heat of vaporization" required to convert the evaporating water from liquid into vapor. Once the boiling point (temperature at which $P_e = P_0$) is reached, the temperature rise proceeds very little farther. Such further temperature rise as may be achieved leads to a relatively large increase in P_e. With $P_e > P_0$, the rate at which the liquid walls of the vapor bubbles are pushed back becomes very great; bubbles grow quickly to a large size. The total free surface available for evaporation is great, the total rate of evaporation is great, and the heat required for evaporation is great. The temperature reaches equilibrium when the rate at which heat is used in evaporation equals the rate at which heat enters the liquid from the stove. Because the former rate increases very rapidly with excess of P_e over P_0, and P_e in turn increases very rapidly with temperature, equilibrium is usually reached at a temperature only a fraction of a degree above the boiling point (Figure 19.06). It is important to remember, however, that for a *precise* determination of the boiling point the boiling should not be vigorous.

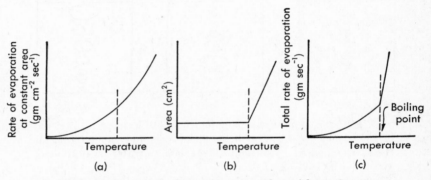

Fig. 19.06.   Variation of rate of evaporation with temperature.

Compare evaporation and boiling on the one hand with melting on the other. Melting is a "microscopic" or molecular process which (for crystalline substances) happens at temperatures close to the temperature called the melting point. Evaporation is another "microscopic" or molecular process, but it goes on at any temperature, provided there is a free surface, a liquid/gas surface, through which it can proceed. The rate of evaporation increases more and more rapidly as the temperature rises. There is no molecular phenomenon about boiling, other than that of evaporation. Boiling is a "macroscopic" or mechanical process, a large-scale thing, that sets in when the equilibrium vapor pressure of the evaporation phenomenon reaches the pressure existing within the liquid. It is of such a nature, increasing the area of free surface available for evaporation very rapidly as the temperature increases, as to prevent any further great rise in temperature. The onset of boiling as temperature is increased is readily observable and clear-cut, occurring at exactly the temperature at which $P_e = P_0$, so that the "boiling point" temperature can be measured and studied with great precision.

19.07 "BUMPING"

Boiling in the absence of dissolved gases is a less simple and less obvious matter. Thus if the beaker of water which we followed to the boil in the previous section were allowed to go on boiling for a few minutes, the temperature would (after a few minutes) rise somewhat, and the boiling become "bumpy", almost explosive in nature. At this stage the dissolved gases are all gone. Gases coming out of solution served the purpose of breaking apart the water, or breaking the water away from the wall, to make the initial opening, the initial bubble, into which water vapor could evaporate. The temperature of the water, by itself, may not achieve this breaking-apart until it is several degrees above the boiling point. When the breaking-apart finally does come about, the rate of evaporation into the cavity or bubble is very rapid, and the violent expansion called "bumping" ensues.

Dissolved gases are not the only way of avoiding bumping. A few bits of crushed stone in the beaker, in some way connected with their having rough edges and points, assist the boiling process in breaking apart the water at a temperature close to the boiling point.

19.08 BOILING BY PRESSURE ADJUSTMENT

For any pressure, there is a boiling-point temperature: A lower pressure will have a lower boiling-point temperature. In the preceding section we have considered the process of raising the temperature under fixed pressure until the liquid boils. Alternatively, one may achieve boiling at any temperature by reducing the pressure P_0 until it equals the equilibrium vapor pressure of the liquid at its existing temperature. If no heat is available for transfer from an outside source to the liquid, the boiling will tend to reduce the temperature of the liquid. Under this circumstance, boiling can be maintained by continuing to reduce the pressure as the temperature of the liquid drops. At lower boiling points, the rate of evaporation is of course much lower, and this affects the nature of the boiling: The rate of evolution of vapor may only become considerable when P_0 is considerably less than P_e, i.e., when the existing temperature is considerably above the boiling point. But water can be boiled at 0C, and the heat required for the evaporation then comes not from a further reduction in temperature but from the formation of ice.

19.09 EXPANSION OF MIXED GAS AND VAPOR

Suppose that a container of adjustable volume, designed for experiments on Boyle's Law, contains some gas, a very little liquid, and vapor in equilibrium with the liquid. Let the pressure in the container be

$$P = P_v + P_g \qquad (19.13)$$

where P_v is the pressure of the vapor and P_g the pressure of the gas. Let the volume of the container be V, and neglect the small volume occupied by liquid.

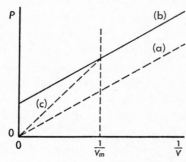

For the gas, Boyle's Law holds, and we have

$$P_g V = \text{constant} = c \qquad (19.14)$$

as long as the existence of heat transfer permits the temperature to remain constant. For the vapor, as long as there is liquid present, and provided we proceed slowly enough for equilibrium to be maintained,

$$P_v = P_e \qquad (19.15)$$

where P_e is the equilibrium vapor pressure.

Fig. 19.07. Behavior of mixed gas and vapor; (a) gas, (b) gas plus vapor in equilibrium, (c) gas plus vapor, in absence of liquid, behaving as all gas.

If the volume becomes great enough, say V_m, the liquid will all be converted to vapor. Proceeding to still greater volumes, the vapor at pressure less than P_e (and in the absence of liquid) will obey Boyle's Law approximately,

$$P_v V = \text{constant} = P_e V_m \qquad (19.16)$$

although the approximation is not as good for the vapor, only just removed from equilibrium vapor pressure, as it is for the gas.

For volumes less than V_m, the volume at which the liquid is just used up, equations (19.13) to (19.15) hold, and combining them we obtain as a pressure/volume relation

$$P = \frac{c}{V} + P_e \qquad (19.17)$$

For volumes greater than V_m, where there is no longer any liquid, equations (19.13), (19.14), and (19.16) hold, and the relation between P and

V is

$$P = \frac{c}{V} + \frac{P_e V_m}{V} = \frac{1}{V}(c + P_e V_m) \qquad (19.18)$$

Since, c, P_e, and V_m are all constants, this is Boyle's Law.

A convenient way to plot Boyle's Law data is on a chart of P against $1/V$. In Figure 19.07, equations (19.17) and (19.18) have been plotted on such a chart. Curve (a) on that chart is the curve we might have had for the gas by itself, that is

$$PV = c \qquad (19.19)$$

Curve (b) is the locus of equation (19.17) and holds only to the right of the vertical line $1/V = 1/V_m$. The vertical distance from line (a) to line (b) is the constant P_e, the equilibrium vapor pressure. Indeed, a "Boyle's Law" experiment performed with a small sample of volatile liquid in the container along with the gas is a good way of determining the equilibrium vapor pressure of the liquid. Curve (c) is the locus of equation (19.18) and holds only to the left of the vertical line $1/V = 1/V_m$, and even then only approximately, for it assumes that Boyle's Law holds for vapors near their equilibrium vapor pressures.

PROBLEMS

1. Ethyl alcohol has a boiling point of 78.3C (at a pressure of 1 atm.) and a heat of vaporization at that temperature of 854 joules gm^{-1}. Its specific heat is 2.43 joules gm^{-1} deg^{-1}. What heat will be required to raise 100 gm of this alcohol and its 200-gm iron container (specific heat 0.45 joules gm^{-1} deg^{-1}) from 20.0C to the boiling point and then boil all the alcohol away? How long will this take if the heat is available at a constant rate of 100 watts?

2. The vapor pressure of a substance is 10.0 mm Hg at temperature 10C, 100 mm Hg at 50C. At what temperature will it be 1000 mm Hg, according to the Clausius-Clapeyron equation?

3. For naphthalene ($C_{10}H_8$) over the range 0C to 80C the equilibrium vapor pressure in millimeters of mercury is given by $\log_{10} P_e = -3720 T^{-1} + 11.45$. Calculate the equilibrium vapor pressure of this solid for 0C, 40C, and 80C.

4. The equilibrium vapor pressure of carbon tetrachloride (CCl_4) at 0C is 33 mm Hg. Its boiling point at a pressure of 1 atm. is 77C. Calculate the values of A and B for the relation $\log_{10} P_e = -AT^{-1} + B$, where P_e is in millimeters of mercury.

5. A closed vessel contains 1000 cm^3 of moist air and some water, all at 10.0C. The vapor being in equilibrium with the water has a pressure of 9 mm Hg, and the total pressure is 760 mm Hg. If the temperature should be raised

to 20.0C (at which temperature the equilibrium vapor pressure of water is 18 mm Hg), what would then be the total pressure?

6. A constant-pressure cylinder at exactly 1 atm. and 20C contains a small amount of liquid carbon disulphide (CS_2) in addition to 10 cm^3 of a mixture of gas with vapor in equilibrium with the liquid. What will be the volume of mixed gas and vapor at 30C? ($P_e = 298$ mm Hg at 20C and 433 at 30C.)

7. Plot pressure against 1/(volume) for a mixture of 1.00 gm nitrogen and 1.00 gm water at 80C.

8. A faulty mercury barometer contains some air and some water vapor (in equilibrium with liquid water) above the mercury. As a result the height of the mercury column is 70.0 cm when the atmospheric pressure is 74.0 cm Hg. (Room temperature is 22C, so that the vapor pressure of water is 20.0 mm Hg.) The distance from the top of the mercury to the sealed top of the glass tube is 10.0 cm. What is the atmospheric pressure when the barometer reads 72.0 cm, the temperature remaining the same?

9. The closed end of a barometer tube comes at 80.0 cm on the scale. At constant temperature, the barometer reads 72.5 and 74.0 cm, respectively, when it should read 74.5 and 76.5. Does the barometer contain gas, vapor in equilibrium, or both?

10. What volume is occupied by 1.00 gm water vapor at pressure 0.0100 atm., temperature 100C, assuming $PV = nRT$? at pressure 1.00 atm.? What work is done in expanding a container by this amount at this pressure, in each case? What fraction is this of the latent heat of vaporization of water at 100C (2260 joules gm^{-1})?

11. Mercury vapor ($M_0 = 200.6$ gm) is poisonous at concentrations as low as 1 mgm m^{-3}. What is the pressure of this concentration at 20C?

20

Water Substance

20.01 DENSITY

Water is the working substance in so many thermal processes that its properties are of particular interest. First let us consider its density, or the reciprocal of density, which is called specific volume. Starting with ice, say at $-20C$, and increasing the temperature, we find that ice expands, like most solids, until at 0C its specific volume is 1.09117 cm^3 gm^{-1}. Liquid water at the same temperature has a specific volume of 1.00016, which decreases to a minimum value of 1.00003* at 3.98C. Then it starts to expand, reaching its zero-degree value again at about 8C and expanding more and more rapidly to achieve a specific volume of 1.0435 at 100C, as shown in Figure 20.01(a). The density or specific volume of water vapor is of course of a different order altogether. It can be calculated with reasonable accuracy (and usefully) from its molecular weight.

The minimum (at about 4C) in the plot of specific volume against temperature in Figure 20.01(b) is peculiar to water, and considerable philosophical comment has been engendered about the rigors of life in a world without this anomaly. As to the microphysical basis of the anomaly, there have been two notable suggestions. One is that liquid water is composed of different polymeric molecules, $(H_2O)_2$, $(H_2O)_3$, etc., the more complex having larger specific volumes, and that the proportion of more complex molecules increases as the temperature is lowered. More recently, it has been noted from X-ray studies that the molecules in a liquid arrange themselves in a somewhat orderly fashion, a sort of low-grade crystalline structure, rather than disposing themselves completely

---

* While the intention was that one gram should be the mass of one cubic centimeter of water at its temperature of maximum density, the platinum "standard kilogram" came out a bit heavy. Thus, one cubic centimeter of water at maximum density has a mass of 0.99997 gm, one "milliliter" by definition a mass of 1.00000 gm, and the "specific gravity" is by definition 1.00000.

randomly like the molecules of a gas. A change in this structure with temperature could lead to an increase in the specific volume as the temperature drops. The normal behavior of liquids is to contract as the temperature decreases. The processes suggested above, tending in the opposite direction, might combine with the normal contraction to give the anomalous behavior observed for water.

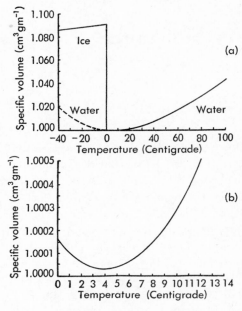

Fig. 20.01. Specific volume of ice and water.

20.02 SUPERCOOLED LIQUID

If clean, distilled water in a clean, smooth beaker is kept perfectly still as its temperature is lowered through the ice-point temperature, it may reach a temperature many degrees below 0C before any ice appears. Clouds of water droplets in the atmosphere may cool (by rising above the freezing level) to −20C or more before the droplets freeze. Ice forms rapidly on the surfaces of an aircraft traveling through such a cloud.

Many other liquids behave similarly. A liquid at a temperature less than the normal freezing point is said to be supercooled. Researches on the phenomenon of supercooling tend to involve the careful observation and measurement of the physical properties of a liquid, say viscosity, or its dielectric constants, or its scattering of X-rays, as its temperature is lowered through the normal freezing point.

20.03 SPECIFIC HEAT

The specific heat of water has particular importance because a common unit of heat energy, the calorie, is based on it. The specific heat of water, like its density, is peculiar in its variation with temperature, first decreasing and then increasing as the temperature goes from 0C to 100C, with a rather flat minimum between 30C and 40C (Figure 20.02). One calorie is, by definition, the amount of heat required to raise the temperature of one gram of water one Centigrade degree. Obviously this definition by itself is not precise enough. With greater precision, we normally use the "15C calorie": the amount of heat required to raise the temperature of one gram of water from 14.5C to 15.5C. This specification was chosen when it was thought that it equaled just one-hundredth of the heat required to raise the temperature of one gram of water from the ice point to the steam point. Actually, this latter "average calorie" is slightly greater. On the basis of experiments performed at

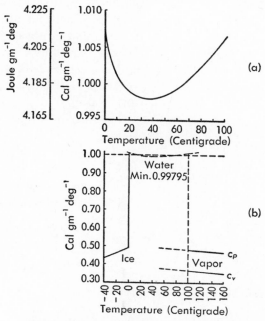

Fig. 20.02. (a) Specific heat of water.
(b) Specific heats of ice, water, and water vapor.

the National Bureau of Standards in 1939, one 15C calorie equals approximately 4.186 joules.

If you glance through a table of specific heats, you will find that only the very occasional and unusual substance has a specific heat higher than one calorie per gram.

The specific heat of ice at 0C is approximately 0.5 cal per gram; as the temperature is reduced, the specific heat decreases; see Fig. 20.02(b). Water vapor or steam has of course two quite different specific heats, at constant pressure and at constant volume. The former has a value at the steam point about equal to the specific heat of ice at the ice point.

20.04 HEAT OF VAPORIZATION AND HEAT OF FUSION

The heat of vaporization of a substance varies with temperature, becoming zero at the critical temperature, above which the substance cannot exist as a liquid. That of water is plotted against temperature in Figure 20.03. The variation with temperature is related to the specific heat (at constant pressure) of the vapor and that of the liquid.

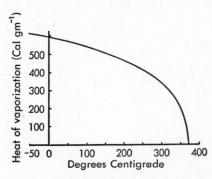

Fig. 20.03. Variation of the heat of vaporization of water with temperature.

Thus the heat of vaporization of water decreases from 595.9 cal gm^{-1} at 0C to 539.6 cal gm^{-1} at 100C, at a nearly linear rate of 0.563 cal gm^{-1} deg^{-1}; over this temperature range the specific heats of water and water vapor are nearly constant at 1.00 and 0.44 cal gm^{-1} deg^{-1}, for a difference of 0.56 cal gm^{-1} deg^{-1}. The heat of sublimation of ice is 676 cal gm^{-1} at 0C and remains nearly constant as the temperature is decreased, the specific heats of ice and water vapor being about equal.

The heat of fusion of water is 79.7 cal gm^{-1} at 0C and decreases with decreasing temperature at about the same rate as the heat of vaporization decreases with increasing temperature.

20.05 EQUILIBRIUM VAPOR PRESSURE

The equilibrium vapor pressure of any substance increases faster and faster as the temperature increases; the relationship can usually be represented by an equation of the form $\log P_e = -\dfrac{A}{T} + B$, as noted in equation (19.01). In the case of water, a relation of this simple form is not as good a fit as in most cases. This limitation can be overcome by changing to different values of A and B for different temperature regions, or going to a more complex relation, say

$$\log P_e = a - \frac{b}{T} - \frac{c}{T^2} \tag{20.01}$$

or by referring always to a graph (Figure 20.04) or table of the experimental data; precise tables are now available.

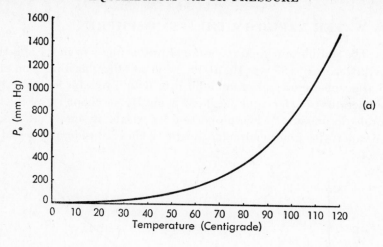

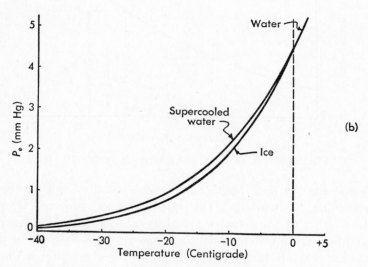

Fig. 20.04. (a) Equilibrium vapor pressure over water.
(b) Equilibrium vapor pressure over ice and supercooled water.

Solids as well as liquids have equilibrium vapor pressures, and so at and below 0C there are two equilibrium pressures: the pressure of vapor in equilibrium with the solid and the pressure of vapor in equilibrium with the (supercooled) liquid; see figure 20.04(b). Both these pressures vary with the curvature of the surface involved. This variation becomes important for radii of curvature less than one micron, as in the case of very small cloud droplets and ice crystals.

20.06 WATER VAPOR IN THE ATMOSPHERE

The equilibrium vapor pressure of water ranges from 0.1 mm Hg at −40C (over ice) to 55 mm Hg at 40C, and so ranges as a fraction of the total atmospheric pressure from a bit over 0.01% to a bit less than 10%. At temperature 7C, for example, it is 7.5 mm Hg, or about 1% of the total atmospheric pressure. The proportion by weight is somewhat less, for water vapor with gram-molecular weight 18 gm is considerably less dense than air.

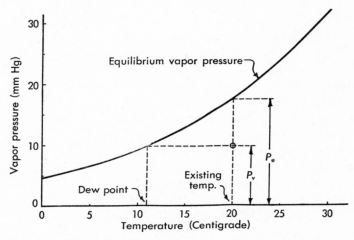

Fig. 20.05. Dew point and relative humidity (P_v/P_e).

The pressure of water vapor in the air is usually less than the equilibrium value, fortunately. The existing vapor pressure is usually described either by the **relative humidity,** i.e., the fraction it forms of the equilibrium value at the existing temperature, or by the **dew point,** i.e., the temperature for which the existing vapor pressure is the equilibrium value. Consider the circled point in Figure 20.05, for which the vapor pressure is P_v. The relative humidity is P_v/P_e, while the dew point is the temperature for which the line $P = P_v$ intersects the locus of equilibrium vapor pressures.

20.07 HYGROMETERS

The relative humidity can be read directly from a **hair hygrometer,** for the variation in length of a hair with the dampness is a function of the relative humidity and is independent of the temperature. Thus a hair will have, nearly enough, the same length at 25C, relative humidity 60%, as at 15C, relative humidity 60%.

The dew point can be obtained directly from a **dew-point hygrometer.** In that instrument, a vessel with a highly polished surface is cooled below the temperature of the surrounding air. A thin film of air next to the surface cools to the temperature of the surface. The pressures of water vapor and air in this cooled film remain the same as those in the warmer air, but the *relative* humidity rises. When the surface and the adjacent film of air have been cooled to the dew point, so that the relative humidity in the cooled film of air has reached 100%, water condenses from the cooled film onto the solid surface. On this highly polished and strongly illuminated surface, even a very small amount of condensation can be seen. The temperature at which such condensation is first seen is the dew point. By the use of photoelectric cells, an automatic dew-point hygrometer can be built, and can be used not only to register the dew point but also to control humidifying machinery so as to maintain the dew point at a constant value.

Dew point, relative humidity, and temperature are interrelated, so that a direct determination of the dew point can be converted to give the relative humidity, and vice versa. In common meteorological practice, however, both dew point and relative humidity are obtained from a **wet-and-dry-bulb hygrometer,** the direct reading of which is neither one thing nor the other. In this hygrometer, there are two matched thermometers side by side. The bulb of one is bare, the bulb of the other is covered by a thin muslin wick, kept moist by capillary flow from water in a small reservoir. The water should be pure, and the wick and the dry bulb should both be clean.

Because of evaporation, the wet bulb will tend to be cooler than the dry bulb (section 19.02). Let us consider the matter a little more closely. The vapor pressure prevailing in the atmosphere, or in the room, is presumably below the equilibrium value for the air temperature. Whatever it may be, we may safely assume that the vapor in the immediate vicinity of the moistened wick will be in equilibrium with the water on the wick. That is to say, the vapor pressure at the surface of the wet bulb will be the equilibrium vapor pressure for the temperature of the wet bulb.

Water evaporates at the surface of the wet bulb and travels out into the surrounding air as vapor. The rate of flow of vapor outward from the wet bulb is proportional to the excess of the vapor *density* at the bulb over the "ambient" or prevailing vapor density in the atmosphere or room. So the rate of evaporation and the rate of heat loss by evaporation will be proportional to this vapor-density excess.   If the temperature of the wet bulb were at the dew point, this excess would be zero.   If the temperature of the wet bulb is higher than the dew point, this excess is positive, and so is the heat loss by evaporation.   The top broken-line curve of Figure 20.06 shows the manner in which heat loss by evaporation would vary if the wet-bulb temperature were varied relative to the dew point.

If a thermometer bulb, wet or dry, is at a temperature above or below the temperature of the surrounding air, there is heat transfer from or to the bulb.   This transfer is proportional to the difference between the

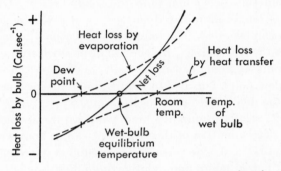

Fig. 20.06.   Heat flow and evaporation in wet-bulb thermometer.

temperature of the bulb and that of the surrounding air.   The bottom broken-line curve of Figure 20.06 shows the manner in which heat loss by heat transfer would vary if the wet-bulb temperature were varied relative to room temperature.

The broken lines show what would happen if the wet-bulb temperature were varied.   What is there to cause it to vary; what determines the wet-bulb temperature?   For any wet-bulb temperature between the dew-point and room temperature, the wet bulb will lose heat by evaporation, gain heat by heat transfer.   The nature of the net change, the sum of these two, is shown by the solid line of Figure 20.06.   If the net change is a loss, the wet bulb will get colder; if it is a gain, the wet bulb will get warmer.   In either case, the temperature of the wet bulb will tend toward an equilibrium position where the gain equals the loss, so that the net change is zero.   For any pair of room-temperature and dew-point values, there is just one such wet-bulb equilibrium temperature.   This is the wet-bulb reading that is taken from the hygrometer.   From it and the room temperature (i.e., the "dry-bulb" reading), the dew point and the relative humidity can be determined. **Psychrometric tables,** charts (Figure 20.07), and slide rules are available for achieving this determination in a few seconds. For precise work or for high-altitude use where the atmospheric pressure departs considerably from standard, tables must be chosen that take account of the barometric pressure.

The equation of heat flow is similar to that of diffusion of water vapor, on which the rate of evaporation depends. Increased ventilation should affect both, transferring heat to the bulb faster but at the same

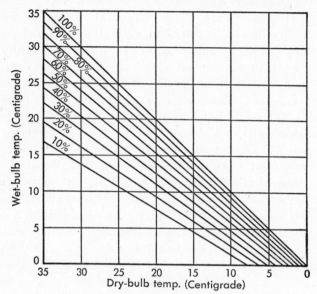

Fig. 20.07. Relative humidity from ventilated wet- and dry-bulb thermometer readings at an air pressure of one atmosphere.

time increasing the rate of evaporation, and so not affecting the equilibrium temperature of the wet bulb. There will be some heat flow down the stem of the thermometer, however, and there is no matching mode of evaporation to balance this. Increasing the rate of flow of air past the bulbs increases the rates of evaporation and heat transfer, and so improves the chance of making the heat flow along the stem negligible by comparison. This ventilation is most simply achieved in the sling psychrometer, in which a frame on which the two thermometers are mounted is swung around a handle by a simple motion of the wrist.

The hair hygrometer is the simplest of these devices; it is direct-reading, but requires occasional calibration to maintain an accuracy of the order of two per cent. The dew-point hygrometer is accurate when carefully used, but is rather elaborate. The wet-and-dry-bulb gives good accuracy at temperatures above freezing (and useful accuracy below freezing, when the wick is replaced by a thin coating of ice) and is reasonably simple.

20.08 HUMIDIFYING AND AIR CONDITIONING

Evaporation from its surface is an important factor in the disposal of heat by the human body. It is important to this process that the relative humidity be neither too high (more than 70%, say) nor too low (less than 40%). Low humidity is also hard on the respiratory passages, particularly when they double as speech organs, so efforts may be made to remove undue moisture in the humid weather, or to add moisture in the winter. In a cold climate, air that is saturated or less than saturated at, say, −10C is brought indoors and heated to 20C, whereupon without change in its actual moisture content its relative humidity becomes extremely low. This humidity may be raised by the evaporation into the air of water from wicks or from fine sprays. It should be recognized that this evaporation requires a good deal of heat, which must come directly or indirectly from a heating plant. It is a useful and enlightening experience to calculate the relative cost of providing a roomful of warm, dry air and one of warm, moistened air, when the available "raw materials" are cold, dry air and liquid water.

In a warm climate, it is considered desirable to cool the air. The relative humidity is likely to be too high even before it is cooled. When the air is cooled, the relative humidity would be likely to approach or even reach 100%. In air conditioning, therefore, cooling coils are used not only to cool the air but also to condense out water and so reduce the vapor content.

20.09 CONDENSATION IN THE ATMOSPHERE

In determining humidity by the dew-point method, the surface of a vessel is chilled below the temperature of the surrounding air; this is done by an independent system of evaporation inside the vessel. In the natural formation of **dew** on the ground at night, the cooling of the solid surface below that of the adjacent air is achieved by radiation losses. On a cloudy night, the ground radiates to, and receives radiation from, the clouds, and the difference between radiation emitted and radiation absorbed is not great. On a clear night, more heat is radiated than is received. The clear night sky has a low temperature; the clear air is transparent to radiation, and so the ground, instead of looking at relatively warm clouds, spends the night looking through the clear air at empty space. Little radiation is received to balance radiation emitted, and the temperature of the ground drops. If it drops to the dew point, there is condensation, and the release of latent heat helps to some small extent to keep the ground temperature from falling lower still. If the dew point is below 0C, and the ground temperature drops to 0C, the condensation will appear in the form of **hoar frost,** even though the air temperature a few feet above the ground is greater than 0C.

Air does not lose much heat by radiation. It does lose heat by conduction, on contact, to colder ground and water. When moist air is thus cooled to such an extent that supersaturated water vapor is present, condensation occurs on tiny hygroscopic **condensation nuclei** that are always present, to form a **fog.**

Cloud and fog are the same sort of thing. They differ only in the manner in which the air is cooled, creating supersaturation. In the case of fog, the cooling is by contact or in part by radiation. In the case of cloud, the cooling is principally effected by the rising of the air to higher levels and lower pressures, i.e., by a nearly adiabatic expansion of the gas. Sometimes the rising of the air is the result of instability in the atmosphere. The air near the ground becomes so heated and moistened in the summertime that it becomes less dense than the air above it. Not only is it less dense, but even after it has risen and expanded, it is still lighter than the air about it, and goes on rising to a great distance, say 10 miles. That is how we get towering summer thunderstorms. Alternatively to rising spontaneously, the air may be forced up as two air masses of different temperature press against each other, and one slides up over the other. In this way we get a general overcast of layer-type clouds.

The process of cloud formation may usefully be considered with reference to Figure 20.08. The coordinates there are density and temperature. Curves relating equilibrium vapor density, for water and for ice, to temperature have been drawn. These resemble the equilibrium vapor pressure curves of Figure 20.04(b). Consider now air which, when it leaves the earth's surface, has temperature and density of water vapor given by the high-temperature end of curve A. As the air rises, the point representing it moves right-to-left along the curve, expansion leading to a decrease in temperature and a decrease in the grams per cubic meter of water substance. The water substance remains all in the vapor phase until the dew point is reached (intersection with water equilibrium curve).

Any further cooling leads to the condensation of water substance in the form of a cloud of water droplets a few microns in diameter, the density of water *vapor* being given then by the water equilibrium curve. Thus, at 0C the air following curve A contains 4.8 gm m^{-3} of water vapor and 3.6 gm m^{-3} of cloud droplets.

A sample proceeding from right to left along curve B reaches the frost point (intersection with the ice equilibrium vapor curve) before the dew

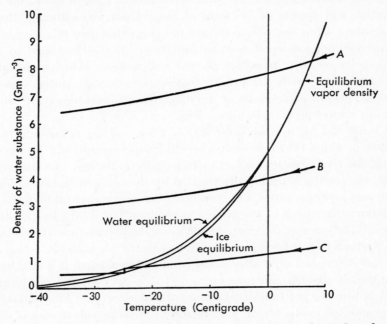

Fig. 20.08. Approximate paths (A, B, C) followed on plot of vapor density against temperature by air parcels rising through atmosphere.

point. It is found, however, that there is no formation of ice particles at the frost point. Again as before, water cloud forms at the dew point, even though the liquid water formed is at a temperature several degrees below 0C.

A sample proceeding along curve C passes the frost point without incident, as in the previous case, but when it reaches the dew point, ice is observed to form, rather than water. Water substance indicated by any point on C to the left of the dew point is made up of vapor plus ice crystals.

These somewhat idealized observations can be explained as follows. The condensation nuclei required for the formation of water droplets are always present in the atmosphere, permitting condensation whenever air is cooled to its dew point. There are no "sublimation nuclei" in the atmosphere, and so the air can be cooled below its frost point without occurrence of sublimation. At low temperatures such as the $-25C$ dew point of curve C, there are **freezing nuclei** capable of freezing water cloud droplets as soon as they form, or not long afterward. These frozen droplets serve then as sublimation nuclei. Aircraft form condensation trails or "contrails" by flying through air colder than about $-20C$ and adding enough further water substance to it to achieve water equilibrium. Apart from adding water substance, the passage of the aircraft may expand, and thereby cool, the air temporarily (by the action of the propellers or the wing tips), and thus achieve water equilibrium temporarily. In either case, water droplets form, freeze, and grow by sublimation until the vapor content has dropped to ice equilibrium.

20.10 PRECIPITATION IN THE ATMOSPHERE

Cloud droplets range from 4 to 40 microns or from 0.004 to 0.04 mm in diameter. They are surprisingly stable, being capable of continuing to exist within this size range for hours. They fall through the air with speeds of a few centimeters per second. Raindrops have diameters a hundred times as great, and fall a hundred times as fast. The processes by which clouds precipitate to form rain and snow are not known with certainty, and can only be sketched out.

Ice crystals continue to grow as long as vapor in excess of ice equilibrium is available on which to feed. Precipitation is simple, therefore, in case C of Figure 20.08. The ice crystals simply grow big enough to achieve a considerable fall speed, and fall out. The amounts of water substance involved are so small, however, and the heights at which the process occurs are so great, that little if any snow or rain arrives at the ground as a direct result. Rather, we have here the basis of the "mare's-tail" clouds occasionally seen in a blue sky.

In case B, continued rising and cooling beyond the dew point leads to a continually increasing density of supercooled water cloud until a temperature is reached at which freezing nuclei become active. Then ice crystals grow within the water cloud and either fall out as single crystals or join together to fall out as aggregate snowflakes. These may reach the ground as snow, or falling into warm air, melt and reach the ground as rain, or fall into dry air and evaporate.

The continued growth of cloud droplets by condensation is slow, but in case A it may be sufficient, by the time the density of cloud water has reached about 4 gm m^{-3}, to produce droplets large enough for them to begin to grow by coalescence, as one overtakes another in its fall, and so initiate precipitation as rain, without the ice phase being involved at all. Again, there are known to be present in the air particles of sea salt. Droplets forming about these will grow more rapidly than the rest, and so become big enough to initiate rain. If neither of these processes has led to precipitation by the time the cloud has cooled to about -15C, ice crystals may grow as in case B, leading to snow or hail and so to rain.

In cases A and B there is the possibility of situations where precipitation would occur except for the absence of freezing nuclei. This possibility has led to "weather modification" operations, in which the atmosphere is seeded with silver iodide crystals, which may serve as freezing nuclei at temperatures as warm as -4C. This is just one possible technique for inducing precipitation artificially. The merits of it and of other techniques can be better assessed when the precipitation processes involved are more fully understood.

PROBLEMS

1. The introduction of an ice nucleus into a 10-gm sample of supercooled water at -20C transforms it to a mixture of ice and water, both at 0C. What is the mass of ice? (Take the specific heat of water as 1.00 cal gm^{-1} deg^{-1} at all temperatures. Calculate what heat would be needed to take the whole sample to 0C, and how much ice would be formed if this heat were then removed.)

2. Convert 1.00 kw to calories per second. By how much will 1.00 kw for 10.0 min raise the temperature of 4.00 kgm water?

3. From Figures 20.01(a) and 20.02(a), calculate and plot a curve against temperature, 0C to 100C, of the heat required to raise 1.00 cm^3 water 1.00 degree (C).

4. What heat would be required to evaporate 1.00 gm water at 0C, then heat the vapor at constant pressure to 100C? (Treat the vapor as a triatomic gas of gram-molecular weight 18.0 gm, with 6 degrees of freedom per molecule.) What heat would be required to heat 1.00 gm water from 0C to 100C, then evaporate it?

5. One hundred grams steam at 100C are passed into a mixture of ice and water at 0C and condense there. Assuming that some ice remains, how much ice is melted in this process?

6. In the Bunsen ice calorimeter, the heat to be measured is introduced into a mass of ice, surrounded by water, with both the ice and the water around it

at 0C.   The measurement made is the decrease in the total volume of ice and water due to conversion of some ice to water.   Taking the latent heat of fusion to be 80 cal gm^{-1} and the density of ice at 0C as 0.917 gm cm^{-3}, what addition of heat will lead to a decrease in volume of 1.00 mm^3?

7. (a) Plot the logarithm to base 10 of the equilibrium vapor pressure (in millimeters of mercury) of water, against the reciprocal of the Kelvin temperature, over the range −10C to 150C, from the accompanying data.   Then (b) from the graph, determine P_e at 15C, 50C, and 150C; (c) select best values for A and B in the equation $\log P = -(A/T) + B$ for the ranges −10 to +20C, 100 to 150C.

Temperature (C)	P_e (water) (mm Hg)
−10	2.0
0	4.6
10	9.2
20	17.6
30	31.8
40	55.1
60	149
80	355
100	760
120	1489
140	2710

8. If the temperature is 25C and the dew point 18C, what is the existing vapor pressure?   What is the relative humidity?   (See Figure 20.05.)

9. (a) If the temperature is 20C (so that $P_e = 17.6$ mm Hg) and the relative humidity is 60%, what is the vapor pressure?   What is the vapor density? ($\rho = PM_0/(RT)$, $M_0 = 18.0$ gm.)   (b) If the vapor density remains constant at its value in problem 9(a), while the temperature varies, plot (1) vapor pressure, (2) dew point, and (3) relative humidity, all against temperature, from 15C to 30C.   Note the relatively small change in the first two items.

10. What is the relative humidity, relative to ice, if at −10C the humidity relative to water is (a) 50%, (b) 100%?

11. How many grams water vapor are there in a room 10.0 m by 20.0 m by 7.0 m at 20C, at relative humidity 26%? at relative humidity 50%?   How much heat is needed (heat of vaporization 585 cal gm^{-1}) to evaporate the difference at 20C?   The answer may usefully be compared with that of problem 15 of Chapter 14.

12. What is the mass of 1.000 lit. of dry air ($N_0 = 29.0$ gm) at a pressure of 1.000 atm., temperature 27C?   What is the mass at the same temperature and total pressure of 1.000 lit. of saturated air, i.e., a mixture of air with water vapor at its equilibrium pressure for 27C of 26.74 mm Hg?

21

Heat Transfer by Conduction and Convection

21.01 FORMS OF HEAT TRANSFER

Heat may be transferred through matter, notably through solids, by **conduction,** the passing-on of energy of random motion from particle to particle through the substance without any related transfer of the substance itself. An alternative form of heat transfer is **convection.** In convection, which is limited to fluids, a heated portion of the substance itself is transferred, and its heat content with it. The one other form of transferring heat energy is by the radiation of electromagnetic waves generated by thermal motion. These waves are a most important phenomenon, to which the theory of heat as developed in this book so far gives no clue, and to which the next chapter is devoted.

21.02 CONDUCTION ALONG AN INSULATED ROD

If one end of a metal rod of length l is maintained (by supplying heat to it) at temperature θ_1, and the other end (by removing heat from it to colder material) at a lower temperature θ_2, and if (by thermal insulation) the amount of heat transferred out through the side wall of the rod is kept negligible, then heat flows steadily along the rod, and a plot of temperature against distance along the rod is a straight line (Figure 21.01). (We will use θ as a symbol for temperature to avoid confusion between temperature and time.) The rate at which heat enters the rod equals the rate at which it leaves the rod; this rate is proportional to the temperature difference between the two ends of the rod $(\theta_2 - \theta_1)$, proportional to the cross-sectional area of the rod (A), and inversely proportional to the length of the rod (l).

Let ΔQ be the amount of heat (in calories or ergs or joules) transferred in time Δt. Then the rate at which heat is transferred is $(\Delta Q)/(\Delta t)$. When Δt becomes very small, so does ΔQ, and the value of their ratio as both Δt and ΔQ approach zero is written in the symbolism of calculus, dQ/dt. A constant rate of heat transfer may be referred to either as $\Delta Q/\Delta t$ or dQ/dt; for a constant rate they are exactly the same.

Using the symbol dQ/dt to represent the rate of heat transfer, the proportionalities mentioned above may be written

$$\frac{dQ}{dt} \propto A \qquad \text{(other factors constant)}$$

$$\propto (\theta_2 - \theta_1) \qquad \text{(other factors constant)}$$

$$\propto \frac{1}{l} \qquad \text{(other factors constant)}$$

Combining these statements, we have

$$\frac{dQ}{dt} \propto A \frac{\theta_1 - \theta_2}{l}$$

or $\qquad \dfrac{dQ}{dt} = KA \dfrac{\theta_1 - \theta_2}{l} \qquad$ (21.01)

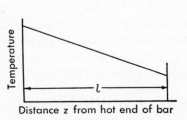

The constant of proportionality K is found to vary from substance to substance. It is a measure of how well the substance transfers heat by conduction and is called the **conductivity**.

One should note that there is a rate on each side of equation (21.01). On the left is dQ/dt, the rate of heat transfer with time. On the right, $(\theta_1 - \theta_2)/l$ is the rate of temperature decrease, or more generally $-(\theta_1 - \theta_2)/l$ is the rate of temperature change along the rod in the direction of flow of the heat. This rate is called the temperature "gradient" along the rod. If instead of the full length of the rod we consider just a slice of it, anywhere along its length, then a relation of the form of equation (21.01) is still applicable. Let the thickness of the slice be Δz, and the temperature change across it $\Delta\theta$ (Figure 21.02). Then

Fig. 21.01. Steady heat flow and temperature distribution for cylinder losing no heat from side.

$$\frac{dQ}{dt} = -KA \frac{\Delta\theta}{\Delta z}$$

or in the limit as the slice becomes very thin (and this is important here

only as a matter of form),

$$\frac{dQ}{dt} = -KA\frac{d\theta}{dz} \tag{21.02}$$

This is just a somewhat more generally applicable form of equation

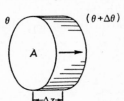

(21.01). Either form may be applied to any cylinder, from a long, slim rod to a large, thin plate. In any case, it neglects heat transferred from the side walls, a term much less important in the case of a plate.

Fig. 21.02. Arrow indicates direction of heat flow for $\Delta\theta$ negative.

21.03 HEAT CONDUCTION ALONG A BARE ROD

If there is an appreciable escape of heat from the side walls, then more heat goes in one end of the rod than comes out the other. Indeed, more heat goes in any thin slice than comes out the opposite face of the slice. Under this circumstance, dQ/dt becomes smaller as we proceed along the rod, and so therefore must the temperature gradient $d\theta/dz$, as shown in Figure 21.03.

21.04 CONDUCTION THROUGH COMPOSITE WALLS

Consider two parallel-sided slabs S_1 and S_2, Figure 21.04, of thickness z_1 and z_2 and conductivities K_1 and K_2. When a steady state has been reached, let the temperatures of the outer faces of S_1 and S_2 be θ_1 and θ_2 respectively, and let θ be the temperature of the interface. Let A be the area of cross section of the slab, and dQ/dt the rate of flow of heat through the composite slab from θ_1 to θ_2. Then

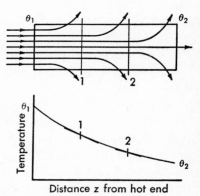

Fig. 21.03. Heat conduction along a bare rod. Rate of flow of heat through (2) is less than through (1). Gradient at (2) is less than at (1).

$$\frac{dQ}{dt} = \frac{K_1 A(\theta_1 - \theta)}{z_1} = \frac{K_2 A(\theta - \theta_2)}{z_2} \tag{21.03}$$

From this double equality the value of the rate of flow of heat and the temperature of the interface can be found.

21.05 THE CONDUCTIVITIES OF METALS

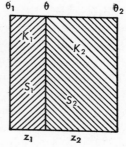

Equation (21.02) or (21.01) serves to define conductivity. With this in mind, we rearrange (21.02) to the form

$$K = - \frac{\frac{dQ}{dt}}{A \frac{d\theta}{dz}}$$

Fig. 21.04. Composite wall or bar.

that is to say, conductivity is the quantity of heat conducted per second, per unit area of cross section, per degree-per-unit-length. Its units might be

$$\frac{\text{calories}}{\text{second}} \times \frac{1}{\text{cm}^2} \times \frac{1}{\text{degrees/cm}}$$

that is, $\qquad$ calories sec^{-1} cm^{-1} deg^{-1}

These are the units most frequently used, although the present trend in usage would replace calories by joules. Conductivities in these units are given in Table 21.01 for several pure metals.

TABLE 21.01.

Metal	Conductivity [cal sec^{-1} cm^{-1} deg^{-1} (C)]
Silver	1.01
Copper	0.92
Gold	0.70
Aluminum	0.50
Zinc	0.27
Iron	0.16
Lead	0.08
Mercury	0.02

Metals are better conductors of heat than nonmetals. Metals are very much better conductors of electricity than other substances, and according to the **Wiedemann-Franz Law,** *for all pure metals, for any given temperature, the ratio of electrical to thermal conductivity is the same.* This "law" is not perfectly true, but is true enough to be worth remembering. Metals contain "free electrons", free to break loose from their orbits about the atoms and wander randomly through the crystal lattice. It is these free electrons that carry an electric current through the metal, and it is they that pass along the energy of thermal motion well enough to qualify the metals as good conductors of heat. On the basis of classical theory, these free electrons would be expected to contribute greatly to the number of degrees of freedom, and so to the specific heats of metals. They do not, and a reason for this can be found in wave mechanics.

There is another point of comparison between electrical and thermal conductivity. Conductivity is an economical way, in fact the only economical way, of transporting electricity. The charging of a capacitor and transport of the charged capacitor would be quite out of the question as an alternative. The thermal case is just the reverse. To transport heat even the short distance around a house from furnace to radiators by conduction is uneconomical, while heating a substance and transporting the substance (convection) is the normal and economical procedure.

21.06 CONDUCTIVITY OF NONMETALLIC SOLIDS

Nonmetallic crystalline solids hardly conduct electricity at all, indicating an absence of free electrons. They do conduct heat, though considerably less well than the metals, presumably by the passing-on of vibrations through the crystal lattice. (Metals can be assumed to conduct heat in the same way, as well as by the much more effective medium of the free electrons.)

In Table 21.02, the conductivities of a few nonmetallic solids are listed. The best of them is less than that of the poorest metal; these substances

TABLE 21.02.

Nonmetals	Conductivity [cal sec^{-1} cm^{-1} deg^{-1} (C)]
Graphite	0.012
Glass	0.002
Wood (along grain)	0.006
Wood (across grain)	0.0002
Ice	0.005
Pressed snow	0.0005
Dry soil	0.00033
Manufactured insulating materials	0.0001

are considered not for their worth as conductors but rather for the excellence of some of them as insulators, i.e., nonconductors. Wood, in its considerable difference in conductivity parallel to the grain and conductivity across the grain, resembles other anisotropic substances such as mica and large single crystals.

Solids are still poorer conductors when they are porous, since the non-circulating air in the pores is a very poor conductor. The manufactured insulating materials are very light meshes which prevent the circulation of the large amount of air trapped in them. A lower limit for the conductivity of these insulators is provided by the conductivity of air itself.

21.07 CONDUCTIVITY OF LIQUIDS AND GASES

The conductivities of liquids and gases are the lowest there are, as can be seen from Table 21.03.

TABLE 21.03.

Fluid	Conductivity [cal sec^{-1} cm^{-1} deg^{-1} (C)]
Water	0.0014
Other liquids	0.0006 to 0.0003
Hydrogen	0.00033
Air	0.00006

The conductivities of gases can be calculated from kinetic theory, in similar fashion to the calculation of viscosity (section 14.13). Suppose that in Figure 14.10 the temperature increased upward, rather than the flow velocity, so that $d\theta/dz$ was positive. As in section 14.13, the number of molecules crossing unit area of the XY plane in unit time would be $\frac{1}{2}\bar{c}\nu$, and the average magnitude of the z-distance traveled by these molecules between collisions would be $\lambda/2$. The average energy of a molecule is $\frac{1}{2}fk\theta$, and when a molecule moves in the z direction by *minus* $\lambda/2$, its energy will exceed that of its new neighbors, on an average, by $\frac{1}{2}fk(d\theta/dz)\lambda/2$. Thus this is the average amount of thermal energy transferred across the XY plane (or any surface parallel to it) by one molecule crossing it.

The energy transferred across unit area in unit time is thus

$$\frac{1}{2}\bar{c}\nu \times \frac{1}{2}fk\frac{d\theta}{dz}\frac{\lambda}{2}$$

in the opposite direction to the temperature gradient (i.e., with temperature increasing upward in Figure 14.10, the energy will be transferred downward). In terms of the quantities involved in equation (21.02), this energy transferred across unit area in unit time is

$$-\frac{dQ}{dt} \times \frac{1}{A}$$

Thus we can extend equation (21.02) to read, for gases,

$$K = -\frac{\dfrac{dQ}{dt}}{A\dfrac{d\theta}{dz}} = \tfrac{1}{2}\bar{c}\nu \times \tfrac{1}{2}fk \times \frac{\lambda}{2} \qquad (21.04)$$

The product $\tfrac{1}{2}fk\nu$ on the right-hand side of equation (21.04) is the thermal energy of the gas per unit volume, equal to $c_v\rho$. (This equality can be derived explicitly from information contained in Chapter 14.)   So

$$K = \tfrac{1}{4}\rho\bar{c}\lambda c_v$$

But in section 14.13 similar considerations gave, for the viscosity, $\eta = \tfrac{1}{4}\rho\bar{c}\lambda$, and so

$$K = \eta c_v \qquad (21.05)$$

that is, the conductivity equals the viscosity times the specific heat at constant volume. Conductivities of gases, determined experimentally, are found to be roughly twice the product of viscosity times specific heat, these quantities also being determined experimentally. So equation (21.05) is correct only as to order of magnitude. But the conductivity of a gas, like its viscosity, is independent of pressure over a large range of pressures and temperatures.

21.08 THE NATURE OF CONVECTION

The easiest way of transferring heat from one point to another is to heat some fluid and transfer the substance by fluid flow. Heated fluid is less dense than colder fluid, and so is buoyant in it and tends to rise. Thus, when a beaker of water is placed over a burner, the water at the bottom of the beaker becomes the hottest, but at the same time it becomes the least dense, and rises and is replaced by less dense and less warm water. Again, in the heating system of a house, water heated in the boiler rises through one set of pipes while the cooled water in the radiators flows down through another set. The pressure of the column of warm, less dense water is somewhat lower than that of the less warm water, and so circulation is maintained.

Whether the circulation occurs in a simple volume of fluid as in the beaker or in a planned system of pipes, it is called *natural convection* as long as it relies on the effect of gravity on fluid of varying density. Nowadays, the heating system of a house is likely to include a small electric pump to provide (and control) the circulation. Such circulation is usually called "forced convection".

Convection in gases occurs similarly to that in liquids. The "radiators" in a room would have to be much larger or much hotter than they are to provide much heat by radiation. Actually, they heat the air close to them, this rises, and a convective circulation is set up. Because of the compressibility of gases, convection in gases differs somewhat from that in liquids. Thus columns of convectively rising air form and develop into showers and thunderstorms, even though the temperature *decreases* as the height increases (section 15.17).

For convective circulation to be set up in a body of fluid, heat must be applied at the bottom, or taken away from the top. Hot pipes near the ceiling of a room will raise the temperature of the air near the ceiling by local convection, but will not affect the air at lower levels. Again, an immersion heater in the top few inches of a tall beaker of water can bring the water at the top to the boiling point without affecting the temperature at the bottom of the beaker. In measuring the *conduction* of heat by fluids, it is necessary to avoid convection, and this can be done by observing a downward flow of heat.

21.09 NONCONVECTING FILMS

If a beaker of hot water is set out on a table, it cools, and the principal cause of its cooling is convection. The air next to the beaker becomes heated, rises, and is replaced by cooler air. But the region close to the beaker requires careful consideration.

When fluid is flowing parallel to a wall, the velocity of flow drops as you approach the wall, becoming zero at the wall surface. Close to the wall, the lines of flow of the fluid are all neatly parallel to the surface; the flow is said to be "laminar". Farther removed from the wall, somewhere between 1 and 10 mm, the flow lines become nonparallel, the flow is "turbulent" (Figure 21.05). Now in the region of laminar flow, a minute sample of air at distance x from the wall remains just that far from the wall. There is thus no convection—transfer of heat by transfer of substance—across that fluid film, the region of laminar flow. The heat must get across this film by conduction. The conductivities of liquids are low, those of gases even lower, and so these fluid films, even though they are thin, are very effective insulators. The hot beaker with which we introduced this section cools much more slowly by virtue of the film of air, the region of laminar flow, against its surface. In the case of the beaker, the film would be something like 5 mm thick.

It is a simplification to give the film an exact thickness, for there is no

sharp boundary but rather a gradual transition through a "buffer zone"
from the region of laminar flow to the region
of turbulence.   This is a fair and reasonable
simplification, however, for we can consider
an "effective thickness" through which transfer is by conduction only.   The effective
thickness varies with the nature of the fluid
and its rate of flow, with the smoothness and
shape of the surface, and with its disposition:
vertical, horizontal, or oblique.   Just to indicate the complexity of the calculation of this
"effective thickness", here is an example.
For a large, vertical wall at temperature t_w
surrounded by a gas at temperature t_g, the
results of dimensional analysis combined with
experiment indicate that the effective thickness as a function of other factors is

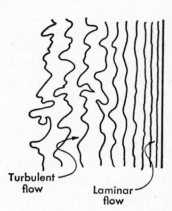

Fig. 21.05. Transition
from laminar flow, adja-
cent to wall, to turbulent
flow at a distance from
wall.

$$7.8 \left(\frac{\eta}{\rho^2 c_p \beta g (t_w - t_g)} \right)^{\frac{1}{3}} \qquad (21.06)$$

where η is the viscosity of the gas, ρ the density, c_p the specific heat
at constant pressure, β the coeffi-
cient of volume expansion, and g
the acceleration of gravity.

Once the effective thickness is
known, its use is fairly simple.
Thus for heat to be lost from a
room through a glass windowpane,
it must be conducted through three
parallel slabs (Figure 21.06): first,
a slab 5 mm thick (say) of nonconvecting air, then one of glass,
then another one of air.   The
outer film of air is liable to be
reduced in thickness by the wind.
(Similarly, if we want to eliminate
the film between a flame and a
metal surface, we can use a jetlike
flame to drive the film away and

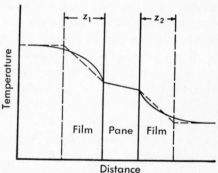

Fig. 21.06.   Temperature drop across
a windowpane and the nonconvecting
films on either side of it is shown,
approximately, by the solid line.   If we
assume films having quite definite thicknesses, z_1 and z_2, and sharp outer edges, we
obtain the pattern of temperature against
distance indicated by the broken line.

force the hot gases of the flame right up against the metal.)   In the case of a windowpane, a 5-mm film of air is thirty-three times as good an insulator as a similar thickness of glass, and so we find only a small fraction of the total temperature drop across the glass itself. There is no point in doubling the thickness of the glass pane; it is by doubling the number of panes and so doubling the number of air films that we reduce the heat lost through windows.

When heat is to be transferred through the wall of a vessel, be it an industrial boiler or a pot on the stove, the fluid films prove a great hindrance. The outer film can be blown away. The inner film, of the liquid inside the vessel, can be reduced by stirring or rapid flow. Its thickness may not be so great as the 5 mm mentioned above. (Thus for boiling water flowing with an average speed of 2 ft sec^{-1} through a smooth copper pipe of one-inch internal diameter, the equivalent thickness of the conducting layer is 0.009 in.) Its conductivity, while low, will be many times that of a gas: Water has more than twenty times the conductivity of air. If bubbles or a complete layer of vapor forms in the liquid against the wall of the vessel or pipe, the rate of heat transfer becomes very poor indeed.

PROBLEMS

1. At what rate is heat conducted along a copper bar of length 20.0 cm, cross section 20.0 cm^2, temperature drop 30.0 deg (C) from one end to the other, losses from the side walls being negligible? Express your answer first in calories per second, then convert it to watts.

2. What is the temperature gradient in problem 1? What would the temperature gradient need to be in an iron bar of the same cross section to provide the same heat flow?

3. Heat is conducted along a bar of length 20.0 cm, cross section 20.0 cm^2, without loss from the sides. Temperatures at the end of the bar are 90.0C and 60.0C. The first 10.0 cm of the bar are copper, the rest iron. What is the temperature of the interface between copper and iron? At what rate is heat conducted along the bar?

4. A pond is covered by a layer of ice 1.00 cm thick. The top surface of the ice is at −2.00C (although the atmosphere above is many degrees colder), the bottom surface obviously at 0.00C. At what rate is heat being transferred through the ice? How long will it take for an additional thickness of 1.00 mm of ice to form on the under side of the layer?

5. In 100 sec, how much heat will be *conducted* down a column of air 10.0 cm deep, cross section 10.0 cm^2, temperature drop 15.0 deg (C)? By how much would this quantity of heat raise the temperature of 0.100 lit. of air at 1.00 atm. 0C, at constant pressure?

6. A house 7.0 m by 10.0 m has walls 7.0 m high, insulated by 5.0 cm of rock wool of conductivity 1.00×10^{-4} cal sec^{-1} cm^{-1} deg^{-1}. At what rate (in calories per hour) is heat lost *through the walls* if their inside surfaces are maintained at 20.0C when their outside surfaces are at 0.0C?

7. Draw diagrams to show, approximately, the temperature variation from a room at 20C through a glass windowpane to the outside atmosphere at −20C (a) when there is little wind, (b) when there is a strong wind against the window. Repeat these for a double pane with a sealed air space between the two panes. Estimate the factor by which the double glazing reduces the rate of heat loss in case (a) and in case (b).

8. A windowpane 5.0 mm thick has a nonconvecting layer of air of effective thickness 5.0 mm clinging to each side of it. Room temperature is 20.0C, outdoor temperature −10.0C. At what rate is heat conducted through the window, per square meter? What would be the rate per square meter if there were no air films?

9. Repeat problem 8 with the same layers of air, but with a pane of glass 20.0 mm thick. Comparing your answer with that for problem 8, by what percentage is the rate of heat loss reduced by increasing the thickness of the glass?

10. A shopkeeper, faced with the situation of problem 8, directs an electric fan at the inner surface of the window and so reduces the thickness of the inner surface film to 1.0 mm. This brings the temperature of the inner surface to a value above the dew point and so avoids condensation. What will be the temperature of the inner surface of the glass? By how much will the fan increase the conduction of heat through the window, per square meter?

22

Radiation

22.01 INTRODUCTION

We have considered the transfer of heat through a substance, and the transfer of heat by transfer of the substance. There remains a mode of transfer that does not require substance at all. Our whole study of heat so far has been with reference to matter, randomly energized matter. But matter cannot possess this random energy without setting up a corresponding random energy in the form of electromagnetic radiation. By looking on atoms and molecules as point masses, without recognizing their essentially electrical structure, we have missed entirely the possibility of this electrical concomitant of thermal motion. The experimental study of heat, however, cannot go far without revealing its existence.

22.02 THE NATURE OF ELECTROMAGNETIC RADIATION: RADIO WAVES

Suppose that a vertical wire is connected to the ground through a battery (Figure 22.01). Then the voltage of the wire will differ from the voltage of the ground. There will be an electrostatic field due to this charged conductor, extending out indefinitely, but detectable to only a short distance.

Now suppose we throw a switch and ground the wire. The wire is rapidly discharged; its voltage drops to zero. The electrostatic field must disappear too, but it will not disappear all at once. The field nearest the wire will disappear first; the disappearance will travel out as a wave (Figure 22.02). The wave will not limit itself to the

Fig. 22.01.

region where the static field was appreciable, but will travel out to much greater distances. It will travel out at high speed, at a speed known most commonly as the velocity of light.

So much for electrostatics. But when the charge was being removed from the wire, a current must have been flowing. When an electric current flows, a magnetic field is set up. This momentary current would lead to a sudden increase in the magnetic field, then a sudden decrease. And the change in the magnetic field takes time to travel, too. It likewise travels with the velocity of light, and keeps traveling to great distances. In fact, the magnetic and electric variations traveling out are intimately related; you cannot get a wave of one without the other. The combination is known as electromagnetic radiation.

As an alternative to the sudden discharging of a conductor, you can arrange circuits which will cause the charge in the wire to vary continuously between a large positive and a large negative value. There will then be a continuously varying current in and out of the wire. A succession of continuous waves will be sent out: continuous electrical waves interlaced with continuous magnetic waves.

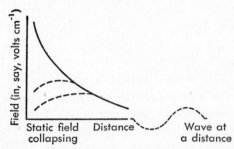

Fig. 22.02. Manner in which static field collapses and wave is formed when switch of Figure 22.01 is thrown from battery to ground.

There are continuously changing charges and continuously changing currents in the wiring of a building, but not much energy is radiated from it. The variations occur too slowly, or more specifically, too slowly for the size of the system. Whatever radiation there may be will travel how far during one cycle of the current? In one-sixtieth of a second, at 3×10^{10} cm sec^{-1}, it will travel 5×10^8 cm, or 5,000,000 m. That is the wavelength of the radiation.

The longest wavelength used is about 25,000 m (corresponding to a frequency of 12,000 cycles per second), and that takes a very long aerial. The shortest, used in radar, is about, shall we say, 1 cm, corresponding to a frequency of 30,000 million cycles, i.e., 30,000 megacycles, per second.

22.03 ELECTROMAGNETIC RADIATION: RADIO TO X-RAY

By setting up oscillations in electrical circuits, electromagnetic radiation can be generated at wavelengths from about 10^5 m down to about 1 cm, a geometrical range of 10^7 from the longest to the shortest. Waves over this range are referred to as radio waves. The most notable naturally occurring source of radiation in this range is lightning, although radiations from the sun and from outer space at the shorter end of the range are the basis of "radio astronomy".

By bombarding metal targets with fast electrons, "X-rays" of wavelength from 10^{-7} to 10^{-10} cm are produced; the gamma rays emitted by radioactive nuclei range from 10^{-9} cm to shorter wavelengths.

Thus at wavelengths from 1 cm upward we have radio waves, from 10^{-7} cm downward we have X-rays and γ-rays. Let us now turn our attention to the region from 1 cm to 10^{-7} cm, from the short-wavelength limit of radio to the long-wavelength limit of X-rays (Figure 22.03). In this region, radiations may be generated by various means. The most notable landmark in this range of wavelengths is the narrow band from

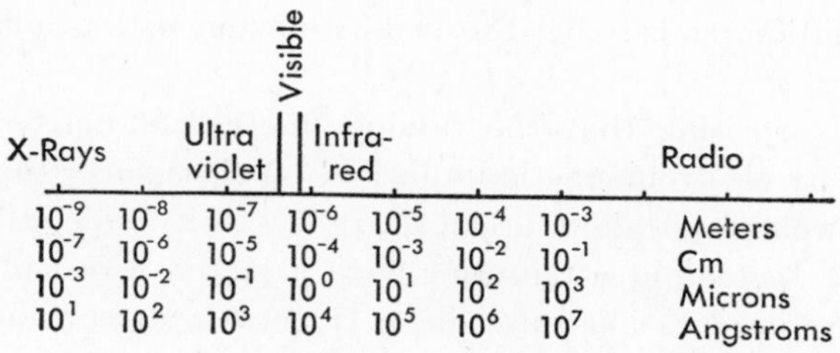

X-Rays		Ultra violet	Visible	Infra- red				Radio	
10^{-9}	10^{-8}	10^{-7}	10^{-6}	10^{-5}	10^{-4}	10^{-3}		Meters	
10^{-7}	10^{-6}	10^{-5}	10^{-4}	10^{-3}	10^{-2}	10^{-1}		Cm	
10^{-3}	10^{-2}	10^{-1}	10^{0}	10^{1}	10^{2}	10^{3}		Microns	
10^{1}	10^{2}	10^{3}	10^{4}	10^{5}	10^{6}	10^{7}		Angstroms	

Fig. 22.03. Position of the visible region in the spectral range between X-rays and radio.

0.4 to 0.75 $\times$ 10^{-4} cm; (10^{-4} cm is called one "micron", i.e., one micrometer or millionth part of a meter). This region is defined not by the means of generation, but by the means of detection; it is the *visual range* of the human eye. The adjacent region on the short-wave side, extending down to about 10^{-6} cm, is called the ultraviolet region, i.e., beyond and above (in frequency) the violet end of the visible region. The region adjacent to the visible on the long-wave side, extending up to about 40 microns, is called the infrared, i.e., below (in frequency) the red end of the visible.

It is in these regions, roughly halfway (on a logarithmic scale) between the shortest radio waves and X-rays, that radiant heat—the electromagnetic radiation emitted by bodies by virtue of their temperature—is important. Matter consists of electrically charged particles, and the random motion of matter that we have been calling heat involves many random accelerations of these charged particles. The acceleration of a charged body, or a charged particle, involves the sending out of electromagnetic radiation, in keeping with the statements of section 22.02. It is not surprising, therefore, that this random motion should always be accompanied by the emission of electromagnetic radiation having similarly random properties. Where the thermal motion is random as to speed, the radiation is random as to wavelength. Where for any particular temperature there is a continuous distribution of molecular speeds, the corresponding radiation is found to have a continuous distribution of wavelengths. Thermal radiation is emitted by matter in random motion. On the other hand, electromagnetic radiation of thermal or other origin may be absorbed by matter, and this absorption leads to an increase in the thermal motion, and so an increase in the temperature, of the absorbing material. We are accustomed to the absorption of light waves by matter, and of heat waves from the sun and from less-hot electric heaters by our bodies. It should be borne in mind that although certain substances are transparent over limited ranges of wavelengths, all electromagnetic radiation tends to be absorbed by matter, with resultant heating of the matter.

It is not surprising that the random motion of matter should be accompanied by electromagnetic radiation, but it is surprisingly difficult to obtain a simple physical picture of the processes by which this radiation is generated. Instead of attempting such a picture, we will proceed to observational considerations (and hence macroscopic considerations) of thermal radiation and its relationship to matter.

22.04 THE THERMOPILE

If an object is hot enough, the radiation it emits by virtue of its temperature can be detected by eye, for some of it is at wavelengths in the visible region. Below about 500C there will no longer be a visible glow, but the radiation can still be felt by its warming effect on the body, for it is absorbed by the skin and converted into heat.

For more sensitive and quantitative observations of the radiation associated with heat, we can turn to detecting instruments, notably the thermopile. One very useful way of measuring temperature is by means of thermocouples, junctions of two dissimilar metals. If we have a closed circuit consisting of a galvanometer and two thermocouples, then any difference between the temperatures of the two couples, even a small fraction of a degree, results in a detectable deflection of the galvanometer. A thermopile consists of a number of thermocouples in series. One designed for the detection of radiation is shown in Figure 22.04.

The thermopile is set behind a slit, so that the blackened silver plates (very lightweight affairs) are exposed to the radiation, whereas the alternate junctions are hidden from it.   When the pile is "looking at" something hot, an electromotive force (emf) is set up, indicating that the irradiated junctions have become slightly warmer than the alternate, sheltered junctions.   The temperature difference between the junctions, and so the emf, levels off when the temperature of the irradiated junctions has risen sufficiently for their rate of heat loss by conduction and convection to equal their rate of heat gain by the absorption of radiation.

When the pile is looking at something at the same temperature as itself, there is no emf. When it is looking at something cooler than itself, there is an emf of the opposite polarity to the first case mentioned, indicating that the exposed junctions are actually losing heat by radiation.   To do this, they must radiate themselves and lose more heat by outgoing radiation than they gain by radiation absorbed.   Since this reverse emf goes on increasing as the temperature of the objects at which the pile looks is

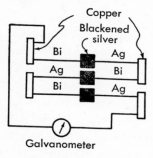

Fig. 22.04.   Thermopile elements and connections.

continually reduced, it would appear that there is some radiation from any object, and that the amount of this radiation goes on decreasing as long as the temperature itself goes on decreasing.

22.05 LESLIE-CUBE SURFACES AS REFLECTORS

Sir John Leslie, experimenting with radiant heat in 1804, used a piece of apparatus that is still useful for demonstration purposes.   It consists of a cubical vessel, each face of whose outer surface is of a different material, or differently finished.   Although the experiments for which the Leslie Cube was designed are dealt with in section 22.07, it will be convenient to think of the present subject matter in terms of this equipment.

If the thermopile is set facing a hot body, say one hot enough to glow, it produces a large current, or at any rate a large deflection of a sensitive galvanometer.   Now if the thermopile faces away from the hot body, it is found that the polished metal surfaces of the cube can be used to reflect the radiation from the body toward the thermocouple, and so again produce a large current.   The surface of the cube must be held at just the right angle to give this reflection, for the reflection is specular, i.e., with the radiation coming back at one particular angle, just like the reflection of light by a mirror.

If a white surface of the cube is used instead of a mirrorlike surface, a reflection is still obtained.   In this case, the reflected radiation is not so intense, i.e., the current produced is not so large.   At the same time, the angle of reflection is not so critical.   This is a case of diffuse reflection, with the reflected radiation coming back at all angles, as opposed to the previous case of specular reflection with the reflected radiation coming back at one particular angle.   It is just like the reflection of light by an opaque white wall.

If a black surface of the cube is used, no reflection is detected at all, at any angle.   The radiation is then being absorbed.   That is why the absorbing surfaces of the thermopile are themselves painted black: so that they will be good absorbers.

Other surfaces of the cube, of varying lightness and texture, reflect to varying extents and with varying degrees of diffusion.   And so they vary in absorption, for the radiation not reflected either specularly or diffusely must be absorbed.   Positive evidence of this absorption exists in the thermopile itself, where the energy of the absorbed radiation is converted into heat and so actuates all the little thermocouples.

Direct evidence of absorption may be obtained from the Leslie Cube. Suppose it is made airtight and connected to a water-filled manometer, to make an air thermometer out of it.   Then the rate at which its temperature rises is found to be greatest for the nonreflecting, least for the reflecting surfaces.

22.06 BLACK BODIES

Although no reflection is detected from the black surface, there will actually be some, just a little.   For no surface is perfectly absorbing. The best approach to a perfect absorber is achieved, not by studying the various black paints available, but by considering the possibilities of geometry.   The windows of a house, viewed from outside, by daylight, tend to look black.   The walls within the house are not black; they may be almost white.   But such daylight as enters the window is reflected about the room several times before it gets out, and at each reflection there is some loss by absorption.   As a result, only a small fraction of the light entering through the window re-emerges from the window.   The window may be looked on as a good absorber.

There are two ways of making a window, say the single window in a room, a better absorber.   One is by making the interior walls darker, so that there is more loss by absorption at each reflection.   The other is to make the window smaller, so that the probable number of reflections that the light undergoes between the time it enters and the time it leaves is greater.

In considering radiant heat, a perfect absorber, i.e., a surface that absorbs all the radiation falling on it, whatever the wavelength, is called a "black body". It is a useful abstraction. The nearest laboratory approach to a perfect absorber is obtained by stressing the latter of the two methods mentioned above, by making a small window or opening or aperture in a relatively large vessel. Just as with a small window in a large room, the chance that any radiation which enters the opening will ever get out again is very small. It can be made vanishingly small by reducing the relative size of the aperture. Any close approach to a perfect absorber formed in this way, like the theoretical perfect absorber whose performance it approaches in the limit, is also called a "black body".

22.07 RADIATION FROM A LESLIE CUBE

If a Leslie Cube is filled with hot water or circulating steam, all its surfaces are brought to the same temperature, considerably above room temperature. If the various surfaces all at the same temperature are set facing the thermopile, one after another, it is found that they radiate to various extents. The dull black surface radiates a good deal, and so effects a large thermocouple current. The white and the polished metallic surfaces radiate very little. The radiation from the mirrorlike surfaces may not even be detectable. It is notable, and important, that a list of the various surfaces in the order of the extent to which they radiate by virtue of their own temperature is just the reverse of a list in the order of the extent to which they reflect. Or more pertinently, the order in which they radiate by virtue of their own temperature is exactly the same as the order in which they absorb.

22.08 DEFINITION AND KIRCHHOFF'S LAW

It appears from the foregoing section that there is a proportionality between the emission of radiation and its absorption. To become more precise about this relation, precise definitions are required.

Absorptivity or *total surface absorptivity* is the fraction of the total radiation falling on a surface that is absorbed. The radiation not absorbed is thrown back, either in all directions (diffusely) or in a direction bearing a particular relation to that from which it came (specularly).

Reflectivity or *total surface reflectivity* is the fraction of the total radiation falling on a surface that is thrown back, reflected either diffusely or specularly. If we avoid cases of transparent materials, we can say that the radiation that is not reflected must be absorbed. Letting I denote the amount per unit area, or intensity, of radiation incident on (i.e., falling on) a surface, then

$$AI + RI = I \qquad (22.01)$$

or, dividing by the intensity I,

$$A + R = 1 \qquad (22.02)$$

where A and R denote the absorptivity and the reflectivity of the surface for the radiation being considered.

The **emissive power** of a surface is the energy emitted by a surface in the form of radiation per unit area (cm^2) per unit time (second). Let us denote this by e.

The proportionality noted above between emission and absorption is shown by more precise experiments to be exact, and may be stated as

$$e \propto A$$

or
$$e = \text{constant} \times A \qquad (22.03)$$

This is Kirchhoff's Law (after Gustav R. Kirchhoff, 1824).

Now, the largest value that A can have is unity: This is the case of total absorption, the case of a black body. So the greatest possible emissive power is that of a black body at the same temperature. Letting BB as a subscript denote a black body, then for any specified temperature the emissivity equals e_{BB} when A equals unity. Substituting in (22.03) gives

$$e_{BB} = \text{constant} \qquad (22.04)$$

where the constant is that of equation (22.03). **Kirchhoff's Law** can now be rewritten as

$$e = e_{BB}A \qquad (22.05)$$

If, to match the quantities reflectivity and absorptivity we define **emissivity** as the emissive power of a surface expressed as a fraction of the emissive power of a black body at the same temperature, and if we denote emissivity by the symbol E, then

$$E = \frac{e}{e_{BB}} = A \qquad (22.06)$$

22.09 THE STEFAN-BOLTZMANN LAW

So far we have considered the relative emission from various surfaces, assumed to be all at the same temperature. The rate at which energy is emitted varies rapidly with the temperature. In 1879 Stefan suggested from a study of experimental data that the rate is proportional to the fourth power of the absolute temperature. A few years later, Boltzmann provided a theoretical basis for such a relation in the case of a black body. So we can write

$$e_{BB} = \sigma T^4 \tag{22.07}$$

This is known as the **Stefan-Boltzmann Law**; the constant of proportionality in this equation is called the Stefan-Boltzmann constant.

Combining equation (22.07) with (22.06), we obtain for any body

$$e = E\sigma T^4 \tag{22.08}$$

or, since $E = A$,
$$e = A\sigma T^4$$

It should be borne in mind that although E is always equal to A, this quantity by either name depends on physical properties of a surface which vary with the temperature. Thus E or A may vary with the temperature, and although it is perfectly true to say, for a black body, that

$$e_{BB} \propto T^4$$

it does *not necessarily* hold that for any body at all

$$e \propto T^4$$

Many experiments have been carried out to evaluate the constant σ. It is now generally accepted that

$$\sigma = 5.672 \pm 0.003 \times 10^{-12} \text{ watt cm}^{-2} \text{ deg}^{-4} \tag{22.09}$$

22.10 NET EMISSIVE POWER

The Stefan-Boltzmann Law as we have stated it in equation (22.07) and its combination with Kirchhoff's Law in equation (22.08) refer to the radiation coming out from a body. At the same time that radiation is being emitted, radiation from the surroundings is being absorbed. This applies even if the surroundings are colder than the body in question, although the surroundings need not be much cooler for the inflow to become insignificant compared with the emission. In the simplest case, where the black body at temperature T is surrounded by other black bodies at temperature T_0,

$$(e_{BB})_{net} = \sigma(T^4 - T_0^4) \tag{22.10}$$

In another extreme case, if the surroundings are all perfect reflectors,

$$(e_{BB})_{net} = \sigma(T^4 - T^4) = 0 \tag{22.11}$$

There would seem to be a moral in this. If you cannot keep the walls of your room warm, then make them good reflectors, and keep yourself warm by the heat you yourself radiate, reflected back at you.

22.11 THE DISTRIBUTION WITH WAVELENGTH OF BLACK-BODY RADIATION

The radiation from a body by virtue of its temperature has a wide and continuous assortment of wavelengths. The distribution of

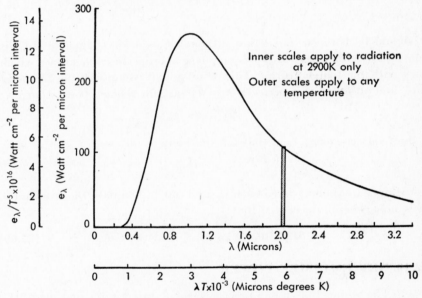

Fig. 22.05. Thermal radiation: Plank's Distribution Law for radiation from a black body.

the power radiated with the wavelength of that radiation is shown in Figure 22.05 for a black body at a temperature of 2900K, which is approximately the temperature of an incandescent tungsten lamp. The ordinate, e_λ, varies with the wavelength. At any wavelength λ, the product $e_\lambda \, \Delta\lambda$ gives the emissive power at wavelengths between λ and a slightly longer wavelength $\lambda + \Delta\lambda$. The shaded column at $\lambda = 2$ microns in Figure 22.05 has an area $e_\lambda \, \Delta\lambda$, where $e_\lambda = 100$ watts cm^{-2} per micron and $\Delta\lambda = 0.1$ micron. This area, then, represents 100 watts cm^{-2} micron^{-1} $\times$ 0.1 micron $= 10$ watts cm^{-2}, and this is (approximately) the power per square centimeter emitted by a black body at temperature 2900K at wavelengths between 2.0 and 2.1 microns. The approximation consists in taking the area of a rectangular column of height e_λ, rather than just the area within the column and below the continuous e_λ curve. The approximation improves as the interval $\Delta\lambda$ is decreased, and approaches perfection as $\Delta\lambda$ approaches zero. The total emissive power, i.e., at all wavelengths, is represented by the total area under the curve. The ordinate e_λ corresponding to a given value of λ is actually $\Delta e/\Delta\lambda$, or more precisely $de/d\lambda$, where e is the emissive power for all wavelengths less than that value of λ.

For the temperature of 2900K, the maximum value of e_λ comes at a wavelength (λ_m) of one micron. According to **Wien's Displacement Law** (Wilhelm Wien, 1864), the product $\lambda_m T$ is constant, i.e.,

$$\lambda_m T = 2900 \text{ microns} \times \text{degrees} \qquad (22.12)$$

So for a temperature of 290K, the peak comes at 10 microns. The peak for 290K is not only displaced along the wavelength scale by a factor 10 from that for 2900K; it is also lower by a factor of 10^5, so that the area under the curve will be less by a factor 10^4, in keeping with equation (22.07). The whole curve as given for 2900K will be correct for 290K if the scale of the abscissas is changed by a factor 10, i.e., $(T_2/T_1)^{-1}$, and the scale of ordinates by a factor 10^{-5}, i.e., $(T_2/T_1)^5$. In fact, if we plot e_λ/T^5 against λT, the very same curve will hold for a black body at any temperature.

Brunt* points out:

$\cdots$ on account of the steep slope of the curve on the side of low wavelengths the amount of radiation below a limit $\lambda T = 1,000$ [micron $\times$ degree Kelvin] is negligible, being considerably less than 0.1 per cent of the total radiation. The slope of the curve is far less steep on the side of high wavelengths, and the limit is not so readily set. Only 0.1 per cent of the total radiation will be neglected if we stop at an upper limit set by $\lambda T = 54,000$, and 1 per cent will be neglected if the upper limit is set by $\lambda T = 24,000$.

Thus black-body radiation at 6,000K, approximately the temperature of the sun, is contained (or 99 per cent of it is contained) within the limits of 0.17 and 4 microns, and has its maximum intensity in the blue-green at about 0.5 microns.

* Sir David Brunt, *Physical and Dynamical Meteorology*, Cambridge University Press, 1941.

Black-body radiation at terrestrial temperatures of roughly 300K will be contained within the limits 3 and 80 microns, having its maximum intensity at 10 microns.

22.12 LESS-GOOD EMITTERS

Actual radiating surfaces are all less good than the perfect and theoretical black bodies. Their energy distributions therefore always fall below the distributions for black bodies at the same temperatures. These distributions do not necessarily fall below by the same fraction at all wavelengths. Thus a white surface at 300K is obviously a good reflector (and so a poor absorber, poor emitter) in the visible region, from 0.4 to 0.7 microns. But some white-painted surfaces are quite good absorbers and emitters at somewhat longer wavelengths; you cannot tell for sure from the visible what the behavior of a surface will be over a much wider range of wavelengths.

Tungsten at temperatures between 2000K and 3000K has an emissivity E of only about 0.3. It happens, however, to have about the same value of E_λ at all wavelengths, so that its distribution is given quite well by the black-body curve whose ordinates have been multiplied by 0.3. The distribution for tungsten at 2450K is much like that for a black body at the same temperature. It is still more closely like that for a black body at 2500K, and so is said to have a "color temperature" of 2500K.

PROBLEMS

1. (a) What is the emissive power of a black body at 2900K, given $\sigma = 5.67 \times 10^{-12}$ watt cm^{-2} deg^{-4}? (b) If the absorptivity is 0.35 for tungsten at 2900K, what area of tungsten at that temperature will be needed to radiate 50 watts?

2. A tungsten wire of length 20.0 cm, diameter 0.100 mm, sends out radiation at a rate of 40 watts. Its absorptivity is approximately 0.30. What is its temperature? What length of the same wire would radiate 40 watts at 2900K?

3. A small spherical source emits radiation uniformly in all directions, with a total rate of 125 watts. How many watts per square centimeter will pass through a spherical surface of radius 1.00 m, whose center is at the source?

4. What must be the temperature of a black body for its emissive power to be 1.00 watt per cm^2?

5. Recalling that a window in a room closely resembles the aperture of an experimental black body, and so radiates at the same rate per unit area as the surface of a black body at the temperature of the room, what is the rate at which heat is radiated from 1.00 m^2 of window in the wall of a room at

20C? (It may be noted that for a window facing the clear sky a loss of this order during the hours of darkness can be avoided by covering the window with curtains of high reflectivity.)

6. Plot the emissive power of a black body against temperature from 0C to 40C. From this, plot over the same range of temperatures the net emissive power $\sigma(T^4 - T_0{}^4)$, where T_0 is the temperature of black-body surroundings, for $T_0 = 20C$, and for $T_0 = 0C$.

7. One face of a wood board 1.00 cm thick is radiating as a black body at 0C, the radiation absorbed by this face at the same time being negligible. The heat lost by radiation is provided by conduction through the wood, with coefficient 2.00×10^{-3} cal sec^{-1} cm^{-1} deg^{-1}. What is the temperature of the other face of the board?

8. The intensity of the sun's radiation at the distance of the earth, per unit area, called the solar constant, equals about 0.14 watt cm^{-2}. The effective area of interception, for the case of a sphere, is πr^2. Radiation by a black body equals $5.67 \times 10^{-12}T^4$ watt cm^{-2}, and the area radiating in the case of a sphere is $4\pi r^2$. What would be the temperature of a spherical black body at the earth's distance from the sun and radiating energy at the same total rate that it received it from the sun?

9. Winter sunshine falling obliquely on a horizontal surface delivers roughly 0.50 cal cm^{-2} min^{-1}. Freshly fallen snow has a density of about 0.100 gm cm^{-3}. If the snow could be made perfectly absorbing by coating it with soot, what depth of snow would be melted per hour of sunshine?

10. All the sunshine falling on a circular mirror of diameter 1.00 m is focused on a small blackened vessel containing 100 gm water. Neglecting losses from the vessel, at what rate does the temperature rise, if radiation arrives at the mirror at a rate of 0.100 watt cm^{-2}?

11. How rapidly (in degrees per minute) would a cup of coffee cool by radiation alone? Assume that the cup is a black body of negligible heat capacity in itself, that it has a radiating area of 200 cm^2, and that it contains 200 gm of coffee having a specific heat of 1.00 cal gm^{-1}. The temperature of the cup is 80C, that of the black-body surroundings 20C.

12. One square centimeter of black body at temperature 1000K emits 5.67 watts of radiation with a wavelength of maximum intensity of 2.90 microns. What will be the power and the wavelength of maximum intensity if the temperature is raised to 2000K? if it is raised to 3000K?

13. A black body at 2900K emits radiation most intensely at wavelength 1.00 micron. At what wavelength, then, will a human body (which is a "black body" in this context) emit radiation most intensely, according to Wien's Displacement Law?

SOUND

23

The Vibrations of Particles

23.01 VIBRATION, WAVE MOTION, AND SOUND

Consider a simple situation in which a gong is struck and heard. When the gong is struck, it moves rapidly to and fro in a fairly regular pattern; that is to say, it **vibrates.** The air close to the vibrating gong is alternately compressed and rarefied. The alternate compressions and rarefactions of the air are passed along through the air as **wave motion,** by which the pattern of to-and-fro motion travels great distances without any one portion of the substance moving very far. The wave motion

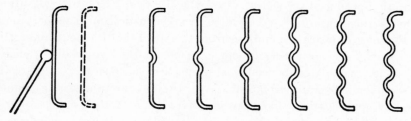

Fig. 23.01.   Fig. 23.02.   Waves on a vibrating gong.

sets up pressure variations at our ears, and so drives our eardrums into vibrations similar to those of the gong, but much less energetic.

Sound passing through the air from the vibrating source to the ear is wave motion. But the vibration of the source is also wave motion. If a perfectly rigid gong were struck, the whole gong would be displaced to one side, without any distortion of its shape (Figure 23.01). This would not lead to any sustained vibration. But there is no such thing as a perfectly rigid substance. When an actual gong is struck, the metal at the point of impact is displaced. Being displaced, it pulls the adjacent metal to a similar displacement, and by virtue of the same force, is itself pulled back. A wave is set up in the sheet of metal and rapidly spreads

417

outward in all directions (Figure 23.02). When the wave reaches the edge of the gong, it is not finished; it is reflected and continues to course to and fro across the sheet of metal: This is the nature of a vibrating system.

The gong can be considered as a vibrating system, independent of its surroundings except that the air around it exerts a damping effect, gradually removing energy from the system. It is this energy continually being removed from the gong that is propagated through the air as wave motion. It is a small share of this energy, gradually transferred to the mechanism of the ear, that maintains this mechanism in motion as another vibrating system. The air through which the sound travels, the **medium** of the wave propagation, may itself be looked on as yet another vibrating system, for every part of it is kept in vibration by the passing waves. It is likely to be looked on as a system, however, only if it is contained within the walls of a room, so that the reflection of the waves from wall to wall set up in it a characteristic pattern, more or less stationary, as do the waves reflected from edge to edge in the gong.

Thus wave motion and vibration are closely interrelated. Those aspects of vibration and wave motion that affect the ear are referred to generally as sound or acoustics. The dictionary defines sound as "the sensation produced through the ear, what is or may be heard; vibrations causing this sensation". The adjective "acoustic" means "pertaining to the sense of hearing", and it is from this word that the noun **acoustics** is derived. In considering a room as a place in which to produce or listen to sounds, we talk of its acoustical properties or acoustics.

Sound waves are mechanical waves; they require a material medium for their propagation, and they involve motion of the particles of the medium. Light and radio waves are electromagnetic waves: changes in the electric and magnetic fields that are propagated on a similar pass-it-on basis. Such fields can exist in regions completely devoid of matter, and so these waves do not require a material medium and do not involve motion. In spite of these differences, the behavior of sound waves has much in common with the behavior of electromagnetic waves, and a consideration of one is helpful to a consideration of the other.

Practically all vibrating systems involve wave motion and must be analyzed in terms of waves. We will first consider the vibration of a single particle, then proceed to waves and so to vibrating systems. In considering the vibration of a particle, however, we will take as a practical example a heavy bob suspended from a light spring. Even here an exact treatment would involve the consideration of waves; the practical example fits the theory of the vibration of a particle only in the limit as all the mass of the system is concentrated in the bob.

23.02 SIMPLE HARMONIC MOTION

The basic item in studying vibration is the simple harmonic motion of a particle. It will be useful now to review briefly the findings of our chapter on simple harmonic motion. This sort of motion was defined there as motion in a straight line obeying the condition

$$a \propto (-y) \tag{23.01}$$

where y is the displacement of the body (or particle, as concerns us now) from its rest position and a its acceleration. Such a motion is produced by a force

$$F = -Ky \tag{23.02}$$

where K is a positive constant, acting on a particle of mass m, so that

$$a = -\frac{K}{m}y \tag{23.03}$$

A massive bob hanging from a light spring was used as an example, since a spring obeying Hooke's Law, pulling against gravity, can produce such a force.

Simple harmonic motion can also exist as the component along a diameter of uniform circular motion. If the radius of the circle is A and the angular speed ω, then for a particle in uniform circular motion,

$$\text{Displacement} = A$$
$$\text{Velocity} = A\omega$$
$$\text{Acceleration} = A\omega^2$$

Displacement is used here for the vector distance from the center of the circle to the position of the particle in uniform circular motion. More commonly, in writing of circular motion, this word is used as the name for distance traveled along the circle, a scalar quantity. Displacement (as used here), velocity, and acceleration are all vector quantities, and their directions at a common instant are indicated in Figure 23.03. Their vertical components are

$$\text{Displacement: } A \sin \theta \tag{23.04}$$
$$\text{Velocity: } A\omega \cos \theta \tag{23.05}$$
$$\text{Acceleration: } -A\omega^2 \sin \theta \tag{23.06}$$

The phase angle θ is measured from the position where the particle is moving vertically upward, and

$$\theta = \omega t + \alpha \qquad (23.07)$$

where α is the phase angle at time zero. Combining (23.04) and (23.06), we find the component motion to be simple harmonic:

$$\text{Acceleration} = -\omega^2 \ (\text{displacement}) \qquad (23.08)$$

The motions described by (23.08) and (23.03) become identical if

$$\omega^2 = \frac{K}{m} \qquad (23.09)$$

The quantity ω is convenient in relating displacement, velocity, and acceleration to time; so is the phase angle $\theta = \omega t + \alpha$. For these and related reasons it is convenient, when simple harmonic motion arises from condition (23.02) being met, even though no circular motion is involved, to envisage a reference circle, with a reference point moving uniformly around it, such that the straight-line component of the motion of the reference point is identical with the motion under consideration (Figure 23.04).

The period of both simple harmonic motion and the motion about the reference circle is

$$T = \frac{2\pi}{\omega} \qquad (23.10)$$

The frequency or number of cycles in unit time is

$$f = T^{-1} = \frac{\omega}{2\pi} \qquad (23.11)$$

The kinetic energy of a particle in simple harmonic motion is

$$\tfrac{1}{2}mv^2 = \tfrac{1}{2}mA^2\omega^2 \cos^2 \omega t$$

The total energy, which is the sum of the kinetic energy and the potential energy, is constant, and equal to the maximum value of the kinetic energy,

$$E = \tfrac{1}{2}mA^2\omega^2 = 2\pi^2 mf^2A^2 \qquad (23.12)$$

Fig. 23.03. Displacement A (i.e., distance from center), velocity $A\omega$, and acceleration $A\omega^2$, of a particle in uniform circular motion.

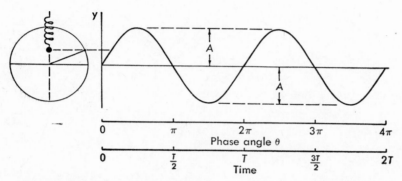

Fig. 23.04. Variation of displacement y with phase angle θ and with time, for a particle in simple harmonic motion of amplitude A, period T.

23.03 THE ADDITION OF SIMPLE HARMONIC TERMS

Very frequently in physics and in engineering there is occasion to add several simple harmonic terms. Suppose that two terms to be added have the same frequency and so the same angular speed ω, and that their amplitudes are A and B, respectively. If the two terms are exactly in phase, the problem is simple arithmetic:

$$A \sin \omega t + B \sin \omega t = (A + B) \sin \omega t$$

If they are not exactly in phase, we have the problem

$$A \sin \omega t + B \sin (\omega t + \alpha) = ?$$

This can be solved by trigonometry, but more simply it can be reduced to a problem in vector addition. Consider the reference circles for the two terms (Figure 23.05). The rates of rotation are the same for the two, the angle between them being always α. Suppose the "radius vector" of the second circle is added as a vector to that of the first circle, so that the vector triangle rotates as a rigid structure about the center

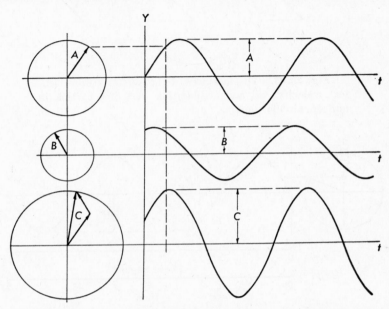

Fig. 23.05. Sum of two simple harmonic motions of the same frequency.

of the first circle. The y-component of the sum is seen to be at every instant the required sum of the two individual y-components.

A simple method of summation now becomes apparent. The reference circles need not be drawn, but only the "radius vectors" or **phasors.** First a line is drawn in any direction, say horizontally to the right, its length denoting the magnitude A (Figure 23.06). This is the phasor representing the first term. Then a second phasor is added to it, differing from it in direction by the phase difference α existing between the two terms. The magnitude of the phasor sum is the amplitude C of the sum of the two terms, and its direction relative to the other terms gives the phase relationship of the sum to the two terms. Thus in Figure 23.06 the sum has amplitude C and leads the first term in phase by the angle β. Any number of terms may be added in this way.

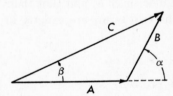

Fig. 23.06. Phasor diagram: $A \sin \omega t + B \sin (\omega t + \alpha) = C \sin (\omega t + \beta)$.

23.04 THE SUM OF MANY RANDOMLY PHASED TERMS

Many occasions arise when several sources, or even a large number of sources, generate signals of the same frequency, but with the phase relationships between the various signals entirely a matter of chance. The signals, we may say, are randomly phased.   Any source of light is an "incoherent source", providing many randomly phased signals in this way.   So also, in the realm of sound, is a symphony orchestra.

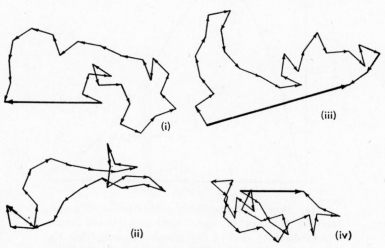

Fig. 23.07.   The resultant of many terms randomly phased.

What is the sum of many randomly phased signals?   It can be zero; at the other extreme the signals can just happen to be all in the same phase, so that the amplitude of the sum equals the sum of the amplitudes of the individual terms.   Figure 23.07 shows four cases in which twenty-five small phasors of magnitudes a, b, $c \cdot \cdot \cdot$ were chosen randomly as to phase and added vectorially to give a sum of magnitude A.   In Figure 23.08 the probability $P(A)$ of any amplitude A is plotted against a scale of A.

The most important point to remember is that, averaging over many cases,

$$\overline{A^2} = a^2 + b^2 + c^2 + \cdot \cdot \cdot \tag{23.13}$$

On the average, that is to say, the squares of the amplitudes are additive. We shall be defining intensity shortly as a quantity proportional to the square of the amplitude.   So we can say that, on the average, when phases are random, intensities are additive. At any instant, the total effect of twenty violins may be anything from zero to the maximum value achieved when the amplitudes are additive. In a short period of time, however, a large number of independent cases present themselves, for the phase relationships not only are random but also are continually

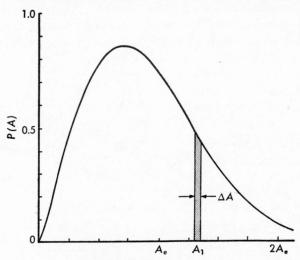

Fig. 23.08. The probability distribution of amplitude for the sum of many randomly phased terms. The probability that at any instant the amplitude lies between A_1 and $A_1 + \Delta A$, for instance, is $P(A)\Delta A$, the area of the shaded column. The X axis is marked in units of A_e, the effective or *root-mean-square* amplitude, where $A_e = \sqrt{\overline{A^2}}$ and $\overline{A^2}$ is the average value of A^2.

and rather rapidly changing. Averaging over even a short period of time, therefore, the average effect produced can be described by equation (23.13) or by the statement that intensities are additive.

23.05 BEATS: THE ADDITION OF TWO TERMS DIFFERING SLIGHTLY IN FREQUENCY

Figure 23.06 shows the phasor diagram of the sum

$$A \sin \omega t + B \sin (\omega t + \alpha) = C \sin (\omega t + \beta)$$

Now suppose that the frequency of the second term, and so its angular velocity, is made slightly greater than that of the first term, i.e.,

$$A \sin \omega_1 t + B \sin (\omega_2 t + \alpha)$$

where ω_2 is slightly greater than ω_1. Then, as both phasors continue to rotate, that for the second term will be rotating slightly faster. The second phasor will slowly rotate counterclockwise relative to the first (Figure 23.09). The sum C of the two phasors will vary continually in magnitude and direction. The magnitude of the resulting simple harmonic motion will vary continuously, reaching a maximum value of $A + B$ when the two terms are exactly in phase and a minimum value of $A - B$ when the two terms are exactly out of phase. The phase of the resulting simple harmonic motion will vary continuously too, relative either to the first term or to the second. This phenomenon of periodically fluctuating amplitude is known as **beats**.

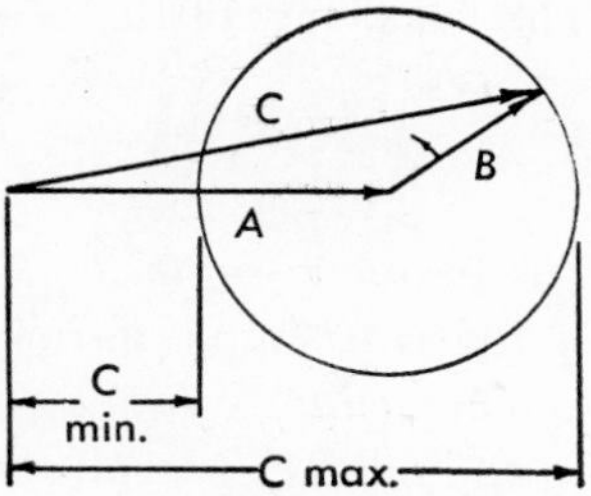

The angular velocity of the second vector relative to the first will be $\omega_2 - \omega_1$. If the variation of the resultant motion goes through one complete cycle (from maximum amplitude to minimum to maximum again) in time T_B (beat

Fig. 23.09. Moving phasor diagram for the sum of two simple harmonic terms differing slightly in frequency.

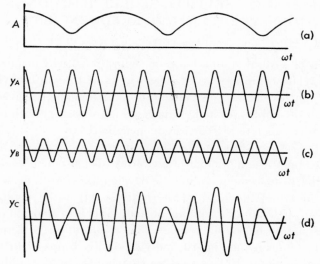

Fig. 23.10. (a) Amplitude of the sum of two beating terms, as given by Figure 23.09, plotted against phase. (b) and (c) Displacement plotted against phase for the individual terms A and B. (d) Displacement of the sum C. Curve (a) forms an envelope to curve (d).

period), then

$$T_B = \frac{2\pi}{\omega_2 - \omega_1}$$

The frequency of the beats will be the reciprocal of the period; thus

$$f_B = \frac{\omega_2}{2\pi} - \frac{\omega_1}{2\pi} = f_2 - f_1 \qquad (23.14)$$

The frequency *of the beating* equals the difference between the frequencies of the two simple harmonic motions. The frequency *of the resultant C* remains close to f_1 and f_2, but varies in a complicated fashion depending on the relative magnitudes of the two terms.

From geometrical construction based on Figure 23.09, one can obtain the amplitude of the sum, C, as a function of time, as in Figure 23.10(a). One does *not* obtain from this construction a plot of *displacement* against time for the sum. That would be obtained by adding y_B, plotted in the (c) part of the figure, to y_A, plotted in the (b) part of the figure, to obtain y_C, shown in Figure 23.10(d). The amplitude plot of 23.10(a) serves as an envelope to the displacement plot of 23.10(d).

23.06 THE SUM OF SEVERAL SIMPLE HARMONIC MOTIONS AT DIFFERENT FREQUENCIES

The complex vibrations of a musical instrument may be described as the sum of several simple harmonic vibrations, with a fairly simple numerical relationship among the frequencies of the various vibrations. An ear listening to such an instrument, or a microphone, receives the sum of a number of simple harmonic signals. Figure 23.11, relating to a violin, shows seven such terms, their frequencies in the ratio $2:3:4:5:6:8:17$. Knowing the relationships among the frequencies and among the amplitudes, we can plot the individual wave forms (displacement against time) and add the displacement values to develop the resultant wave form shown at the top of the figure. Alternatively, given the resultant wave form, we can with suitable equipment analyze it into the sum of a finite number of simple harmonic terms. The resultant wave form can be varied in its details by moving the individual wave forms slightly forward or backward in time. If we consider the simpler case of adding terms 1 and 2, which have frequencies in the ratio of $2:3$, it can be seen that a small shift of one term relative to the other along the time axis will introduce a considerable change in the wave form of the sum. To state the matter conversely, the wave form of the sum depends not only on the frequencies and amplitudes of the terms, but also on their phase relation or relation in time.   The ear, however, like the analyzing equipment above, can distinguish changes in amplitude or frequency of the various terms, but in general has no awareness of phase relationships among them.

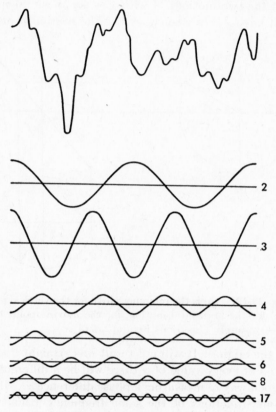

Fig. 23.11.   One complete cycle of the wave form of a violin (top) and its harmonics (2 to 17), all plotted as displacement against time.

23.07 THE COMBINATION OF TWO SIMPLE HARMONIC MOTIONS AT RIGHT ANGLES TO EACH OTHER

Suppose that a point is vibrating up and down, along or parallel to the Y axis, Figure 23.12(a), about a rest position O, according to the equation $y = A \sin \omega t$.   Suppose that at the same time it is vibrating to and fro, along or parallel to the X axis, Figure 23.12(a), about the same rest position, according to the equation $x = B \sin \omega t$.   The combined motion can be determined from the two equations or from the graphical projection of two reference circles, as in Figure 23.12(b), (c). The combined motion is found to be to and fro along a straight but oblique line through the origin or rest position. Now if we introduce a phase difference between the two motions, if with $y = \sin \omega t$ we take $x = B \sin (\omega t + \alpha)$, we will have $x = 0$ when $y \neq 0$. The combined motion will not

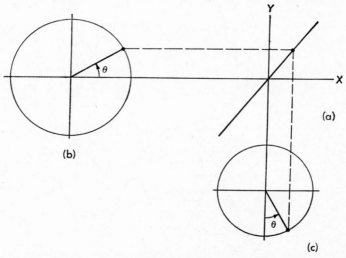

Fig. 23.12. (b) is the reference circle for the vertical motion, and (c) for the horizontal motion, for the moving point tracing out a very simple "Lissajous Figure" at (a).

pass through the origin. It will not result in a straight line, in fact, but in an ellipse. For every value of α there will be a different ellipse.

Here is a good way of measuring a phase difference α. If we have two simple harmonic functions of the same frequency (thus the same ω), we can apply one (as a voltage) to the vertically deflecting plates of a cathode-ray oscillograph, the other to the horizontally deflecting plates. Then the spot of light found where the electron beam strikes the face of the tube will move according to the combination of the two simple harmonic functions. The pattern it traces, its **Lissajous Figure,** will be different for every different value of α. (J. A. Lissajous' paper on the subject was published in 1857.)

If the frequencies of the two functions should differ slightly, the pattern will not remain constant, but will vary continuously. So we have at the same time a way of checking whether two functions are identical in frequency. If the frequency ratio between the two functions, rather than being exactly one to one, is exactly two to one, or seven to three, or any simple ratio exactly, a constant pattern will form. Thus we can use the Lissajous Figures in watching for the simple ratios between different frequencies that are of special interest in music; we can use them in bringing two notes "into tune".

PROBLEMS

1. A particle moving in a vertical line in simple harmonic motion of amplitude 3.00 cm and period 2.00 sec moves upward through its rest position at time $t = 0$. What is the angular velocity of the reference particle? What is the equation of the simple harmonic motion (take upward positive)?

2. Referring to problem 1, what is the velocity of the particle at times $t = 0$, $t = \frac{1}{2}$ sec, $t = 1$ sec?

3. Referring to problem 1, what is the acceleration of the particle at times $t = 0$, $t = \frac{1}{2}$ sec, $t = 1$ sec?

4. Referring to problem 1, draw curves of displacement, velocity, and acceleration against time for 3 sec commencing at $t = 0$. (A good approximation can be achieved by plotting maxima, minima, and zero points, and drawing the appropriate curves through these points. The ability to draw approximations to sinusoidal curves through a series of such points is a useful one to acquire.)

5. What is the energy of vibration of a particle of mass 1.00 gm vibrating in simple harmonic motion with amplitude 0.010 cm at a frequency of 100 cycles sec⁻¹?

6. What is the energy of vibration of a particle of mass 10^{-3} kgm vibrating in simple harmonic motion with amplitude 10^{-4} m at a frequency of 10^2 cycles sec⁻¹?

7. The frequency of a particle vibrating in simple harmonic motion is doubled while its amplitude is trebled. By what factor does its energy of vibration increase?

8. The energy of vibration of a particle is kept constant while its amplitude is increased by a factor five. If the initial frequency was 250 cycles sec⁻¹, what is the final frequency?

9. $A \sin \omega t + B \sin (\omega t + \alpha) = C \sin (\omega t + \beta)$. Determine C and β vectorially for $A = 5$, $B = 3$, and the following values of α: 0, $\frac{1}{4}\pi$, $\frac{1}{2}\pi$, $\frac{3}{4}\pi$, π, $\frac{5}{4}\pi$, $\frac{3}{2}\pi$, $\frac{7}{4}\pi$, 2π.

10. Referring to problem 9, plot C and β against α, from $\alpha = 0$ to $\alpha = 2\pi$.

11. Repeat problems 9 and 10 for $A = 5$, $B = 5$.

12. Determine vectorially the sum of $3 \sin \omega t + 2 \sin (\omega t + \frac{1}{2}\pi) + 4 \sin (\omega t + \pi) + \sin (\omega t + \frac{3}{2}\pi)$.

13. Add 25 simple harmonic terms of amplitude 1 cm and randomly phased. The random phases can be obtained by spinning a matchstick or pencil on a flat table top.

14. Plot a histogram of the resultant amplitudes of a large number of such summations, say 100, obtained by a whole class, using 1-cm intervals of amplitude. The column of maximum height will probably be 2 to 3, 3 to 4, or 4 to 5, the column 3 to 4 being the most probable. Figure 23.13 gives a rather optimistic example.

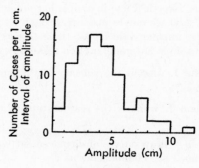

Fig. 23.13.

15. Two simple harmonic terms of equal amplitude, say 1 mm, beat once a second. Working from a diagram resembling Figure 23.09, plot amplitude against time for an interval of 1 sec. (Use something like 5 cm on the scale of ordinates to represent 1 mm.)

16. Draw displacement against time from $t = 0$ to $t = 0.03$ sec, for (a) $y = 2 \sin \dfrac{2\pi t}{0.03 \text{ sec}}$, (b) $y = \sin \dfrac{2\pi t}{0.01 \text{ sec}}$, (c) $y = \sin \left(\dfrac{2\pi t}{0.01 \text{ sec}} + \pi \right)$, (d) the sum of (a) and (b), (e) the sum of (a) and (c).

17. Draw the Lissajous patterns described by a point whose vertical and horizontal motions are given by $y = A \sin \omega t$ and $x = B \sin (\omega t + \alpha)$, where $A = 3$ cm, $B = 3$ cm, and $\alpha = 0, \frac{1}{4}\pi, \frac{1}{2}\pi$.

18. Draw the Lissajous pattern described by a point whose vertical and horizontal motions are given by $y = A \sin \omega t$ and $x = B \sin (\omega t + \alpha)$, where $A = 3$ cm, $B = 1$ cm, and $\alpha = -\pi/2$.

19. Draw the Lissajous pattern described by a point whose vertical and horizontal motions are given by $y = A \sin \omega t$ and $x = B \sin 2\omega t$, where $A = 4$ cm, $B = 2$ cm.

24

Wave Motion

24.01 TRANSIENT WAVES

Consider a hanging cable or string, kept under tension by a bob suspended at its end. If the bob were suddenly pulled to one side, the string would change position as from part (a) to part (b) of Figure 24.01.

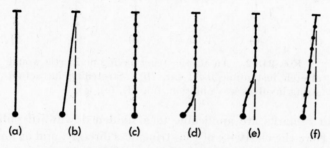

(a)   (b)   (c)   (d)   (e)   (f)

Fig. 24.01. If the end of a vertically hanging string (a) were suddenly displaced to the left, the string would move instantaneously to (b) if the string had no inertia. Actually the string has inertia, (c), and the displacement travels up it as a wave, (d), (e). The same final position (f) is achieved.

That is what would happen if the string were under great tension but had negligible mass, negligible distributed inertia. To exaggerate the actual departure from this motion as a rigid body, picture concentrated masses attached at intervals along the string. With these in place, the sideways pull of the string will require some time to move the lowest of these masses any considerable distance, and this will be true of the next mass, and so on up the string. Thus the transverse deflection applied at the end of the string gradually travels up the string as a **transverse wave.** It may be noted at the same time that the masses, having been accelerated, swing past the final static positions and return before coming to rest finally as in part (f) of the figure.

Any real cable or string does have mass, not lumped as in Figure 24.01(c), but distributed along its length. The tension of the string must accelerate this distributed mass progressively, the nearest part first, to achieve the changed position of the whole string. Thus the response of a real string to a displacement of its end resembles the series (c), (d), (e), (f) more nearly than it does a transition as a rigid body from (a) to (b).

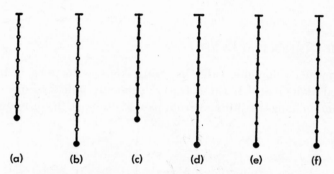

(a)   (b)   (c)   (d)   (e)   (f)

Fig. 24.02. An elastic string having no inertia would stretch instantaneously, (a), (b). Stretching an actual string involves wave motion, (c), (d), (e), (f).

Similar remarks are applicable to a sudden downward pull (Figure 24.02). Here the elasticity of the string acts directly, and as a result the process may be comprehended more explicitly. If the string had no mass, it would immediately stretch uniformly along its whole length, from part (a) to part (b) of Figure 24.02. But if masses are added, or if as in the case of any real string there is mass uniformly distributed along its length, then the downward pull progresses along the string as a wave, as in parts (c) to (f) of Figure 24.02.

In these two examples of wave motion, every particle moves a little way, but it is the wave, a particular configuration of adjacent particles, that moves all the way along the string. In the first example, the particle motion was at right angles to the direction of travel of the wave, and so it was called a transverse wave. In the second example, the particle motion was along the direction of travel of the wave: We call this a **longitudinal wave.** A notable property of any longitudinal wave is the variation it effects in density. In parts (d) and (e) of Figure 24.02 the masses are seen to be more closely spaced, or arranged in greater density, in some parts of the string than others. There is thus on the string a region of greater-than-normal density, or **compression,** and a region of less-than-normal density, or **rarefaction.**

The string along which the waves traveled in the above examples may be referred to as the **medium** along which the waves were **propagated.** It is a one-dimensional medium, but waves are frequently propagated through two- and three-dimensional media. If we strike a block of wood, we suddenly displace and compress the wood in the immediate vicinity of the point of impact. Two sorts of waves thereupon spread out in all directions from that point: transverse waves for which the particle motion is at right angles to the direction of travel or propagation of the wave, and longitudinal waves, involving particle motions along the direction of propagation, and so involving density variations.

If you clap your hands or snap your fingers, you suddenly compress the air, and displace the air, in the immediate vicinity. Again, a small displacement or particle motion and a small density variation spread out through the air in all directions as a longitudinal wave. There is no transverse wave in this case, for in general transverse waves require a medium which offers resistance to distortion or change of shape; fluids have no shear modulus, offer no resistance to a change in shape.

If you drop a pebble into water, longitudinal waves spread out from the point of impact in all directions through the water. There is no corresponding transverse wave spreading out in all directions through the water, as there would be in the case of a block of wood, for water is a fluid and so like air offers no resistance to deformation. There is, however, a surface wave spreading out over the surface of the water, and this is at least in part a transverse wave. It is quite different in its mechanism to the transverse wave that spreads out in three dimensions through a solid. Surface waves are very familiar in everyday life; they appear to be simple things and a reasonable starting-point for the consideration of wave motion. Their simplicity is more apparent than real, however, and so we commenced our consideration of waves with another sort. In the case of surface waves, resistance to distortion is provided both by gravity and by surface tension. For waves on deep water, the individual particles of the surface of the water describe circular paths. The motion of the water dies away very rapidly below the surface; at a depth equal to the wavelength it is only about one five-hundredth that at the surface.* When the total depth of water is less than half a wavelength, the water particles move in elliptical paths, and for very small depths, the particles move

* Ludwig Prandtl, *Essentials of Fluid Dynamics*, Blackie & Son Ltd., 1952.

mainly backward and forward with very moderate rise and fall. Gravity waves are not limited to discrete surfaces like the boundary between water and air. The atmosphere has no such discrete upper boundary, yet because there are more or less pronounced density variations as we proceed upward through the atmosphere, gravity waves very much akin to surface waves are set up in it.

24.02 SPEED OF A TRANSVERSE WAVE ON A STRETCHED STRING

If the end of a stretched string is subjected to a transverse (i.e., lateral or sideways) displacement, there will be a similar transverse displacement of every other point on the string. If a given phase or stage of the motion occurs at the end of the string at time t_1, it will occur at a point a distance x along the string at time $t_1 + (x/c)$, where c is the speed or velocity of the wave motion along the string. Conversely, the motion occurring at distance x along the string at time t_1 occurred at the end of the string at time $t_1 - (x/c)$. The velocity of a transverse wave on a stretched string is given by

$$c = \sqrt{\frac{F}{m}} \qquad (24.01)$$

where F is the tension on the string and m the mass per unit length. Without going into the detailed mechanics from which this relation can be derived, it may be of some interest to derive the form of the relation from "dimensional analysis". On what will the velocity depend? The tension and the heaviness of the wire would seem the most likely factors. Let us assume therefore, that,

$$c \propto F^x m^y \qquad (24.02)$$

where c is the velocity, F the tension, and m the mass per unit length, and x and y are unknowns to be determined from dimensional analysis.

Now denoting the dimensions mass, length, and time by the symbols M, L, T, the dimensions of the quantities involved are,

$$
\begin{aligned}
c: &\quad LT^{-1} \\
F: &\quad MLT^{-2} \\
m: &\quad ML^{-1}
\end{aligned}
$$

Substituting these dimensions in (24.02) gives

$$LT^{-1} = (MLT^{-2})^x (ML^{-1})^y = M^{x+y} L^{x-y} T^{-2x}$$

Therefore,

$$x + y = 0$$
$$x - y = 1$$
$$2x = 1$$

and so,
$$x = \tfrac{1}{2}; \qquad y = -\tfrac{1}{2}$$

Substituting in the proportionality (24.02), we obtain

$$c \propto F^{\frac{1}{2}} m^{-\frac{1}{2}}$$

Having assumed (24.02), or deduced it from experiment, the use of dimensional analysis has given us equation (24.01), apart from a constant of proportionality which in this case happens to be unity.

24.03 SPEEDS OF WAVES GENERALLY

The speed of a wave is always given by a relation of the form of (24.01). For either a transverse or a longitudinal wave through a solid, the speed is given by

$$c = \sqrt{\frac{E}{\rho}} \tag{24.03}$$

For transverse waves, E is the shear modulus or rigidity; for longitudinal waves, it is Young's Modulus. The difference in the two moduli, and so in the speeds of the two different sorts of wave, is used in locating earthquakes from seismographic records, although the procedure is by no means simple. Only longitudinal waves are propagated through fluids. In that case E is the bulk modulus. For surface waves on a liquid, both gravity and surface tension act to resist the change in shape, and the relationship becomes more complicated. For waves on the surface of deep water,

$$c = \sqrt{\frac{g\lambda}{2\pi} + \frac{2\pi T}{\rho\lambda}} \tag{24.04}$$

where g is the acceleration due to gravity, T the surface tension, ρ the density, and λ the wavelength. The speed depends on the wavelength and has a minimum value for the wavelength $\lambda_1 = 2\pi \sqrt{T/(\rho g)}$. Waves having $\lambda > \lambda_1$ are called gravity waves, those having $\lambda < \lambda_1$ are called capillary waves (i.e., surface-tension waves). For the former the speed increases with the wavelength, and for the latter the reverse relationship holds.

24.04 SPEED OF SOUND WAVES IN GASES

For a gas, the bulk modulus is just the pressure, P, if the compression is at constant temperature. The compression and subsequent rarefaction in the case of a sound wave is rapid, however, and is therefore very nearly adiabatic (no heat flow) rather than isothermal (no temperature change). In the adiabatic case, the bulk modulus is γP, where γ is the ratio of the specific heat at constant pressure to that at constant volume.

Equation (24.04), then, for gases becomes

$$c = \sqrt{\frac{\gamma P}{\rho}} \tag{24.05}$$

But for gases,

$$\rho = \frac{P M_0}{R \theta} \tag{24.06}$$

where

$R = $ the universal gas constant
$\quad = 8.31 \times 10^7$ erg mole^{-1} deg^{-1}
$M_0 = $ the gram-molecular weight or mass per mole
$\quad = 29$ gm mole^{-1} (for air)
$\gamma = $ the ratio of the specific heats, a dimensionless quantity
$\quad = 1.4$ (for air)

and θ is the absolute temperature, equal to the Centigrade temperature plus 273. (The symbol T used for temperature in deriving this relationship has been changed to θ here because of the frequent use of T to denote the period of a vibration.)

Combining (24.06) with (24.05) gives

$$c = \sqrt{\frac{\gamma R \theta}{M_0}} \tag{24.07}$$

and for air at $\theta = 273$,

$$c = \sqrt{\frac{1.4 \times 8.31 \times 10^7 \times 273}{29} \frac{\text{erg}}{\text{gm}}}$$
$$= \sqrt{1.095 \times 10^9}\ \text{cm}^2\ \text{sec}^{-2}$$
$$= 33,100\ \text{cm sec}^{-1}$$

For (dry) air at any temperature, then,

$$c = \sqrt{\frac{\theta}{273}} \times 33,100\ \text{cm sec}^{-1} \tag{24.08}$$

While both (24.05) and (24.07) have their uses, the former has one pronounced drawback. It looks as though c varied with the pressure, and this is not the case, for as well as a P in the numerator, there is one contained in the ρ of the denominator, as equation (24.06) shows.

Incidentally, it is interesting to compare the velocity of sound with the velocity of thermal motion of molecules as revealed by the kinetic theory of gases. That theory gives us

$$\frac{R\theta}{M_0} = \overline{u^2} \tag{24.09}$$

where $\overline{u^2}$ is the mean square of u, the component of molecular velocity in any one direction. Combining this with (24.07), we have

$$c^2 = \gamma \overline{u^2} \tag{24.10}$$

that is, the square of the speed of sound equals the mean square of the molecular-velocity component, times gamma, the ratio of the specific heats.

24.05 EQUATION OF A SIMPLE HARMONIC WAVE

So far we have discussed waves only with reference to transient motions: A sudden motion, introduced at some point in the medium, spreads through or along the medium as a transient or isolated wave. More often than not the source of waves is a periodic or regularly repetitive motion of some point in the medium, say the end point of a string. Periodic motions can be analyzed into a number of simple harmonic motions; let us consider therefore the wave propagation of a simple harmonic motion.

Suppose that the end of a string is subjected to a transverse motion,

$$y_0 = A \sin \omega t \tag{24.11}$$

which incidentally may be written slightly differently by substituting for ω:

$$y_0 = A \sin \frac{2\pi}{T} t \tag{24.12}$$

Then any point at a distance x along the string will undergo a similar motion, but the phase that occurs at x at time t will have occurred at the end of the string at time $t - (x/c)$. Therefore, neglecting any change in amplitude with x, the equation of transverse motion at any point on the string is

$$y = A \sin \omega \left(t - \frac{x}{c} \right) \tag{24.13}$$

or substituting $2\pi/T$ for ω we have

$$y = A \sin 2\pi \left(\frac{t}{T} - \frac{x}{cT} \right)$$

$$= A \sin 2\pi \left(\frac{t}{T} - \frac{x}{\lambda} \right) \tag{24.14}$$

where $\lambda = cT$ is called the **wavelength.** It is the distance traveled by the wave in one period. It is the distance between any two points continually in phase with each other. When x is set equal to some fixed

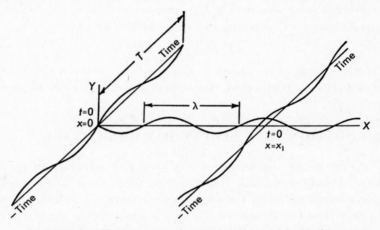

Fig. 24.03. Transverse wave on a string, with displacement plotted against time for $x = 0$ and $x = x_1$.

value, equation (24.14) gives the displacement at that particular point on the string at any time t. Equation (24.12) is the particular case of this where $x = 0$. Similarly, when t is set equal to some fixed value, equation (24.14) gives the displacement at that particular instant at any point along the string. But equation (24.14), as it stands, with both t and x variable, gives us the displacement at *any* point along the string at *any* time. It is the wave equation.

Figure 24.03 may help in the understanding of the wave equation. The horizontal and vertical axes are distance in the directions of wave travel and particle motion, respectively, and time is shown by an oblique axis. Along the X-axis, particle displacement is plotted against x-distance for time $t = 0$. Along the time axis, particle displacement is plotted against time for the end point of the string. Note that the variation of y with x as one proceeds from the origin along the X-axis is similar to its variation with time as one proceeds in the *negative direction* along the time axis. This is in keeping with the opposite signs of the t and x terms in the phase factor $(t/T - x/\lambda)$. A second plot of y against t has been drawn for $x = x_1$. At the intersection of this plot with the x-axis, the same observation can be made: moving backward in time corresponds to moving forward in x-distance, and vice versa. It will be found instructive to develop such a diagram for one's self, drawing several more curves than are shown here.

24.06 LONGITUDINAL SIMPLE HARMONIC WAVES

A longitudinal wave can be represented by the same equation as a transverse one. The equation can still be plotted against rectangular

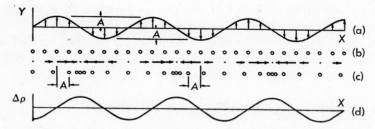

Fig. 24.04. The displacements, of amplitude A, plotted in (a) are applied as longitudinal displacements to a row of uniformly displaced dots (b) to effect the grouping shown at (c). Variations in density about its mean value, plotted in (d), are not in phase with the displacement.

coordinates, but the quantity represented by y and plotted as a displacement at right angles to the x-direction is now actually a longitudinal displacement, a displacement *along* the x-direction. In Figure 24.04 the equation has been plotted against rectangular coordinates; the displacements indicated by the curve have then been applied in their proper longitudinal sense to a row of dots which originally had uniform spacing. From the row of displaced dots, it can be seen that the density, in this linear case the number of dots per unit length, varies periodically with distance. The points of maximum density occur once every wavelength, but rather than coinciding with the points of maximum forward displacement, they occur a quarter of a wavelength further along the direction of travel of the wave, and a quarter of a wavelength behind the points of maximum backward displacement. If the variations with time at a fixed point along the path of the wave are considered, it can be seen that the instant of maximum density will precede the instant of maximum forward displacement by a quarter of the period.

A wave in air may travel along a column of air enclosed in a tube. Then Figure 24.04 is directly applicable. So is equation (24.14), except that y will denote longitudinal displacement rather than transverse displacement. Or y may represent density or pressure, or more precisely the small departure of the density or pressure from the prevailing atmospheric density or pressure, due to the passage of the wave. If y denotes displacement, then the equation must be corrected by a phase change of $\pi/2$ radians or 90° to obtain the pressure or density equation, and vice versa.

Alternatively, a wave in air may be spreading outward in all directions from a point source. In that case, Figure 24.04 represents a cross section along the direction of travel of the wave. Further, in that case, the intensity of the wave (to be discussed in section 24.07) will vary inversely as the square of the distance from the source. Therefore, instead of the constant A for amplitude, we should take A/x, for the amplitude will vary inversely as the distance from the source.

24.07 ENERGY, INTENSITY, AND PRESSURE

The energy of a particle of mass m in simple harmonic motion of frequency f, amplitude A, is $2\pi^2 mf^2 A^2$. If every particle in unit volume of gas has this energy by virtue of the sound waves passing through it, then

$$\text{Energy of sound in unit volume of gas} = 2\pi^2\rho f^2 A^2 \qquad (24.15)$$

where ρ is the mass of unit volume of gas, that is, where ρ is the density of the gas.

Now, the intensity of radiation, of waves radiating through a medium, is defined as follows:

$$\text{Intensity} = \text{rate at which energy flows through unit}$$
$$\text{area at right angles to direction of motion} \qquad (24.16)$$

Let us consider a region in which sound waves have a single direction of travel, i.e., a case of plane waves as opposed to spherical waves spreading out from a nearby source. Imagine a plane fixed in space normal to the direction of travel, through which the waves are continually passing. Picture one particular unit area of this plane. We want to know how much energy passes through this unit area in unit time. If we were to start letting energy through the unit area at the beginning of a unit-time interval, then at the end of the interval all the energy that had passed through would be contained in a definite region of air (Figure 24.05): a rectangular region of volume $1 \times 1 \times c$, where c is the velocity of sound in air. The amount of energy in that volume, and so the amount that flowed through the unit area in unit time, is obtained by multiplying equation (24.15) by c, and thus, denoting the intensity by I, we have for a plane sound wave,

$$I = 2\pi^2 \rho c f^2 A^2 \qquad (24.17)$$

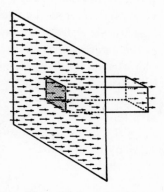

For a plane wave, the intensity need not vary with distance, for the sound that passes through unit area, at some distance x_1, will also pass through unit area at some other distance x_2. Consider, on the other hand, sound spreading out uniformly in all directions from a small source. Let the rate of energy output from the source, the power, be P watts. At a distance r, this power will be passing through a spherical surface of radius r, area $4\pi r^2$. The intensity at that distance will therefore be $P/(4\pi r^2)$. Thus for sound spreading out through a uniform medium from a small source,

Fig. 24.05. If sound traveling west-to-east at speed c is allowed to pass through an aperture of unit area in a north-south wall for unit time, it occupies volume $1 \times 1 \times c$ at the end of that time.

$$I = \frac{P}{4\pi r^2} \qquad (24.18)$$

The intensity varies inversely as the square of the distance, and so the amplitude varies inversely as the first power of the distance from the point of origin.

Observations and calculations in connection with sound in air may involve the displacement, the velocity, or the intensity, and all of these have now been related. They may also involve the pressure variations; most microphones, for instance, are pressure-sensitive. Without waiting to develop the relation between pressure and other quantities, we will note in empirical form the approximate relation for a plane wave in air at 20C and 76 cm Hg:

$$\text{Root-mean-square pressure} = 20,000 \sqrt{\text{intensity}} \qquad (24.19)$$

where the pressure is in dynes per square centimeter and the intensity in watts per square centimeter.

24.08 INTENSITY LEVEL

The range of intensities encountered in dealing with wave motion is very great, involving factors of millions, sometimes millions of millions. A unit of intensity suitably small for one end of the range would be inconveniently small at the other. On this account, it is convenient to use a logarithmic scale of intensity rather than a linear one. A unit increase in the logarithmic scale represents the same percentage increase in intensity at any point on the scale. The quantity log I is given the name **intensity level.** But the log of unity is zero, and so the zero of the level scale would depend on the unit of intensity involved. This is an unnecessary limitation to the use of "levels". To avoid it, we define, not log I as level, but log I_2 − log I_1, or log (I_2/I_1), as difference in intensity level. Thus by definition

$$N = \log \frac{I_2}{I_1} \text{ bels} \qquad (24.20)$$

where N is the difference in intensity level between sounds of intensity I_2 and I_1, and the logarithm is to the base 10. On this basis, a change in intensity level of 1 bel corresponds to an intensity ratio of 10. That is rather a big jump, and so a smaller unit, the **decibel,** is defined by the relation

$$10 \text{ decibels} = 1 \text{ bel} \qquad (24.21)$$

Combining (24.20) and (24.21), we have

$$N = 10 \log \frac{I_2}{I_1} \text{ db} \qquad (24.22)$$

"db" being the abbreviated form commonly used for the decibel. Thus 1 db corresponds to an intensity factor of 1.26, and 3 db to a factor of 2.

24.09 WAVE FRONTS AND EQUIPHASE LINES

A convenient way of dealing graphically with waves is to draw and consider loci of equal phase and loci of constant phase. In Figure 24.06(a), a central source is sending out waves in all directions. The circles that have been drawn are separated one from another by one wavelength, or more generally by an integral number of wavelengths, and so every point on those circles is at the same phase as every other point. Let us say that the diagram refers to time t_1, and that the phase at points on the circles is $(\omega t_1 + \alpha)$. At a slightly later time t_2, the circles of Figure

24.06(a) are at phase $(\omega t_2 + \alpha)$; later again, at t_3, they are at phase $(\omega t_3 + \alpha)$. At all times, this fixed set of circles has every point at the same phase as every other point. The phase keeps changing with time, but all the points on these fixed loci keep in step. Stationary loci of this sort will be referred to as **equiphase lines.**

If we are interested in sticking to the same phase as time moves on, say $(\omega t_1 + \alpha)$, whether the time is t_1 or t_2 or t_3, then our loci must move outward with the phase, at the velocity of the wave motion. Instead of the stationary equiphase lines, we will have steadily expanding circles of

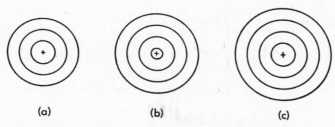

(a)   (b)   (c)

Fig. 24.06. Circular wave fronts expanding outward from a point source.

constant phase—part (a) of the figure at time t_1, part (b) at time t_2, part (c) at time t_3. These moving loci of *constant* phase will be referred to as **wave fronts.** They can be observed readily in the case of ripples on a water surface.

An experimental procedure for obtaining a family of equiphase lines for actual sound waves may be worth describing (Figure 24.07). A small electrically operated source of sound, such as a small single headphone, powered by an electrical oscillator, is fixed in or close to the plane of a blackboard. A small microphone held close to the board is used to intercept the sound waves and convert them into an alternating voltage. This voltage, amplified, is applied to the vertically deflecting plates of a cathode-ray oscillograph. The output voltage of the oscillator, the same voltage that drives the sound source, is applied to the horizontally deflecting plates. The Lissajous pattern that appears on the face of the cathode-ray tube gives the phase relationship between the two voltages.

The microphone is moved to trace out on the blackboard a line for which the Lissajous figure remains the same. The sound along this line bears a fixed phase relationship to the sound at the source. It is an equiphase line. Any given Lissajous pattern, and so any given phase relative to the source, is found to occur along a family of circles centered on the source. The distance radially between two consecutive circles is the wavelength of the sound: the distance between two points exactly in phase with each other. The particular form of the Lissajous figure should not be taken as indicating the phase relationship between the source and the vibrating air at the microphone; various phase shifts will be involved in the transfer from the source to the air, from the air to the microphone,

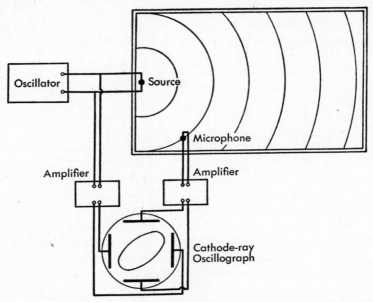

Fig. 24.07. Equiphase lines, loci constantly in phase with each other, about a point source.

and from the input to the output of each amplifier. We assume only that the air at any microphone position giving a particular Lissajous pattern has the same phase, at any instant, as the air at any other position giving the same Lissajous pattern. If the frequency of the sound is known, the velocity of sound in air can be calculated from the relation

$$\lambda f = c \qquad (24.23)$$

i.e., (distance traveled in one cycle) times (cycles per unit time) equals (distance traveled in unit time).

When an experiment like the one described above is attempted on a large scale, say over a whole room, it tends to run into trouble, because the sound at the microphone is the sum of the direct sound and reflected sound from the walls and floor. The sum does not have the same phase as the desired single term.

24.10 INTERFERENCE

The phenomenon of "interference" may be considered with reference to an experiment similar to that of section 24.09. Let there be two sound sources exactly in phase with each other, a few wavelengths apart. (Their distance apart does not need to be an exact or integral number of wavelengths.) Then the equiphase patterns for the two sound sources, obtained one at a time, will appear as in Figure 24.08. Points on the one family of circles, central about A, are in phase with each other, and also

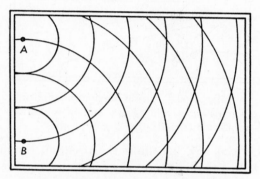

Fig. 24.08. Equiphase lines about two point sources A and B which are in phase with one another. Amplitudes are additive at points of intersection.

in phase with all points on the other family of circles, central about B. Now, the alternating pressure exerted on the microphone at any point on the board is the sum of the pressure due to the waves from A and that due to the waves from B. To obtain the total pressure, we must add two simple harmonic terms, as was done in section 23.03. (It is important to the experiment that the signals be truly simple-harmonic.) Wherever the two waves are exactly in phase, the amplitude of the resultant signal will be the sum of the amplitudes of the two terms. This condition is met wherever equiphase lines intersect. Loci of maximum resultant amplitude may be drawn through such points (Figure 24.09).

Wherever the two waves are exactly out of phase, the amplitude of the resultant signal will be just the difference between the amplitudes of the two terms. This condition is met wherever equiphase lines from A come just halfway between those from B. Loci of minimum resultant amplitude may be drawn through such points (Figure 24.09). The loci of maximum and minimum amplitude provide the **interference pattern** for the two sources. If the exploring microphone is connected through an amplifier to a voltmeter, it can be used to explore the field as to resultant amplitude. If it is moved parallel to the line joining the two sources,

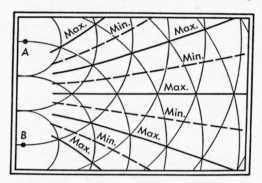

Fig. 24.09.   Loci of maximum amplitude (signals exactly in phase) and of minimum amplitude (signals exactly out of phase).

to cut the calculated loci, one finds the resultant amplitude rising to maximum and falling to minimum values just about where the lines have been drawn.

It is quite possible to derive the interference pattern, or to derive the wavelength from an observed interference pattern, without reference to equiphase lines. At any point on a locus of maximum amplitude, the signals from the two sources are exactly in phase with each other. If the two sources are themselves in phase, this becomes

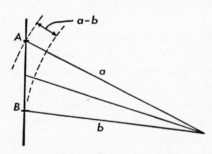

Fig. 24.10.   Path difference.

$$a - b = n\lambda \qquad (24.24)$$

where a and b are the distances from sources A and B and n is zero or a positive or negative integer (Figure 24.10). This is the equation of a family of hyperbolas. Inspection of an interference pattern reveals readily which value of n is applicable to each maximum. The corresponding condition for a locus of minimum amplitude is, of course, $a - b = (n + \frac{1}{2})\lambda$. The maxima and minima are not lines of constant amplitude. Proceeding outward along a maximum, away from the sources, one would find the amplitude decreasing *gradually.* Proceeding from a point on a maximum locus, normally to the locus, one would find the amplitude decreasing relatively rapidly until the adjacent minimum was approached.

At distances from the two sources great compared with the distance between them, the interference pattern of maxima and minima can be described in terms of direction alone. In Figure 24.11 the distance between source points A and B has been denoted by d. A point O has been taken midway between A and B, and a line OO' drawn normal to AB.

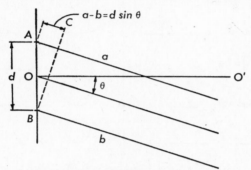

Fig. 24.11. Path difference in the limiting case of a distant point is $d \sin \theta$.

This line can be called the axis of the system. In the limit as the distances a and b of a point from A and B respectively become great,

$$\frac{a - b}{d} = \sin ABC = \sin \theta$$

so that for a fixed value of d the path difference is a function of θ alone:

$$a - b = d \sin \theta$$

and the condition for an interference maximum (24.24) becomes

$$\sin \theta = n\lambda/d \qquad \text{where } n \text{ is zero or an integer} \qquad (24.25a)$$

Any point lying in a direction from O that makes an angle θ with the line OO' is on a locus of maximum signal, provided that θ meets the above condition.

It is of some interest to consider the phasor summation of the signals received from A and B at a distant point, keeping the distance from O to this point fixed and the bearing θ continually increasing. Let the sense in which θ increases be such that the distance from A is steadily increasing, that from B steadily decreasing. If there were a source at O, the phase of the signal from it would remain in the same fixed relationship to that of the source, since the path length remains constant. For the signal from A, however, the path is steadily increasing and the phase of the

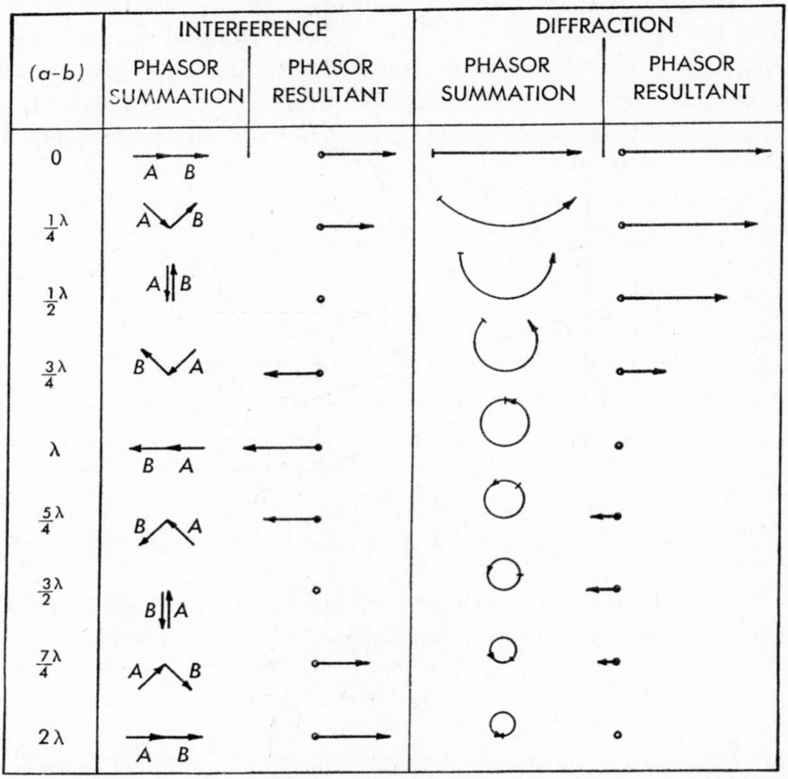

(a-b)	INTERFERENCE		DIFFRACTION	
	PHASOR SUMMATION	PHASOR RESULTANT	PHASOR SUMMATION	PHASOR RESULTANT
0				
$\frac{1}{4}\lambda$				
$\frac{1}{2}\lambda$				
$\frac{3}{4}\lambda$				
λ				
$\frac{5}{4}\lambda$				
$\frac{3}{2}\lambda$				
$\frac{7}{4}\lambda$				
2λ				

Fig. 24.12. Phasor summation for signals at a distant point, for the case of interference between signals from two point sources exactly in phase, and for the case of diffraction at a parallel-edged aperture. The first column gives the difference in path $(a - b)$, from the two sources, for interference, and from the two edges of the aperture, for diffraction. The difference in phase is $2\pi/\lambda$ times the path difference.

signal is lagging more and more. That is, the phasor is rotating clockwise. For the signal from B, the phase is advancing more and more, relative to that of the sources; that is, the phasor is rotating counterclockwise. This is illustrated in the "interference" columns of Figure 24.12. The phase of the sum remains constant, relative to that of the sources, until the first minimum is reached. (At great distances the two signals are nearly enough equal that the minimum is practically zero.)

Then as the amplitude increases again, the phase is exactly reversed. There is a similar exact reversal of phase at each succeeding minimum.

24.11 DIFFRACTION AND HUYGENS' PRINCIPLE

When waves spread out from a point source through a uniform medium, all wave fronts and equiphase lines are concentric circles about the source (or spheres, to go from two dimensions to three). When the medium contains obstacles preventing the passage of waves, determining the location of equiphase lines or the future locations of a wave front becomes more difficult. The obstacle may be such as to prevent the passage of waves in a limited region. For example, a person may be standing between a listener and the source of sound. We know that sound waves pass around this obstacle, so that the sound can be heard in the region behind the obstacle. Establishing just why this is so, and to what extent it is so, is difficult. Alternatively, the obstacle may be such as to prevent passage everywhere except for a limited region. For example, to hear a person through an open door or window, it is not necessary that the person speaking be within line-of-sight of the listener. Again, accounting for the phenomenon in terms of wave motion is not easy. Both in cases of limited obstacles and in cases of limited openings or apertures, the term **diffraction** is applied to the problem. In solving diffraction problems, and in developing relationships applicable to diffraction problems, good use can be made of **Huygens' Principle** (after Christian Huygens, 1629), according to which *any line through which waves pass (once only) can be treated as an infinity of point sources. If the chosen line is an equiphase line, then the hypothetical point sources all have exactly the same phase.*

Use can be made of Figure 24.11 to discuss an important diffraction phenomenon: The spreading-out of waves beyond an aperture. Suppose that A and B are the edges of a slit of width d, viewed in section, cut in a wall normal to the plane of the diagram and to the line OO'. Plane wave fronts normal to OO' approach the slit from the left; in this figure they would be represented by straight lines. In the diagram, then, AB is an equiphase line of length d, and any wave disturbance resulting in the region to the right of AB can be calculated by applying Huygens' Principle and treating that line as an infinity of point sources all having exactly the same phase.

If there were a finite number of sources, uniformly distributed along the length d, phasor diagrams giving the total signal at a distant point would resemble those for interference in Figure 24.12, but would be more complex, in having many terms instead of just two. In any one diagram, the angles between adjacent terms would all be the same, since the sources are uniformly spaced [Figure 24.13(a)]. If the first and last sources along the line were at A and B, their phasors would have the same directions as the phasors shown for interference in Figure 24.12.

In the limiting case of an infinite number of sources, each of infinitesimal amplitude, the succession of small straight phasors with small equal angles between them becomes a continuous circular arc [Figure

(a)   (b)

Fig. 24.13.   The phasor summation for signals from a line array of many point sources (a) approaches a continuous curve (b) as the number of points becomes infinite.

24.13(b)].   The direction of the arc at its start and at its finish are again given by the phase appropriate to signals from sources at A and B.   As before, let us keep the distance of the receiving point from the point O, and so the phase of the signal from O, constant, and vary θ.   The length of the arc is the arithmetic sum of all the individual amplitudes, and so can be kept constant (to a reasonable approximation) as θ is varied. Continuous-curve phasors, drawn with constant length of arc and with their end phases appropriate to A and B, are shown in the "diffraction" columns of Figure 24.12.   A straight line from the start to the finish of the arc is of course the phasor representing the total signal received, in magnitude and phase.

For $\theta = 0$, signals from A and B have the same phase; so do signals from every other point on the line, so that the total signal has the greatest possible value.   Increasing θ from zero, in either direction, reduces the amplitude of the total signal without changing its phase until the continuous-curve phasor summation becomes a complete circle.   At that stage, the total signal is zero.   Signals from A and B have lagged and advanced respectively by π radians, so that the phase difference between signals from A and B is 2π, corresponding to a path difference of zero. Now a phase difference of 2π is the same thing as no phase difference at all, but here it involves a continuous change in phase as we move along the line from A to B, so that the phasor summation is a complete circle with resultant amplitude zero.

Further increase in θ brings the signal amplitude up from zero to reach another maximum when the arc of the phasor summation contains one and a half revolutions, another zero when it contains two revolutions, and so forth. Thus the condition for *zero* signal is

$$\sin \theta = n\lambda/d \qquad \text{where } n \text{ is a zero} \qquad (24.25b)$$

The actual ratio of the amplitude A at any angle θ to the maximum amplitude A_0 occurring at $\theta = 0$ can be shown, from the geometry of the continuous-curve phasor summations, to be

$$\frac{A}{A_0} = \frac{\sin \frac{\Delta}{2}}{\frac{\Delta}{2}} \qquad \text{where} \qquad \Delta = \frac{2\pi d}{\lambda} \sin \theta \qquad (24.26)$$

The quantity Δ is the phase difference between the signals from the end points A and B.

The condition for a zero in the diffraction pattern [equation (24.25b)] is the same as the condition for a maximum in the interference pattern [equation (24.25a)] except that for $n = 0$ both patterns have a central maximum. The phase of the resultant signal is seen to undergo a reversal at every direction of zero signal. All amplitudes beyond the first direction of zero signal are small relative to that at the central maximum, as shown in Figure 24.14(b), contrary to the interference case shown in 24.14(a). (Signals whose amplitudes are plotted downward from the axis of $\sin \theta$ have the opposite phase to those for which the amplitudes are plotted upward.) Bearing in mind that intensity is proportional to the square of the amplitude, we can see that in a plot of relative intensity against angle the intensity in the "side-lobes" would be still smaller, relative to that in the direction of the central maximum, than is the amplitude.

The foregoing two-dimensional treatment of diffraction is applicable to the case of plane wave fronts arriving at a parallel-sided slit of width d and of great length. It is a reasonable approximation regardless of the length. For the particular and important case of a circular opening of diameter d, the value of θ for the first zero of the diffraction pattern is given by

$$\sin \theta = 1.22 \frac{\lambda}{d} \qquad (24.27)$$

and the secondary maxima are weaker than in the case of a slit [Figure

24.14(c)]. Some loudspeakers have a circular opening or aperture which may be assumed filled by an equiphase surace. This relationship is then applicable. For the longer wavelengths there is no direction of zero signal, but for wavelengths considerably less than d there is, so that the ratio of long-wave to short-wave signal strength varies seriously with θ. Our mouths are small enough that all the wavelengths involved receive about the same treatment out to approximately $\theta = 45°$.

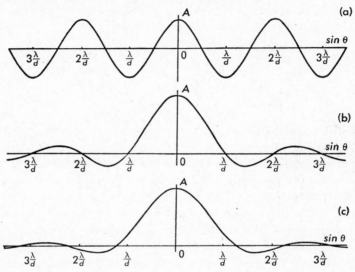

Fig. 24.14. Variation with direction of the amplitude of the signal at a distant point for (a) two point sources separated by a distance d, (b) a parallel-sided slit of width d, (c) a circular aperture of diameter d. Signals whose amplitudes are indicated by distances downward from the horizontal axes have the opposite phase to those with distance upward.

The foregoing treatment of diffraction covers an important but very limited group of cases. Consideration has been limited to signals in the "far field", i.e., to signals at a distance from the aperture several times greater than the width of the aperture. Diffraction in such cases is referred to as "Fraunhofer diffraction". Consideration of the near field ("Fresnel diffraction") requires a different approach not covered in this book. We have not considered diffraction around obstacles, and in general problems involving obstacles are more complex than those involving apertures. Examples are found in diffraction around the human head, which determines, for the far field, the extent to which sounds emitted from our mouths are transmitted to the rear, and for the near field, the signal delivered to the speaker's own ears. Sounds to which the human ear is sensitive have wavelengths in air ranging from 2 cm to 20 m. Most of the structures around us have linear dimensions within this range, and so the diffraction patterns around them vary greatly as the frequency ranges through the audible spectrum.

24.12 WAVES FROM A MOVING SOURCE

If a bullet is fired from an aircraft with a velocity of 2300 ft sec^{-1} relative to the aircraft, and if the aircraft has an air speed of 700 ft sec^{-1},

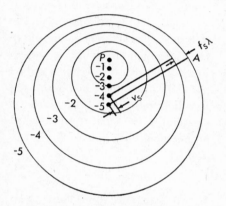

Fig. 24.15. Wave fronts about a source moving with half the speed of sound.

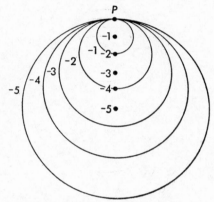

Fig. 24.16. Wave fronts from a source traveling at the speed of sound. Sonic barrier at present position of source, P.

then the bullet will start out through the air with velocity relative to the air of 3000 ft sec^{-1}, if fired straight ahead, or 1600 ft sec^{-1} if fired astern. Any sound produced by the aircraft, however, will travel through the air at the speed of sound in air, a speed independent of that of the aircraft. The speed of a mechanical wave, already discussed, is speed relative to the medium, independent of the speed of the source relative to the medium. As a result, interesting and important patterns are formed when sound originates at a source moving relative to the medium of propagation.

Let us develop diagrams of the sound patterns around moving sources for various situations, as has been done in Figures 24.15 to 24.17. Consider first the case of a source moving through the medium with half the speed of sound (Figure 24.15). First draw a dot to represent the present position of the source. Then draw another dot to represent the position of the source one second earlier. Around this dot draw a circle of radius c, the speed of sound, and so the distance traveled by sound in one second. This circle is the position at time zero of sound emitted at time -1 sec. Repeating, draw a dot for the position of the source at time -2 sec, and around it a circle of radius $2c$. This circle is the position at time zero of sound emitted at time -2 sec. In Figure 24.15 this process has been repeated for a total of five circles.

What is the wavelength? The circles that have been drawn are separated in time by f_s cycles of the source, where f_s is the frequency of the source, and so by f_s wavelengths in distance, if the distance is measured in the direction in which the sound is traveling. The nth circle has radius nc, since the sound has had n sec in which to travel. If the source is stationary, the separation between adjacent circles is $nc - (n - 1)c$, and so

$$f_s\lambda = nc - (n - 1)c = c$$

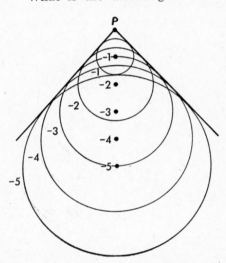

Fig. 24.17. Wave fronts from a source traveling at $\frac{3}{2}$ times the speed of sound, with enveloping shock wave.

In Figure 24.15, lines have been drawn to permit our calculating the separation between adjacent circles in the vicinity of the point A. A radial line has been drawn to the point A from the center of the circle that passes through A, to be referred to as the nth circle. Another radial line parallel to this has been drawn for the $(n - 1)$th circle. Comparing distances along these lines, it can be seen that, approximately,

$$nc - v_s = (n - 1)c + f_s\lambda$$

simplifying to
$$\lambda = \frac{c - v_s}{f_s} \qquad (24.28)$$

where v_s is the component of the velocity of the source in the direction of the sound traveling to A.

What is the frequency of vibration *of the medium*? Wave fronts separated by a distance λ are moving through the medium with velocity c (Figure 24.18), and the frequency is the number of wave fronts passing per second, so

$$f_m = \frac{c}{\lambda} = \frac{c}{c - v_s} f_s \tag{24.29}$$

Recalling from section 24.07 the relationship between the energy of the medium and the frequency, we have for the energy of the medium due to the wave motion passing through it

$$\text{Energy of sound in unit volume of gas} = 2\pi^2 \rho f_s^2 A^2 \left(\frac{c}{c - v_s}\right)^2 \tag{24.30}$$

Thus for v_s equal to 0.1, 0.5, and 0.9 times c, we find the energy of vibration of the medium increased by factors 1.23, 4, and 100 times, respectively. For $v_s = 0.99c$, the energy of the medium is increased 10,000 times, or the energy level by 40 db. The region directly ahead of a sound source moving with speed approaching that of sound can thus be seen to be a region of high frequency and very energetic vibration.

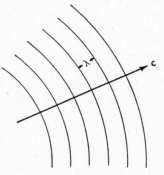

A diagram for the limiting case of a source traveling at the speed of sound is shown in Figure 24.16. It has been developed in the same way as Figure 24.15. Right at the source, all the wave fronts are superim-

Fig. 24.18.

posed for an extremely high concentration of vibrational energy. This concentration constitutes the **sonic barrier** that makes the transition from flight at less than sonic speed to flight at greater than sonic speed a difficult one, especially if made gradually so that the vibrational energy has time to build up. If such a region is formed by an aircraft gradually accelerating from less to more than sonic speed and then dropping back to lower speed again, the region of intense vibration travels forward with the speed of sound. If the aircraft is diving at the time, as is more than likely to be the case, the region arrives at the ground before it has had much time to dissipate, and with enough energy to shake buildings and break their windows.

If a wave-front diagram is drawn similarly to Figure 24.15 but for a source moving with speed greater than that of sound, a new effect is found (Figure 24.17). The source is now out in front of all the sound emitted, and a V-shaped envelope to the family of wave fronts is formed. The energy that was concentrated near the source in the "sonic barrier" case is now distributed along the lines of the V. **A shock wave** is found to exist along this envelope. No sound is heard from the source until this shock wave arrives with a sudden crack. This is the sound heard from a high-speed bullet. In the case of surface waves on water, this is the method of formation of the bow wave of a ship. The speed of surface waves on water is low enough for only a modest speed to be required of a ship to produce a bow wave.

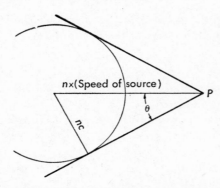

Fig. 24.19. Shock-wave geometry.

To construct a bow-wave or shock-wave diagram, one need draw only one wave front, and draw tangents to it from the present position to the source. From Figure 24.19, it can be seen that the angle between the line of travel of the source and the shock wave or bow wave is given by

$$\frac{\text{Speed of wave}}{\text{Speed of source}} = \sin \theta \qquad (24.31)$$

24.13 DOPPLER EFFECT

When a wave pattern flows past an observer, the frequency heard by the observer is the number of wave fronts passing the observer per second. If the observer is fixed in the medium through which the waves are traveling, then the observed frequency is

$$f_0 = \frac{c}{\lambda} = f_m$$

If the observer is moving in the same direction as the sound with velocity v_0, the observed frequency is reduced to

$$f_0 = \frac{c - v_0}{\lambda} \qquad (24.32)$$

(Of course, if the observer is moving through the medium with the same velocity as the sound, no wave fronts overtake him, and the observed frequency is zero.) Any component of the observer's motion parallel to the wave fronts, and so normal to the direction of travel of the sound through the medium, has no effect on the frequency observed. It is only motion normal to the wave fronts that counts. So equation (24.32) holds generally, if we define v_0 as the component, in the direction that the sound is traveling through the medium, of the velocity of the observer through the medium.

Combining this equation with (24.28) relating the wavelength to the frequency of the source, we have

$$\frac{f_0}{f_s} = \frac{c - v_0}{c - v_s} \tag{24.33}$$

This change in frequency from source to observer is called the Doppler Effect (Christian J. Doppler, 1803).

The velocities in equation (24.33) are all relative to the medium. Suppose that the source and observer are moving relative to the ground with velocities v_{sg} and v_{0g} and suppose that a wind is blowing. Then velocity relative to the ground equals velocity relative to air plus velocity of air relative to ground, that is to say,

$$v_{sg} = v_s + w \qquad \text{and} \qquad v_{0g} = v_0 + w \tag{24.34}$$

These equations are vector if their terms are velocities, but become scalar if the terms are all taken as components in the direction in which the sound is traveling through the air. Substituting (24.34) in (24.33) gives

$$\frac{f_0}{f_s} = \frac{c - v_{0g} + w}{c - v_{sg} + w} \tag{24.35}$$

Thus if the source or the observer is moving relative to the ground, a change in the wind will change the amount of the Doppler Effect. If source and observer are stationary relative to the ground and so to each other, a steady wind will not produce any Doppler Effect.

24.14 BENDING OF SOUND WAVES IN THE ATMOSPHERE

Suppose that a wave front is emitted obliquely from the earth's surface into the atmosphere. If the wind increases with height (Figure 24.20), then the upper end of the wave front will move more rapidly than the lower end. The direction of motion of the sound is altered, and the wave front may actually be returned to the earth. A similar effect will occur if temperature increases with height, for the speed of sound increases with temperature. It should be noted, however, that wind increasing with height is the condition usually existing, but temperature increasing with height is less common and is known as an "inversion".

Winds within a hundred feet of the earth's surface are seldom steady, and when people try to hold a concert or meeting out of doors it is this unsteadiness that makes the wind and its variation with height most troublesome.   A steady wind would merely modify the strength of the sound, and this trouble can be overcome.   Fluctuations in the wind pattern lead, however, to fluctuations in both the strength and frequency of

Fig. 24.20.   Wind increasing with height changes direction of wave fronts from ascent to descent.

the sound heard, and the only way out of this annoyance is to move out of the wind.

PROBLEMS

1. What is the speed of a longitudinal wave on a rod of steel, for which Young's Modulus is 20.0×10^{11} dynes cm^{-2} and density is 7.86 gm cm^{-3}?

2. What is the speed of a transverse wave on a wire of diameter 0.500 mm, of steel of density 7.86 gm cm^{-3}, its tension maintained by a hanging mass of 2.50 kgm?

3. In hanging long cables for power lines and bridges, the tension is determined by measuring the time of travel of a transverse wave.   What would be the speed of the wave for a cable of aluminum (density 2.70 gm cm^{-3}), with a cross-sectional area of 5.00 cm^2, under a tension of 1500 kgm?

4. The surface tension of water at 4C is 75.0 dynes cm^{-1}.   What is the wavelength of the slowest surface waves on deep water at this temperature?   What is the speed?   What is the speed of waves ten times as long?

5. The surface tension of mercury is 6.40 times that of water, its density 13.55 gm cm^{-3}.   On which liquid will short-wavelength ripples travel faster?

6. What is the speed of surface waves of length 10.0 m, a length great enough for surface-tension effects to be neglected?

7. Plot speed c against wavelength λ, using logarithmic scales, from 1 mm to 1 m, for deep water, taking surface tension 75.0 dynes cm^{-1} and density exactly 1 gm cm^{-3}.

8. What is the speed of sound in water vapor ($\gamma = 1.33$, $M_0 = 18.0$ gm) at temperature 0C? in liquid water, for which the bulk modulus is 2.15×10^{10} dynes cm^{-2}?

9. By what factors are the speeds of sound in hydrogen ($\gamma = 1.40$, $M_0 = 2.00$ gm) and helium ($\gamma = 1.67$, $M_0 = 4.00$ gm) greater than the speed in air ($\gamma = 1.40$, $M_0 = 29.0$ gm) at the same temperature?

10. By how many meters per second does the speed of sound in a gas increase when the temperature rises 1 Centigrade degree, for an initial temperature of (a) -20C, (b) 0C, (c) $+20$C?

11. A string extends from the origin positively along the X axis. The origin end moves vertically in simple harmonic motion with amplitude 10 mm and frequency 4 cycles sec^{-1}, and is moving upward through its rest position at time $t = 0$. A traveling wave proceeds outward along the string at a speed of 32 cm sec^{-1}. Draw curves of displacement against distance, for the first 16 cm of the string, at times $t = 0$, $\frac{1}{16}$ sec, $\frac{1}{8}$ sec, $\frac{3}{16}$ sec, $\frac{1}{4}$ sec.

12. Draw a row of vertical lines, about $\frac{1}{2}$ in. tall, spaced $\frac{1}{4}$ in. apart. Redraw them as they would be distributed by the passage of a wave of amplitude $\frac{1}{4}$ in., wavelength 2 in. Indicate the relationship between positions of maximum forward displacement, maximum backward displacement, and maximum density.

13. Longitudinal waves of wavelength 1 cm go out in all directions from a point source. Draw a series of five circular wave fronts 1 cm apart to represent, at an instant, loci of maximum forward displacement. Then draw broken-line circles as loci of maximum backward displacement and dotted-line circles as loci of maximum density.

14. At a frequency of 4000 cycles sec^{-1} the ear can detect sounds of intensity 1.00×10^{-16} watt cm^{-2} in air at standard pressure and temperature 20C. Taking the density of this air as 1.205 gm lit.$^{-1}$, what is the amplitude of the sound waves in air?

15. The power of conversational speech is of the order of 10 microwatts. What is the intensity in watts per square cm at a distance of 1.00 m from a point source of power 10.0 microwatts from which sound spreads out uniformly in all directions? What is the root-mean-square pressure, using the relationship between pressure and intensity for a plane wave in air at 76 cm Hg, 20C?

16. Sound spreads out from a small source, of power 25 microwatt. Plot intensity level, above 10^{-16} watt cm^{-2}, against distance from the source (using a logarithmic scale of distance) from distance 10 cm to distance 10 m.

17. What difference in intensity level should be observed as one moves from a point 3.00 m away to a point 1.00 m away from a point source?

18. An observer at A moves 1.00 m toward a source of sound at B, and notes an increase in intensity level of exactly 1 db. How great is the distance AB?

19. By what factor does the root-mean-square pressure of a plane wave increase when the intensity level rises by 20 db?

20. Waves of wavelength 2 cm spread out from a point source. Draw three (circular) equiphase lines in phase with the source, three more (broken) for which the phase lags that of the source by $\pi/2$ radians, three more (dotted) for which the phase leads that of the source by $\pi/2$ radians.

21. Point sources at A and B are in phase with one another. What condition regarding the distance AB will make those parts of the straight line through A and B, lying outside the region between A and B, a locus of minimum intensity?

22. Two point sources in phase with each other are located on rectangular coordinates (X, Y) at $(x = -4$ cm, $y = 0)$ and $(x = 4$ cm, $y = 0)$, and send out waves of length 2 cm. Draw loci of maximum signal over the rectangle extending from -12 cm to $+12$ cm along the X axis, from -8 cm to $+8$ cm along the Y axis.

23. Repeat problem 22 for wavelength 3 cm.

24. Plane waves are diffracted at a slit of width 4.0 cm. Let the signal at a distant point straight out from the slit have amplitude unity. What then is the amplitude at an equal distance but at an angle of 45°, for wavelengths 20 cm, 10 cm, 5 cm, as given by equation (24.26)?

25. A direct-action loudspeaker emits sound from a circular aperture of width d. Low-frequency sounds are spread out over a wide angle by diffraction, but sounds at higher frequencies are emitted in a relatively narrow beam. Assume plane wave fronts in the aperture. Take as the angular width of the beam the angle between the first direction of zero signal to the right and that to the left. Plot beam width against frequency, from 2500 to 10,000 cycles sec^{-1}, (a) for $d = 5.0$ in., (b) for $d = 12.0$ in. Take the speed of sound to be 1120 ft sec^{-1}.

26. What is the width of beam (defined as in problem 25) in the vertical and in the horizontal, at frequency 5500 cycles sec^{-1}, for a plane sound wave passing through a rectangular aperture of width 3 in., height 12 in., with $c = 1120$ ft sec^{-1}?

27. A road crosses a railway at right angles. A locomotive approaching the crossing at 80 mph emits a whistle of frequency 400 cycles sec^{-1} when 1.00 mile from the crossing. If there is no wind, and if sound travels 0.200 miles sec^{-1}, what frequency is heard (a) by an observer on the crossing, (b) by an observer 1.00 mile up the road, at the time he hears the whistle?

28. Repeat problem 27 for an observer 1.00 mile up the road and approaching the crossing at 40.0 mph.

25

Standing Waves and Vibrating Systems

25.01 REFLECTION AT THE FIXED END OF A STRING

Consider a string along which a transverse wave, simple harmonic for convenience, is traveling from left to right. Its equation might be

$$y = A \sin 2\pi \left(\frac{t}{T} - \frac{x}{\lambda} \right) \tag{25.01}$$

Such a wave is shown in Figure 25.01. The instantaneous position of every point on the string is shown for five different instants in the first five parts of the figure. The fifth instant is exactly one period after the first, and the fifth pattern is therefore identical with the first. The lowest portion of the figure shows how the vibrating string would appear in a time-exposure photograph. Every small portion of the string is vibrating with amplitude A, and so during the course of the time exposure it is observed at every possible displacement between A and $-A$. Because of the persistence of vision, this portion of the figure also represents the way the string would appear to the eye if its motion consisted of a continuous wave of amplitude A moving from left to right. It may be noted that if the string were illuminated by a stroboscope—a flashing light, flashing very briefly at times 0, T, $2T$, $3T$, etc., where T is the period of vibration—the string would appear to the eye or to a camera as the uppermost pattern instead. If the intervals between flashes were lengthened just a little bit, the pattern observed would progress gradually through the series shown.

Now, suppose that some point E on the string is fixed, so that it cannot vibrate. That is,

$$y_E = 0 \tag{25.02}$$

461

According to the wave equation (25.01), the motion of the point E is

$$y_E = A \sin 2\pi \left(\frac{t}{T} - \frac{x_E}{\lambda} \right) \tag{25.03}$$

This, as it stands, is in conflict with equation (25.02).

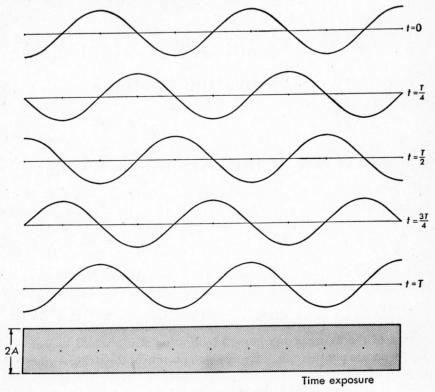

Fig. 25.01.   Transverse wave traveling along a string.

One way of getting around the conflict mathematically is to modify (25.03) by adding a second term to it, similar to the first term but always exactly opposite in phase, so that at every instant the two terms cancel out. The modified form of (25.03) is

$$y_E = A \sin 2\pi \left(\frac{t}{T} - \frac{x_E}{\lambda} \right) + A \sin \left[2\pi \left(\frac{t}{T} - \frac{x_E}{\lambda} \right) \pm \pi \right] \tag{25.04}$$

The reversed-phase term can be looked on as due to the reaction of the mounting on the string, equal and opposite to the force of the string on the mounting. The reaction should, and does, send a "reflected" wave

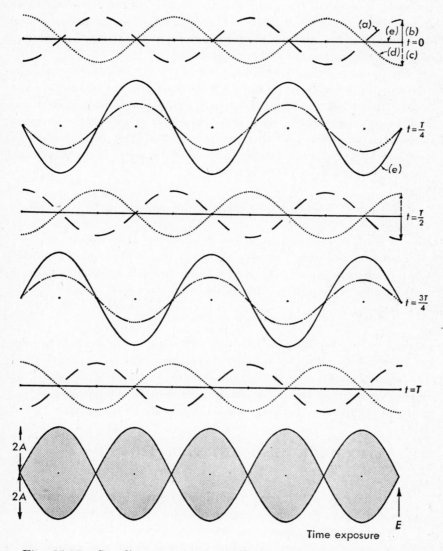

Fig. 25.02. Standing waves. One point of the string of Figure 25.01 is fixed. Curve (*a*) is the primary wave as in Figure 25.01. Line (*b*) is the would-be displacement at the fixed point due to the primary wave. Line (*c*) is the neutralizing displacement which, added to (*b*), gives zero displacement at the fixed point. Curve (*d*) is the wave that would travel from right to left because of the neutralizing term of the motion at the fixed point. Curve (*e*) is the resultant position of the string.

backward, right to left, along the string. This is the same wave that would be sent out if the point E actually did vibrate according to the second term of equation (25.04). Figure 25.02 shows the primary wave, the reflected wave, and the resultant motion of the string. A resultant motion of this sort can actually be observed.

The motion of the rope that we observe is the sum of the two wave motions: the primary wave from left to right and the secondary wave from right to left. Adding these two, either graphically as in Figure 25.02 or by trigonometry, we find zero motion not only at the fixed end, but also at a number of other points, called **nodes,** distant from the fixed end by $\lambda/2$, $2(\lambda/2)$, $3(\lambda/2)$, and so forth, where λ is the wavelength of the traveling wave. That is to say,

$$\text{Distance between adjacent nodes} = \frac{\lambda}{2} \tag{25.05}$$

where λ is the wavelength of the traveling wave. The amplitude at any point remains constant and reaches a maximum value of $2A$ halfway between adjacent nodes. The point of maximum amplitude of displacement is called a **loop,** or an **antinode,** and

$$\text{Amplitude at loops} = 2A \tag{25.06}$$

where A is the amplitude of the traveling wave. The pattern of nodes and loops is referred to as a pattern of **standing waves.** It is not necessary to use a stroboscope now to observe the wavelength. The eye or a camera viewing the string by steady light sees the standing-wave pattern, and the distance between nodes can readily be measured.

25.02 NATURAL OR RESONANT VIBRATIONS OF A STRING

We have been picturing a continuous stream of waves coming in from the left and a continuous stream of reflected waves returning to the left. Where do they come from, where do they go? The easiest solution is a second fixed end, extending out from which is a similar set of nodes and loops (Figure 25.03). This requires that the total length of the string be so adjusted that the patterns match where they meet. This requirement is

$$l = n\frac{\lambda}{2} \tag{25.07}$$

where l is the length of the string and n is an integer, so that there can be a node at each fixed end.

The length of string shown in Figure 25.02 has been so chosen that

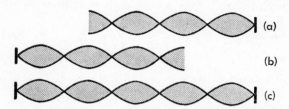

(a)

(b)

(c)

Fig. 25.03. Standing wave patterns from two reflecting ends can be matched by making distance between ends an integral number of internodal distances $(n\lambda/2)$.

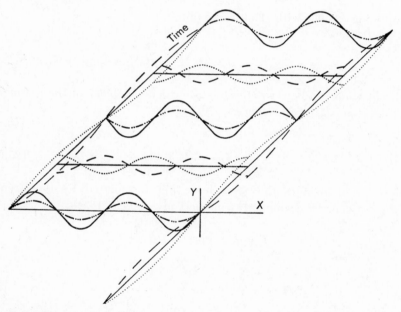

Fig. 25.04. Transverse standing waves. Fixed ends are shown as having two displacement terms, the sum of which is always zero.

it can represent a string fixed at both ends. A similar series of patterns is shown in Figure 25.04, except that here an oblique time axis has been included so that the time variations of the right-traveling and left-traveling waves for the two ends can be shown. At the right end, the broken line is reflected as the dotted line; at the left end, the dotted line is reflected as the broken line.   At each end the sum of the displacements is continuously zero.

We have in equation (25.07) a condition for the length of the string, in terms of wavelength.   But wavelength is related to frequency and velocity:

$$\lambda = \frac{c}{f} \qquad \text{[equation (24.23)]}$$

and velocity is related to tension and mass-per-unit-length:

$$c = \sqrt{\frac{F}{m}} \qquad \text{[(equation (24.01)]}$$

Therefore,
$$\lambda = \frac{\sqrt{\dfrac{F}{m}}}{f} \tag{25.08}$$

Combining (25.08) with (25.07), we obtain

$$l = \frac{n\sqrt{\dfrac{F}{m}}}{2f}$$

This equation can be rewritten to state the dependence of the frequency on the properties of the string:

$$f = \frac{n\sqrt{\dfrac{F}{m}}}{2l} \tag{25.09}$$

This relation includes the three laws first formulated by the French mathematician Mersenne ("Harmonie Universelle", 1636):

$$T \propto l, \qquad \text{or} \qquad f \propto \frac{1}{l}$$

$$f \propto \sqrt{F}$$

$$T \propto \sqrt{m}, \qquad \text{or} \qquad f \propto \frac{1}{\sqrt{m}}$$

The introduction of the integer n indicates that there is a series of **normal modes** of vibration.   The mode having the lowest frequency is called the **fundamental** mode.   Denoting its frequency by f_1, we may write

$$f_1 = \frac{\sqrt{\dfrac{F}{m}}}{2l}$$

Frequencies of all possible normal modes are then given by

$$f = nf_1 \qquad (25.10)$$

where n may have any integral value. If we set a string with two fixed ends vibrating by striking it, we introduce an assortment of waves. Those that "fit" the string by meeting this requirement live on for some time; those that do not fit die out very rapidly. If the striking is not too violent, or if the string is plucked or bowed, only frequencies meeting the requirement are produced. The proportions of the different normal modes may be varied by the manner of exciting the string, and the higher frequencies die out more rapidly than the lower ones. Because the frequencies of all the normal modes of vibration of a string are simple multiples of the fundamental frequency, these modes are called **harmonics.** The value of n in equation (25.09) gives the number of the harmonic; thus the fundamental is itself the first harmonic. (Frequencies other than the fundamental may also be referred to as overtones, the first frequency higher than the fundamental being the first overtone. There is more occasion for this usage with two-dimensional vibrators, which may have normal modes at frequencies other than simple multiples of the fundamental frequency.)

If one end of a string is fixed to a vibrating mount rather than a fixed one, the vibration of the mounting will be transmitted along the string as a wave. It may be reflected back from the other end of the string, and then reflected in turn from the vibrating end. Standing waves of large amplitude can be generated by an end-vibration of small amplitude if the length or tension of the string is so adjusted that the vibrating end comes near a node, i.e., at a position of relatively small amplitude (Figure 25.05). If the frequency of the vibrating end is not the frequency of one of the "normal modes" of the string, then the string will vibrate irregularly, with no fixed pattern of standing waves. The amplitude will nowhere be continuously greater than that of the vibrating end, and the energy delivered by the vibrating mounting to the string will be less than in the previous case. The string is said to be in "forced vibration" rather than "resonant vibration".

If a tuning fork is held against a wooden box on which a string is mounted, the whole box including the two ends of the string will vibrate at the frequency of the fork and with small amplitude. In most cases the string will vibrate with a similar small amplitude. If, however, the frequency of the fork is the frequency of one of the normal modes of the string, then the string will vibrate resonantly with much greater amplitude than the fork or the box (Figure 25.06).   When the original source of vibration, the fork in this case, is removed, the pattern continues as in Figure 25.06.   Energy is gradually released from the resonant string to

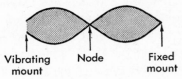

Vibrating   Node   Fixed
mount   mount

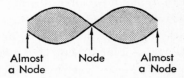

Almost   Node   Almost
a Node   a Node

Fig. 25.05.   Time exposure of a string driven from one end.

Fig. 25.06.   Time exposure of a string mounted on a vibrating box, the string vibrating resonantly.

the box through the slightly vibrating ends, and from the large flat surfaces of the box to the surrounding air.

25.03 CLOSED END OF A PIPE

Standing longitudinal waves also occur.   If the air at one end of a pipe is made to vibrate, then longitudinal waves will travel along the column of air contained in the pipe.   Longitudinal waves can be represented by a plot of displacement against distance on rectangular coordinates, and on that basis Figure 25.01 can be looked on as a series of plots referring to a longitudinal wave traveling along a column of air.   The graphical development of the standing-wave pattern is carried out for longitudinal waves in Figure 25.07(a) as it was for transverse waves in Figure 25.02.   The closed end of the pipe takes the place of the fixed end of the string, for longitudinal displacement of the air is not possible at the closed end of the pipe, just as transverse vibration of the string is not possible at its fixed end.   One discrepancy should be noted.   In Figure 25.07(a) the broken curve represents a wave traveling from left to right, so that a positive displacement is a longitudinal displacement to the right. The dotted curve represents the reflected wave, traveling from right to left, and so a positive displacement is a longitudinal displacement to the left.   Thus, a positive term for a left-to-right wave and an equal positive term for a right-to-left wave have a sum of zero.   For the curve representing the sum, displacement to the right has arbitrarily been taken as positive.

Density in longitudinal standing waves is considered in Figure 25.07(b).   Each curve representing a traveling wave has been transferred from the (a) part of the figure to the (b) part and advanced by a quarter of a wavelength in the direction of travel so that it can represent density. Densities are additive in the same way as transverse displacements, i.e., independently of the direction of travel of the wave. Adding the densities of the two traveling waves, we again find nodes and loops, but with

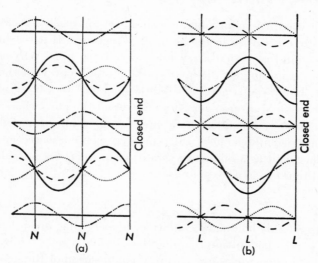

Fig. 25.07.   Standing longitudinal waves.

(a) DISPLACEMENT
Broken line:
   Wave moving left to right; take displacement to right as positive.
Dotted line:
   Wave moving right to left; take displacement to left as positive.   (Dotted line is commenced at right with such a value that the total displacement will always be zero there.)
Solid line:
   Sum, taking displacement to right as positive.
(b) DENSITY: Broken and dotted lines shifted λ/4 from displacement, the shift being in direction in which wave is traveling; then the two terms are added.

a remarkable difference from the displacement case: The density nodes come at the same points as the displacement loops, and vice versa. We obtained the standing-wave pattern by adopting the "boundary condition" that at the closed end, as at a fixed end in the case of transverse waves, the displacement should continuously be zero. We find that the closed end is a point of maximum density variation and therefore a point of maximum pressure variation. And that makes sense, for the closed end that prevents the air from vibrating to and fro does not prevent the pressure from varying. In fact, it is easier to build up a pressure against a wall than it is to build it up at some point part way along the pipe.

25.04 OPEN END OF A PIPE

If a wave traveling along a column of air reaches a closed end, a reflected wave is set up in the opposite direction. If it reaches an *open* end, it is again found that a reflected wave is set up. Why should that be? There is nothing at the open end of a pipe to prevent the vibration of the air, but there is a reason for the pressure to vary less. Just as it is easier to build up pressure at a closed end than anywhere else in the pipe, so it is more difficult to build up pressure at an open end than it is in the relative confinement of the pipe. So where a closed end provides zero displacement as a boundary condition, an open end provides a boundary condition too: approximately

$$\Delta P_E = 0 \qquad \text{or} \qquad \Delta \rho_E = 0 \qquad (25.11)$$

Because of this boundary condition, namely that much less pressure variation is possible outside the pipe than inside, a reflected wave is sent back, and standing waves are set up. The position of the pressure node and displacement loop at an open end does not lie exactly in the plane of the open end of the pipe, but beyond the end of the pipe by $0.3d$, where d is the diameter of the pipe. Realizing that the vibrating system is a column of air contained by the pipe, we can look on the open-end pressure node as the end of a column of air defined by the pipe but extending beyond the end of its container by $0.3d$.

25.05 OPEN AND CLOSED PIPES

A pipe open at both ends is called an **open pipe,** and a pipe open at one end and closed at the other is called a **closed pipe.** (A pipe closed at both ends is not a practical source of sound, and the case seldom arises.)

An open pipe has displacement loops at both ends. Since the distance between adjacent loops is $\lambda/2$, the length of the vibrating column is related to the wavelength by

$$l = n\frac{\lambda}{2} \qquad (25.12)$$

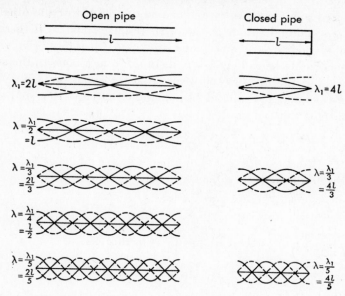

Fig. 25.08. Frequencies of normal modes are in ratio 1:2:3:4, etc., for open pipe, and 1:3:5:7, etc., for closed pipe. Solid and broken lines represent extreme variations of displacement and pressure.

where n is any integer (Figure 25.08). To relate length to frequency, we can recall that

$$\lambda = cT = \frac{c}{f}$$

and so

$$l = \frac{nc}{2f}$$

or

$$f = \frac{nc}{2l} \tag{25.13}$$

The lowest or fundamental frequency is then given by

$$f_1 = \frac{c}{2l} \tag{25.14}$$

and all possible frequencies are related to the fundamental by

$$f = nf_1 \tag{25.15}$$

Thus for an open pipe as for a string, all normal modes are harmonics (frequencies are integral multiples of the fundamental), and all harmonics are possible.

A closed pipe, being open at one end and closed at the other, has a loop at one end and a node at the other (Figure 25.08). If there are no intervening nodes part way along the pipe, therefore, the vibrating column need only be as long as the distance from a node to the adjacent loop, just half the distance between adjacent nodes, or $\lambda/4$. Alternatively, we can add any number of half-wavelengths to this, and say that in general, for a closed pipe,

$$l = n\frac{\lambda}{2} + \frac{\lambda}{4} = (2n + 1)\frac{\lambda}{4} = (2n + 1)\frac{c}{4f} \qquad (25.16)$$

where n is an integer *or zero*, or

$$f = (2n + 1)\frac{c}{4l} \qquad (25.17)$$

The fundamental or lowest frequency is in this case

$$f_1 = \frac{c}{4l} \qquad (25.18)$$

and all possible frequencies are given in terms of the fundamental frequency by

$$f = (2n + 1)f_1 \qquad (25.19)$$

where n is zero or an integer. Thus, for a closed pipe all normal modes are harmonics, but only odd-numbered harmonics (f_1, $3f_1$, $5f_1 \cdots$, etc.) are possible.

25.06 VIBRATING BARS

Flat metal bars are fairly efficient sources of sound. The bar is most conveniently mounted (by felt grommets) approximately one-quarter (more precisely 0.224) of its length from each end as in Figure 25.09(a). If the bar is struck transversely, halfway between the mounting-points, transverse standing waves are set up with nodes at the mounting-points, one loop between the two nodes and one at each free end. The flat bar has the advantage over a string of a fairly large surface area pressing against the air, in that the energy of vibration is transferred more rapidly to the surrounding air.

The tuning fork is effectively a vibrating bar folded into a narrow U, with a short stub extending transversely from the base of the U. When one of the prongs is struck with a felted or rubber hammer, a transverse vibration is set up like that described for the vibrating bar (Figure

25.09). Although the mounting stub is at a loop in the vibration pattern, the fork may be held by this stub without damping out the vibration to any great extent. Presumably the whole fork then vibrates up and down without any great loss of energy. The velocity of traveling waves

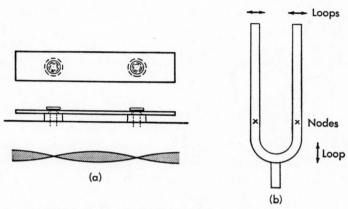

Fig. 25.09. (a) Vibrating bar; (b) tuning fork.

in the curved portion of the U is less than that in the straight prongs, and so the nodes come closer to the U than might be anticipated.

25.07 SOUNDING BOARDS AND BOXES

A tuning fork held by its stub goes on vibrating for some time. The sound from it is not loud, however. The narrow prongs of the fork do not transfer energy very rapidly to the air. If the stub of the fork is pressed down on the top of a light table, the sound becomes considerably louder. The fork is then "driving" the tabletop in forced vibration. That is to say, transverse waves continue to spread out across the tabletop from the point of contact of the tuning fork. Such waves will be reflected from the edges of the table, and so continue to course to and fro across the tabletop. The traveling waves in the tabletop will not set up standing waves unless by chance the frequency of the fork is a resonant frequency for transverse vibration of the tabletop. The condition for resonant frequency of the tabletop would be similar to that for a stretched string, but more complex because the tabletop has two dimensions instead of one and because its mounting is more complex.

A tabletop is not a good vibrator in the way that a tuning fork is: When it is struck with a hammer, the vibrations set up in it die out rapidly. But it *is* a good "transducer" for leading the energy across from one system (the tuning fork) to another (the air of the room). It is good at this because it has such a large area vibrating against the surrounding air. Without such a **sounding board,** the fork delivers energy very gradually to the surrounding air, while at the same time there is a gradual conversion of energy of vibration into heat through the continual bending of the metal fork. Connected to a sounding board, the fork must also work at bending the sounding board, and delivers energy through the wide expanse of the board to the air at a much greater rate. In this case, the energy of the vibrating fork is used up more rapidly, but while it lasts the sound from the fork is much more intense, much louder.

Tuning forks are often bolted to **sounding boxes** open at one end. Then, if the cavity formed by the box is just the right size, the air in that cavity vibrates resonantly at the frequency of the fork. The air at the open end of the box vibrates with great amplitude, and sound waves of great intensity spread out into the room from this open end. Thus, if just a single frequency is involved, a relatively small sounding box can be as effective at its purpose of transferring vibrations to the air of the room as a much larger nonresonant sounding board.

The wires of a piano transfer energy to the air around them only very gradually: The wire cuts through the air much too readily. The piano is built, however, with its wires fixed at their ends, through the frame, to a large sounding board. The vibrations of the wires are transferred through their "fixed" ends to the sounding board. With its very large area, the sounding board is very good at transferring the vibrations in turn to the air of the room. Since it must be effective for all the notes of the piano, and all their overtones, the sounding board cannot be resonant at any frequency within the range covered by the piano. If it were, the resonant frequency or frequencies would receive undue emphasis. The wood used for the sounding boards of pianos is chosen for the high velocity with which it propagates sound waves. Thus the phase of the waves traveling across the sounding board varies only gradually with distance. In this way the sounding board is made to approximate as nearly as possible a rigid piston, for which at any given instant every point would be in exactly the same phase.

Almost every stringed instrument is designed with a sounding board, since strings do such a poor job in themselves of transferring their vibrations to the surrounding air. The design of most of these instruments has been empirical, rather than scientific. Thus through a gradually evolved craftsmanship the Italian violinmakers centuries ago built instruments not equaled since. Modern science with its powerful methods of analysis and measurement is hard put to explain just where the excellence of these instruments lies. It was suggested in the previous paragraph that a sounding board that must deal with a wide range of frequencies should not be resonant anywhere within that range of frequencies. It is of interest to note that the violinmakers did not observe this rule: The sounding boxes of their violins do have resonant frequencies within the audible range. Yet in thus flouting a reasonable rule, they achieved the utmost in musical quality.

25.08 MUSICAL STRINGS AND PIPES

We have worked out the laws for standing waves on a string or in a column of air. The musical quality or **timbre** of a vibrating system depends on just which modes are present, and in just what proportions. These factors can be influenced in many ways, some of them subtle. One may choose between striking a string, or plucking it, or bowing it. (In plucking, some point on the string is pulled aside and let go. In "bowing", the resined hairs of the bow are continually pulling the string aside, letting go, and pulling aside again.) This choice affects the quality. So does the point of attack, for none of the modes of vibration set up can have a node at the point of attack. Again, the manner in which the vibrations are transferred to the air—the transducer or sounding board involved—may emphasize high frequencies or low frequencies.

The column of air contained in a pipe may be set in motion by directing a stream of air at a lip cut into the wall of the pipe. A steady stream of air directed at this lip flips in and out of the pipe at a frequency determined by the vibration of the air column and provides the energy for that vibration. Alternatively, the steady air stream may be throttled at the required frequency by the vibrations of a reed. Some wind instruments use lips, some reeds. The nature of the device and the shape of the pipe affect the timbre. The pipe may, for instance, be made slightly conical. We have already noted that different sets of harmonics are set up by open and closed pipes. For strings and for pipes, the possibilities for variation of musical quality or timbre are infinite.

25.09 TRANSDUCERS

Sounding boards have already been described as transducers, "leading across" the vibratory energy from the resonant vibrator to the air.   The word has come into wide use, and so it may be worth quoting an authoritative definition of it:* "A **transducer** is a device by means of which energy may flow from one or more transmission systems to one or more other transmission systems.   The energy transmitted by these systems may be of any form (for example, it may be electrical, mechanical or acoustical) and it may be the same form or different forms in the various input and output systems".   Thus microphones, loudspeakers, and phonograph pickups are all transducers.   In general, it is desirable that transducers should not be resonant at any of the frequencies with which

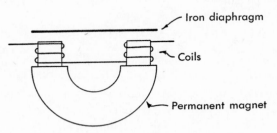

Fig. 25.10.   Telephone receiver.

they deal; otherwise undue emphasis will be given to the resonant frequency.

In the telephone receiver (Figure 25.10) an electric current varying in proportion to the pressure or the displacement of the sounds spoken at the other end of the line is fed through an electromagnet.   An iron diaphragm is thus driven in forced vibration, and it is desirable that the displacement of the diaphragm of the receiver should be proportional to the electric current and so to the displacement of the corresponding diaphragm in the microphone.   To obtain such proportionality, the resonant frequency of the diaphragm is kept outside the range of frequencies that the receiver reproduces.   Also, the magnetic circuit includes a permanent magnet.   Otherwise the diaphragm would be attracted toward the magnet twice in each cycle, once when the current was positive and again when it was negative.   Further, the permanent magnet increases sensitivity and reduces the distortion that tends to arise because the pull on the diaphragm is proportional to the *square* of the field.

The dynamic direct-radiator speaker is the form most commonly found in radio receivers.   A "voice-coil" through which the signal current flows is mounted, at the small end of a paper cone, in a strong, steady magnetic

* Harry F. Olson, *Elements of Acoustical Engineering*, 2nd Ed., Copyright 1947 by D. Van Nostrand Co., Inc.

field (Figure 25.11). Variations in the voice-coil current cause the coil to vibrate to and fro along its own axis, which is also that of the cone. Transverse waves are sent out from it along the cone, which thus finds itself in forced vibration of the same frequencies as the signal current and so as the sound at the distant microphone. A light frame (not shown in the figure) connects the magnet rigidly to the baffle, but the connection of the cone to the frame and baffle is made flexible by corrugations in the paper cone. The voice-coil must be kept light to achieve

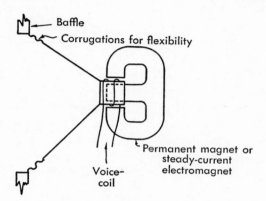

Fig. 25.11. Dynamic or direct-action speaker.

high-frequency response. Usually its resistance, and in fact its total impedance to the alternating signal currents, is just a few ohms.

The baffle, or panel in which the speaker is mounted, should be more than half a wavelength across, to avoid cancellation of the sounds of opposite phase arising at the front and back of the speaker. Thus for a frequency of 200 cycles, with a wavelength over five feet, the baffle should have a "diameter" of three feet or more. It is better that the baffle should be irregular in shape, to minimize the occurrence of marked interference effects at particular frequencies. For efficiency and simplicity, we would like to look on the speaker as a piston in an infinite baffle. Even that "ideal" has the limitations of being very directional at high frequencies, where its aperture may be several wavelengths across, and rather ineffective at transferring energy to the air, with an efficiency of just a few per cent. Actually, the forced vibration of the cone is really very complex, departures from pistonlike performance becoming more and more pronounced as the frequency is increased. Further, there is a resonant frequency to be avoided. Because of the weight of the voice-coil, the system is usually designed for a low resonant frequency: somewhere between 70 and 100 cycles sec^{-1}, and so below the usual range of audiofrequencies (although not below the audible limit). (Sixty cycles per second is particularly to be avoided, of course, because of the presence in the circuits of some current at this frequency picked up from the power line.) The amount of engineering development that has gone into this type of speaker during the past twenty-five years is very great. Olson's text, previously mentioned, manages to survey the characteristics of such speakers and their baffles in an intensive sixty pages.

The telephone receiver, the dynamic speaker, and in fact most "speakers" can be operated backward as microphones, producing electrical signals similar to the sound waves falling on them. Office intercommunication sets use a small dynamic speaker both as speaker and as microphone. A specially designed microphone will usually be more delicately constructed than any speaker, however. "Dynamic" microphones operate on the same principle as dynamic speakers, but with considerable differences in actual design. Crystal microphones use crystals of Rochelle salt, which at temperatures between -40 and $+130$F develop an electrical voltage on bending. In the microphone, the crystals are either fixed in a simple mechanical system such that the crystals will be bent by rapidly changing pressure, or else they are connected to a diaphragm to achieve the same result with greater sensitivity. In either case, it is rapid changes in pressure to which crystal microphones are sensitive. Being pressure-sensitive devices, they are nondirectional: Sounds coming at the microphone from any direction are almost equally effective.

"Velocity" microphones give signals proportional, not to pressure, but to the rate of change of displacement. Thus the very light ribbon of a free-ribbon microphone "floats in the breeze", sways to and fro with the air as the sound wave passes by. The ribbon lies in a strong magnetic field and generates a voltage proportional to the rate at which magnetic flux is cut, proportional thus to the velocity of the ribbon, the velocity of the vibrating air. A sound wave arriving obliquely will have less effect on the ribbon than one arriving normally, and one striking the ribbon edgewise will have no effect on it at all. Thus velocity microphones are directional, according to a cosine law, with sensitivity a maximum to the front and to the back, and zero to the sides.

A "cardioid" pattern of sensitivity with direction, giving maximum sensitivity to the front and minimum to the back, can be obtained by mounting a small nondirectional microphone, usually of the dynamic type, in a suitably designed case. There is a tendency for the pattern to vary with the frequency, but this tendency can be minimized by careful design. As was said about the dynamic speaker, the amount of engineering development that has been applied and is being applied to microphones is very great, and any comprehensive treatment would be correspondingly long.

25.10 THE VOICE*

The voice starts with the so-called vocal cords (Figures 25.12, 25.13). These organs are in the form of a double reed: in effect a pair

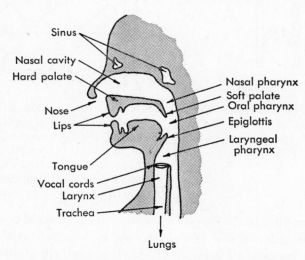

Fig. 25.12. Anatomy involved in speech. (From H. F. Olson, *Elements of Acoustical Engineering*, 2nd Ed., D. Van Nostrand Co., Inc., 1947.)

of lips, not unlike the lips of the human mouth. The edges can be brought together, and air from the lungs can be forced through between them. They will then be set in vibration and will produce a periodic interruption of the air blast, much as do the lips of a bugler or cornet player. The pitch of the note produced depends on the thickness, tension, and vibrating length of the two cords, factors that can be varied. The two cords lie in the same horizontal plane and run from front to back. They open widely during the act of breathing, and are about three-quarters of an inch long in the case of men, about half an inch in the case

* Taken almost verbatim from Alexander Wood, *The Physics of Music*, Methuen & Co. Ltd., 1944.

of women.   The "cracking" of the adolescent boy's voice is due to a comparatively rapid change in the length of the cords to about twice the previous value.   The male speaking voice has an average fundamental frequency of about 145 cycles sec^{-1}, female 230, each with a range of about two octaves (i.e., a factor 4).   The lowest frequency of a cathedral-choir bass is about 66 cycles sec^{-1}, the highest fundamental of a soprano about 1056.   (There are exceptions going as much as an octave higher.)

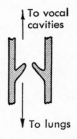

Fig. 25.13. Schematic view of vocal cords. (From H. F. Olson, *Elements of Acoustical Engineering*, 2nd Ed., D. Van Nostrand Co., Inc., 1947.)

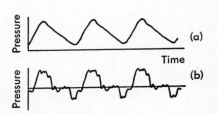

Fig. 25.14. Wave form of speech sound, (a) at vocal cords, (b) embellished by resonance in cavities of the head. (From H. F. Olson, *Elements of Acoustical Engineering*, 2nd Ed., D. Van Nostrand Co., Inc., 1947.)

The wave form of the vibrations of these reedlike vocal cords, and of the resulting pulsations of the air flowing past, is saw-toothed rather than simple harmonic; Figure 25.14(a).   Resonant vibration of the air in the "vocal cavities" embellishes this wave form into something much more complicated; Figure 25.14(b).   The shapes of the vocal cavities may be varied, the tongue playing the major part in these alterations. The true vowels and diphthongs are produced as outlined above.   The so-called "unvoiced consonants", as for example "s", are produced by air from the lungs passing over the sharp edges and through the narrow passages in various parts of the mouth and nose, the vocal cords not being used for these sounds.   The "voiced consonants" are produced by a combination of the two systems.   In whispering, the vocal cords remain silent.

25.11 THE EAR

You wouldn't think of speaking in a loud voice less than five inches away from someone else's ear.   Yet whether your voice is loud or soft, your own ears are only that far away from your mouth. Diffraction around the head is such that one's own speech is only one one-hundredth as intense at the ear as at the mouth. So the location of the ear has something in its favor. It is said to help in determining the direction from which sounds come, too. The pinna, the flap on the outside, would help lead the sound into the ear, if it were bigger, and if we could move it around better. As it is, it does not count for much; yet a cupped hand can help considerably. Also under the heading of "external ear" comes

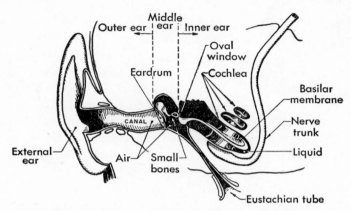

Fig. 25.15. The ear. (After A. P. G. Peterson and L. L. Beranek, *Handbook of Noise Measurement*, General Radio Company, 1953.)

the auditory canal leading into the eardrum (Figure 25.15). The canal is slightly crooked, about 2.5 cm long and 0.75 cm in diameter, so that it resonates (closed-pipe fundamental) with a broad maximum at a frequency of about 3000 cycles sec^{-1}. This is approximately the frequency at which the ear is most sensitive.

The canal is terminated in the eardrum or tympanic membrane, the beginning of the "middle ear." Vibrations of the eardrum are carried through a curious linkage of three bones, the memorably named hammer, anvil, and stirrup, to the inner ear. At first glance at this complicated mechanism, one would say that nature was achieving this transmission job the hard way. Modern physiologists have a skillfully devised explanation, though. According to it, the mechanism is so designed that it transmits the proper vibrations of the eardrum, those due to air-pressure variations, without transmitting or setting up noises due to movements of the head—disturbances arriving by conduction through the bone. Bearing in mind that the sound of a microphone stand being slid across the floor or table is pretty disconcerting, consider the sounds that might be picked up, while one was eating, by a microphone strapped to the head!

The inner ear or cochlea is the transducer, where vibrations are converted to nerve impulses. Embedded in the thick wall of the temporal bone, it is shaped like a snail shell of two and three-quarter turns, and is filled with fluid. Uncoiled (in imagination, as by a mathematician), it would form a tube about 35 mm long, with area of cross section ranging from 4 mm² at the end where the snail would come out (the base) to one-fourth as much at the apex. The nerve endings of the cochlear nerve are attached to thousands of hair cells, distributed along the length of the cochlea and supported by the basilar membrane (Figure 25.16). The membrane is narrowest at the base of the cochlea, widest at the apex. Introduction of a simple harmonic wave into the cochlea sets the basilar membrane into vibration over a large part of its length, but with maximum amplitude at a point which moves from apex to base as the frequency is increased. Vibration of the basilar membrane stimulates the nerve endings, which transmit electrochemical pulses to the brain. The number of pulses per second depends on the strength of the sound, and the frequency of the sound is judged, apparently, by the distribution of activity among the many nerve fibers.

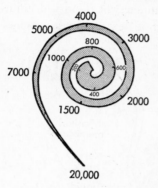

Fig. 25.16. Basilar membrane. Greatest width $\frac{1}{2}$ mm. Positions of greatest response at frequencies from 200 to 20,000 cycles per second are marked.

PROBLEMS

1. A string vibrates with a frequency of 80 cycles per second. The speed of wave propagation on the string is 100 m sec⁻¹. What is the wavelength? What is the distance between adjacent nodes due to reflection from a fixed end?

2. Draw the five lowest-frequency patterns of standing waves that can be formed on a string of length 1.00 m between fixed ends. What are their wavelengths? What are their frequencies, if the speed of wave propagation is 200 m sec⁻¹?

3. Wires A, B, C all have the same length and same tension, and are made of the same metal, but have different diameters. They all vibrate with the same frequency when the number of intermediate nodes between the two ends is

zero for A, 1 for B, 2 for C.   If the diameter of wire A is 0.100 mm, what are the diameters in millimeters of B and C?

4. A wire vibrates with frequencies 100, 200, 300, etc., cycles sec^{-1}.   A change in temperature causes the lowest frequency to increase by exactly 1 cycle sec^{-1}.   Is the change in temperature an increase or a decrease?   By what amounts are the other frequencies changed?

5. Two strings a and b have the same mass per unit length, but have lengths 50.0 and 60.0 cm, respectively.   What is the ratio of the frequency of b to the frequency of a if their tensions are the same?   What is the ratio of the tension of b to the tension of a if their frequencies are the same?

6. What is the lowest frequency of vibration of a column of air 30.0 cm long, one end closed, at temperature 20C?   What length of pipe of diameter 6.0 cm will contain such a column, allowing for an open-end correction?

7. What are the five lowest frequencies at which the air at 20C in a cylindrical glass vessel, of length 57.0 cm and diameter 10.0 cm, will resonate?

8. Referring to problem 7, show on a set of diagrams the positions of displacement nodes for each case.

9. What are the five lowest frequencies at which the air at 20C in a glass cylinder, open at both ends, of length 54.0 cm and diameter 10.0 cm, will resonate?

10. Referring to problem 9, show on a set of diagrams the positions of displacement nodes for each case.

11. A column of air resonates at a frequency of 1000 cycles sec^{-1} when the temperature is 20C.   What increase in temperature will increase the frequency by exactly 1 cycle sec^{-1}, if the length of the column remains constant?

12. Taking the dimensions of the auditory canal as given in the text and the temperature of the air as 30C, calculate the resonant frequency of the column of air contained in the canal.

26

Acoustics

26.01 AUDIBILITY

The sensation produced in the human mind, by way of the ear, in response to a pure sound, depends on the frequency of the sound and the amplitude of the pressure variations in the air at the ear. The pressure is fairly directly related to the intensity and so to the intensity level. The performance of the ear and the audibility of sounds can therefore be studied against coordinates of frequency and pressure or intensity. Because the range of frequencies and the range of intensities involved are both very great, logarithmic scales are generally used. These scales have added convenience because the response of the ear is in a way an approximately logarithmic response. In Figure 26.01, therefore, the coordinates are frequency and pressure on logarithmic scales. The scales extend from less than the lowest frequency to more than the highest frequency that any ear can hear, and from less than the smallest pressure variation that any ear can detect to more than any pressure variation that is healthy for the ear to encounter. Alternative ordinate scales are provided, of intensity (on a logarithmic scale) and intensity level (with a linear scale). These scales bear the correct relationship to the pressure scale on the assumption that the sound waves are plane waves in air at room temperature and a pressure of one atmosphere. (The "pressure" scale refers to the very small pressure variations of the sound wave about an average value of one atmosphere.) On the same assumptions, oblique lines of constant amplitude (amplitude of longitudinal displacement) have been drawn.

The lowest curved line is in effect the **threshold of hearing** for the 5% of the population having the most acute hearing. During the World's Fairs at New York and San Francisco in 1939, the Bell Laboratories tested the hearing of more than half a million people. Five per cent of those tested could hear sounds falling below the 5% curve. The lowest point on this curve lies just under 2×10^{-4} dyne cm^{-2}; because of this, intensity level is generally used with an intensity of 2×10^{-4} dyne cm^{-2} as the zero level. The "thermal noise" due to random molecular motion amounts to 0.5×10^{-4} dyne cm^{-2} in this frequency range, so that the threshold for acute hearing is not far above this ultimate limitation. Half

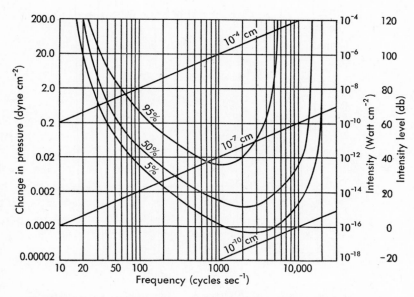

Fig. 26.01. Audibility diagram, showing thresholds of hearing bettered by 5%, 50%, and 95% of the population. (Threshold curves after Steinberg, Montgomery and Gardner, *Jour. Acous. Soc. Amer.*, Vol. 12, No. 2, p. 291, 1940.)

the people tested could hear some sounds falling below the 50% curve, and 95% could hear some sounds falling below the 95% curve. Comparison of the curves shows that the spread between the best 5% and the poorest 5% is between 30 and 40 db at frequencies below 1000 cycles sec^{-1}, then increases rapidly to 100 db at 5000 cycles sec^{-1}.

At about 120 db or 200 dyne cm^{-2}, at all frequencies, there is a **threshold of feeling.** The feeling involved is a tickle in the middle ear due to the linked bones there vibrating against the walls of the cavity containing them. This sensation comes just before dangerously large vibrations which may damage the structure of the inner ear, somewhat in the same way that a loudspeaker driven until it rattles is in danger of permanent damage.   The threshold of feeling thus serves as a practical upper limit to the range of intensities that the ear can hear.

For most of us, acuity of hearing drops off steadily with age, beyond an age of about twenty years, particularly at high frequencies.   At age

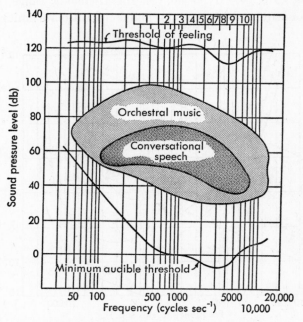

Fig. 26.02. Audibility diagram, showing regions of speech and music.   Numbered regions of top band contribute equally to intelligibility of speech.   (After V. O. Knudsen and C. M. Harris, *Acoustical Designing in Architecture*, John Wiley & Sons, Inc., New York, 1950.)

60, your hearing is likely to be down 5 to 10 db at voice frequencies, 25 db at frequencies over 3000 cycles sec^{-1}.

The displacement amplitudes indicated by the oblique lines are amazingly small.   An amplitude of 1 mm is above the threshold of feeling; the smallest amplitudes detectable by ear are less than 10^{-9} cm.

The approximate range in frequency and intensity of conversational speech is shown in Figure 26.02, along with the range of orchestral music as heard in a concert hall.   All the portions of the frequency spectrum do not contribute equally to the intelligibility of speech, and at the top of the figure 10 bands are indicated that do provide equal contributions.

It is only in the absence of other sounds that pure tones can be heard down to the threshold levels indicated in Figure 26.01. Usually there is present an assortment of noises of various frequencies tending to mask sounds of lesser intensities. This establishes a threshold for hearing quite independent of the capabilities of the ear. Samples of such thresholds established by the presence of noise are shown in Figure 26.03. Comparing this figure with 26.01 it can be seen that the best 5% of listeners seldom have the chance to gain by their acuity, whereas in an average factory the poorest 5% appear to do almost as well as the rest.

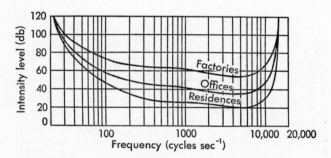

Fig. 26.03. Typical thresholds due to masking by noise. (From H. F. Olson, *Elements of Acoustical Engineering*, 2nd Ed., D. Van Nostrand Co., Inc., 1947.)

Masking is considerably worse for listening with a single ear. We train ourselves to judge by the difference in time of arrival at our two ears the direction from which a sound comes. With our ears in a horizontal plane, it is only horizontal direction that can be judged this way. A microphone acts like a single ear. A person listening at home to the radio can use his binaural hearing to separate the sounds of the radio from the assorted sounds of the noise background, coming from an assortment of directions. He cannot separate in the same way such noises as occurred in the studio and were picked up by the one-eared microphone. The requirements for quiet and for good acoustics in a radio studio are thus especially severe. For the same reason, the noise background in the output of a hearing aid or a single-channel tape recorder tends to be startlingly high.

Now compare the masking thresholds with the regions of speech and music in Figure 26.02. A residence is quiet enough for conversation. It is quiet enough for orchestral music, too, if the music is at the normal concert-hall level. Reproduction in the home of orchestral music, at this level, is apt to startle the neighbors, however. If the loudest sounds are kept down to the socially acceptable maximum and the softest sounds are similarly reduced, the latter are bound to be lost in the noise-masking. The tendency in practice is for the extreme range of orchestral music to be considerably reduced for home reproduction.

26.02 LOUDNESS

Intensity is an objective quantity, the measurement of which can be achieved without involving personal judgment. Loudness is the subjective quantity, entirely a matter of personal judgment, that varies with

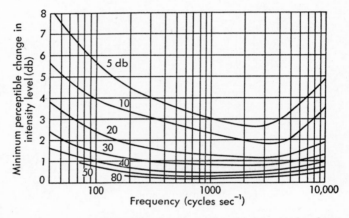

Fig. 26.04. Minimum perceptible changes in level at various levels marked on curves. (After H. Fletcher, *Speech and Hearing*, 2nd Ed., D. Van Nostrand Co., Inc., 1953.)

varying intensity. Subjective quantities are difficult to measure. One way of measuring the manner in which the subjective response varies with the intensity is the method of minimum perceptible changes. A change in intensity can be detected by ear, if the change is big enough, but will pass undetected if it is less than the minimum detectable change. Let the smallest possible change in response, corresponding to the minimum perceptible change in intensity, be looked on as a unit of response, a unit of loudness. If the intensity is increased progressively by the least perceptible amount, it is found that the increments in intensity become progressively larger. It is found, however, that the increments in the intensity level remain roughly the same over a wide range of levels. On this basis, we can say that the ear has logarithmic response, for equal small changes in level correspond to equal increments in the logarithm of the intensity. It can be seen in Figure 26.04 that the minimum perceptible changes in level are only roughly constant, but more nearly so for moderate frequencies and intensities than for extremely high or low values.

The quantity known as **loudness level** is in keeping with this notion of logarithmic response. Its measurement is a useful step toward determining loudness in any case. The loudness level of a 1000-cycle note, in **phons,** is by definition numerically equal to the intensity level in decibels.

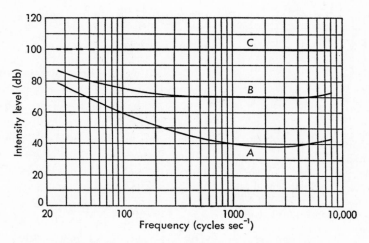

Fig. 26.05. Lines of equal loudness, used in specifying performance of sound-level meters.

The loudness level of a note of any frequency is by definition numerically equal to the intensity level in decibels of the 1000-cycle note that sounds equally loud.

Lines of equal loudness are plotted in Figure 26.05. That is to say, there is general agreement that every note on one of these lines has the same loudness as every other note on the same line. These lines have been drawn to pass through 1000 cycles sec^{-1} at 40, 70, and 100 db. They are used to specify the relative response to varying frequency that a sound-level meter shall have. Ordinarily, the response specified by curve *A* is used when loudness levels below 55 phons are being measured, curve *B* for levels between 55 and 85 phons, and the flat curve *C* for levels above 85 phons.

The system of loudness levels permits our saying when two sounds are equally loud, or which of two sounds is the louder. When it comes to saying how much louder one sound is than another, however, the scale of loudness levels is not viewed with general favor. Going beyond this, a scale of **loudness** has been developed (Figure 26.06) which permits us to say "how much louder." The unit in this scale is the "sone". It is necessary in the use of this scale to distinguish between a pure note, of frequency, say, 1000 cycles per second, and a sound containing many unrelated frequencies, described as "wide-band noise".

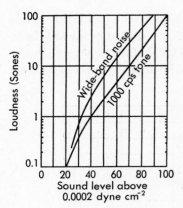

26.03 PITCH

Just as with intensity, the ratio of the minimum detectable change in frequency to the initial frequency is a quantity that varies only gradually with frequency and intensity, except for extreme values of these quantities (Figure 26.07). Thus the subjective response to frequency, called **pitch**, varies roughly as the logarithm of the frequency. Pitch is not entirely independent of intensity: At frequencies below 1000 cycles

Fig. 26.06. Loudness related to intensity level for a pure note and for noise covering a wide range of frequencies. (After A. P. G. Peterson and L. L. Beranek, *Handbook of Noise Measurement*, General Radio Company, 1953.)

sec^{-1}, if a note of constant frequency is raised steadily in intensity level, from 60 to 100 db, its frequency seems to decrease by several per cent. Its pitch, then, being subjective, can be said actually to decrease.

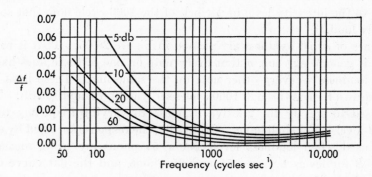

Fig. 26.07. Minimum perceptible change in frequency at various levels marked on curves. (After H. F. Olsen, *Elements of Acoustical Engineering*, 2nd Ed., D. Van Nostrand Co., Inc., 1947.)

"Wow" is an interesting demonstration of the perception of frequency change. If a phonograph record is rotated about a point differing slightly from its proper center, the frequencies of the reproduced music rise and fall with the period of rotation of the record. A small error in centering the record can produce this effect to a disconcerting extent, particularly as the needle nears the center of the record, and if there are sustained notes of high frequency.

26.04 MUSICAL SCALES

Some notes sound pleasant when played together or in close succession—some don't. The aim of music is much more than the production of pleasing combinations of tones, but in establishing the scales of musical notes as a framework on which music can be composed, this business of pleasant and unpleasant combinations is important. The reasonable aim in establishing a scale is not to provide consonance, and thus to make composing easy. It is rather to provide a reasonable number of notes having a minimum of dissonance, of unpleasantness. Then the composer can take over, and invent the positive qualities that make music something more than "pleasant". Helmholtz (1821) developed a theory of consonance and dissonance in terms of beats. To avoid dissonance, he said, avoid fast but perceptible beats between the two notes being played together, and avoid such beats between any overtones of the two notes. And how can this be done? By keeping to simple ratios between any notes played together.

If one tries to set up for oneself a sequence of frequencies that will give simple ratios, one comes with very little steering to the **diatonic scale**. For example, follow the development in Figure 26.08; follow it if possible to the accompaniment of pairs of notes played by oscillators.

In the figure, a logarithmic scale has been ruled off, so that lines of equal horizontal length represent equal ratios. The scale extends from 1 (to represent the base frequency) to 2. Now we fit in the simplest ratios we can think of, 2:1, 3:2, 4:3, 5:3, 5:4. The ratio of 6:5 does not require another frequency, for it exists twice already. If you are playing the ratios as you work through the diagram, you will be finding the sound of ratios involving sevens unsatisfactory. Arbitrarily, let us omit them. The ratio 8:5 exists already. Let us take stock of our position, (j). Consecutive ratios are now 5:4, 16:15, 9:8, 10:9, 6:5. We have two large ratios (5:4 and 6:5), two medium (9:8 and 10:9), and one small (16:15). The next ratio to be considered, in order of decreasing simplicity, is 9:8. It already exists, although not terminating at either end of the scale. Let us introduce it twice more to break down the two large ratios (k):

$$9:8, \ 10:9, \ 16:15, \ 9:8, \ 10:9, \ 9:8, \ 16:15$$

At this stage we have the diatonic scale. You can get a close approach to it by playing the white keys on a piano from one C to the next (Figure 26.08). The musician names the intervals by the number of these keys,

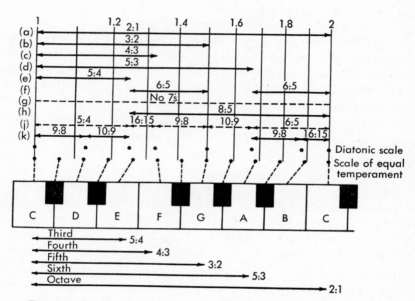

Fig. 26.08. Development of musical scale and its relationship to piano keyboard.

including the end ones in each case. Thus his names octave, fifth, etc., have no direct connection with the frequencies involved. The exact frequencies used are unimportant; it is the frequency ratios that count. If we take 24 (or 240) as our base frequency, all the other frequencies are integers. Musicians are in fairly good agreement nowadays about taking 440 cycles sec^{-1} as the frequency of the note A above middle C. In physics it is often convenient to emphasize the scale-of-two by taking middle C itself equal to 256, which is the eighth power of two.

The diatonic scale consists of five large intervals (whole tones), almost but not exactly identical in size, and two small intervals (semitones), approximately half as large. If each whole tone were split in two, the octave would contain twelve semitones, all approximately the same size. The scale of equal temperament (S.E.T.) does split the octave into twelve semitones, and does make them all exactly the same size. This size must be one-twelfth of an octave, or $\sqrt[12]{2} = 1.0595$. The resulting scale is compared with the diatonic in Table 26.01. The final column of Table 26.01 gives the interval from the diatonic frequency to that of the scale of equal temperament. In three cases it is almost 1%, quite enough for the ear to detect. The scale of equal temperament is not "good music" in the way that the diatonic scale is. It gives fair approximations to simple ratios, whereas the diatonic really does give

TABLE 26.01.

Diatonic Ratio (n)	S.E.T. Ratio (m)	m − n	(m − n)/n
1:1 = 1.000	1.0000		
	1.0595		
9:8 = 1.125	1.1224	−0.0026	−0.002
	1.1892		
5:4 = 1.250	1.2599	+0.0099	+0.008
4:3 = 1.333	1.3348	+0.0015	+0.001
	1.4144		
3:2 = 1.500	1.4983	−0.0017	−0.001
	1.5874		
5:3 = 1.666	1.6818	+0.0152	+0.009
	1.7822		
15:8 = 1.875	1.8878	+0.0128	+0.008
2:1 = 2.000	2.0000		

simple ratios. But with the scale of equal temperament the notes of a keyboard instrument become a uniform series. With it, music can be played equally well in all keys, without stopping to retune the instrument. Quoting now from Sir James Jeans:*

On the other hand its defects are many. The most obvious is that of all the seventy-eight intervals that lie within the range of a single octave, not a single one is in perfect tune; every one could be improved if there were not the others to think about. The pianist and organist accept this accumulation of lesser evils in order to escape the major evils of badly discordant intervals. But the violinist and singer are under no such necessity; as each interval comes along, they can make it what they like, and so naturally tend to make it that which gives most pleasure to the ear. Observations show that the intervals which such performers produce when they are left to themselves differ greatly from those they produce when accompanied by an instrument tuned to equal temperament.

* Sir James Jeans, *Science and Music*, Cambridge University Press, 1937.

26.05 THE ABSORPTION OF SOUND

The air transmits sound with very little **attenuation,** that is to say, very little loss by absorption. The intensity of a spherical sound wave spreading out from a small source will decrease as the square of the distance, because the energy is distributed over a continually lengthening wave front, but the total energy in the wave front remains effectively constant, because very little of the energy is absorbed. Such energy as *is* absorbed is converted into heat. Absorption by air at high frequencies is appreciable and changes with the humidity of the air. The effect is

TABLE 26.02.

Material	Absorption Coefficient		
	at 128 cps	at 512 cps	at 4096 cps
Painted brick wall	0.012	0.017	0.025
Wood sheeting, 0.8-in. pine	0.10	0.10	0.11
Masonite, $\frac{1}{2}$-in., set out from wall	0.18	0.32	0.31
Rock wool, 1-in.	0.35	0.63	0.83
$\frac{1}{2}$-in. carpet, on $\frac{1}{8}$-in. felt, on concrete	0.11	0.37	0.27
Individual Object	Absorption in Sabins		
Man with coat	2.3	4.8	7.0

just great enough to make it important, in order for music to retain its quality in a large auditorium, to maintain the humidity at an appropriate value.

Absorption of sound does occur at some solid surfaces. This is fortunate, for otherwise sound energy released in the air of a closed room would remain in the air of the room for a long time, and a listener in the room would hear at any instant all the sounds made in the room in the previous several seconds. Fortunately, too, the amount of absorption varies greatly from one sort of surface to another. The quality of sound heard in a room can be varied by incorporating some surfaces that absorb greatly, some that absorb hardly at all, and by recognizing that some locations in the room are better for the absorbing materials, some for the nonabsorbing.

If a surface reflects all the sound arriving at it, it has a "reflection coefficient" of unity and an **absorption coefficient** of zero. A painted brick wall approaches this limit; at a frequency of 256 cycles sec^{-1} it reflects 99% of the sound, absorbs 1%; its reflection coefficient is 0.99, its absorption coefficient 0.01. At the other extreme comes an open window. Unless the room is so shaped that it reflects like the open end of a pipe, it has an absorption coefficient of 1.00, reflection coefficient zero. One square foot of perfect absorber is said to have an absorption of one "sabin" (after Wallace C. Sabine, 1868); thus a surface of area S with absorption coefficient a has an absorption of Sa sabins. One average man with his coat on has an absorption (for frequency 512 cycles sec^{-1}) of 4.8 sabins. As far as the acoustics of the room are concerned, he corresponds to 4.8 ft^2 of open window. Some sample coefficients are given in Table 26.02.

26.06 INTENSITY OF SOUND IN A ROOM

Although a room may contain some highly absorbent surfaces, the average coefficient of absorption, averaging over all surfaces, tends to be quite low. As a result, sound waves in a room are reflected several times, possibly many times, before they are reduced to negligible strength. Because of these multiple reflections, we find at any point in a room sound waves traveling in almost every conceivable direction. We find too that the energy of the sound is distributed fairly uniformly throughout the volume of the room (except close to a source of sound): If the sound energy in the room is E, then the sound in any unit volume is approximately E/V, where V is the volume of the room.

To meet this situation, we must develop further our notion of intensity. The intensity of a plane wave has been defined (section 24.07) as the rate at which energy passes through an aperture of unit area, the aperture lying in a plane to which the direction of motion of sound is normal. On that basis,

$$I = \mathcal{E}c$$

where $\mathcal{E}$ is the energy per unit volume due to the wave. If the plane sound wave arrived at the aperture obliquely, the rate at which energy passed through would be reduced to $\mathcal{E}c \cos \theta$, where θ is the angle between the direction of the sound wave and the normal to the aperture. In the case now postulated, in whatever plane an aperture is considered, sound waves will arrive with every conceivable value of θ. Averaging over every direction subtended by a hemisphere, an average value of $\frac{1}{4}$ is obtained for $\cos \theta$. We will therefore define intensity, for the case of sound traveling in all directions, by

$$I = \frac{c}{4} \mathcal{E}$$

Recalling that $\mathcal{E} = E/V$, we can write for the intensity of sound in a room

$$I = \frac{c}{4V} E \tag{26.01}$$

where E is the sound energy in the room, c the speed of sound, and V the volume of the room.

If we cut a hole of area A in the wall of a room, sound energy will leave the room at a rate IA. If the hole is replaced by the same area of perfect absorber, the rate is still the same. It is still the same if we have larger areas of partially absorbing material, the total absorption of which is A sabins, for this is the equivalent of A ft² of perfect absorber. A room can be considered as a reservoir of sound, to which sound is being added from a source at a rate P and from which it is being removed at a rate IA. The change in E in time Δt is then given by

$$\Delta E = (P - IA)\,\Delta t \tag{26.02}$$

Since $I \propto E$, any change ΔE in E will effect a corresponding change ΔI in I, and since $I = [c/(4V)]E$, it can be seen that

$$\Delta I = \frac{c}{4V}\Delta E = \frac{c}{4V}(P - IA)\,\Delta t \tag{26.03}$$

26.07 GROWTH OF SOUND IN A ROOM

Equation (26.03) is a differential equation. For specified conditions it can be solved to give the algebraic relationship between intensity and time. Suppose that a sound of power P is turned on at an instant that we shall denote by $t = 0$ in a room that was previously quiet. Then the algebraic relation is

$$I = I_e(1 - e^{-\frac{cA}{4V}t}) \tag{26.04}$$

The form of this relationship is plotted in Figure 26.09(a). At the start the rate of rise is rapid, because the intensity in the room is zero, and the rate of loss of energy to the absorber is proportional to the intensity. As the intensity builds up, so does the rate of loss, and an equilibrium condition is approached in which rate of loss IA equals rate of gain P. Using I_e to denote the intensity in this condition,

$$I_e = \frac{P}{A} \tag{26.05}$$

The equilibrium value of the intensity is proportional to the power of the source, inversely proportional to A. By making A small, we can make the intensity great. This is a virtue of making sound in rooms instead of in the open: We can make them more intense, and uniformly intense throughout the room. It takes time for the intensity to rise to a value comparable with I_e, of course. This delay is seldom troublesome,

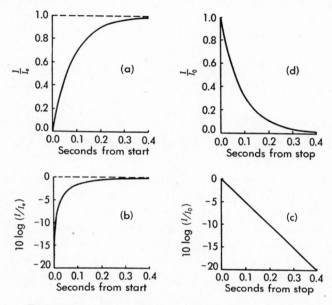

Fig. 26.09. Theoretical growth (a), (b), and decay (c), (d), of sound in a room.

as can be seen more readily from Figure 26.09(b), where intensity *level*, to which the response of the ear is more nearly linear, is plotted. The time for the level to come within one or two decibels of the equilibrium value is almost always short enough.

26.08 DECAY OF SOUND IN A ROOM

Now let us consider what happens if a source of sound, after it has been operating long enough to fill the room fairly uniformly with sound, is turned off. With no source in operation, equation (26.03) becomes

$$\Delta I = - \frac{cA}{4V} I \, \Delta t \tag{26.06}$$

The use of $\Delta \log x$ in place of $\Delta x/x$ was discussed in Chapter 15. Introducing $\Delta \log I$ according to equation (15.19), we have

$$\Delta \log I = 0.434 \frac{\Delta I}{I} = -0.434 \frac{cA}{4V} \Delta t$$

Thus a plot of $\log I$ against t is a line of constant slope, $-0.434cA/(4V)$. If at time zero the intensity is I_0, the equation of the line is

$$\log I = \log I_0 - 0.434 \times \frac{cA}{4V} t$$

Replacing $(\log I - \log I_0)$ by $\log (I/I_0)$ and at the same time introducing a factor 10 to give intensity level, we have

$$10 \log \frac{I}{I_0} = -4.34 \frac{cA}{4V} t \text{ db} \tag{26.07}$$

When sources of sound are turned off, then, the intensity level in a room decreases linearly with time; Figure 26.09(c). The rate is proportional to the amount of absorption A and inversely proportional to the volume of the room. To complete the set of curves, I is plotted against t for the case of decay in Fig. 26.09(d).

This continuation of the sound after the sources are turned off is known as **reverberation.** The measure that is used for the amount of reverberation in a room is **reverberation time:** *the time required for the level to decrease by 60 db.* Denoting this quantity by t_{60} and substituting in equation (26.07) gives

$$-60 = -4.34 \frac{cA}{4V} t_{60} \tag{26.08}$$

Taking the velocity of sound as 1130 ft sec^{-1} (for a room temperature of 72F), we obtain

$$t_{60} = \frac{60}{4.34} \times \frac{4}{1130 \text{ ft sec}^{-1}} \times \frac{V}{A}$$

$$= 0.049 \frac{V}{A} \text{ ft}^{-1} \text{ sec}$$

or nearly enough $= \dfrac{V}{20A} \text{ ft}^{-1} \text{ sec} \tag{26.09}$

Substituting values of V in cubic feet and A in square feet (of perfect absorber) gives t_{60} in seconds. Therefore the amount of absorption required to give a reverberation time of 1 sec (which is of the right order) is given by

$$A = \tfrac{1}{20} V \text{ ft}^{-1}$$

Thus for a room of volume 20,000 ft³, the total amount of absorption needed is of the order of 1000 sabins, or the equivalent of 1000 ft² of perfect absorber.

The need for a short reverberation time can be seen in Figure 26.10. The four shaded areas in the (a) part of the figure represent in extremely simplified form four successive speech sounds, occurring at intervals of

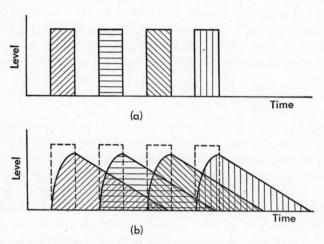

Fig. 26.10. Sequence of speech sounds, (a) as produced (very roughly) and (b) as heard in a room.

0.1 sec. In practice they would occur at this rate on the average, but they would not be so uniformly spaced, so widely separated by intervals of no sound, or so uniform in level. The (b) part of the figure shows the pattern of intensity level as heard in a room. With a reverberation time of 1 sec, each sound is down by an average of only 6 db from its maximum level at the time the next sound has reached its maximum. Each sound tends to mask its successor. Recognizing that the consonants tend to have much less power than the vowels, many of the consonants will be completely masked. Fortunately there is sufficient redundancy in normal speech to permit the listener to fill in subconsciously the sounds missed, but this is a poor substitute for the intelligible delivery of every sound, which can be achieved only by careful enunciation *and* well-controlled reverberation.

The principal beneficial effect of the reverberant sound is to provide a reasonably uniform intensity level throughout a room. The average power of a man's speaking voice is 24 microwatts, providing at a distance of 1 m an intensity of

$$\frac{24 \times 10^{-6}}{4 \times 3.14 \times 10^4} \simeq 2 \times 10^{-10} \text{ watt cm}^{-2}$$

for a level of 63 db above threshold. At a distance of 10 m the intensity will have dropped by a factor of $10^2 = 100$, and the level by 20 db to 43 db. In a room, however, the equilibrium intensity will be $I = P/A$. Let us take a room of volume $40 \times 25 \times 16$ ft $= 16,000$ ft^3. For a reverberation time of 1 sec, the amount of absorption needed will be 800 sabins, or 7.44×10^5 cm^2 of perfect absorber, and so an equilibrium intensity will be obtained, more or less, everywhere in the room, of

$$\frac{24 \times 10^{-6}}{7.44 \times 10^5} = 3.2 \times 10^{-11} \text{ watt cm}^{-2}$$

for a level of 55 db. This is the same as the level of the direct sound alone at a distance of just 2.5 m or 8 ft from the speaker, and 12 db better than would be provided otherwise for the more distant listeners.

It takes time for the reverberant sound to build up, and there is no point in attempting to enhance sounds of short duration by a long reverberation time. Music contains sounds of longer duration than speech, and so there is more chance of this advantage accruing with it. Further, the blending of successive sounds may actually be desirable. Even for speech, a very short reverberation time has a disadvantage in that it sounds unnatural. Lecturers adjust the level and rate of their delivery according to the reverberant sound that they hear, and musicians playing together use it to keep in touch. Optimum values of reverberation time, based on attempts to take all these factors into account, range from 0.7 sec for a small room used for speech to 2 sec for sacred music in a large church.

26.09 IMAGES

Let us consider now in greater physical detail the case of a closed room containing a source of sound, say a man talking, and a listener. The listener hears sound that has traveled straight from the source, and in addition sound that has been reflected at the walls, floor, and ceiling of the room. We can obtain aid in determining the path followed by the reflected sound from the notion of images. The image of a point source due to a plane reflecting surface can be located by drawing a perpendicular from the source to the surface and continuing the perpendicular an equal distance beyond the surface. Reflected radiation, whether we are considering sound or light, travels as from the image. Furthermore, the distance traveled from source to observer is equal to the distance from the image to the observer. This is useful information in the case of sound, for it tells us how long it will take the sound to travel from source to listener. Figure 26.11 shows four such images. Adding to these the images due to the ceiling and due to the floor, there are six images as compared with just one source. The signals reaching the listener from

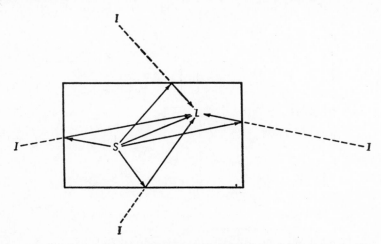

Fig. 26.11.   Plan view of room showing source (S), listener (L), and primary images of source in walls (I).

them, or apparently from them, are bound to be weaker than the direct sound, because of the greater distances traveled. There will not only be a set of six images due to reflection, but images of those images, and images of those images of images, and so on to infinity.

Let us reconsider the case of a source of sound commencing at the instant $l = 0$ in a previously quiet room. Figure 26.12 is a plot of intensity, at the position of the listener, against time, for such a case. No sound is heard until the direct sound has had time to travel from source to listener; then the intensity jumps suddenly. A little later there is another somewhat smaller jump, due to the nearest image, followed in rapid succession by the other primary images. The broken line has been drawn for a room with perfectly reflecting surfaces. The jumps become progressively smaller but at the same time more numerous; the set of irregular steps can be represented to a first approximation by a straight line through the origin. The solid line has been drawn, more realistically, for a room in which the surfaces, or some of them, are partially absorbent.

There are just as many steps, but they tend to be smaller, some of them very much so. The corresponding approximation for this case is the curve of Figure 26.09(a), and equation (26.04). By the time an equilibrium value of intensity is approached, the steps have become imperceptibly small.

When the source stops, the direct sound will be lost to the listener first, then the sound from the nearer images, and gradually the sound from more and more distant images. The steps of the decay curve will

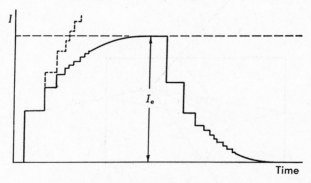

Fig. 26.12. Growth of sound in room, showing discontinuous jumps in intensity as various images join in and drop out. Broken line is for hypothetical room with zero absorption.

be those of the building-up taken in the same order, but downward instead of up. The discontinuous curve of decay will approximate to the continuous decay curve of Figure 26.09(d).

The mathematical derivation of the continuous curve assumes that the room is uniformly filled with sound. The true curve will approximate to the smooth curve only if there are many reflections during the time under consideration. For relevance, this time must be of the order of the time between individual sounds in speech, or roughly 0.1 sec. Thus for "reverberation time" theory to be applicable, the time between successive reflections of the sound waves must be small compared with 0.1 sec. In this interval of time, sound travels about 110 ft. So the distance between successive reflections, and therefore the dimensions of the room, should be small compared with 110 ft—should be, say, 30 ft or less—for this theory to be applicable. For larger rooms, it is possible from considering the pattern of images to so locate the areas of high absorption that an array of near images is retained to reinforce the sound (any signal arriving within 0.05 sec is acceptable to the ear as reinforcement), while more distant images, which would be heard as echoes, are effectively deadened.

Correct acoustical design is a complex business for any size of room. Behavior at all frequencies must be considered. In a small room the problem of reverberation can be reduced to the consideration of reverberation time, but the related problem of resonance, which emphasizes certain low frequencies, becomes important. In any case noise must be kept down. If it cannot be brought well below the speech level, then that level must be raised by amplifiers. It is the interrelation of many factors that makes acoustical engineering complex work, demanding and deserving the greatest care.

PROBLEMS

1. Which is higher, the threshold of the average ear (50% curve, Figure 26.01) or the threshold due to masking in a residence (Figure 26.03), (a) at 1000 cycles sec^{-1}, (b) at 5000 cycles sec^{-1}?

2. How many of the ten frequency regions contributing equally to the intelligibility of speech (at conversational level, Figure 26.02) are lost to the 5% of the population with poorest hearing (95% curve, Figure 26.01)?

3. Two sounds of frequency 100 and 1000 cycles sec^{-1} have the same loudness level as measured by a sound-level meter set to weighting A. By how much do they differ in intensity level?

4. By what factor is the loudness (in "sones") increased when the intensity level of a 1000-cycle tone is raised from 40 db above threshold to 60 db above threshold?

5. (a) A phonograph has a spiral groove, of radius diminishing from 15.0 cm at the outside to 5.0 cm at the inside of the record. (i) What is the linear speed of travel of the needle along the groove, at the outside, in centimeters per second, if the record rotates at a rate of $33\frac{1}{3}$ rpm? What will be the maximum and minimum linear speeds if the record is rotated about a center 1.00 mm distant from the center used when the record was made? If a note having a constant frequency of 1000 cycles sec^{-1} was recorded, what will be the maximum and minimum frequencies heard when the record is played, using this wrong center? By what percentage will the maximum frequency exceed the minimum? (ii) Repeat for the inside of the record (radius 5.0 cm).

   (b) What inaccuracy in centering a phonograph record can be permitted if the "wow" (percentage variation in frequency of playback) must not exceed 1 part in 200 when the radius of the groove is 5.0 cm?

6. What is the ratio of the frequency of the note G to that of the note E in the diatonic scale and in the scale of equal temperament?

7. If the note A is given a frequency of 440 cycles sec^{-1}, what is the frequency of the next note C above, in the diatonic scale and in the scale of equal temperament?

8. A room contains panels of rock wool (see Table 26.02), designed so that the amount of absorbing surface can be varied to maintain the total absorption within the room when the number of people in it changes. By what amount must the area of rock wool be increased to compensate exactly at frequency 512 cycles sec^{-1} for the departure of 50 people?

9. Referring to problem 8, what change will be effected in the absorption at 128 cycles sec^{-1} and at 4096 cycles sec^{-1} when 50 people have been replaced by an amount of rock wool equivalent to them at 512 cycles sec^{-1}?

10. A room is 12 ft high by 20 ft by 32 ft. How much absorption must there be, in sabins or equivalent square feet of perfect absorber, to give a reverberation time of 1.0 sec?

11. A steady sound is suddenly stopped in a room having a reverberation time of 1.20 sec. By what factor does the intensity drop in the next 0.10 sec?

12. All surfaces of a room of volume $10 \times 15 \times 18$ ft have an absorption coefficient of 0.10 at all relevant frequencies, and there is no other absorber of any account. What is the reverberation time?

13. Referring to problem 12, what is the reverberation time at 512 cycles sec^{-1} with 5 people in the room? with 30 people?

14. Repeat problem 13 for frequencies 128 cycles sec^{-1} and 4096 cycles sec^{-1}.

LIGHT

27

Light and Color

27.01 LIGHT IN THE ELECTROMAGNETIC SPECTRUM

It is known, these days, that electromagnetic radiation exists at just about every conceivable wavelength. The velocity of this radiation, in empty space, has a fixed value, roughly 3×10^{10} cm sec^{-1}, regardless of the wavelength. The longer wavelengths are generated by electrical circuits, and are used for radio. The very short wavelengths are generated by bombarding metal targets with beams of electrons, the electrons themselves having very nearly the velocity of light; they are used as X-rays. There is a narrow region in the spectrum, from 0.38 to 0.76×10^{-6} m in wavelength, that holds a particular interest. The reason is in our eyes; that is the range of wavelengths, approximately, to which they are sensitive. Radiations in this range of wavelength, and sometimes a bit beyond it, are called light. The units of length used for these short wavelengths are the Angstrom unit (A) and the micron (for which the abbreviation μ will be used only sparingly, since this symbol is used for refractive index). One meter equals 10^6 micron equals 10^{10} A.

The wavelength to which the eye is most sensitive comes at about 0.5550 micron. Although there is variation from person to person, a standard curve of sensitivity against wavelength has been established by the International Commission on Illumination. This I.C.I. curve is shown as curve a, Figure 27.01. This curve is for **photopic** vision: vision by a reasonably bright light. When the light is very faint, the eyes change to **scotopic** vision: We no longer distinguish as well among colors (a fact to be considered as incidental in the present section), and our sensitivity curve shifts to shorter wavelengths. The scotopic curve is shown as curve b in Figure 27.01. Each curve has been "normalized" for a maximum sensitivity of unity. That is to say, the ordinate is actually

$$\frac{\text{Sensitivity at the given wavelength}}{\text{Sensitivity at best wavelength for this type of vision}}$$

so that both curves have the same peak ordinate value of unity.   With-

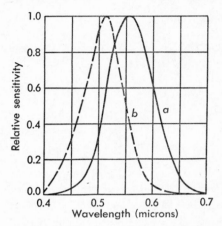

out this normalization, the scotopic curve would rise far above the photopic curve, since the eye adapts its sensitivity to the brightness of the light.

27.02 OTHER SENSITIVE SURFACES

At any wavelength, we can detect and measure radiation by absorbing it in some substance that is a good absorber at that wavelength.   Then the rate that heat is generated in the substance equals the power of the incoming radiation.   A thermopile working on this principle can be uniformly sensitive over a wide range of wavelengths.   The retina of the

Fig. 27.01.   Standard Luminosity Curves, giving sensitivity of the eye: curve *a* for photopic vision, when light is bright, and curve *b* for scotopic vision, when light is weak.

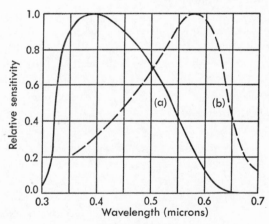

Fig. 27.02.   Sensitivity curves for photoelectric cells: curve (a), example of a photoemissive cell, and curve (b), example of a photovoltaic cell, as used in exposure meters.

eye, we have noted, is sensitive over a narrow range of wavelengths. But in that range, particularly in the middle of that range, it is very sensitive. Other devices have been developed that are very sensitive over limited ranges of wavelengths. Thus curve *a* of Figure 27.02 gives the variation with wavelength of the sensitivity of an R.C.A. photocell, type 929. Like the curve for the retina, the sensitivity units are arbitrary, chosen for a maximum of unity. With a photocell, though, we can go farther, and say just what the maximum of unity stands for. At wavelength 4000 A, an average 929 photocell has a sensitivity of 0.042 μa per microwatt. The current in a single cell will never exceed a few microamperes. The output, being an electrical current, is measurable. The output of the eye, being in nervous impulses, is harder to deal with. A variety of photocells is available with different sensitivity distributions. The distribution for the photovoltaic cells commonly found in photographic exposure meters is shown by curve *b* in Figure 27.02.

The emulsions on photographic films must have sensitivity distributions resembling that for the eye, at least to some extent, if pictures recorded on them are to resemble the original scene as observed directly by the eye. The silver salts in these emulsions are sensitive at shorter wavelengths than the eye; their sensitivities drop to zero at about 5000 A

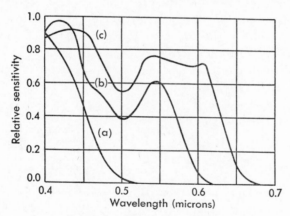

Fig. 27.03. Relative sensitivity curves for three types of emulsion: Curve (a), a blue-sensitive or unsensitized type, curve (b), an orthochromatic type of emulsion or one sensitive to both blue and green regions, and curve (c), a panchromatic type of emulsion sensitive to blue, green, and red radiation. (From R. M. Evans, *An Introduction to Color*, John Wiley & Sons, Inc., 1948.)

(Figure 27.03). The sensitivity may be extended throughout the visible spectrum and beyond by the use of special dyes, known as "sensitizers", which have the property of absorbing light and transmitting its effect

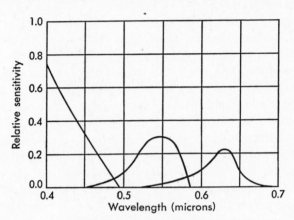

Fig. 27.04. Effective spectral-sensitivity curves of a typical three-color photographic process. (From R. M. Evans, *An Introduction to Color*, John Wiley & Sons, Inc., 1948.)

to the crystals so that they become developable. In Figure 27.03 curves *b* and *c* are for an "orthochromatic" and a "panchromatic" emulsion such as are now in common use. By a combination of such sensitized emulsion and the use of transparent colored "light filters" it is possible, therefore, to restrict the region of the spectrum which affects the emulsion. Thus Figure 27.04 shows the effective spectral sensitivity curves of a typical three-color photographic process.

27.03 SOURCES

Light from the sun has about the same intensity at all wavelengths in the visible region (Figure 27.05). Its wavelength of maximum intensity comes in or close to that region, varying somewhat with atmospheric absorption. The maximum is broad, at any rate in comparison with the breadth of the visible region. Incandescent lamps operate at temperatures roughly half that of the sun. As a result, their maximum intensity comes at longer wavelengths, and in the visible region their intensity drops rapidly with decreasing wavelength (Figure 27.06).

A tungsten filament in an evacuated envelope is efficient in the sense that over 90% of the power input comes out as radiation (Table 27.01). But most of that radiation is at wavelengths too long for the eye; only 6%

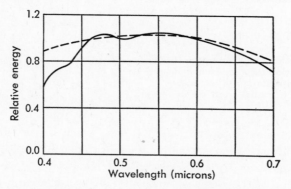

Fig. 27.05. Noon summer sunlight (solid line) compared with radiation from a black body at 5740K (broken line). (From R. M. Evans, *An Introduction to Color*, John Wiley & Sons, Inc., 1948.)

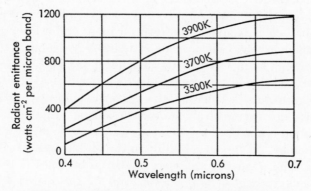

Fig. 27.06. Variation with wavelength of radiation emitted by a "black body." (From R. M. Evans, *An Introduction to Color*, John Wiley & Sons, Inc., 1948.)

of the power comes out as radiation in the visible region. If a gas is introduced into the bulb, a new form of loss through heat transfer is introduced. At the same time, the gas reduces evaporation of the tungsten and permits its operation at a higher temperature. Thus while the fraction of the power going into radiation is reduced, the fraction of the total power going into *useful* radiation is actually increased.

TABLE 27.01   Power Distribution in 100-Watt Lamps.

Mode of heat transfer	Vacuum (%)	Gas-filled (%)
Conduction and Convection through gas	0	20
Conduction through leads and supports	8	5
Infrared radiation (λ too long)	86	67
Light (i.e., radiation in visible region)	6	8
	100	100

At best, the incandescent lamp is very inefficient. Gas discharge tubes have always been attractive as more efficient artificial sources. In them, an electric current is carried through gases at low pressure by ions. Collision of the ions with molecules of the gas creates further ions to continue the supply and to maintain atoms and molecules in excited states. Recovery from these states involves release of light of specific wavelengths, and we get the emission of line spectra. The light then has a finite number, possibly very large, of discrete wavelengths. A mercury discharge lamp is a good source of light, in large part because much of its energy is emitted at 5461 A, near the peak sensitivity of the eye (Figure 27.07). For "color balance", however, a more uniform distribution of energy throughout the visible region is desirable.

The mercury lamp has two shortcomings, the long-wave (infrared) radiation it lacks, and the ultraviolet (shorter-than-visible) radiation that it generates to no useful end, the eye being insensitive to it. These shortcomings are overcome in fluorescent lamps. In them, the ultraviolet radiation is absorbed by chemicals on the inside of the glass, which fluoresce thereby, giving out radiation in the visible region. By keeping the coating thin, a considerable part of the visible lines of the mercury discharge gets through. The combination of the mercury lines and fluorescent light has a reasonably good distribution with wavelength (Figure 27.08).

27.04 COLOR

Light of different wavelengths affects the eye in different ways. We have already noted that the sensitivity of the eye, the amount of sensation for a given intensity of radiation, varies with the wavelength. But that is not all; the nature of the sensation also varies. Wavelength 5500 A makes us see green, 6500 red, 4500 blue. The nature of the sensation varies continuously as the wavelength is varied from one end of the visible region to the other. (The sensation at the short-wavelength end of the visible region is "violet". Radiations of still shorter wavelength, beyond the visible limit, are known as ultraviolet radiation or ultraviolet

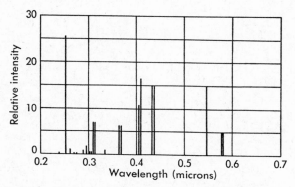

Fig. 27.07. Relative intensity of lines emitted by a low-pressure mercury-vapor lamp. (From R. M. Evans, *An Introduction to Color*, John Wiley & Sons, Inc., 1948.)

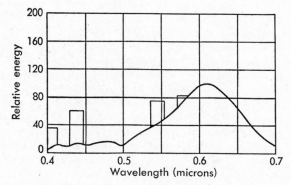

Fig. 27.08. Spectral distribution for a "white" fluorescent lamp. (From R. M. Evans, *An Introduction to Color*, John Wiley & Sons, Inc., 1948.)

light. Similarly, radiations of wavelength longer than the long-wave limit of the visible are referred to as infrared radiation. The radiation from a hot body may include ultraviolet, visible, and infrared. At temperatures as we find them until we get up to the high temperature of the sun, most of the energy of thermal radiation is in the infrared region.)

The "color" of light of a given wavelength is characteristic of the wavelength. If one knows that the light is **monochromatic,** i.e., light of a single wavelength, one can judge its wavelength by its color. This can be done, though, *only* if the light is known to be monochromatic. For the very same color that is produced by a single wavelength can be produced alternatively by two other wavelengths. Color, then, is not the direct subjective concomitant of wavelength (or frequency) in the way that pitch is in the case of sound. To go further into the subject, we will quote from *An Introduction to Color*, by R. M. Evans.* But first, it should be noted that "white" is the color sensation produced by light with a uniform distribution of intensity with wavelength from one end of the visible region to the other. Quoting now from Evans,

Thomas Young, and later James Clerk Maxwell, pointed out and demonstrated that if only three widely separated monochromatic lights are chosen and these three are projected on top of each other on a white surface it is possible to match the appearance of any of the other parts of the spectrum. Further investigation has shown that this effect has fundamental validity, and from it has arisen our basic knowledge of the color sensitivity of the eye. Without attempting to trace the history of the studies we may state the results briefly as follows:

(1) The mixture of any two wavelengths of light will give rise to a color falling between the two in the spectrum, except at the extreme ends where they form a series of purples related to the extreme short-wavelength colors (around 4000 Angstroms in the region known as violet). The exact wavelength matched varies with the relative intensity of the two, being continuous from one to the other as the percentage varies from 0 to 100.

(2) There are a whole series of pairs of monochromatic lights which when mixed give white light. These pairs are called the complementary wavelengths.

(3) There are no complementary wavelengths for the central region of the spectrum (the greens).

(4) Any known color may be matched by light of a single wavelength mixed with white light, with the exception of the colors which we call purple or magenta.

(5) Those colors which cannot be matched by monochromatic plus white light may all be made into white light by the addition of some line from the green spectral region (i.e. they are all complementary to some spectral region).

27.05 TRICHROMATIC THEORY

Results of experiment as summed up in the preceding section can all be explained by a three-color theory, according to which the retina should possess three sorts of receptor or sensitive element. Each sort would have sensitivity varying continuously with wavelength over a con-

* Ralph M. Evans, *An Introduction to Color*, John Wiley & Sons, Inc., 1948.

siderable part of the visible region of wavelengths. The sensitivity curves for the three might resemble roughly those shown for three-color-process color film in Figure 27.04. Suppose that the "green" and "red" receptors were excited in the proportion of 3 to 2. There is just one single wavelength that could excite the two in this exact ratio. There are, on the other hand, many *pairs* of wavelengths that could do the same job. All the experimental findings can be explained by the trichromatic theory.

When you turn to studies of the retina, the trichromatic theory is immediately in difficulties. There are two sorts of nerve endings, not three. These are the rods and cones. The rods are responsible for the scotopic vision that comes into play when the light is of very low intensity. They appear to have no sense of color. That leaves us with just one sort of receptor, the cones, as color-sensitive elements. How can a trichromatic theory be fitted to a single type of receptor? Polyak, at Chicago, has found only one kind of cone, but at least three different kinds of nerve connection to each cone. It may be that each sort of nerve connection is specifically sensitive to the photochemical reaction of one of several different substances mixed within a single cone. It may be. The mechanism of color vision cannot be said to be understood.

27.06 INTENSITY DISTRIBUTION AND COLOR

A source of light has a certain color because of its distribution of intensity with wavelength. Another source may have the same color owing to quite a different distribution with wavelength. Thus the distribution for a "daylight" fluorescent lamp will be quite different from that for natural daylight from the sky.

"White" surfaces reflect all wavelengths equally well. Thus they take on the color of the source by which they are lit. "Colored" surfaces reflect in different proportions at different wavelengths. Thus a red surface reflects more at long wavelengths, and white light comes back preponderantly red. The distribution of intensity with frequency for reflected light is the product of the distribution for the light source and the distribution (of reflectivity) for the reflecting surface. That is to say, each ordinate in the final graph is the product of the ordinates of the other two graphs for the same wavelength.

Now, suppose that two lights have distribution D_1 and D_2, and that a particular reflecting surface has a reflectivity distribution D_3. Then the light coming back from this surface will be D_1D_3 or D_2D_3, depending on which source is used. Distributions D_1 and D_2 may be quite different,

yet have the same color.   Multiply them both by D_3, and they will again
be quite different.   The fact that D_1 and D_2 gave the same color does not
mean that D_1D_3 and D_2D_3 give the same color.   A "daylight" lamp may
make white paper look the very same as true daylight, and yet make a
piece of colored cloth look quite different.   For an artificial source to
make any colored object look just as it does by daylight, the artificial
source must have the very same distribution as daylight: Being itself
the same color as daylight is not enough.

PROBLEMS

1. Using the data of Figure 27.01, and assuming that scotopic and photopic
   sensitivities are the same at wavelength 0.60 micron, calculate the ratio
   of scotopic to photopic sensitivity at 0.45, 0.50, and 0.55 micron.

2. A filter can be used to modify the sensitivity of a photovoltaic cell [Figure
   27.02(b)], so that it resembles the photopic sensitivity of the eye.   Assuming
   that such a filter does not reduce the sensitivity of such a cell at all at wavelength 0.55 micron, calculate the reduction that it must effect at wavelengths
   0.45, 0.50, 0.60, and 0.65 micron.

28

Reflection, Refraction, and Dispersion

28.01 LIGHT IN MATERIAL MEDIA

Mechanical waves require a material medium for their propagation, and the speed of propagation depends on the medium. Electrical and magnetic fields can exist in regions quite free of matter, and so electromagnetic waves can travel through empty space. They can also travel through some forms of matter. In empty space, the speed of electromagnetic waves is 2.99790×10^{10} cm sec^{-1}, or approximately 3×10^{10} cm sec^{-1}. The effect of matter is to reduce this speed. The reduction in speed varies from substance to substance. For a given substance it also varies somewhat with the wavelength; this variation is of the order of 1% from one extreme of the visible range to the other. (Unless specifically stated otherwise, "wavelength" refers to wavelength in empty space.) The speed of light in a substance is described by the **index of refraction** of the substance, μ, where

$$\mu = \frac{\text{speed in empty space}}{\text{speed in substance}} \qquad (28.01)$$

Thus μ varies inversely as speed-in-substance and is always greater than unity. The more a substance retards radiation, the greater its index of refraction. Denoting speed in empty space by the symbol c, we have

$$\text{Speed in substance} = \frac{c}{\mu} \qquad (28.02)$$

and

$$\text{Distance traveled in time } \Delta t = \frac{c}{\mu} \Delta t \qquad (28.03)$$

At the boundary line between media of different indices, or between empty space and substance, some radiation is reflected, and the radiation that passes through the boundary is liable to a change in direction. Consider the case of light spreading out from a point source in a medium of index μ_a, and arriving at the plane boundary of a second medium of index μ_g. Let the subscripts a and g stand for air and glass, if you like; we will find it convenient in the present discussion to refer to the two media as air and glass, and to construct the diagrams accordingly.

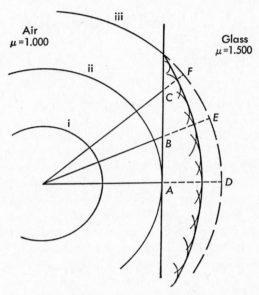

Fig. 28.01. Huygens development of transmitted wave front, from point source, at plane surface, air to glass.

Consider a single wave front expanding outward from the point source. Until the boundary is reached, the wave front will be a continually expanding sphere. Figure 28.01 shows, in section, three subsequent positions of the spherical wave front (the circles i, ii, iii). The last position lies in part in the glass; the circular line is carried into the glass as a broken line, to indicate what might have been if there were no glass present.

According to Huygens' Principle, any surface through which a wave front passes can be treated as an array of point sources. Any envelope to the wavelets spreading out from these point sources—any line, that is, to which all the wavelets are tangent—is a future position of the wave front. This procedure is useful when a wave front passes from one medium to another, for although we are uncertain about the direction in which the radiation travels upon entering the new medium, we can readily ascertain from the speed in the new medium *how far* it travels. Let us, then, draw wavelets about an array of points on the boundary, making their radii the distances traveled in glass in the time that the wave front would have required to reach the broken line if there had been

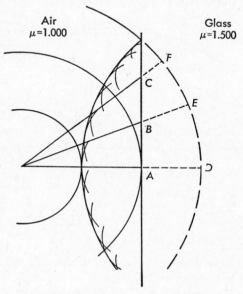

Fig. 28.02. Huygens development of reflected wave front, from point source, at plane surface, air to glass.

no change in speed. Thus, in Figure 28.01, the wavelets about A, B, C have radii (μ_a/μ_g) times AD, BE, CF. These radial lines are of course the shortest distances from points A, B, C to the might-have-been wave front. The wave front in glass is the envelope to these wavelets. It is apparently a circle of less curvature than the broken line, i.e., a circle about a center more distant than the actual point source.

Accepting the notion that not all the radiation enters the glass, but that some is reflected, we can use Huygens' Principle again to develop the reflected wave front (Figure 28.02). The wavelets about A, B, C, in the backward direction have radii equal to AD, BE, CF. The reflected wavefront is a circle about a point as far behind the surface of the glass as the

point source is in front of it.   This image point is on the same line normal
to the surface as the source point.

The case of light from a point source in a more-dense medium (glass)
reaching the boundary of a less-dense medium (air) is shown in Figure
28.03.   Two positions of the wave front in air have been developed.   In
both positions the wave front is nearly circular, and the circles have a
common center.   The smaller wave front is the better approximation to
a circle, and all the wavelets drawn for it are tangent to the envelope.

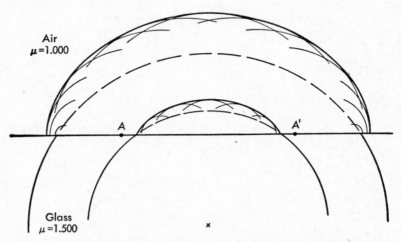

Fig. 28.03.   Huygens development of transmitted wave fronts, from
point source, at plane surface, glass to air.

In the case of the larger wave front, wavelets whose centers fall between
A and A' are all tangent to the common envelope, but wavelets whose
centers lie on the surface, but outside the region AA', fall short of the
envelope.   As a matter of fact, light arriving at the surface beyond A in
the one direction or A' in the other does not emerge into the air, but
instead is totally reflected, as will be discussed in section 28.04.

28.02 A PLANE WAVE FRONT AT A PLANE SURFACE

Suppose that a section of plane wave front AB (Figure 28.04) is
traveling through air and approaching the flat surface of a piece of glass
in which the velocity of light is 2×10^{10} cm sec^{-1}.   If the glass were not
present, the plane wave front would move straight ahead and arrive at a
later position CD.   That is, the time taken to travel from A to C would
equal that taken to travel the equal distance from B to D, both at the

velocity in air of 3×10^{10} cm sec⁻¹. With the glass present, travel
beyond the line JK is at the reduced velocity 2×10^{10} cm sec⁻¹, and it can
be assumed that some light will be reflected. What direction will be
taken by the light that enters the glass? What direction will be taken
by the light that is reflected? We can apply Huygens' Principle to find
out.

Let us draw wavelets about a number of points on the surface of the
glass, wavelets exactly in phase with the might-have-been wave front

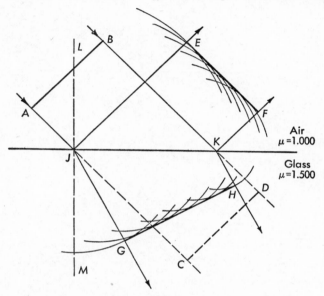

Fig. 28.04. Huygens development of transmitted and
reflected wave fronts when a plane wave front traveling
through air arrives at the plane surface of a block of glass.

CD. What will the radii of these wavelets be? In the air, the radius of
the wavelet about a given point will be just the distance from that point
to the line CD. That is the distance that light can travel through air in
the time it would have taken to get to CD, through air. In the glass, the
radius of the wavelet about a given point will be only two-thirds the distance from that point to the line CD. That is the distance that light can
travel *in the glass* in the time it would have taken to get *through air* to CD.

Having drawn two families of wavelets, one in air and one in glass, we
find that they have envelopes along the lines EF and GH. These are the
new wave fronts, the wave fronts of the reflected light and of the refracted
light, respectively.

We can obtain a relationship between the directions of travel before and after reflection, and between the directions of travel before and after passing through the surface, from Figure 28.04.   We can obtain the relationships more readily from simplified versions of the figure.   Figure 28.05 contains the essential construction for the case of reflection.   The

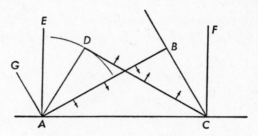

Fig. 28.05. Geometry of plane wave front reflected at plane surface.

wave front AB is reflected as the wave front CD, located by drawing an arc of radius AD equal to BC.

$$\angle EAD = \frac{\pi}{2} - \angle DAC = \angle DCA = \angle BAC =$$

$$\frac{\pi}{2} - \angle BCA = \angle BCF = \angle EAG$$

The angle EAG, between the normal to the surface and the direction of travel of the light before it reaches the surface, is the **angle of incidence.** Similarly, EAD is the **angle of reflection.**   Our finding, then, is that the

$$\text{Angle of incidence} = \text{angle of reflection} \qquad (28.04)$$

Another important relationship gives the change in direction of light proceeding from one medium to another.   In Figure 28.06, another simplified version of 28.04, the light travels distance AD in the medium of index μ_g (glass) in the time that it travels a distance BC in the medium of index μ_a (air).   Hence

$$\frac{BC}{AD} = \frac{\dfrac{c}{\mu_a}}{\dfrac{c}{\mu_g}} = \frac{\mu_g}{\mu_a}$$

But
$$\frac{BC}{AD} = \frac{\dfrac{BC}{AC}}{\dfrac{AD}{AC}} = \frac{\sin CAB}{\sin ACD} = \frac{\sin GAE}{\sin FAD}$$

So

$$\frac{\text{Sine of angle from normal to direction of travel in medium } a}{\text{Sine of angle from normal to direction of travel in medium } g} = \frac{\mu_g}{\mu_a}$$

Referring to these angles as the angle of incidence (i) and the **angle of refraction** (r), and to the first and second media by subscripts i and r, this may be stated more briefly as

$$\frac{\sin i}{\sin r} = \frac{\mu_r}{\mu_i} \qquad (28.05)$$

If the first medium were empty space, or if the difference of μ_i from unity were negligible, the ratio of the sines would equal simply μ_r.

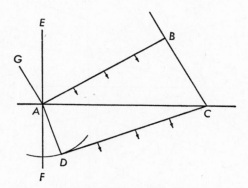

Fig. 28.06. Geometry of plane wave
front refracted at plane surface.

Equation (28.05) holds whether the index of the first medium is less or more than that of the second medium. So does the construction of Figure 28.06. The construction does not give an answer for light in a dense medium approaching the boundary of a less-dense medium very obliquely. The fact is, there is no answer; no light is transmitted through the boundary in that case. This phenomenon, called total reflection, will be discussed in section 28.04.

28.03 RAYS

Wave fronts have been defined as loci of points all in the same fixed phase. **Rays** are lines pointing in the direction of travel of the radiation. Thus wave fronts and rays form two related families of lines: The rays intersect the wave fronts everywhere at right angles. The laws of change in direction on reflection or refraction at a surface, derived by use of wave fronts, enable us to carry rays through a surface, so that we can now use either wave fronts or rays in solving an optical problem. Sometimes one is more convenient, sometimes the other. When the goal is not just the solution of the immediate problem, but a better mental picture of optical processes, it is best always to keep both families in mind. The behavior

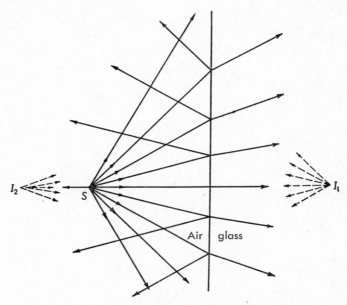

Fig. 28.07. Ray development of reflection and refraction when light from a point source S in air arrives at the plane surface of a block of glass. Reflected light appears to come from point I_1. Transmitted light appears to come from vicinity of I_2.

of a point source and a plane surface, discussed in section 28.01, can be dealt with very well by drawing rays outward from the source and applying the laws of section 28.02 to them where they intersect the surface (Figure 28.07). The image points, the apparent points of origin of the reflected and refracted light, are more readily located in this way than by the wave-front constructions of section 28.01.

All the reflected rays spread out from a common **image** point, as far behind the surface as the point source is in front of it. The refracted rays do not have a common point of intersection, but refracted rays not far from the normal all pass close to a point on the normal line through the source point, and (μ_r/μ_i) times as far from the surface. This is then an approximate image point, and is the center of the circles fitting the approximately circular emergent wave fronts of Figure 28.01.

28.04 TOTAL REFLECTION

When light goes from a denser to a less-dense medium, the angle of refraction r is greater than the angle of incidence i. When r reaches its

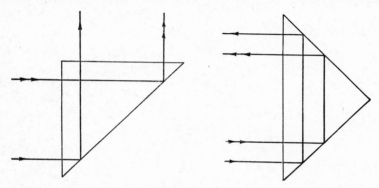

Fig. 28.08. Prisms providing totally reflecting surfaces for optical systems.

maximum value of $\pi/2$ radians, i is still less than $\pi/2$. If i is increased beyond this critical value, which we shall call i_c, no light passes through the surface, and there is total reflection. Substituting i_c for i and $\pi/2$ for r in equation (28.05), we find

$$\frac{\sin i_c}{\sin \dfrac{\pi}{2}} = \frac{\mu_r}{\mu_i}$$

$$\sin i_c = \frac{\mu_r}{\mu_i} \qquad (28.06)$$

If we attempt to introduce a value of i greater than i_c into the constructions of Figures 28.06 and 28.07 (applied to the case of progress from a denser to a lighter medium), the construction breaks down. No refracted wave front or ray can be found; none exists. There is evidence of total reflection in Figure 28.03, too, in the separation between the emergent and incident wave fronts when a large angle of incidence is involved. The phenomenon of total reflection inside prisms of glass is used in preference to metallic reflection in many optical instruments (Figure 28.08). The reflectivity is practically perfect, and does not deteriorate with time as a result of tarnishing.

Apart from this mention of total reflection, we have discussed only the direction of the reflected light, not the fraction of light reflected. A plot of fraction reflected against angle of incidence (Figure 28.09) shows the fraction increasing continuously with the angle, to reach 100% just as the critical angle is reached.

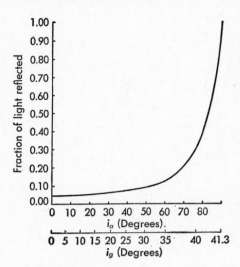

Fig. 28.09. Fraction of light reflected when light in air strikes glass ($\mu = 1.515$) at angle of incidence i_a, or when light in glass strikes air at angle of incidence i_g.

28.05 PRISMS

Quite apart from their use to provide totally reflecting surfaces, prisms can be used to deviate a beam of light by refraction. The amount of the deviation or bending is a function of the index of refraction, and this in turn varies somewhat with the wavelength of the light, as will be discussed in the next section. Prisms therefore can be used to sort a beam of light according to the wavelengths of its components.

A ray of light is bent when it passes obliquely through the surface separating two media of different refractive index (Figure 28.04). When a ray passes through a sheet of plate glass with parallel surfaces, however, the bending at the second surface exactly cancels out that at the first; there is no net deviation. If the surface of a block of glass by which a ray emerges is not parallel to that by which it enters, however, there is a net deviation. This is so in the case of a prism (Figure 28.10). Here A is the angle of the prism, δ the net deviation. Usual practice is followed in lettering the ray-angles within the prism r_1 and r_2 and those outside i_1 and i_2. Light may follow the direction shown by the ray drawn here

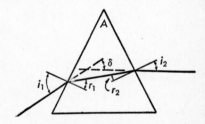

Fig. 28.10. Deviation of ray of light (traveling either left to right or right to left) by a prism.

either from left to right or from right to left. Taking the case of light
traveling from left to right, the ray changes direction at the left-hand surface by a clockwise angle $i_1 - r_1$ and at the right-hand surface by a clockwise angle $i_2 - r_2$ for a total deviation

$$\delta = i_1 - r_1 + i_2 - r_2 \qquad (28.07)$$

Considering the triangle formed by the surfaces of the prism and the ray
through the prism, we have

$$A + (90° - r_1) + (90° - r_2) = 180°$$

that is,
$$A = r_1 + r_2 \qquad (28.08)$$

Further, if the index of the prism material is μ_r and that of the surrounding
medium μ_i,

$$\frac{\sin i_1}{\sin r_1} = \frac{\sin i_2}{\sin r_2} = \frac{\mu_r}{\mu_i} \quad (28.09)$$

The foregoing equations permit
us to calculate δ as a function of i_1
or of i_2. A typical plot of δ against
i_1 or i_2 appears in Figure 28.11.
Such a plot can be obtained either
by calculation or by experiment.
For each value of δ there are two
values of i. These are simultaneous or conjugate values of i_1 and i_2.
These conjugate values approach

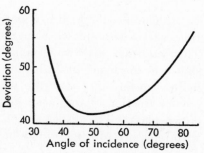

Fig. 28.11. Typical plot of deviation against angle of incidence for a
prism.

each other as δ is reduced, until at the minimum value of δ we have
$i_1 = i_2$. Then $r_1 = r_2$, and setting $i_1 = i_2 = i$ and $r_1 = r_2 = r$, we have
for this symmetrical case

$$i = \frac{\delta + A}{2}, \qquad r = \frac{A}{2} \qquad (28.10)$$

At the point of minimum deviation the rate of change of deviation
with angle of incidence is zero, i.e., the curve of Figure 28.11 is parallel to
the i axis. Since the minimum of the curve is broad, there is a considerable range of i-values over which the variation in δ is small. This insensi-
tivity of δ to the angle of incidence is desirable, and prisms are most often
used in the symmetrical condition giving minimum deviation in order to
make δ insensitive to small variations in the angle of incidence.

Another case of particular interest is the case of a prism of small angle, so used that the angle of incidence is also small.   Then equation (28.09) approaches the simpler form

$$\frac{i_1}{r_1} = \frac{i_2}{r_2} = \frac{\mu_r}{\mu_i} \tag{28.11}$$

This equation, combined with (28.07) and (28.08), gives

$$\delta = \left(\frac{\mu_r}{\mu_i} - 1\right) A \tag{28.12}$$

or for the case of a thin prism of index μ surrounded by a medium of index approximately unity,

$$\delta = (\mu - 1)A \tag{28.13}$$

28.06 DISPERSION

The speed of light in a material medium, and so the index of refraction, varies with the wavelength-in-vacuum of the light (Figure 28.12). This variation with wavelength is called **dispersion**.   The flint glass shown in the figure has a higher index than the crown glass.   It is also more dispersive, in that the variation in index with wavelength is a greater fraction of the mean index for the flint glass than it is for the crown glass.   The dispersion of a substance is conveniently described with reference to three specific wavelengths, those of

> The F line of hydrogen, $\lambda = 0.4861$ microns, a blue line
> The D_2 line of sodium, $\lambda = 0.5890$ microns, a yellow line
> The C line of hydrogen, $\lambda = 0.6563$ microns, a red line

The change in direction of travel of light due to a thin prism of index μ surrounded by empty space or a medium of index unity is proportional to $(\mu - 1)$.   We shall see later that the focusing power of a lens is also proportional to $(\mu - 1)$.   The important thing about dispersion, then, is the variation in $(\mu - 1)$ as we travel across the range of visible wavelengths, as a fraction of the average value of $(\mu - 1)$.   Taking the F and C lines as representative of the blue and red ends of the spectrum, and the D_2 line as providing an average value, we define the **dispersive power** of a substance, denoted by ω, by

$$\omega = \frac{(\mu_F - 1) - (\mu_C - 1)}{\mu_D - 1}$$

or more simply

$$\omega = \frac{\mu_F - \mu_C}{\mu_D - 1} \tag{28.14}$$

where the subscripts F, C, and D denote the F, C, and D lines.

If F and C light enter a thin prism, traveling in the same direction, they leave it differing in direction by

$$(\mu_F - 1)A - (\mu_C - 1)A = (\mu_F - \mu_C)A$$

This is called the **angular dispersion** of the prism. The mean deviation

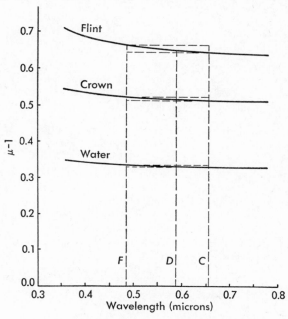

Fig. 28.12. Plot of $(\mu - 1)$ against wavelength, to show dispersion, for selected flint and crown glasses and for water.

of the prism is best represented by the deviation of the D light, $(\mu_D - 1)A$. Thus, for a thin prism,

$$\frac{\text{Angular dispersion}}{\text{Mean deviation}} = \frac{\mu_F - \mu_C}{\mu_D - 1} = \omega \qquad (28.15)$$

By using two thin prisms, made of glasses differing in dispersive power, it is possible to achieve a net deviation with zero net angular dispersion, or dispersion without deviation. These are both useful achievements.

PROBLEMS

1. A point source of light lies 3 cm above the surface of water contained in a vessel. Taking the indices of refraction of air and water as unity and $\frac{4}{3}$,

respectively, develop below the surface of the water the wave front which in air has a radius of 8 cm.

2. Referring to problem 1, develop the reflected wave front.

3. A block of glass 7 cm thick, index of refraction 1.5, is placed over a point source of light, so that the source lies in the bottom surface of the glass. Develop from Huygens wavelets the wave front in the air above the glass that has a radius in the glass of 10 cm.

4. Repeat problem 3 for a block of thickness 4 cm.

5. Use the construction of Figure 28.06 to develop the refracted wave front when a plane wave front passes through a plane surface from a medium of index unity to a medium of index 1.5, with angle of incidence 30° and again with angle of incidence 60°.

6. Referring to problem 5, develop a relation between the lengths of the wave front in the two media and the indices of refraction of the media.

7. Repeat problem 5 for light proceeding from the denser (higher index) to the less-dense medium.

8. A point source of light lies 8 cm below the surface of water (index $\frac{4}{3}$) contained in a vessel. Draw rays from the source arriving at the surface with angles of incidence 0°, 15°, 30°, 45°, 60°. Use the laws of reflection and refraction (and graphical construction, preferably, rather than tables) to locate the reflected and refracted rays.

9. Show for a ray of light passing through a prism (as Figure 28.10) that $\delta = i_1 - r_1 + i_2 - r_2$ and $A = r_1 + r_2$.

10. Draw a 60° triangle, each side 8 cm long, to represent a prism of index 1.5. Draw a ray passing symmetrically through the prism, i.e., with the ray in the glass parallel to the wall of the prism. (Draw all three parts: in air, in glass, in air again.)

11. A thin prism made of glass of index of refraction (for the D_2 line) of 1.650, is required to bend light through an angle of exactly 4°. What must be the angle of the prism?

12. Referring to the prism of problem 11, by how much more is blue light (the F line, for which $\mu = 1.664$) bent than red light (the C line, for which $\mu = 1.644$)?

29

Lenses and Mirrors

29.01 USE OF LENSES TO ALTER CURVATURE

The curvature of a small section of wave front can be altered by passing it through a lens of any transparent substance. In Figure 29.01, the central portion B of the wave front passes through the maximum

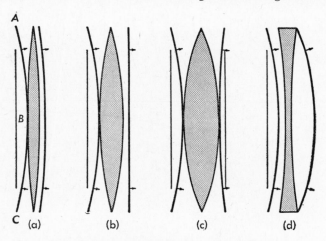

Fig. 29.01. Modification of wave fronts by lenses.

thickness of the lens l, and the outer portions at A and C pass through zero thickness of the lens. Let the material be glass, of refractive index 1.5, i.e., material in which the speed of light is $\frac{2}{3}c$, and let it be surrounded by air, with refractive index very nearly unity, velocity very nearly c. Then in the time taken for the central portion of the wave front to pass through thickness l of the glass (time $= l/\frac{2}{3}c = \frac{3}{2}l/c$), the outer portions will travel half as far again ($c \times \frac{3}{2}l/c = \frac{3}{2}l$) in the air. Thus the outer portions advance by half the maximum thickness of the lens ($\frac{3}{2}l - l = \frac{1}{2}l$)

531

relative to the central portion.   For any index the outer portions advance
by $(\mu - 1)l$ relative to the central portion.   This can reduce the magnitude of the curvature of the wave front, Figure 29.01(a), or bring it to
zero, 29.01(b), or even convert it to a curvature of the opposite sense,
29.01(c).   Similar considerations for a lens *thinner* at the center than
at the edges show that such a lens could have the opposite effect, 29.01(d),
increasing the magnitude of the same sort of curvature that the thick-
centered lens decreased.

29.02 RADIUS, CURVATURE, AND CONVENTION

   The **curvature** of a line, its rate of change of direction with distance along the line, equals $1/r$ where r is the **radius of curvature**.   A

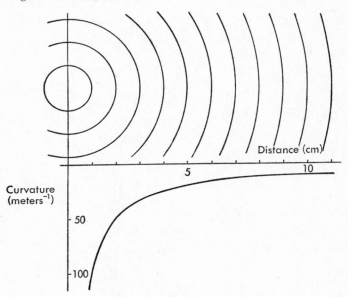

Fig. 29.02.   The magnitude of wave-front curvature
decreases continuously with distance traveled.

wave front about a point source in a uniform medium is a sphere, **or in**
two dimensions a circle.   Its curvature is infinite at the source, its magnitude decreasing rapidly at first with increasing distance from the source,
decreasing more and more gradually as the distance increases (Figure
29.02).
   It will be necessary in dealing with lenses and mirrors to define distances and curvatures algebraically.   That is, we must define them as to

direction and sense by the labels plus and minus. To make this possible, let us define the radius of curvature of any curve as the distance *from* the curve *to* its center of curvature. Further, let us define the positive direction as that in which the light is traveling. (For mirrors, the definition is extended by adding the words *after reflection.*)

On the basis of these arbitrary definitions, distance increases positively from left to right in Figure 29.02. The wave fronts shown there have negative radius of curvature, and so have negative curvature. On the convention proposed here, wave fronts spreading out from a point source always have negative curvature. In the limit, as the distance becomes very great, the curvature approaches zero, and we approach the condition of a plane wave front. This corresponds, in "ray" terminology, to a "parallel beam", for all the rays will then be parallel to each other. For some purposes, a wave front just a few feet distant from its source has negligible curvature and may be considered as a plane wave front, and the corresponding rays may be considered as parallel rays. For almost any purpose, light arriving at the earth from a star or from some point on the sun may be considered as having plane wave fronts, parallel rays.

Curvature keeps changing with distance. A sudden change may be introduced in a section of wave front by passing it through a lens (Figure 29.03). This change is not exactly discontinuous, i.e., it does not occur in exactly zero distance. It does occur in the distance that the wave front must travel to pass through the lens. This distance is small enough for the amount by which the curvature would change in this distance, with the lens absent, to be negligible by comparison with the change effected by the lens.

The various parts of Figure 29.03 deal with the same cases as the corresponding parts of Figure 29.01. In part(a), negative curvature is changed to a negative curvature of smaller magnitude. Before the lens, the wave fronts are spreading out from the point source, are circles about the source as center. Beyond the lens, the wave fronts are spreading out as from a point more distant than the source, the **image point.** In the (b) part, the lens reduces the curvature to zero: The image point has gone to minus infinity, if you like.

In part (c), the wave fronts emerging from the lens have positive curvature (on the foregoing sign convention): Their centers of curvature lie ahead of them. Just as a circular wave front of negative curvature expands as an arc subtending a fixed angle at a fixed center of curvature, so a circular wave front of positive curvature contracts as it proceeds,

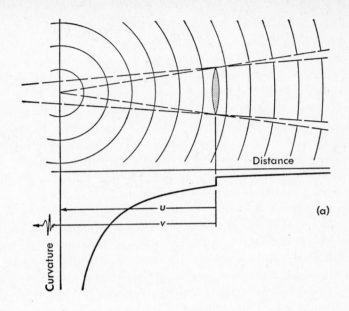

(a)

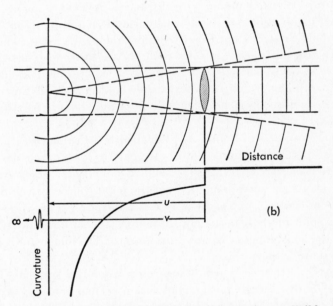

(b)

Fig. 29.03. Lenses change curvature during negligible distance of wave-front travel (*cf.* corresponding parts of Figure 29.01).

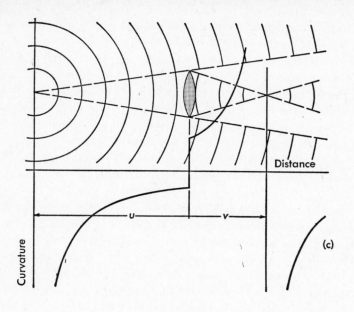

(c)

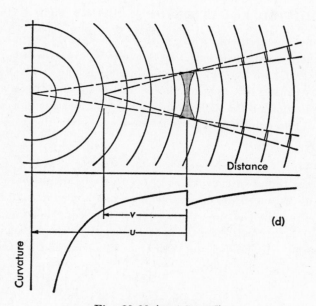

Fig. 29.03 (continued)

continuing as an arc subtending a fixed angle at a fixed center of curvature. When the wave front arrives at the center of curvature, it has zero length, and all the energy of the wave front is concentrated at that point. Beyond the center of curvature, the wave front spreads out again, but within the limits of this angle rather than in all directions. The center of curvature is the image point in this case. It is a **real image point,** since the energy is actually concentrated at it. Compare with the case of part (a). There the wave front beyond the lens has a fixed center of curvature. The light spreads as from that point, but since the light was never concentrated at that point, it constitutes only a **virtual image point.**

Part (d) deals with a lens thinner at the center than at the edges. This lens increases the magnitude of the existing negative curvature, so that the emerging wave front proceeds with a fixed center of curvature behind the lens, i.e., a virtual image point. The virtual image point lies between the source and the lens. Compare this with the case of a lens thicker at the center. In that case the image point is either virtual and located to the left of the source, as in Figure 29.03 (a), (b), or real and so lying to the right of the lens.

29.03 MODIFIED EQUATION OF A SHORT CIRCULAR ARC

In dealing mathematically with the passage of a spherical wave front through a spherical lens, the sort of situation drawn in Figures 29.01 and 29.03, we find ourselves dealing with short arcs of circles all having their centers on a common line. It is convenient to have a simplified form of equation for such arcs. Let us take rectangular coordinates X and Y. The equation of a circle passing through the origin, with its center on the x axis, is

$$(x - r)^2 + y^2 = r^2 \tag{29.01}$$

where r is the radius of curvature. Accepting the definition of radius of curvature as distance from curve to center, introduced in establishing our sign convention in the preceding section, this equation holds without modification whether the center is to the right or the left of the origin (Figure 29.04). Expanded and rewritten, this equation becomes

$$x^2 - 2xr + r^2 + y^2 = r^2$$
$$x(x - 2r) + y^2 = 0$$

In the region near the origin, where x is small enough to be neglected in comparison with $2r$, i.e., where $x - 2r \simeq -2r$, this relation can be simplified to the approximate form

$$-2xr + y^2 = 0$$

$$x = \frac{y^2}{2}\frac{1}{r} \qquad (29.02)$$

This is actually the equation of a parabola, but near the origin it serves as a good and simple approximation to the equation of a circular arc of small

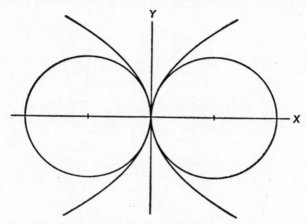

Fig. 29.04.   Parabolas as approximations to circles.

curvature.   Incidentally, it suggests a simple way of drawing such an arc: Rather than using compasses of great radius, lay off a series of points with their x-values increasing approximately as the square of their y-values.

For a circle passing through $(x_0, 0)$ rather than the origin, but still with its center on the x axis, the equation becomes, instead of (29.01),

$$(x - x_0 - r)^2 + y^2 = r^2 \qquad (29.03)$$

The approximate form, applicable near $x = x_0$, then becomes

$$(x - x_0) = \frac{y^2}{2}\frac{1}{r} \qquad (29.04)$$

This is the particular form of equation for which we will have most use.

29.04   EQUATION FOR THE THICKNESS OF A THIN SPHERICAL LENS

Consider a lens bounded by two spherical surfaces.   If the centers of the spheres are in the XY plane, these surfaces will appear in that plane as circles of the same radii as the spheres. If the centers are on the X axis, the circles can be represented, approximately, near the X axis, by

$$x_1 - x_{01} = \frac{y^2}{2} \frac{1}{r_1}$$

$$ (29.05) $$

and

$$x_2 - x_{02} = \frac{y^2}{2} \frac{1}{r_2}$$

where the first and second surfaces of the lens are denoted by subscripts 1

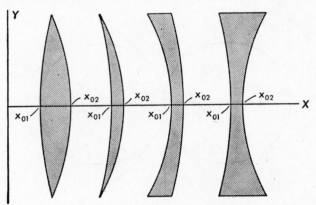

Fig. 29.05. Various lenses: double-convex, concave-convex (2), double-concave. Equation (29.06) gives lens thickness as a function of y for any of these shapes.

and 2, and they cut the X axis at x_{01} and x_{02}, respectively (Figure 29.05). The thickness of the lens, parallel to the X axis, is then

$$x_2 - x_1 = (x_{02} - x_{01}) + \frac{y^2}{2}\left(\frac{1}{r_2} - \frac{1}{r_1}\right)$$

$$ (29.06) $$

29.05 THE THIN-LENS RELATIONSHIP

Provided all the circular arcs have their centers on a common line, we can now show that when a spherical wave front passes through a thin spherical lens it emerges as an approximately spherical wave front. We can at the same time obtain a simple relationship between the curvatures of the incident (or entering) and emergent wave fronts.

Let the subscript u denote the incident wave front, of radius u and curvature $1/u$, shortly before it enters the lens (Figure 29.06). Then its equation is

$$x_u - x_{0u} = \frac{y^2}{2} \frac{1}{u}$$

$$ (29.07) $$

Let the surfaces of the lens be described by (29.05), so that its thickness is given by (29.06). Now allow a time Δt to elapse, long enough for the passage of the wave front through the lens to be completed. The equation of the wave front after that time interval will be the equation of the "emergent" wave front. Part of the time Δt will be spent, by each portion of the wave front, in passing through lens material.

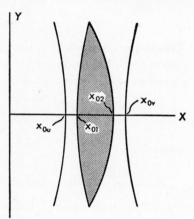

Distance through lens material $= x_2 - x_1$

If μ is taken as the index of the lens material, the speed in it will be c/μ, and so

$$\text{Time through lens material} = \frac{\mu(x_2 - x_1)}{c}$$

Therefore

$$\text{Time not in lens} = \Delta t - \frac{\mu(x_2 - x_1)}{c}$$

Fig. 29.06. Passage of wave front through lens.

Taking the index of the surrounding medium as unity (as it would be for empty space, and approximately for air) and so the speed as c, we have

$$\text{Distance not in lens} = c\,\Delta t - \mu(x_2 - x_1)$$

Therefore

$$\begin{aligned}
\text{Total distance traveled} &= x_2 - x_1 + c\,\Delta t - \mu(x_2 - x_1) \\
&= c\,\Delta t - (\mu - 1)(x_2 - x_1)
\end{aligned}$$

This total distance traveled, added to x_u, will give the x of the emergent wave front, which we will denote by a subscript v:

$$x_v = x_u + c\,\Delta t - (\mu - 1)(x_2 - x_1) \tag{29.08}$$

and as a particular case of this, on the x axis,

$$x_{0v} = x_{0u} + c\,\Delta t - (\mu - 1)(x_{02} - x_{01})$$

Subtracting the terms of the latter equation from those of the former, we obtain

$$x_v - x_{0v} = (x_u - x_{0u}) - (\mu - 1)[(x_2 - x_1) - (x_{02} - x_{01})]$$

Substitution now from equations (29.07) and (29.06) gives

$$x_v - x_{0v} = \frac{y^2}{2}\frac{1}{u} - (\mu - 1)\frac{y^2}{2}\left(\frac{1}{r_2} - \frac{1}{r_1}\right)$$

$$= \frac{y^2}{2}\left[\frac{1}{u} + (\mu - 1)\left(\frac{1}{r_1} - \frac{1}{r_2}\right)\right]$$

This is the equation of a circular arc with its center on the X axis, with curvature equal to the square bracket. If we call this curvature $1/v$, the equation of the emergent wave is

$$x_v - x_{0v} = \frac{y^2}{2}\frac{1}{v} \tag{29.09}$$

where

$$\frac{1}{v} = \frac{1}{u} + (\mu - 1)\left(\frac{1}{r_1} - \frac{1}{r_2}\right) \tag{29.10}$$

Equation (29.10) is the general equation for a thin lens, relating

$1/v$, curvature, and v, radius of curvature, of emergent wave front
$1/u$, curvature, and u, radius of curvature, of incident wave front
$1/r_1$, curvature, and r_1, radius of curvature, of first surface of lens
$1/r_2$, curvature, and r_2, radius of curvature, of second surface of lens

Rather than assigning new symbols, we will look on $1/u$, $1/v$, $1/r_1$, and $1/r_2$ as themselves the symbols for the various curvatures.

The length u is the distance from the lens to the point of origin, or apparent point of origin, of the incident wave front. (The relatively small, and in part arbitrary, distance from the wave front, as it is shown in Figure 29.06, to the central plane of the lens is neglected.) This length u is called the source distance or **object distance.**

If the emergent wave front is converging (has positive curvature), v is similarly the distance from the lens to the point at which it will converge to form a "real image" point. If the emergent wave front is diverging (has negative curvature), v is the distance from the lens to the apparent point of origin, the "virtual image" point. The length v is called the **image distance.** The reader may usefully refer to Figure 29.03 in considering these statements.

The image distance, for the case of a plane incident wave front ($u = \infty$, $1/u = 0$), is called the **focal length** of the lens, and denoted by f. Substituting in equation (29.10) gives

$$\frac{1}{f} = 0 + (\mu - 1)\left(\frac{1}{r_1} - \frac{1}{r_2}\right)$$

Thus equation (29.10) can be written

$$\frac{1}{v} = \frac{1}{u} + \frac{1}{f}$$
where
$$\left.\frac{1}{f} = (\mu - 1)\left(\frac{1}{r_1} - \frac{1}{r_2}\right)\right\} \tag{29.11}$$

The quantity $1/f$ is called the **focusing power** of the lens, or just the "power" of the lens. Expressed in words, the equation states that the curvature of the emergent wave front equals the curvature of the incident wave front plus the power of the lens. Or we can say that *the lens adds its power to the curvature of the wave front passing through it.* The height of each vertical step in Figure 29.03 is the power of the lens, added as a sudden increment to the wave-front curvature which is otherwise changing continuously.

Focusing power has the dimension (length)$^{-1}$, and may be expressed in units of (centimeters)$^{-1}$ or (meters)$^{-1}$, or for that matter (feet)$^{-1}$. It is usually expressed in units of (meter)$^{-1}$, which unit is for the purpose called the **diopter**. We will then find it convenient to express lengths in meters, and reciprocal lengths in (meter)$^{-1}$, which we shall usually refer to, especially in the case of focusing power, as diopters. The symbol for diopter will be m^{-1}.

29.06 ADDITIVE POWERS OF ADJACENT LENSES

Suppose that we have two lenses on the same axis, in contact or nearly so. Let us denote the first and second lenses by subscripts 1 and 2. Then the emergent wave front of lens 1 is the incident wave front of 2:

$$\frac{1}{u_2} = \frac{1}{v_1} = \frac{1}{u_1} + \frac{1}{f_1}$$
$$\frac{1}{v_2} = \frac{1}{u_2} + \frac{1}{f_2} = \frac{1}{u_1} + \frac{1}{f_1} + \frac{1}{f_2}$$
$$= \frac{1}{u_1} + \frac{1}{f}$$
where
$$\frac{1}{f} = \frac{1}{f_1} + \frac{1}{f_2} \tag{29.12}$$

We can treat the two lenses together as a single lens whose power is the sum of the individual powers. We can do this, in general, only if the two lenses are close together, because the curvature of a wave front keeps changing as it proceeds on its way (Figure 29.03). If there is appreciable change in curvature from the time it leaves the first lens until it enters the second, we can no longer equate $1/u_2$ to $1/v_1$. Then we must go into more detail, locating the image formed by the first lens and so determining u_2, the distance from the second lens to this image.

29.07 CHROMATIC ABERRATION

The power of a lens contains two factors, first $(\mu - 1)$, which depends on the material of which the lens is made, and second $(1/r_1 - 1/r_2)$, which depends on the geometry of the surfaces. Because of dispersion, as noted in section 28.06, $(\mu - 1)$ varies with the wavelength as well as with the substance, and the proportional or percentage variation in $(\mu - 1)$ is greater for some substances than it is for others. If we multiply the ordinates of Figure 28.12 by $(1/r_1 - 1/r_2)$, the graph becomes one of focusing power against wavelength.

By what proportion of its average value (that for the D line) does the focusing power of a lens of a given substance increase as we change the wavelength from the C line to the F line?

$$\frac{\dfrac{1}{f_F} - \dfrac{1}{f_C}}{\dfrac{1}{f_D}} = \frac{(\mu_F - 1)\left(\dfrac{1}{r_1} - \dfrac{1}{r_2}\right) - (\mu_C - 1)\left(\dfrac{1}{r_1} - \dfrac{1}{r_2}\right)}{(\mu_D - 1)\left(\dfrac{1}{r_1} - \dfrac{1}{r_2}\right)}$$

$$= \frac{\mu_F - \mu_C}{\mu_D - 1} = \omega \tag{29.13}$$

The **chromatic aberration,** or spread in focusing power with wavelength, is proportional to the dispersive power of the lens material.

It is possible to combine two lenses (subscripts 1 and 2) of different lens material so that $(1/f_F - 1/f_C)$ for the second lens is equal and opposite to that for the first. Since

$$\frac{1}{f_{1F}} - \frac{1}{f_{1C}} = \frac{\omega_1}{f_{1D}} \quad \text{and} \quad \frac{1}{f_{2F}} - \frac{1}{f_{2C}} = \frac{\omega_2}{f_{2D}} \tag{29.14}$$

we need only set

$$\frac{\omega_1}{f_{1D}} + \frac{\omega_2}{f_{2D}} = 0 \tag{29.15}$$

Then $$\frac{1}{f_{1F}} + \frac{1}{f_{2F}} = \frac{1}{f_{1C}} + \frac{1}{f_{2C}}$$

The power of the combination is the same for F and C wavelengths, and indeed just about the same for all wavelengths. Equation (29.15), then, is the condition to be met for a combination to have no variation in power with wavelength. Since ω is always positive, this condition for an **achromatic combination** requires that the two components have opposite focusing powers. The materials of the two components must differ in dispersive power; otherwise the power of the combination will be zero.

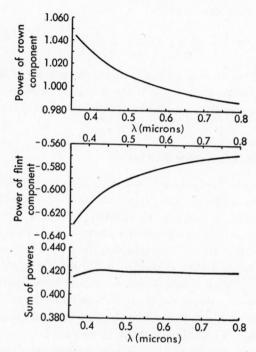

Fig. 29.07. Focusing power plotted against wavelength for the components of an achromatic combination and for the combination.

In Figure 29.07, a lens of crown glass (the glass of Figure 28.12) of average (or D-line) focusing power 1.000 diopter is combined with a lens of flint glass of average focusing power -0.580 diopter to give a combination of power very nearly constant at 0.420 diopter. A combination of positive power has been formed by taking a more powerful lens of crown glass (which has relatively small dispersion) and correcting it by a negative lens made of a material of high dispersion.

Suppose that an achromatic combination of power $1/f$ is required, to be made of glasses of dispersive powers ω_1 and ω_2. Then concerning the two components (subscripts 1 and 2) we know that

$$\frac{1}{f_{1D}} + \frac{1}{f_{2D}} = \frac{1}{f}$$

and
$$\frac{\omega_1}{f_{1D}} + \frac{\omega_2}{f_{2D}} = 0$$

Combining these equations gives

$$\frac{1}{f} = \frac{1}{f_{1D}}\left(1 - \frac{\omega_1}{\omega_2}\right) = \frac{1}{f_{2D}}\left(1 - \frac{\omega_2}{\omega_1}\right) \tag{29.16}$$

If the difference between ω_1 and ω_2 is small, the powers of the components must be much greater than $1/f$. If the dispersive powers differ by a factor 2, the more powerful component will have twice the power of the combination.

29.08 SPHERICAL ABERRATION

Approximate methods were used in deriving the lens relationship (29.10). Equation (29.02) is an approximation, and it is the basis for the subsequent equations through to (29.10). Further, in proceeding to equation (29.10) we assumed implicitly that all portions of the wave front travel parallel to the X axis, thus ignoring the gradual change in curvature with distance traveled that is shown in Figure 29.03. The wave front actually emerging from a simple spherical lens is not perfectly circular. If it has positive curvature, the portions further removed from the X axis tend to converge on a point closer to the lens than the image point given by the equations. The failure to achieve an emergent wave front with a common center of curvature is known as **spherical aberration.** The approximations that we have used are good for lenses of diameter small in comparison with their focal length, say $d < f/10$, where d is the diameter of the lens and f the focal length. For $d > f/10$, spherical aberration may be serious, unless steps are taken to keep it small.

A lens could be designed, with other than spherical surfaces, that would eliminate spherical aberration for one particular value of u, but this lens would have greater errors when u was varied. It would also be a considerable more difficult lens to manufacture. If we agree to spherical surfaces, however, and so a thickness relation of the form of (29.06), it is still possible to minimize the spherical aberration for a particular value of u by a suitable distribution of curvature between the front and back surfaces of the lens. Thus for a distant source, and for index of refraction 1.50, spherical aberration is reduced to a minimum by taking $r_2 = -6r_1$.

To eliminate this aberration entirely, with spherical lenses, combinations of at least two lenses must be used.

29.09 ASTIGMATISM

A spherical surface is represented in section by a circle, but a circle in a sectional diagram does not necessarily represent a spherical surface.

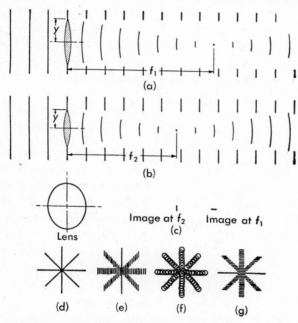

Fig. 29.08. Astigmatic lens. (a) Wave-front pattern in vertical section. (b) Wave-front pattern in horizontal section. (c) Lens and images at f_2 and f_1, looking along the axis of the lens. (d) Object. (e) Image at f_2. (f) Image between f_2 and f_1. (g) Image at f_1.

Thus a lens may have vertical and horizontal sections as indicated in parts (a) and (b) of Figure 29.08. Its projection on a plane perpendicular to its axis will then be as shown in the (c) part of the figure. The wave patterns of parts (a) and (b) are both correct, yet there is no point focus. At distance f_2 the beam of light converges to a vertical line; at f_1 it converges to a horizontal line. Somewhere between, its cross section is circular and may be referred to as the **circle of least confusion**. Consider an extended source such as shown in the (d) part of the figure as an array of point sources. The image of this array will appear as the (e) part of the figure at distance f_2, as the (g) part at distance f_1, and as the (f) part at an intermediate distance. Such reproduction is of course unsatisfactory. The lenses and corneas of our eyes are liable to grow **astigmatic,** i.e., to have different powers in different planes through the axis because of the sort of asymmetry described here. Astigmatic lenses are manufactured for use in spectacles to correct astigmatic eyes. Further, a simple lens, quite symmetrical in itself, behaves astigmatically for any point source not exactly on the axis of the lens. This point will be discussed in the next section.

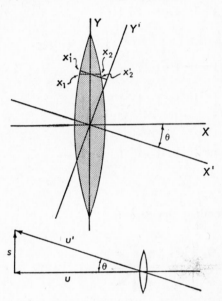

Fig. 29.09. Oblique axis for source off the axis of the lens.

29.10 SOURCES OFF THE AXIS OF THE LENS

Consider a point source of light not on the axis of the lens. Continuing to denote the axis of the lens as the X axis, take a new X' axis passing through the source and the center of the lens, the latter continuing to serve as origin, and take a new Y' axis, rectangular to the X' axis through the origin. Let the new axes form an angle θ with the old (Figure 29.09). Let the distance from lens to source, along the X' axis, be u', and let u be the component of u' along the X axis.

The thickness of lens material to be traversed by light traveling parallel to the X' axis, or nearly so, varies with y' in much the same way as it varies with y for light from a point on the X axis traveling parallel or nearly parallel to that axis. An image on the X' axis can be anticipated. Some modifications must be made to equation (29.06), however. For one thing, to a first approximation,

$$\frac{x_2 - x_1}{x_2' - x_1'} = \cos \theta \qquad (29.17)$$

[This approximation contains the most serious inaccuracy to be introduced; the bending of the light at the first surface of the lens causes the light to travel less obliquely through the lens; in place of θ we could with greater precision use θ', where $(\sin \theta)/(\sin \theta') = \mu$.] Further,

$$\frac{y'}{y} = \cos \theta \tag{29.18}$$

Introducing these two modifications into (29.06) makes it read

$$[(x_2' - x_1') - (x_{02}' - x_{01}')] \cos \theta = \frac{(y')^2}{2} \left(\frac{1}{r_1} - \frac{1}{r_2} \right) \frac{1}{\cos^2 \theta} \tag{29.19}$$

As a result of this change in (29.06), the lens relationship for light traveling along the X' axis becomes, instead of (29.11),

$$\frac{1}{v'} = \frac{1}{u'} + \frac{1}{f \cos^3 \theta} \tag{29.20}$$

where v' and u' are distances to image and object points along the X' axis. Using the components along the X axis, which are

$$u = u' \cos \theta \qquad \text{and} \qquad v = v' \cos \theta \tag{29.21}$$

this becomes

$$\frac{1}{v} = \frac{1}{u} + \frac{1}{f \cos^4 \theta} \tag{29.22}$$

If by focal length we refer to a distance along the X axis, then for light traveling at an angle θ to that axis, the focal length is $f \cos^4 \theta$.

Now take a Z axis, normal to both the X and Y axes. It will also be normal to both the X' and Y' axes. Consider the diagram in the $X'Z$ plane. Variations in θ do not affect the variation of lens thickness with z, in the way that they affect its variation with y. Thus there is no modification corresponding to (29.18). The other modifications, based on equations (29.17) and (29.21), still apply, and so for the diagram in the $X'Z$ plane,

$$\frac{1}{v} = \frac{1}{u} + \frac{1}{f \cos^2 \theta} \tag{29.23}$$

Thus for any value of θ, the lens has different focal lengths in two planes at right angles to each other, both containing the direction of travel of the light. That is to say, for $\theta \neq 0$, the lens is no longer symmetrical, but has the property of astigmatism described in the preceding section. For $\theta \neq 0$, there will be no point images, but instead two line images, at distances from the lens given by equations (29.22) and (29.23). These images are both closer to the lens (if the lens has positive power) than the point image on the axis located by (29.11). The best approximation to a point image for $\theta \neq 0$, (the circle of least confusion, section 29.09) lies somewhere between the two line images.

Equations (29.22) and (29.23) give the focal lengths for line images normal to the plane of Figure 29.09 and in the plane of that figure as

$$f_t = f \cos^4 \theta \simeq f(1 - 2 \sin^2 \theta) \qquad (29.24)$$

and
$$f_s = f \cos^2 \theta = f(1 - \sin^2 \theta) \qquad (29.25)$$

respectively. These equations exaggerate the magnitude of $(f_t - f)$ and

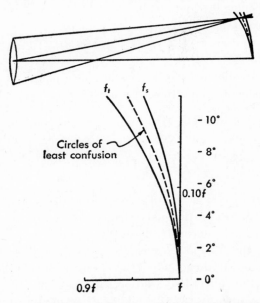

Fig. 29.10. Loci of line images and circles of least confusion, for a distant line-array of source points normal to the axis of the lens.

$(f_s - f)$, because of the inaccuracy in equation (29.17) already noted; they give $(f_s - f_t)$ quite accurately. Figure 29.10 gives the loci of images of three sorts for a distant line-array of source points normal to the axis. The focus for least confusion departs from the focus given by the simple lens relation by about 1% for $\theta = 5°$, by about 4% for $\theta = 10°$. The amount of astigmatism, as indicated by the magnitude of $(f_s - f_t)$ increases similarly as the square of θ, approximately.

Suppose that a lens of power 10 diopters, i.e., of focal length 10 cm, is set up at a distance great compared with 10 cm, say a distance of 5 m, from a flat wall, on which a pattern of concentric circles and radial lines has been drawn (Figure 29.11). The axis of the lens should pass through the center of the pattern. An "image" will be formed approximately 10 cm behind the lens. The center point of the pattern will be imaged as a point on the axis of the lens apart from the limitations of spherical aberration. No other point of the pattern will be imaged anywhere as a point. If in Figure 29.10 we rotate the f_t and f_s loci about the horizontal axis, we obtain the surfaces on which points on the pattern or "object" are imaged as short line-elements. On the f_t surface the elements are all tangential (hence the subscript t), so that on this surface the circles of the pattern are in apparently good focus. On the f_s surface, the elements are all radial or "sagittal" (hence the subscript s), so that on this surface the radial lines are in apparently good

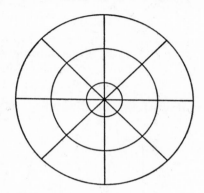

Fig. 29.11. Object pattern for consideration of astigmatism resulting from source being off the axis.

focus. The best compromise, with every point of the pattern imaged as a circle of least confusion, is obtained on some surface intermediate between these two.

If, instead of using these surfaces, we let the image form on a flat surface normal to the axis, at the correct axial image distance behind the lens, each point on the pattern will be imaged as an elliptical patch, the linear dimensions of the patch increasing as the square of the distance from the axis of the lens.

The spherical aberration that exists for $\theta = 0$ takes on a somewhat more complicated form for light passing obliquely through a lens, and is referred to then as **coma**. It is usually difficult to observe, being mixed with a relatively large amount of astigmatism. Coma gives rise to a comet-shaped focus of each point source. We have seen now that for a simple lens there is a curvature of the surface of best images corresponding to a flat object-surface. Further, everywhere off the axis there is astigmatism, so that the best image is a compromise between two line-element alternatives.

A further problem arising with photographic lenses is that of **dis-**

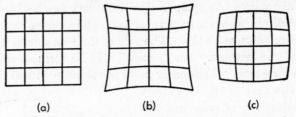

Fig. 29.12. Distortion of rectilinear grid: (a) object, (b) image with positive or "pincushion" distortion, (c) image with negative or "barrel-shaped" distortion.

tortion: the imaging of straight lines as curves, and curves in general as other curves. This is primarily due to a variation of the magnification with θ. The effect of magnification increasing with distance off the axis (positive or "pincushion" distortion) is shown in part (b) of Figure 29.12. The reverse effect, negative or "barrel-shaped" distortion, is shown in the (c) part of the figure, and the (a) part indicates the rectilinear object.

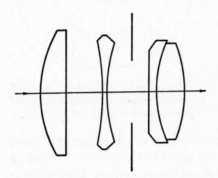

Fig. 29.13. Kodak Ektar Lens. Focal length = 44 mm. Effective diameter of f/3.5 aperture = 12.6 mm. Angle of view = 52° (i.e., 26° from axis).

All these defects, and chromatic aberration too, can be reduced to any practical specification by the careful optical design of a lens of three or more components. Figure 29.13 shows, for example, a four-element lens designed for a "miniature" camera taking pictures 24 by 36 mm.

29.11 IMAGE PLANES, MAGNIFICATION, AND CONVENTIONAL RAYS

The thin-lens relation

$$\frac{1}{v} = \frac{1}{u} + \frac{1}{f}$$

relates the curvatures $1/v$ and $1/u$ to the power of the lens $1/f$. At the same time it relates distances along the axis of the lens. In describing these distances we neglect the thickness of the lens, and so treat it as though it existed in a plane normal to its axis. Then u is the object distance, or distance from the lens to the **object point,** the location on the axis of a point source; v is the image distance, or distance from the lens to the **image point;** and f is the focal length of the lens.   If we set $u = -f$, then $v = \infty$.   Let us call the object point in this case the **first focal point** of the lens.   Then light from a point source at the first focal point emerges as a parallel beam, with all emergent rays parallel to the axis (Figure 29.14).   If we set $u = -\infty$, then $v = f$.   Let us call the image point in this case the **second focal point** of the lens (Figure 29.15).

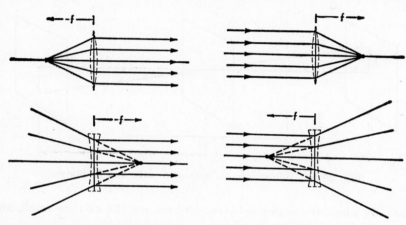

Fig. 29.14.   When the incident rays originate or intersect at the first focal point, the emergent rays form a beam parallel to the axis.

Fig. 29.15.   When the incident rays form a beam parallel to the axis, the emergent rays intersect at the second focal point.

Now, in order to develop a simplified approximate method for dealing with sources off the axis and with extended objects, let us consider planes normal to the axis of the lens.   The **lens plane** will be the plane in which, by neglecting the thickness of the lens, we consider the lens to exist.   The **object plane, image plane,** and **first and second focal planes** are parallel to the lens plane at distances u, v, $-f$, and f, respectively.   The preceding section has indicated that for an array of point sources in the object plane, the best images will lie on a curved surface to which the image plane is tangent.   Let us adopt the image plane as a useful approximation to this surface.   The approximation improves as we approach the axis.   Let us assume (as indeed we already have in Figure 29.09) that a ray proceeding toward the center of the lens (i.e., the intersection of the axis with the lens plane) passes through the lens without any change.   Then a straight line, from a source point in the object plane, through the center of the lens, cuts the image plane at the corresponding image point. Suppose that as an object we have a line of length s in the object plane and cutting the axis. On the assumptions made above, the image of this line is a line in the image plane and cutting the axis (Figure 29.16). If the length of the image line is i, then

$$\frac{i}{s} = \frac{|v|}{|u|} \tag{29.26}$$

The ratio i/s is called the **magnification**. Our approximations are

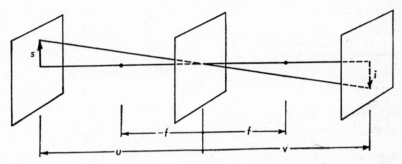

Fig. 29.16. Linear object, normal to axis, and its image.

good only where the angles between the rays and the axis are small, and so we can also say that approximately

$$\frac{i}{|v|} = \frac{s}{|u|} = \theta \tag{29.27}$$

where θ is the angle subtended at the lens by both object and image. If the light arrives at or leaves the lens in a parallel beam, $s/|u|$ or $i/|v|$ becomes the ratio of two infinite quantities, but the equation in this second form can still be used.

Equation (29.26) gives the magnification as a function of u and v. It can be combined with the basic lens relationship (29.11) to relate the magnification to u and f, for a positive lens and a real image, by

$$\frac{i}{s} = \frac{f}{|u| - f}$$

In the stadia system of measuring distances, surveyors observe the length of object (a "stadia rod") that can be seen between two fine lines of known separation in the real-image plane of their telescope objective, and so establish the magnification i/s. Since they know f for this objective accurately, the above relation gives them $|u| - f$, the distance from the object to a point a distance f in front of the objective. The relation can be derived alternatively from "conventional rays", as in Figure 29.17. Similarly, in dealing with picture projectors and enlargers, it is convenient to calculate the size of the large real image at distance v from the relation

$$\frac{i}{s} = \frac{v - f}{f}$$

obtained by combining equations (29.26) and (29.11).

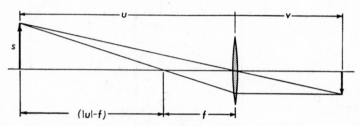

Fig. 29.17. Surveyors use magnification relation $(|u| - f)/f = s/i$.

We have located the images of objects which are lines normal to the axis by locating the image plane and drawing one ray: a straight line through the center of the lens. If we use as our construction the drawing of two rays, then the image plane is itself located by the ray construction. The second ray may be a line through the first focal point as an incident ray, and so emerge parallel to the axis (Figure 29.14). Alternatively, it may be a line parallel to the axis as an incident ray, and so emerge as a line through the second focal point of the lens (Figure 29.15). The rays used are **conventional rays** or principal rays, devised to locate an image plane distant v from the lens plane, in keeping with the thin-lens relation. Such rays would not reveal lens aberrations. In the designing of lenses, use is made of the technique of ray tracing. Many rays are drawn and carried through each of the lens surfaces according to equation (28.05). Rays traced in this way reveal the departure from a point of the image of a point source, and so reveal the extent of lens aberrations.

The use of conventional rays is illustrated in Figure 29.18. It should be noted that these rays are merely a convenient device for geometrical construction and have no special physical significance. Figure 29.19 shows that we may draw such a ray where there is no light traveling at all. The position of an image having been located by such rays, there is often

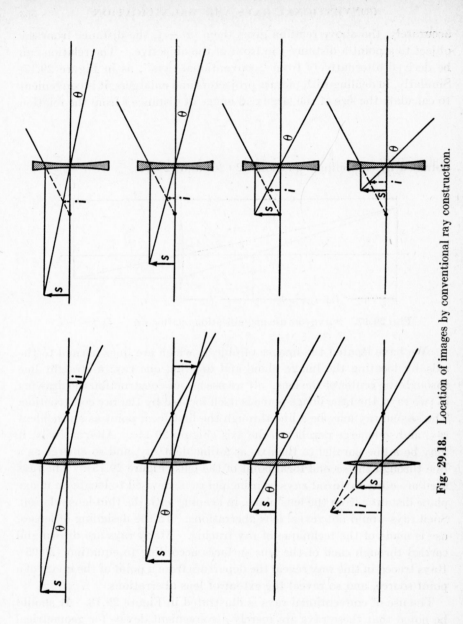

Fig. 29.18. Location of images by conventional ray construction.

virtue in shading-in the beam of light for the top of the image and the beam for the bottom of the image.

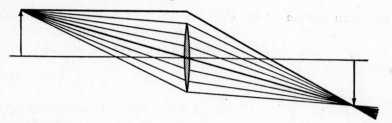

Fig. 29.19. Rays used in conventional construction can fall outside the beam.

29.12 USE OF MIRRORS TO ALTER CURVATURE

When a spherical wave front is reflected from a plane reflecting surface, its direction of travel is reversed, and at the same time, its curvature is reversed. There is no change in the curvature relative to the direction of travel. Therefore, an expanding wave front continues to expand, and a converging wave front continues to converge toward a point. If the reflecting surface is itself given a concave curvature (Figure 29.20), the central portion of the wave front is given a slight extra distance to travel, and as a result the curvature of the reflected wave front differs from that of the incident wave front in magnitude as well as in sense or sign. Before deriving the mathematical relationship between incident and reflected curvatures, we should make a modest extension to our sign convention. For lenses, we take the direction in which the light travels as the positive direction. With mirrors, this is ambiguous, and so we specify more explicitly that the direction of travel of the light *after reflection* will be taken as positive.

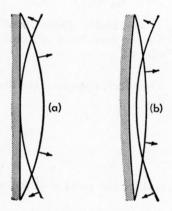

Fig. 29.20. Change in wave-front curvature effected by (a) plane mirror, (b) concave mirror.

29.13 THE MIRROR RELATION

Consider a spherical reflecting surface of radius of curvature r, with its center on the X axis, so that the equation of its section in the XY plane is

$$x_m - x_{0m} = \frac{y^2}{2}\frac{1}{r} \tag{29.28}$$

in line with section 29.03. Let a wave front, incident at the mirror and centered at a point on the X axis (Figure 29.21), have the equation

$$x_u - x_{0u} = \frac{y^2}{2}\frac{1}{u} \tag{29.29}$$

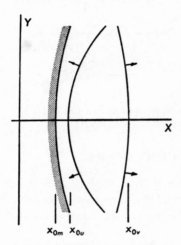

Consider the reflected wave front after a time Δt long enough to permit all parts of the wave front to be reflected. Each part of the wave front, assumed for convenience to be traveling exactly parallel to the axis, must travel a distance $x_u - x_m$ to reach the mirror, then a further distance $x_v - x_m$ in the remaining time.

$$\text{Time to reach mirror} = \frac{x_u - x_m}{c}$$

Fig. 29.21. Reflection of a wave front by a spherical mirror.

Time spent traveling away from mirror

$$= \Delta t - \frac{x_u - x_m}{c}$$

Therefore, regarding the distance traveled away from the mirror, we can say

$$x_v - x_m = c\left(\Delta t - \frac{x_u - x_m}{c}\right)$$
$$= c\,\Delta t - (x_u - x_m)$$

and for the portion of the wave front on the X axis,

$$x_{0v} - x_{0m} = c\,\Delta t - (x_{0u} - x_{0m})$$

Subtracting, we have

$$x_v - x_{0v} = -(x_u - x_{0u}) + 2(x_m - x_{0m}) \tag{29.30}$$

Combining (29.30) with (29.29) and (29.28) gives

$$x_v - x_{0v} = \frac{y^2}{2}\left(-\frac{1}{u} + \frac{2}{r}\right)$$

This is the equation of a circular arc having its center on the X axis.

Denoting the radius of curvature of this arc by v, we have the mirror relation

$$\frac{1}{v} = -\frac{1}{u} + \frac{2}{r} \tag{29.31}$$

As for lenses, the image distance for the case of a plane incident wave front ($u = \infty$, $1/u = 0$) is called the focal length of the mirror and is denoted by f. Substituting in equation (29.31) gives

$$\frac{1}{f} = -0 + \frac{2}{r}$$

that is, the focal length equals half the radius of curvature. Thus equation (29.31) can be written

where

$$\left. \begin{array}{l} \dfrac{1}{v} = -\dfrac{1}{u} + \dfrac{1}{f} \\[2mm] \dfrac{1}{f} = \dfrac{2}{r} \end{array} \right\} \tag{29.32}$$

Again, the quantity $1/f$ is called the focusing power, or just the power, of the mirror. In words, we can say that *the mirror reverses the curvature of the wave front reflected from it and adds twice its own curvature.*

29.14 ABERRATIONS WITH MIRRORS

The law of reflection does not involve any wavelength-sensitive index, and so mirrors do not have chromatic aberration. Similar approximations were made in deriving the mirror relationship as in deriving the lens relationship; there is a spherical aberration for spherical mirrors similar to that for spherical lenses. It may be noted in this connection that it is simpler to draw ray or wave-front diagrams (the latter using Huygens wavelets) to reveal this condition for the case of mirrors than it is for the case of lenses. Curvature of the image plane, astigmatism, and coma exist for spherical mirrors as for lenses, for much the same reasons, and there is usually less opportunity to correct for them by a system of several elements.

29.15 PLANES, RAYS, AND MAGNIFICATION

As we did with lenses, we can use the approximation that for purposes of applying the relation ($1/v = -1/u + 2/r$), the mirror lies in a plane normal to its axis, and that all points on an object plane distant from the mirror plane by u are imaged in an image plane distant from the mirror plane by v. A spherical mirror has a single focal point, halfway

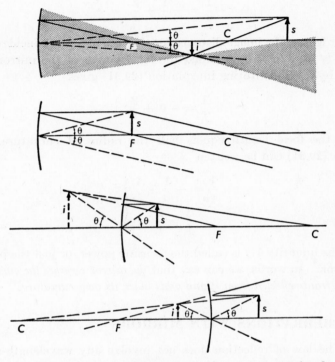

Fig. 29.22. Location of mirror images by conventional ray construction.

between the mirror and its center of curvature. For conventional ray construction (Figure 29.22), we have three conditions:

(1) A ray through the center of curvature (C) strikes the surfaces of the mirror normally, and so is reflected back on itself.

(2) A ray parallel to the axis is reflected back through the focal point (F) and *vice versa*.

(3) At the point of intersection of the mirror and its axis, incident and reflected rays make equal angles with the axis.

Again with mirrors, having located an image by conventional rays, it is desirable to draw beams in outline for the extremes of the object, to maintain an awareness of where the light really goes.

Regarding magnification, the linear size of the image is to that of the object as the image distance is to the object distance, equations (29.26), (29.27), just as for lenses.

29.16 ELLIPSOIDAL AND PARABOLOIDAL MIRRORS

Lines drawn from the two foci of an ellipse to any point P on the ellipse make equal angles with the normal to the ellipse at P (Figure 29.23).   Therefore if we have an el-lipsoidal mirror and mount a point source at one of its foci, all the light from the source that is reflected from the mirror is brought to an image point at the other focus.   The mirror need not be a complete ellipse, of course, unless it is required that all the light that is emitted by the source contribute to the image.

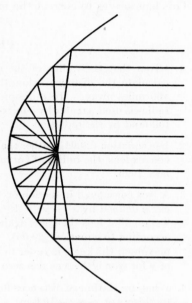

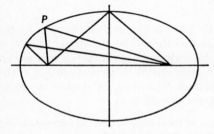

Fig. 29.23.   An ellipsoidal mirror brings all light from a point source at one focus of the ellipse to a point image at the other focus.

Fig. 29.24.   A paraboloidal mirror brings the light from a point source into a perfect parallel beam.

A parabola may be regarded as an ellipse of which one of the foci has gone to infinity.   If we mount a point source at the one finite focus of a paraboloidal mirror, every reflected ray will be parallel to the axis of the paraboloid (Figure 29.24).   For any mirror requirement where the object or the image is on the axis and at infinity, a paraboloidal mirror avoids all the aberrations found in a spherical mirror.   More generally, these aberrations could be avoided in any case where the object and image are at fixed distances, and on the axis, by the selection of the appropriate ellipsoidal mirror.

Large telescopes employ parabolic mirrors, ground from glass and

front-silvered.   These are simpler to make than lenses, the glass need
not be so free from flaws, and diameters as great as one-fifth the focal
length can be achieved.   Spherical mirrors are used, however, in the
"Schmidt" telescope, which not only has a larger diameter of aperture,
relative to the focal length (diameters actually a bit greater than the
focal length), but also operates satisfactorily at greater angles from the
axis than most telescopes.   In this use of a spherical mirror, an irregularly
shaped diverging lens is located at the center of curvature of the reflector.
This lens serves to correct the major defects of the large-aperture mirror.

PROBLEMS

1. Given that the radius of the earth is 3957 miles, use equation (29.04) to
   calculate the distance below the horizon of a point on the earth's surface
   100 miles away.   (In radio-propagation studies, an enhanced value of the
   radius is used, greater by a factor 4/3, to allow for slight curvature of the path
   followed by the radiation.)

2. Use equation (29.04), rather than a compass of great radius, to draw a double-
   convex lens, the radius of curvature of each side 50 cm, the maximum thickness 2 cm.

3. A lens considered in section on the XY plane is bounded on the right by the
   circle defined by $x^2 + y^2 = 10^2$ cm^2 and on the left by the straight line $x =$
   9 cm.   Plot lens thickness against y, first without approximation and second
   according to equation (29.06).   Both plots should be accurate to 1% of the
   maximum thickness in order to reveal their differences.   Calculate the value
   of y for which the lens has zero thickness in each case.

4. What are the image distances for a lens of focal length 10.0 cm corresponding
   to objects at $-\infty$, -10.0 m, -5.00 m, -2.00 m, -1.00 m?

5. Suppose that the maximum image distance in a camera is 2.0 cm greater
   than the focal length.   What is the shortest possible object distance, (a) for
   $f = 20$ cm, (b) for $f = 10$ cm, (c) for $f = 5.0$ cm?

6. A lens has focal length 10.0 cm.   For what value of u are u and v equal and
   opposite?

7. Keeping the image distance fixed at exactly 2 cm, by how much must the
   focusing power of a lens be increased to go from an object at $-\infty$ to an
   object at -25 cm?

8. Two lenses lying close together on the same axis have focal lengths 10.0 cm
   and 20.0 cm.   What is the focal length of the combination?

9. An achromatic combination has power 5.0 diopters.   What are the powers of
   the components, if the dispersive power (ω_1) of the glass of the first component is just half that (ω_2) of the glass of the second component?

10. Calculate the dispersive powers of the substances for which refractive indices are given in the following table:

Substance	Refractive Indices for Wavelengths		
	F	D	C
Borosilicate crown	1.530	1.524	1.522
Light barium flint	1.581	1.574	1.571
Barium flint	1.576	1.568	1.565
Light flint	1.590	1.580	1.576
Dense flint	1.669	1.655	1.650

11. A lens of index of refraction 1.50 has $r_2 = -6r_1$ in order to minimize spherical aberration (section 29.08). If the lens has power 10.0 diopters, calculate r_1 and r_2.

12. Show from a figure similar to 29.16 that $1/v = (1/u) + (1/f)$. First derive a relationship among the magnitudes of the quantities involved, then replace the magnitudes by the algebraic quantities.

13. Taking as object a line extending normally upward 1 cm from the axis of a lens of power 40 diopters, use conventional rays to locate the image for object distances -8 cm, -4 cm, -2.5 cm, -1.5 cm.

14. Repeat problem 13 for a lens of power -40 diopters.

15. What magnification is provided by a lens of power 2.00 diopters with an image distance of 20.0 m?

16. Object and real image are separated by a distance of 1.00 m. A magnification of exactly 3 is required. What must be the focusing power of the lens?

17. What object distances are required with a mirror of curvature $1/r$ to produce images distant r, $2r$, $3r$, $4r$, $5r$, from the mirror?

18. Taking as object a line extending normally upward 1 cm from the axis of a mirror of radius 5 cm, use conventional rays to locate the image for object distances 8 cm, 4 cm, 2.5 cm, 1.5 cm.

19. Repeat problem 18 for a mirror of radius -5 cm, i.e., a convex mirror.

30

Simple Lens Systems

30.01 A MORE GENERAL FORM OF THE LENS RELATION

The change in curvature of a wave front by a lens can be considered in two stages: first the change as the wave front enters the lens and then the change as it leaves. Consider now the passage of a wave front from a medium of index μ_p, where its radius of curvature is p, into a medium of index μ_q, the boundary surface itself having radius of curvature r (Figure 30.01). Let the equations of the incident wave front and of the lens be

$$x_p - x_{0p} = \frac{y^2}{2}\frac{1}{p}$$

and

$$x_r - x_{0r} = \frac{y^2}{2}\frac{1}{q}$$

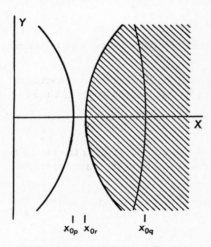

Then by allowing a time Δt sufficient for the wave front to enter the second medium, it may be shown much as in section 29.05 that the equation of the wave front in the q medium is

$$\frac{\mu_q}{q} = \frac{\mu_p}{p} + \frac{\mu_q - \mu_p}{r} \quad (30.01)$$

Fig. 30.01. Passage of a wave front from air through a spherical surface into glass.

If the curvature of the boundary surface is zero, this reduces to

$$\frac{\mu_q}{q} = \frac{\mu_p}{p}$$

This is the case already treated in section 28.01. Again, for any value of $1/r$, suppose the first medium has index unity. Then we no longer

562

need the subscript q for the index of the second medium and can set $\mu_p = 1$, $\mu_q = \mu$. Then equation (30.01) reduces to

$$\frac{\mu}{q} = \frac{1}{p} + \frac{\mu - 1}{r}$$

Similarly if we set $\mu_p = \mu$ and $\mu_q = 1$,

$$\frac{1}{q} = \frac{1}{p} - \frac{\mu - 1}{r}$$

We can use these special forms or the general form of (30.01) to deal with thick lenses, that is, with lenses of sufficient thickness for the curvature of a wave front to change appreciably in the distance traveled within the lens.

Our purpose now, however, is to derive a more general *thin-lens* relationship than we have had previously for the case of a wave front proceeding from a region of index μ_u, where its curvature is $1/u$, through a lens of index μ_e, where its curvature is $1/e$, into a region of index μ_v, where its curvature is $1/v$ (Figure 30.02). Let the lens surfaces have curvatures $1/r_1$ and $1/r_2$. Applying equation (30.01) for the transition from incident medium to lens, we have

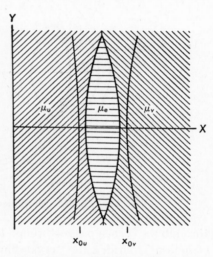

Fig. 30.02. Passage of a wave front from medium μ_u through the lens of index μ_e into medium μ_v.

$$\frac{\mu_e}{e} = \frac{\mu_u}{u} + \frac{\mu_e - \mu_u}{r_1}$$

Applying it again for the transition from the lens to the emergent medium gives

$$\frac{\mu_v}{v} = \frac{\mu_e}{e} + \frac{\mu_v - \mu_e}{r_2}$$

Combining these two equations to eliminate the curvature of the wave front in the lens, $1/e$, we obtain

$$\frac{\mu_v}{v} = \frac{\mu_u}{u} + \frac{\mu_e - \mu_u}{r_1} - \frac{\mu_e - \mu_v}{r_2} \qquad (30.02)$$

This is the generalized relation we need. If we set $\mu_e = \mu$ and $\mu_u = \mu_v = 1$, it reduces to equation (29.10).

30.02 OPTICS OF THE EYE

Referring to Figure 30.03, it will be seen that the eyeball is covered by the fibrous white "sclerotic coat". The front portion of this is transparent and horny (hence "cornea"), and more curved. Light entering

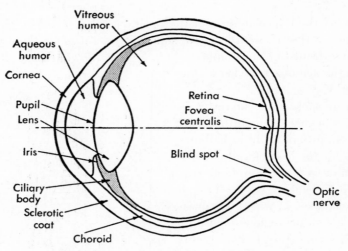

Fig. 30.03.   Simplified cross section of the eye.

through the cornea passes through the "aqueous humor" (a weak solution of sodium chloride), the "crystalline lens" (composed of flexible layers of different refractive indices), and the gelatinous "vitreous humor", to reach the light-sensitive "retina". Back of the retina, lining the sclerotic coat, is the "choroid", composed of numerous blood vessels that nourish the eye and dark pigment cells that absorb light and minimize the amount of stray light inside the eye. The size of aperture of the lens, i.e., the size of the "pupil", is regulated by involuntary muscular control of the "iris" diaphragm, the diameter ranging from 8 to 2 mm with the brightness of the light. The eye is focused by the muscles of the "ciliary body". Contraction of these muscles relaxes the ligaments around the rim of the lens, allowing the lens to thicken by its own elasticity. This process of focusing is known as **accommodation**. Distances, curvatures, and indices for the average eye are given in Table 30.01.

The normal eye can focus on objects as close to it as 0.25, or as far

away as you please. By using the meter as our unit of length, we can
have simple reciprocity between our units of length and power, the meter
and the diopter. That is to say, the lens system can deal with incident
wave-front curvatures ranging from 0 to -4 diopters. The cornea and
the lens are too powerful to be analyzed correctly by thin-lens theory;
further, they are not close enough together to be considered properly as
lenses in contact, with additive powers. A thin-lens treatment does seem
to be a good enough approximation, however, to be worth carrying
through. Let us take the cornea as a thin lens (between two different
media) and the lens as another thin lens; let us assume that their powers

TABLE 30.01 Concerning the Eye.

	Radius (mm)		Thickness along axis (mm)	Index refraction
	Front	Back		
Cornea	7.8	7.3	0.5	1.38
Lens, min. power	10.0	−6.0	3.6	avg., 1.40
Lens, max. power	6.0	−5.5	4.0	
Aqueous humor				
min. lens power			3.6	1.33
max. lens power			3.2	
Vitreous humor			15.9	1.33

are additive. Let $1/r_1$, $1/r_2$, $1/r_3$, and $1/r_4$ denote the curvatures of the
front and back surfaces of the cornea and the front and back surfaces of
the lens. Let μ_c, μ_h, and μ_e be the indices of the cornea, the humors, and
the lens.

Applying equation (30.02) to the cornea, we obtain the relation

$$\frac{\mu_h}{v_a} - \frac{1}{u} = \frac{\mu_c - 1}{r_1} - \frac{\mu_c - \mu_h}{r_2}$$

Applying the same relation to the crystalline lens gives

$$\frac{\mu_h}{v} - \frac{\mu_h}{v_a} = \frac{\mu_e - \mu_h}{r_3} - \frac{\mu_e - \mu_h}{r_4}$$

In these equations, v_a has been used for the radius of curvature of the
wave fronts in the aqueous humor; the change in curvature from the time
the wave front leaves the cornea until it enters the crystalline lens has
been neglected. Combining these equations, to eliminate v_a, we have

$$\frac{\mu_h}{v} = \frac{1}{u} + \frac{\mu_c - 1}{r_1} - \frac{\mu_c - \mu_h}{r_2} + \frac{\mu_e - \mu_h}{r_3} - \frac{\mu_e - \mu_h}{r_4}$$

Substituting numbers for the indices gives

$$\underbrace{\frac{1.33}{v}}_{\substack{\text{con-}\\\text{stant}}} = \underbrace{\frac{1}{u}}_{\substack{\text{min. 0}\\\text{max. } -4\\\text{diop-}\\\text{ters}}} + \underbrace{\frac{0.38}{r_1} - \frac{0.05}{r_2}}_{\substack{\text{power of}\\\text{cornea con-}\\\text{stant at 42}\\\text{diopters}}} + \underbrace{\frac{0.07}{r_3} - \frac{0.07}{r_4}}_{\substack{\text{power of lens}\\\text{min. 19.5}\\\text{max. 23.5}\\\text{diopters}}} \qquad (30.03)$$

The powers written under equation (30.03) were obtained using curvature values taken from Table 30.01, and values for the index of refraction of the lens just above and just below 1.40. It can be seen that the eye in accommodation from an infinite object-distance to 0.25 m changes its total power by less than 10%.

30.03 THE RETINA

The retina is a very complex structure of nerve endings; the light passes through this structure to reach the array of light-sensitive tips of two sorts, "rods" and "cones". Approximately in the center of the retina is the "fovea"; a patch of diameter 0.5 mm, where there are cones only. These cones are squeezed closely together in a mosaic of six-sided cells, the average diameter of a cell being 0.003 mm. This is the image-size corresponding to an object of diameter about 0.3 mm at a distance of 2 m. The whole fovea would be covered by the image of a 5-cm disk at this distance. Around the fovea is the "macula", an area corresponding to a 25-cm disk at 2 m, over which the degree of resolution is almost as good. The rest of the retina is of increasing coarseness and serves more for the detection of the presence of objects than for their close examination. In view of these data, consider what happens when we are looking at something, say a few people, at a distance of 6 ft. Only one face can be "imaged" on the macula at one time, and so observed with good definition. The rest can be kept track of, but cannot be scrutinized in detail simultaneously. And even in the case of that one face, only one feature, a nose or a mouth or an eye, can be commanding the ultimate scrutiny of the fovea. Beyond the fovea, the retina is populated by a mixture of cones and rods, the proportion of the former decreasing until at the outer edge of the retina only rods are present. Since the total number of nerves is far less than the number of cones and rods and in the central portions there is one nerve to each cone, it is apparent that in the outer parts of the retina many cells must affect the same nerve. Thus resolution decreases, but sensitivity increases, as we move outward from the center. Sensitivity to color decreases, however, for it is only cones, or networks including cones, that are color-sensitive. The outer areas of the field of vision are used primarily for the detection of motion.

30.04 COMMON OPTICAL DEFECTS OF THE EYE

The specifications of the "normal eye", in terms of which the optics of the eye have been described, are somewhat arbitrary. With muscles relaxed, this normal eye focuses distant objects (plane wave fronts arriving at the eye) on the retina. (As the object moves in from infinity to 6 m, the image moves by no more than the thickness of the retina, so everything beyond 6 m can be classed as "infinity" when one is considering focusing.) With muscular effort, the power of the lens can be increased by several diopters. For the "normal eye" the greatest amount of such increase has been set at 4 diopters. With this added power, objects 0.25 m distant are focused on the retina. The normal eye is thus considered as having a **far point** at infinity ($1/u = 0$, $u = -\infty$) and a **near point** at 0.25 m ($1/u = -4 \text{ m}^{-1}$, $u = -0.25$ m).

Actually, the optics of the average eye change with age, as shown in Figure 30.04. The far point is at infinity, as specified for the normal eye, until age 50, or almost 50. The power of the lens, with muscles relaxed, gradually increases from age 50 onward. The accommodation, i.e., the added power that can be achieved by muscular effort, gradually decreases throughout life, from about 14 diopters at ten years to zero at age about seventy-five. Thus, after middle age the average eye can no longer focus on objects as close as the normal near point, or on objects at a distance of a few meters. These changes with age in the lens and its accommodation are known as **presbyopia.** The resultant shortcomings can be overcome by the wearing of spectacles, but no single lens can correct for the loss of accommodation: One set of lenses is needed for vision at short range, another for vision at long range. The continuous nature of the changes with age shown in the figure is the result of averaging; changes in the eyes of any one individual are more likely to occur over relatively short periods of time, but with the same general trend.

There are other optical defects that may become apparent at earlier ages. In **myopia** or nearsightedness, an abnormally long eyeball places the retina beyond the principal focus with muscles relaxed. The far point, imaged on the retina with muscles relaxed, comes at some distance less than infinity, or in practice at some distance less than 6 m. When the ciliary muscles are contracted to increase the focusing power of the lens by 4 diopters, such an eye focuses to distances a bit less than the standard 0.25 m. In **hypermetropia** or farsightedness, the eye generally has a flattened eyeball; the retina is too close to the lens. Then some of the extra power achieved by muscular effort must be added-in before even objects at infinity come to a focus on the retina, and the full 4

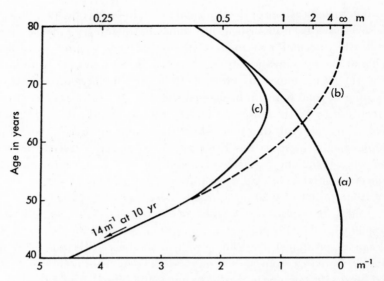

Fig. 30.04. Nature of the variation with age of the focusing power of the eye. (a) Curvature and radius of curvature of incident light focused by relaxed eye. (b) Accommodation. (c) Curvature and radius of curvature of incident light focused by eye with maximum accommodation.

diopters of extra power will only focus objects at a near point considerably farther away than the standard 0.25 m. Either of these defects can be fully corrected by the wearing of suitable spectacles.

Astigmatism is another common defect of the eye. It is generally due to a nonspherical cornea, although sometimes the crystalline lens is astigmatic. If the ciliary muscles do not act equally around the periphery of the lens, the amount of astigmatism will change with accommodation. Effectively, an astigmatic eye has maximum power in one axial plane, and minimum power in the axial plane at right angles to this. It can be corrected by a cylindrical spectacle lens suitably oriented so that it increases the minimum power to equal the maximum, without affecting the latter.

30.05 LENS AT THE EYE

A lens may be placed immediately in front of the eye, with a view to correcting the optical defects described above, or so that an object can be brought closer than 0.25 m and so seen better. Then the wave front arriving at the eye is that emerging from the lens, which has curvature $1/v_s$, (s being used as a subscript to denote this accessory lens). This curvature is related to the power of the lens and the curvature of the wave front incident on the lens by the usual lens relation,

$$\frac{1}{v_s} = \frac{1}{u_s} + \frac{1}{f_s} \qquad (30.04)$$

To determine what power of lens is needed to correct the sight of a myopic eye, we need only substitute the far point of the unaided eye for v_s and the required far point $(-\infty)$ for u_s. Similarly, for the correction of a hypermetropic eye, substitute the near point of the unaided eye for v_s and the required near point $(-0.25$ m$)$ for u_s.

When the other common defect, astigmatism, was mentioned in the preceding section, the correction was said to be a cylindrical lens. Most prescriptions for spectacle lenses specify "spheres" of so many diopters, plus "cylinders" of so many diopters, the required directions of the axes of the cylinders being specified. Effectively, assuming that lenses are being used to correct short or long sight, these lenses are themselves made astigmatic, their astigmatism being at right angles to that of the eye. These astigmatic lenses can be specified in terms of their spherical power and their cylindrical power.

30.06 THE MAGNIFIER OR SIMPLE MICROSCOPE

As we bring a small object closer to the eye, say from 1 m to 0.5 m, we see it better, because the size of the image on the retina is approximately proportional to the angle subtended by the object at the eye, and for a fixed size of object this is inversely proportional to the object-distance. The amount of accommodation required of the eye also varies inversely as the object-distance. Thus, as the object is brought closer, the amount of accommodation required increases, and so does the muscular effort required. If the object is brought closer than the near point, the image on the retina, although bigger than ever, is less good, and at the same time the eye muscles undergo undue strain. We therefore take the size of the image on the retina given by $|u| = 0.25$ m, as in Figure 30.05(a), as the best that can be obtained, unless the eye is aided by some accessory device.

Microscope is the general name for devices permitting the eye to achieve a larger clear image on the retina, and as a measure of the performance of a microscope we use **magnifying power** (M.P.), the ratio of the size of the retinal image when the microscope is used, to its size when

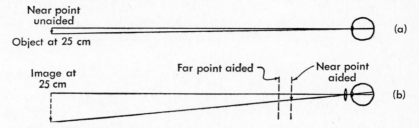

Fig. 30.05. Use of magnifier or simple microscope to increase angle subtended at eye.

the object is held 0.25 m from the unaided eye. Since these image-sizes are proportional to θ, the angle subtended at the eye, it is more convenient to define magnifying power specifically by

$$\text{M.P.} = \frac{\text{angle at eye when microscope is used}}{\text{angle at unaided eye, object at 0.25 m}}$$

The simplest microscope, called a **magnifier** or **simple microscope,** is a lens of positive power held at the eye like a spectacle lens; Figure 30.05(b). (It is not essential that such a magnifying glass be held at the eye, and a low-power reading glass very often is not. In any case, though, this is the most convenient position for theoretical consideration.)

To determine the far point when a lens is held in front of a normal eye, we need only substitute the normal far point $(-\infty)$ for v_s in equation (30.04):

$$\frac{1}{u_s} = \frac{1}{-\infty} - \frac{1}{f_s} = -\frac{1}{f_s} \tag{30.05}$$

Similarly, for the near point, substitute the normal near point (-0.25 m) for v_s:

$$\frac{1}{u_s} = \frac{1}{-0.25 \text{ m}} - \frac{1}{f_s} = -\left(4 \text{ m}^{-1} + \frac{1}{f_s}\right) \tag{30.06}$$

The angle subtended at the eye, for the case of the magnifier, is simply $|s|/|u_s|$, and the angle that would be subtended at the unaided eye from

0.25 m is $|s|/0.25$ m. Thus we can readily obtain the magnifying power:

$$\text{M.P.} = \frac{\dfrac{|s|}{|u_s|}}{\dfrac{|s|}{0.25 \text{ m}}} = \frac{0.25 \text{ m}}{|u_s|} \tag{30.07}$$

Thus with the object at the far point,

$$\text{M.P.} = \frac{0.25 \text{ m}}{f_s} \tag{30.08}$$

and with the object at the near point,

$$\text{M.P.} = 0.25 \text{ m} \left(4 \text{ m}^{-1} + \frac{1}{f_s} \right)$$
$$= 1 + \frac{0.25 \text{ m}}{f_s} \tag{30.09}$$

Thus in using a lens of positive power held at the eye as a magnifier, we can achieve a magnifying power of $(0.25 \text{ m})/f_s$ with the eye muscles relaxed. By applying the muscular effort needed for an accommodation of 4 diopters, as we normally do in looking at things 0.25 m distant, we can increase this magnifying power by unity. A lens of focusing power 40 diopters provides a magnifying power of 10 if the object is held at the far point, so as to leave the eye relaxed. Bringing the object to the near point, the nearest we can bring it, without undue strain of the eye muscles, increases the magnifying power to 11. When a lens of focusing power 4 diopters is used with the object at the far point (which is -0.25 m) the magnifying power is unity. This does not make the use of the lens in this way pointless, though. It provides as good seeing with the eye muscles relaxed as would be achieved without it by the muscular effort required for an accommodation of 4 diopters.

30.07 POINT OF VIEW AND FIELD OF VIEW

It is simple, by the use of the conventional ray construction, to locate the image that a given lens (or mirror) will form of a given object. Suppose that after this is done the object and the lens are set up in the laboratory. How is the image "located" in practice? If it is a real image, a sheet of paper or ground glass can be placed in the image plane, and the real image will be "formed" on the opaque or diffusing surface, and will send out light in all directions. But this is not necessary; in the case of a virtual image it is not even possible. How can we see the image, without thus "forming" it on a diffusing surface? It is all a matter of putting your eye in the right place, all a matter of the point of view.

Consider the situations drawn in Figure 30.06, all for a lens of positive power. Light is spreading out in all directions from every point on the object. Such of this light as falls on the lens is redirected. In parts (a)

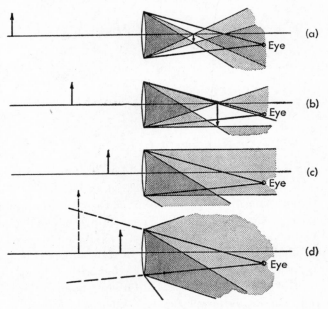

Fig. 30.06. Point of view and field of view.

and (b) of the figure, the redirected light converges, light from each point on the object converging to a point on the real image, then spreading out again. The spreading-out from the real image is not in all directions, however, but in a limited range of directions specified by the size of the lens.

Now consider the eye drawn in part (a). It receives light from the top of the object, and when this light arrives at the eye, it is spreading out from the "top" of the image. If the eye is more than 0.25 m from the image, the eye will focus this light at a point on the retina. Similarly, the eye receives light from the bottom of the object. When this light arrives at the eye, it is spreading out from the "bottom" of the image. This light will come to a focus at another point on the retina. Every other point on the object will be "imaged" similarly, first at a point on the real image formed by the lens, then again on the retina of the eye. The eye sees the whole of the real image.

Let us turn now to the (b) part of the figure. This time, the eye catches light from the bottom of the object (spreading out from the bottom point of the image), but it does not catch any light from the top. To catch light from the top, the eye would have to be lowered, and it would then not catch any light from the bottom. At the particular distance

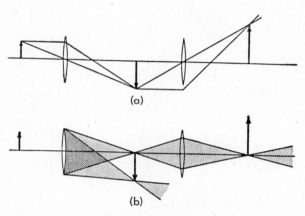

(a)

(b)

Fig. 30.07. According to conventional ray construction, second lens forms second real image of first real image of arrowhead. Drawing of beams indicates light at base of this real image, but no light at arrowhead.

from the lens at which the eye has been drawn, it cannot see the whole of the object, or if you prefer it, the whole of the image, from a single point of view. Just how much can it see?

Lines have been drawn, in each part of the figure, from the eye to the edges of the lens. That part of the image falling inside these lines can be seen by the eye. Points on the image outside these lines are not seen by the eye, for they do not send any light in the direction of the eye. This statement can be checked by drawing further beams of light. It holds not only for the real images of parts (a) and (b), but also for the case of a virtual image in part (d). With suitable interpretation, it holds in part (c), in which the image is at infinity.

In Figure 30.07(a), the image formed by the first lens has been located by the use of conventional ray construction. The light that reaches this image proceeds to spread out from points on the image. For the purposes of the second lens, the image formed by the first lens is the object.

It can be treated as such, and rays can be drawn from it (or the thin-lens relation can be applied) to locate the image formed by the second lens. This is true whether the images are real or virtual.

It should be noted, however, that when we proceed to draw beams of light, no light from the top of the object strikes the second lens. There will be a final image of the bottom of the object, and of an adjacent portion of the object, but no final image of the top of the object. There would be, if the diameter of the second lens were greater. The ray construction locates the final image, but only consideration of where the light actually goes, taking lens apertures into account, will indicate what portion of that image actually exists.

30.08 PARALLAX

To an observer at A in part (1) of Figure 30.08, the circle lies to the right of the cross, as it does also to an observer at B or C or D or E. In part

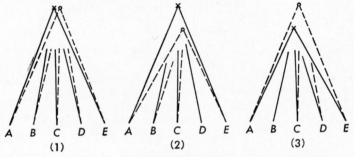

Fig. 30.08. Parallax.

(2) of the figure, circle lies well to the right of cross for an observer at A, progressively less so at B and C, and an observer at E sees the cross to the right of the circle. In part (3) the situation is reversed. **Parallax** is the name given to the angular displacement of one object relative to another, caused by an actual change in the point of observation.

There is one case of zero parallax in Figure 30.08, and that is the case of an observer at C in part (1) of the figure. If an observer at A or B moves to the right, he notices a gradual increase in the angular separation of circle and cross. If an observer at D or E moves to the right, he notices a gradual decrease. At C the rate of change in this angular separation with distance moved along the line AE is zero. At C the cross and circle are equidistant from the observer, and the observer can use the absence of parallax as an indication that cross and circle are equidistant.

The elimination of parallax is a useful method of locating an image. Suppose that the cross is the image, or an element of it, and you are looking at it from C, without knowing how far away it is. A pointer (or an image of a pointer) represented here by the circle, is placed at a point lying in the same direction from C as the image, and at your best guess as to the right distance. If when you move your eye to the right or left the image appears to move with your eye, then the image is farther away than the pointer. (Similarly the moon appears to move with you relative to the intervening trees.) If it is the pointer that appears to move with you, then the pointer is farther away. If there is no apparent relative motion—that is, if parallax is eliminated—then pointer and image are equidistant. Frequent application for the technique is found in the use of optical instruments.

The technique of eliminating parallax is applied by using one eye, and moving the head from side to side, say between points C and D, in Figure 30.08. We apply the related technique of **stereoscopic vision** extensively in everyday life. With reference to Figure 30.08, we look from point C with one eye and from point D with the other. Years of experience in the use of two eyes enable us to judge the relative distances of the various objects in the field of view by the slight differences in their relationship as observed from the two points of view. Further, we avoid any undue awareness that our two eyes are providing us with two (slightly) different pictures. But just try looking at a pencil held at arm's length against a distant background, paying attention to both at the same time; you won't like it.

PROBLEMS

1. A glass vessel has a thick glass bottom, 3.00 cm thick, index 1.50. Over this there is a 10.0 cm depth of water, index 1.33. A point source of light lies in the lower surface of the glass base. Considering first the change in curvature of wave fronts proceeding from glass to water, then the further change from water to air, what is the apparent depth of the source below the top surface of the water to an observer looking down from above?

2. A lens has $r_1 = 10.0$ cm, $r_2 = -10.0$ cm, index of refraction 1.50, so that its power, on simple lens theory, is 10.0 diopters, its focal length 10.0 cm. A source point at -10.0 cm will be focused, on simple lens theory, at infinity. Treat the effect of the lens, one surface at a time, to determine the distance from the second surface to the image, for the following thicknesses of lens: (a) 1 mm (which gives a diameter for zero thickness of 2 cm), (b) 1.0 cm, (c) 10.0 cm.

3. Treating the goggles worn by divers as plane boundaries between water ($\mu = 1.33$) and air ($\mu = 1.00$), what curvatures of the incident wave front

in water will produce curvatures of 0 and -4.00 m^{-1} in air? What, then, are the far and near points of a normal eye, thus equipped, under water? (Note that a normal eye naked under water loses much of its focusing power and is unable to focus wave fronts of negative curvature.)

4. An underwater camera can be made using a thin meniscus lens that can be treated simply as the curved boundary between the water outside the camera and the air inside. Taking $\mu = 1.33$ for water and $\mu = 1.00$ for air, what is the radius of curvature of this lens if a distant source ($\mu = -\infty$) is to be focused at a distance of 30.0 cm ($v = 30.0$ cm)?

5. When objects at infinity are focused on the front of the retina, objects distant 6.00 m from the eye are focused at the back of the retina. Writing the lens relation for the eye, Equation (30.03), in the form

$$\frac{1.33}{v} = \frac{1}{u} + P$$

and setting $v = 20$ mm (to the front of the retina), what is the thickness of the retina?

6. Continuing from problem 5, if a new value of P is adopted so that an object at -6.00 m is focused on the front of the retina, what is the distance of an object focused on the back?

7. In line with problem 5, it would appear that the minimum perceptible change in curvature of the wave front incident at the eye is the change effected when the object-distance is moved from infinity to -6.00 m. How many changes in curvature of this amount occur as an object is brought from infinity to -0.25 m?

8. A nearsighted person has the normal 4.00 diopters of accommodation, but his far point is at -50 cm. Where is his near point?

9. A farsighted person has his near point at -40 cm. What power of lens will bring his near point to -25 cm?

10. What power of lens will bring the near point of a normal eye to -10 cm? Where will its far point be then?

11. Where are the far and near points of a normal eye when using a magnifier of focusing power 40 diopters?

12. What percentage increase in magnifying power can be achieved when using a magnifier of focusing power 30 diopters by bringing the image from infinity to -0.25 m?

13. A lens of focusing power 10 diopters, diameter 3.0 cm, is held 20 cm from the eye. A small object is held 5.0 cm beyond the lens. How far off the axis of the lens can the object be moved and still be seen?

14. Four masts, a, b, c, d, are arranged in a square, 0.1 mile to a side, a being due north of d and b due north of c. An observer sees c due north of him, with b hidden behind it. The angle between c and d is $2°$. How far away is he from c? What angle would he observe between d and a?

31

Illumination and
Optical Instruments

31.01 POWER OF RADIATION

Any form of wave propagation transmits energy in the direction of the wave motion. Electromagnetic radiation thus involves the transmission of energy through space, and we can consider the rate of this transmission as the power of the radiation. Thus when energy enters a tungsten lamp at a rate of 100 watts, 75% of the energy leaves as radiation. We say that there are 100 watts of electrical power entering the lamp, and 75 watts of radiant power or **radiant flux** leaving the lamp.

How much of this 75 watts falls on a book cover of area 20 × 30 cm lying 2 m from the lamp? This is typical of the sort of problem that arises in the field of illumination. (We shall take into account in a subsequent section the "luminosity" of the radiation—its effectiveness on the eye—which is a function of wavelength.) Similar problems arise in the field of acoustics, but the methods commonly employed in the two fields are different.

31.02 SOLID ANGLE

Illumination theory makes considerable use of solid angles. Any area A (of any shape) on the surface of a sphere of radius r subtends a solid angle of A/r^2 **steradians** at the center of the sphere. This may be taken as the definition of a solid angle, in the same way that an angle may be defined as the ratio of the length of an arc to the length of its radius of curvature. Since the area of a sphere is $4\pi r^2$, a whole sphere subtends a solid angle of 4π steradians at its center. You do not need a sphere in order to have a solid angle, of course, any more than you need a circle in order to have an angle. Small solid angles are readily evaluated. Sup-

577

pose a flat sheet of area A lies at a distance r from a point O, and lies normal to the radius vector r as in Figure 31.01.   If the linear dimensions of A are small in comparison with r, then the solid angle subtended at O by the sheet differs only slightly from that subtended by an area A on a sphere of radius r.   Calling the solid angle subtended by the small flat sheet ω, we have, approximately,

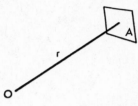

$$\omega = \frac{A}{r^2}$$

If the sheet is turned in any direction by an angle θ (so that the normal to its surface makes an angle θ with the line Or), then more generally

Fig. 31.01.   Area A normal to radius vector subtends a solid angle $\omega = A/r^2$ steradians.

$$\omega = \frac{A \cos \theta}{r^2} \qquad (31.01)$$

is the solid angle subtended by an area A at a point distant r, where θ is the angle from the normal to the surface to the radius vector, provided that the linear dimensions of A are small in comparison with r.   The product $A \cos \theta$ may be referred to as the projection of the area A in the direction of r.

31.03 THE CASE OF A SPHERICALLY UNIFORM SOURCE

Let us take as a source of light a small sphere of hot metal, emitting radiant flux P (watts) by virtue of its temperature.   We choose a spherical source so that we can assume that the flux emitted is distributed uniformly with direction over the total solid angle around the source of 4π steradians.   Thus the flux emitted per steradian is $P/(4\pi)$.   The amount of this flux intercepted by a flat sheet of area A at distance r is then

$$\frac{P}{4\pi} \times \frac{A \cos \theta}{r^2}$$

The flux emitted per steradian, which in the case of a spherical source is the same in all directions and equal to $P/(4\pi)$, is called the **radiant intensity**.   Multiplication of this quantity by the solid angle ω subtended by the sheet gives the flux intercepted by the sheet.   Thus denoting the radiant intensity from a spherical source by I_{rs}, we have

$$I_{rs} = \frac{P}{4\pi} \qquad (31.02)$$

and $$\text{Flux intercepted} = I_{rs}\omega \qquad (31.03)$$

where ω is the solid angle subtended at the source by the intercepting sheet.

31.04 THE CASE OF A SMALL FLAT SOURCE

The sun is a small spherical source.   It is small compared with the distance from it at which its light is considered.   The sun does not look like a sphere, but like a disk.   (One does not look at the sun in a clear sky except through a *dense* filter, many times more dense than "sun glasses", but everyone can recall the flat red disk of the sun when it is dimmed by

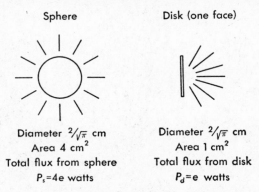

Sphere   Disk (one face)

Diameter $2/\sqrt{\pi}$ cm   Diameter $2/\sqrt{\pi}$ cm
Area 4 cm^2 Area 1 cm^2
Total flux from sphere   Total flux from disk
$P_s = 4e$ watts $P_d = e$ watts

Fig. 31.02.   Comparison of self-luminous disk of unit area with sphere of same diameter.

hazy or smoky air.)   The reason is that the radiant intensity in any direction is proportional to the projected area normal to that direction. The projection of a sphere in any plane is a disk of the same diameter; this provides us with a convenient lead in determining the radiant intensity for a small flat source.   In Figure 31.02 are shown a disk and sphere emitting the same flux per unit area.   The disk has been given unit area. The sphere has been given the same diameter as the disk and so has four times the area; its total emission of flux will be four times as great.   The radiant intensity of the disk, in the direction normal to its surface, is the same as that of the sphere in any direction:

$$I_{rd(\text{normal})} = I_{rs} = \frac{P_s}{4\pi} = \frac{P_d}{\pi}$$

For a direction making an angle ϕ with the normal, the projected area of the disk is reduced by $\cos \phi$, and so we can say more generally that

$$I_{rd} = \frac{P_d}{\pi} \cos \phi \qquad\qquad (31.04)$$

This relationship between radiant intensity and total flux emitted holds not only for a small flat disk but for any small flat element. And again, the word small is relative: The linear dimensions of the element should be small compared with the distance away from the source that is involved.

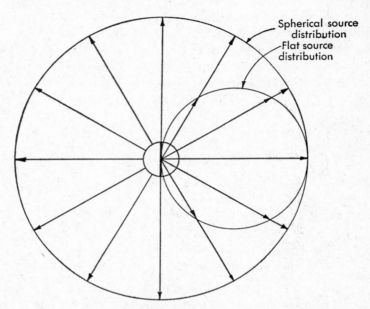

Fig. 31.03. Angular distribution of intensity for disk and for sphere of same diameter.

The radiant intensity of a small flat element, and its variation with direction, are compared in Figure 31.03 with the case of a sphere of four times the area.

31.05 LUMINOSITY

The effectiveness of power or flux of radiation on the eye cannot be measured simply in watts; the effectiveness on the eye of a flux of one watt will depend on the wavelength or, if more than one wavelength is involved, on the composition with wavelength, for the sensitivity of the eye varies with wavelength. A new quantity termed **luminous flux** is therefore set up, analogous to radiant flux except that its unit is a measure of eye-effectiveness. By changing the wavelength or wavelength-distribution, it is possible to change the luminous flux while keeping the radiant flux constant. The unit of luminous flux is the **lumen.** It is based on the performance of a standard candle, a candle made and burned according to definite specifications. *The luminous intensity of a standard candle in a horizontal direction is one lumen per steradian.* It has been found over the years that even with rigid specifications as to manufacture and use, actual standard candles do not give accurately reproducible results. The **new candle** adopted in the United States and the United Kingdom in 1948 is, in effect, a flat element of area $\frac{1}{60}$ cm² of a "black body" at the temperature of freezing platinum.

The eye is most sensitive at wavelength 0.5550 micron. At this wavelength (where the color sensation is green), each watt of radiant flux corresponds to a luminous flux of 685 lumens. Knowing this relationship and the distribution of power with wavelength for any source makes it possible to calculate for any source the lumens of luminous flux per watt of radiant flux. This ratio is called the **luminosity** of the source. Figure 31.04 shows the procedure. Part (a) is the distribution with wavelength of the radiant flux emitted by 1 cm² of "black body" at temperature 3500K. The value of the ordinate, multiplied by the width $\Delta\lambda$ of any narrow column (such as the one indicated) expressed in microns, gives the watts of radiant flux in the wavelength interval $\Delta\lambda$. This product is the area of the column. The total area under the curve (extending from less than 0.3 micron to much more than 0.7 micron) gives the total radiant flux emitted by the source, in watts.

Part (b) is the "standard luminosity curve". Using the left-hand scale of ordinates, it gives the sensitivity of the eye at any wavelength relative to its sensitivity at 0.5550 micron. The ratio of lumens to watts at this wavelength being known, an alternative scale of ordinates (the right-hand one) can be added, by which the figure gives lumens per watt at any wavelength.

Multiplying the watts per micron band of part (a) by the lumens per watt for the same wavelength from part (b), we obtain the lumens per micron band, part (c). Thus the area under the curve of part (c), between any wavelength limits, gives the lumens emitted by the source between those limits. The area under the whole curve gives the total lumens emitted by the source. The ratio of total lumens, from part (c), to total watts, from part (a), gives the luminosity of this particular source.

The luminosity of a black body is plotted against its temperature in Figure 31.05. The values are all well below the 685 lumens per watt that would be achieved by a source emitting radiation only at the wavelength to which the eye is most sensitive, although it should be noted that

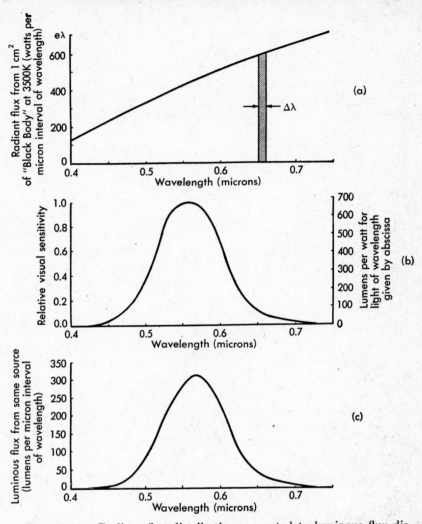

Fig. 31.04. Radiant flux distribution converted to luminous flux distribution by multiplying ordinates by those of standard luminosity curve.

everything seen by such a source would be either green or black. An incandescent lamp consuming 100 watts of electrical power sends out about 75 watts of radiant flux, about 1500 lumens of luminous flux, for a luminosity of 20 lumens per watt. The same number of lumens can be obtained from a fluorescent lamp of considerably greater physical size, but consuming only 30 watts of electrical power.

It needs to be borne in mind that when we refer to a lumen as effective power, we mean effective to the eye. In dealing with ultraviolet radiation and its effect on the skin, the use of the lumen as a unit is quite pointless. Similarly, in the use of a photocell, say in an electric-eye system for opening a door, there is no place for the response curve of the eye, or for the lumen. (Measuring instruments used in illumination studies employ photocells, but are designed to have response curves similar to that for the eye, and the lumen is the obvious unit.) Photographic films have

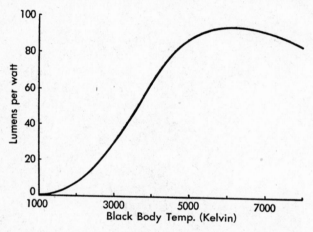

Fig. 31.05. Luminosity of a black body as a function of temperature.

response curves resembling those of the eye only in a general fashion, and the introduction of lumens is scarcely justified. Consequently, there is a trend toward the description of the behavior of radiation-sensitive surfaces, other than that of the eye, in watts and response curves, rather than in a system involving lumens. When the eye is involved directly, so are lumens.

31.06 DIFFUSION AND ABSORPTION

At the smooth boundary between regions differing in index of refraction, some light is transmitted and some reflected. The transmission and reflection are **specular,** meaning essentially that they obey the laws $\sin i = \mu \sin r$ and $i = r$. In these phenomena, there is one specific direction of transmission, one of reflection, for each angle of incidence. Polished metal surfaces also provide specular reflection. Consider now a sheet of white paper. It reflects light, in the sense that it returns light to the incident side of the paper, but the direction of the reflected light is no longer specifically related to the direction of the incident light: The reflection is nonspecular or **diffuse**. A thin sheet of paper may also transmit some light, in the sense that light emerges from the far side of the paper, but again the direction of the emergent light is not specifically related to the direction of the incident light. The transmission, too, is diffuse.

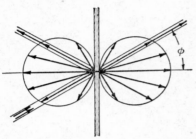

Referring to Figure 31.06, let us list all the things that may happen when a parallel beam of light strikes a thin sheet of material, say ground glass (where the diffusing occurs at the surface of the glass) or opal glass (where the diffusing occurs throughout the depth of the sheet).

Fig. 31.06. Specular and diffuse transmission and reflection of a parallel beam of light by a thin sheet.

T_s: *Specular Transmission*. Some of the light may be transmitted straight ahead, or bent as by a lens.

T_d: *Diffuse Transmission*. Some of the light may be transmitted, but spread out continuously with direction. The simplest assumption about the spread-out light is that the illuminated patch of the screen itself acts as a flat source, so that its luminous intensity varies with $\cos \phi$ just as it would for a primary source.

R_s: *Specular Reflection*. Some of the light may be reflected according to the law (angle of reflection equals angle of incidence) already developed.

R_d: *Diffuse Reflection*. Some of the light may be thrown back to the side of the screen from which it came, but in all directions, like T_d. Again we can assume the illuminated patch of screen to be a source, varying with direction according to a cosine law.

A: *Absorption*. Finally, some of the light may be absorbed in the screen.

Taking the symbols used above as coefficients denoting the fraction of the incident light going each way, we can say that the sum of the coefficients should be unity:

$$T_s + T_d + R_s + R_d + A = 1 \tag{31.05}$$

In setting up this relationship, we considered "a thin diffusing sheet". It is applicable to a thin sheet of just about anything. The pattern on a photographic negative consists of variations in T_s and A; while the values for the diffuse coefficients are relatively small. The white paper of a book must have a high value for R_d, reduced by the black ink to a negligible value. Its T_d will be smaller, but not negligible. If the paper is coated, its R_s will be appreciable; the paper will serve as a low-grade mirror, producing virtual images of concentrated light surfaces. Care must be taken in reading from coated or glossy paper, then, that no such **glare** images fall in the field of view.

In devising projection screens for slide and film projectors, a sheet having a high R_s is chosen, so that most of the light from the projector is thrown back at the audience. If the hall is wide, so that some of the viewers are observing the screen obliquely, a **matte** surface obeying the cosine law for diffuse reflection is chosen. If the hall is narrow, so that all viewers are within an angle of 30°, say, from the normal to the screen, a surface covered with tiny glass beads may be used, so that the diffusely reflected light is concentrated in a narrower angle. A brighter picture is thus achieved for viewers at small angles; the picture viewed obliquely, say from an angle of 45° to the normal, is correspondingly less bright.

All five of the coefficients may vary with the wavelength. Consideration of them as functions of wavelength permits the complete description of colored materials.

31.07 PHOTOGRAPHIC EMULSIONS

To make photographic films and papers, light-sensitive chemicals are suspended as an emulsion in transparent gelatin, which is then applied as a thin coating either to a transparent plastic sheet (to produce "film") or to white paper. In a camera, an image is formed on a flat sheet of film, and a photochemical reaction takes place in the emulsion. The amount of such reaction is a function of the product

Flux per unit area × time of exposure

This product is known as the **exposure.** Subsequent chemical processing results in a blackening of the film which also varies with the exposure. The amount of such blackening can be described by the transmission coefficient T_s of the processed film, or more conveniently by the **density,** which for film is defined as

$$D = - \log T_s \tag{31.06}$$

The sort of relationship achieved between exposure and density is shown in Figure 31.07(a). The slope of the approximately straight-line portion of the curve is called γ (gamma). Choice of emulsion, processing chemicals, and processing time permits any value of gamma up to about five.

The processed film from the camera, called a **negative,** has thus great density and small transmission coefficient where the flux per unit area was great. If now light is shone through the negative onto another sheet of film, a **transparent positive** is formed. The transmission coefficient of

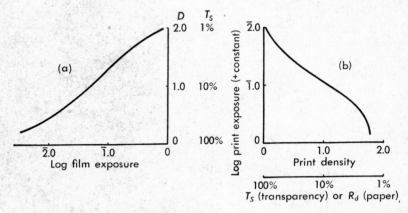

Fig. 31.07. Characteristic curves of negative film (a) and positive print (b). The usual unit of exposure is the meter-candle-second, equal to one lumen meter^{-2} second.

the positive is great where the flux per unit area within the camera was great. When the positive is inserted in a projector, the projected picture resembles the scene observed by the camera. Similarly, if paper instead of film is used, to produce an **opaque positive,** the coefficient of diffuse reflection of the positive is great where the flux per unit area within the camera was great, and the picture on the paper print resembles the scene observed by the camera. For paper, density is defined as

$$D = -\log R_d \qquad (31.07)$$

The relationship of the positive-printing process to the negative is shown in Figure 31.07(b). The use of $\gamma = 1$ in both processes, or some equivalent combination of gammas, should reproduce the original scene with fidelity. It should be noted, however, that the smallest value of R_d that can be achieved in an opaque print is not much less than 1%, and so the range of intensities that can be reproduced in an opaque print is limited.

31.08 CONCENTRATION OF FLUX AT A REAL IMAGE

Let us take as object a small flat surface of area A, on the axis of the lens and normal to the axis (Figure 31.08), and compare the flux per unit area at the image with that falling on the object. Let the diffuse

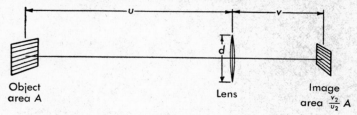

Fig. 31.08. Two-dimensional object and image for camera considerations.

reflectivity of the object be R_d and the flux per unit area falling on it be E (watts cm^{-2}). Then

$$\text{Flux leaving object} = EAR_d \qquad \text{(watts)} \qquad (31.08)$$

Radiant intensity of object in direction of lens

$$= \frac{EAR_d}{\pi} \qquad \text{(watts per steradian)}$$

Solid angle subtended by lens of diameter d at object

$$= \frac{\pi d^2}{4u^2} \qquad \text{(steradians)}$$

Flux intercepted by lens

$$= \frac{EAR_d}{\pi} \times \frac{\pi d^2}{4u^2} \qquad \text{(watts)}$$

Flux passing through lens of transmission coef. T_s to form image

$$= \frac{EAR_d d^2 T_s}{4u^2} \qquad \text{(watts)} \qquad (31.09)$$

Applying the magnification v/u to both linear dimensions of the object, we find

$$\text{Area of image} = \frac{v^2 A}{u^2}$$

Therefore

$$\text{Flux per unit area at image} = \frac{EAR_d d^2 T_s}{4u^2} \times \frac{u^2}{v^2 A}$$

$$= \frac{ER_d T_s}{4 \left(\dfrac{v}{d} \right)^2}. \qquad (31.10)$$

31.09 EXPOSURE TIME FOR A CAMERA

Photographic film requires a certain exposure, just how much depending upon the type of film, where

$$\text{Exposure} = \text{flux per unit area} \times \text{time of exposure} \qquad (31.11)$$

as described in section 31.07.   Thus

$$\text{Required time of exposure} = \frac{\text{required exposure}}{\text{flux per unit area}} \qquad (31.12)$$

If, as is usually the case in using a camera, $|u| \gg v$, we can take $v = f$ as a fair approximation.   Then

$$\text{Flux per unit area} = \frac{ER_d T_s}{4 \left(\dfrac{f}{d}\right)^2}$$

and

$$\text{Required time of exposure} = \text{required exposure} \times \frac{4 \left(\dfrac{f}{d}\right)^2}{ER_d T_s} \qquad (31.13)$$

The required exposure time is thus independent of the distance away of the object. If the lens is a simple one, the coefficient of specular transmission will be almost unity.   If it is a complicated one with many air-to-glass interfaces, T_s may be considerably less than unity, but may be brought back close to unity by applying nonreflecting coatings to the glass surfaces. In any case,

$$\text{Required time of exposure} \propto \left(\frac{f}{d}\right)^2 \qquad (31.14)$$

By using a lens of short focal length, forming a correspondingly small image on the film, a lens of proportionately small diameter may be used.

31.10 CALIBRATION OF LENS APERTURE

The size of aperture or lens-opening on a camera is usually adjustable, and the adjustment is usually marked in diameter as a function of focal length, as for instance $f/3.5$.   The oblique stroke following the f is important, for "$f/3.5$" means $d = f/3.5$, where f is the focal length, so that $f/d = 3.5$ and $(f/d)^2 = (3.5)^2$.   It is unfortunate that the power of 2 appearing in equation (31.14) is not taken into account in this scheme of aperture calibration, for it leaves the photographer with the work of squaring the value of f/d. Thus if at $f/3.5$ the required time of exposure is 1 sec, then at $f/7$ it will be $2^2 \times 1$ or 4 sec.

In Table 31.01, a series of possible exposure times is given, each one twice as long as the former. For each, values of f/d and d are given that will lead to the same total exposure. The f-numbers are seen to increase as the square root of the relative times of exposure. Cheap camera lenses have maximum diameters of about $f/11$. Larger values of d/f require careful lens corrections. They are more readily achieved for small values of f. Regardless of the size of f, it is extremely difficult to achieve $d = f$.

TABLE 31.01.

d Aperture diameter, as a function of focal length f, as given on camera	f/d Sometimes referred to as f-number	$(f/d)^2$ Relative exposure time (see eq. 31.14)
$f/1$	1.0	1
$f/1.4$	1.4	2
$f/2.0$	2.0	4
$f/2.8$	2.8	8
$f/4$	4.0	16
$f/5.6$	5.6	32
$f/8$	8.0	64
$f/11$	11	128
$f/16$	16	256
$f/22$	22	512
$f/32$	32	1024
$f/45$	45	2048
$f/64$	64	4096

31.11 FOCUSING SCALE AND DEPTH OF FIELD

To photograph an object at distance u so as to obtain the sharpest possible image on the film, it is necessary that the distance from the lens to the film be v, where

$$\frac{1}{v} = \frac{1}{u} + \frac{1}{f} = \frac{f + u}{uf}$$

so that

$$v - f = \frac{-f^2}{f + u} \tag{31.15}$$

and as long as f is negligible as a term added to u,

$$v - f \simeq \frac{-f^2}{u} \tag{31.16}$$

In order to obtain this sharpest possible focus, v is made adjustable, and a focusing scale, resembling the lowest scale of Figure 31.09(a), is installed, calibrated in object-distances from infinity down to about 1 m. For $u = -\infty$, of course, $v - f = 0$. For $u = -2$ m, and $f = 10$ cm, the value of $v - f$ is 0.5 cm by equation (31.16), and $v - f$ varies as the square of the focal length.

Suppose now that with the film at distance v behind the lens, light enters the camera from a source point at more or less than the chosen value of u, and so converges on a point distant $v + \Delta v$ from the lens, Fig. 31.09(a). This light will form a small disk on the film, called a **circle of confusion**. Denoting the diameter of this disk by c and the diameter of the lens opening by d, we have

$$\frac{c}{d} = \frac{|\Delta v|}{v + \Delta v} \simeq \frac{|\Delta v|}{v} \tag{31.17}$$

Provided that v never differs from f by more than a few per cent, we can approximate further and write

$$\frac{c}{d} \simeq \frac{|\Delta v|}{f}$$

or

$$|\Delta v| \simeq \frac{f}{d} c \tag{31.18}$$

If we establish a maximum acceptable value for c, this relation can be used to determine the maximum acceptable value of $|\Delta v|$ (or of $\Delta|v - f|$, which is the same thing). For a fairer comparison of lenses of different focal lengths, we adopt instead a maximum acceptable value of c/f, since negative films having the same value of c/f will all give the same size of circle of confusion when enlarged to a standard size.   Then

$$|\Delta v| \simeq f \frac{f}{d} \frac{c}{f}$$

Since the quantity related to the object-distance u by equation (31.16) is $(v - f)/f^2$, we can conveniently rewrite this statement as

$$\frac{\Delta|v - f|}{f^2} = \frac{1}{f} \frac{f}{d} \frac{c}{f} \tag{31.19}$$

The size of this increment is compared in Figure 31.09(b) with the focusing scale established by equation (31.16).   Loci have been drawn for various focal lengths, all for $c/f = 10^{-3}$. This value of c/f is frequently adopted for good miniature and cine cameras.   For commercial and copying work, a value of 2 minutes of arc or 1/1720 is frequently used.   If the increment in $(v - f)/f^2$ is transposed to any part of the related reciprocal scale of u, it will give the range of acceptable focus in either direction from the chosen

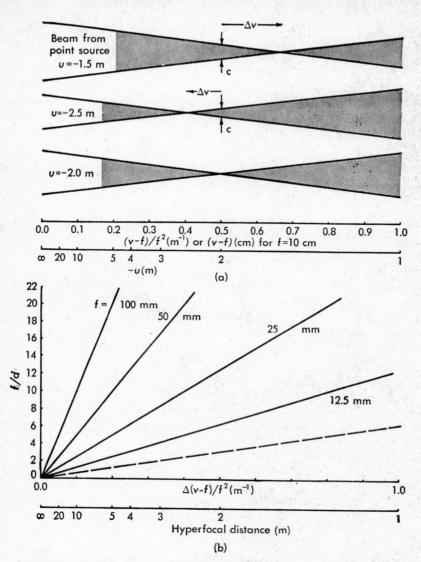

Fig. 31.09. In part (a), the diameter of the circle of confusion is denoted by c, for $u = -1.5$ m and $u = -2.5$ m, camera focused at $u = -2$ m. Part (b) gives $\Delta|v - f|/f^2$ for any f/d, for selected values of f, for $c = 10^{-3}f$. Transfer of this increment to any point on the reciprocal scale of u permits calculation of depth of field for any value of u.

value of u.   The distance from the near to the far limit of this range is known as the **depth of field**.   The value of u for which the acceptable focus extends to infinity is known as the **hyperfocal distance**.   The near limit of the range of acceptable focus then lies at just half the hyperfocal distance.

For small values of u, the depth of field is very small and increases as u^2.   As for variation with focal length and aperture, it can be seen from equation (31.19) that for a given c/f the quantity $\Delta|v - f|/f^2$ is (a) proportional to f/d when f is fixed, and (b) inversely proportional to f when f/d is fixed.   Item (a) indicates that when f/d is reduced in order to reduce the exposure time, depth of field is reduced, and increased care is required in focussing the camera.   Item (b) indicates that the choice of a lens of short focal length offers greater depth of field.   The pictures obtained are small, but even when they are enlarged to a standard size their depth of field is greater than if they had been taken with a lens of greater focal length.

By making f and/or f/d small, it is possible to design a fixed-focus camera that will give tolerable focus from infinity in to an acceptable minimum distance.   Thus a lens of focal length 50 mm and $d = f/10$ will meet the specification we have set from infinity to $2\frac{1}{2}$ m; with the lenses of focal length 12.5 mm that are used with 8 mm cine film, this same performance can be obtained at $d = f/2.5$.

31.12 PROJECTORS

The projection of large images of opaque pictures, say pictures in a book, is much to be desired; however, although this is a simple process,

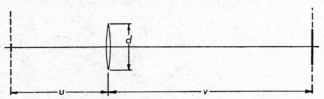

Fig. 31.10.   Schematic diagram of simplest projector.

it has severe limitations because so little of the flux diffusely reflected by the "object" is intercepted by the lens.   If an element of the picture on the axis of the lens (Figure 31.10) reflects flux L, its radiant intensity in the direction of the lens is L/π, and the lens intercepts flux

$$\frac{L}{\pi} \times \frac{\frac{\pi d^2}{4}}{u^2} = \frac{d^2}{4u^2} L$$

The image distance v is usually great compared with u in this case, so that $u \simeq f$. Even if there is no transmission loss in the lens,

Fraction of light from object going to form image

$$= \frac{1}{4}\left(\frac{d}{u}\right)^2 \simeq \frac{1}{4\left(\frac{f}{d}\right)^2} \quad (31.20)$$

Since the object-pictures to be projected tend to be large, compared with lantern slides or motion pictures, f must be about 20 in., and $d = f/4.5$ is

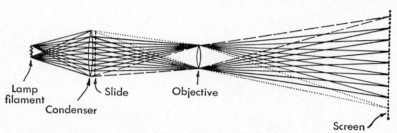

Fig. 31.11. Double-lens system of slide or film projector.

about as large a lens as can be hoped for. Thus the fraction of light utilized is not likely to exceed one part in eighty. Incidentally, the system as drawn in Figure 31.10 would show the picture backward. This difficulty is met by inserting a front-surfaced plane mirror into the optical system.

If lantern slides and motion-picture films were diffusing screens rather than transparencies, projection from them would have the same inherent inefficiency as projection from opacities. With transparencies, however, a system can be devised in which practically all the light passing through the slide or object-picture goes on to form the image. In Figure 31.11, the objective forms an image of the slide on the screen, while the condenser, somewhat larger than the slide, forms an image of the filament of the lamp on the objective. Light from every point on the filament is distributed uniformly over the screen; beams have been drawn for the extreme points of the filament. All the light that passes through the slide reaches the screen. The pattern on the slide is reproduced in reverse on the screen, for, as the figure shows, all the light from the topmost point on the slide goes to the lowest point on the screen, and all the light from the lowest point on the slide goes to the topmost point on the screen. Indeed, as with the opaque projector, light from each point on the slide goes to a corresponding image point on the screen. The difference is that light from any point on the slide spreads out, not in all directions, but in a narrow cone contained by the objective. The primary condition is that the objective should have sufficient area to contain the whole image of the filament. It is also necessary that the condenser lens or system of condenser lenses illuminate the slide uniformly and be reasonably achromatic. If a smaller slide were placed halfway between the condenser and the objective, it would not be uniformly illuminated, for a blurred but appreciable pattern of the filament would fall on it and be reproduced on the screen.

The total radiant flux arriving at the slide may amount to more than 100 watts and, particularly if the slide is dark or deeply colored, an appreciable fraction of this radiation may be absorbed and heat the slide. This heating is frequently reduced by inserting in the condenser-lens system a sheet or lens of heat-absorbing glass which removes a large percentage of the infrared radiation to which the eye is insensitive and a relatively small proportion of the radiation at visible wavelengths.

The lens system described here is the basis of those in both slide and motion-picture projectors, the aperture at the condenser lens ranging from a few millimeters for the smallest motion-picture film to 25 cm for the sort of projector used in place of blackboards, where the lecturer writes on the slide while it is in place.

31.13 THE COMPOUND MICROSCOPE

The greatest magnifying power that can be built into the single unit of a magnifier is not much over 10. Even that calls for a lens of focusing power 40 diopters. A greater magnifying power can be obtained by using a lens of high positive focusing power, B, Figure 31.12, to form an enlarged real image C, then using a magnifier D as an aid in viewing this enlarged image. The system is called a **compound microscope;** the first lens B is called the **objective** and the magnifier is called the **eyepiece.** The magnifying power (M.P.) exceeds that of the eyepiece alone by a factor v_1/u_1, the magnification produced by the objective. Thus

M.P. of compound microscope
$$= \frac{|v_1|}{|u_1|} \times \frac{0.25 \text{ m}}{|u_2|}$$
$$= \text{magnification of objective} \times \text{M.P. of eyepiece} \quad (31.21)$$

The magnification of the objective v_1/u_1 ranges in actual microscopes from 3 to 100, while the magnifying power of the eyepiece ranges from 3 to 10. The two factors multiplied together thus give an over-all magnifying

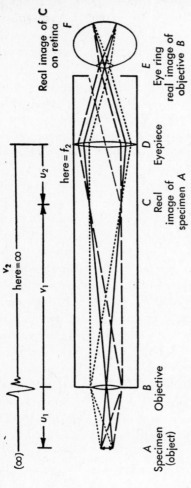

Fig. 31.12. Compound Microscope.

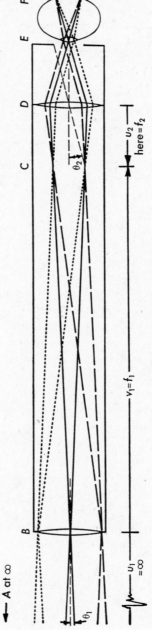

Fig. 31.13. Telescope.

595

power ranging from $3 \times 3 = 9$ to $100 \times 10 = 1000$. A microscope usually possesses a choice of objectives and a choice of eyepieces, so that the one instrument offers a choice of several magnifying powers covering this wide range.

Figure 31.12 has been drawn for the object-distance u_2 of the eyepiece equal to its focal length; thus the virtual image is at infinity, parallel rays emerge, and the eye is focused for infinity. It is permissible to decrease u_2 until v_2 is reduced to -0.25 m. The increase in magnifying power thus achieved is not large enough to be important; in normal practice any value of v_2 between $-\infty$ and -0.25 m is acceptable.

Light from each point of the real image C remains concentrated in a small cone as it proceeds toward the eyepiece. The use of a magnifier as an eyepiece for viewing this real image therefore differs somewhat from its use for the direct viewing of a small object, in which case light would be spreading out in all directions. If in Figure 31.12 one follows the pair of rays from the top of the objective and the pair of rays from the bottom of the objective, one finds that the members of these pairs intersect at E. A real image *of the objective*, then, is formed at E, and all the light emerging from the objective and passing through eyepiece C passes through this real image of the objective at E. This real image is called the **eye ring.** If the pupil of the eye is located at the eye ring, it will collect light from every point on the image C and so from every point on the specimen A. Since the eye ring is the real image of the objective, increasing the size of the objective increases that of the eye ring. Until the eye ring becomes equal in size to the pupil of the eye, increasing the size of the objective increases the amount of light entering the eye and so increases the flux per unit area at the retina.

The lens system of a microscope of good quality is more complex than the basic system shown here. The objective possesses several separate components; a high-power objective may have a focal length as small as 2 mm and subtend a large angle at the specimen. The eyepiece will usually be a combination of two separated lenses, providing greatly reduced spherical and achromatic aberration and bringing the eye ring much closer to the final lens.

31.14 THE TELESCOPE

The angle subtended at the eye, and so the size of the retinal image, can be increased for objects at a distance by the use of a **telescope** (Figure 31.13). The optical system is similar to that of a compound microscope, in that an objective forms a real image, and the eye observes this real image at close range through an eyepiece. Telescope objectives are lenses of great focal length; the object-distance tends to be great compared with this focal length in turn, so that the image-distance is very nearly the focal length. Since telescope objectives have greater image-distances than microscopes, they must have proportionately larger diameter to provide the same diameter of eye ring.

The magnifying power of a telescope, like that of a microscope, is the ratio of the sizes of the retinal image with and without the instrument. In the case of the telescope, however, it would not be in order to use the case of object at 0.25 m as a standard of comparison, so the definition reduces to

$$\text{M.P. of telescope} = \frac{\text{angle subtended at aided eye}}{\text{angle subtended at naked eye}} \quad (31.22)$$

The angle that would be subtended at the naked eye is the same as the angle θ_1 subtended at the objective (Figure 31.13), and the angle subtended at the eye in Figure 31.13 is the angle subtended at the eyepiece θ_2. Denoting the linear size of the real image at C by i, we have

$$\theta_1 = \frac{i}{|v_1|}, \qquad \theta_2 = \frac{i}{|u_2|}$$

$$\text{M.P.} = \frac{\theta_2}{\theta_1} = \frac{|v_1|}{|u_2|}$$

If the object is distant so that $|v_1| = f_1$, and the eyepiece is so adjusted that $|u_2| = f_2$, then

$$\text{M.P. of telescope} = \frac{\text{focal length of objective}}{\text{focal length of eyepiece}} \quad (31.23)$$

As with a microscope, the flux per unit area at the retina increases as the diameter of the objective is increased until when the diameter of the eye ring equals that of the pupil a maximum value is reached. This maximum value is equal to that which would exist (with a much smaller image) for the naked eye. In daylight, the diameter of the pupil is about 2 to $2\frac{1}{4}$ mm. Telescopes or binoculars designed for use in good light will provide an eye-ring diameter of 3 or 4 mm to give an adequate margin over this pupil diameter. In dim light the diameter of the pupil increases to 5 mm or more, and "night glasses" for use in dim light have eye-ring diameters as high as 7 mm. In good light, their performance will be no better than those of glasses with smaller objectives and correspondingly smaller eye rings, but in dim light a marked improvement can be noted.

In a good practical telescope, the objective is an achromatic combination, and the real image at C is viewed through an eyepiece having two separate components. An erect image may be obtained by incorporating a set of erecting lenses; this increases the over-all length of the instrument. In the **Galilean** type of telescope commonly used in opera glasses, a single lens of negative power is used as an eyepiece, placed at a distance from the objective less than f_1, so that the real image C is not formed. This has advantages in that the over-all length of the instrument is reduced, while at the same time the image viewed by the eye is erect. The field of view is limited, however, and the quality is not of the highest.

In telescopes used in surveying, a diaphragm approximately at C supports a **graticule** or array of fine lines: either filaments of spider web or lines ruled on a thin glass plate. The point of intersection of two diametric lines is useful in establishing the axis of the system, and two parallel horizontal lines, one above and one below the center, are used in the stadia system of measuring distances.

31.15 SPECTROMETER

Light may be sorted out according to its wavelength by passing it through a prism, or, as we shall see later, through a diffraction grating. It is desirable that the light should arrive at the prism (or the grating) in a parallel beam. To produce a parallel beam, a **collimator** is used (Figure 31.14), consisting of a narrow slit at the principal focus of a lens of positive power. When a concentrated source of light is placed behind the slit, the beam of light projected from the lens of the collimator is a parallel one, assuming that the width of the slit is negligible.

With a parallel beam, the angle of incidence on the first surface of the prism is the same for all the light, and so all light of a given wavelength is turned through the same angle of deviation. Thus when the light emerges from the prism it has been sorted according to wavelength: Each wavelength has its own direction. On the emergent side of the prism, a telescope receives the parallel beams. Each direction of the light entering the telescope is brought to a focus at a different point on the focal plane of the objective, so that by looking through the eyepiece, the spectrum of the light can be observed as a series of images, in light of different wavelengths, of the slit of the collimator.

The prism is mounted on a turntable. The telescope is mounted in a bracket that can be rotated about the same axis as the turntable. To measure the angle of deviation for a given spectral line (identified by its color and its relationship to the other lines observed), the telescope bracket is rotated until that line is imaged on the axis of the objective (as indicated by cross hairs in the telescope), and the angle of deviation is read from an engraved bearing circle.

Since the slit of the collimator has finite width, light emerges from the lens of the collimator over a small range of angles rather than in a single

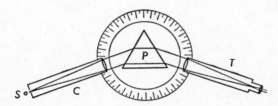

Fig. 31.14. Spectroscope, consisting of source S, collimator C, prism P, telescope T. Angles are read from a bearing circle around the turntable on which the prism is mounted.

perfectly parallel beam. It is therefore desirable that the deviation produced by the prism should be insensitive to small differences in angle of incidence. As noted in section 28.05, this requirement is met when the angle of incidence is chosen to give minimum deviation, in which case the light passes symmetrically through the prism, i.e., parallel to its base.

Having rotated the prism to the position of minimum deviation, one can calibrate the prism. The resultant plot of deviation against wavelength is not simple, involving as it does the variation with wavelength of the index of refraction that is discussed in Chapter 28 under the heading of "Dispersion". Therein lies an advantage of the diffraction grating; the relationship between angle and wavelength when it is used in place of a prism is a function of geometry and does not involve the physical properties of any substance in any such direct fashion.

A **spectrograph** records the spectrum on a photographic plate; the spectrometer of Figure 31.14 could be converted to a spectrograph by removing the eyepiece of the telescope and placing a plate with its emulsion-coated surface in the focal plane of the telescope objective, thus converting the telescope to a camera.

PROBLEMS

1. A room is 15.0 ft wide.   One wall contains a window 2.0 ft across by 3.0 ft high, its bottom edge 4.0 ft above the floor.   (a) What solid angle does the window subtend at a point on the opposite wall, directly across from the window and 5.5 ft off the floor?   (b) What solid angle does the window subtend at a point on the opposite wall, directly across from the window but at floor level?

2. A sheet of paper 8.5 in. × 11 in. lies on a tabletop, 4.0 ft directly under a small lamp.   What solid angle does the sheet subtend at the lamp?   A second sheet lies on a similar tabletop and is distant horizontally from the first sheet by 6.0 ft.   What angle does it subtend at the lamp?

3. If the lamp of problem 2 is a spherically uniform source, emitting a total radiant flux of 60 watts, what radiant flux is intercepted by each sheet of paper?

4. What is the radiant intensity of a small flat source emitting a total of 500 watts, in a direction making an angle of 60° with the normal to the plane of the source?   What would be the total emission, in watts, of a spherically uniform source providing this radiant intensity?

5. Plot the radiant intensity of a small flat source emitting a total flux of 100 watts, against angle from the normal to the plane of the source, using rectangular coordinates, from 0° to 90°.

6. What percentage increase in luminosity is achieved by raising the temperature of a black body from 3000K to 3100K?   (See Figure 31.05.)

7. A reader finds the illumination of his book satisfactory when the book is lying on a flat tabletop 5.0 ft directly below a 100-watt tungsten lamp. If the lamp emits a total radiant flux of 75 watts, has a luminosity of 20 lumens per watt, and is assumed to be a spherically uniform source, how many lumens per square foot are falling on the book?

8. How many lumens per square foot fall on a horizontal tabletop, due to a small (1 ft²) flat source of 3000 lumens let into the ceiling, 6.0 ft above the tabletop, (a) if the source is directly above the tabletop, (b) if the source is displaced horizontally by 6.0 ft?

9. A small flat source of 2000 lumens is let into the wall of a room, 8.0 ft above point p on the floor.   What luminous flux is intercepted by a map of area 3.0 ft² lying on the floor at point q, where qp is 12.0 ft and normal to the wall?

10. A beam of 1000 lumens is projected onto a sheet of tracing paper, illuminating a small patch of the paper (a circle, say, of diameter 10 cm).   The specular transmission of the paper is zero, the diffuse transmission 30%.   What flux will fall on a card 5.0 cm × 8.0 cm held 60 cm straight out from the illuminated patch, so that the line joining patch and card is normal to both?

11. A camera with lens of focal length 5.0 cm is used (at $d = f/4.5$) to photograph some flowers from a distance of 2.00 m (so that $v \simeq f$), and it is found that an exposure time of 0.040 sec is required. Then the camera is moved closer, so that its lens is 30.0 cm from the flowers. What are the two image distances, and what exposure time will be needed in the second case?

12. After a satisfactory exposure has been obtained with a camera with aperture setting $f/5.6$, exposure time $\frac{1}{25}$ sec, it is desired to repeat the picture at exposure time $\frac{1}{100}$ sec, without changing the illumination. What new aperture should be used?

13. A motion-picture camera takes pictures at 8, 16, 24, 32 frames per second, and the exposure time is inversely proportional to the frames per second. If aperture setting $f/8$ is correct at 8 frames per second, what are the correct settings at the other speeds?

14. If a circle of confusion of (focal length)/1000 is acceptable, what is the depth of focus at object-distance 2.00 m with aperture setting $f/3.5$, with lenses of focal length (a) 100 mm, (b) 25 mm?

15. Repeat problem 14 for aperture setting $f/11$.

16. If the required exposure time at $f/3.5$ is 0.010 sec, what will it be at $f/11$?

17. What focal length of lens is required to project an image 6.0 ft × 6.0 ft on a screen 20.0 ft from the lens of an opaque picture 6.0 in. × 6.0 in.? If the lens has a 3.0-in. diameter, what fraction of the light diffusely reflected by the picture will go through the lens to form the image?

18. A photographic enlarger may have a condenser lens like that of a projector, so that all the light transmitted by the negative passes through the objective and goes to form an image on the photographic paper. Suppose that such a system is used, and with aperture $f/4.5$ is found to require the rather short time of exposure of 1.0 sec. Such a system shows up scratches on the film rather badly, and so it is decided to insert immediately behind the negative a diffusing screen whose specular transmission is zero and diffuse transmission 30%. What time of exposure will then be required?

19. Referring back to section 29.11, what focal length is required in a lens to project an image, 9.0 ft × 12.0 ft on a screen 60 ft away, of a slide 3.0 in. × 4.0 in.?

20. The image-distance of the objective of a compound microscope is 10 cm. The magnifying power of the eyepiece (focused for image at infinity) is 10. What diameter of objective is required to give an eye-ring diameter of 3.0 mm?

21. A pair of binocular telescopes has magnifying powers of 8 times and objectives of diameter 30 mm (and so is labeled 8 × 30). What is the diameter of the eye rings?

22. What diameter of telescope objective is required to give (a) an eye ring of 3.0 mm at magnifying power 4 times, (b) an eye ring of 7.0 mm at magnifying power 12 times?

32

Diffraction, Interference, and Polarization

32.01 DIFFRACTION

Diffraction phenomena are essentially the same for electromagnetic waves as for sound waves. Thus the diagrams and relations developed for sound waves are applicable to radio waves. Short radio waves such as used in radar have much the same wavelengths as audible sound waves, so that even the scale of the patterns is similar. The phenomena are essentially the same for light waves too, but these electromagnetic waves are shorter than radar waves and sound waves by a factor of about a million, and as a result the manner of observing the pattern tends to be different. Thus in dealing with sound waves, the aperture of a loudspeaker will not be more than a few wavelengths in diameter. The diameter of a radar antenna is somewhat greater than this, but rarely more than one hundred wavelengths in diameter. Apertures in optical systems, on the other hand, are very rarely less than one hundred times the wavelength. The wavelength of light waves is only of the order of 0.5 micron, and in optics apertures as small as $100 \times 0.5 = 50$ microns are uncommon except in devices such as diffraction gratings designed to make use of the phenomenon. Nevertheless, diffraction is important in optical instruments, both as an ultimate limit to the performance of instruments of considerable aperture and as the physical basis of wavelength-measuring devices.

32.02 THE PINHOLE CAMERA

Quite acceptable photographs can be taken by a camera having a small aperture and no lens at all. No focusing is required, but the image of a point source at any image-distance is a circle somewhat larger than the aperture. By decreasing the aperture we decrease the image-circle and increase the required time of exposure. Diffraction provides a limit to the decrease in the image-circle that can be achieved in this way, however. Suppose the light comes from a distant point source, so that all the light arriving at the aperture is traveling in the same direction; then some of the light proceeding from the aperture into the camera will change direction somewhat, as part of the diffraction pattern, so that there is a spreading-out of the beam within the camera. If the diameter of the aperture is equal to many wavelengths, the spreading-out is slight, so that unless the distance traveled within the camera is great, the diameter of the image-circle is equal to that of the aperture. If at the other extreme the diameter of the aperture equals very few wavelengths, the spreading-out of the light will be considerable, like the spreading-out of sound from a loudspeaker,

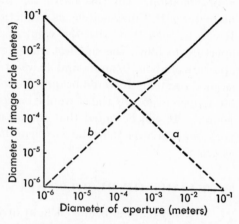

Fig. 32.01. Diameter of circle of confusion in pinhole camera of image-distance 10 cm, being the sum of a, diameter of central spot of diffraction pattern, and b, diameter of aperture.

and when the light from a point source falls on the film at the back of the camera, it will form on the film a cross section of the diffraction pattern. Even the central maximum of the pattern will be broad compared with the aperture.

The diffraction pattern resulting when plane wave fronts passed through a small aperture in a plane parallel to the wave fronts was discussed in section 24.11. The intensity is maximum along the axis of the aperture, and for a circular aperture of diameter d, equation (24.27), it drops to zero at an angle $1.22\lambda/d$. At greater angles the intensity rises and falls through a series of secondary maxima, all much smaller than the central maximum. On the cross section of the diffraction pattern recorded on the film of the pinhole camera, then, the distance from the center of the pattern to the first minimum is $l \times 1.22\lambda/d$, where l is the distance from the pinhole to film and d is the diameter of the aperture. Neglecting all the pattern beyond the first minimum, we can treat this cross section as a disk of radius $1.22\lambda l/d$, or diameter twice that much. With $\lambda = 0.4$ micron and $l = 0.1$ m, this diameter is plotted against the diameter of the aperture as curve a in Figure 32.01.   The diameter of the aperture is plotted against itself as curve b.   When a is much greater than b, or vice versa, the larger of the two can be taken as the diameter of the image-circle.   When they are comparable, their sum will serve as a fair approximation.   On this basis, the solid line has been drawn for the diameter of the image-circle, as a function of the diameter of the aperture. It can be seen that with the value of 10 cm taken for l (distance from aperture to film), the smallest image of a point source is formed by an aperture of about 0.3 mm, and an aperture of diameter 1 mm gives almost as good results.   It would be quite pointless to go below 0.3 mm, however, for longer exposure times would be required and the results would be poorer.   It will be noted that the optimum diameter of the aperture is very much greater than the wavelength, approximately a thousand times as great.

32.03 LIMIT OF RESOLUTION

When parallel beams of light arrive at a lens from different directions, they are brought to foci in the focal plane of the lens, there being one point on the focal plane for each direction of the incident light.   When a parallel beam of light arrives at an aperture, it emerges from the aperture distributed over a range of directions; the resultant "diffraction pattern" of the emergent light has been studied.   If the aperture is filled by a lens, the distribution with direction of the diffraction pattern is converted to a distribution with position on the focal plane, just as though the light had had that distribution with direction when it arrived at the lens.   Thus Figure 32.02 gives the distribution of intensity with direction for light emerging from an aperture of diameter d, for a parallel beam incident on the aperture, θ being the angle from the axis of the aperture to the direction of the emergent light.   The beam of light may have been coming from a distant point source on the axis of the aperture.   If the aperture is filled by a lens of power $1/f$, an image of this point source will be formed at a distance f beyond the lens.   The image will not be a point, however, but a diffraction pattern in cross section, and the same Figure 32.02 can be used to show the distribution with distance from the axis of the flux in this image.

Suppose now that a second point source is located at a similar great distance from the lens, but off its axis, so that the light arrives at an angle

ϕ to the axis. Its image will be a similar diffraction pattern, displaced from the first by a distance $f\phi$. If $\phi = 1.22\lambda/d$ (more precisely if $\sin \phi = 1.22\lambda/d$, but ϕ is sure to be small since d is sure to be $\gg\lambda$), the maximum of the second image will coincide with the first minimum of the first image. This is taken as the limit of resolution; two point sources

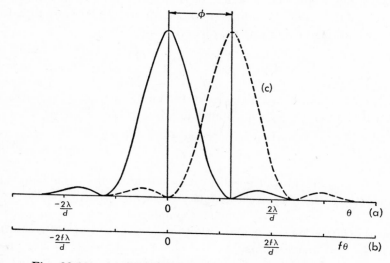

Fig. 32.02. (a) Distribution with angle θ of intensity of light emerging from a circular aperture of diameter d. (b) Distribution with distance off axis, $f\theta$, of concentration of light in focal plane if aperture is filled by a lens of focal length f. (c) Broken line gives same distributions for light arriving at an angle ϕ.

separated in angle by less than $1.22\lambda/d$ will not be recognized as separate sources. The limit of resolution thus effected for the human eye is very much the same as that set by the diameter of the close-packed cells at the center of the retina.

If the eye is looking through a telescope, the limit of resolution imposed by the effective aperture of the eye, d (which is the diameter of the pupil or the diameter of the eye ring, whichever is smaller), is

$$\phi_2 = \frac{1.22\lambda}{d}$$

where ϕ_2 is the limit in terms of the angle *at the eye*. But

$$\frac{\phi_2}{\phi_1} = \text{magnifying power} = \frac{f_1}{f_2}$$

where ϕ_1 is the corresponding angle at the objective, and f_1 and f_2 are the focal lengths of objective and eyepiece, respectively. Further,

$$\frac{f_1}{f_2} = \frac{d_1}{d_2}$$

where d_1 and d_2 are the diameters of the objective and eye ring, respectively. So the limit of resolution imposed by the effective aperture of the eye, in terms of the angle at the objective, is

$$\phi_1 = \frac{d_2}{d_1} \phi_2 = \frac{d_2}{d_1} \times \frac{1.22\lambda}{d} \tag{32.01}$$

If d_2 is made equal to the diameter of the pupil (the smallest value for it that will give an image of maximum brightness), this reduces to

$$\phi_1 = \frac{1.22\lambda}{d_1} \tag{32.02}$$

which is the same limit of resolution as that imposed by the diameter of the objective. Increasing the diameter of the objective beyond the value (magnifying power) times (diameter of pupil) not only fails to increase the brightness of the image, it also fails to decrease the limit of resolution. When the real image formed by the objective is recorded on a photographic plate, the limitation imposed by the eye is of course removed, and continued increase in the diameter of the objective continues to increase the resolution and at the same time to decrease the required time of exposure.

The resolving power of a microscope is a more complicated matter, because the specimen is close to the objective, so that the light arriving at the objective from a point on the specimen is not in a parallel beam. The minimum linear separation between adjacent points that can be distinguished on the specimen is

$$d_{\text{min.}} = \frac{1.22\lambda}{2\mu \sin A} \tag{32.03}$$

where A is half the angle subtended by the objective at the specimen, and μ is the index of refraction of the medium in which the specimen is immersed. Thus it can be seen that better resolution can be obtained by increasing A, by immersing the specimen in a liquid of high index of refraction (not exceeding that of the front component of the objective), and by using a short wavelength. If 90° and 1.5 are taken as upper limits for A and μ, the limit of resolution becomes about 0.2 micron for visual observation, and about 0.1 micron for ultraviolet light recorded photographically.

32.04 INTERFERENCE. THE DOUBLE SLIT OR YOUNG'S EXPERIMENT

In discussing sound, an interference pattern was described that was developed by setting up two loudspeakers a short distance apart. The two speakers were kept in exactly the same phase, or a fixed phase relationship was maintained between them. The same sort of thing can be done with short-wave radio. Light differs from radio and sound, though, quite apart from the enormous difference in wavelength, in one essential respect. The oscillations in a radio aerial driven by a radiofrequency oscillator are continuous, just as are the mechanical oscillations of a loudspeaker driven by an audiofrequency oscillator. The "oscillations" of a sodium atom when it is emitting light are discontinuous. The light from a sodium flame or discharge lamp comes from a very large number of atoms, all emitting occasional bursts of radiation. The radiation has a specific wavelength, but just what atoms will be emitting at any one moment is a matter of chance. Thus we cannot have the exact phase relationship between two discharge lamps that we can have between two radio-aerials or two loudspeakers. In order to obtain two light sources with an exact phase relationship between them, we must start with a single primary source, and channel its radiation through two separated outlets.

In order to obtain two sources of light in phase with each other, pass light through a very narrow slit, from which because of diffraction it will spread out considerably in direction. Let this light illuminate some distance further along its path *two* narrow slits, close together. Beyond these two slits, light will spread out from each of the slits, and there will be a constant phase relationship between the two slits considered as sources (Figure 32.03). The situation beyond the slit will be essentially that for sound waves in section 24.10. The separation of the sources will tend to be greater in terms of the wavelength, and the field will probably be explored by placing an opaque screen across it rather than by a single-point probe corresponding to the microphone of the sound experiment. Let us develop the theory, therefore, in terms of intensity variations along a line normal to the axis of the system, Figure 32.03(b).

Let the receiving screen be distant D from the plane of the slits. Now let a point on the screen be distant y from the axis and distant a and b, respectively, from the two sources. Then

$$a^2 = \left(y - \frac{d}{2}\right)^2 + D^2 = y^2 + \frac{d^2}{4} - yd + D^2$$

$$b^2 = \left(y + \frac{d}{2}\right)^2 + D^2 = y^2 + \frac{d^2}{4} + yd + D^2$$

$$(b - a)(b + a) = (b^2 - a^2) = 2yd$$

$$(b - a) = \frac{2yd}{b + a}$$

Let $b = D + \delta_2$ and $a = D + \delta_1$. When D is great compared with both

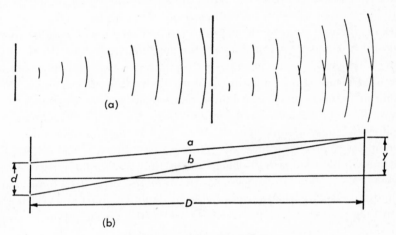

(a)

(b)

Fig. 32.03. The double slit.

d and y, δ_1 and δ_2 become negligible as terms added to D. Then, approximately, $(b + a) = 2D$, and the relation becomes

$$b - a \simeq \frac{yd}{D} \qquad (32.04)$$

The condition for maximum intensity is

$$b - a = n\lambda \qquad (32.05)$$

where n is an integer. Combining (32.04) and (32.05), the condition becomes

$$\frac{yd}{D} = n\lambda \qquad \text{or} \qquad y = \frac{n\lambda D}{d} \qquad (32.06)$$

That is, the maxima are uniformly spaced, with distance between adjacent maxima $(D/d)\lambda$. Thus the spacing can be increased by increasing D, decreasing d, or increasing λ. Let $\lambda = 0.5$ micron. Then, if we want fringes 0.5 mm = 500 microns apart, we must have $D/d = 1000$, say D one meter and d one millimeter. The scale, you see, is quite different from that of the acoustical analogue.

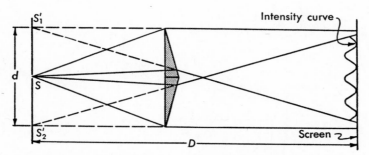

Fig. 32.04. Light from a single slit S passing through a Fresnel Biprism proceeds as from two images of the slit S'_1 and S'_2, which behave like the two members of a double slit, maintaining similarly a fixed phase relationship. (Actually, $D \gg d$.)

Since D, like a and b, is great compared with d, we could have recalled from section 24.10 that the condition for maximum signal at a distant receiving point is given by equation (24.25a):

$$\sin \theta = \frac{n\lambda}{d}$$

where n is zero or an integer. When D is also great compared with y,

$$\sin \theta \simeq \theta \simeq \frac{y}{D}$$

Combining these two relations gives us equation (32.06) rather more directly.

The Fresnel Biprism (Figure 32.04) provides two virtual images of a single slit, the waves from which interfere in accordance with the above theory.

32.05 NEWTON'S RINGS

In this experiment a lens, flat on top and convex on the bottom, lies on a flat plate of glass (Figure 32.05). A small region around the point of contact of lens and plate is viewed through a microscope on the axis of the lens. Illumination is provided by an extended source of monochro-

matic light, such as a sodium flame or a discharge lamp. A glass plate
between the lens and the microscope, set at an angle of 45°, reflects enough
of the light (a few parts per cent) downward on to the lens, while at the
same time transmitting most of the up-coming light to the microscope.

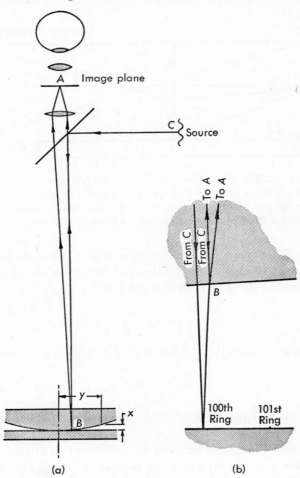

Fig. 32.05. Schematic diagram of apparatus for
observing Newton's Rings.

Consider the light brought to a focus at some specified point A in the
image plane of the microscope.   It all came from a related point B on the
bottom surface of the lens, the surface on which the microscope is focused.
Consider now, more specifically, such of this light as originated at any one
point C on the source.   Some of this light was reflected at the bottom sur-

face of the lens, some penetrated this surface and was reflected from the top surface of the flat plate. (We are concerned with the region within a very few millimeters of the point of contact of the lens and the flat plate, so that the bottom surface of the lens is never far from parallel to the top surface of the plate.)

If we take x as the distance from the flat plate up to the curved surface of the lens, and y as the distance outward from the point of contact, the approximate equation of the spherical surface is

$$x = \frac{y^2}{2r}$$

where $1/r$ is the curvature of the surface. The path difference between the two reflected components is $2x$. If this path difference were equal to $n\lambda$, with n an integer, we would expect the amplitudes to add and give a maximum. There is, however, a phase reversal in the air-to-glass reflection that is not present in the reflection at the glass-to-air surface, and so we have

$$2x = n\lambda$$

as the condition, not for a maximum, but for a *minimum*, a dark ring. Eliminating x, the condition for a dark ring becomes

$$n\lambda = \frac{1}{r} y_n{}^2 \qquad (32.07)$$

where y_n is the diameter of the nth dark ring. (The central dark spot is effectively the *zero*th ring. For it there is no path difference, only the difference between reflection with phase reversal and reflection without it.) Rewriting (32.07) for the $(n + m)$th ring, where m is another integer, we have

$$(n + m)\lambda = \frac{1}{r} y_{n+m}{}^2$$

Subtracting gives

$$m\lambda = \frac{1}{r} (y_{n+m}{}^2 - y_n{}^2)$$

$$\lambda = \frac{y_{n+m}{}^2 - y_n{}^2}{mr} \qquad (32.08)$$

The wavelength can thus be determined from the measurement of two y-values, i.e., the radii of two rings.

Setting $m = 1$ in equation (32.08), we obtain for two adjacent rings

$$y_{n+1}{}^2 - y_n{}^2 = r\lambda$$

$$y_{n+1} - y_n = \frac{r\lambda}{y_{n+1} + y_n} \simeq \frac{r\lambda}{2y_n}$$

Thus the spacing between adjacent rings is inversely proportional to y. Figure 32.05(b) shows the region of the 100th and 101st rings for $r = 0.1$ m, $\lambda = 0.5$ micron. The value of y is then 2.236 mm. Even with this large n and small r, the lack of parallelism between lens and plate surfaces is slight.

Adjusting laboratory apparatus to reveal Newton's Rings has its difficulties. Even so, the rings sometimes appear where they are not wanted. For instance, the required gradual separation between reflecting surfaces may occur in a photographic enlarger, where not-quite-flat film is pressed down against a flat glass plate, leading to the reproduction of "Newton's Rings" in the large photographic print.

32.06 COATED LENSES

The interference between light reflected from closely spaced surfaces is used to reduce greatly the reflections from air-to-glass surfaces in an optical system.

Consider radiation arriving at a smooth surface separating a medium where its speed is c/μ_1 from a different medium where its speed is c/μ_2. Some of the radiation is reflected, and for small angles of incidence, it can be shown that

$$\frac{A_r}{A_i} = \frac{\dfrac{c}{\mu_1} - \dfrac{c}{\mu_2}}{\dfrac{c}{\mu_1} + \dfrac{c}{\mu_2}} \tag{32.09}$$

where A_r and A_i are the amplitudes of the reflected and incident radiation, respectively. In the case of air and glass, if we take the index of refraction of air as unity, this can be written

$$\frac{A_r}{A_i} = \frac{\mu - 1}{\mu + 1} \tag{32.10}$$

Now suppose that between the regions of index μ_1 and μ_2 we introduce a thin layer where the index is μ_a, intermediate between μ_1 and μ_2. The amplitude of the wave reflected from the first surface will then be given by

$$\frac{A_{r1}}{A_i} = \frac{\dfrac{c}{\mu_1} - \dfrac{c}{\mu_a}}{\dfrac{c}{\mu_1} + \dfrac{c}{\mu_a}} \tag{32.11a}$$

and the amplitude of the wave reflected from the second surface, neglecting the slight diminution of A_i at the first surface, by

$$\frac{A_{r2}}{A_i} = \frac{\dfrac{c}{\mu_a} - \dfrac{c}{\mu_2}}{\dfrac{c}{\mu_a} + \dfrac{c}{\mu_2}} \tag{32.11b}$$

[It should be noted that the coefficient of reflectivity R_s is the ratio of two fluxes, effectively of two powers. Power is proportional to amplitude squared, and so $R_s = (A_r/A_i)^2$.] By making the thickness of the intermediate layer a quarter-wavelength, the two reflected terms can be set exactly out of phase; their resultant amplitude is then $A_{r1} - A_{r2}$. The condition that the resultant amplitude be zero is

$$A_{r1} - A_{r2} = 0 \tag{32.12}$$

That is,
$$\frac{\dfrac{c}{\mu_1} - \dfrac{c}{\mu_a}}{\dfrac{c}{\mu_1} + \dfrac{c}{\mu_a}} - \frac{\dfrac{c}{\mu_a} - \dfrac{c}{\mu_2}}{\dfrac{c}{\mu_a} + \dfrac{c}{\mu_2}} = 0$$

which reduces to

$$\mu_a^2 = \mu_1\mu_2 \tag{32.13}$$

For a nonreflecting coating on a glass lens used in air, the index of the coating must then be the square root of that of the glass. If the condition is met for green light, reflection is much reduced at all wavelengths; the residual reflections at the ends of the visible spectrum give the lens a purple tinge. Magnesium fluoride is much used to provide a thin, hard coating meeting the required conditions.

32.07 MICHELSON'S INTERFEROMETER

This instrument makes use of the phenomenon of interference to provide a direct relationship between the wavelength of light and the distance moved in a mechanical system. The light first strikes the glass plate A obliquely (Figure 32.06). The back face of the plate is half-silvered, i.e., lightly silvered so that half the light reaching it is specularly reflected, half specularly transmitted. The reflected light goes out to mirror M_1 and back, the transmitted light to mirror M_2 and back. Half of each component then proceeds in the direction of the eye. Block B is inserted in the system so that both components pass through the same amount of glass. The eye receives two components, comparable in strength, both belonging originally to the same beam of light, but the one having traveled a slightly different path than the other. The resultant of the two components will vary with the phase relationship between the two, and this of course depends on the difference in the lengths of paths traveled by the two. (Let us assume that we have monochromatic light; just one wavelength.) Thus for any particular point on the half-silvered

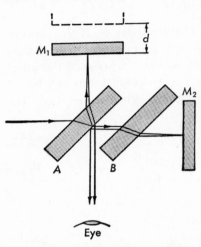

surface, say the one for which rays have been drawn, a gradual motion of mirror M_1 toward or away from the eye will lead to a periodic variation in the intensity of the light reaching the eye. If exactly n cycles are counted in the variation of intensity of the light while mirror M_1 is moved back a distance d, then

$$n\lambda = 2d \qquad (32.14)$$

Actually, the path difference tends to vary somewhat with position on the half-silvered mirror. If the mirror M_1 is held stationary, the eye sees an array of fringes over the face of the half-silvered mirror. When M_1 is moved, the array of fringes is observed to move across the face of the mirror.

Fig. 32.06. Michelson's Interferometer.

Michelson used his interferometer to measure the standard meter in terms of light wavelengths. The standard meter, kept at the International Bureau of Weights and Measures in France, defines the unit of length in terms of the distance between two scratches on a bar of platinum-iridium alloy. It is important that this length should be known in terms of a still more permanent unit. Michelson used the red line of cadmium, and found the meter to equal 1,553,163.5 wavelengths (in dry air at 15C, 760 mm Hg) to an accuracy of one part in two million. Recent developments in the artificial production of isotopes have produced isotopes capable of emitting spectral lines more monochromatic than any hitherto obtained; there is now a trend toward the use of one of these rather than the cadmium line as a primary standard of length.

32.08 THE DIFFRACTION GRATING

A spectrometer has been described in section 31.15 with a prism as the device that gives every wavelength a different angle of deviation. A diffraction grating can be used, alternatively, with the same spectrometer, as shown in Figure 32.07(a). Again, the collimator provides light with a single direction of travel. Again, the telescope objective focuses emergent light of a given deviation θ at its focal point. Light for which the deviation is somewhat more or somewhat less comes to a focus in the focal plane too, but at positions somewhat displaced from the focal point.

The grating consists of many narrow slits, produced by ruling many fine parallel lines on a transparent sheet, or by some development of this

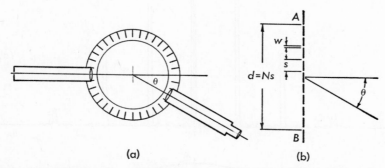

Fig. 32.07. The transmission grating that can take the place of a prism in a spectrometer (a) can be represented by a regularly spaced array of parallel slits (b). The grating with its edges at A and B has width d. Each of the N elements of width s contains a transparent slit of width w.

process. In Figure 32.07(b) a grating of width d contains N elements each of width s. A reasonable width would be 5 cm, with 4000 elements per cm. For simplicity of consideration, each element has been taken as consisting of a transparent slit of width w plus a wider opaque strip. Assuming that the parallel beam from the collimator is exactly normal to the plane of the grating, the line AB of Figure 32.07(b) is an equiphase line.

The slit-width w is narrow enough that the light passing through a single slit spreads out in a diffraction pattern of considerable width. From section 24.11, the signal-amplitude from a single slit will be greatest at $\theta = 0$, will decrease with increasing θ, and reach zero at the value of θ for which

$$\sin \theta = \frac{\lambda}{w}$$

Thus as w is narrowed down to approach λ, the value of θ for zero signal approaches $\pi/2$. The following paragraphs will discuss the manner in which the signals interfere to yield maxima in certain directions which are functions of the wavelength, and will call further on diffraction theory to show that the signal drops off rapidly with departures of θ from its

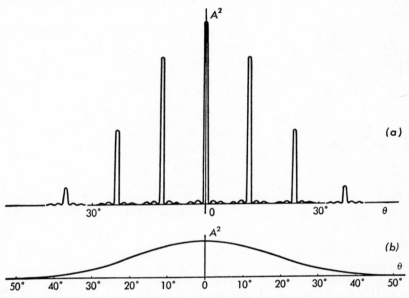

Fig. 32.08. The square of the amplitude, which is proportional to the intensity, plotted against angle, in part (a) for a grating, in part (b) for a single slit of the grating. The width of the whole grating has been taken as just 0.03 mm in order that the individual diffraction patterns in (a) would be wide enough that they could be drawn. In practice the grating would be at least 1000 times wider, the orders at least 1000 times narrower.

values of maximum signal. The nature of the results is indicated in Figure 32.08(a).

At $\theta = 0$, path lengths from all the slits to a distant receiving point are all the same and so all signals arriving at a distant point have the same phase. The phasor summation is a straight line, for the greatest possible amplitude of the resultant phasor. With departures from $\theta = 0$ the phasor summation becomes the arc of a circle, closing to a complete circle and zero resultant amplitude when

$$\sin \theta = \frac{\lambda}{d}$$

just as for a slit of width d (see section 24.11 and particularly Figure 24.12). Thus a grating of total width d gives the same diffraction pattern centered on $\theta = 0$ as does a slit of width d. The width of a grating is so great compared with the wavelength that the values of θ involved are very small; $\sin \theta$ is thus very nearly identical with θ, and the condition for zero amplitude can be written

$$\theta = \frac{\lambda}{d}$$

At the large values of θ for which

$$\sin \theta = \frac{n\lambda}{s} \tag{32.15}$$

where n is an integer (and a small integer; otherwise $n\lambda/s$ will be greater than unity), the path difference between signals from adjacent slits is exactly one wavelength, and so again the signals from all the slits have exactly the same phase, the phasor summation is a straight line, the resultant amplitude is a maximum. Again, small departures $\Delta\theta$ from this direction of maximum signal result in a rapid dropping-off of resultant amplitude, to zero amplitude at

$$\Delta\theta = \frac{\lambda}{d} \tag{32.16}$$

Thus the pattern of signal amplitude at a distant point, against θ, consists of sharp maxima at values of θ given by

$$\sin \theta = \frac{n\lambda}{s}$$

where n is zero or a small integer, as indicated in Figure 32.08(a). These maxima or diffraction patterns are called the zeroth, first, second, etc. orders of the grating. The amplitudes at the maxima are proportional to the amplitudes of the single-slit signals, shown in Figure 32.08(b), of which they are the sum. At all orders except the zeroth, the value of $\sin \theta$ is proportional to the wavelength, and so each wavelength is given a different direction, as required for the operation of a spectrometer.

The condition that yields maximum signal at a distant receiving point also yields maximum signal in the focal plane of the telescope objective, and so this lens can be introduced to concentrate at a single position on its focal plane all the light of a given direction that is intercepted by it.

The grating described above is specifically a transmission grating.

There are also reflection gratings, working on the same principle. In both sorts, the value of d may be a few times greater than the 5 cm mentioned above. In practice, the method of inscribing or embossing the lines of the grating affects the fraction of the light used, and the relative performance of the grating in its different orders.

32.09 POLARIZED LIGHT

Polarization is a property of transverse waves, and so it is worthwhile recalling something of transverse mechanical waves. If a string or spring is stretched from O to some point along the X axis (Figure 32.09), there is just one sort of motion of the end at the origin that will generate longitudinal waves on it, and that is a small motion, let us say a rapid periodic one, along the X axis. When we turn to transverse waves, there is an infinite choice of direction of vibration. Vibrating the origin-end along the Y axis will generate transverse waves in the XY plane. Vibrating it along the Z axis will generate waves in the XZ plane. Vibrating it along any line in the YZ plane will generate waves in a plane containing that line and the X axis. Such waves can be completely described by their components in the XY and XZ planes. Physically, these components can be separated out: For instance, if at some point along the X axis the string passes through a narrow vertical slot, the vertical (y) component will be transmitted through the slot, the x-component reflected.

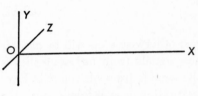

Fig. 32.09.

Waves are not limited to a one-dimensional medium, such as a string, of course. A transverse vibration at some point in an elastic solid can send out transverse waves in all directions. (The amplitude of the wave will vary with the direction, and will drop to zero for the case of direction of propagation identical with the direction of vibration.)

Electromagnetic waves are transverse; they do not involve *motion* across the direction of propagation; they consist of variations in electric and magnetic fields across the direction of propagation, the direction of motion of the wave. That leaves an infinite number of directions in which those variations can occur. In any particular case, the electrical variations occur in a plane at right angles to the magnetic variations

(Figure 32.10), but our consideration can go to some length without involving this.

By the nature of the aerial arrays in which they originate, radio waves are **polarized,** given a specific direction for their electrical variations (and another at right angles for their magnetic variations). Thus radio waves radiated from a vertical mast involve electrical variations in the vertical, magnetic in the horizontal; they are best received by a

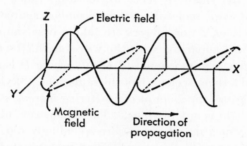

Fig. 32.10. Relationship of variations in electric and magnetic fields.

vertical receiving antenna, and are received not at all by a receiving system of zero vertical extent.

A beam of light consists of very many wave trains, each wave train originating in a single atom and having its own plane of polarization. At any point in the beam at any instant, many wave trains from many atoms are passing by, and since the atoms are randomly oriented or directed one to another, every conceivable plane of polarization is represented in the beam. The light is unpolarized. In the interaction between light and matter, there are a few ways in which light, originally unpolarized, may become sorted-out according to the planes in which the electrical and magnetic variations occur, i.e., in which it may become polarized.

The most familiar device for polarizing light is the "Polaroid" filter. This contains a layer of herapathite, an iodosulphate of quinine, between glass plates or celluloid sheets. These crystals are much more strongly absorbent to waves of one polarization (relative to their structure) than to that at right angles. Such a filter does not separate out one component perfectly, and in a thickness great enough to provide a satisfactorily high ratio of flux of one component to flux of the other, even the favored component is reduced appreciably. The degree of polarization falls off at both ends of the visible spectrum, so that crossed filters, which should transmit no light, actually transmit a little light of a purple hue. Although this form of polarizer is somewhat inefficient, it is very convenient and extremely useful.

32.10 SCATTERING

Particles too small to serve as reflectors, such as molecules or aggregates of not many molecules, act as secondary sources and so **scatter** light in all directions. For spheres (to take a case simple in theory) of diameter small in comparison with the wavelength, the amount of scattering of radiation is proportional to D^6/λ^4, where D is the diameter of the scatterer and λ the wavelength of the radiation. Skylight is scattered sunlight, and because the amount of scattering increases with decreasing wavelength, skylight is notably blue. The setting sun, observed through a great thickness of atmosphere, is correspondingly red, since a greater proportion of the shorter wavelengths has been scattered out. When light is diffused by a haze or cloud of particles of diameter greater than the wavelengths of visible light, the amount of light diffused is not very dependent on the wavelength. Thus the haze usually observed near the horizon is more nearly white, sunlit clouds are a brilliant white, and clouds in general tend to colorless gray.

Scattering polarizes light. Consider a scatterer located at the origin of a coordinate system, with unpolarized light traveling in the positive direction parallel to the X axis. The incident light will possess electrical and magnetic variations in all directions perpendicular to the X axis, that is, in all directions that can be contained in the YZ plane. The scattered light can only have directions of electrical and magnetic variations possessed by the incident light. Radiation scattered along the Z axis must have its variations normal to that axis, so that it can be propagated as a transverse wave in that direction. It must have its variations normal to the X axis, since it was initially propagated in that direction. The direction of the Y axis is the only one meeting this condition: Light scattered along the Z axis is polarized, its electrical variations limited to the YZ plane. In this way, all the radiation scattered at 90° is polarized, and all the scattered radiation, whatever the direction, is partially polarized. Although most skylight has undergone multiple scattering, we find that a large part of it, particularly at suitable angles from the sun, is polarized, and can be absorbed by a Polaroid filter suitably oriented.

32.11 POLARIZATION BY REFLECTION

The amount of light reflected at the surface of a transparent medium varies with the angle of incidence, as shown in Figure 28.09. Actually, the amount reflected depends on the polarization of the light,

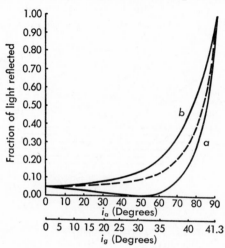

Fig. 32.11. Fraction of light reflected when light in air strikes glass ($\mu = 1.515$) at angle of incidence i_a or when light in glass strikes air at angle of incidence i_g. Broken line, like Figure 28.09, is for unpolarized light. Curve a is for component polarized in plane of Figure 32.12, curve b for component polarized normal to plane of that figure. (Adapted in part from Joseph Valasek, *Introduction to Experimental and Theoretical Optics*, John Wiley & Sons, Inc., New York, 1949.)

except for the cases of zero incidence; Figure 28.09 is for unpolarized light and averages values for all possible planes of polarization. Figure 32.11, for the same index of refraction, repeats the curve of the earlier figure (broken line) and adds the separate curves for light with its electrical variations respectively *in*, curve a, and *normal to*, curve b, the plane of incidence (i.e., the plane of Figure 32.12). For the a case, it can be proved that the reflection drops to zero when

$$\tan i = \mu \tag{32.17}$$

This is known as Brewster's Law, or the angle as Brewster's Angle.   It can be seen from the figure that there is very little reflection of the a-component for five degrees to either side of this angle.   In the same range of angles about 14% of the b-component is reflected.

One good source of polarized light is a pile of glass plates (Figure 32.12).   The top surface of the first plate reflects about 14% of the b-component (and none of the a), the bottom surface 14% of the residue,

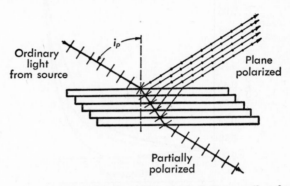

Fig. 32.12. Polarization of light by a pile of plates. The angle i_p is Brewster's Angle. Dots along rays indicate polarization (of electrical variations) normal to plane of diagram, and correspond to curve b, Figure 32.11. Cross lines indicate polarization *in* the plane, corresponding to curve a.

and so on, until with a pile of plates a large fraction of the b-component is returned and the transmitted component is fairly pure a.

32.12 ANISOTROPIC MEDIA

Substances having the same properties in every direction are called isotropic, and those that do not are called **anisotropic.**   These words are frequently applied to substances serving as media for the transfer of energy: the conduction of heat or electricity, or the transmission of sound or light.   If we used such words in everyday life, we could refer to a cornfield as an anisotropic region in which to walk, since walking in the direction of the rows is easier and quicker than walking across them.

Some crystals are anisotropic media for the transmission of light, since the speed of light with a certain plane of polarization varies with the direction in which the light is traveling.   For one class of crystals whose anisotropy has important applications, the propagation of light can be described with reference to a particular direction relative to the structure of the crystal. These crystals are called uniaxial, and the direction is called the **optic axis** of the crystal.

In Figure 32.13, let the direction called the optic axis be parallel to the Y axis. Let us first consider radiation proceeding from the point O in any direction normal to OY. The direction of the electrical variations involved in the wave, which we shall call the direction of vibration,

must of course be perpendicular to the direction of propagation. It is found that waves for which the direction of vibration is also perpendicular to the optic axis, called **ordinary** radiation, travel at one speed (which we shall denote by c/μ_0), and waves for which the direction of vibration is parallel to the optic axis, called **extraordinary** radiation, travel at another speed (which we shall denote by c/μ_e). Waves that meet neither of the above specifications regarding direction of vibration are broken

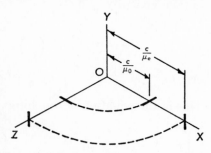

Fig. 32.13. Speed and direction of vibration of ordinary and extraordinary radiation traveling normal to optic axis (parallel to OY) of uniaxial anisotropic medium.

into two components that do. Figure 32.13 shows $c/\mu_e > c/\mu_0$. Crystalline substances for which this is the case are called **negative**. For **positive** crystals the reverse is true. Some uniaxial crystals are:

	μ_e	μ_0
Iceland spar (negative)	1.486	1.658
Tourmaline (negative)	1.62	1.64
Quartz (positive)	1.553	1.544
Ice (positive)	1.307	1.306

To depart from the limitation applied above, that the direction of propagation should be normal to the optic axis, let us now consider light proceeding from O in any direction in the XY plane, as representative of any plane containing the optic axis and the direction of propagation (Figure 32.14). For propagation along the optic axis, all possible directions of vibration are normal to the axis, and so we find that any radiation is propagated with speed c/μ_0, and without being broken into components. For any other direction in the XY plane, radiation with its direction of vibration normal to the optic axis is propagated as ordinary radiation at speed c/μ_0. Radiation with its direction of propagation normal to that of the ordinary radiation, and so with a component parallel to the optic axis, is called extraordinary radiation, and travels with a velocity c_e. This velocity c_e can be described with reference to its components (normal to the optic axis, c_{ex}, and parallel to the optic axis, c_{ey}) so that

$$c_e{}^2 = c_{ex}{}^2 + c_{ey}{}^2 \tag{32.18}$$

The speed of the extraordinary wave in any direction in the XY plane is then given by

$$\frac{c_{ex}{}^2}{\left(\dfrac{c}{\mu_e}\right)^2} + \frac{c_{ey}{}^2}{\left(\dfrac{c}{\mu_0}\right)^2} = 1$$

or

$$\mu_e{}^2 c_{ex}{}^2 + \mu_0{}^2 c_{ey}{}^2 = c^2 \tag{32.19}$$

This is the equation of an ellipse. In Figure 32.14 the velocities of the ordinary and extraordinary radiation are given by lines from the origin to the circle and to the ellipse, respectively. Radiation having a direction of vibration other than those specified above is broken up into two components that do meet those specifications.

The XY plane treated above might have been any plane containing the direction called the optic axis. If we consider radiation proceeding from O in any direction, then, we will find it traveling in two components:

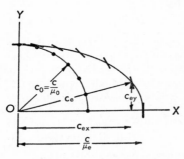

Fig. 32.14. Speed and direction of vibration of ordinary and extraordinary radiation, shown for XY plane where optic axis is parallel OY.

(1) The ordinary component has its direction of vibration normal to the direction of propagation and normal to the optic axis. Its speed is given by the distance from O to the surface of a sphere of radius c/μ_0 (of which the circle of Figure 32.14 is the line of intersection with the XY plane). That is to say, its speed is c/μ_0, independent of direction.

(2) The extraordinary component has its direction of vibration normal to that of the ordinary component proceeding in the same direction. Its speed is given by the distance from O to the ellipsoid of revolution about the axis OY (a line through O in the direction of the optic axis) for which the line of intersection with the XY plane is given by equation (32.19). Figure 32.15 is a repetition of Figure 32.13, with the sphere

and ellipsoid indicated by their intersections with the XY, ZY, and XZ planes.

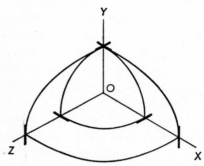

This optical anisotropy is sometimes called **birefringence,** because a ray of light passing obliquely through a surface from an isotropic medium, where there is just one speed for light, to an anisotropic medium undergoes double refraction. It is split into two polarized components traveling at different speeds and so refracted by different amounts, to travel in two directions (Figure 32.16). In particular cases the Huygens wavelets for both ordinary and extraordinary components may have circular sections in the plane of the diagram, but there will be different amounts of refraction.

Fig. 32.15. For a uniaxial medium, speed of ordinary radiation in any direction is given by distance from origin to sphere. Speed of extraordinary radiation in any direction is given by distance from origin to ellipsoid of revolution about OY (parallel to optic axis).

There will be refraction of the extraordinary component even for normal incidence, except for the particular cases of light traveling in the direction of the optic axis or normal to it.

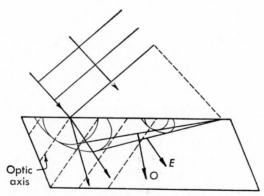

Fig. 32.16. Huygens' construction for locating ordinary and extraordinary wave fronts when plane waves are incident obliquely on the surface of an anisotropic crystal. (After J. K. Robertson, *Introduction to Optics*, 4th Ed., Copyright 1954, D. Van Nostrand Co., Inc.)

32.13 THE NICOL PRISM

The Nicol Prism is designed to make use of double refraction to trap one plane-polarized component by double refraction while transmitting the other plane-polarized component.   It can achieve perfect polarization and a very good efficiency.   Its use in instruments, therefore, continues in spite of the development of more generally convenient "Polaroid" filters.

The Nicol Prism is made from a crystal of Iceland Spar about three times as long as it is broad (Figure 32.17).   End pieces (from the broken-line to the solid-line ends) are removed.   The crystal is then cut into

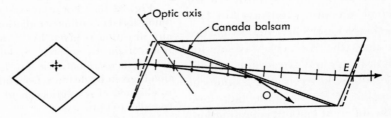

Fig. 32.17.   The Nicol Prism.

two pieces which are recemented in their original relation, using Canada Balsam as cement.   The index of refraction of Canada Balsam, 1.55, is less than that of the spar for the "ordinary" wave, but more than that for the "extraordinary" wave.   The angles of the end faces and the diagonal cut are so chosen that the ordinary wave is totally reflected at the Canada Balsam surface, and absorbed at the side, while the extraordinary wave passes on through.   By rotating the Nicol around its long axis the plane of vibration of the transmitted light may be rotated.

32.14 THE POLARIMETER AND OPTICAL ACTIVITY

A convenient device for many measurements involving polarized light is called a **polarimeter.**   It consists of two polarizing devices such as sheets of Polaroid to provide a large field, or Nicol prisms for precise work (Figure 32.18).   These are mounted on a common axis, with a space along the axis between the two for introducing samples. The second device, called the **analyzer,** can be rotated about the common axis relative to the first device, called the **polarizer.**   The angle through which the analyzer is rotated can be measured accurately.

When plane-polarized light enters certain types of crystals and certain liquids, the direction of polarization gradually rotates with distance traveled through the material. Crystalline quartz is **optically active** in this way. So are solutions containing molecules that are asymmetrical. The angle of rotation due to the column can be measured. If the specific

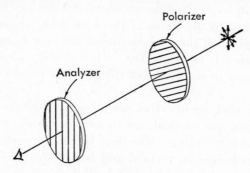

Fig. 32.18. The Polarimeter.

rotation of the solute is known—i.e., the rotation produced by a column 10 cm long, divided by the grams of active substance per cubic centimeter of solution—then the concentration can be determined. Much commercial use is made of the polarimeter in this way.

32.15 CIRCULAR AND ELLIPTICAL POLARIZATION

In Figure 32.19(a), let the oblique line PP denote the plane of polarization of the light emerging from the polarizer of a polarimeter, as viewed from the analyzer. The vibration can be described by two com-

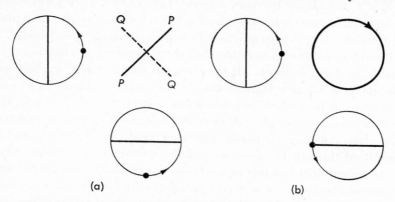

Fig. 32.19. Vertical and horizontal components of (a) plane-polarized radiation, plane at 45° to vertical; (b) same after passing through quarter-wave plate to become circularly polarized.

ponents, one vertical and one horizontal, their phase relation being indicated by the relative positions of the dots on the two reference circles. (The arrangement of the diagram is that used in discussing Lissajous figures in section 23.07.) Suppose that there is no sample between polarizer and analyzer. Then the amplitude transmitted by the analyzer will be proportional to the cosine of the angle from the plane PP of the polarizer to the plane of the analyzer, being greatest when the latter lies along PP, zero when it lies along QQ. The intensity of the signal is, of course, proportional to the square of the amplitude and so to the square of the cosine.

Now suppose that we insert as sample a sheet of doubly refracting substance, its optic axis vertical and its surface normal to the direction in which the light is traveling. The light travels through this substance in components polarized in vertical and horizontal planes. One component, say the one with a horizontal plane of polarization, travels more slowly than the other, so that the phase of the horizontal component lags the vertical component more and more with increasing distance into the sample. There will be some depth into the substance at which the horizontal component lags the vertical by 2π radians. At that depth the two components will go together just as they did initially, to form a vibration along the same line PP. At half the depth, with phase lag π, they will combine to form a vibration along the line QQ. A plate of just that thickness is called a **half-wave plate.** At any other intermediate depth the resultant vibration will not be linear, but will be elliptical, as shown in section 23.07. At the depth for which the phase lag is $\pi/2$, the ellipse becomes a circle, Fig. 32.19(b). A sheet of such thickness as to provide a phase lag of $\pi/2$ is called a **quarter-wave plate,** and the light emerging from it is said to be **circularly polarized.**

Consider now the passage through the analyzer of the light emerging from the anisotropic sheet. If the sheet has the thickness of a half-wave plate, no light will pass through the analyzer when its plane is PP, and a maximum will pass when its plane is QQ, just the reverse of the settings when there was no sample. If the sheet has the thickness of a quarter-wave plate, yielding circularly polarized light, the intensity of light transmitted through the analyzer is independent of its setting. Circularly polarized light has this property in common with unpolarized light, that transmission by an analyzer is independent of the setting of the analyzer. For any other thickness of anisotropic sheet, yielding elliptically polarized light, there is transmission for every setting of the analyzer, but the intensity of transmitted light varies with the setting.

The indices of refraction of anisotropic media, like those of isotropic media, vary with the wavelength, and so the pattern of polarization emerging from an anisotropic sheet varies with the wavelength. Thus, if a half-wave plate for red light is followed by an analyzer, and white light enters with polarization PP (Figure 32.19), the light emerging from the analyzer will be preponderantly blue for the PP setting of the analyzer and preponderantly red for the QQ setting.

32.16 OPTICAL STUDY OF STRAIN

If the analyzer of a polarimeter is set with its plane of polarization at 90° to that of the polarizer, no light emerges. Then, if an anisotropic sample is inserted, some light will pass, unless the light is monochromatic and the sheet is a full-wave plate for the wavelength used. Glasses and plastics are normally isotropic substances, but straining them can make them slightly anisotropic. Thus, if a sheet of glass is placed between polarizer and analyzer with their planes crossed as described above, any transmission of light is an indication of strain. This provides a method of detecting undesirable strains in optical glass before it has been worked into a lens. In the technique of photoelasticity, models of newly designed structures are built of transparent material before the structure itself has been built, and are studied in this way to determine the stresses involved.

PROBLEMS

1. A pinhole camera with image-distance 10.0 cm comes reasonably close to its best resolution with an aperture of diameter 1.00 mm. If a camera having aperture setting $f/10$ requires an exposure time of $\frac{1}{25}$ sec, what will this pinhole camera require?

2. What is the limit of resolution of the eye, stated as an angle, based on diffraction theory, when the diameter of the pupil is 3.0 mm? (Take 0.50 micron as the relevant wavelength.) How far apart must two lines be, then, to be recognized as two separate lines by the eye at a distance of (a) 25 cm, (b) 20 m? How far apart must they be at 20 m if opera glasses (binocular telescopes), of perfect optical quality and rated 4×12 (i.e., magnifying power 4, objective diameter 12 mm) are used?

3. Adopting the limit of resolution established for optical systems, what must be the diameter of a radar antenna for it to distinguish separately two targets $\frac{1}{4}$ mile apart at a distance of 25 miles, if the wavelength is (a) 10.2 cm, (b) 5.6 cm, (c) 3.2 cm?

4. What is the radius of the 25th Newton ring, for a lens of radius of curvature 30 cm and light of wavelength 0.50 micron?

5. Draw, enlarged 10 times, the first 10 dark rings of a pattern of Newton's rings formed between the spherical surface of a lens, of radius of curvature 5.0 m, and an optically flat plate, the wavelength of the light being 0.50 micron.

6. Using light of wavelength 0.5890 micron, a grating gives a value of θ for the first order of 13°37′30″. How many lines does the grating have per centimeter?

7. Referring to problem 6, the angular width of the line observed, from zero intensity on the left of the central maximum to zero on the right, is 10.0 min. What is the width of the grating?

ELECTRICITY
AND
MAGNETISM

33

.

Electric Current

With this chapter we start a new section of physics, the study of electric and magnetic phenomena. These phenomena are complicated, very different from most things we are used to, and seem rather mysterious at first, principally because most of them make no direct impression on our sense organs as heat, light, and sound do. Electricity and magnetism is a relatively new branch of physics—very little was known about it prior to a hundred and twenty-five years ago, and the commercial applications date back only some seventy-five years. The enormous effect on our method of living hardly needs retelling.

33.01 NATURE OF ELECTRICITY

What is electricity? It is natural to ask this question, but one need not be too surprised that physics does not provide an answer, any more than it answers similar questions about matter and time. The aim of physics is to reduce the description of nature to as few laws as possible—the emphasis is on *how* things work rather than *why*. Electricity has many of the properties of a fluid, which may be at rest (**electrostatics**) or in motion (**electrodynamics**). On investigation the electric fluid turns out to be made up of discrete particles or pieces of electricity. The pieces are of two kinds which cancel out each other's effects and so, by convention, are called positive and negative. The smallest quantity of electricity which has ever been found is called the electronic charge, represented by the symbol e. Charge is always associated with matter, and any electric charge has mass. Two of the fundamental constituents of matter are the **proton**, which has a charge of e, and the **electron**, which has a charge of $-e$. The simplest of the chemical elements is hydrogen, and the atom of hydrogen consists of one proton and one electron. Atoms of all elements, and hence all forms of matter, contain protons and electrons, showing the close relationship between matter and electricity. Normal atoms are electrically neutral, that is, do not show the properties of charged bodies, and thus must contain equal quantities of positive and negative charge. These facts come from atomic physics, a subject we shall discuss in Chapter 43, and were discovered after most of the main effects of electricity and magnetism were well established, so it is clear that we can go a long way before invoking atomic theories. This arises from the fact that any electric charge you are likely to encounter will consist of literally billions of electrons or protons, so the atomic nature of electricity does not intrude itself.

This property of electric charge is the fundamental one. The effects of electric charge are easily demonstrated. If you run a comb through your hair, the comb will then attract and pick up tiny scraps of paper. Everyone has experienced the shock one gets by shuffling about on a carpet and then touching a metal radiator or another person. The chain dangling from a gasoline truck is to allow the electric charge which accumulates from friction with the air to leak away to ground so that there will be no danger of a spark igniting the gasoline when it is poured out. For the same reason, when an airplane lands it *must* be grounded before refueling. This list of examples of electric charges at rest, or "static" electricity, could be extended indefinitely, but if static charges are easy to demonstrate, they are hard to measure exactly, and so it is now customary to base electrical definitions on the electric current.

Electric charges in motion constitute an electric current, but the very fact of the motion produces quite different effects from those when the charges are at rest. The three principal effects of electric currents are as follows.

(1) MECHANICAL AND MAGNETIC EFFECTS

Every electric current produces a magnetic field. By the word "field" we mean that there is a region of space, surrounding the wire in which the charges move, where magnetic phenomena can be detected. The concept of the magnetic field is one of the key ideas in electricity and magnetism and will be developed at length later. For the present we merely note that if there are two currents, each produces a field and each experiences a mechanical force due to the presence of the other. Similarly, charges moving in a magnetic field due to a permanent magnet (in which there doesn't seem to be any current) will be acted on by a force. This mechanical force is used to define current, to operate instruments measuring current and other electrical properties, and to cause electric motors to rotate, converting electrical energy into mechanical work.

(2) HEATING EFFECTS

Whenever electric charges flow through matter, heat is produced. Sometimes this is an advantage—as in incandescent lamps, toasters, irons, and so on. Most of the time it is a costly nuisance, but whether we want it or not, heat is always produced and allowance must be made for it.

(3) CHEMICAL EFFECTS

When an electric charge flows through some substances (notably water solutions of acids, bases, and salts), chemical changes take place. This is the basis of enormous industries such as the production of aluminum and is also important as a method of "storing" electrical energy in batteries.

33.02 INSULATORS AND CONDUCTORS

We spoke in the last section of charges flowing through matter. One finds that they flow very easily through some kinds of matter and virtually not at all through other kinds. Substances of the first type are called **conductors** and those of the second type **insulators**. All metals are conductors, some better than others, and so are a few other substances such as carbon and water solutions, although these are not nearly as good conductors as the metals. Most other materials are insulators. The best insulators (that is, those which allow the least current) include glass, rubber, plastics, dry cotton, most oils, and porcelain—to name the materials most commonly used for this purpose. The best conductor is silver, but it is rarely used because of expense. The next is copper, which is the principal conductor used in electrical work. Aluminum is also widely used because it is a good conductor and is also very light. For carrying electric charge from one place to another, the conducting material is usually in the form of a wire which is wrapped with cotton and rubber or plastic to insulate it—that is, to prevent another conductor such as a person from touching it accidentally. It is important to realize that electricity, which is such a useful servant, can be extremely dangerous and must be handled with great caution. Improper design of circuits and electrical equipment has caused many serious fires. Personal danger must also be heeded. A small electric current in a person's body produces a rather unpleasant tingling sensation and involuntary contraction of the muscles, a somewhat larger current causes severe burns at the point where it enters the body, and a sufficiently large current is fatal. Most of the cells in the body contain a saline solution and are very good conductors. Dry skin is a poor conductor and is our principal protection against electric current. *Don't* touch electrical equipment with wet hands.

33.03 THE UNIT OF ELECTRIC CURRENT

If currents flow in two adjacent wires, there is a mechanical force on each wire, as stated earlier. These forces are equal in magnitude and opposite in direction, as would be expected from Newton's Third Law of Motion. Why these forces act we cannot say, any more than we offer any explanation of *why* the Law of Universal Gravitation should be true.

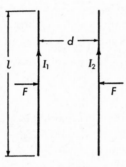

Fig. 33.01.

In Figure 33.01 two parallel wires carry currents I_1 and I_2. We shall imagine that the wires are very long and that we can measure the force F which acts on a length l of either wire. If I_1 and I_2 flow in the same direction, the wires are attracted to each other and the forces F act in the directions shown. If I_1 and I_2 flow in opposite directions, the wires repel each other. These are experimental results, as also are the following:

$$F \propto l, \qquad F \propto I_1 I_2, \qquad F \propto \frac{1}{d}$$

and F depends on the medium in which the wires lie (i.e., F will be much larger if the wires run in two holes in a solid block of iron than if the wires are in empty space).

This dependence of the force on the medium is one of the singular features of electricity and magnetism. It is represented in equations by the product $\mu\mu_0$ where μ_0 represents the effect of free space and μ is a factor which expresses how much greater F is for a given medium than it is for free space. Thus μ is a ratio relating the effectiveness of one medium to another and has no units. Evidently $\mu = 1$ exactly for free space, that is, in a vacuum. We call μ_0 the **permeability of free space** and μ the **relative permeability**. The unit in which μ_0 is to be measured raises another problem. It is found that the electrical quantities cannot be expressed satisfactorily in terms of the mechanical quantities of mass, length, and time, and so we choose one of the electrical units and give it the same fundamental status as the meter, the kilogram, and the second. We shall chose as this unit the unit of current, the ampere, and refer to our system of units as the mksa system.

Writing our experimental results in algebraic form, we have

$$F \propto \frac{\mu\mu_0 I_1 I_2 l}{d}$$

or

$$F = \frac{k\mu\mu_0 I_1 I_2 l}{d} \tag{33.01}$$

Now we still have not chosen the size of the ampere, and so k and μ_0 can be given any numerical values we wish. We take

$$k = \frac{1}{2\pi} \quad \text{and} \quad \mu_0 = 4\pi \times 10^{-7}$$

These are *definitions*, and if they seem like odd choices, it is because we are not following the historical development of these ideas, but are "jumping" right into the presently accepted method of choosing units. These oddly chosen numerical factors will result in as simple a form as possible for the more important equations of electromagnetism. If you have occasion to refer to other books and articles, it may be worth knowing that these definitions lead to what is called the *rationalized mksa system of units*.

Equation (33.01) can now be written in "dimensional" form, that is, we write in the units of each quantity, disregarding any purely numerical factors such as μ and 2π.

$$\frac{[\text{Newtons}] = [\mu_0][\text{amperes}][\text{amperes}][\text{meters}]}{[\text{meters}]} \tag{33.01a}$$

Hence μ_0 has the dimensions of newtons per square ampere. It is more commonly stated in henrys per meter, which we shall see later is exactly the same unit. Thus the definition is:

$$\mu_0 = 4\pi \times 10^{-7} \text{ henrys/meter}$$

If the numerical values are substituted, and if the wires are in empty space where $\mu = 1$, (33.01) becomes

$$F = 2 \times 10^{-7} \times \frac{I_1 I_2 l}{d} \qquad (33.01b)$$

and this equation is used to define the ampere. In words, the definition is: If equal but oppositely directed currents in two infinitely long parallel wires 1 meter apart in a vacuum cause a force of repulsion between them of 2×10^{-7} newtons per meter length, then each current is 1 ampere.

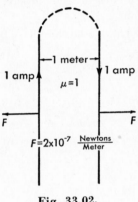

This is illustrated in Figure 33.02. Infinitely long wires do not exist, but (33.01b) will give the force between parallel wires if $l \gg d$.

The unit of current will normally be abbreviated as amp or a. Thus 6.70 amp, 43.6 ma, and 104 μa stand respectively for 6.70 amperes, 43.6 milliamperes, and 104 microamperes.

The Current Balance. Ordinary currents in light bulbs, car ignition systems, electric irons, and so on are of the order of 1 to 10 amp, and a little arithmetic will show that the forces between wires carrying currents of this order are very small unless the length of the wires is very great. Hence, for a practical instrument using our definition, we take long wires but wind them up in coils to conserve space. The instrument

Fig. 33.02.

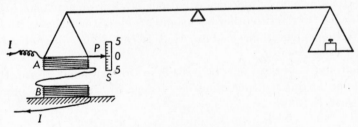

Fig. 33.03. The current balance.

is called a current balance and is illustrated in Figure 33.03, where A and B are two coils of many turns of wire, wound in the same sense so that if there is a current in the circuit they will be attracted. Equation (33.01) is not directly applicable to this case, but a very similar equation can be derived by integrating the force of attraction between the elements of length of the wires in each coil. The geometry is complicated, making the integration rather difficult to perform, but the resultant total force of attraction is

$$F = KI^2$$

where K is a constant depending on μ_0 and the geometry of the coils, i.e., the number of turns of wire, the spacing of the turns, their radii, and the separation of the coils. The value of K is calculated from these factors for a certain definite separation corresponding to the pointer P being at the zero of scale S. Coil B is clamped rigidly in place. Coil A, with its attached pointer P, is suspended from one arm of an ordinary balance, the other arm supporting a scalepan to which standard "weights" can be added.

To use the instrument, weights are added to the scale until the pointer is at zero, when there is no current. Let the mass of the weights be m_1. The current I is then turned on. The coil A moves toward B, and additional weights are added until the coil returns to the zero position. If the total mass on the scale pan is now m_2, then

$$KI^2 = (m_2 - m_1)g$$

Thus the current I has been measured absolutely, that is in terms of mass, length, time, and the defined constant μ_0.

The current balance is a very rare instrument, being used primarily in standards laboratories to calibrate accurately-made current meters of another type which are used as secondary standards. Actual current balances are naturally more elaborate than this brief description would indicate but operate in just this way.

33.04 JOULE'S LAW AND RESISTANCE

Joule was one of the pioneer experimenters in the study of heat. Among other effects he measured the heat liberated in a wire when there is an electric current in it. He found that

Rate of production of heat $\propto$ (current)^2

or in equation form,

$$P_H = RI^2 \tag{33.02}$$

where P_H is the rate of production of heat, and R is a constant independent of I (provided the temperature of the wire does not change). The constant R is a most important property of the wire and is called its **resistance.** In mks units power is measured in watts and current in amperes, so from (33.02) the unit of resistance is the watt/ampere^2. This unit occurs so frequently that it is given a special name, the ohm.

The resistance of a wire or any electrical conductor is thus defined by the equation

$$R = \frac{P_H}{I^2} \qquad (33.03)$$

and is measured in ohms in the mks system. If R is known, the heat H generated in time t can be found from (33.02).

$$P_H = RI^2 \text{ watts}$$
$$H = P_H t = RI^2 t \text{ joules} \qquad (33.04)$$

If preferred, H can be expressed in calories. Since 1 cal = 4.186 joules,

$$H = \frac{RI^2 t}{4.186} \text{ cal} \qquad (33.05)$$

Fig. 33.04. Circuit diagram for a resistance.

In circuit diagrams—that is, schematic pictures of an electric circuit—resistance will be indicated by the symbol of a jagged line, and the Greek letter omega (Ω) will be an abbreviation for ohm. Thus in Figure 33.04 there is a resistance of 10 ohms between A and B. By convention the straight lines are considered to have no resistance— we can think of them as representing very heavy wires.

33.05 POTENTIAL DIFFERENCE

Consider an electric current going from point A to point B in Figure 33.04. We have seen in the last section that, as a result of the current, heat is generated in the resistance R. Thus, as long as there is a flow of charge, energy is given off by R. Where does this energy originate? It must be due to a loss in energy by the moving charges in going from A to B. This loss might be a loss of kinetic energy owing to the charges moving with a slower average velocity at B than at A. All experimental evidence, however, shows that the average velocity of the moving charge is constant in a conductor with a steady current, so we conclude that the charges lose *potential energy*. The decrease in potential energy of a unit positive charge in moving from A to B is defined as the **electric potential difference** (P.D.) between these points. It may be represented by the symbol V, or more explicitly by $V_A - V_B$. Then

$$V_A - V_B = V = \frac{\text{loss of potential energy}}{\text{charge moved}}$$

or

$$V_A - V_B = V = \frac{W}{Q} \qquad (33.06)$$

where W represents the loss of potential energy which will also be the work done or energy given off, and Q is the charge. This is an equation of great importance—the concept of potential difference is fundamental to electrical theory. In mechanics a falling or rolling body tends to go downhill, that is, to a region of lower potential energy. We can think of the difference in potential energy as the cause of the motion of the body. Similarly in electricity, positive charges tend to move from a region of high electric potential to a region of lower potential. That is, *potential difference is the cause, current is the result.*

This important concept can be looked at in another way, one which we shall develop more completely in Chapter 40 when we study electrostatic phenomena. The primary cause of motion is force. If there is an electric potential difference between two points A and B, any charge placed between them will be acted on by a force. If $V_A > V_B$, the force F on a positive charge Q acts toward B. If the charge is made to move from B to A, work must be done by an external agent; and if F is constant, the amount of work is Fs, where s is the distance between the two points. (As in section 5.01, this result is modified to $W = \Sigma \mathbf{F} \cdot \Delta \mathbf{s}$ if F is a variable.) This work is the extra potential energy possessed by Q when it is at A, and the analogy with the added gravitational potential energy possessed by a mass raised through a height h is a very close one. It is only an analogy, however. Electrical potential energy arises from a completely different kind of force, and the word "high" in "high electric potential" is used in a metaphorical sense only.

What happens if a particle of charge Q is permitted to move? The electric force F causes it to accelerate, and it will soon move with a high velocity if there are no obstructions. This sort of motion is observed in vacuum tubes. In a solid conductor, however, the atoms are quite close together, and before the charged particle can move far it collides with one of the atoms and is brought to rest, its kinetic energy being converted to heat. The electric force then causes it to accelerate again, and the process is repeated. Thus the charged particle moves down the conductor by fits and starts, its velocity varying continually but having a constant average value. The electrical potential energy of each charge in a current is converted bit by bit into kinetic energy and thence into heat.

Units. Let us pause and bring our definitions of units up to date. First, what is the relation between current and charge? Current is the rate at which charge passes a point in a circuit per unit time. In symbols,

$$I = \lim_{\Delta t \to 0} \frac{\Delta Q}{\Delta t} \quad \text{or} \quad I = \frac{dQ}{dt} \tag{33.07}$$

where ΔQ is the charge passing the point in the short time interval Δt. If I is a steady current, this can be integrated readily:

$$\int dQ = I \int dt$$
$$Q = It \qquad (33.07a)$$

The rough analogy with water flowing in a pipe may help illustrate this. If the water is flowing at a rate of 10 gal/sec (current), what quantity of water would be recorded by a flowmeter in 10 sec? The answer is 100 gal. Thus unit electric charge is the quantity of electricity when one ampere flows for one second. This unit quantity is called a *coulomb* and

$$1 \text{ coulomb} = 1 \text{ ampere-second}$$

From (33.06), electric potential will be measured in units of energy per unit of charge, and we name this unit the *volt*. Then

$$1 \text{ volt} = 1 \text{ joule per coulomb}$$

Zero of Potential. The discussion so far has dealt with potential difference only. What shall we mean by absolute potential, that is, from what zero is potential measured? As we continue our study of electricity it will be seen that we never have to answer this question, we are always concerned only with potential differences. Hence we may pick any arbitrary definition of zero potential if it simplifies things. The usual definition adopted is that the surface of the earth is at zero electric potential. There is an excellent reason for this choice, and that reason is personal safety. The earth is a very good electrical conductor, and our bodies are never very different in potential from the earth, since we make frequent contact with it during each day, either by touching it directly, or indirectly through metal railings, water pipes, radiators, etc., all of which are good conductors in close contact at some point with the earth. When high-voltage electrical equipment is built, it is customary to enclose it, as far as possible, in a metal shield which is connected to the earth. (Any point in electrical circuits or equipment connected to the earth is said to be "grounded".) Thus since we are at or near ground potential, we may safely touch this shield, although we might be killed if we touched the parts of the machine which are at high potential with reference to ground.

Sources of Electric Energy. In Figure 33.04 we showed a resistance giving off heat, and we have stated that this heat is due to a loss of electrical potential energy. Going farther back, we must find the source of this electrical energy. In all cases it originates in some device which transforms nonelectrical energy in electrical form. In 5.07 a hydroelectric power system was illustrated. The original energy came from the sun, was stored as mechanical potential energy, and finally was converted by an electric generator into electrical energy. Virtually all electric power is produced by generators, driven where possible by hydroelectric power and where necessary by heat engines burning coal or oil. Another source of electrical energy is a battery, which is a device for storing energy in the form of chemical potential energy and converting it into electrical energy on demand. Batteries are used extensively in automobiles, flashlights, and science laboratories, and many of our circuits in this book will have batteries in them. The conventional symbol for a battery is ———$\overset{+}{\dashv}$|—— where the longer line is considered to be the higher potential (positive) side of the battery. Generators and batteries are thus devices for establishing a difference of electric potential which will cause a current to exist if a conducting path exists, that is, if there is a complete circuit.

Direction of Current. Electric currents cannot be seen, and so when they were first studied it was to some extent a guess to say that anything was moving. Similarly the earlier workers had to guess which type of charge was moving. They assumed that only positive charges were capable of motion, so that current would be a motion of charges from high potential to low potential. Unfortunately it isn't quite as simple as that. It is now established that there are several mechanisms for the conduction of electric charge, and these mechanisms are quite different for currents in the different states of matter. In liquids and gases, both positive and negative charges move, so that the total current is the result of a two-way stream of moving charges. In solid conductors, positive charges are held firmly in place by atomic forces while negative charges (in this case electrons) can move. In vacuum tubes (radio tubes) electrons are freed from ordinary matter, and their motion constitutes the current. Conduction through solids is by far the most important case, and therefore current usually consists of moving negative charges or electrons. It is unfortunate that the original guess about current direction is opposite to this. Nevertheless, since we have based our definition of potential on the motion of positive charges, we shall continue to consider that the direction of current flow is that in which a positive charge would

move, namely from high to lower potential.   This is the universal practice, which is maintained because so many of the "rules" of electricity
are based on this conventional direction of current.   They could be
changed, but the amount of confusion which would result is considered
to be worse than the relatively minor confusion due to the present choice
of current direction.   When we get to a discussion of electron tubes, just
remember that the directions of conventional current and actual electron
flow are opposite to each other.

Power Equation.   An alternative, very useful form of equation
(33.06) is obtained by dividing both sides of it by time as follows:

$$W = QV$$
$$\frac{W}{t} = \frac{QV}{t}$$

Now work per unit time is power, and from (33.07) $Q/t = I$.

$$P = IV \tag{33.08}$$

That is, power (in watts) equals product of current (in amperes) and
potential difference (in volts).   This equation applies to any circuit or
part of a circuit at any given instant of time.   The circuits we shall consider first are those in which the current and voltage are steady, that is,
not changing with time.   Such circuits are called **direct-current** (**d-c**)
circuits, and equation (33.08) is very useful, applying to them at all
times.   Actually, electric power is usually handled in a form in which
the current and voltage change regularly with time.   These are called
alternating-current (**a-c**) circuits, and when we get to them we shall
have to modify (33.08) because while it is still true at any instant, unfortunately average P does not equal average I times average V any more,
and it will be average power we shall need to calculate.

33.06 OHM'S LAW

Let us look at the circuit of Figure 33.05.   Here a battery delivers
energy to the circuit, consuming its own chemical energy in the process.
The negative side of the battery is grounded (indicated by the conventional symbol at B), and the effect of the battery is to keep A at a potential V above ground.   In consequence a current I flows through the
resistance R, dissipating the electrical energy as heat as fast as it is
produced.   By (33.08), the power produced by the battery is $P = IV$

and, since all the electrical energy is dissipated as heat, $P = P_H$, that is,

$$IV = I^2R$$

Dividing both sides by I gives

$$V = IR \tag{33.09}$$

This is known as **Ohm's Law** and most d-c circuits can be solved by using it. We have deduced it from Joule's Law, which is rather more general, and the derivation shows the limitations of Ohm's Law. It is only valid for a complete circuit when all the electrical power is changed into heat energy—thus it will not work for a battery-charging circuit (in which electrical energy is changed back into chemical energy) or in a motor circuit (when electrical energy is changed into mechanical work). It will, however, apply to the resistances in all d-c circuits.

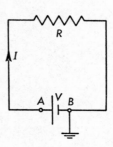

Fig. 33.05.

Our derivation also tacitly assumed that the current was steady (d-c) since we used $P = IV$. In a-c circuits the ratio of voltage to current is usually a constant, as required by Ohm's Law, but this constant does not equal the resistance. It is for this reason that we defined resistance from Joule's Law. This definition applies equally to d-c and a-c circuits.

Finally, we must mention that there is a group of electrical devices, notably electron tubes (radio tubes), which do not follow Ohm's Law at all. These exceptional conductors have numerous important applications but require a quite different and more difficult theoretical treatment.

We have listed the limitations of Ohm's Law for the sake of accuracy, but it applies to, and will be used in, practically all the d-c theory which we shall study. It is worth repeating.

Ohm's Law. *For most d-c circuits, or parts of circuits, the ratio of potential difference to current is a constant, called the resistance, provided the temperature remains unchanged.*

33.07 SUMMARY OF UNITS

In this chapter we have defined several of the most important of the electrical units. We summarize these definitions in Table 33.01

and emphasize that they *must* be known. As indicated in the table, the basic units of power and energy in electrical work, as in mechanics, are the watt and joule. A derived unit of work widely used is the *kilowatt-hour* (kwhr), that is, the work done in one hour by a source of power delivering 1000 watts.

TABLE 33.01   Definitions of Units.

Quantity	Symbol	Defining Equation	Definition
Current	I	$F = 2 \times 10^{-7} \dfrac{I^2 l}{d}$	A current of 1 *ampere* is that current which, flowing go-and-return in two infinitely long parallel wires 1 m apart in a vacuum, causes a force of repulsion between them of 2×10^{-7} newtons per meter length.
Charge	Q	$Q = It$	A *coulomb* is that charge which passes a point in a circuit in 1 sec when the current is 1 amp.
Resistance	R	$R = \dfrac{P_H}{I^2}$	The resistance of a conductor is 1 *ohm* when power is dissipated in it as heat at the rate of 1 watt when the current is 1 amp.
Potential	V	$V = \dfrac{W}{Q}$	1 *volt* is the potential difference between two points when 1 joule of energy is released when 1 coulomb of charge moves from the point of higher potential to the other.

PROBLEMS

1. Two wires are parallel to one another, each 10.0 m long and 10.0 cm apart. Each wire carries a current of 2.00 amp, and the current is in the same direction in each. Find the force acting on each wire if they are situated in air ($\mu = 1.00$).

2. In the above problem, if the wires are separated by iron of permeability $\mu = 90.0$, find the force.

3. For a certain current balance such as that in Figure 33.03 it is calculated that the force of attraction (in newtons) between the coils is $2.90 \times 10^4\ I^2$ when the pointer is at zero. When there is no current, a mass of 524.6 gm balances the weight of the coil. When a current is turned on, a mass of 541.3 gm is needed for balance. Find the current.

4. Calculate the power expended as heat in 100-Ω, 10.0-Ω, 1.00-Ω resistors for the following currents: 5.00 amp, 2.00 amp, 10.0 ma (milliamperes).

5. The power expended as heat in an ordinary toaster is 550 w (watts). If the current through the heating element is 5.00 amp, what is the resistance of the toaster heating element?

6. An electric kettle holds 2.00 kgm of water. Its heating element has a resistance of 7.00 Ω and carries a current of 14.0 amp. The initial temperature of the water in the kettle is 20.0C. How long does it take to bring the water to the boil? (N.B., Water boils at 100C and it takes 1 calorie to raise the temperature of 1 gm of water one Centigrade degree.)

7. An electron (charge -1.60×10^{-19} coulomb) moves from a point at -5.00 v (volts) to another point 1.00 cm away which is at a potential of $+5.00$ v. Find (a) the potential energy lost by the electron; (b) the average force experienced by the electron.

8. The current in a wire is 1.00 amp. Find the number of electrons which pass a given point in 1 sec. The charge on the electron is 1.60×10^{-19} coulomb.

9. The heating element in an electric oven has a power rating of 4.40 kw. If the potential difference across the ends of the element is 220 v, find (a) the current through the element; (b) the resistance of the element.

10. A resistance of 10.0 Ω dissipates 22.5 w as heat. Find (a) the current through the resistance; (b) the voltage across the ends of the resistance.

11. A battery-charging circuit contains a battery and a resistance. The total power supplied is 200 w. If 40 w are used to provide the necessary chemical action to recharge the battery and if the charging current is 4.00 amp, find (a) the size of the resistance; (b) the potential difference between the ends of the resistance.

12. In the above problem assume the battery itself has a resistance of 0.50 Ω, the total power supplied is 200 w, 40 w is used for the chemical action, and 4.00 amp is the charging current. Find (a) the size of the resistance; (b) the potential difference between the ends of the resistance.

13. A d-c electric motor is connected to 110-v mains and draws a current of 2.00 amp when it is running at normal speed. Under these conditions it delivers 160 w of mechanical power and frictional losses amount to 20 w. What is its resistance?

14. Radio resistors come in a wide range of sizes from a few ohms to several megohms and with various power ratings. The power rating is the maximum power the resistor may safely dissipate as heat. Calculate maximum values of current through, and potential difference across, resistors of 10 Ω, 1 kΩ, 50 kΩ, and 2 MΩ for power ratings of $\frac{1}{2}$, 2, and 5 w.

15. The circuit diagram of Figure 33.06 illustrates a triode radio tube in which a current $I_p = 15$ ma flows under the conditions shown. If $R = 10$ kΩ, what is the potential difference between points P (for plate) and F (for filament)? (Note that the resistance between ground connections is negligible.)

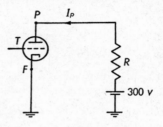

Fig. 33.06.

16. The resistor R in Figure 33.07 is made by winding a uniform wire in equally spaced turns around an insulating cylinder. The point B is connected one-third of the way along the wire; therefore, as one would expect, the resistance between A and B is $R/3$. What is the potential difference between A and B?

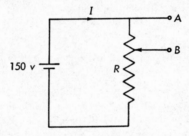

Fig. 33.07.

34

Resistance

34.01 SERIES AND PARALLEL CIRCUITS. KIRCHHOFF'S LAWS

Series Circuit.   When several circuit elements are connected one after another so that there is only one possible path for current, they are said to be in series.   Thus Figure 33.05 shows a battery and a resistance in series; Figure 33.06 is a series circuit with the tube, resistance, and battery connected one after another, the circuit being completed through the ground.   Figure 34.01 shows three resistors in series.

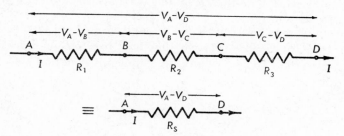

Fig. 34.01.   Resistors in series and equivalent resistance.

Let us first discuss a matter of terminology.   The words resistor and resistance have just been used.   The word ending in *-or* refers to the actual piece of physical apparatus, and that ending in *-ance* is the numerical value of the electrical property of the apparatus defined by equation (33.03).   The same terminology is applied to other electrical circuit-elements, e.g., capacitor and capacitance.

The main property of a series circuit is that the current has the same value at all points.   This current is analogous to the flow of water in a pipe with no leaks and no branch lines.   As much water must come out one end per second as enters the other.   Electric current shares this property. Current is *not* used up in a circuit regardless of how much work it may do. In Figure 34.01, a current I is shown entering at A and leaving at D. By Ohm's Law,

$$V_A - V_B = IR_1$$
$$V_B - V_C = IR_2$$
$$V_C - V_D = IR_3$$

The total potential difference is therefore

$$V_A - V_D = I(R_1 + R_2 + R_3) \tag{34.01}$$

Suppose a single resistor R_S had been connected between A and D instead of the train of resistors. If the same current had resulted for the same

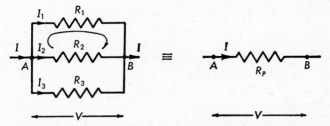

Fig. 34.02. Resistors in parallel and equivalent resistance.

potential difference between A and D, no measurement made externally could have distinguished between the three resistors in series and the single resistor R_S. Hence, we say they are equivalent and since

$$V_A - V_D = IR_S \tag{34.02}$$

equating (34.01) and (34.02) gives

$$R_S = R_1 + R_2 + R_3$$

In a series circuit of any number of resistors the equivalent single resistance is

$$R_S = \sum_n R_n \tag{34.03}$$

Parallel Circuit. If two or more resistors are arranged in a circuit so that they present *alternative* paths for current, they are said to be in parallel. This is illustrated in Figure 34.02 on the left. As in the previous case, it is possible to find a single equivalent resistor R_P, shown at the right. The current I at A has three alternative paths and divides into the three currents as shown. Since current cannot be destroyed,

$$I = I_1 + I_2 + I_3 \tag{34.04}$$

Let the potential drop from A to B by the top path be V_1, by the middle path be V_2, etc. Then

$$V_1 = V_2 = V_3 = V \qquad (34.05)$$

for if $V_1 > V_2$, a charge Q could be moved from B to A by path 2 by doing work QV_2 on it. It could then be allowed to return by path 1 doing work QV_1 for us. Thus we would have a net gain of energy of $Q(V_1 - V_2)$ and could get any amount of work out of the system with no net expenditure of energy by repeating this sequence. This is contrary to the law of conservation of energy. Therefore equation (34.05) must be true.

We now use (34.05) to relate the individual currents to the resistances of the branches and the common potential difference.

$$\begin{aligned} V = V_1 &= I_1 R_1 \\ = V_2 &= I_2 R_2 \\ = V_3 &= I_3 R_3 \end{aligned}$$

Therefore

$$\frac{V}{R_1} + \frac{V}{R_2} + \frac{V}{R_3} = I_1 + I_2 + I_3 = I \qquad \text{[by (34.04)]}$$

Since the equivalent resistance R_P must equal V/I,

$$V\left(\frac{1}{R_1} + \frac{1}{R_2} + \frac{1}{R_3}\right) = I = \frac{V}{R_P}$$

Therefore

$$\frac{1}{R_P} = \frac{1}{R_1} + \frac{1}{R_2} + \frac{1}{R_3}$$

or in general

$$\frac{1}{R_P} = \sum_n \frac{1}{R_n} \qquad (34.06)$$

Working with an equation of this type is tedious, so it is sometimes convenient to introduce the **conductance** G defined by

$$G = \frac{1}{R}$$

The unit of conductance is the *mho* (represented by ℧). In terms of conductance (34.06) becomes

$$G_P = \sum_n G_n \qquad (34.07)$$

A very common case of parallel circuits is one of only two resistors in parallel. If we remove the third arm from Figure (34.02),

$$I = I_1 + I_2$$
$$I_1 R_1 = I_2 R_2$$
$$= (I - I_1) R_2$$

so that
$$I_1 = I \frac{R_2}{R_1 + R_2} \qquad (34.08a)$$

Similarly,
$$I_2 = I \frac{R_1}{R_1 + R_2} \qquad (34.08b)$$

These equations show that the current in *one* branch equals the total current times the resistance in the *other* branch divided by the total resistance. This result is used often enough to be worth remembering. It applies only to a two-branch circuit, and there is no relation of this type for three or more branches simple enough to be of much use.

Electromotive Force. Any device which transforms or can transform energy from a nonelectrical form to electrical energy produces an **electromotive force** (**emf**). This emf establishes the difference in potential which causes current, and is measured by the potential difference of the device on open circuit, that is, the potential difference between the terminals when no current is flowing. The reason for this definition of the numerical value of an emf is that all sources of emf have some resistance. The output voltage invariably drops as the current drawn from a source of emf increases. The sources of emf in approximate descending order of importance are:

(a) Electromagnetic generators which convert mechanical energy
(b) Batteries which convert chemical potential energy
(c) Thermocouples which convert heat energy
(d) Photovoltaic cells which convert light energy
(e) Piezoelectric crystals which convert mechanical energy

Of these, only (a) and (b) are of any importance as power sources, but the others are useful in instruments.

Figure 34.03 shows a battery of emf E and internal resistance R_e delivering current to a load resistance R. This circuit diagram shows the conventional method of indicating E and R_e. It should be noted that the battery has only two terminals, A and B, and that it is impossible to connect a wire *between* E and R_e. For the moment, however, let us think of E and R_e as separate parts of the battery and consider from an energy point of view what happens as a positive charge Q moves counter-clockwise around the circuit. Starting at the negative "terminal" of E, the charge Q gains electrical potential energy EQ as it moves to the positive terminal. This energy has been derived from the chemical potential energy of the battery and will be converted to heat energy in the resistors. The work transformed to heat as Q moves through the resistor R is QV, and a further amount QV_e will be produced in R_e if V_e is the potential difference across it. Since the charge is now back to its starting point, the conservation of energy requires that

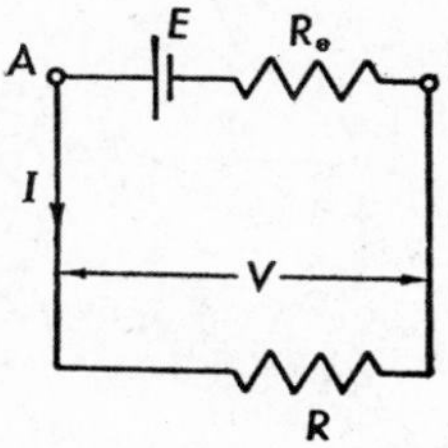

$$QE = QV + QV_e$$

That is,

$$E = V + V_e$$

Fig. 34.03.

and by Ohm's Law, $V = IR$ and $V_e = IR_e$, where I is the rate at which the charge is flowing. Therefore

$$E = IR + IR_e$$

or

$$I = \frac{E}{R + R_e}$$

Thus there is a unique value of I for a particular battery and load resistance. The potential difference V across A and B, i.e., across the load, is called the output voltage. Solving the above equations gives

$$V = E - IR_e$$

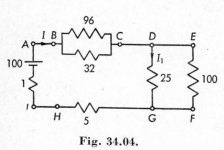

Fig. 34.04.

and this equation shows why the output voltage of a source of emf drops as the current drawn from it increases. The potential difference across a resistor is often called the IR drop or potential drop in the resistor.

Example I. In the circuit of Figure 34.04 resistances are in ohms, the emf of the battery is in volts, and all numerical values are exact. Find

- (a) the current drawn from the battery
- (b) the current I_1
- (c) the energy transformed to heat in the 32-ohm resistor in 10 min.

The first step in the solution of this problem is to examine the circuit and decide which parts can be considered as entirely in series and which entirely in parallel.   Between B and C there are two branch paths. Hence the 96-ohm and 32-ohm resistors are in parallel.   Similarly, current reaching D may go direct to G through the 25-ohm resistor or to G via E and F.

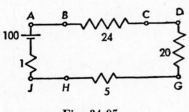

$$\tfrac{1}{96} + \tfrac{1}{32} = \frac{1}{R_P} \qquad \text{or} \qquad R_P = 24 \ \Omega$$

$$\tfrac{1}{25} + \tfrac{1}{100} = \frac{1}{R_{P'}} \qquad \text{or} \qquad R_{P'} = 20 \ \Omega$$

Fig. 34.05.

The circuit can now be redrawn with these resistors replacing the parallel combinations, as shown in Figure 34.05.

It is seen that the circuit has been reduced to a series one with total resistance R, and

$$R = 24 + 20 + 5 + 1 = 50 \ \Omega$$

(a) We can now calculate the total current:

$$E = IR$$
$$100 = I \times 50$$
$$I = 2 \text{ amp}$$

Knowing the current in Figure 34.05 permits us to calculate the potential drop between any two points in the circuit.   For example,

$$V_D - V_G = I \times \text{resistance between } D \text{ and } G$$
$$= 2 \times 20$$
$$= 40 \text{ volts}$$

(b) Since the circuits of Figures 34.04 and 34.05 are equivalent, this result applies equally to the first circuit.   Hence

$$I_1 = \frac{V_D - V_G}{25} = \tfrac{40}{25} = 1.6 \text{ amp}$$

This result can also be obtained using equation (34.08), from which

$$I_1 = I \times \frac{100}{100 + 25} = 2 \times \tfrac{100}{125}$$

$$= 1.6 \text{ amp}$$

(c) Similarly, the current through the 32-ohm resistor can be found by working out $V_B - V_C$ or by applying (34.08):

$$I_2 = 2 \times \frac{96}{96 + 32} = 2 \times \tfrac{3}{4} = 1.5 \text{ amp}$$

$$\begin{aligned} W &= I_2{}^2 \times 32 \times t \\ &= 2.25 \times 32 \times 600 \\ &= 4.32 \times 10^4 \text{ joules} \end{aligned}$$

Kirchhoff's Laws.   The methods outlined in Example I are sufficient to solve any circuit containing only one source of emf, and resistance elements arranged in series and parallel combinations.   For more complex circuits we use two generalizations known as Kirchhoff's Laws. These are:

(I) *The algebraic sum of the currents at any point in a circuit is zero.*

(II) *The algebraic sum of the IR drops around any closed path is equal to the algebraic sum of the emf's in that path.*

The first law is a mathematical statement of the indestructibility or conservation of current which we have already assumed.   To apply it, we adopt the sign convention that current flowing away from a point is considered positive, and current approaching a point is taken as negative.   (The reverse convention would serve equally well.)   Applying this convention to point A of Figure 34.02, we have

$$-I + I_1 + I_2 + I_3 = 0$$

i.e.,
$$I = I_1 + I_2 + I_3$$

which is equation (34.04).

The second law requires a choice of the direction to be followed around the closed path.   Referring again to Figure 34.02, let us apply the second law to the closed path made up of the top two resistors and their connecting wires, going around this path in the direction of the curved arrow shown.   An IR drop will be considered positive if the sense of the current is the same as the direction being followed and negative if the two directions are opposed.   Hence, since there is no emf in this path,

$$I_1R_1 - I_2R_2 = 0$$

i.e.,
$$I_1R_1 = I_2R_2$$

or
$$V_1 = V_2$$

In this case Kirchhoff's Second Law reduces to the statement, already proved, that the potential differences across the various branches of a parallel circuit are the same. This was proved earlier by combining Ohm's Law and the law of conservation of energy, and this same proof applies to Kirchhoff's Second Law in the general case when the path includes sources of emf. The emf of a source equals the work done by it when unit charge passes through it in the direction from low potential to high potential:

$$E = \frac{W}{Q}$$

(As pointed out earlier when emf was defined, not all of this work will be delivered to the external circuit because of the internal resistance of the source.) For a loop containing several sources of emf, the net emf is the net *increase* of potential and, by Ohm's Law, the sum of the IR terms is the net *decrease* in potential. Since potential is work per unit charge, equating these two is equivalent to saying that if a charge were moved completely around the loop, the work done by the sources of emf would equal the energy liberated as heat. The convention of signs used for emf is best illustrated by an example.

Example II. In Figure 34.06 resistances are in ohms, emf's in volts, and the numerical values are exact. Find the current in each branch. (A branch is a part of a circuit in which all components are in series and which thus has the same value of current throughout its length.)

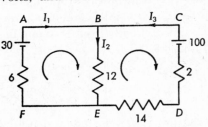

Fig. 34.06.

The first difficulty is that we don't know the directions of the various currents. We can guess or we can put directions on them at random. If the final result for a particular current is negative, it means that the actual direction of current is opposite to that indicated. It is with this understanding that the arrows for current directions have been placed on the diagram. At point B,

$$-I_1 - I_3 + I_2 = 0, \qquad I_2 = I_1 + I_3 \qquad (34.09)$$

To apply the Second Law, we must choose closed paths and directions of following them. The possible paths are $ABEFA$, $BCDEB$, and $ACDFA$. It will be found that only two of these yield independent equations, and the first two have been chosen with directions indicated. The sign of an emf is taken as positive if it tries to send current in the direction chosen, as negative if the directions are opposite. Applying this rule, we obtain

For path $ABEFA$: $\qquad\qquad 12I_2 + 6I_1 = 30$ $\qquad\qquad$ (34.10)
For path $BCDEB$: $\quad -2I_3 - 14I_3 - 12I_2 = -100$ $\qquad\qquad$ (34.11)

Equations (34.09), (34.10), and (34.11) give three independent relations between the three unknown currents. Solving, we obtain

$$I_1 = -1 \text{ amp}, \qquad I_2 = 3 \text{ amp}, \qquad I_3 = 4 \text{ amp}$$

Thus the directions of I_2 and I_3 are shown correctly in the diagram, but the current in the left-hand branch is going in the direction $BAFE$.

The circuit of Figure 34.06 consists of three branches and two meshes, where a mesh is a closed loop which (taken by itself) forms a series circuit. The number of meshes in a circuit is the mini- mum number of closed loops to traverse each branch at least once. Figure 34.07 shows a 6-branch, 3-mesh circuit. Its solution by Kirchhoff's Law requires that six independent equations be obtained since there are six cur- rents, one for each branch. These equations are obtained by applying the First Law to three of the four junctions and the Second Law to each of the meshes. It is readily seen

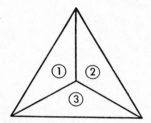

Fig. 34.07. A 6-branch, 3-mesh circuit.

that as the number of meshes increases, the algebraic complexity increases rapidly. More powerful methods of circuit analysis can be developed from Kirchhoff's Laws, but they will not be needed in the problems con- sidered here.

34.02 MEASUREMENT OF R WITH AMMETERS AND VOLTMETERS

Resistance is the basic circuit element in d-c circuits, so its meas- urement is one of the first experimental problems. Its measurement is so important that a wide variety of methods have been developed, vary- ing in accuracy and in suitability for measuring R's of various sizes.

The simplest method uses meters to measure the current through a resistor and the potential difference across it. A meter for measuring current is called an **ammeter** (or a milliammeter or a microammeter if it measures small currents). One for the measurement of potential difference is called a **voltmeter**. These instruments operate by using the mechanical forces existing between currents and magnetic fields and will be described in detail in a later chapter. The current in a series circuit is the same everywhere. Hence if an ammeter is put in series, it measures the current in the circuit. Preferably its insertion into the circuit should not alter this current at all. This will be the case only if the ammeter has zero resistance. Such an ammeter as this has yet to be invented, but actual instruments have quite low resistances (usually $\ll 1 \; \Omega$). Since the voltage drop across parallel branches is the same, if a voltmeter is placed in parallel with a part of a circuit whose potential difference we wish to know, it will measure the potential difference across itself, which will be equal to the one we wish to measure. Voltmeters also should disturb conditions in the circuit as little as possible and so should have very high resistances, preferably infinite. Even cheap voltmeters have resistances of several hundred ohms, but the price of a voltmeter goes up with its resistance.

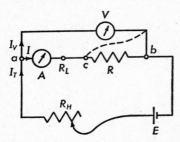

Fig. 34.08. Ammeter-voltmeter circuit suitable for the measurement of high resistance.

Figure 34.08 shows an ammeter-voltmeter circuit, where R is the unknown resistance, A the ammeter, V the voltmeter, E the driving battery, and R_H a resistance with a sliding contact so that any desired fraction of its total resistance can be included in the circuit. A resistor of variable resistance such as R_H is called a **rheostat**. Let R_A be the resistance of the ammeter, R_V that of the voltmeter, and R_L the resistance of the lead connecting R and A.

Assume first that A and V are ideal instruments; that is, $R_A = 0$, $R_V = \infty$. Then V measures the potential difference across a, b, but since $R_A = 0$, there is no IR drop across it, and if R_L is also negligible,

$$R = \frac{V}{I}$$

For convenience R_H can be adjusted to make I an even number like 1 amp or 0.5 amp.

If R_A and R_L are not negligible,

$$\frac{V_1}{I_1} = R + R_L + R_A$$

where the subscripts 1 refer to the circuit of the solid lines. If now the right-hand lead of the voltmeter is transferred to the point c (as shown by the dotted connection) and the new readings of the meters are indicated by the subscript 2,

$$\frac{V_2}{I_2} = R_A + R_L$$

Subtracting gives $\qquad\qquad R = \frac{V_1}{I_1} - \frac{V_2}{I_2} \qquad\qquad\qquad (34.12)$

It can be seen that the circuit of Figure 34.08 is best suited to the measurement of high resistance. If R is large enough, the correction for $R_A + R_L$ becomes negligible, but if R is comparable to R_A or smaller, equation (34.12) involves taking the difference between two quantities of the same
order of magnitude, which magnifies any
inaccuracies of the meter readings.

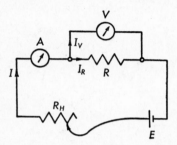

The division of resistances into the
classes high and low is, of course, arbitrary,
but if $R < 1$ Ω, the above circuit is quite
inaccurate and better results are obtained
with the circuit of Figure 34.09. In this
circuit the voltmeter is directly across R
and so measures the exact potential difference across R. The ammeter, however,
measures the total current, which includes

Fig. 34.09. Ammeter-voltmeter circuit suitable for the measurement of low resistance.

the current drawn by the voltmeter. If I_1 and V_1 are the meter readings
of current and potential difference, respectively,

$$I_1 = I_R + I_V$$
$$= \frac{V_1}{R} + \frac{V_1}{R_V} \qquad\qquad\qquad (34.13)$$

The resistance R can be calculated from this equation if R_V is known, or
R_V can be measured by disconnecting R (open circuit in the lower branch)
and noting the new values of the meter readings, say I_2 and V_2. Then
the ratio $V_2/I_2 = R_V$. In any event, if $R < 1$ Ω and $R_V > 100$ Ω, as is
usually the case, the error in neglecting R_V is less than 1%. The equations take on a particularly simple form in terms of conductance. Since

$$\frac{I_1}{V_1} = G_T$$

the total conductance, and

$$G_T = G + G_V$$

where G is the conductance of the unknown resistor and G_V that of the voltmeter, then

$$G = G_T - G_V = \frac{I_1}{V_1} - \frac{1}{R_V}$$

$$= \frac{I_1}{V_1} - \frac{I_2}{V_2} \tag{34.14}$$

34.03 THE WHEATSTONE BRIDGE

Figure 34.10 shows an arrangement of resistors, together with a power source, which is known as a **bridge**. It will be noted that no two of the resistors are in a direct series connection, nor are any two in parallel.

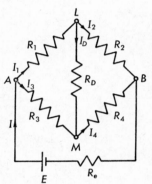

This is a 3-mesh circuit, and its general solution will require six equations and much tedious algebra. Fortunately, we are usually concerned with the special case of the "balanced" bridge, which has a much simpler solution. The bridge is said to be balanced when there is no current in the arm LM, that is, when the points L and M are at the same potential. Applying Kirchhoff's First Law at these points, we have

Fig. 34.10. The Wheatstone Bridge network.

$$\left.\begin{array}{c} I_1 = I_2 + I_D \\ I_3 + I_D = I_4 \end{array}\right\} \quad \text{or} \quad \left.\begin{array}{c} I_1 = I_2 \\ I_3 = I_4 \end{array}\right\} \quad \text{if } I_D = 0 \tag{34.15}$$

If V_L is the potential at the point L, etc., then for a balanced bridge

$$V_L = V_M$$

Therefore
$$V_A - V_L = V_A - V_M$$
$$I_1 R_1 = I_3 R_3 \tag{34.16}$$

Similarly,
$$V_L - V_B = V_M - V_B$$
$$I_2 R_2 = I_4 R_4$$

i.e., by (34.15),
$$I_1 R_2 = I_3 R_4 \tag{34.17}$$

Dividing (34.16) by (34.17) gives

$$\frac{R_1}{R_2} = \frac{R_3}{R_4} \tag{34.18}$$

Equation (34.18) is called the balance condition for the bridge. It expresses the numerical relation which must exist between the four "arms" of the bridge in order that the potentials of L and M shall be the same. The important feature of (34.18) is that the balance condition is independent of the battery voltage and internal resistance, of the resistance in the branch LM, and of the sizes of the various currents. The arm AL is said to be adjacent to the arm AM and opposite to the arm MB. A convenient way to remember the balance condition is found by cross multiplying (34.18), getting $R_1R_4 = R_2R_3$. Putting this into words, we have:

The products of the resistances of the two pairs of opposite arms are equal for a balanced Wheatstone Bridge.

This bridge is named after Sir Charles Wheatstone (1802), who introduced it in 1843 as an accurate method for measuring resistance. For this purpose it is necessary to have three known resistors, at least one of which can be varied in a known manner. The arm LM contains a sensitive instrument for measuring small currents called a **galvanometer** (usually a milliammeter or microammeter with a zero-centered scale so that currents in either direction can be measured). If R_4 is the unknown and R_3 the variable resistor, R_3 is adjusted until the galvanometer shows no current in LM. The bridge is then balanced, and R_4 can be calculated from (34.18). Figure 34.11 shows one simple, practical form called a *slide-wire* or *meter bridge*. Two brass strips A and B are mounted on a

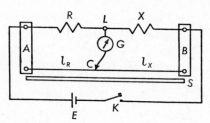

Fig. 34.11. Slide-wire form of Wheatstone Bridge.

wooden base, and a wire of uniform diameter is stretched between them. A known resistance R and the unknown X are also connected between A and B as shown. A galvanometer G is connected between L and a contact C which can be slid along the wire. A battery line with a key K completes the circuit. Lengths on the slide-wire can be measured from the scale S, usually a meterstick. With K closed, C is moved along the slide-wire until G gives a null reading. If r is the resistance per unit length of the wire,

$$R \times rl_X = X \times rl_R$$

$$X = R \frac{l_X}{l_R}$$

A more compact form is the *Post Office Box*, so named because it was invented by engineers of the British Post Office, which operates the telephone and telegraph system in Great Britain. It consists of a number of coils of wire mounted in a case. Each coil has an accurately known resistance.   In the nomenclature of Figure 34.10, R_1 and R_2 are called the ratio arms, and each consists of coils of resistance 1, 10, 100, or 1000 ohms. An arrangement of plugs or dial switches enables R_1 (and R_2) to be set at any one of these four values.   Resistor R_3 consists of coils of resistance totaling 10,000 ohms or more, so chosen that any integral resistance from 1 ohm to the maximum may be obtained.   Figure 34.12 shows a section

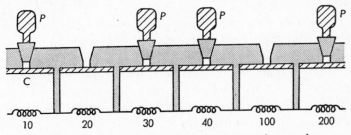

Fig. 34.12.   Construction of a plug-type resistance box.

of a plug box.   Shaded parts are solid metal, usually brass.   The top of the box, C, is a sheet of bakelite, which is a good insulator.   Each brass block is separated from the others but is connected to the train of resistance coils as shown.   The plugs P have insulated knobs for handling and brass tips which fit snugly between the blocks.   The heavy brass parts form a complete short circuit across a coil when a plug is inserted.   The values of the resistances are indicated in the figure, and it is seen that the part of the box shown is contributing a resistance of 120 ohms to the circuit of which it is a part.   The Post Office Box contains the coils making up R_1, R_2, and R_3 wired together to form three sides of the bridge. Terminals on top provide for connecting the unknown resistor, the battery, and the galvanometer.

Many modifications of the Wheatstone Bridge have been designed, and are used with both direct and alternating current for making accurate measurements not only of resistance but also of capacitance, inductance, frequency, and other quantities of interest in electricity.   Bridge methods form the basis of the highly accurate science of electrical measurements.   In the discussion above the labeled values of the resistance coils were treated as exact.   This is not the case, but most components in bridges are accurate to 0.1% or better.

34.04 RESISTIVITY

Compare the resistances of two wires A and B of the same material and diameter but with the length of A twice that of B.   Each half of A

must have the same resistance as B, and the two halves of A are in series, so we would expect R_A to be twice as great as R_B. Measurement verifies this conclusion. In general, if l is the length of a wire,

$$R \propto l$$

Similarly, if A and B are two wires of the same material and length but A has twice the cross-sectional area of B, A can be thought of as equivalent to two wires like B in parallel, so that $R_A = R_B/2$. In general,

$$R \propto \frac{1}{\text{area}}$$

Combining these results, the resistance of a conductor is given by

$$R \propto \frac{l}{A}$$

or
$$R = \rho \frac{l}{A} \tag{34.19}$$

where l and A are the length and cross-sectional area of the conductor, and the constant of proportionality ρ is a number depending on the material of the conductor. The constant ρ is called the **resistivity**. The resistivities of the commoner conductors are given in Table 34.01, and with this information and equation (34.19) we can calculate the resistance of any sample of regular dimensions.

Units. In the mksa system

$$[\rho] = \frac{[R][A]}{[l]} = \frac{[\text{ohms}][\text{meters}^2]}{[\text{meters}]}$$

and the unit of ρ is the *ohm-meter*. Another unit often used is the *microhm-centimeter* ($\mu\Omega\text{-cm}$).

$$1\ \mu\Omega\text{-cm} = 10^{-8}\ \Omega\text{-m}$$

In electrical engineering, a mixture of units is common, mksa electrical units being combined with fps units of length. This combination leads to a very convenient unit of resistivity which we shall now develop. Most electrical conductors are wires of circular cross section, and the sizes used are fairly well standardized. The system followed is known as the AWG (American Wire Gauge), and a wire size is referred to as AWG No. 12, for example. The sizes run from No. 0000 to No. 40 (44 in all) in order of decreasing size. The diameter of No. 0000 wire is

0.460 in. and that of No. 36 is 0.0050 in. These diameters are usually expressed in thousands of an inch, this unit being called the *mil*. A unit of area based on this is called the *circular mil* (cir mil). The area of a circle of diameter d mils is d^2 circular mils, that is, the circular mil is the area of a circle whose diameter is one one-thousandth of an inch. This unit permits calculation of area by squaring the diameter and avoids the number π which, of course, is concealed in the conversion factors relating circular mils to more orthodox units of area like the square meter or square inch.

$$1 \text{ cir mil} = 5.07 \times 10^{-10} \text{ m}^2 = 7.85 \times 10^{-7} \text{ in.}^2$$
$$1 \text{ cm}^2 = 1.97 \times 10^5 \text{ cir mils}$$

In dealing with the resistances of round conductors, electrical engineers measure R in ohms, l in feet, and A in circular mils.

$$[\rho] = \frac{[\text{ohms}] \, [\text{circular mils}]}{[\text{feet}]}$$

Thus resistivity has to be measured in *ohms-circular mils per foot*. This name is abbreviated, when there is no danger of ambiguity, to *mil-ft*.

Example. Find the resistance of a wire of AWG No. 10 copper 20.0 miles long.

$$\text{Diameter of AWG No. 10} = 0.102 \text{ in.} = 102 \text{ mils}$$
$$\text{Area} = 10,400 \text{ cir. mils}$$

From Table 34.01,
$$\rho = 10.4 \text{ mil-ft}$$

Therefore
$$R = \frac{10.4 \times 20.0 \times 5280}{1.04 \times 10^4}$$
$$= 106 \, \Omega$$

34.05 VARIATION OF RESISTANCE WITH TEMPERATURE

Resistance is found to depend on temperature, increasing with temperature for most conductors and decreasing with temperature for all insulators. Carbon is anomalous, being a fairly good conductor but having a negative temperature coefficient. Another group of substances, in which there has recently been a great revival of interest, is the class known as semiconductors. As the name implies, these have resistivities between those of metals and insulators, a typical value of ρ being 10 Ω-cm. The temperature coefficients of semiconductors are invariably negative.

Over a limited range of temperature variation, the fractional change in resistance is almost proportional to the temperature change. In equation form,

$$R_\theta = R_S[1 + \alpha_S(\theta - \theta_S)] \tag{34.20}$$

or

$$\frac{R_\theta - R_S}{R_S} = \alpha_S(\theta - \theta_S)$$

$$\alpha_S = \frac{\Delta R}{\Delta\theta}\frac{1}{R_S} \tag{34.21}$$

where R_θ and R_S are the resistance values at temperature θ and standard temperature θ_S, and α_S is the temperature coefficient of resistance at the standard temperature. Note that if the variation is accurately linear, $\Delta R/\Delta\theta$ is a constant, but α_S from (34.21) depends on the temperature which is chosen as standard. Two different standard temperatures are used, 0C and 20C (approximately room temperature). Values of α_{20} are listed in Table 34.01.

TABLE 34.01 Resistivities and Temperature Coefficients of Resistance at 20C.

Material	Resistivity ($\mu\Omega$-cm)	Resistivity (mil-ft)	Temperature Coef. ($\Omega/\Omega/°C$)
Aluminum	2.83	17.0	39×10^{-4}
Carbon	3000	—	-5×10^{-4}
Copper	1.72	10.4	39×10^{-4}
Graphite	800	—	-5×10^{-4}
Iron	12.0	72.1	50×10^{-4}
Manganin	44	260	6×10^{-6}
Mercury	95	570	9×10^{-4}
Nichrome	100	600	2×10^{-4}
Silver	1.63	9.79	38×10^{-4}
Steel	20	120	—
Glass	5×10^5	—	—
Mica	9×10^9	—	—
Polystyrene	10^{12}	—	—
Rubber	10^{10}	—	—

For wider temperature changes a linear relation breaks down, and we must write R_θ/R_S as a power series in temperature

$$\frac{R_\theta}{R_S} = 1 + \alpha_S(\theta - \theta_S) + \beta_S(\theta - \theta_S)^2 + \gamma_S(\theta - \theta_S)^3 + \cdots \tag{34.22}$$

where β_S and γ_S are second- and third-order temperature coefficients. Since $\alpha_S \gg \beta_S \gg \gamma_S$, etc., terms of higher order than shown can almost invariably be neglected. In most electrical work the temperature of the conductors is not permitted to rise more than 40 Centigrade degrees above the ambient temperature (the temperature of the air and other materials surrounding the conductors), and the linear approximation of (34.20) is quite satisfactory.

Several alloys such as constantan (60% Cu, 40% Ni) and manganin (84% Cu, 12% Mn, 4% Ni) have very small temperature coefficients. Standard resistors such as the coils in a Wheatstone Bridge are made of these materials to reduce the error due to temperature changes.

34.06 THE MEASUREMENT OF HIGH TEMPERATURES

The ordinary instruments for temperature measurement such as gas thermometers, mercury-in-glass thermometers, etc., are useless or awkward for measuring temperatures of several hundred degrees, and electrical methods replace them. One type of instrument uses the change of resistance with temperature. The commonest form is the *platinum resistance thermometer*, which consists of a fine coil of platinum wire enclosed in a quartz tube. Leads from the coil are connected to an arm of a bridge, and a measurement of its resistance can be used to give the temperature of the platinum from equation (34.22) since the various coefficients for platinum are well known. The R, θ relation is usually plotted as a graph for the particular platinum coil, permitting one to read the temperature directly from the graph. Since quartz softens at about 1400C, this puts an upper limit on the temperatures which can be measured with this instrument.

Thermal emf's. If two different metals are joined to form a complete circuit and the two junctions are at different temperatures, an emf is set up which causes a current to flow. This is a direct conversion of heat energy to electrical energy. The phenomenon is called the Seebeck Effect. A little thought shows that the law of conservation of energy requires that a reverse process must also exist. If a current is sent through the circuit, one of the junctions must be *heated* by the current and the other *cooled*. This is called the Peltier Effect. Figure 34.13(a) shows an experimental arrangement for observing the Seebeck Effect. The emf of a copper-iron combination is measured with a high-resistance millivoltmeter V. The high resistance keeps the current small and avoids complications due to the Peltier Effect. One of the junctions is kept at 0C, and the emf is measured as a function of the temperature θ of the other junction. The results are shown in Figure 34.13(b). The emf varies parabolically with temperature difference, reaching a maximum at 270C and then decreasing. The direction of the emf in the range 0C to 540C is indicated by the current arrow.

This combination is called a copper-iron **thermocouple** and is useful for temperature measurements in the ranges −100C to 200C and 400C to 800C. Combinations of other metals frequently used in thermocouples are platinum-rhodium, copper-constantan, chromel-alumel, and bismuth-antimony. All thermocouples have parabolic emf-temperature curves, but in many cases the point of maximum emf, A in Figure 34.13(b), is

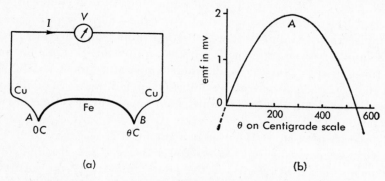

Fig. 34.13. Copper-iron thermocouple and thermal emf.

above the operating region of the thermocouple, and there is no possible ambiguity of temperature because of two branches. Suitable thermocouples can be chosen to measure temperature accurately from −200C to 1700C. Another advantage of electrical measurement of temperature is the ease with which the reading can be displayed at a considerable distance from the region of high temperature. If desired, the reading can be repeated, or displayed at a number of different locations.

The **thermopile** is an instrument in which a large number of pieces of two metals (normally bismuth and antimony) are joined in series to form many junctions. One type of junction is at the front of the instrument and the other type at the rear. If a temperature difference exists between front and rear, the emf's of the junctions are added to produce an observable emf for a very small temperature difference. The thermopile is usually used to detect radiant energy (heat and light), and the forward surface is blackened to aid the heat absorption.

34.07 POWER DISSIPATION

Heat is the great enemy of electrical equipment. All conductors have resistance and so produce heat when current is present. This heat will raise the temperature of the conductor and its surroundings until an equilibrium is reached in which the amount of heat lost per second by conduction, convection, and radiation equals its rate of production. This equilibrium temperature cannot usually be calculated but must be established by tests. High temperatures will destroy insulation, melting shellac, charring cotton, and fusing rubber and plastics. If the insulation is weakened or destroyed, short circuits complete the destruction.

Manufacturers of electrical equipment test components by passing a steady current and noting the equilibrium temperature. The current is increased by steps, and temperature is noted, sometimes until the component is destroyed. In this way the maximum safe current is established, and a power rating is given the equipment. A rule-of-thumb sometimes used is that the equilibrium temperature must not be more than 40 Centigrade degrees above ambient temperature. In many cases, such as house wiring enclosed in walls, more conservative ratings are used for safety.

To specify a resistor to be used in a circuit, it is necessary to give not only its resistance value but also its power rating. The size and cost of components increases rapidly as the power rating goes up. A 100-Ω, $\frac{1}{2}$-w radio resistor is less than half an inch long and costs about ten cents. A 100-Ω, 200-w resistor is a foot long and costs three or four dollars.

Small, cheap radio resistors are made of a carbon-clay mixture, the resistance depending on the proportion of carbon. Excessive temperature will cause an abrupt and irreversible change in the resistance of this type of resistor. Greater accuracy and stability are obtained, at a higher price, with resistors made by depositing a film of carbon on a ceramic or glass rod.

PROBLEMS

1. Resistors of 8.0, 12.0, and 24.0 Ω are connected first in series, then in parallel. Find the equivalent resistance in each case.

2. A resistor is intended to have a resistance of 120.00 Ω, but careful measurement shows its value to be 120.14 Ω. What resistance placed in parallel will give the desired value?

3. Resistors of 40.0, 100.0, and 80.0 Ω are connected in series, and a potential difference of 110 v is established across the combination. What is the potential difference across the 100-Ω resistor?

4. Two resistors of 6.00 and 12.00 ohms are in parallel, and the combination is in series with an 8.00-Ω resistor and a battery of emf 1.20 v and negligible internal resistance. Find (a) the current through the battery; (b) the potential difference across the 6.00-Ω resistor; (c) the current in the 12.00-Ω resistor.

5. A storage battery has an emf of 6.30 v and an internal resistance of 0.0160 Ω. What is the output voltage for currents of 1.00 amp, 30.0 amp, 200 amp?

6. The emf of a battery is 90.6 v. When a current of 1.00 amp is drawn from it, the output voltage drops to 89.8 v. What is the internal resistance of the battery?

7. An aluminum bus bar has a cross-sectional area 5.00×2.00 cm². Find the resistance of 1000 m of the bar.

8. A heater element is made of nichrome wire 0.0300 in. in diameter. If the heater contains 25.0 ft of wire, what is its resistance at 20C?

9. A telephone cable is constructed of AWG No. 24 copper wire (404 cir mil in area). A telephone set of 600-Ω resistance is connected across the end of a pair of wires, and the total resistance of the line must not exceed that of the set. What is the maximum length of the cable?

10. A resistance is measured with the circuit of Figure 34.08. The voltage across a, b is 20.1 v when the ammeter reads 0.500 amp. When the current through the meter is 1.000 amp the voltage across a, c is 0.20 v. Find the resistance R.

11. A resistor of large conductance is measured with the ammeter-voltmeter circuit of Figure 34.09. The potential difference across the resistor is 150 mv when the circuit current is 5.43 amp. The resistor is now removed, and the rheostat is adjusted until the voltmeter reads 300 mv and the ammeter 2.00 ma. Find the conductance of the resistor and the resistance of the voltmeter.

12. The resistance of the armature of a motor is 2.063 Ω at 20.0C. After the motor has been running for some time, the resistance of the armature is measured as 2.455 Ω. Find the operating temperature of the armature if it is wound with copper wire.

13. In Figure 34.10, $R_1 = 1000$ Ω, $R_2 = 100.0$ Ω, $R_3 = 4637$ Ω, and the current I_D is zero. Find R_4.

14. In Figure 34.10, $R_1 = 4.00$, $R_2 = 20.0$, $R_3 = 12.0$, $R_4 = 60.0$, $R_D = 120$, and $R = 2.00$, all in ohms. If $E = 2.00$ v, find all the currents.

15. In a Wheatstone Bridge the ratio arm resistors are restricted to 1, 10, 100, or 1000 ohms, and the resistance of the third arm is adjustable by 1-Ω steps up to a maximum of 10,000 Ω. Assuming that the nominal values of these resistors are exactly correct, what range of values of resistance can be measured with the bridge if four-figure accuracy is required?

16. Figure 34.14 illustrates a bridge invented for the accurate measurement of low resistances. The resistors B, B are variable (indicated by the arrows) and are adjusted so that their values are always equal. Find the condition such that the galvanometer G will give a zero reading.

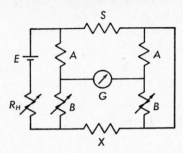

Fig. 34.14. Kelvin double bridge.

17. In Figure 34.15 the emf is in volts, and resistances are in ohms. All numerical values are exact. Find (a) the current drawn from the battery; (b) the potential difference across the 200-ohm resistor; (c) the power dissipated in the 200-ohm resistor; (d) the current in the 60-ohm resistor.

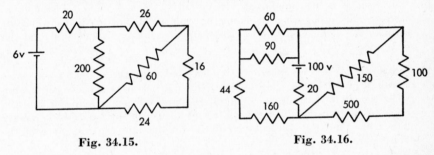

Fig. 34.15.   **Fig. 34.16.**

18. In Figure 34.16 resistance values are in ohms. Find the total resistance of the circuit, the current drawn from the battery, and the current in the 100-Ω resistor. What are the potential differences across the resistors of values 44 Ω and 500 Ω?

19. In Figure 34.17, emf's are in volts, resistances in ohms, and currents in amperes. Find the missing values.

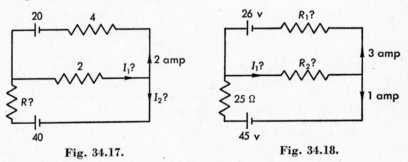

Fig. 34.17.   **Fig. 34.18.**

20. In Figure 34.18 find the missing values.

21. In Figure 34.19(a), AB, $A'B'$ are two identical uniform wires in a telephone cable which have become connected at some interior point C by an unknown shorting resistance r. Each wire is 5000 ft long and has a resistance of 250 Ω. The resistance between A and A' is measured with B, B' open as 600 Ω, and with B, B' short-circuited as 420 Ω. Find the distance AC and the resistance r.

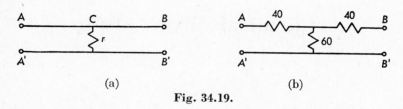

(a)   (b)

Fig. 34.19.

22. In Figure 34.19(b) the resistances are in ohms. What resistance R must be connected across B, B' in order that the resistance between A and A' shall be R?

23. A 100-ohm resistor is made of a copper section in series with a carbon section. What must the resistance of the copper part be if the 100-ohm resistor is to be independent of temperature, to a first approximation?

24. Figure 34.20 illustrates a method of measuring the emf E and internal resistance R_e of a battery. A high-resistance voltmeter is denoted by V

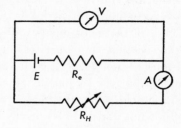

Fig. 34.20.

and an ammeter by A. The rheostat R_H is set to its maximum value, and the meters give readings of 2.11 v and 0.20 amps. The resistance R_H is reduced until current through the ammeter is 2.00 amp, at which time V reads 1.12 v. Find E and R_e.

25. A rheostat is to be made by winding a single layer of wire on a porcelain cylinder of external diameter 2.00 in. The wire is insulated with enamel whose thickness is negligible, and the adjacent turns are in contact. The length of the form which can be used is 10.0 in. Find the proper size of wire of resistivity 300 mil-ft to produce a rheostat of 50-ohm resistance. If the rheostat can safely dissipate 6.0 w/in.² of winding surface, what is the maximum current through the rheostat?

35

Chemical Effects of Current

35.01 HISTORICAL

Electrostatics and magnetostatics have been familiar, if completely mysterious, since antiquity. Current electricity is relatively new because naturally occurring currents are usually either too small to detect or too rapid (e.g., lightning flashes) to study. Investigation of currents had to await the discovery of continuous sources of electric current such as batteries.

Galvani (1737), an Italian medical doctor, in dissecting a dead frog, discovered that if a nerve was touched by two instruments of different metals the frog was likely to jump, or at least kick. The effect took place *only* if the other ends of the instruments were in contact with each other. Volta (1757) showed that the effect was electrical and that the dead frog's nerves and muscles were serving as a detector of electric current. He invented the first battery by placing zinc and copper rods in a dilute solution of sulphuric acid. When the rods were connected by an external wire, the wire got hot and bubbles of gas arose from the **electrodes,** as the conducting rods or plates immersed in a solution are now called. Volta also showed that the copper rod had a positive charge and the zinc rod a negative one, regardless of whether a complete circuit existed or not.

Shortly after Volta's work, it was discovered that if current from a battery is passed through a dilute acid solution, chemical action takes place, and hydrogen and (usually) oxygen are released from the solution. This phenomenon was studied in detail by Michael Faraday (1791), one of the truly great experimental scientists. He introduced the terminology now used—chemical change due to the passage of an electric charge is called **electrolysis,** the electrode which is positive the **anode,** and that which is negative the **cathode.** Faraday's Laws of Electrolysis are a

672

masterly summation of the experimental results. He realized that they implied an intimate connection between electricity and the structure of matter and also that they implied that electricity is discrete in structure.

Pure water is a very poor conductor of electricity, but even weak solutions of acids, bases, and salts conduct current readily. Svante Arrhenius (1859) advanced the now generally accepted theory of dissociation in 1887 to account for electrolytic conduction. According to this theory a molecule of solute in solution has a tendency to break up into charged particles called **ions**. For example, some of the common salt molecules in a saline solution dissociate according to the equation

$$NaCl \rightarrow Na^+ + Cl^-$$

where Na^+ is a sodium atom less one electron, and Cl^- is a chlorine atom plus one electron. The chemical properties of ions are completely different from those of neutral atoms. If a potential difference is set up between the electrodes (Figure 35.01), the Na^+ ion will move toward the

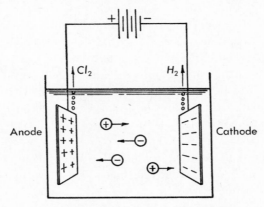

Fig. 35.01. Electrolysis of a solution of NaCl in water. The positive ions are Na^+ and the negative ones Cl^-.

low potential electrode, the cathode, while the Cl^- ion will move to the anode. On reaching the electrodes the electrical charges of the ions are neutralized, i.e., Na^+ receives an electron from the cathode to become a neutral Na atom and Cl^- gives up an electron to the anode. Chlorine is a gas at ordinary temperatures and pressures, so the chlorine atoms group themselves into molecules and bubble up from the anode. Neutral sodium metal reacts vigorously with water according to the equation

$$2Na + 2H_2O \rightarrow H_2 + 2NaOH$$

and hydrogen is given off from the cathode.   The electrolysis of the NaCl solution is a simple example, as far as the chemical reactions are concerned, but it is quite typical of the general nature of electrolytic processes.

Arrhenius' theory has been extended by Nernst (1864) to give a qualitative explanation of the action of a voltaic cell.   Suppose a rod of copper is placed in a dilute acid solution (or in pure water—the acid serves to reduce the internal resistance of a cell but does not affect the establishment of the emf).   There is a tendency for copper atoms to go into solution as copper ions, leaving the copper rod negatively charged. This process will continue until a certain concentration of copper ions exists in the solution.   When this equilibrium concentration exists, as many copper ions are deposited on the rod in unit time as go into solution.   A similar process results if any other metal is placed in the solution, but the charge, and hence the potential of the metallic rod, differs for each metal. Thus zinc ions develop a higher concentration than copper ions, and if a solution contains both a copper and a zinc rod, both will have negative potentials with respect to the solution, but that of the zinc rod will be the more negative.   Hence there is a potential difference between the two rods, and the copper one is positive with respect to the zinc.   The potential differences is characteristic of the two metals and is virtually independent of the nature of the solvent, although it varies slightly with temperature.   The potential difference of each rod with respect to the solution depends on the equilibrium of two completing processes—ions going into solution from the electrode and ions being deposited on the electrode from the solution.   The rates of both processes change with temperature, but not equally, so that the potential difference between each electrode and the solution (and hence between the two electrodes) depends on the temperature.

If, now, the electrodes are joined externally by a metallic conductor, current will flow through the wire from the copper to the zinc (more accurately electrons flow from the zinc to the copper).   This current reduces the charges on both electrodes, and these charges are replenished by the deposition of copper (and hydrogen) ions on the anode and by more zinc going into solution, using up the zinc rod.   The redistribution of ionic concentrations in the cell results in a slight reduction of its emf. This phenomenon is called **polarization** and can be considered as the setting up of an emf opposing the static emf of the two rods in the solution. An extreme case of polarization results when the neutralized ions on either or both electrodes form gas molecules.   This happens in the simple Cu-Zn-H_2SO_4 solution cell of Volta, where hydrogen is formed on the anode and oxygen on the cathode. One effect of the collection of gas bubbles is to interpose an insulating layer of gas on the electrode. The gas bubbles may be too small for their buoyancy to overcome the adhesion forces between the liquid and the metal, so that they remain on the surface of the electrode. The process of gas formation is cumulative, and polarization may cause the current delivered by the cell to drop rapidly. Several ingenious methods of counteracting polarization effects are used in practical voltaic cells such as the Daniell and the Leclanché.

35.02 THE DRY CELL

Electric cells are classed in two groups: (1) *primary cells* such as those described in the preceding section, in which the original materials of the cell are consumed when it delivers current; and (2) *storage cells*, which are first charged by sending electric current through them and can then deliver current by reversing some chemical change which has taken place. A battery was originally a *group* of cells but the term is now applied also to a single cell such as a flashlight "battery". Cells may be connected in series to form a battery, in which case they are connected with all their polarities so directed as to send current the same way. The emf of the battery is then the sum of the emf's of the cells, and its internal resistance is the sum of the individual internal resistances. Alternatively, cells may be connected in parallel if large currents are needed, *provided* that the cells in parallel all have the same emf. If this proviso is not observed, the cells will rapidly destroy themselves. The internal resistance R_e of a battery of cells in parallel is given by equation (34.06) for resistors in parallel:

$$\frac{1}{R_e} = \sum_n \frac{1}{R_n}$$

where R_n is the internal resistance of the nth cell.

The only primary cell of any importance as a source of power is the *dry cell*, which is a cell enclosed in a liquid-tight case. This is the reason for its name—the interior is actually quite moist. It is a modified Leclanché cell. The central electrode is carbon and is positive with respect to the outer case, which is zinc and acts as cathode. An ammonium chloride solution is the solvent, and manganese dioxide, which oxidizes hydrogen, is added to take care of polarization. The NH_4Cl and MnO_2 are mixed with powdered carbon, sawdust, and other ingredients to form a thick paste, which is packed between the electrodes, the top being sealed off with wax or plastic. The dry cell has an initial emf of just over 1.5 v, which decreases slightly with use. The internal resistance depends on size and age. In a new No. 6 dry cell (6 in. high by $2\frac{1}{2}$ in. in diameter) it is about 0.05 ohm. Dry batteries are available up to emf's of several hundred volts, the standard radio "B" battery having an emf of 45 v.

35.03 STORAGE CELLS

The most widely used storage cell is the lead-sulphuric acid type, familiar to everyone in the automobile battery. It consists of two sets of plates, alternately positive and negative and separated by insulators. The plates are immersed in a solution of H_2SO_4 and water. Each plate consists of a grid or framework into which a thick paste is pressed during manufacture. The paste is composed of red lead (Pb_3O_4) and a binder for the positive plates and litharge (PbO) and a binder for the negative ones.

When a cell is initially charged by passing current through it the Pb_3O_4 is reduced to PbO_2 and the PbO to pure lead. The pure lead which forms on the cathode is a thick, rather spongy, mass. A charged battery supplies energy, when connected to an external circuit, by the following reactions:

At the anode: $\quad PbO_2 + H_2SO_4 \rightarrow PbSO_4 + H_2O + O$

At the cathode: $\quad Pb \quad + H_2SO_4 \rightarrow PbSO_4 + 2H$

These reactions maintain a potential difference of 2.1 v between the electrodes. If an external voltage larger than this is applied in the reverse direction to the electrodes, a charging current flows through the cell and the chemical equations reverse, changing lead sulphate ($PbSO_4$) back to lead peroxide and lead.

The car battery usually consists of three cells in series, giving an emf of 6.3 v. The internal resistance is so low that currents of several hundred amperes may be drawn for a short time. This is necessary as an electric starting motor on an automobile draws from 75 to 200 amp, depending on the size of the main motor which it must turn. This starting current does *not* pass through the instrument panel ammeter. The battery is kept charged by an electromagnetic generator connected via the fan belt to the motor of the car. Figure 35.02 shows a schematic diagram of the arrangement. The generator G has an emf slightly greater than 6.3 v at the normal driving speed of the car. The battery's emf and internal resistance are E and R_e, respectively, A is the ammeter, and R_L is the load, consisting of some combination of the ignition system, headlights, radio, heater, etc. The starter motor M is connected into the circuit by the starting switch S, and K is the ignition key. The current directions shown are the normal ones for steady driving, the generator current I_G being slightly larger than the load current I_L, and the balance going as charging current I_C through the battery. If R_L is decreased by connecting an additional load in parallel, I_L increases and the battery delivers current to add to I_G. In this arrangement the battery is said to be "floating" across the generator. The voltage regulator and "cutout"

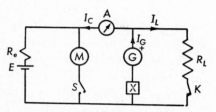

Fig. 35.02. Electrical system of an automobile.

X prevents the battery being overcharged, and also acts to disconnect the generator circuit when the motor is stopped.

Battery Charging. As a lead storage battery discharges, the plates are converted to lead sulphate and the amount of sulphuric acid in the solution decreases. Since H_2SO_4 has a greater density than water, the density of the solution decreases as the battery discharges. The state of charge of a battery can thus be measured with a hydrometer. The specific gravity of the solution in a fully charged battery is about 1.28, and it should not be allowed to fall below 1.15 before recharging. The electrical system of a car is designed to keep the battery in a properly charged condition, but unusual load conditions, particularly in winter, may cause it to become excessively discharged. Figure 35.03 shows a battery-charging circuit in which several batteries are being recharged at the same time. The emf of a partially discharged battery is virtually the same as that of a charged one, and internal resistance is still usually negligible. A control resistance R is necessary to limit the current. Note that Ohm's Law is not followed by this circuit as a whole, in the sense that if the emf of the generator G is doubled, the current increases by more than a factor two, for constant R. For example, if $R = 10 \ \Omega$ and the emf of G is 110 v,

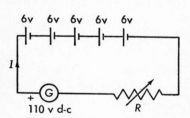

Fig. 35.03. Battery-charging circuit.

$$\text{Net emf} = 110 - 5 \times 6 = 80 \text{ v}$$
$$I = \tfrac{80}{10} = 8 \text{ amp}$$

If the emf of G is 220 v,   Net emf $= 220 - 5 \times 6 = 190$ v

$$I = \tfrac{190}{10} = 19 \text{ amp}$$

Lead batteries have many disadvantages. They are very heavy, and the amount of charge they can deliver is comparatively small. A popular size is 120 amp-hr, and this battery will give a current of 12 amp for 10 hr. As the discharge rate increases, the total charge which can be withdrawn safely decreases. The same battery will be discharged in about 3 hr if a current of 24 amp is drawn. Lead batteries will be at least seriously damaged, if not destroyed, if left standing uncharged, if frozen, or if subjected to much mechanical vibration.

A sturdier type of storage battery is the Edison cell. It uses nickel and iron plates, and a potassium hydroxide solution as electrolyte. Its mechanical advantages are rather outweighed by electrical disadvantages as its emf is smaller (initially 1.4 v) and drops off steadily to 1.0 v as the battery discharges. Despite this, Edison cells are used in aircraft where the vibration would destroy a lead cell rapidly. A similar cell, which uses nickel and cadmium electrodes and an alkaline solution, has certain advantages over the Edison cell. Use of the nickel-cadmium cell is increasing rapidly.

35.04 THE STANDARD CELL AND THE POTENTIOMETER

The standard cell is a primary cell whose emf is accurately known and very steady with time, provided no appreciable power is drawn from the cell. Two different types of standard cells are used, the Weston and the Clark, the former being more common. The Weston cell is a small H-shaped glass tube with mercury and a mercury-cadmium amalgam as electrodes and a saturated solution of cadmium sulphate as electrolyte. Mercurous sulphate is added as a depolarizing agent. Details of construction are unimportant, but two precautions in the *use* of a standard cell are vital: *first*, never draw a current of more than one microampere from the cell—it is not a power source; *second*, never tip a standard cell—it is a sealed tube and won't spill, but because the electrodes are liquid, if it is tipped they may mix, completely changing its emf. The emf of a Weston cell is found to be

$$E = 1.0187[1 - 0.00004(\theta - 20)] \text{ volts}$$

where θ is the temperature of the cell on the Centigrade scale.

Absolute Electrical Measurements. The absolute measurement of current using a current balance was described in section 33.03. Resistance can be measured absolutely by a method introduced by Lorentz (1853) in which its value can be determined from a frequency, the defined number μ_0, and geometrical measurements. The emf of a standard cell can then be compared with the IR drop across a resistor to obtain a voltage absolutely. These absolute measurements are usually restricted to standards laboratories. Experimental and test laboratories in industry and at universities generally use standard cells and carefully calibrated resistors as the basis of accurate electrical measurements.

The Potentiometer. One of the key instruments in electrical measurements is the potentiometer, which serves primarily to compare emf's. Its simple principle is illustrated in Figure 35.04, where AB is a long, uniform wire with a scale for measuring length. A battery E sends a current, whose size is controlled by the rheostat R_H, through the wire. A standard cell E_S can be connected (by key K_1) between A and a sliding contact C on the wire through a galvanometer G. The emf E must be greater than

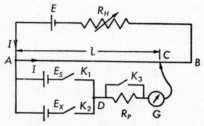

Fig. 35.04. The potentiometer circuit.

E_S or any emf to be measured, but need not be known. All cells must be connected with the same polarity toward A as shown in the figure. Two opposing factors control the current in the galvanometer. The potential at A is higher than at C, tending to cause a current from left to right. The cell E_S tends to send current from right to left. For some position of C these factors balance out, and the galvanometer gives a null reading. When this is the case, applying Kirchhoff's Second Law to the loop $ACGE_SA$ gives

$$Irl_S + 0 \cdot (R_G + R_P + R_e) = E_S$$

where r is the resistance per unit length of AB, l_S is the distance AC corresponding to a null reading of the galvanometer with E_S in the circuit, R_G is the resistance of G, and R_e is the internal resistance of the cell E_S. That is,

$$E_S = Irl_S \tag{35.01}$$

The procedure is simple. With K_1 closed, the sliding contact is moved until a null reading on G is obtained. Then K_3 is closed, effectively removing R_P from the circuit and improving the sensitivity (R_P is there to ensure that the current drawn from E_S is very small at any time). The balance is then adjusted more accurately and l_S is noted. The procedure is repeated with K_1 open and K_2 closed. If the length of wire for balance is now l_X, the emf of the cell being tested is

$$E_X = Irl_X \qquad (35.02)$$

Dividing (35.02) by (35.01) gives

$$\frac{E_X}{E_S} = \frac{l_X}{l_S} \qquad (35.03)$$

Since at balance there is no current through the cell under test, I is the same in both tests, being controlled solely by E, R_H, and the resistance of the wire. Furthermore, the E's in equations (35.01) to (35.03) are actual emf's since they are measured with no current being delivered by the test cell or battery.

A simple potentiometer can readily be constructed in a laboratory, or commercial instruments of great accuracy and ease of operation are available. Potentiometers can be used for the calibration of ammeters and voltmeters and for precision resistance comparisons as well as for direct measurements of emf. Figure 35.05(a) shows a circuit for volt-

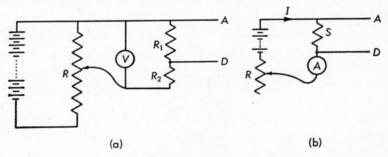

(a)   (b)

Fig. 35.05. Potentiometric calibration circuits for voltmeters and ammeters.

meter calibration. The potential applied to the voltmeter V can be varied from zero to its maximum reading by the rheostat R. The maximum emf measurable with a potentiometer is less than E (in Figure 35.04) and is usually about 1.8 v. Hence a **potential divider** or "volt box" is connected in parallel with V. This consists of precision resistors R_1 and R_2, and the potential difference across R_1 is $R_1/(R_1 + R_2)$ times the total potential difference. The leads A, D are connected to the corresponding points in the circuit of the potentiometer, and V_{AD} is measured. Then the correct potential difference across V is $[(R_1 + R_2)/R_1] \times V_{AD}$, which can be compared with the voltmeter reading. Figure 35.05(b) shows an ammeter calibration circuit. The potential difference across a precision resistor S is measured with the potentiometer. Since a balanced potentiometer draws no current from the source of emf connected between the points A and D, the current through S and the ammeter A is the same and

$$I = \frac{V_{AD}}{S}$$

35.05 FARADAY'S LAWS OF ELECTROLYSIS

Faraday's studies of electrolysis led him to two experimental laws relating the products of electrolytic decomposition and the electric charge passed through the electrolyte.

I. *The mass (M) of the substance which appears at an electrode is proportional to the electric charge passed.*

$$M \propto Q \qquad \text{or} \qquad M = ZQ \qquad (35.04)$$

where Z, the constant of proportionality, is called the **electrochemical equivalent.** It is a property of the substance in question, and can be related to other atomic properties, as is seen from the second law, which shows what happens when the same quantity of electricity is passed through different solutions.

II. *The mass of the substance which appears at an electrode is proportional to its gram-atomic weight (A_0) and inversely proportional to its valence (v).*

$$M \propto \frac{A_0}{v} \qquad (35.05)$$

Combining these two laws, we obtain

$$M \propto Q\,\frac{A_0}{v}$$

or $$M = \frac{Q}{F}\frac{A_0}{v} \qquad \text{(grams)} \qquad (35.06)$$

The constant of proportionality F is written in the denominator for convenience. If $Q = F$ and $v = 1$, $M = A_0$. Thus F has the dimensions of charge and is that charge which will result in the production of one gram-atomic weight of a monovalent substance, half a gram-atomic weight of a bivalent one, and so on. This quantity of charge is called 1 **faraday** and it is found experimentally that

$$F = 96,520 \text{ coulomb}$$

Equation (35.06) is the most convenient form for numerical calculations regarding electrolysis. Values of Z, the electrochemical equivalent, need not be known, but if desired, they can be found from the equation

$$Z = \frac{A_0}{Fv} \tag{35.07}$$

obtained by comparing (35.04) and (35.06).

Example. Oxygen is to be produced electrolytically from a dilute solution of H_2SO_4. The oxygen is to be sold in tanks of 120-lit capacity at a pressure of 10.0 atm at 0C. If the potential difference applied across the electrolytic cell is 2.00 v and the cost of the electrical energy is 4.00 cents per kwhr, find the cost of producing a tankful of oxygen.

In this method of producing hydrogen and oxygen, water is electrolyzed in a cell with platinum electrodes. The ions from the sulphuric acid carry the current, but the quantity of H_2SO_4 remains constant. The chemical reactions are:

$$\begin{aligned}
\text{Dissociation:} \quad & H_2SO_4 \rightarrow H^+ + H^+ + SO_4^{--} \\
\text{Anode:} \quad & SO_4^{--} \rightarrow SO_4 + 2(-e) \\
& SO_4 + H_2O \rightarrow H_2SO_4 + O\uparrow \\
\text{Cathode:} \quad & H^+ + (-e) \rightarrow H\uparrow
\end{aligned}$$

It is probable that in an intermediate stage the H^+ ions attach themselves to neutral water molecules to form positive ions $(H_3O)^+$ which break down at the cathode into water and free hydrogen. The only thing we need from the chemistry is that $(SO_4)^{--}$ carries two extra electrons and thus has a valence of two and each ion delivers only one atom of oxygen.

$$120 \text{ lit at } 10.0 \text{ atm} = 1200 \text{ lit at N.T.P.}$$
$$22.4 \text{ lit have a mass of } 32.0 \text{ gm of } O_2$$
$$\text{Mass of } O_2 = \frac{1200}{22.4} \times 32.0 = 1.71 \times 10^3 \text{ gm}$$

By (35.06)
$$1.71 \times 10^3 = \frac{Q}{96.5 \times 10^3} \times \frac{16}{2}$$
$$Q = 20.6 \times 10^6 \text{ coulombs}$$
$$\text{Work} = QV = 20.6 \times 10^6 \times 2.00 = 41.2 \times 10^6 \text{ joules}$$
$$1 \text{ kwhr} = 10^3 \times 1 \times 3600 \text{ joules} = 3.6 \times 10^6 \text{ joules}$$

Therefore $\text{Cost of oxygen} = \dfrac{41.2 \times 10^6}{3.6 \times 10^6} \times 4.00 = 45.8 \text{ cents}$

35.06 PRACTICAL APPLICATIONS OF ELECTROLYSIS

Electrolysis is of great importance industrially. A few of the major uses of the process follow.

(1) PRODUCTION OF GASES

The example of the preceding section described briefly the production of pure hydrogen and oxygen by electrolysis. Large quantities of these gases are used, and a considerable fraction of the total amount is made electrolytically, especially when a high degree of purity is needed. Electrolysis of salt is the principal method of producing chlorine.

(2) PRODUCTION OF METALS

Many metallic salts, when heated and fused into a liquid, ionize and conduct current electrolytically. Several metals are produced in this way, the most important being aluminum. Others are sodium, potassium, and magnesium. The current through the salt serves a double purpose; not only does it cause the electrolytic separation, but also it keeps the material molten through the heat it produces. To be economical, cheap power is required, and aluminum-extraction plants are usually located near great hydroelectric power stations. Thus the Aluminum Company of Canada ships the raw material *bauxite* (a mixture of hydrated aluminum oxides) from British Guiana to northern Quebec, a distance of over 2000 miles, in order to extract the metal at a plant a few miles from the million-horsepower Shipshaw hydroelectric development.

(3) ELECTROPLATING

If the positive ion is an ion of a metal which does not react with the solution, the metal will be deposited as a coating on the cathode or will fall as a sludge on the floor of the cell. Figure 35.06 shows the method

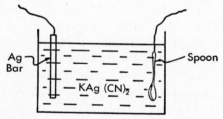

Fig. 35.06. Electrolytic silver-plating.

used in silver-plating cutlery. A spoon is made of steel or other alloy of base metals and is connected as the cathode in an electrolytic bath. The anode is a silver bar, and the electrolyte is a solution of potassium silver cyanide which ionizes into silver, potassium, and cyanide ions. Under proper conditions of current and potential, silver is deposited on the cathode and the potassium ions remain in solution. The cyanide ions, on reaching the anode, are neutralized and react with the silver to form silver cyanide, which dissolves in the solution. The concentration of the solution remains the same, and the current causes a gradual transfer of silver from the anode to the cathode. When the spoon has received a sufficiently thick coating of silver it is removed and burnished. Platings of a wide variety of metals, including gold, copper, tin, and chromium, can be applied by a similar method. The chemistry and electricity of electroplating are complex, and the processes require a high degree of skill if uniform protective coatings are to be applied properly.

(4) ELECTROLYTIC REFINING

Many metals are originally produced in an impure form and are refined or purified electrolytically. Copper is the most important case as the electrical industry requires copper of great purity. The impure copper, containing small quantities of metals such as iron, lead, and gold, is formed into anodes which are placed in an electrolyte of copper sulphate. Pure copper sheets form the cathodes, and if the current and voltage are properly adjusted, pure copper is deposited on the cathodes and the impurities (with the exception of gold) remain in solution. The gold falls to the bottom as a sludge and forms a valuable by-product.

35.07 SIGNIFICANCE IN ATOMIC THEORY

Faraday's work established the close connection between matter and electricity, and his original papers (published as "Experimental Researches in Electricity", by Michael Faraday: J. M. Dent & Sons) are fascinating reading. He believed that a definite quantity of electricity was associated with each atom in electrolysis, but he was unable to calculate this charge because the number of atoms in a gram-atomic weight— Avogadro's number—was not known at that time.

Faraday's Laws of Electrolysis are readily understood in terms of the dissociation theory. This theory assumes that a univalent element (or compound) is one which forms a singly charged ion in solution by giving up or attaching to itself a single electron. Similarly, a bivalent substance forms ions with a charge of $\pm 2e$ (e being the electronic charge), and so on. The charge on an ion is thus ve, where v is the valence, and if N ions are transported to an electrode, the charge Q involved is

$$Q = Nve$$

If the charge reaching the electrode is one faraday, the number of ions is the number of atoms in a gram-atomic weight (or the number of molecules in a gram-molecular weight) divided by the valence of the ion. That is, if $Q = F$,

$$N = \frac{N_0}{v}$$

where N_0 is Avogadro's number. Therefore

$$F = \frac{N_0}{v} \times ve = N_0 e \tag{35.08}$$

This important equation connecting three of the fundamental atomic constants has been used many times. The earliest estimate of N_0 was obtained from kinetic theory and was used with the measured value of F to obtain the order of magnitude of the electronic charge. This is a statistical approach—measurements involve vast number of atoms and electrons and merely give an average value of e with no assurance that electrons are all the same, with identical charges. Millikan, in a famous experiment described in section 43.03, showed in 1909 that all electrons have the same charge, namely 1.60×10^{-19} coulombs. Equation (35.08) was then used to determine N_0. Later N_0 was obtained more accurately from X-ray measurements on crystals, and at present the equation is used to derive the accepted value of e. The values are $N_0 = 6.025 \times 10^{23}$ and $e = 1.602 \times 10^{-19}$ coulombs.

PROBLEMS

Atomic weights are listed in Table A.1 in the appendices.

1. A certain type of cell has an emf of 2.03 v and an internal resistance of 0.257 ohm. How many cells must be used to deliver a current of 100 amp to a load of resistance 0.0100 Ω?

2. Ten storage batteries, each of emf 6.30 v and internal resistance 0.0100 Ω, are to be charged at a rate of 10.0 amp from a d-c source of 110 v with a negligible internal resistance. What series resistor is needed? If each battery is to be given a charge of 120 amp-hr and electrical energy costs 3.00 cents/kwhr, calculate the cost of charging each battery in this circuit.

3. A single storage battery (emf 6.30 v, internal resistance 0.0100 Ω) is to be given a quick charge of 120 amp-hr at a rate of 75.0 amp from a d-c source of emf 40.0 v and resistance 0.080 Ω. Find the series resistor needed and the cost of charging the battery if electrical energy costs 3.00 cents/kwhr. What is the efficiency of this arrangement?

4. A potentiometer circuit is used to compare the emf's of an unknown cell and a Weston cell. The lengths of slide-wire for null galvanometer readings are 4.033 and 1.983 m, respectively. The temperature is 15C. Find the unknown emf.

5. In the circuit of Figure 35.04 $E = 2.3$ v, $AB = 20.00$ m. The temperature is 20C and E_S is a Weston cell. The point C is moved until $AC = 10.187$ m, and with K_1 and K_3 closed, R_H is adjusted until the galvanometer gives a zero reading. Rheostat R_H remaining fixed, the potentiometer is now said to be *direct-reading*. The unknown E_X is now connected, and C is adjusted for null deflection. If $l = 16.374$ m, find the emf. What is the maximum range of the potentiometer?

6. The output voltage of the cell E_X of problem 5 is measured with a voltmeter of resistance 100.0 Ω as 1.603 v. What is the internal resistance of the cell?

7. In Figure 35.07, R_1 and R_2 are resistors in a series circuit through which a current I passes. The potential differences between K, L and M, N are measured by connecting these pairs of points in turn to A and D of Figure 35.04 and balancing the potentiometer in each case. The lengths are respectively 8.004 and 19.214 m. Resistor R_1 is a precision resistor of 40.000 Ω. If the potentiometer has

Fig. 35.07.

been previously adjusted to be direct-reading, as in problem 5, find the current I and the resistance R_2.

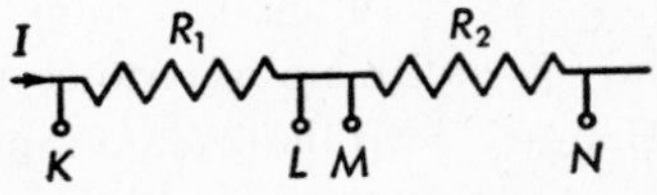

8. A voltmeter of nominal range 0–50 v is calibrated with the circuit of Figure 35.05(a). Determine the error of the meter in the lower half of its range and plot the calibration curve.

Voltmeter reading	0.00	10.00	20.00	30.00	40.00	50.00
R_1 (ohms)	10.000	10.000	4.0000	4.0000	4.0000	2.0000
R_2 (ohms)	90.000	90.000	96.000	96.000	96.000	98.000
V_{AD} (volts)	0.0000	1.0500	0.8400	1.2712	1.7044	1.0740

9. A current of 10.0 amp is sent for 4.50 hr. through a brine solution (NaCl). Calculate the volume of chlorine (at 0C and 760 mm Hg) released.

10. Aluminum is produced by the electrolysis of molten alumina (Al_2O_3) using a current of 1.50×10^4 amp. What is the rate at which the aluminum is obtained? If the potential difference across the electrolytic furnace is 5.00 v and electrical energy cost is 1.00 cents/kwhr, find the cost of separating 1 lb of aluminum.

11. Copper is to be refind electrolytically, using $CuSO_4$ as the electrolyte. If each unit is to produce 100 lb of copper per 24-hr day, what current must it carry?

12. Ten steel knives, each of area 105 cm², are to be silver-plated with a deposit 0.100 mm thick. The current density is to be 0.200 amp/cm² with a poten-

tial difference of 2.00 v between each knife and the anode. How long should the knives be left in the plating bath, and what is the cost of plating each knife if silver costs \$19.00/kgm and electrical energy 3.00 cents/kwhr? (Specific gravity of silver is 10.5.)

13. A lead-sheathed cable is 6.00 cm in diameter, and the sheath is 2.00 mm thick. The cable is buried in moist earth, and a stray current of 10.0 amp flows from the cable to the earth. The valence of lead in the reactions involved is 4. If the current comes uniformly from a length of 3.00 m of the cable, how long will it take the sheath to dissolve?

14. How many atoms of silver are deposited per second from a solution of $AgNO_3$ by a current of 1.00 ma?

15. Calculate the number of copper atoms per cubic centimeter. Assuming that each atom contributes one electron to carry the current, how fast do the electrons move in a wire of cross-sectional area 1.00 cm^2 carrying a current of 100 amp?

36

Magnetostatics

36.01 ELECTRIC CURRENTS AND MAGNETISM

A magnetic field exists in any region of space in which a mechanical force will be exerted on an electric current. It was stated in Chapter 33 that a magnetic field is *always* set up by moving electric charges, and it is now believed that motion of charge is the *only* primary cause of a magnetic field. In apparent contradiction to this is the behavior of a piece of iron. If a bar of iron is placed horizontally pointing approximately north and south and struck several blows, it will thereafter produce a magnetic field and exert a force on an electric current. The iron is said to be a **magnet.** Certainly no moving charges are in evidence here, but a consistent explanation of the observed phenomena is obtained by attributing the magnetic field to the resultant magnetic effects of circulating currents within the iron. This theory was first suggested by Ampere (1775), and the currents are often called *amperian currents.* He postulated that these currents dissipated no energy and would thus continue indefinitely, but he could offer no explanation of their origin. With the discovery of the electron and the investigations into atomic structure, the picture has become somewhat clearer. It is believed that all the electrons in an atom circulate about a small massive center or nucleus, spinning about their own axes as they move. This motion is somewhat similar to that of the earth, with its annual revolution about the sun and its daily rotation. Both motions of an electron constitute currents, and both are important in the theory of magnetism. The orbital motion offers a satisfactory explanation of diamagnetism (see section 36.09), and the phenomenon of electron spin is the principal cause of the magnetic properties of iron and the other ferromagnetic materials.

A superficial knowledge of the phenomena of magnetostatics or magnetism is very old. There is some evidence that the Chinese used magnets in navigation fifteen hundred years ago, and the magnetic compass came into general use in Europe in the sixteenth century. One of the first voyages using a magnetic compass was that of Christopher Columbus in 1492, and he is credited with the discovery of **magnetic variation,** as well as America. He observed that his compass did not point exactly toward north and that the direction in which it did point varied as he sailed across the Atlantic. The subjects of magnetism and electricity developed completely independently of each other until 1819, when Oersted (1777) observed the magnetic field of a current.

36.02 THE BAR MAGNET

Certain minerals, notably magnetite (Fe_3O_4), exhibit magnetic properties, which are shown still more strongly by pure samples of three elements, iron, cobalt, and nickel, and by some alloys of these elements. Magnetite in its natural state is usually magnetized, but samples of iron, etc., frequently have to be treated specially, or magnetized, to show these properties. The simplest magnet is a long rod or bar of iron.

(1) METHODS OF MAGNETIZATION

A bar of iron can be magnetized in several ways:

(a) By placing it north and south and subjecting it to mechanical shock or vibration.

(b) By taking another magnet and stroking the bar repeatedly with one end of the magnet. The motion of the magnet over the bar must always be in the same direction, from left to right, say.

(c) By placing it north and south, heating it to a red heat, and then allowing it to cool.

(d) By placing it within a helix of insulated wire (a solenoid) and passing a direct current through the wire.

(2) MAGNETIC PROPERTIES

The bar of iron treated by one of these methods shows the following properties:

(a) If suspended by its mid-point, it will turn until its long axis points approximately north and south.

(b) It will exert a force on a conductor carrying an electric current.

(c) It will attract to itself pieces of other magnetic material which are initially unmagnetized.

(d) If the ends of two bar magnets are brought close together, they may attract each other or the force may be one of repulsion. If the force between the ends is attractive, reversing *one* of the magnets end for end will produce repulsion.

(3) MAGNETIC POLES AND MAGNETIC AXIS

The third property above is readily demonstrated by sprinkling iron filings on a bar magnet. It is seen that the iron filings adhere most thickly at the ends of the bar as in Figure 36.01, showing that the magnetic forces are strongest in these regions. The center of one of these

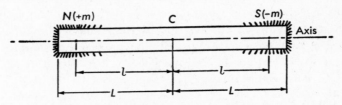

Fig. 36.01. Bar magnet with iron filings adhering to poles. Magnetic and geometric lengths.

active regions is called a magnetic **pole.** If the magnet is suspended by a string tied to it at C, it will swing until one end will point toward the north. The pole at this end is called the north-seeking or north or positive pole. It is marked in the diagram as the point N. The opposite pole S is a south or negative pole. Each pole is a distance l from C, the center of the magnet. The distance $2l$ is called the magnetic length of the magnet. It is slightly less than the geometric length $2L$, the ratio l/L being of the order of 0.85. The line through N, C, and S is called the magnetic axis of the magnet. In terms of poles, the fourth magnetic property above can be stated as *like poles repel and unlike poles attract.*

(4) MAGNETIC HARDNESS

Magnetic materials vary greatly in the ease with which they can be magnetized. Pure iron can be magnetized very easily by any of the methods listed but loses its magnetic properties very quickly. It is said to be magnetically *soft*, and one speaks of soft iron, which seems a peculiar phrase the first time you encounter it. Most steels are magnetically *hard*, that is, they are hard to magnetize and retain their magnetic properties for a long time. A group of iron-aluminum-nickel-cobalt alloys, known as *Alnico* alloys, are exceptionally hard magnetically. "Permanent" magnets are made of magnetically hard materials, which are usually very hard mechanically as well.

(5) MAGNETIC INDUCTION

If a piece of soft iron is brought near a permanent magnet, it becomes magnetized temporarily. The polarities are shown in Figure 36.02. No contact between the magnet and the soft iron is necessary, and this action at a distance is called **magnetic induction.** The soft iron will be attracted to the magnet because of the attraction between the adjacent S and N poles. If the soft iron is removed some distance from the magnet, it will be found to have lost its magnetic properties.

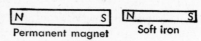

Permanent magnet   Soft iron

Fig. 36.02.   Magnetization by induction.

36.03 COULOMB'S LAW. PERMEABILITY

The law of force between magnetic poles was established by C. A. Coulomb (1736), who measured the forces between poles with a torsion balance similar to that used by Cavendish in measuring the gravitational constant. (See section 10.03.) He found that poles are of different sizes. If $+m$ is the **pole strength** of the north pole of a magnet, the south pole always has a pole strength of $-m$. If two poles of two magnets are close together, the others being some distance away, he showed that

$$F \propto \frac{m_1 m_2}{r^2} \tag{36.01}$$

where m_1, m_2 are the pole strengths, r is the distance between the poles, and F is the force exerted on either pole. The force F is one of attraction if m_1 and m_2 have opposite signs and one of repulsion if the signs are the same.

The mathematical similarity of (36.01) to Newton's Law of Gravitation is striking. Two important differences should be noted, however. Gravitational forces are always attractive, but magnetic forces may be either attractive or repulsive. Gravitational forces are independent of the medium between the two masses, but Coulomb found that the force between two poles depends on the matter placed between them. Dependence of force on the nature of the medium has already been encountered in connection with the forces between parallel currents (section 33.03), and the same property of the medium, permeability, is involved in the forces between magnets as in the forces between currents. This is not surprising if magnetism is a property always associated with current. What is surprising is that, if the relative permeability μ is greater than unity, forces between magnets are *decreased* whereas forces between currents are *increased*. Historically, permeability was first introduced in connection with Coulomb's Law, and its bearing on forces between currents developed as the fundamental laws of the magnetic field were better understood. As we shall see in the succeeding chapters, the development leads inevitably to the results of section 33.03. This section represents a relatively late stage in the theory.

Experiment thus requires us to write the permeability factors $\mu\mu_0$ in the denominator of (36.01), which becomes

$$F \propto \frac{m_1 m_2}{\mu\mu_0 r^2} \tag{36.02}$$

Units. In the mks system units have already been chosen for F (newtons), μ (dimensionless), μ_0 (henrys meter^{-1}), and r (meters). We can still choose any constant of proportionality we wish, but doing so determines the size of the unit of pole strength. For reasons of later convenience the constant is chosen as $1/(4\pi)$. Coulomb's equation is then

$$F = \frac{1}{4\pi\mu_0} \frac{m_1 m_2}{\mu r^2} \tag{36.03}$$

The name of the unit of pole strength to fit this equation is the *weber*. Remembering the numerical value of μ_0, we see that the force between two poles of one weber each, placed one meter apart in vacuum, is

$$F = \frac{10^7}{4\pi \times 4\pi} \frac{1.1}{1.1^2} = \frac{10^7}{16\pi^2} \text{ newtons}$$

The Unit Pole. Another peculiar experimental property of magnets is illustrated in Figure 36.03. If the bar magnet in (a) is cut in half transversely, we do not get a piece with a north pole and a piece with a south pole. Instead we have two magnets, and each of the four poles has the same pole strength as the original poles. This division of the magnet can be repeated indefinitely with the same result. No isolated pole, north or south, is ever found, and for any system of magnets

$$\Sigma m = 0 \tag{36.04}$$

It is, nevertheless, a great simplification in electromagnetic theory to base the discussion on an isolated unit pole (the weber), which is further assumed not to disturb any system in which it is introduced. A complete development of the theory is possible without introducing this fictitious concept, and advanced books on electricity often omit all references to

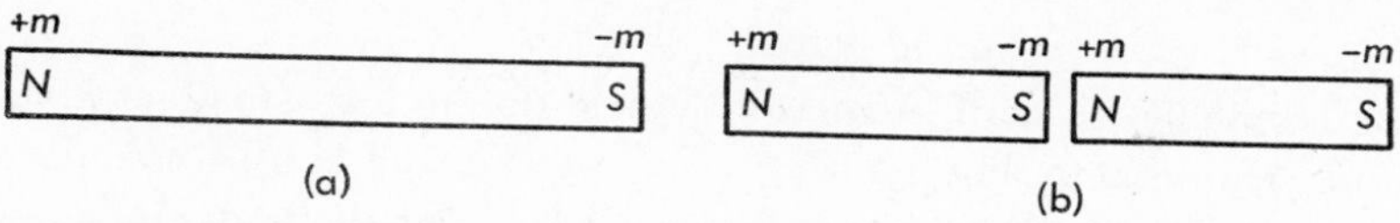

Fig. 36.03. Magnetic poles always occur in pairs. A bar magnet, shown in (a), when cut in two pieces becomes two magnets, as shown in (b).

magnetic poles. The mathematical analysis is more difficult but leads to the same results we shall obtain, which is the justification we need for following the simpler approach.

36.04 MAGNETIC FIELD STRENGTH

The space surrounding a magnetic pole or collection of poles contains a magnetic field. The **magnetic field strength** at any point in the field is defined as the force per unit pole at that point. It is represented by the letter H. At a point P a unit pole would experience a force

$$F = 1 \cdot H$$

By (36.03) if a pole of two webers were at P, the force would be

$$F = 2 \cdot H$$

or in general,

$$F = mH \tag{36.05}$$

so that field strength is a measure of the force a field could exert on a pole or a magnet. Pole strength is a scalar, so field strength is a vector whose direction is that of the force which would be exerted on a positive pole. The unit of H could be called the newton weber^{-1} from (36.05), but it is more customary to call it the *ampere-turn per meter* (amp m^{-1}), which will be seen later to be exactly equivalent to newton weber^{-1}. The word "turn" in the unit is unnecessary because the "turn" has no dimensions—the number of turns or loops of wire in a coil is a pure number—but it is helpful later on in indicating the nature of magnetic field strength and related quantities. It has been dropped in the abbreviation, which may be read as "amperes per meter" if desired.

We can calculate the field strength at any distance from an isolated pole of strength m from (36.03). If we put $m_1 = m$ and $m_2 = 1$, the force on m_2 is H, by definition. Therefore

$$H = \frac{m \times 1}{4\pi\mu_0\mu r^2} \tag{36.06}$$

In section 36.06 we shall calculate the field due to a bar magnet along its lines of symmetry. The number of cases where H can be calculated is quite small, but methods of measuring H have been devised, and a knowledge of H at every point in a field gives us full information about the effect it would have on a magnet placed in the field. Faraday introduced a valuable graphical description of a magnetic field in terms of lines of force or lines of magnetic intensity. A line of magnetic intensity is any line in a field such that the tangent to it at any point gives the direction of H there. The lines of magnetic intensity in the field due to an isolated pole are radii drawn to or away from the pole according to its polarity.

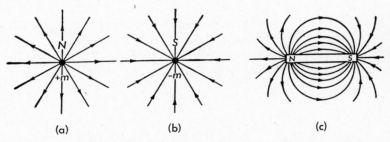

(a)   (b)   (c)

Fig. 36.04.   Maps of magnetic fields by lines of magnetic intensity.

Figure 36.04(a) and (b) show the two cases. Figure 36.04(c) is a two-dimensional cross section through the field of a bar magnet. Lines of force are purely imaginary but are of great assistance in visualizing the effect of a field. Any number may be drawn, but observation of the resulting patterns shows that they have several properties and restrictions. No two lines may cross since the direction of H must have a unique value at every point. A qualitative idea of the action of the field can be obtained by thinking of the lines as being under tension and mutual repulsion. The density of the number of lines at any point is an indication of the magnitude of H there. Magnetic fields extend away from their sources for an indefinite distance but usually decrease rapidly in size, so that the force on a test magnet is usually too small to measure if it is more than a few feet from the magnet or current producing the field.

36.05 TORQUE IN A UNIFORM FIELD. COMPARISON OF FIELDS

Most magnet fields are irregular, with the size and direction of H varying rapidly from point to point. A uniform field is one in which H has the same size and direction everywhere. Let us examine the effect of such a field as this on a small bar magnet pivoted at its center. This is called a compass needle and forms an important magnetic instrument. Figure 36.05(a) illustrates the uniform field and shows the forces on the

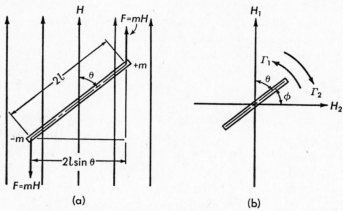

Fig. 36.05. (a) Torque on a compass needle in a uniform field. (b) Use of torque to compare magnetic fields.

compass needle, which has poles of strength m a distance $2l$ apart. The force on each pole is $F = mH$ acting with the field on the N pole and against it on the S pole. The net force is thus zero, but if the axis makes an angle θ with the field, the forces are not in line and constitute a force couple whose torque is

$$\Gamma = mH \times 2l \sin \theta$$
$$= (2ml)H \sin \theta$$

The quantity in parentheses is pole strength times magnetic length. It recurs frequently in magnetic calculations and is called the **magnetic moment** M of the magnet. It can be measured quite readily, although both m and l are difficult to measure with any accuracy.

$$\Gamma = MH \sin \theta \qquad\qquad (36.07)$$

From this equation we see that the torque vanishes if $\theta = 0$, that is, the effect of the field is to try to align the compass needle with the line of magnetic intensity through its center. Two methods of field mapping in two dimensions are based on this property. In the first, a small compass with a needle about half an inch long is placed on a horizontal sheet of paper in the field. Pencil dots are placed opposite the north and south ends of the needle. The compass is shifted until the south end of the needle is over the pencil dot marking the original position of the north end. Another pencil dot is placed opposite the new position of the north end. Repeating this process many times and joining the pencil dots gives a line of magnetic intensity. As many lines as necessary may be drawn in this way. The second method uses iron filings. A sheet of paper is placed horizontally over a magnet or system of magnets, and iron filings are sprinkled lightly on the paper. By induction each piece of iron becomes a magnet, and tapping the paper gently to overcome friction causes the iron filings to line up to show the field direction everywhere.

Comparison of Fields. Figure 36.05(b) shows a compass needle placed in two perpendicular, uniform magnetic fields. The field strength H_1 produces a torque Γ_1 trying to turn the needle counterclockwise, and H_2 produces Γ_2, a clockwise torque. The needle will take up an equilibrium position with

$$\Gamma_1 = \Gamma_2$$
$$H_1 M \sin \theta = H_2 M \sin \phi$$

But $\qquad\qquad \phi = 90 - \theta, \qquad \sin \phi = \sin (90 - \theta) = \cos \theta$

Therefore $\qquad H_2 = H_1 \tan \theta \qquad\qquad (36.08)$

Equation (36.08) permits the comparison of the two fields. Note that since $\tan \theta$ ranges from 0 to ∞ as θ ranges from 0 to $\pi/2$ radians, an equilibrium angle exists for any ratio of H_2/H_1.

36.06 THE MAGNETIC FIELD OF A BAR MAGNET

Figure 36.06(a) shows the method of calculating the field of a bar magnet at an exterior point on its axis. Let the distance of the point P from the center be x. Set up Cartesian axes as shown, with the origin at the center of the magnet. The distance $NP = x - l$ and $SP = x + l$. Applying (36.06) gives

$$H_A = \frac{m}{4\pi\mu_0\mu(NP)^2} - \frac{m}{4\pi\mu_0\mu(SP)^2}$$

$$= \frac{m}{4\pi\mu_0\mu}\left[\frac{1}{(x-l)^2} - \frac{1}{(x+l)^2}\right]$$

$$= \frac{m}{4\pi\mu_0\mu}\frac{x^2 + 2xl + l^2 - x^2 + 2xl - l^2}{(x^2 - l^2)^2}$$

$$= \frac{m}{4\pi\mu_0\mu}\frac{4xl}{(x^2 - l^2)^2}$$

$$= \frac{2Mx}{4\pi\mu_0\mu(x^2 - l^2)^2} \tag{36.09}$$

The medium surrounding the magnet is normally air, for which μ differs from unity by a negligible amount. Equation (36.09) applies exactly at any point on the X axis exterior to the magnet. It takes on a particularly simple form if $x \gg l$. In that case l^2 is negligible compared to x^2 and

$$H_A \doteq \frac{2M}{4\pi\mu_0\mu x^3} \tag{36.10}$$

That is, the field of a bar magnet drops off as the inverse cube of the distance except very near the magnet. Considerable use is made in the theory of magnetism of an idealization called a **magnetic dipole,** which is defined as the limit reached by a bar magnet as $l \to 0$ with M remaining finite. Equation (36.10) is exact for a dipole.

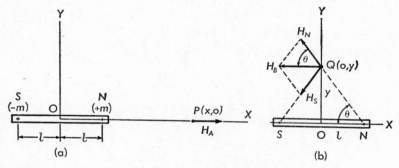

Fig. 36.06. Field caused by a bar magnet or magnetic dipole. (a) Gauss "A" position. (b) Gauss "B" position.

Figure 36.06(b) shows the field at a point on the Y axis.

$$QN = QS = (y^2 + l^2)^{\frac{1}{2}}$$

$$|H_N| = |H_S| = \frac{m}{4\pi\mu_0\mu(QN)^2} = \frac{m}{4\pi\mu_0\mu(y^2 + l^2)}$$

Since H_N and H_S are vectors with directions as shown, we resolve them parallel to the X and Y axes to find their resultant. The Y components cancel, and the resultant in the X-direction is

$$H_B = 2|H_N| \cos \theta$$

$$= 2 \frac{m}{4\pi\mu_0\mu(y^2 + l^2)} \frac{l}{(y^2 + l^2)^{\frac{1}{2}}}$$

$$= \frac{M}{4\pi\mu_0\mu(y^2 + l^2)^{\frac{3}{2}}} \tag{36.11}$$

If $y \gg l$, $\qquad\qquad H_B \doteqdot \dfrac{M}{4\pi\mu_0\mu y^3}$ $\qquad\qquad\qquad$ (36.12)

The two cases illustrated in Figure 36.06 are known as the Gauss "A" and "B" positions, after the German mathematician Gauss (1777), who first developed the analysis. A little thought will show that the relative simplicity of these calculations is due to the symmetry of the points on the axes. The problem of finding the field at a point with arbitrary coordinates (x, y) can be solved in a similar manner, but the calculation is lengthy and we shall not need the result.

36.07 THE DEFLECTION AND OSCILLATION MAGNETOMETERS

The results of the preceding three sections are used in instruments called a deflection magnetometer and an oscillation magnetometer, which together permit absolute measurements of the magnetic moment M of a magnet and of the magnetic field strength H. A sketch of the deflection magnetometer is shown in Figure 36.07. A small bar magnet A with a

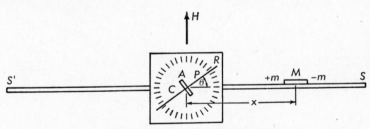

Fig. 36.07. Deflection magnetometer.

light pointer P is pivoted at C. The pointer moves over a scale R, measuring angles in degrees. The scale R is sometimes called a compass rose. This part of the apparatus is enclosed in a wooden case with a glass top. Scale arms S and S' are attached to the box and serve as supports for a bar magnet M, at the same time giving a measure of distance from C. Initially M is removed and the instrument placed in a uniform field of strength H. Using the compass, the arms S, S' are aligned at right angles to H. The magnet M is then placed as shown and x and θ are measured. If M is the magnetic moment of the magnet, and if x is large enough compared to l for equation (36.10) to be used, the field at C due to M is

$$H_A = \frac{M}{2\pi\mu_0 x^3}$$

Since H_A is perpendicular to H, equation (36.08) gives

$$\frac{M}{2\pi\mu_0 x^3} = H \tan \theta$$

$$\frac{M}{H} = 2\pi\mu_0 x^3 \tan \theta \tag{36.13}$$

This equation gives the ratio of the two unknown quantities. Next, the magnet M is suspended by its center in the field H, using a fine thread of negligible rigidity. By (36.07), it will take up a position along the direction of H. If it is rotated through an angle θ, the restoring torque is

$$\Gamma = MH \sin \theta \doteq MH\theta$$

if θ is a small angle. That is, since torque equals moment of inertia I times angular acceleration α,

$$I\alpha = -MH\theta$$

which is the equation of a simple harmonic motion of period

$$T = \frac{2\pi}{\sqrt{\dfrac{MH}{I}}}$$

or

$$MH = \frac{4\pi^2 I}{T^2} \tag{36.14}$$

where I is the moment of inertia of the magnet. The thread and magnet are usually contained in a glass-sided box, to avoid the effects of stray currents of air, and the whole arrangement is called an oscillation magnetometer. Equations (36.13) and (36.14) permit the calculation of M and H separately, and the measurements are absolute since they involve only μ_0 and mechanical quantities.

36.08 TERRESTRIAL MAGNETISM AND NAVIGATION

For hundreds (and possibly thousands) of years it has been known that if a magnet is suspended or pivoted, so that it can turn in a horizontal plane, it will point approximately north. It was first suggested by Sir William Gilbert (1544), the physician to Queen Elizabeth I, that this phenomenon was caused by the earth itself being a gigantic magnet. To a very rough approximation, the magnetic field of the earth is the same as that of a small bar magnet or dipole near the center of the earth, with its axis inclined at an angle of about 17° to the earth's axis of rotation. In general, the lines of force of the magnet are parallel neither to the surface of earth nor to the geographical meridians. If a compass needle is mounted to swing horizontally, the angle from the direction of true north (the geographical meridian) to the rest position of the compass is called the magnetic variation v (or sometimes the declination). It is given in tables or maps as degrees east or west of *true* north. If a compass needle is mounted to swing vertically, the angle of its rest position below the horizontal is called the dip D, or magnetic inclination. Both v and D are measured with respect to the north pole of the compass. The regions on the earth's surface where $D = 90°$ are called the earth's magnetic poles. In 1949 the north magnetic pole (which is, in fact, a south-seeking pole) was in northern Canada about 1200 miles from the north geographic pole at latitude 73°N, longitude 95°W. The south (north-seeking) magnetic pole is in Antarctica and is not exactly opposite the south-seeking magnetic pole. The poles are not stationary but move in an irregular manner.

The earth's field at any point is described in terms of three magnetic elements: variation, dip, and the total magnetic field strength, R_e. Even more important than R_e itself are its horizontal component H_e and vertica component Z_e. Figure 36.08 shows the relations between the various quantities. The points N, P, M lie in a horizontal plane, the triangle PAB in a vertical plane. It is seen that

$$H_e = R_e \cos D \qquad (36.15)$$
$$Z_e = R_e \sin D \qquad (36.16)$$

The earth's field is highly irregular, and because of its importance, magnetic surveys have been made of considerable portions of the surface. The quantities v, D, and H_e are the ones usually measured, and from a knowledge of these values at a sufficient number of points, maps are prepared showing the various magnetic properties. Isogonic charts show the variation at various points by means of lines called isogonals through

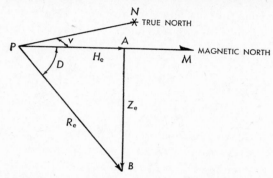

Fig. 36.08. The magnetic elements of the earth's field.

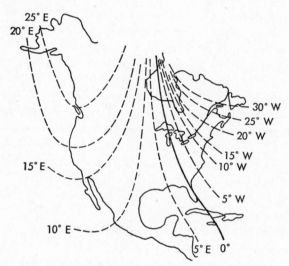

Fig. 36.09. Isogonic chart of North America. The heavy line is the agonic line joining points of zero variation while the dotted lines are the isogonals.

points having the same variation (see Figure 36.09). Isogonals differ in variation by 1° or more, depending on the scale of the map. For points between isogonals, the variation can be found by interpolation. Isoclinic charts show lines of constant dip and isodynamic charts lines of constant horizontal magnetic intensity.

None of the magnetic elements are constant at any given location but vary with time in a most complex manner. The most important of the changes is called secular and is a gradual change over a long period of years. The secular rate of change of any one of the elements is usually shown on the appropriate map or chart. To illustrate orders of magnitude, at Montreal in 1953

$$v = 16°W, \text{ increasing } 2' \text{ per annum}$$
$$D = 75°$$
$$H_e = 12 \text{ amp m}^{-1}$$

Throughout North America below 50°N latitude the variation ranges from about 24°E at Vancouver to 20°W in Newfoundland.

The magnetic compass is an instrument which is far from ideal, but it remains one of the basic tools in surveying and in most forms of navigation because of its ability to give a direction indication regardless of weather and location. The directive force is the horizontal component of the earth's field, and its small size is the controlling factor in compass design. Pivot friction must be reduced to a minimum, and for this reason most sensitive compasses are suspended from a single pivot, with the center of gravity of the compass appreciably lower so that the needle will hang horizontally. This increases the sensitivity but makes the compass susceptible to acceleration errors, since if it is mounted in a ship or aircraft, acceleration of the support produces a torque on the compass. This torque is often comparable in size with the restoring torque due to the magnetic field, and the compass reading may often be in error by an unknown amount for this reason and has to be interpreted with care. Compasses may also be in error because of permanent or induced magnetism in magnetic materials in its vicinity. A discussion of methods of allowing for local magnetism of this type will be found in any textbook on navigation.

In addition to secular changes in the earth's field, it has a very smal daily fluctuation. This is mentioned here only because it is the one feature of the earth's field whose cause is known. The daily changes are caused by electric currents which circulate in the upper atmosphere. It has been shown that only 6% of the total field is due to these causes, the other 94% being due to some effect below the earth's surface. No accepted explanation of the cause of this major part of the earth's field is known, despite intensive work on the problem during the last thirty years.

36.09 THEORIES OF MAGNETISM

The relative permeability μ serves to classify materials into three groups with different magnetic properties. These are:

(1) **Diamagnetic** substances, which are those with μ very slightly less than unity. A typical example is silver, for which $\mu = 0.99997$.

(2) **Paramagnetic** substances, which are those with μ very slightly greater than unity. A typical example is platinum, with $\mu = 1.0003$.

(3) **Ferromagnetic** substances, including iron, cobalt, nickel, some alloys containing one or more of these elements, and a few alloys containing none of the magnetic elements. Relative permeabilities in this group are of the order of 1000 and are dependent on the size of the external magnetic field in which the ferromagnetic material is placed *as well as* the past mechanical, thermal, and magnetic history of the sample. The properties of ferromagnetic materials are quite complicated but extremely important because the electrical industry existing today depends on the use of ferromagnetic substances.

The vast majority of substances are either diamagnetic or paramagnetic, and for all practical purposes their relative permeabilities can be taken as unity. Modern theories of matter have been quite successful in accounting quantitatively for the origins of diamagnetism and paramagnetism.

Ferromagnetic materials consist of atoms, at least some of which have a permanent magnetic moment. When the material is in a crystalline form, interatomic forces favor the formation of small magnetic **domains** in which the atoms are all aligned so that their magnetic moments add. A typical domain of this type is about 2.5×10^{-3} cm to the side and contains about 10^{15} atoms. The alignment of the atoms in domains is a permanent feature of the material at ordinary temperatures, but each domain breaks up suddenly into individual, randomly oriented atoms at a critical temperature called the **Curie temperature,** which is around 500C to 700C for most iron alloys.

In an unmagnetized sample the orientation of the domains is completely random, their magnetic fields cancel, and the sample shows no over-all magnetic properties. If an external field is applied, each domain is a small magnet and tries to turn along the direction of the field. Its motion is opposed by the frictional forces between the domains. These forces are large, so that a very strong magnetic field is needed to change the direction of a domain as a whole. An alternative mechanism is available, however. When a small field is applied, some of the domains will already be aligned with this field direction, or nearly so. These domains tend to grow at the expense of adjacent domains which are inclined at a considerable angle to the field, that is, individual atoms tend to "flip over" and join the properly aligned domains. This process occurs principally at domain boundaries, which thus move as the field is applied. For any given applied field, a certain fraction of the atoms will line up with the field. As the external field increases, the fraction of aligned atoms increases. Since this fraction has unity as a limit, every ferromagnetic material has the property of saturation, that is, its degree of magnetization tends to a limit as the applied field increases. Actual rotation of domains takes place near saturation. Figure 36.10 is a schematic representation of the process of magnetizing a bar of iron. The three sketches indicate progressive stages. Each square represents

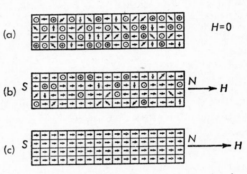

Fig. 36.10.   Stages in the magnetization
of a bar of ferromagnetic material. H in
each case is the external field.

a domain (shown much larger relative to the bar than they actually are), although domains are not necessarily of this shape. No attempt has been made to illustrate the changes of domain boundaries as the magnetizing field is increased. The arrows show the direction of the magnetic moments, the arrowhead being the north pole. A circle with a dot shows a magnetic moment pointing out of the paper, and one with a cross a moment pointing into the paper.

Examination of Figure 36.10(c) shows that each north pole of one domain is immediately adjacent to a south pole of the next domain except at the ends of the bar. Thus their fields cancel out except at the ends, and the poles of the magnet are located there. If the bar is cut in half transversely, this condition obtains at each of the four ends. Figure 36.10(c) also explains the phenomenon of **demagnetization**. If the magnetizing field H is removed, the bar loses some or all of its magnetism, because mutual repulsion between all the north poles of the domains at the north end of the bar and similar repulsions at the south end will tend to turn the domains. Some will actually rotate, but in most cases domain boundaries will shift in an analogous but reverse manner to that described above. Thus the ordered array at the ends is destroyed and disorder spreads into the bar until it ultimately reverts to the condition of Figure 36.10(a). The length of time this demagnetizing process takes depends on the particular ferromagnetic material. The same forces between domains which resist magnetization also resist demagnetization; a magnetically hard material can be magnetized appreciably only by a strong external field and tends to remain magnetized for a long time after the external field is removed.

The reality and size of the domains is now well established, notably by the magnetic powder pattern method. In this method the surface to be studied is ground smooth and etched lightly with acid. A drop of colloidal suspension of finely ground ferromagnetic material is placed on the surface. On examining the surface through a microscope, the colloidal particles are observed to be concentrated along certain lines which are interpreted as being the domain boundaries. When a magnetic field is applied, these lines are observed to move, and for strong fields actual rotation of domains can be seen. Motion pictures taken through a microscope at the Bell Telephone Laboratories show the domains gradually taking on an ordered appearance as the applied magnetic field increases.

Motion of a domain boundary proceeds in a series of jumps, that is, the motion is irregular or discontinuous. If the magnetic sample is placed in a coil connected through an amplifier to a loudspeaker, a series of individual clocks are heard when a magnetic field is applied or changed. This noise is called the Barkhausen Effect and is due to the irregular motion of the domain boundaries. (The clicks are caused by small emf's induced in the coil as the magnetization of the sample changes. Induced emf's will be discussed in Chapter 39.)

PROBLEMS

1. The magnetic moment of a bar magnet 20.0 cm long is measured as 8.00×10^{-6} weber-meter. If the magnetic length is 85% of the geometric length, find the pole strength.

2. Two north poles of strengths 10.0 and 180 μ webers (microwebers) are placed 16.0 cm apart in air. Calculate the force on either of them.

3. Two identical bar magnets have pole strengths of 4π μwebers and magnetic lengths of 12.0 cm. They are placed side by side 5.00 cm apart with

north poles together at one end and south poles at the other. If the medium between them is air, calculate the force of repulsion on either magnet. Sketch the pattern of lines of force of this system.

4. A short bar magnet has a magnetic moment of 5.00×10^{-6} weber-meter. Find the field strength at points on its axis 1.00, 2.00, 5.00, and 10.00 cm from its center. Find also the field strengths at the same distances away from the center along a line perpendicular to the axis of the dipole.

5. If in problem 3 a line is drawn through the centers of the two magnets, what is the field strength at a point on this line 5.00 cm from the nearer magnet?

6. In a Cartesian coordinate system the unit of distance is 1 cm. A pole of $+500$ μwebers is situated at $(0, -4)$ and a pole of -100 μwebers at $(2, 0)$. Find the field strength at the origin if μ is unity.

7. What is the maximum torque which a field of 1000 amp m^{-1} can exert on a magnet of moment 20.0×10^{-6} weber-meter?

8. A compass needle of magnetic moment 60.0×10^{-6} weber-meter is mounted in jeweled bearings which exert a maximum frictional torque of 1.00×10^{-5} newton-meter (Nm). What is the minimum value of the horizontal component of the earth's magnetic field which will cause the compass needle to point within $2.00°$ of magnetic north?

9. At a location where the horizontal component of the earth's field is 12.5 amp m^{-1}, a second magnetic field is set up perpendicular to H_e. A compass needle acted on by both fields points $64.3°$ from magnetic north. Find the unknown field.

10. H_e is measured as 10.6 amp m^{-1} at a place where the angle of dip is $68.0°$. Find the total strength of the earth's field and its vertical component at this place.

11. Lighthouse A is 3000 yd due north of lighthouse B. A navigator on a ship observes the directions of the two lighthouses to be $030°$, $120°$ by his compass. (In navigation, angles are measured clockwise from north.) If the variation is $15°$E, how far is the ship from each lighthouse?

12. In Figure 36.07, $x = 45.0$ cm, $\theta = 30.0°$, and $H = 40.0$ amp m^{-1}. Find M. if the length of the magnet is negligible.

13. The horizontal component of the earth's field is measured with oscillation and deflection magnetometers. The magnet used has a moment of inertia of 4.00×10^{-5} kgm m^2 and oscillates in the earth's field with a period of 6.53 sec. When it is set up as in Figure 36.07 with $x = 30.0$ cm, the deflection θ is $40.7°$. The magnetic length of the magnet is 5.00 cm. Find H_e.

14. An oscillation magnetometer is used to make a survey of the value of H_e in the cockpit of a stationary aircraft in order to determine the best location for a magnetic compass. The magnet executes 40.0 swings in 2.00 min when

the magnetometer is placed outside the aircraft at a place where H_e is known to be 12.4 amp m^{-1}.   In 2.00-min tests at positions A, B, C in the cockpit it makes 20.0, 16.5, and 32.0 swings, respectively.   Find H_e at the three positions.   Which is the best location for a compass?

15. A small compass needle has a moment of inertia of 4.80×10^{-6} kgm m^2 and a magnetic moment of 1.02×10^{-6} mks units.   What is its period of oscillation at a place where $H = 12.0$ amp m^{-1}?

16. A bar magnet is placed horizontally with its axis pointing magnetic north and south.   A compass needle, when placed with its center magnetic south of the magnet, points north and oscillates with a period of 15.00 sec.   When the magnet is reversed but left in the same position, the needle still points north, but its period is now 5.00 sec.   Find its period of oscillation if the magnet is removed.

37

Magnetic Effects of Current

37.01 OERSTED'S EXPERIMENT

The discovery in 1819 by Oersted of the magnetic field of an electric current has already been mentioned. This discovery was made by him while performing a demonstration experiment in a lecture to his students. Figure 37.01(a) shows a simple apparatus for demonstrating

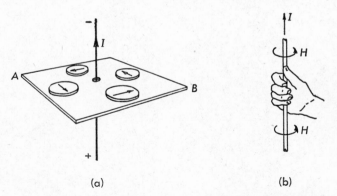

(a)   (b)

Fig. 37.01. Magnetic field of a current and right-hand rule.

the effect. A wire is run vertically through a hole drilled in the center of AB, a horizontal surface such as a table top. Small compass needles placed on AB point north. When a current is established in the wire, the compass needles swing around perpendicular to the wire, showing that the current produces a magnetic field. If the field is mapped as described in section 36.05, the lines of force are circles about the wire. Figure 37.01(b) illustrates a convenient rule for remembering the direction of the field.

Right-Hand (Current) Rule.   Imagine you are grasping the wire with your right hand, your thumb being along the (conventional) direction of current.   Then your fingers point in the direction of the magnetic field.

The word "current" in the name is to distinguish it from another right-hand rule we shall introduce in the next chapter.

37.02 BIOT'S LAW

Within a few years of Oersted's discovery, the magnetic fields due to currents were studied intensively by a number of French scientists including Biot (1774), Savart (1791), Ampere, and Laplace (1749).   It was found that the relation between the size of the current and the strength of the field could be put into a simple form only in terms of differential elements.   That is, the field depends on the current and various geometrical factors, but the relation is best expressed in terms of the contribution to the field of a very short piece of the current-carrying conductor.   This is quite typical of field relations in electromagnetic theory.   The law has been attributed to all the scientists listed above, but it seems probable that Biot was the first to announce it.   In Figure 37.02, which illustrates the law, AB is a conductor carrying a current I.   We wish to find the field strength H at some point P.   We choose some short piece of the wire Δl and join the center of it to P.   This line of length r is called the radius vector, and the angle it makes with Δl is θ.   Then the current in the length of wire Δl will produce a field ΔH at P where

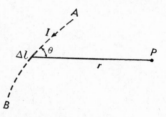

Fig. 37.02.   Biot's Law.

$$\Delta H \propto \frac{I \, \Delta l \sin \theta}{r^2} \tag{37.01}$$

Note that $\Delta l \sin \theta$ is the projection of Δl perpendicular to the radius vector, that is, the apparent length of Δl as seen from P.   The field ΔH is at right angles to the plane containing Δl and r, and in the figure must be coming out of the paper, by the right-hand rule.   To find the total field, the contributions from each element Δl of the entire circuit must be added, remembering that since H is a vector the addition must be vectorial.

In the last chapter, the magnetic field strength H was defined in terms of force and magnetic pole strength, but the name of the unit of H (the ampere per meter) indicated a connection with electric current. This connection is shown explicitly in (37.01), and we see that this proportionality gives the dimensions of H as amperes per meter as before. Hence the constant of proportionality to turn (37.01) into an equation must be a pure number.   For many years (37.01) was used to define the unit of current by making an arbitrary choice of this constant of proportionality, but as we have already defined the ampere in section 33.03 we must choose the constant to be consistent with that definition.   Considerable development of the theory lies ahead of us in order to show the connection between (37.01) and (33.01), so for the present we shall state the value of the constant of proportionality, which is $1/4\pi$, and show in section 38.06 that we are led back to equation (33.01).   With this choice, Biot's Law is written as

$$\Delta H = \frac{I\,\Delta l\,\sin\,\theta}{4\pi r^2} \qquad\qquad (37.02)$$

(1) FIELD AT THE CENTER OF A CIRCULAR COIL

Suppose the circuit consists of a wire bent in the form of a circular coil of radius r, and we wish to find the field at the center.   Figure 37.03 shows an element Δl.   Since $\theta = 90°$,

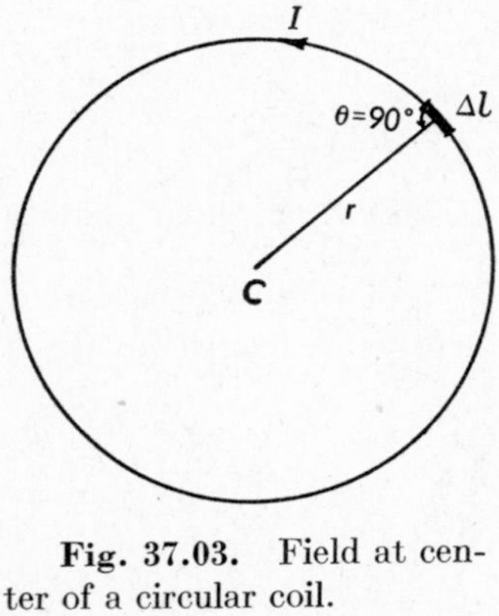

$$\Delta H = \frac{I\,\Delta l}{4\pi r^2}$$

The values of I and r are the same for any element Δl of the circle.   Furthermore, the ΔH for each element acts through C perpendicular to the plane of the wire and out of the paper.   Therefore

Fig. 37.03.   Field at center of a circular coil.

$$H_C = \Sigma\,\Delta H = \Sigma\,\frac{I\,\Delta l}{4\pi r^2} = \frac{I}{4\pi r^2}\,\Sigma(\Delta l)$$

$\Sigma(\Delta l)$ is the total length of the wire, that is, the number of turns, N, times the circumference.   Hence

$$H_C = \frac{I}{4\pi r^2}\,N(2\pi r) = \frac{NI}{2r} \qquad\qquad (37.03)$$

This calculation of H_C is quite straightforward because of the symmetry of the point C.   However, general expressions for the field due to an electric current in a circuit are calculable in relatively few cases. In principle, all that is involved is the adding up of the components given by (37.02), but this adding up or integration is usually very difficult to perform. A valuable indirect method will be outlined in section 37.05. Three further important results are stated here.

(2) LONG, STRAIGHT WIRE

If current flows in a long, straight wire, as in Figure 37.04(a), the return circuit being at some distance, the field at any point is

$$H = \frac{I}{2\pi d} \tag{37.04}$$

where d is the perpendicular distance from the point to the wire. This result was found experimentally by Biot and Savart before equation (37.01) was formulated and is sometimes called the *Biot-Savart Law*.

(3) SOLENOID

The field inside a long solenoid is uniform and is given by

$$H = nI \tag{37.05}$$

where n is the number of turns per unit length; see Figure 37.04(b).

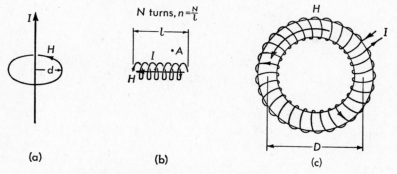

(a) (b) (c)

Fig. 37.04. Magnetic fields of various circuits.

This field is virtually confined to the inside of the solenoid, that is, the field at point A is very small.

(4) TOROID

Figure 37.04(c) illustrates a toroidal coil, which is a coil wound completely around a closed cylindrical form. The field of a toroid is confined entirely within the rim and is

$$H = \frac{NI}{\pi D} \tag{37.06}$$

where N is the total number of turns and D the average diameter of the rim.

37.03 ELECTROMAGNETS

Equation (37.05) is exact only for a solenoid of infinite length but gives a fairly good approximation for the field in the interior of a helix whose length is several times as great as its diameter. For a solenoid of finite length, what is the field outside the coil? This can be found by mapping the field by either of the methods of 36.05, and the pattern is shown in Figure 37.05(a). Comparing this diagram with Figure 36.04(c),

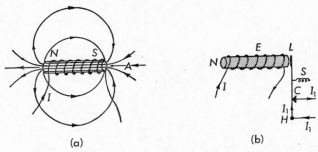

(a)   (b)

Fig. 37.05. The magnetic field of a solenoid and its application in a relay.

we see that the external field of a solenoid can be used in place of a bar magnet, with the added advantage that the field can be turned on and off at will. For a reasonable current the field at an external point such as A will not be very large, but it can be increased greatly, without an increase of current, if a soft iron core is placed inside the coil. A qualitative explanation of this increase is easy to find. When the current I is present, the field it sets up inside the coil acts on the soft iron, converting it into a bar magnet by induction. Its N pole is at the "north" end of the solenoid, so the external field of the magnet adds to that of the coil. The effect of the core may easily be to increase the field at A by a factor of 20 or more. A coil with a soft iron core is called an **electromagnet** and acts as a magnet only when there is current in the coil, since soft iron loses its magnetism almost immediately when the inducing magnetic field is turned off. Electromagnets are not restricted to solenoids but may be of many different shapes. The most powerful external magnetic fields are produced by making the iron core an almost-closed ring with a thin air gap.

Solenoids are used extensively in **relays**, which are devices for causing an impulse in one part of a system to have an effect on a different part. Figure 37.05(b) shows one type of solenoid-operated relay, in which E is the iron-cored solenoid, L a lever hinged at H, S a spring, and C a fixed contact. The lever ends in a soft iron plate which is attracted toward the electromagnet E. As the diagram is drawn, the pull of E is less than that of the spring, and L remains in contact with C, permitting the current I_1 to flow. If I is increased sufficiently, the pull of E overcomes that of the spring, L moves to the left, and the circuit for the current I_1 is broken. The relay is then said to be open.

Figure 37.06(a) shows the forces on a piece of soft iron in a magnetic field whose strength varies. Pole strengths of $+m$ and $-m$ are produced

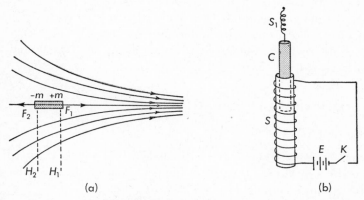

Fig. 37.06. (a) Forces acting on iron in a nonuniform field. (b) Plunger action in a solenoid.

in the iron by induction. The force on the $+m$ pole is $F_1 = mH_1$ and that on the $-m$ pole is $F_2 = mH_2$. Since $H_1 > H_2$, the iron moves to the right. We have already seen that a *uniform* field can only produce rotation of a piece of iron. If the field is *nonuniform*, in addition to the torque trying to align the bar with the field, there is a translational force trying to move it to the strongest part of the field. Figure 37.06(b) shows a solenoid S in which the motion of the core C is controlled by the field. With K open, the spring S_1 holds the core up. When K is closed, the field set up by the solenoid draws the core down into the higher field region. This plunger action is widely used in electrical switches when motion is required over a greater distance than in an ordinary relay.

Lifting magnets are often used in handling steel and other ferromagnetic material. The core C is made of soft iron in a cylindrical shape,

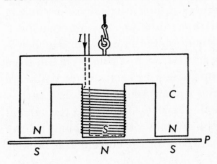

shown in cross section in Figure 37.07. It is lowered onto the steel plate P, and the current is turned on. The plate forms part of the electromagnet, and strong forces are developed between the core and the plate (which have polarities induced in them as shown). When the plate has been moved to the desired location, it can be released by turning off the current.

Fig. 37.07. Lifting electromagnet.

Electromagnets can be operated by either steady currents (direct current) or alternating currents. When alternating current is used to energize the magnet, the magnetic field reverses in direction every time the current reverses, but as the induced magnetism in the soft iron being attracted also reverses, the force on it remains one of attraction although fluctuating rapidly in size.

37.04 SOME CIRCUIT APPLICATIONS

(1) ELECTRIC BELL

Figure 37.08 shows a circuit for ringing a bell. A lever L, hinged at H, is held up by a spring S. It carries a clapper C, which can strike the gong G when the circuit is completed. When the key K is closed, current energizes the electromagnet E, which attracts the soft iron segment A of L. The motion of L breaks the circuit at the fixed contact B, and the spring pulls L back. As long as K is closed, L will thus move back and forth several times

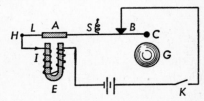

Fig. 37.08. Electric bell circuit.

a second, ringing the bell. The inertia of the bar HC and the tension of the spring regulate the number of times per second the bell is struck.

(2) TELEGRAPH SYSTEM

In the Morse code a system of "dots" (short sounds) and "dashes" (long sounds) is used to represent the individual letters of the alphabet.

Thus the international Distress Call SOS is (·· ·−−−·· ·). By means of this code any message could be spelled out, one letter at a time, with the circuit of Figure 37.08.   This is the principle of the telegraph system. To increase speed, the circuit is modified so that a single click is made in the sounder when K is closed.   The difference between a dot and a dash is indicated by the time interval between clicks (and a slightly different code is used).   The speed possible with this system is surprising—a skilled operator can transmit or interpret the clicking sounds at a rate of fifty or more words per minute.   In the "teletype" system the message is typed on a keyboard and coded automatically.   At the receiving end the machine interprets the signal received and types out the message again.

(3) TELEPHONE CIRCUITS

A telephone circuit includes a microphone to convert the pressure variations in a sound wave into variations in an electric current and a receiver to convert the fluctuating current back to sound.   The microphone used consists of two graphite disks with loosely packed granules of carbon between them.   In Figure 37.09(a) the sound wave striking

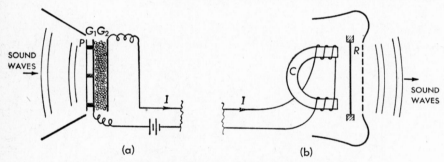

Fig. 37.09.   Carbon microphone and telephone receiver.

the plate P causes it to vibrate in and out with the frequency of the sound wave.   One graphite plate G_1 is rigidly connected to P, and the other is fixed.   The resistance of the carbon microphone decreases as the plates G_1, G_2 are pushed together, and the variation in resistance causes the size of I to fluctuate with the sound frequency.   The microphone is connected by a pair of wires with the receiver at the other end as in Figure 37.09(b). The wire makes many turns around a steel core C of a permanent horseshoe magnet.   This permanent magnetism is necessary to prevent doubling the frequencies.   A thin iron plate R clamped around its rim is attracted by this magnet and vibrates with the frequency of the fluctuations of I, generating sound waves which are very similar to those falling on the microphone.

A telephone set has a microphone and receiver in parallel across the wires, and the line leads to a central office with switching arrangements by which the line may be connected with any other telephone set. In most cases the switching is automatic and is controlled by a dial on the calling set, which can send a series of timed pulses. Telephone circuits are a very interesting combination of electrical and mechanical devices. As a measure of their complexity, the completion of a connection made by dialing a seven-digit number involves the action of approximately sixty relays similar in principle to that of Figure 37.05(b) but often having five or six contacts instead of the single one shown in the figure.

37.05 CALCULUS METHODS. MAGNETOMOTIVE FORCE

Figure 37.10(a) shows a current in a long, straight wire. The field at P due to the length Δl is

$$\Delta H = \frac{I \, \Delta l \sin \theta}{4\pi r^2} \tag{37.07}$$

and acts at right angles to the plane of the diagram independently of the position of the element of length. The total field can thus be found by an

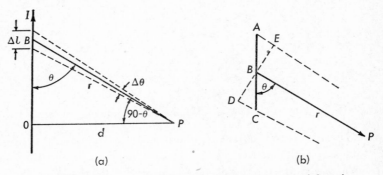

Fig. 37.10.   Magnetic field of current in a long, straight wire.

arithmetical addition or integration of (37.07). The equation contains three variables, l, r, and θ, and these must be transformed to a single variable before we can integrate. The (b) part of the figure shows an enlarged view of Δl; DE is an arc of a circle of radius r and center P, and $AC = \Delta l$. As pointed out before when Biot's Law was introduced, the term $\Delta l \sin \theta$ is the apparent length of Δl as seen from P. That is,

$$\Delta l \sin \theta \doteq DE = r \, \Delta \theta$$

where $\Delta \theta$ is the angle subtended at P by the length Δl. As $\Delta l \rightarrow 0$ (and hence $\Delta \theta \rightarrow 0$), the relation becomes exact and

$$\sin \theta \, dl = r \, d\theta \qquad\qquad (37.08)$$

In the triangle OBP of Figure 37.10(a),

$$d = r \sin \theta \qquad\qquad (37.09)$$

where d is the perpendicular distance of P from the wire. Substituting these results in (37.07), we have

$$dH = \frac{Ir \, d\theta}{4\pi r^2} = \frac{I \, d\theta}{4\pi r} = \frac{I \sin \theta \, d\theta}{4\pi d}$$

The wire is assumed to be infinitely long, so that at the top $\theta = 0$ and at the bottom $\theta = \pi$. Therefore

$$
\begin{aligned}
H &= \frac{I}{4\pi d} \int_0^{\pi} \sin \theta \, d\theta \\
&= \frac{I}{4\pi d} \left[-\cos \theta \right]_0^{\pi} = -\frac{I}{4\pi d} [-1 - (+1)] \\
&= \frac{I}{2\pi d} \qquad\qquad (37.10)
\end{aligned}
$$

Magnetomotive Force. Figure 37.11 shows a cross section perpendicular to the wire of Figure 37.10(a). In this rather common type of diagram the convention for showing the direction of current is modified. A small circle represents the wire, and the arrow for current direction is considered to be in the wire. If the current is approaching, a dot representing the point of the arrow is shown as follows: $\odot$. If the current is receding, or away, the symbol $\otimes$ is used, the "$\times$" in the circle representing the receding "feathers" of the arrow. Thus in Figure 37.11 the current I is coming out of the paper.

Consider the work done in carrying a unit positive magnetic pole once around a circular path in the direction $ABCA$. The force on the pole is numerically equal to H. Hence the work done is force times distance or

$$2\pi d \times H = 2\pi d \times \frac{I}{2\pi d} = I$$

This work per unit pole around a closed path we call the **magnetomotive** force (mmf) and represent by $\mathfrak{F}$. It is analogous to the emf, which is the work done in carrying a unit positive *charge* around a closed path or circuit. For the path *ABCA*

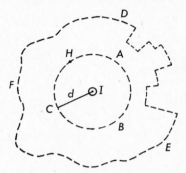

$$\mathfrak{F} = I \qquad (37.11)$$

Since the radius d of the path does not appear in (37.11), $\mathfrak{F}$ is the same for a circular path of any radius. Line *DEFD* is any irregular path about the wire. It can be approximated with any desired accuracy by a succession of arcs of circles connected by radii as shown in the part *DE*. Adding up the work done along each of the arcs, we get (37.11), and this must be the mmf, since no work is done in moving a pole along a radius, because the displace-

Fig. 37.11. Magnetomotive force about a long, straight wire.

ment is perpendicular to the direction of the force. Thus the mmf around a wire is given by (37.11), regardless of the path followed as long as the path encloses the wire.

If there had been two wires, each with current I, the mmf would have been twice as great. For N wires the mmf is given by

$$\mathfrak{F} = NI \qquad (37.12)$$

This result has been proved here only for the case of long, straight wires, but a more general analysis shows that it holds good in all cases. It is in fact more general than Biot's Law, which is not valid in a medium of varying permeability.

In Figure 37.12 *ABCA* is a closed path, and we wish to find the mmf. Consider any element Δs of the path. In general H will not be perpendicular to Δs, so that

$$\Delta \mathfrak{F} = H \, \Delta s \cos \theta = \mathbf{H} \cdot \mathbf{\Delta s} \quad (37.13)$$

using the "dot" product notation introduced in section 5.01. The total mmf is found by adding up all these contributions from each Δs, or in equation form,

$$\mathfrak{F} = \oint \mathbf{H} \cdot \mathbf{ds} \qquad (37.14)$$

Fig. 37.12.

where the small circle on the integral sign means that the addition or integration is carried out over a closed path. Equation (37.14) is the rigorous definition of the mmf and does not involve the fictitious concept of an isolated pole in defining $\mathfrak{F}$. The unit of $\mathfrak{F}$ is the *ampere-turn (amp-turn)* from (37.12). Since the number of turns is a dimensionless number, $\mathfrak{F}$ could be measured in amperes, but the more explicit name avoids confusion. Equation (37.13) shows the origin of the name ampere-turn per meter for the unit of H.

Magnetomotive force is of considerable importance theoretically, but its utility for us lies in the fact that if a coil of wire has a marked symmetry, $\mathfrak{F}$ can often be expressed in terms of H. Equating this expression for $\mathfrak{F}$ to that found from (37.12) gives a method for evaluating H in some cases where direct integration of Biot's Law is difficult or impossible. Finding the field of a toroidal coil is an example of the method.

Toroid and Solenoid. Figure 37.13(a) shows a toroidal coil with only part of the winding indicated for clarity. Consider three paths of

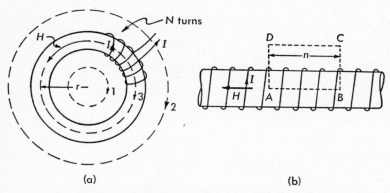

(a)   (b)

Fig. 37.13.   Calculation of H for toroid and solenoid.

integration, numbered 1, 2, and 3. Path number 1 includes no current-carrying conductor. Hence by (37.12) $\mathfrak{F} = 0$, and by (37.14) it follows that $H = 0$, since by symmetry H must have the same value at every point on a circle about the center of the toroid. Similarly, path 2 encloses no conductors and hence $H = 0$. If you prefer, you can say that path 2 enclosed $2N$ conductors, half carrying I upward and half I downward. From either point of view $\mathfrak{F}$ and H vanish. Thus $H = 0$ at all points inside the rim of the toroid and outside it, and the field is contained entirely within the rim. Path 3 encloses N conductors, each carrying current I. By (37.12),

$$\mathfrak{F} = NI$$

Along path 3, H must be constant and parallel to ds.   Equation (37.14) gives

$$\mathfrak{F} = \oint \mathbf{H} \cdot \mathbf{ds} = H \oint ds$$
$$= 2\pi r H = NI$$
$$H = \frac{NI}{2\pi r} = \frac{NI}{\pi D} = nI$$

where n is the number of turns per unit length.

The solenoid can be thought of as a toroid of infinite radius with n turns per unit length, and the toroid equation can be used directly in the form

$$H = nI$$

or (37.14) can be evaluated around the path $ABCD$ in Figure 37.13(b) where $AB = CD =$ unit length.

PROBLEMS

1. A toroidal coil has a rim 4.00 cm in diameter. The radius of the outer edges of the rim is 50.00 cm. The coil has 10,000 turns and carries a current of 12.0 ma. Find the average field in the rim.

2. In the coil of problem 1 calculate the minimum and maximum fields within the rim.

3. What current is needed in a long, straight wire to produce a field of 20.0 amp m^{-1} at a distance of 6.00 m?

4. A long, straight wire carries a current of 10.0 amp. If the effect of a magnetic field of less than 1 amp m^{-1} on an instrument can be neglected, how far away from the wire must the instrument be kept?

5. A long solenoid is 5.00 cm in diameter and 75.0 cm in length. It has 6000 turns. Find the field strength in the solenoid when it carries a current of 100 ma.

6. A more exact formula for the field at a point on the axis of a solenoid of finite length is

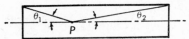

$$H_p = \frac{nI}{2} (\cos \theta_1 + \cos \theta_2)$$

Fig. 37.14.   The angles θ_1 and θ_2 are shown in Figure 37.14. Use this equation to find the field at the center of the solenoid of problem 5 and compare with the result found by the simple equation. Find the field at a point on the axis 10.0 cm from either end.

7. Derive the equation for the field of an infinitely long solenoid by working out the mmf for the path $ABCD$ in Figure 37.13(b).

8. Figure 37.15 represents a top view of a circular coil of N turns. A small compass needle M is mounted horizontally at its center. The coil is aligned magnetic north and south. When a current I flows in the coil, the compass deflects through an angle θ. Prove that

$$I = \frac{2rH_e}{N} \tan \theta$$

where H_e is the horizontal component of the earth's field at the location. This instrument, now obsolete, is called a tangent galvanometer and provided the first method for the absolute measurement of current.

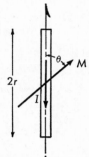

9. The coil of a tangent galvanometer is 25.0 cm in diameter and has 400 turns. It is at a place where $H_e = 12.0$ amp m^{-1}. What current in the coil will produce a deflection of 60.0°?

Fig. 37.15. The tangent galvanometer.

10. A compass needle of magnetic moment M and moment of inertia I is found to have a period of π sec in the earth's field H_e. When there is a downward current of 10.0 amp in a vertical wire due magnetic west of the needle and 10.0 cm distant, the needle still points north and has a new period of oscillation of $\pi \sqrt{5}$ sec. Calculate the strength of the horizontal component of the earth's field.

11. Biot and Savart's original experiment is illustrated in Figure 37.16. A long, straight wire carries a current I. A loop L of insulating material supports a magnet M so that the latter is free to turn about the wire. Biot and Savart had expected that the field of the current would diminish inversely as the square of the distance from the wire, by analogy with Coulomb's Law, and they set up this equipment to demonstrate the rotation of the magnet about the wire. No rotation took place, so they concluded that the field must follow an inverse first-power law. Explain their original expectation and final conclusions.

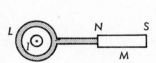

Fig. 37.16. Biot and Savart's experiment.

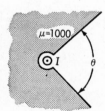

Fig. 37.17. Effect of permeability on magnetic field strength.

12. In Figure 37.17 a long, straight wire is partially surrounded by iron of relative permeability 1000. The angle θ measures the angular width of the sector

without iron. The relative permeability is unity in this sector. It is found experimentally that the lines of magnetic intensity are still circles about the wire but that the size of H in each sector is governed by the fact that μH is constant. Use the mmf law to find H at points 10.0 cm from the wire in both iron (H_I) and air (H_A) if $I = 100$ amp and θ is (a) 90.0°, (b) 5.00°.

13. A wire is bent to form a square of side 20.0 cm. If there is a current of 2.00 amp in the wire, what is the field at the center of the square?

38

Magnetic Flux Density

38.01 FORCE ON A CURRENT IN A MAGNETIC FIELD

In the preceding chapter we saw how a current sets up a magnetic field, measured by the field strength H, and can exert a force on a magnet placed in the field. By Newton's Third Law of Motion we expect that the magnet must therefore exert a force on the current. This force is most easily described in terms of the magnetic field. Experimentally it is found that a force *is* exerted on a conductor carrying a current when it lies in a magnetic field. The field may be due either to a permanent magnet or to a second electric current. This force increases with the strength of the field and acts in a direction at right angles to the plane containing the current and the field. Only the component of the field perpendicular to the current contributes to the force. The property of the field which determines the force on a current is called the **magnetic flux density** and will be represented by the symbol B. Once again the only convenient general law relating B, I, and the force is a differential law which we shall call **Ampere's Law.** (There is no general agreement on the naming of these laws.) It is

$$\Delta F = BI \, \Delta l \sin \theta \qquad (38.01)$$

and is illustrated in Figure 38.01, where ΔF is the element of force acting on the element Δl of the conductor. A convenient rule for remembering the direction of the force is stated in the following paragraph.

Left-Hand (Motor) Rule. The thu**M**b, **F**orefinger, and **C**enter finger of the *left* hand are held mutually perpendicular. If the **F**orefinger points in the direction of the **F**ield and the **C**enter finger in the direction of the **C**urrent, the thu**M**b points in the direction of the force, that is, in the direction of **M**otion.

The letters in boldface type serve as a mnemonic aid.

723

Units. Since units of F (newtons), I (amperes), and l (meters) have already been chosen, equation (38.01) establishes the size of unit flux density. The unit of B is the *weber per square meter*. This choice of name shows that a close connection exists between pole strength and flux density.

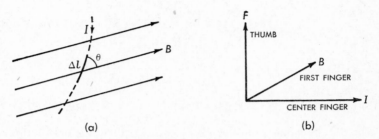

(a)   (b)

Fig. 38.01. Ampere's Law and the left-hand (motor) rule.

The magnetic flux density B is a vector property of the field having in all cases of importance the same direction as H, to which it is evidently closely related. If B is known, equation (38.01) must be integrated over the entire circuit of the current I to find the force on the circuit. The calculation is often difficult, but we shall need only two simple cases. First, if we are interested only in the force acting on a straight portion of the circuit and if B is uniform, (38.01) becomes

$$F = BIl \sin \theta \qquad (38.02)$$

38.02 TORQUE ON A COIL

The other, and more important, case is the effect of a uniform field on a coil carrying a current. The axis of rotation of the coil is usually at right angles to B, and this is the only case discussed here. Figure 38.02 shows a rectangular coil of height l and breadth b with N turns. The current I enters and leaves by connections through the pivots, P. The angle between B and the plane of the coil is ϕ. Consider the sides WX and ZY. Unless $\phi = 0$ there is a field component $B \sin \phi$ normal to the wires on these sides, and hence the total force on side ZY is

$$F' = BIb \sin \phi$$

and there is a similar force on WX. Applying the left-hand rule, we see that these forces act in the plane of the coil and, for the angle ϕ as shown, merely try to shorten the length l of the coil. The framework on which the wire is wound is strong enough to resist these forces, which can be ignored from now on.

The side ZW is at right angles to B for all values of ϕ and will be acted on by a force

$$F = BINl$$

This force, together with a similar but oppositely directed one on XY, is

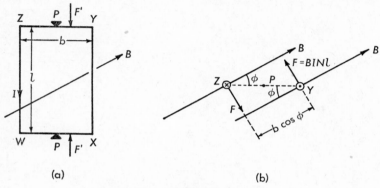

Fig. 38.02. Torque on a coil.

shown in the plan view of the coil in Figure 38.02(b). They produce a couple

$$\Gamma = BINl \times b \cos \phi$$
$$= BIN(lb) \cos \phi$$
$$= BINA \cos \phi \qquad (38.03)$$

where A is the area of the coil.

This important result is proved here for a rectangular coil, but the proof can readily be extended to a flat coil of any shape by approximating the coil shape with short elements of length parallel and perpendicular to the axis of rotation. Forces on the perpendicular elements will contribute nothing to the torque, and the result shown by (38.03) is obtained.

Radial Field. The $\cos \phi$ term in (38.03) can be a nuisance. It is seen to arise because of the angle between B and the plane of the coil and could be eliminated if ϕ were always zero. This would be the case for the type of field shown in Figure 38.03(a), which is called a radial field. It cannot be produced over any large area, but Figure 38.03(b) shows an arrangement to give an approximately radial field in an air gap. The pattern of lines of force or lines of flux density is controlled by their marked preference for passing through media of high permeability such as the soft iron core C. The poles of a permanent magnet or an electromagnet, N and S, are joined by a closed iron path (not shown). The position of the coil is indicated, and it is seen that the coil can turn through about

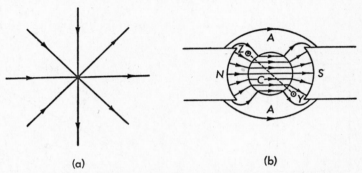

(a)   (b)

Fig. 38.03.   (a) Radial field; (b) radial field in an air gap.

120°, with the field B always parallel to the plane of the coil.   Within this range

$$\phi = 0, \qquad \cos \phi = 1, \qquad \Gamma = BINA \qquad (38.04)$$

38.03 THE D'ARSONVAL GALVANOMETER

The basic d-c measuring instrument is a moving-coil permanent-magnet mechanism called a **d'Arsonval galvanometer**. The coil is placed in a radial field as shown in Figure 38.03(a), and when a current is passed through the coil, an electromagnetic torque, given by (38.04) and denoted here by Γ_e, is developed. The elastic properties of the suspension produce a restoring torque Γ.

$$\Gamma = k\theta$$

where k measures the elasticity of the suspension and θ is the angle through which the coil is turned from its rest position.   For equilibrium,

$$\Gamma_e = \Gamma$$
$$BINA = k\theta$$
$$I = \frac{k}{BNA}\,\theta = K_i'\theta \qquad (38.05)$$

where K_i' is a constant of the meter called its **ampere sensibility**. Equation (38.05) shows that a meter of this type is linear within a range of θ such that the magnetic field is uniform in size and perfectly radial. Theoretically, K_i' can be calculated from the geometry of the suspension and coil and from a measurement of B, so that a meter of this type could be used for an absolute measurement of I. In practice, however, the accuracy obtained in this way is low, and although (38.05) is used in the design of instruments, they are calibrated using a potentiometer and standard cell.

Suspensions are of two types. In the more sensitive type the coil is supported by a phosphor-bronze fiber which also serves to introduce the current to the coil. The current leaves through a loose helix of fine wire which exerts no appreciable torque. This type of suspension was discussed in section 9.06. The coil carries a mirror, and the deflection is noted by observing through a tele-scope the reflection in the mirror of a scale. A light beam is thus act-ing as a pointer of great length but no inertia. If the deflection d is measured on a circular scale a dis-tance D from the center of the mirror,

$$d = 2(D\theta) \qquad (38.06)$$

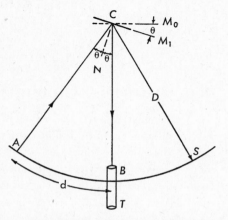

The factor 2 arises because if the mirror turns through an angle θ, the beam of light turns through an angle 2θ. This is illustrated in Figure 38.04, where T is the tele-scope, S the scale, M_0 the zero cur-rent position of the mirror, M_1 the new position of the mirror after rotation through angle θ, N the

Fig. 38.04. Scale and telescope for reading deflection of a d'Arsonval galvanometer. In some instruments T is replaced by a lamp which projects a spot of light on the mirror and thus on the scale.

normal to M_1, and ACB the path of the light ray. Usually D is either 0.50 or 1.00 m. Combining (38.05) and (38.06) gives

$$I = \frac{K_i'}{2D}\, d = K_i d \qquad (38.07)$$

where K_i is also called the ampere sensibility, although its units differ from those of K_i'. Values of K_i as low as 10^{-11} amp mm^{-1} can be obtained in the most sensitive meters of this type.

The vast majority of meters in use need to be sturdier or more portable than is possible with the fiber suspension, and the coil is mounted between two jeweled bearings, the restoring torque being provided by a small

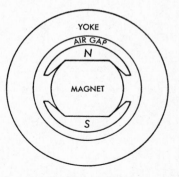

spiral spring. The magnet may be of the type shown in Figure 38.03(b), but recently with the advent of Alnico alloys there has been a trend to a magnet design in which a permanent magnet with specially shaped pole pieces is situated inside the coil and surrounded by a cylindrical soft iron yoke. This design is illustrated in Figure 38.05 and has the advantage of great permanence in the value of B together with extremely effective shielding against external mag-

Fig. 38.05.   Magnet system for moving coil meters.

netic influences.   The pole pieces are N and S, and the coil moves in the air gap.   This design was developed by the Weston Electrical Instrument Company.

38.04 AMMETERS, VOLTMETERS, AND OHMMETERS

The instruments described in the preceding section are known as galvanometers or milliammeters or microammeters. The currents they can be designed to carry are small because the moving coil must have many turns of fine wire. The two most important properties of a galvanometer are the full-scale current I_M and resistance R_G. These are specified by the manufacturer or may be measured if necessary. It is vital that no current larger than I_M be allowed to enter the galvanometer G. Usually I_M is $\not> 50$ ma.

Ammeters.   In order to measure larger currents than I_M it is necessary to provide an alternative low-resistance path which will carry the bulk of the current, allowing an accurately known fraction of the total to pass through the meter. This parallel resistor is known as a **shunt.** An ammeter for measuring currents up to about 10 amp consists of a galvanometer with an appropriate shunt contained in the instrument case. For larger currents the ammeter shunt is external to the case to assist in heat dissipation. The calculation of the resistance of the shunt is straightforward. Figure 38.06(a) shows an ammeter. The dotted line is the outline of the case, and S is the shunt resistor. Let I be the full-scale current for which the meter is designed. Then if I enters at the input terminal, it must divide into a current I_M through G and $I - I_M$

through S. Since the potential difference across G and S must be the same,

$$(I - I_M)S = I_M R_G \qquad (38.08)$$

permitting us to solve for S. The scale is engraved to read I when a current I_M goes through the meter.

Frequently it is convenient to have different ranges available on an ammeter. For this purpose a design known as an Ayrton-Mather shunt is used. It is shown in Figure 38.06(b). The input terminal is common

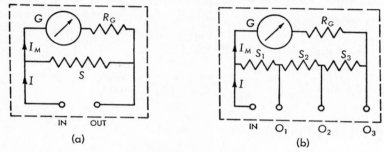

(a)   (b)

Fig. 38.06. Ammeters.

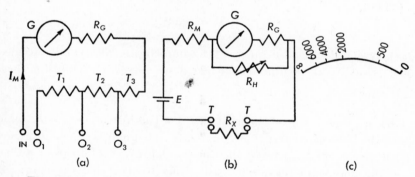

(a)   (b)   (c)

Fig. 38.07. (a) Multirange voltmeter; (b) ohmmeter; (c) typical ohmmeter scale.

for all ranges, and the desired range is selected by using O_1, O_2, or O_3 as the output terminal. If, for example, O_2 is used, the shunt resistor consists of $S_1 + S_2$, and the effective galvanometer resistance is $R_G + S_3$. The terminal for the *high* current range is O_1.

Voltmeters. Figure 38.07(a) shows the modification of a galvanometer into a voltmeter to measure potential difference. If a voltmeter is designed for a maximum voltage V, when this potential is applied across the input and output terminals the current through the meter must be I_M. The current is restricted to this value by a series resistor T of appropriate size.

$$V = I_M(T + R_G) \tag{38.09}$$

The figure shows a three-range voltmeter. The common input terminal and O_1 give the highest range.

Example. A galvanometer gives full-scale deflection for a current of 20.0 ma and has a resistance of 50.0 Ω. What shunt and series resistors would be needed to convert it to an ammeter of range 0–5 amp and a voltmeter of range 0–100 v? By (38.08),

$$\left(5.00 - \frac{20.0}{1000}\right)S = \tfrac{20}{1000} \times 50.0$$

The shunt should therefore have a resistance

By (38.09),
$$S = \tfrac{1000}{4980} = 0.201 \ \Omega$$
$$100 = \tfrac{20}{1000}(T + 50.0)$$
$$T = 4950 \ \Omega$$

Note how the effective resistances of the ammeter (0.200 Ω) and voltmeter (5000 Ω) satisfy the requirements laid down in section 34.02 for these instruments.

Ohmmeters. One of the most useful of test instruments is the ohmmeter, which measures resistance directly. Its circuit is shown in Figure 38.07(b), where T, T are test leads usually ending in metal tips or probes for making momentary contacts easily, and R_M is a series resistor. It will be seen on study of this circuit that the instrument is very similar to a voltmeter with a self-contained power source. Usually E is a flashlight battery. In use, the leads T, T are first short-circuited, permitting maximum current in G. This current is adjusted to a preset value with R_H. This value is marked zero ohms on the scale, and the R_H adjustment allows for small changes in E as the battery ages. The test leads are then clipped to the resistor R_X to be measured, and the current decreases. From a knowledge of E, R_M, and R_G the scale of the meter can be calibrated to read R_X directly. For example, if we neglect the effect of R_H, the resistance of the meter is $R_M + R_G$ and maximum current is

$E/(R_M + R_G)$. This current will be cut in half if $R_X = R_M + R_G$ since the total resistance is then doubled. Thus the mid-point of the scale is marked with the resistance of the meter. When the circuit is closed there will always be some current unless R_X is very large. Hence the zero current indication on the scale is marked as infinite resistance. The scale will be far from linear in R_X, and its general appearance is shown in Figure 38.07(c) for an ohmmeter of internal resistance 2000 Ω. The pointer shows a value of R_X of about 1600 Ω.

Ohmmeters are not accurate instruments, and because of the non-linearity of the scale are practically useless for measuring resistances of more than three times the meter resistance. Even for resistances below this the error may easily be 10%. Nevertheless, they are very valuable for testing continuity in a circuit and for obtaining approximate resistance values. Most ohmmeters have several different resistance ranges.

38.05 MOTORS

Electric motors are of many different types and sizes, and a discussion of their design belongs to electrical engineering. Here we are concerned only with principles. In Figure 38.03(b) application of the left-hand rule (the significance of the word "motor" in its name now becomes clear) shows that a counterclockwise torque exists for the current direction shown. If the coil is free to turn, it will rotate until it occupies the position indicated by the points A, A where the field and hence the torque vanish. In a galvanometer, the core C is fixed, and the coil moves about it. In a motor, the coil is wound on the core, which is mounted on bearings. The iron core with its windings is called the **armature.** Its inertia carries the coil past the position of zero field. If the current direction in the coil remains the same, the torque builds up but is now clockwise and will cause the armature to oscillate, finally coming to rest with the coil in the zero field region. Suppose, however, the current is reversed in the coil when it passes through A, A. The torque will then always be counterclockwise, and continuous rotation results.

The device for reversing the current direction at every half-revolution of the armature is called a **commutator.** It is illustrated (in principle) in Figure 38.08, where LL is the axis of rotation of the armature, and the ends of the coil slide on a ring with two gaps, placed so that contact is broken when the coil is near the field-free region. Current always enters by one half (R_1) of the ring and leaves by the other (R_2), but the direction of the current in the coil reverses each time the leads cross the gaps.

The rotation of a d-c motor with a single coil would be continuous but uneven in speed because of the variation in torque. To avoid this, actual motors have several armature coils evenly spaced around the core to ensure that the torque remains fairly uniform. The coils are terminated in insulated copper segments, and the sliding contacts are made with graphite blocks called **brushes.**

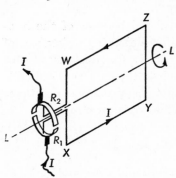

Fig. 38.08. Principle of the split-ring commutator.

Very small electric motors sometimes have permanent magnets to supply the field, but above about $\frac{1}{10}$ hp all electric motors have a magnetic field established by an electromagnet. The armature core and the iron framework of the motor form an almost closed path, with the armature coils moving in the air gap. **Field coils** are wound around the iron framework and magnetize it when the current is turned on. The field coils may be in series with the armature (series-wound motor), in parallel with it (shunt-wound), or part in series and part in parallel (compound-wound). These three types of motors have quite different performance characteristics and different applications.

In addition to the d-c motors discussed briefly above, motors can be designed to operate on alternating current, and in fact the majority of motors are a-c driven. This is partly because alternating current is the type of power usually available and also because an a-c motor is intrinsically simpler to build. It requires no commutator, for instance, and commutators are a source of much trouble in both construction and maintenance of motors. A-c motors operate on the same principle as d-c motors, the force being produced by the interaction of current and magnetic field, but they differ quite considerably in design and performance. One basic difference is that a-c motors operate at an essentially constant rotational speed, whereas the speed of a d-c motor can be varied within wide limits.

Finally, it should be noted that an electric motor is a device for converting electrical power into mechanical power, and one of great efficiency. The power output may be as high as 30,000 hp in a single motor or as low as $\frac{1}{100}$ hp. Efficiencies are as high as 95% in large motors and are rarely below 75%.

38.06 RELATION BETWEEN FLUX DENSITY AND FIELD STRENGTH

We wish now to obtain the relation between B and H, two properties of the magnetic field. In Figure 38.09 a current I flows in a single-turn, circular coil of radius r. At the center of the coil is a single magnetic pole of strength $+m$. The current produces a magnetic field of strength H_I, say. This field will produce a force F_I on the pole. The pole produces a second field, described by H_M, B_M, which will produce a force F_M on the wire. Force F_I acts straight *out* from the diagram by the right-hand (current) rule, and F_M acts straight *into* the diagram by the left-hand (motor) rule. Forces F_I and F_M are the equal and opposite forces of

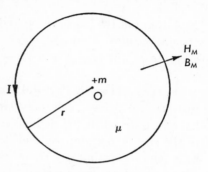

Fig. 38.09. $B = \mu\mu_0 H$.

Newton's Third Law of Motion and must be equal in size. At the center O, by (37.03),

$$H_I = \frac{I}{2r}$$

Therefore
$$F_I = \frac{mI}{2r} \qquad (38.10)$$

The value of B_M at the wire is everywhere the same, by symmetry, and perpendicular to I. By (38.01),

$$\Delta F_M = B_M I \, \Delta l$$

for every element of the wire, and all the elements of force have the same direction. Therefore

$$F_M = B_M I \cdot 2\pi r \qquad (38.11)$$

Equating (38.10) and (38.11) gives

$$\frac{mI}{2r} = B_M I \cdot 2\pi r$$

$$B_M = \frac{m}{4\pi r^2} \qquad (38.12)$$

Since m is in webers, this equation shows why B is measured in webers per square meter. Now if the entire system is in a medium of uniform relative permeability μ, H_M at the wire is given by (36.06) as

$$H_M = \frac{m}{4\pi\mu\mu_0 r^2}$$

Substituting in (38.12) and dropping the subscript M, we have

$$B = \mu\mu_0 H \qquad\qquad (38.13)$$

Equation (38.13) has been proved for the field of a single pole, but it is a general result of great importance and applies to magnetic fields set up by currents as well as to the fields set up outside permanent magnets.

Forces Between Parallel Currents. We are now in a position to justify the various, arbitrary choices of proportionality constants we have introduced in the definition of μ_0 (the permeability of free space), in the size of the ampere, and in the constant in Biot's Law. We saw in section 37.05 that, by choosing this last constant as $1/(4\pi)$, the magnetomotive force law took on the particularly simple form

$$\mathfrak{F} = \oint \mathbf{H} \cdot \mathbf{ds} = \sum_n I_n \qquad\qquad (38.14)$$

where the summation is over all currents enclosed within the path over which $\mathfrak{F}$ is calculated. The simplicity of this equation is very desirable because, although we deduced it from Biot's Law in a special case, it can be shown that (38.14) is more general than Biot's Law and hence finds a wider range of use.

To investigate the forces between parallel currents, on which our original definition of the ampere was based, we recall equation (37.10) for the field H due to current in a long, straight wire:

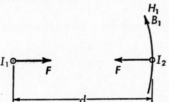

$$H = \frac{I}{2\pi d}$$

Substituting in (38.13) gives

Fig. 38.10. Forces between parallel currents.

$$B = \frac{\mu\mu_0 I}{2\pi d} \qquad\qquad (38.15)$$

Consider now two long, parallel wires carrying currents I_1 and I_2 as shown in Figure 38.10 in plan view. Both currents are coming out of the diagram. The direction of the field at I_2 due to I_1 is shown. Applying the left-hand rule, we see that the resulting force acts to the left. The size of the force on a length l of the wire is given by (38.02) as

$$F = B_1 I_2 l$$
$$= \mu\mu_0 \frac{I_1 I_2 l}{2\pi d} \qquad (38.16)$$

Proceeding in the same way to calculate the force on length l of wire No. 1, we find that the size of the force is given by (38.16), but its direction is opposite to that on wire No. 2. Hence the wires attract each other in this case and would repel each other if one of the currents were reversed.

Comparing (38.16) with equation (33.01) we see that they are identical if k is chosen as $1/2\pi$ as was done in section 33.03. The choice of μ_0 controls the size of the unit current and the value $4\pi \times 10^{-7}$ was chosen to make the long-established "ampere" serve as our unit of current.

38.07 FERROMAGNETISM

Reference has already been made to the peculiar properties of the ferromagnetic materials, and a brief description is needed of how these properties vary. The usual method of measurement is to form the magnetic material into a closed ring and wind a uniform coil of insulated wire around it to form an iron-cored toroid. When a known current is sent through the coil it produces a primary or magnetizing field H in the iron which can be calculated using equation (37.06) for the field inside the rim of a toroid. This field magnetizes the iron, resulting in a high value of flux density B in the ring. A second coil is wound on top of the first winding and is connected to a galvanometer. Any change in the current in the toroidal coil changes H and hence B as well. The change in B causes a momentary current in the galvanometer (these induced currents will be discussed in the next chapter), and this meter can be used to measure B. The theory and a complete description of the method will be found in any good textbook on electrical measurements. Here we shall only discuss the results. Two cases must be distinguished.

Magnetization Curves. If the magnetic sample is initially completely unmagnetized and the magnetizing field H is increased gradually and *never* decreased, the resulting values of B are as shown in Figure 38.11. The numerical data are typical of the behavior of soft iron. Other magnetic materials show similar behavior, although the numerical results may differ by several orders of magnitude. The saturation of the iron (see section 36.09) shows up clearly. The second curve in the figure is the relative permeability μ, obtained by dividing B by $\mu_0 H$. The sharp peak is the most important feature of this curve. In electromagnetic machinery the object is to get a large flux density since, for example, it is B which determines the force a motor can exert. The cost of getting this flux density depends largely on H, which is proportional to the current in the field coils. But the ratio $B/H \propto \mu$, which shows that μ is a measure of how much flux we get for our money. The most economical **magnetic circuit** (as the entire system of magnetic material is called) is

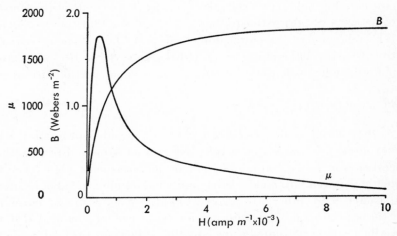

Fig. 38.11. Magnetization of soft iron.

the one with the maximum permeability. The figure shows that for soft iron this requires a low magnetizing field and a relatively low flux density. If we must have a larger flux density, approaching saturation of the iron, we must be prepared to pay heavily for it.

Hysteresis Loops. Suppose that having magnetized our sample we start to reduce H, measuring B as we do so. We find that B does *not* decrease as fast as Figure 38.11 would indicate, and, in fact, when H becomes zero B is not zero. This phenomenon is called **hysteresis** and is the result of "permanent" magnetism showing up in the iron. If H is varied cyclically, B always "lags" behind the value of H, and the graph of Figure 38.12(a) shows the resulting B-H curve for soft iron. The original magnetization curve is OA. The hysteresis loop for an **Alnico** alloy is shown in Figure 38.12(b).

The use of the hysteresis loop is twofold. If the field coils are excited by an alternating current, the value of H varies in this manner once a

cycle, i.e., usually 60 times per second.   The continual modification of
the magnetic domains is opposed by forces similar to friction, and so heat
develops.   This heat represents an energy loss.   It can be shown that
the area enclosed by the hysteresis loop measures the energy loss due
to this cause per cycle per unit volume of the magnetic material.   To
reduce this loss, the magnetic circuits of a-c machinery are constructed
of a material with a hysteresis loop of small area.   On the other hand,
the size of the loop indicates the amount of permanent magnetism in the

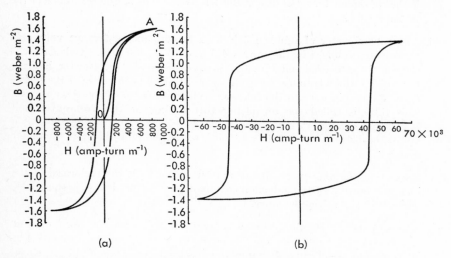

Fig. 38.12.   Hysteresis loops of (a) soft iron; (b) Alnico 5.   [Note expanded
H scale in (a).]

sample, and good permanent magnets are made from materials with
large loops, such as Alnico 5 (51% Fe, 24% Co, 14% Ni, 8% Al, 3% Cu).

PROBLEMS

1. A long, straight wire carrying a current of 100 amp lies in a magnetic field
   of flux density 0.800 weber m^{-2}, the angle between B and I being 30.0°.
   Find the force per meter of wire and draw a sketch to show the direction of
   this force.

2. A coil of 300 turns of wire is 16.0 cm by 5.00 cm in area and its axis of rotation
   is perpendicular to a uniform field of flux density 3.00×10^{-3} weber m^{-2}.
   If the coil carries a current of 125 ma, what is the maximum torque on it?

3. A galvanometer coil has an area of 8.00 cm^2 and consists of 500 turns of
   fine wire.   It is suspended by a phosphor-bronze wire so that its axis is
   perpendicular to a radial magnetic field of strength 3.18×10^4 amp m^{-1} in

the air gap. Find the flux density in the air gap and the torque on the coil for a current in it of 12.2 μa.

4. In the galvanometer of problem 3, the restoring constant of the suspension is 1.22×10^{-6} Nm (newton-meters) per radian. The deflection is measured on a circular scale 0.500 m away, using a telescope and a mirror mounted on the coil. Find the ampere sensibility in microamperes per millimeter.

5. A galvanometer gives full-scale deflection for a current of 50.0 μa. What shunt resistance is needed to convert it to a milliammeter of range 0–500 ma if the galvanometer resistance is 100 Ω? What will be the resistance of the milliammeter?

6. The galvanometer of problem 5 is used to construct a 3-range voltmeter to measure voltages in the ranges 0–1 v, 0–10 v, 0–100 v. Calculate the series resistors needed and draw the circuit diagram of the voltmeter, indicating which terminals to use for each range. Calculate the ratio of the resistance of the voltmeter to the full-scale voltage for each of the three ranges. This ratio is called the **ohms-per-volt rating of the voltmeter** and is a simple quality rating of the meter—the higher this rating the less a voltmeter disturbs a circuit to which it is connected (and the more the meter costs).

7. Prove that the ohms-per-volt rating of a voltmeter is the reciprocal of the full-scale current of the galvanometer used to construct it and is thus independent of the voltmeter range.

8. A galvanometer of resistance 60.0 Ω gives full-scale deflection for a current of 1.00 ma. Calculate the shunt and series resistors needed to convert it into an ammeter of range 0–1 amp and a voltmeter of range 0–10 v. Draw the circuit for a combined meter of this type (put a push button in series with the shunt—this button has to be pushed to get the correct voltage reading when using the instrument as a voltmeter).

9. A galvanometer of resistance 50.0 Ω gives full-scale deflection for a current of 4.00 ma. It is to be used to make an ammeter of ranges 0–50 ma, 0–500 ma, 0–5 amp. Calculate the components of the appropriate Ayrton-Mather shunt and draw a circuit diagram.

10. The total resistance of an ohmmeter of the type shown in Figure 38.07(b) is 1500 Ω, and the emf of the battery is 1.50 v. If the meter scale is divided linearly into 10 divisions, the beginning indicating zero current, calculate the external resistance corresponding to each division if the meter reads full-scale with the leads short-circuited. (Neglect the effect of R_H.)

11. Figure 38.13 illustrates a different ohmmeter circuit called a shunt ohm-meter, which is particularly suitable for measuring small resistances. The unknown is connected in parallel with a voltmeter V of resistance R_V. If $R_x = 0$ (short-circuit), the voltmeter reads zero. The maximum reading of V is obtained for R_x open-circuit. The key is necessary to prevent drain

on the battery when the ohmmeter is not in use. If $E = 3.00$ v, $R_S = 100$ Ω, $R_V = 200$ Ω, and the range of V is 0–2 v, calculate the value of R_X corresponding to each quarter-volt reading of the meter.

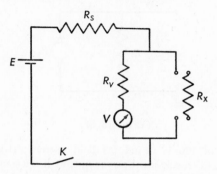

Fig. 38.13.   Shunt ohmmeter.

12. What is the relative permeability of a material in which (a) $B = 1.00$ weber m^{-2}, $H = 400$ amp m^{-1}; (b) $B = 0.395$ weber m^{-2}, $H = 3.64 \times 10^3$ amp m^{-1}; (c) $B = 0.250$ weber m^{-2}, $H = 35.0$ amp in^{-1}?   This last unit of H is widely used in engineering.

13. Two conductors are parallel and 10.0 cm apart in air.   The force of attraction between them is 0.0500 newton on each wire.   When the space between and around the conductors is filled with sheets of steel, the force increases to 40.0 newtons.   Find the relative permeability of the steel.

14. Two parallel conductors are horizontal, one directly above the other.   The lower one is fixed to a wooden tabletop, and the upper is floating between vertical guides.   If the wire has a mass of 20.0 gm m^{-1} and a current of 140 amp goes out one wire and returns by the other, what is their spacing for equilibrium?

15. Two parallel, horizontal conductors are suspended by light, vertical threads 75.0 cm long.   Each conductor has a mass of 40.0 gm m^{-1}, and when there is no current they are 0.500 cm apart.   Equal currents in the two wires result in a separation of 1.500 cm.   Find the sizes and direction of the currents.

16. A d-c motor draws a current of 20.0 amp at 100 v under steady load conditions.   The armature has 36 equally spaced coils of 16 turns each, connected in two circuits in parallel so that each coil carries a current of 10.0 amp.   The field produced by the field coils is radial over most of the armature surfaces, with essentially no-field regions midway between the poles.   The field acting on 27 of the coils at any time is 1.00 weber m^{-2}, and the field on the other coils is zero.   The effective area of each coil is 0.150 m^2.   If the armature turns at 1500 rpm, find the output power in horsepower and the efficiency of the motor.

17. Figure 38.14 represents schematically a shunt-wound d-c motor. The armature coils have a resistance $R_a = 3.00$ Ω, and the field coils a resistance $R_f = 240$ Ω. The total current drawn by the motor is 4.50 amp for an

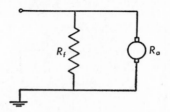

Fig. 38.14.

applied voltage of 120 v. Find (a) field current; (b) armature current; (c) power input; (d) mechanical power output if frictional losses amount to 32 watts; and (e) efficiency of the motor.

(*Note:* The armature current must be the difference between the total current and the field current. The *IR* drop in the armature is readily seen to be considerably less than the voltage applied to the armature. The difference is called the **back emf** and arises from the fact that the spinning armature coils act as a generator, developing a voltage opposing the applied one. This generator action will be discussed in the next chapter.)

18. The hysteresis curve of a sample of iron is found, and the area enclosed by the loop is measured as 400 webers m^{-2} × amp m^{-1}. If this type of iron forms the core of a transformer, the core having a volume of 0.125 m^3 of iron, calculate the power lost through hysteresis when this transformer is handling 60.0-cycle power with the same maximum magnetic flux density as used in the loop test.

39

Electromagnetic Induction

39.01 FARADAY'S LAW AND LENZ' LAW

The electromagnetic phenomena we have discussed so far are those caused by currents which are unvarying in size and direction, resulting in steady magnetic fields. If the current is allowed to change in any way which causes a variation in the magnetic field with time, new phenomena appear which are classed under the heading of **electromagnetic induction.** These phenomena were first discovered by Faraday and shortly afterward, independently, by the American scientist Joseph Henry (1797).

Figure 39.01 illustrates some simple experiments for demonstrating induced currents. In (a), a magnet is thrust into the center of a coil of

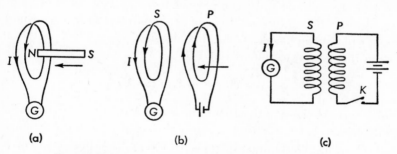

| (a) | (b) | (c) |

Fig. 39.01. Electromagnetic induction experiments.

wire connected to a galvanometer. As long as the magnet is *moving*, a small current is indicated by the galvanometer. The polarity of the magnet and direction of motion shown result in the current direction marked. As soon as the motion of the magnet stops, so does the current. In (b), the magnet is replaced by a coil of wire P, through which a battery sends a steady current. If the coil P is moved toward the coil S, connected to G, a small current I results. If the motion of P stops, so does I.

741

In both (a) and (b), if the motion of the magnet or coil is reversed, the direction of the induced current reverses. In (c) the relative positions of the two coils are fixed, but the current in P (known as the primary coil) can be interrupted with a key K. When K is first closed, a momentary induced current I appears in the coil S (the secondary coil), but it soon dies away to zero and remains zero as long as the current in the primary is constant. When K is opened, a momentary induced current is observed in the secondary in the reverse direction. This arrangement of two coils is called a **transformer.** The size of the induced current is increased greatly if both P and S are wound around a closed iron ring to form an iron-cored transformer.

Suppose in Figure 39.01(c) the galvanometer is replaced by a voltmeter of infinite resistance. No current is then possible in the secondary circuit, but when K is opened or closed, momentary readings of the voltmeter are obtained. This induced voltage or induced emf E is considered to be the basic phenomenon.

All three cases considered have one feature in common—the induced emf appears in the secondary coil when and only when the magnetic field in which S lies changes with time. Faraday showed that, measuring the field by its flux density B, the induced emf is proportional to the rate of change of B and that the maximum emf is obtained when B is perpendicular to the coil. He also showed that the emf was proportional to the area A of the coil and to the number of turns of wire N. Let us define the **magnetic flux** ϕ through the coil as the product of its area times the perpendicular component of the flux density. Then if θ is the angle between the normal to the area and B,

$$\phi = (B \cos \theta)A = \mathbf{B} \cdot \mathbf{A} \tag{39.01}$$

where we are considering the area to be a vector quantity whose direction is that of its normal. If B changes in direction or size throughout the area of the coil, (39.01) must be replaced by a summation or integration.

$$\phi = \sum_{\text{area}} \mathbf{B} \cdot \Delta \mathbf{A} = \int_{\text{area}} \mathbf{B} \cdot d\mathbf{A} \tag{39.02}$$

Faraday's experimental results are summed up in the equation

$$E = N \frac{\Delta \phi}{\Delta t} \tag{39.03}$$

where $\Delta \phi$ is the total change of flux through the coil in the time interval

Δt. This equation should strictly be regarded as giving only the average emf E during Δt. The instantaneous emf is the limit of this ratio as $\Delta t \to 0$.

$$E = N \frac{d\phi}{dt}$$

(39.03a)

Equation (39.03) is known as **Faraday's Law of Electromagnetic Induction.**

The direction of the induced emf is given by **Lenz' Law** which states:

The induced emf is such as to send a current in the secondary circuit in a direction to oppose the change in the magnetic field which produces it.

Figure 39.02 shows the system of Figure 39.01(a) again. The secondary coil S has an induced current I and thus acts as a magnet with north and south faces as shown. It repels the moving magnet as required by Lenz' Law. Suppose, for a moment, that I were in the opposite direction. Then the coil would attract the magnet, and its motion would continue without any work being done on it. Its continued motion would maintain the induced current, which does do work, so that the system would supply work with none being done on it—in violation of the law of conservation of energy. Thus Lenz' Law is seen to be a necessary consequence of the conservation of energy.

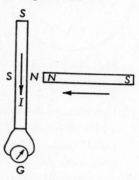

Fig. 39.02. Illustration of Lenz' Law.

The Right-Hand (Generator) Rule. The following rule is a consequence of Lenz' Law and is sometimes easier to apply. Spread the thumb and first two fingers of the *right* hand to be at right angles to each other. Then if the thu**M**b is pointed in the direction of **M**otion of the conductor and the **F**orefinger in the direction of the **F**ield, the **C**enter finger points in the direction in which the induced emf attempts to send a **C**urrent. The boldface letters serve as a mnemonic aid.

Units. From (39.01), flux is the product of flux density (webers per square meter) times area (square meters). Hence flux is measured in *webers*, the same unit as that used for magnetic pole strength. This choice can be justified by calculating the flux from a magnetic pole of strength m webers. Let P be an isolated pole of this strength. Draw a sphere of radius r about P. If it is assumed that the region has a uniform permeability $\mu\mu_0$, then at any point on this sphere (Figure 39.03)

$$H = \frac{m}{4\pi\mu\mu_0 r^2} \quad \text{and} \quad B = \frac{m}{4\pi r^2}$$

Since B is uniform in size over the surface of the sphere and normal to each element of area,

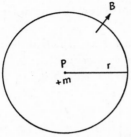

$$\phi = BA = \frac{m}{4\pi r^2} \times 4\pi r^2 = m$$

Therefore, from a pole of strength m webers,

$$\phi = m \text{ webers}$$

The Magnetic Field. We have now introduced three numerical properties of the magnetic field. Let us summarize their meanings and the connections between them.

Fig. 39.03. Flux from an isolated pole.

H, the **magnetic field strength**, is that *vector* property of the field which determines the force exerted on a magnetic pole placed at any point in it. The force on any *magnet* can be deduced, at least in principle.

B, the **magnetic flux density**, is that *vector* property of the field which determines the force exerted on a current element placed at any point in it. The force on any *current-carrying circuit* can be deduced, at least in principle.

ϕ, the **magnetic flux**, is that *scalar* property of the field, the time rate of change of which determines the emf induced in a loop of a conductor in the field.

Of these three, B and H are point properties. That is, they are defined at a point and may vary from one point to another, but ϕ is defined only in terms of the area of a closed loop.

$$\mathbf{B} = \mu\mu_0\mathbf{H} \qquad \phi = \mathbf{B} \cdot \mathbf{A}$$

39.02 THEORY OF ELECTROMAGNETIC INDUCTION

The induced emf can be shown to be a necessary result of Ampere's Law and the existence of free electrons in a conductor. Figure 39.04 shows a conductor LM moving through a constant, uniform magnetic field of flux density B which is perpendicular to both LM and the direction of motion of the conductor and is into the diagram. Consider any electron in the metal. A charge $-e$ moving to the right with velocity v is equivalent to a current I_e moving (conventionally) to the left. By Ampere's Law there is a force on the electron. The direction of the force is given by the left-hand (motor) rule as from L to M. If the electron is free to move, it will therefore drift toward M. Since all the free electrons tend to move toward M, there is an accumulation of negative charge at M and a shortage of electrons around L, that is, an excess positive charge. This separation of charge means that L is at a higher potential than M and hence an emf is produced, just as separation of charge in an electric cell results in an emf.

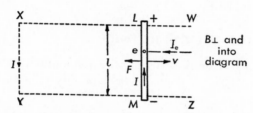

Fig. 39.04.　Generation of an emf.

In Figure 39.04, if the conductor does not form part of a closed circuit, there will be no current and the emf will do no work. A small amount of work will be needed to accelerate LM from rest to the velocity v. This work is made up of two parts, the work required to give the conductor the kinetic energy corresponding to its mass and velocity, and the work required to separate the charges to set up the emf. Once LM has reached a steady velocity, no further work need be done on it to keep it moving.

The situation is quite different if LM forms part of a closed circuit. Suppose LM slides on a fixed conductor $WXYZ$. The induced emf E will cause a current I in the path $LXYML$. There are two consequences of this current. First, electrical power EI is dissipated in the conductor. Second, Ampere's Law shows that a force $F = BIl$ will act on the moving conductor LM in the direction shown. Hence, if LM is to continue to move with a velocity v, mechanical power equal to Fv must be applied. Equating mechanical and electrical power, we have

$$EI = BIlv$$
$$E = Blv$$

The product lv of the length of LM and its velocity is just the rate at which the area of the loop $LXYM$ is increasing. Therefore

$$E = B\frac{\Delta A}{\Delta t} = \frac{\Delta(BA)}{\Delta t}$$

since B is constant. That is,

$$E = \frac{'\Delta\phi}{\Delta t}$$

which is Faraday's Law for this single-turn circuit. A more elaborate derivation based, as is the above, on Ampere's Law and the conservation of energy leads to (39.03) in the general case in which the flux density B is also a function of time.

39.03 A-C AND D-C GENERATORS

Suppose a coil of N turns of wire is mounted with its axis perpendicular to a uniform magnetic field of flux density B (see Figure

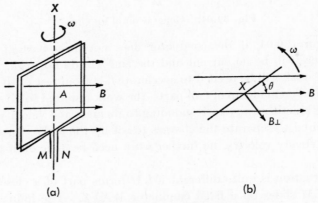

(a)   (b)

Fig. 39.05. Principle of an a-c generator.

39.05) and is caused to rotate at a uniform angular velocity ω. Let the plane of the coil make an angle θ with the direction of B. The flux through the coil (of area A) is

$$\phi = \mathbf{B} \cdot \mathbf{A}$$

If $B_\perp$ is the component of B along the normal to A,

$$\phi = B_\perp A$$

or
$$\phi = BA \sin \theta$$

The induced voltage between the terminals M, N is

$$E = N\frac{\Delta\phi}{\Delta t} = N\frac{\Delta(BA \sin \theta)}{\Delta t}$$
$$= \frac{NBA}{\Delta t}\,\Delta(\sin \theta)$$

since B and A are constants. Let θ increase by an angle $\Delta\theta$ in Δt. Then the change in $\sin \theta$ is the difference between the sine of $\theta + \Delta\theta$ and the sine of θ.

$$\Delta(\sin \theta) = \sin (\theta + \Delta\theta) - \sin \theta$$
$$= \sin \theta \cos \Delta\theta + \cos \theta \sin \Delta\theta - \sin \theta$$

For small $\Delta\theta$, $\cos \Delta\theta \doteq 1$ and $\sin \Delta\theta \doteq \Delta\theta$. Therefore

$$\Delta(\sin \theta) \doteq \sin \theta \cdot 1 + \cos \theta \cdot \Delta\theta - \sin \theta$$
$$\doteq \Delta\theta \cos \theta$$

Substituting gives $\qquad E \doteq NBA \dfrac{\Delta\theta}{\Delta t} \cos \theta$

But $\Delta\theta/\Delta t = \omega$, and in the limit as $\Delta t \to 0$ the equation becomes exact. The induced emf in the coil is

$$E = NBA\omega \cos \omega t \qquad (39.04)$$
$$= E_M \cos \omega t \qquad (39.05)$$

where $\qquad\qquad E_M = NBA\omega \qquad\qquad (39.06)$

The output voltage of the coil thus varies between a maximum of $+E_M$ and a minimum of $-E_M$ since the value of $\cos \omega t$ varies between ± 1. Such a voltage is called a **sinusoidal a-c voltage**.

Virtually all the electrical power used in North America is produced by a-c generators operating on this principle. The power required to turn the coil may come from the energy of falling water in a hydroelectric system or from burning coal or oil in a steam-operated electric power plant. The magnetic field is produced by an electromagnet energized or **excited** by a separate d-c source of power. The coil leads M, N slide on two continuous rings called **slip rings** from which the a-c power is drawn.

If the leads M, N are connected to a commutator, the generator can be used to produce d-c power, and the output of the generator is said to be **rectified**. To obtain a smoother voltage from a d-c generator, several coils are wound on the armature, equally spaced about it. The voltage outputs of these coils are added. Figure 39.06 illustrates many of these features.   Part (a) shows the output of a single-coil a-c generator and is a plot of equation (39.05).   Part (b) shows the effect of a commutator on the output of a generator.   The commutator acts to reverse the output voltage every half-revolution, and (b) is obtained from (a) by reversing all the half-cycles where the voltage is negative.   The average d-c voltage obtained is $\bar{E}$.   In Figure 39.06(c), the voltage-time curves are shown for a d-c generator with three coils spaced 120° apart around the armature. These three voltages are added to give the output voltage E_T of the

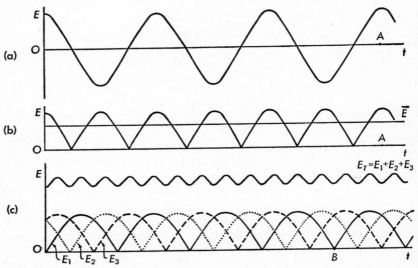

Fig. 39.06.   Wave forms of various generators: (a) single-coil, uniform-field a-c generator; (b) single-coil, uniform-field d-c generator; (c) three-coil, uniform-field d-c generator.

generator.   The time scale in (c) has been expanded slightly for clarity. Thus the time interval OA in the first two diagrams is the time for the armature of the generator to make three complete revolutions, whereas OB in (c) is the time for two complete revolutions.

Back emf.   Generators and motors have marked similarities in construction—in fact, the same machine can frequently be used for both purposes.   Both have two electrical circuits (field circuit and armature), linked by a common magnetic circuit.   It is important to note that a motor also acts as a generator while running.   The armature coils carry a current which interacts with the magnetic field to cause motion, and once the coils are turning in the field, they generate an emf.   This is called the **back emf** because by Lenz' Law it must be so directed as to attempt to produce a current opposing the motion causing it. The back emf is usually a large fraction of the voltage applied to the motor, and this has important consequences in starting motors. An example shows this.

Example. A shunt-wound d-c motor has a rating of 150 hp for an applied voltage of 600 v and current of 202 amp. These are full-load conditions. The resistance of the field coils is 300 Ω and of the armature 0.150 Ω. Find the back emf under full load, and the initial current in the armature if the full voltage is applied in starting the motor.

Under full load the current in the field coils is

$$I_F = \tfrac{600}{300} = 2.00 \text{ amp}$$

Therefore the armature current is

$$I_A = 202 - 2.0 = 200 \text{ amp}$$

The IR drop across the armature is $200 \times 0.150 = 30.0$ v. The back emf is $600 - 30.0 = 570$ v. If the armature is at rest, there is no back emf and the starting current in the armature is

$$I_A = \frac{600}{0.15} = 4000 \text{ amp}$$

Although this current is only momentary, it would probably burn out the armature winding and would also produce a very high accelerating torque which might damage the motor. To avoid these dangerous results of a full-voltage start, it is customary to place a rheostat in series with the armature with enough resistance to limit the starting current to about 150% of full-load current. As the angular speed of the armature builds up, so does the back emf, and the series resistance is gradually decreased to zero.

39.04 MUTUAL INDUCTANCE

Faraday stated his law of electromagnetic induction in terms of a magnetic field property, the flux. Henry stated the same result in terms of the current producing the magnetic field. In Figure 39.07(a) two coils are shown wound around a common form. A current I_P in the primary coil P produces a magnetic field B within the secondary coil S. If the geometry of the two coils is completely known, it is possible, in theory at least, to calculate the flux ϕ through S. By geometry we mean number of turns, radii of coils, spacing, etc.   If the current I_P varies, the flux ϕ will change, and an emf will be induced in the secondary, given by

$$E_S = N_S \frac{\Delta \phi}{\Delta t}$$

where N_S is the number of turns on the secondary coil.   Now ϕ depends on I_P, so this equation can be written

$$E_S = M \frac{\Delta I_P}{\Delta t} \tag{39.07}$$

where M is a geometrical constant of the two coils which involves N_P and N_S and the other factors listed above.   It is constant as long as the spacing of the coils does not change and is called the **mutual inductance**

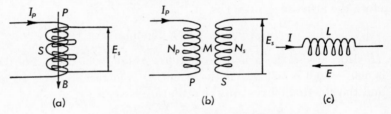

Fig. 39.07.   Mutual and self inductance.

of the two coils.   It is not necessary for the two coils to be wound on the same form (although this is the method used to obtain large values of M), and a mutual inductance will exist between any two coils when flux produced by one threads the turns of the other.   Figure 39.07(b) shows the conventional symbol for M used in circuit diagrams.

From the symmetry involved in the definition of M, it is reasonable that, if a current varies in the secondary, the voltage induced in the primary will be

$$E_P = M \frac{\Delta I_S}{\Delta t} \tag{39.08}$$

and this is always found to hold, M having the same value regardless of which coil is acting as the primary.

The calculation of M is simple in theory and very difficult in practice. The calculations have been made only for a few simple coil structures, but several methods are available for measuring mutual inductance.   If one or both of the coils are wound around an iron core, B, ϕ, and M are increased by a large factor, approximately equal to the relative permeability of the iron.   However, as the magnetic field depends on the current and the value of B does not depend linearly on H in iron, M is no longer a constant for an iron-cored coil but is a function of the current.

Units. From (39.07), the unit of M may be obtained. It is

$$[M] = \frac{\text{volts} \times \text{seconds}}{\text{amperes}} = \text{ohms} \times \text{seconds}$$

M is thus measured in ohm-seconds, a unit to which we give the name, the *henry*.

39.05 SELF INDUCTANCE

Current through a single coil produces a magnetic field which threads through the turns of wire. If the current, and hence magnetic field, are varied, an emf will be generated in the coil itself. The size of the voltage can be found from an equation similar to (39.07).

$$E = L \frac{\Delta I}{\Delta t} \tag{39.09}$$

where L is called the **self inductance** of the coil. By Lenz' Law the direction of E will be such as to oppose the change in current producing it. Figure 39.07(c) shows the conventional symbol for representing self inductance. If I is increasing, the direction of E will be as shown, that is, it will oppose the current and cause a drop in potential. If I is decreasing, E is in the opposite direction, and the coil acts as a source of power which tries to maintain a current of the original size and direction.

As in the case of mutual inductance, L can be calculated only for a few simple coil shapes, but many methods have been developed for measurement of self inductance. Like M, L is measured in henrys or millihenrys (abbreviated h and mh). A device for introducing inductance into a circuit is called an **inductor** and is usually some type of coil. If large values of L are needed, the coil may be wound on an iron core, but if this is done, L is not a constant, its value depending on the current.

A steady, or d-c, current is, by definition, one in which I does not change with t: $\Delta I = 0$ for any Δt. From (39.09), $E = 0$ for direct current and self inductance plays no role in d-c circuits. A coil of wire is no different from an equal length of straight wire of the same resistance, at least insofar as the size of the steady current is concerned. However, steady currents do not last indefinitely. They had to be turned on at some time and eventually they will be turned off. Inductance becomes important during these transition times when the current is varying in size. Consider the circuit of Figure 39.08. When the key K has been closed for some time, the current is

$$I = \frac{E_B}{R} \tag{39.10}$$

since L has no effect. However, when K was first closed, the current I did not jump immediately to this value but increased gradually from zero to the value given by (39.10). It can be shown that the time for this growth of current to take place is about $5L/R$ where L/R is called the **time constant** of the circuit. (Remembering that L is in henrys and that a henry is an ohm-second, we see that L/R is a time in seconds.) Unless an extraordinarily large inductance is used, the time constant is usually small (measured in milliseconds), and the growth of current takes place too rapidly to be of interest to us. When K is opened later on, events of more importance take place. The current cannot drop to zero instantly, for if it did, ΔI would be finite for Δt zero, giving an *infinite* voltage of self-induction. Infinite voltages do not exist, but E *will* be large enough to keep the current flowing for a short time after K opens. It can do this only by breaking down the insulation of the air between the two contacts of the key, and the result is a spark. Most circuits contain some inductance and thus produce a spark when opened, as when you pull a toaster or iron cord out of the wall socket. The effect is unimportant in these cases, but if the current and inductance are large, elaborate arrangements must be made to break the circuit. Sparking is a serious cause of deterioration of electrical contacts.

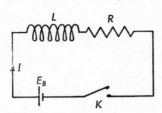

Fig. 39.08. L-R d-c circuit.

Inductance is sometimes referred to as electrical inertia, and the analogy is a good one. Mechanical inertia is the property of a mass by which it resists change in velocity or angular velocity. Inductance is the circuit property by which it resists change in current. If a large inductor is placed in series with the output of the generator of Figure 39.06(c), E_T will still have the wave form shown, but the current will be held constant by the inductance. There is an interesting analogy here with the action of a flywheel in a gasoline engine, such as a two-cylinder outboard motor, for example. The energy supplied by the engine comes in short bursts or pulses, as the cylinders fire. The flywheel has a large moment of inertia, and hence considerable kinetic energy which it gives up gradually to the propeller during the intervals between firing. When a cylinder fires, the flywheel gains back the energy it lost and thus maintains a reservoir of energy which smooths out the fluctuating power of the engine so that the power delivered to the propeller is almost constant.

An inductor stores energy in the magnetic field which the current produces. The amount of energy stored can be found by considering the work done in establishing the final current I in the circuit of Figure 39.08. Let the current increase from i to $i + \Delta i$ in time Δt. The average emf induced in the inductor is

$$e = L \frac{\Delta i}{\Delta t}$$

and since this opposes the increase of current, the power required is $p = ei$. Hence the work done to produce this increase of current is

$$\Delta W = p\, \Delta t = ei\, \Delta t = L \frac{\Delta i}{\Delta t}\, i\, \Delta t = Li\, \Delta i$$

$$W = \Sigma\, \Delta W = L\Sigma i\, \Delta i = L \frac{I}{2} \Sigma\, \Delta i$$

since the average value of i is half the initial value (0) plus the final value I. The sum of all the increments of currents is just I, so that

$$W = \tfrac{1}{2}LI^2$$

The vital role of inductance in a-c circuits will be discussed in Chapter 41.

PROBLEMS

1. The magnetic flux through a 100-turn coil changes from 0.360 weber to zero in 1.00 sec. Find the average emf induced in the coil.

2. A flat coil has 5000 turns, each of area 7.00 cm². It lies in a uniform field of strength 6000 amp m⁻¹, the angle between the normal to the coil and the direction of the field being 60.0°. If there is no ferromagnetic material in the vicinity, find the flux through the coil. What is the voltage induced in the coil if the field decreases uniformly to half its former strength in 0.100 sec?

3. A uniform magnetic field varies with time according to the equation

$$B = 0.800 \sin \omega t \qquad \text{(webers m}^{-2}\text{)}$$

A flat coil of N turns each of area 10.00 cm² is mounted so that the plane of the coil is perpendicular to B. Show that the voltage induced in the coil is $E = E_M \cos \omega t$, where $E_M = 0.800NA\omega$, A being the area of the coil. Note that the peak values of the a-c voltage occur at the times of zero field. How

many turns of wire should the coil have to give a peak voltage of 155 v if
$\omega = 2\pi \times 60 = 377$ radians/sec?

4. A wire 60.0 cm long moves with a velocity of 20.0 m sec⁻¹ perpendicular to a
uniform magnetic field of 10,000 amp m⁻¹. What is the potential difference
between the ends of the wire?

5. In Figure 39.09, if the slider is moved down on the rheostat to increase the
resistance, which of A or B will be at the higher potential?

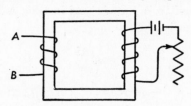

Fig. 39.09.

6. At a certain location the angle of dip of the earth's field is 60.0° and the
total flux density is 8.00×10^{-5} weber m⁻². A car driving west at a speed
of 30.0 m sec⁻¹ carries a vertical radio aerial of height 1.50 m. What emf
is induced in the aerial?

7. The armature of an a-c generator carries a single coil of 500 turns, each of
area 0.200 m². It rotates at 1200 rpm in a uniform magnetic field of flux
density 4.00×10^{-2} weber m⁻². Find the maximum value of the a-c voltage.

8. The axis of a flat coil of 400 turns is perpendicular to a uniform magnetic
field. The coil has an area of 100 cm² and rotates at 1500 rpm. What
magnetic flux density is needed in order that the maximum output voltage of
the generator shall be 155 v? What is the frequency of the a-c voltage?

9. The resistance of a d-c generator armature is 0.500 Ω and the generated voltage
is 240 v. What is the output voltage for a current of 1.00 amp?, 50.0 amp?

10. Two coils have a mutual inductance of 0.200 h. If a current of 10.00 amp
is decreased uniformly to zero in 10.0 sec in one coil, what voltage is induced
in the other?

11. The current in a coil of self inductance 220 mh is increased from zero to
500 ma in 10.0 msec. What average back emf is developed?

12. The primary current in a transformer is changing at a uniform rate of 0.400
amp sec⁻¹. A steady voltage of 140 mv is observed in the secondary coil.
What is the mutual inductance?

13. The current in a 150-turn coil is changing at a uniform rate of 0.800 amp
sec⁻¹. This causes the flux in the coil to change at a rate of 3.60×10^{-4}
weber m⁻² sec⁻¹. What is the self inductance of the coil?

14. A solenoid is 60.0 cm long and has 4000 equally spaced turns, each of area
5.00 cm², wound on a nonmagnetic core. Calculate the self inductance

of the coil. (Assume a current I in the coil. Calculate H, B, and ϕ. Then since $E = L(\Delta I/\Delta t) = N(\Delta\phi/\Delta t)$, $L = N(\Delta\phi/\Delta I) = N\phi/I$ since $\phi \propto I$.)

15. In Figure 39.08, $L = 2.00$ mh, $R = 50.0$ Ω, and $E_B = 60.0$ v. Find the steady current in the circuit, the time constant of the circuit, and the approximate time for the steady current to be established after K is closed.

16. In Figure 39.10, $R_S = 500$ Ω, $R = 181$ kΩ, $E_B = 6.30$ v. What steady current results if K_1 is closed, K_2 open? After this current is established,

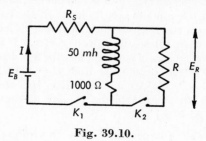

Fig. 39.10.

K_2 is closed and K_1 opened. What is the initial value of E_R? (The inductance will not allow an instantaneous change of current. Thus the switching diverts the current through R and its value is initially unchanged.)

17. The insulating properties of air break down if too large a potential difference exists between two conductors separated by air. The required electric field for breakdown is about 30 kv/cm. If this figure is also applicable to the gasoline-air mixture in the cylinder of a car, what potential difference will cause a spark plug to "fire" if the distance between the points is 0.0100 in.? (If the resistor R in Figure 39.10 is replaced by the spark plug, we have a rudimentary automobile ignition system. Actual systems are more complex but use this same principle to develop potential differences of several hundred volts from an automobile battery of 6.3 v.)

18. Calculate the energy to be disposed of (by a spark or otherwise) when (a) a current of 100 ma in an inductor of 300 mh is broken, (b) a current of 625 amp in a 10.0-h coil is interrupted. How high would this latter amount of energy raise a mass of 1000 kgm above the surface of the earth?

19. A shunt-wound d-c motor has an armature resistance of 0.350 Ω and a field coil resistance of 110 Ω. A 220-v line supplies the power, and under full load the motor draws a total current of 20.0 amp. In addition to heating losses in the coils, frictional losses and other miscellaneous ones amount to 117 w. Find the back emf in the armature, the mechanical power output in horsepower, and the efficiency of the motor.

20. The motor of problem 19 rotates at 1200 rpm under full load. What torque does it develop? If the starting armature current is limited to 1.50 times full-load current, what series resistor is needed initially? What is the initial torque? The series resistor is gradually reduced, resulting in an

average torque midway between the two values just calculated. If the moment of inertia of the armature is 200 kgm m², how long does it take to bring the motor to full speed?

21. Under certain conditions a galvanometer can be used to measure charge and for this purpose is referred to as a **ballistic galvanometer.** In Figure

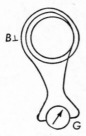

39.11, a small coil, called a **search coil,** is placed in a magnetic field with its plane perpendicular to the lines of flux. It is connected to a galvanometer, and the total resistance of the coil and G is R ohms. If the coil is removed rapidly from the magnetic field, a voltage is induced in the coil and a charge flows through the meter. If the coil has 140 turns and an area of 5.00 cm², find the flux density when the charge $Q = 105$ μcoulombs and $R = 400$ Ω. (Induced voltage $E = N(\Delta\phi/\Delta t)$ and also $E = IR$, where I is the current in the galvanometer at any instant; $\Delta\phi = \phi - 0$ and $I\,\Delta t = Q$.)

Fig. 39.11.

22. **An earth inductor** is a large search coil with a spring-and-trigger arrangement to permit the coil to be rotated rapidly 180° about a diameter as axis. This rotation reverses the position of the coil with respect to any flux through it. An earth inductor, mounted with its axis horizontal, is connected to a galvanometer. The total resistance is 300 Ω. When the coil (2000 turns, area 250 cm²) is reversed, a charge of 1.14×10^{-5} coulomb is measured. The earth inductor is next mounted with its axis vertical and the normal to the coil pointing north and south. Rotation of the coil produces a charge of 6.71×10^{-6} coulomb. Find the horizontal component and total strength of the earth's field (in ampere per meter) and the angle of dip.

23. Figure 39.12 shows the secondary of a mutual inductor M connected to a galvanometer. A steady current in the primary can be reversed with the

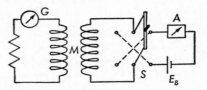

Fig. 39.12. Measurement of mutual inductance with a ballistic galvanometer.

switch S. The total resistance of the galvanometer circuit is 500 Ω. When a current of 1.00 amp is reversed in direction in the primary, a charge of 2.40×10^{-4} coulomb goes through the galvanometer. Find the mutual inductance.

40

Electrostatics

40.01 GENERATION OF CHARGE

We return now to a discussion of isolated electric charges at rest. Suppose an ebonite rod (E) is rubbed with fur (F) and that the rod and piece of fur are then suspended by light strings so that they are close together but not touching. It is found that they attract each other with a small force. Similar results are obtained with a glass rod (G) and a piece of silk (S), which also attract each other after being rubbed together. Each of the four bodies is said to be electrified or to possess electric charge. We can represent the attractions schematically as follows:

$$E\ (-)\rightarrow\ \leftarrow F\ (+)$$
$$G\ (+)\rightarrow\ \leftarrow S\ (-)$$

If now we test the bodies in different combinations, repulsion is observed between the glass rod and the fur, and so on. Summarizing the other possibilities, we have

$$G\ (+)\leftarrow\ \rightarrow F\ (+) \qquad G\ (+)\rightarrow\ \leftarrow E\ (-)$$
$$E\ (-)\leftarrow\ \rightarrow S\ (-) \qquad F\ (+)\rightarrow\ \leftarrow S\ (-)$$

These results are readily explained if, by analogy with magnetostatics, we assume that electric charges are of two types, positive and negative, and that like charges repel and unlike attract. The charges on the glass and the fur are arbitrarily called positive. As pointed out in 33.01, equal quantities of charge of opposite sign neutralize each other—hence the use of the algebraical signs.

The basic facts of electrostatics have been known much longer than the corresponding information about current electricity; in fact, the name electricity comes from the Greek word "electron", which means amber, and the ancient Greeks were familiar with the electrostatic properties of amber. The arbitrary labels, plus and minus, for the two kinds of electricity were first assigned to electrostatic charges and then were taken over into theories of current electricity.

A negatively charged body is one which has a surplus of electrons, and a positively charged body has a deficiency of them. Matter in its normal state is neutral, having equal numbers of protons and electrons, and in solids the positively charged protons are fixed in place, being part of the permanent structure of the solids. The negatively charged electrons are more or less firmly attached to the structure, but at least some of them can be detached fairly readily. If any two solids of different materials are placed in close contact, as by rubbing them together, some electrons will be transferred from one body to the other, leaving them both charged. For any two given substances, the transfer of electrons always takes place in the same direction. Thus, when ebonite and fur are placed together, electrons always move from the fur to the ebonite.

The four substances we have used as examples are all insulators, and for a long time it was thought that only insulators had this property of electrification by contact between dissimilar substances. That this is not true can be shown by mounting metal plates on insulating handles. If two different metals are pressed or rubbed together and then separated, they will be found to be charged. Because conductors allow the motion of charge to take place freely, if the two metals are held in your hands, your body allows the charges to leak away before they can be detected, and this was the reason for the failure to detect electrostatic charging of metals in early experiments.

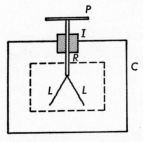

Fig. 40.01. A leaf-type electroscope.

Electroscopes. The repulsion of like charges is used in an instrument called an electroscope to detect small charges. Figure 40.01 shows a simple design. A metal (or metal-lined) box C has glass windows in front and back. A metal plate P is mounted on a metal rod R, passing through an insulator I. Two light, metal strips L are attached to the ends of the rod. The strips or "leaves" are often made of gold because it can be beaten very thin to form light leaves. If a charge is transferred to P, it is distributed rapidly throughout the connected metal parts, including L and L. The electrostatic repulsion between the leaves causes them to move apart, the angle of divergence being a measure of the charge. The electroscope can be discharged by connecting P to ground. The earth can be considered a conductor at zero potential, with an inexhaustible supply of free electrons. If P (and the metal system connected to it) has a surplus of electrons, its potential is negative, and on grounding it a momentary current flows in the conventional sense from earth to P. Since it is the electrons which actually move in solid conductors, what really takes place is that the surplus electrons flow to ground until P is uncharged. Touching P with your finger is equivalent to grounding it since the charge it can hold is very small and for this charge your body is a large conductor at (approximately) zero potential.

Charging by Induction. An electroscope can indicate the charge on a body without any actual contact taking place. In Figure 40.02(a)

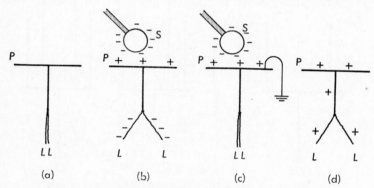

Fig. 40.02. Charging an electroscope by induction.

we see a discharged electroscope. A metal sphere S, mounted on an insulating handle, is given a negative charge and brought near P without touching it. The result is indicated in (b). The repulsion between the charges on S and the electrons in the metal parts of the electroscope causes some of the free electrons to move down to the leaves, which diverge. The total charge on the metal system is unchanged but has been rearranged, with P now having a net positive charge and L, L a negative one.

An interesting effect is observed if, without removing S, P is now grounded as in (c). The repulsive force exerted by S causes some free electrons to escape to ground, and the leaves collapse. The net charge on the electroscope is no longer zero. If the ground connection is first removed, and S is then taken away, the electroscope's net charge is positive, and free electrons will move about until the charge is uniformly distributed. The leaves now have positive charges and once again diverge as in Figure 40.02(d). This method of producing a charge on the electroscope, opposite in sign to that on S, is called **charging by induction.** If S had had a positive charge, the final result would have been a negative charge on the electroscope.

Faraday's Experiment. According to the explanation offered above there is no creation of charge when two substances are electrified by contact, only a transfer of existing charge from one body to another. Thus the positive and negative charges appearing on the two bodies must be equal and opposite. An ingenious experiment of Faraday's can be repeated easily in the laboratory to verify this. In Figure 40.03(a) a

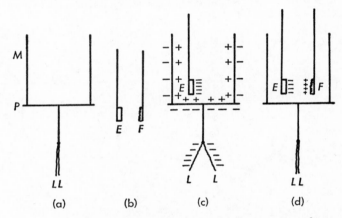

Fig. 40.03. Faraday's ice-pail experiment to show equality of charge.

metal can or pail M, open at one end, is seated on the plate of an electroscope. The electroscope is discharged. In (b) two insulating handles are terminated in a small ebonite disk E and a small pad of fur F, which are tested separately in the electroscope to ensure that they have no charges. They are then rubbed together briskly. In (c) E is inserted into the can and the leaves diverge, showing that the ebonite is now charged. In (d) the fur piece is also lowered into the can but does not touch E. Nevertheless, the leaves of the electroscope collapse, showing that the net charge inside the can is zero.

A second simple but important experiment which can be done with the pail and electroscope of Figure 40.03 is the following. Suspend a small piece of metal on an insulating string and give the metal a charge, negative say, and equal to $-Q_1$. Ground the pail momentarily to ensure that it and the electroscope are neutral. Now lower the metal on the string gradually down toward the pail and into it (not touching the sides) and watch the electroscope. As the charged metal approaches, the leaves diverge more and more until the metal is actually inside the pail. After this there is no increase, and the metal can be moved about anywhere within the pail without altering the position of the leaves. From this we conclude that the amount of charge which can be separated by induction has a maximum value, say Q_2. Then the inside of the pail has a charge $+Q_2$, and the total charge on the outside of the pail and on the electroscope is $-Q_2$.

Now, lower the metal to touch the inside of the pail, watching the electroscope as contact is made. Nothing happens—the leaves show no change in charge at all. The metal can now be removed from the pail without any effect on the electroscope, and when the metal is tested it is found to be completely discharged. Since the electroscope showed no change when contact was made, the external charge $-Q_2$ on pail and electroscope remained the same. Since removal of the metal had no effect, there can have been no charge left on the inside of the pail. Hence the inescapable conclusion is that $-Q_1$ on the metal neutralized $+Q_2$ on the inside of the pail. That is, $Q_2 = Q_1$: the maximum induced charge equals the inducing charge, and the two will be equal if the second conductor surrounds or almost surrounds the charged conductor. Actually the two charges will be equal (or have a negligible difference) if the two conductors are separated by a distance small compared to their extent. This is demonstrated well in one type of electrostatic device illustrated in Figure 40.05. The two metal plates are close together, and if one is given a charge, the induced charge on the other will be of the same size.

Charge Remains on the Outside of a Closed Conductor. If a closed metal surface, such as a sphere, is given a charge, mutual repulsion between the individual electrons will cause them to take up positions as widely separated from each other as possible. Since the external surface has a larger area than the internal one,

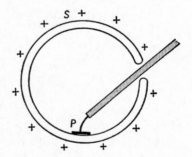

Fig. 40.04. Testing inside of a sphere for a charge with a proof plane.

it follows that *all* the charge must be found on the outside. Figure 40.04 shows a method of verifying this conclusion. The charged sphere S has a small hole in it, and a small metal plate P (called a **proof plane**), mounted on an insulating handle, is inserted through the hole until it makes contact with the interior surface. The plate is then removed and tested with an electroscope and is found to be uncharged.

40.02 COULOMB'S LAW. PERMITTIVITY

The exact form of the law of force between electric charges was investigated by Coulomb, using a torsion balance. He found the law to be similar in form to the one governing magnetostatic forces, that is, the force is proportional to the product of the charges, inversely proportional to the square of the distance between them, and dependent on the nature of the medium in which the charges lie. In equation form **Coulomb's Law of Electrostatic Force** is

$$F = \frac{Q_1 Q_2}{4\pi\epsilon\epsilon_0 r^2} \tag{40.01}$$

where F is the force between charges Q_1 and Q_2 a distance r apart. The properties of the medium are included via the terms $\epsilon\epsilon_0$, where ϵ_0 measures the effect of having the charges in vacuo, and ϵ is a factor which indicates the ability of any medium, relative to that of a vacuum, in reducing the force of attraction. The factor ϵ is called the **relative permittivity** or **dielectric constant.** Being a ratio, it has no units. By definition it is unity for a vacuum and differs from unity by only a few parts in ten thousand for gases, including air. Table 40.01 shows some typical values of ϵ. No substance is known with $\epsilon < 1$.

TABLE 40.01 Values of the Dielectric Constant.

Substance	ϵ
Air at N.T.P.	1.0006
Transformer oil	2.5
Wax	2
Glass	6
Water	80

The term ϵ_0 is called the permittivity of free space. To make equation (40.01) balance dimensionally,

$$[\epsilon_0] = \frac{[\text{coulomb}]^2}{[\text{newton}][\text{meter}]^2} = \frac{[\text{farad}]}{[\text{meter}]}$$

The two units given for ϵ_0 are identically equal, and the second is the one normally used. The farad is the unit of capacitance and will be defined in 40.06. The numerical value of ϵ_0 must be found experimentally and is

$$\epsilon_0 = 8.85 \times 10^{-12} \doteq \frac{10^{-9}}{36\pi} \text{ farad m}^{-1} \qquad (40.02)$$

40.03 FIELD STRENGTH AND POTENTIAL

The mathematical similarity between Coulomb's Laws of Magneto-statics and Electrostatics shows that we can develop the theory of the electrostatic field along lines very similar to those used in Chapter 36 for the magnetic field. Just as a magnetic field surrounds a distribution of magnetic poles, so an electrostatic field surrounds a distribution of electric charges. The **electric field strength** at any point is defined as the force which would be exerted on a unit positive charge ($+1$ coulomb) if it were placed at that point. We shall use the symbol $\mathcal{E}$ for field strength (not to be confused with E for emf), and the force equation

$$F = Q\mathcal{E} \qquad (40.03)$$

which gives the force exerted on a charge, corresponds to

$$F = mH$$

of section 36.04. The simplest type of electric field is a uniform field which is obtained with the system shown in Figure 40.05. In this diagram P_1 and P_2 are parallel metal plates whose length and breadth are very large compared to the distance d between them. Plate P_2 is grounded, and P_1 is at a potential V. From the symmetry of this arrangement it is plausible that $\mathcal{E}$ will have the same direction and size everywhere between the plates, and this is confirmed experimentally. Let us consider moving a charge Q from a point on P_2 to P_1 by the shortest path, that is, along a line perpendicular to the plates. Such a line is a line of force of the electric field, and the force is given by (40.03):

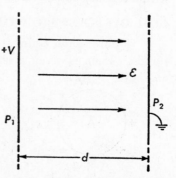

Fig. 40.05. Parallel-plate capacitor giving a uniform electric field.

$$F = Q\mathcal{E}$$

The work done equals force times distance, or

$$W = Fd = Q\mathcal{E}d$$

and the work per unit charge was defined in Chapter 33 as the potential difference. Thus

$$V - 0 = \frac{W}{Q} = \mathcal{E}d$$

or
$$\mathcal{E} = \frac{V}{d} \tag{40.04}$$

This simple equation applies only for a uniform field, but it indicates how $\mathcal{E}$ and V are related in one case, and it explains the choice made for the unit of $\mathcal{E}$.

Units. From (40.03), $\mathcal{E}$ could be measured in newtons per coulomb, but the usual unit is *volts per meter*. These two units are identically equal.

$$\frac{\text{newton}}{\text{coulomb}} = \frac{\text{newton} \times \text{meter}}{\text{coulomb} \times \text{meter}} = \frac{\text{joule}}{\text{coulomb} \times \text{meter}} = \frac{\text{volt}}{\text{meter}}$$

Most electric fields are not uniform, but (40.03) enables us to predict the force on any charge if we can calculate or measure the field strength. In this book we shall have little occasion to use equations relating to nonuniform electric fields, but they are very important in connection with electronics and radio.

40.04 DISTRIBUTION OF CHARGE ON A BODY

Figure 40.06 shows three metal bodies supported on insulating stands. Each is given a charge, and the distribution of the charge is

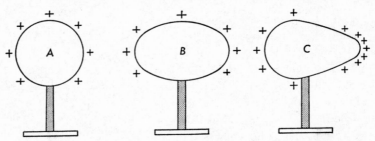

Fig. 40.06. Distribution of charge on bodies of various shapes.

examined by placing a small proof plane in contact with various points on the surface and then testing the proof plane with an electroscope (discharging proof plane and electroscope after each test). The body A is a sphere, and the charge is found to be uniformly distributed. The charge on B, an ellipsoid, is no longer uniformly distributed but is slightly more concentrated on the pointed ends of the ellipsoid. Body C is still more sharply pointed at one end, and here the charge is found to be almost entirely concentrated in the vicinity of the point.

If a body is constructed with a very sharp point, it will not retain a charge; that is, any charge placed on it will gradually disappear. This is caused by the great concentration of charge at the point, which sets up a strong electric field in its vicinity. The surrounding air is normally an excellent insulator, but all insulators "break down", or become conductors, if a sufficiently large electric field strength is applied across them. In the case of air at normal temperature and pressure, the breakdown field strength (or **dielectric strength** as it is sometimes called) is 3000 volts per millimeter ($= 3 \times 10^6$ v m^{-1}). Such a field strength as this is easily set up near a sharp point, and the air becomes conducting and allows the charge to leak away. This phenomenon is called a point discharge. If the quantity of charge involved is small and if the other conductor to which the charge moves (frequently the earth) is some distance away, the discharge proceeds slowly and with little or no visible effects. For larger quantities of charge, the discharge may be rapid enough for a visible **corona** of light to appear. This consists of fine, branching, irregular lines of purplish light.

In contrast to the point discharge is the spark discharge which occurs between two smooth-surfaced electrodes (spheres are often used) when the charges on them are made sufficiently great. Careful observation of a spark shows it to have a very complicated structure, and if the potential difference between the electrodes is maintained, separate sparks follow each other rapidly. Each spark seems to follow a different path and to have no connection with the others. There has been considerable study of high-voltage sparking both because of intrinsic interest and because of the similarity to lightning flashes, but the details of the process are still obscure.

40.05 ELECTROSTATIC MACHINES

A considerable number of devices have been invented for the generation of electric charge by electrostatic means. The quantities of charge are almost invariably small, but the voltages may be quite large. For example, if you shuffle your feet across a carpet when the humidity is low and then touch a radiator, a spark about 0.1 mm long jumps from your finger to the radiator. From the figure quoted in the previous section it follows that your body must have been at a potential of about

300 v with respect to ground.   The most important of these electrostatic machines are described below.

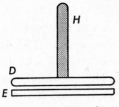

Fig. 40.07.   An electrophorus.

(1) THE ELECTROPHORUS

This is a simple device used in laboratories in electrostatic experiments.   It is illustrated in Figure 40.07 and consists of a metal disk D, mounted on an insulating handle H, and an ebonite disk E. To use the device, the disk E is first rubbed vigorously with a piece of fur.   This leaves a considerable amount of negative charge on the surface of E.   The disk D is placed on top of E and grounded by touching it with one's finger.   When D is now removed it is found to have a positive charge.   This is an example of charging by induction, and the details are similar to those shown in Figure 40.02. Even when D is resting on E, because of the irregularities of the surface

Fig. 40.08.   A Wimshurst machine.   (Photograph courtesy of Central Scientific Co. of Canada Ltd.)

the number of points of contact is small, and actual transfer of charge from E to D is negligible. The attraction of the charge on E for the positive charges in the metal, however, results in a separation of charge, with positive charges on the lower side of D and negative on the upper side. Grounding D permits the separated negative charges to go to earth, leaving a net positive charge.

(2) THE WIMSHURST MACHINE

This machine, illustrated in Figure 40.08, consists of two parallel glass disks which are rotated in opposite directions by turning a crank. Each disk carries a number of segments of tinfoil, and the tinfoil segments develop charges as they are rotated. The charges are collected from the segments by wire brushes and stored in foil-lined glass cylinders called **capacitors** (see section 40.06). The theory of operation is rather involved and is omitted here as it has little bearing on the rest of our subject matter. It is possible to develop potential differences of several thousand volts with this machine.

(3) THE VAN DE GRAAF GENERATOR

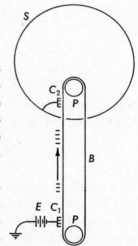

Biggest of the electrostatic machines, this generator is a very important tool in nuclear physics. It is sketched in Figure 40.09, where S is a large metal sphere. An endless belt B passes through two holes in S, going around the pulleys P, P. The belt is made of insulating material (woven, rubber-impregnated nylon is a favorite) and is motor-driven in the direction shown. At its lower end the belt passes close to a metal comb C_1 of sharp points, maintained at a high negative potential by the emf E. The potential difference between comb and belt, aided by the point-discharge phenomenon, causes negative charge to jump to the belt, where it is carried up to the inside of the sphere and is there collected by

Fig. 40.09. Principle of the van de Graaf generator.

another comb C_2 connected to the inside of S. Since the charge immediately flows to the outside of the sphere, no charge builds up on C_2 to prevent the transfer of charge to it from the belt. The process is continuous, and the quantity of charge on the outside of S and, hence, the potential difference between S and ground are limited only by the available insulation. Potentials of five and six *million* volts have been achieved with generators of this type. In the diagram S becomes negative with respect to ground but could equally well be raised to a positive potential by reversing the polarity of E. In actual van de Graafs, the d-c emf E is usually obtained from an electromagnetic generator.

40.06 CAPACITANCE

Figure 40.10(a) shows two conductors separated by some insulating medium. If a potential difference is established between the conductors,

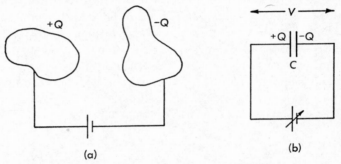

(a)   (b)

Fig. 40.10. Capacitance and its representation in a circuit diagram.

it is found that they acquire equal and opposite charges Q. If the potential difference V is varied in size, Q varies also, and it is found that

$$\frac{Q}{V} = \text{a constant, } C; \qquad Q = CV \qquad (40.05)$$

This constant, written as C, is called the **capacitance** of the arrangement and is a third type of circuit element, the other two being resistance and inductance. Like inductance, capacitance is a geometrical property, depending on the size and spacing of the conductors and on the properties of the intervening medium. In all cases the capacitance is directly proportional to the dielectric constant of the medium. The unit of capacitance is the *farad*, and we see from (40.05) that

$$1 \text{ farad} = 1 \frac{\text{coulomb}}{\text{volt}}$$

Any device introduced into a circuit to produce capacitance is called a **capacitor.** The arrangement of parallel plates in Figure 40.05 and the foil-lined glass cylinders used in the Wimshurst machine to store charges are examples of capacitors. The parallel-plate type is the most important, and the conventional symbol for capacitance, or for a capacitor, in a circuit is a pair of equal, parallel lines as shown in Figure 40.10(b).

It can be shown that two metal plates, each of area A, a distance d apart have a capacitance of

$$C = \frac{\epsilon \epsilon_0 A}{d} \qquad (40.06)$$

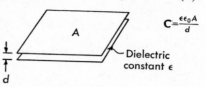

where ϵ is the dielectric constant of the medium between the plates. Figure 40.11 illustrates the factors in this equation.

Fig. 40.11. Parallel-plate capacitor.

Capacitors in Parallel and Series. Earlier it was shown that combinations of resistors in series and parallel connections could be reduced to a single equivalent resistor. The same can be done with capacitors. If two or more capacitors are connected in parallel, we simply add their capacitances to get the equivalent capacitance. Formal proof of this result is left as a problem for the student (problem 9), but the equation is almost self-evident when we compare two capacitors in parallel (and hence with the same potential) to two pails filled with water to the same height. The analogy between electric potential and hydrostatic pressure is close, and the total quantity of water stored is certainly the sum of the quantities in the two pails.

Problem 10 deals with the case of capacitors in series. The result is not so obvious but follows readily when we realize that capacitors in series must all have the same charge (reread the description of Faraday's ice-pail experiment in section 40.01). Comparing equations (40.16) and (40.17) with the corresponding ones for resistance, (34.06) and (34.03), we note that capacitors in parallel are analogous to resistors in series, and capacitors in series to resistors in parallel.

Energy Stored in a Capacitor. If a capacitor is charged by a battery which is then disconnected, the plates remain charged for a considerable time. Eventually the charge "leaks" away through the insulating material, since no insulator has an infinite resistance, but the capacitor may retain most of its charge for days or months. For this reason it is wise to "short" the terminals of capacitors in high-voltage equipment such as radar or television sets before doing any servicing. The shock one gets by touching both terminals of even a small capacitor charged to a potential difference of 1000 v is not lightly forgotten. When a capacitor is discharged by connecting its terminals together, a spark is produced, showing that energy was stored in the capacitor.

The charging of a capacitor consists of removing a charge from one plate and transferring it to the other. Suppose we mentally divide the total charge moved, into a large number of small charges and consider that these are transferred in succession. No work is involved in moving the first small charge, because initially there is no potential difference between the plates. As a result of this first movement of charge, however, a small potential difference now exists, equal to the ratio of the charge moved, to the capacitance. The second small charge must thus be moved against a small potential difference, and each successive charge against a larger potential difference until the last one is raised through the full final voltage on the capacitor. The total work done is the total charge moved times the average voltage. Calling this work W, we write

$$W = Q \times \frac{0 + V}{2} = \tfrac{1}{2}QV \tag{40.07}$$

This can be written in several ways by eliminating Q or V between (40.07) and (40.05). The work done in charging a capacitor, which is the energy stored in it, is thus

$$W = \tfrac{1}{2}QV = \tfrac{1}{2}CV^2 = \tfrac{1}{2}\frac{Q^2}{C} \tag{40.08}$$

The calculus proof of this relation is short. At some stage, let the charge on the plates be q. Then the potential difference is $v = q/C$. The work done in transferring an increment of charge dq is

$$dW = v\, dq$$
$$W = \int_0^Q v\, dq = \int_0^Q \frac{q}{C}\, dq$$
$$= \tfrac{1}{2}\frac{Q^2}{C}$$

Example. Find the capacitance of two parallel plates, each of area 400 cm², clamped on either side of a sheet of mica ($\epsilon = 6.30$) which is 0.500 mm thick. If the dielectric strength of mica is 100 kv/mm and a safety factor of 4 is required, what is the maximum voltage which may safely be applied to this capacitor? What is the charge stored for this maximum potential difference, and how much energy can the capacitor release?

To apply (40.06), we must express area and separation in square meters and meters, respectively.

$$A = 400 \text{ cm}^2 = 400 \times 10^{-4} \text{ m}^2$$
$$d = 0.500 \text{ mm} = 5.00 \times 10^{-4} \text{ m}$$

Therefore
$$C = \frac{6.30 \times 8.85 \times 10^{-12} \times 400 \times 10^{-4}}{5.00 \times 10^{-4}}$$
$$= 4.46 \times 10^{-9} \text{ f}$$

where f is the abbreviation for farad. We see that the capacitance of our capacitor is an extremely small number of farads. For this reason, capacitances are usually quoted in millionths of a farad or microfarads, or even in micromicrofarads.

$$1 \ \mu\text{f} = 10^{-6} \text{ f}, \qquad 1 \ \mu\mu\text{f} = 10^{-12} \text{ f}$$

Thus the capacitance found above is

$$C = 4.46 \times 10^{-9} \text{ f} = 0.00446 \ \mu\text{f} = 4460 \ \mu\mu\text{f}$$

If the dielectric strength of mica is 100 kv/mm, the 0.5-mm mica insulator might break down if a voltage of $0.5 \times 100 = 50$ kv were applied across it. A safety factor of 4 thus limits the voltage to one-fourth of this or 12.5 kv. For this potential difference the charge is given by (40.05) as

$$Q = CV$$
$$= 4.46 \times 10^{-9} \times 12.5 \times 10^3 = 55.8 \times 10^{-6} \text{ coulomb}$$

The energy which can be obtained from the capacitor is given by (40.08) as

$$W = \tfrac{1}{2}QV = \tfrac{1}{2} \times 55.8 \times 10^{-6} \times 12.5 \times 10^3 = 0.349 \text{ joule}$$

From the above example we see that the amount of charge (or energy) which can be stored in a capacitor is very small compared to the charge (or energy) which a storage battery can deliver. A 120-ampere-hour battery can produce charge $Q = 120 \times 3600 = 4.32 \times 10^5$ coulombs. Thus capacitors do *not* furnish a useful method of storing any appreciable quantity of electricity. Despite this, capacitors are extremely important circuit components, particularly in a-c circuits and electronics. One reason is that, since there is no contact between the plates, a capacitor is a complete block to a direct current—a capacitor offers an infinite resistance to a steady voltage. If the voltage is varying however, as in a-c circuits, the charges on the plates vary, and we shall see that this is equivalent to the passage of an alternating current. Thus a capacitor may be used to prevent the passage of direct current while allowing alternating current to pass. A capacitor used in this way is called a *blocking capacitor*, and this application is common in electronic circuits. Other uses will be discussed in the next chapter.

Effect of a Dielectric. To conclude this discussion of capacitors, let us investigate qualitatively the reason why the presence of an insulating material between the plates of a capacitor increases its capacitance. In order to be specific we shall consider a parallel-plate capacitor, but similar arguments apply to any capacitor. From equation (40.06), if the capacitor of Figure 40.11 is placed in a vacuum, its capacitance is $\epsilon_0 A/d$ since by definition $\epsilon = 1$ in vacuo. If any dielectric (that is, any solid, liquid, or gaseous insulator) is placed between the plates, the capacitance increases by a factor ϵ, the dielectric constant characteristic of the material.

We have assumed earlier the existence of "free" electrons in metallic conductors, and we interpreted electric current as due to the motion of these free electrons under the influence of a potential difference. Using the terms introduced in this chapter, we may say that the potential difference sets up a field which exerts a force on the electrons—the drift of the free electrons constituting the current. The field also exerts a force on the positive parts of the atoms, but as these are fixed in place by interatomic forces, they play no part in an electric current. In an insulator the situation differs because the number of free electrons is negligible and each atom (or molecule) remains in its place when an electric field is applied. However, the field may cause a rearrangement of charge within the atom. That is, positive charges move slightly toward the cathode and electrons toward the anode. These displacements are infinitesimal in size and do *not* (for ordinary field strengths) result in any rupture of the atom, as in ionization. They do apparently elongate the atom slightly along the lines of force of the field. The situation is illustrated schematically in Figure 40.12(a), which shows the effect of the field. This phenomenon is unfortunately called **polarization,** a thoroughly overworked word in physics.

Figure 40.12(b) shows a parallel-plate capacitor in a vacuum, and (c) shows the same capacitor with a dielectric between the plates. A few of the polarized atoms in the dielectric are shown. In the body of the dielectric the polarization gives no net charge. The positive charge of one atom is adjacent to the negative charge of the next atom, and their effects cancel. It is seen, though, that at the anode and cathode surfaces there is an unbalanced surface charge on the dielectric. These surface charges have been labeled $-Q_P$ and $+Q_P$, respectively. (There is an analogy here with the magnetized bar of iron where the poles appear at the ends.)

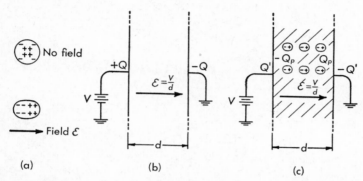

Fig. 40.12. Polarization and the effect of a dielectric on capacitance.

The same potential difference is applied in (b) and (c), and hence the field strength is the same. Now the field strength can be calculated from a knowledge of the charges on the plates, and hence the net charges at the plates must be the same to keep the same value of $\mathcal{E}$. That is,

$$Q = Q' - Q_P$$

where Q' is the externally supplied charge on the plates in (c), and Q is the charge in (b). The capacitance is the ratio of the external charge to the applied potential difference. Hence in (b) $C = Q/V$, and in (c)

$$C' = \frac{Q'}{V} = \frac{Q}{V} + \frac{Q_P}{V} = \frac{Q}{V}\left(1 + \frac{Q_P}{Q}\right)$$

$$= C\left(1 + \frac{Q_P}{Q}\right) > C$$

That is,
$$\epsilon = \frac{C'}{C} = 1 + \frac{Q_P}{Q}$$

In most cases ϵ is found experimentally to be a constant for a particular material, so that the surface charge due to polarization increases with applied potential difference at the same rate as Q does. Dielectrics of this type are called *linear*.

40.07 SYSTEMS OF UNITS

The mks system of units has been the preferred one throughout this text, principally because of its advantages in electricity and magnetism. Now that we have introduced Coulomb's Laws of Magnetostatics and Electrostatics, it is appropriate to discuss briefly the older systems of units based on these laws. Both systems use cgs mechanical units.

The Electromagnetic System of Units (emu). Coulomb showed that the force law between poles is

$$F \propto \frac{m_1 m_2}{\mu r^2}$$

using the notation of section 36.03. The constant of proportionality can be chosen arbitrarily since the size of the unit pole has not been assigned. The most obvious choice is to make the constant unity and write

$$F = \frac{m_1 m_2}{\mu r^2} \tag{40.09}$$

If now cgs units of force and distance are chosen, the size of the unit pole in emu is automatically determined. The development of other magnetic and electrical units follows along lines similar to those in Chapters 36–39. The names and sizes of some of these units are listed in Table 40.02.

TABLE 40.02   The Electromagnetic Units and Their Relations to Corresponding mks Units.

Quantity	Name	Conversion Factor (1 unit of column 2 =)
Pole strength	Abpole	$4\pi \times 10^{-8}$ weber
Magnetic field strength	Oersted	$1000/(4\pi)$ amp m^{-1}
Flux density	Gauss	10^{-4} weber m^{-2}
Flux	Maxwell	10^{-8} weber
Current	Abampere	10 amp
Potential difference	Abvolt	10^{-8} v
Resistance	Abohm	10^{-9} Ω
Inductance	Abhenry	10^{-9} h

The Electrostatic System of Units (esu). In a similar fashion the electrostatic force law can be written

$$F = \frac{Q_1 Q_2}{\epsilon r^2} \tag{40.10}$$

and used to define a unit of charge called the *statcoulomb* in terms of cgs mechanical units. Electrostatic units of potential, field strength, current, etc., follow readily and are summarized in Table 40.03.

TABLE 40.03 The Electrostatic Units and Their Relations to Corresponding mks Units.

Quantity	Name	Conversion Factor (1 unit of column 2 =)
Charge	Statcoulomb	$\frac{1}{3} \times 10^{-9}$ coulomb
Current	Statampere	$\frac{1}{3} \times 10^{-9}$ amp
Potential difference	Statvolt	300 v
Electric field strength	Statvolt cm^{-1}	30,000 v m^{-1}
Capacitance	Statfarad	$\frac{1}{9} \times 10^{-11}$ f ($\doteq 1\ \mu\mu$f)
Resistance	Statohm	$9 \times 10^{11}\ \Omega$

It must be stressed that *some* of the equations relating electrical and magnetic quantities have slightly different forms for use with emu or esu than those we have derived in the mks system. The difference is usually a factor of 4π and is due to the explicit appearance of this factor in the mks forms of Coulomb's Laws.

Practical Units. Long before the invention of the mks system it was found that the emu or esu of current, potential, resistance, etc., were of an inconvenient size, and the so-called practical units were adopted by engineers and others concerned with the industrial application of electricity. The practical units chosen were the ampere, volt, ohm, etc., and they were defined by arbitrary conversion factors from emu and esu. Thus three sets of units were in use, two absolute systems and one arbitrary system. The arbitrary, practical system was of limited use in theoretical work, so that it was customary to develop electrical theory in one or both of the absolute systems and then convert to the practical system in order to make calculations about applications of the theory. The mks system replaces these three sets and has been chosen to make the practical units serve also as the absolute units for theoretical work.

Ratios of the Units. Before leaving the subject of units, one curious experimental fact should be noticed.

$$\frac{1 \text{ abampere}}{1 \text{ statampere}} = \frac{1 \text{ statvolt}}{1 \text{ abvolt}} = \sqrt{\frac{1 \text{ statohm}}{1 \text{ abohm}}} = \sqrt{\frac{1 \text{ abfarad}}{1 \text{ statfarad}}}$$
$$= 3 \times 10^{10} \text{ cm sec}^{-1}$$

The numerical value of each ratio can be found from Tables 40.02 and 40.03, and it can be shown that each term has the dimensions of velocity. The numerical result is identical with

$$c = 3 \times 10^{10} \text{ cm sec}^{-1}$$

where c is the velocity of light. This result was one of the first indications of the electromagnetic nature of light.

Similarly, in the mks system

$$\frac{1}{\sqrt{\epsilon_0 \mu_0}} \doteq \left(\frac{10^{-9}}{36\pi} \times 4\pi \times 10^{-7}\right)^{-\frac{1}{2}} = (9 \times 10^{16})^{\frac{1}{2}} = 3 \times 10^8 \text{ m sec}^{-1}$$

It is important to note that ϵ_0 is determined by a purely electrical experiment, having no connection with optics. The quantity μ_0 is arbitrarily defined.

40.08 FIELD STRENGTH AND POTENTIAL. CALCULUS METHODS

In Figure 40.13(a), A and B are two points in an electrostatic field of field strength $\mathcal{E}$ which may vary in both size and direction from point

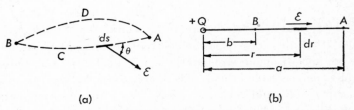

(a)   (b)

Fig. 40.13. (a) Rigorous definition of potential difference and emf. (b) Potential distribution near a point charge.

to point. Let us calculate the difference in potential between A and B. Choose any path ACB joining the points and divide it into infinitesimal elements of length ds. The potential at B is greater than that at A by the amount of work done in moving a unit charge from A to B against the field. Consider this unit charge being moved through the distance ds.

The force exerted on it by the field is ε, so that an equal and opposite force $-\varepsilon$ must be applied to move it. The work done is the component of this force along ds multiplied by the distance. That is,

$$dW = dV = -\varepsilon \cos \theta \, ds \qquad (40.11)$$

where θ is the angle between ε and ds. The total potential difference is found by adding up the work done in each element of the path, that is, by integrating (40.11) along the path. Symbolically,

$$V_B - V_A = \int_a^b -\varepsilon \cos \theta \, ds = \int_b^a \varepsilon \cos \theta \, ds \qquad (40.12)$$

where the limits on the integral refer to the positions of the points A and B. This equation is the mathematical definition of potential difference.

At first sight the result of the calculation of (40.12) might be thought to depend on the path chosen between A and B. This is not the case, however, as may be seen by choosing a second path ADB. Suppose

$$(V_B - V_A)_{ACB} < (V_B - V_A)_{ADB}$$

The work done on a unit charge in carrying it from A to B by a certain path is returned if the charge is allowed to "fall" back to A along the same path. Let us carry the unit charge around the path $ACBDA$. Then more work is obtained on the return trip than was done in going to B, in violation of the law of conservation of energy. Hence, we conclude that $(V_B - V_A)_{ACB}$ must equal $(V_B - V_A)_{ADB}$, and therefore that $V_B - V_A$ is independent of the path and depends only on the positions of A and B. A field with this property is known as a **conservative field**. A very neat mathematical notation for the result just proved is

$$\oint \varepsilon \cos \theta \, ds = \oint \varepsilon \cdot \mathbf{ds} = 0 \qquad (40.13)$$

where the circle on the integral sign means that the integral is calculated over a closed path such as $ACBDA$.

One important exception to (40.13) exists. If the path includes a source of emf, net work numerically equal to the emf will be done if a unit charge moves around the closed path. This does not conflict with the law of conservation of energy since the source of emf provides the energy from a nonelectrical source. In this case

$$E = \oint \varepsilon \cdot \mathbf{ds} \qquad (40.14)$$

Equation (40.14) is a generalized form of Kirchhoff's Second Law. Note the complete parallel with (37.14) for mmf.

Let us apply (40.12) to find the potential distribution near a point charge. The situation is illustrated in Figure 40.13(b). Since the lines of force are radial, the potential will be constant on any spherical surface centered about the charge Q. Field strength $\mathcal{E}$ and the element of distance along a radius dr are parallel. That is, $\theta = 0$ and $\cos \theta = 1$. The field strength $\mathcal{E}$ is given by Coulomb's Law. Setting $Q_1 = Q$ and $Q_2 = 1$ in (40.01), we have

$$F = \mathcal{E} = \frac{Q}{4\pi\epsilon\epsilon_0 r^2}$$

$$V_B - V_A = \int_b^a \mathcal{E} \, dr = \int_b^a \frac{Q}{4\pi\epsilon\epsilon_0} \frac{dr}{r^2}$$

$$= \frac{Q}{4\pi\epsilon\epsilon_0} \left[-\frac{1}{r} \right]_b^a$$

$$= \frac{Q}{4\pi\epsilon\epsilon_0} \left(\frac{1}{b} - \frac{1}{a} \right)$$

If we now let $a \to \infty$

$$V_B - V_\infty = \frac{Q}{4\pi\epsilon\epsilon_0} \frac{1}{b}$$

Any arbitrary value may be given to V_∞, since it is only potential difference which we can measure, and the choice $V_\infty = 0$ is a convenient one. Then, if we replace b by r, the potential at any distance from a point charge is

$$V_r = \frac{Q}{4\pi\epsilon\epsilon_0 r} \tag{40.15}$$

PROBLEMS

1. Point charges of 20 and 60 microcoulombs are opposite each other on different sides of a sheet of glass 2.00 mm thick. Find the force on either of them.

2. It is found that 0.800 joule of work is needed to move a charge of 0.500 millicoulomb from one insulated conductor to another. What is the potential difference between the two conductors? If their separation is 10.0 cm, what is the average electric field strength?

3. What is the electric field strength between two large parallel plates 3.00 cm apart if a potential difference of 500 v is applied to them?

4. If an electron (charge 1.60×10^{-19} coulomb, mass 9.11×10^{-31} kgm) starts with zero velocity at the cathode of problem 3, calculate the force acting on it, its acceleration, and its transit time to the anode.

5. Charges are placed at three points A, B, C in a straight line. $AB = 10.0$ cm, $BC = 5.00$ cm, $AC = 15.0$ cm. If charges of $+8$ μcoulombs and -10

μcoulombs are placed at A and B, respectively, what charge must be placed at C so that there is no net force on the charge at B?

6. In problem 5, calculate the field strength at C due to the charges at A and B, assuming unit dielectric constant.

7. Charges of -8.00×10^{-8} coulomb and -5.40×10^{-7} coulomb are placed at A (30, 0) and B (0, 90), respectively, where the coordinates of the points are in centimeters on a Cartesian diagram. Find the field strength at the origin, giving its direction as the positive angle it makes with the X-axis. ($\epsilon = 2.00$.)

8. Find the capacitance of a parallel-plate capacitor, the plates being of area 6.00 m² and separated 0.885 mm from each other by a glass plate. ($\epsilon = 6.00$.)

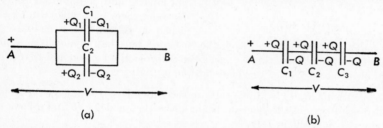

(a)   (b)

Fig. 40.14. Capacitors connected in parallel and series combinations.

9. Figure 40.14(a) shows two capacitors connected in parallel. Prove that this arrangement is equivalent, from the point of view of charge stored, to a single capacitor whose capacitance is

$$C_P = C_1 + C_2 \tag{40.16}$$

Write down a general equation for the equivalent capacitance of any number of capacitances in parallel.

10. Figure 40.14(b) shows three capacitors connected in series. Prove that this arrangement is equivalent, from the point of view of charge stored, to a single capacitor whose capacitance is C_S where

$$\frac{1}{C_S} = \frac{1}{C_1} + \frac{1}{C_2} + \frac{1}{C_3} \tag{40.17}$$

The charge stored is considered to be the quantity Q available at either output terminal of the system.

11. In Figure 40.14(b), $C_1 = 12.0$, $C_2 = 6.00$, $C_3 = 4.00$, all in microfarads. Find the equivalent capacity and the potential difference across each capacitor if $V = 120$ v.

12. What thickness of polystyrene of dielectric strength 2.20 kv mm⁻¹ is needed between metal surfaces for a potential of 3.00 kv, allowing a safety factor of 4?

13. A capacitor is designed to have a capacitance of 0.100 μf and to operate safely at a potential difference of 1000 v. If the dielectric used is mica ($\epsilon = 6.30$, dielectric strength 100 kv mm^{-1}), and a safety factor of 4 is required, what must be the area of either plate?

14. An *electron gun* is a device which produces a fine beam of electrons, projecting them in a certain direction with a definite velocity v. In Figure 40.15 a

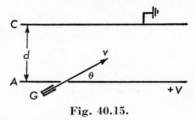

Fig. 40.15.

gun G projects an electron beam through a small hole in the anode A so that the beam has an initial velocity v and makes an angle $\theta = 30.0°$ with the anode. The anode A and the cathode C are large, parallel plates a distance $d = 10.0$ cm apart, and a potential difference between them of V volts can be established as shown. If $V = 49.5$ v, it is found that the electrons reach the cathode, but they do not if $V = 50.5$ v. Find v. (Note that this is a problem in projectile motion and that e/m for an electron $= 1.76 \times 10^{11}$ coulombs kgm^{-1}.)

15. In Figure 40.15, if $v = 1.00 \times 10^7$ m sec^{-1} and $V = 100$ v, how far from the entrance hole will the electron beam strike the anode? (θ and d have same values as in problem 14.)

16. Figure 40.16 shows the essential mechanism of a cathode-ray oscillograph (C.R.O.). An electron gun G fires a fine beam of electrons at a fixed velocity v along the axis of the tube. The beam passes centrally between the plates P_1, P_2 of a parallel-plate capacitor and strikes a fluorescent screen S at the end of the tube. This screen glows at the point where electrons strike it. If a potential difference is established between P_1 and P_2, the beam will be deflected vertically (as shown by the dotted line). A second set of plates (not

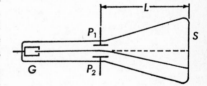

Fig. 40.16. Essentials of a cathode-ray oscillograph.

shown), placed at right angles to P_1 and P_2, can deflect the beam horizontally.

If $v = 3.00 \times 10^6$ m sec^{-1} and $L = 20.0$ cm, find the vertical movement of the beam due to a potential difference of 50.0 v applied to P_1 and P_2. The plates have a length of 1.00 cm along the beam and are 1.00 cm apart. Assume the electrostatic field is uniform and confined entirely between the plates.

17. If an a-c voltage $e = 30.0 \cos \omega t$ is applied to the deflector plates of the oscillograph of problem 16, find the length of the bright, vertical line which appears on the screen.

41

Alternating Currents

41.01 ALTERNATING-CURRENT CIRCUITS

Virtually all the electric power produced in North America is obtained from a-c generators. The simplest of these was described in section 39.03. We saw in that section that a coil rotated in a uniform magnetic field generates an emf of form

$$e = E_M \cos \omega t \qquad (41.01)$$

where ω is the angular velocity of the coil. Practical generators do not have uniform fields. Instead, the rotating coil, or rotor, turns in the field of an electromagnet having several pairs of poles. The result is an emf of the form of (41.01), but ω is now equal to the angular velocity of the rotor times the number of pairs of poles. For this reason ω is renamed and called the **angular frequency.** The renaming is also appropriate for emf's with higher values of ω. These are produced by electronic oscillators which contain no (visibly) moving parts at all.

Equation (41.01) is of a type considered in detail in the discussion of the simple harmonic motion of a particle in section 8.02. This section can be reread with profit at this point. We recall in particular the connection between ω and the frequency f and period T.

$$\omega = 2\pi f = \frac{2\pi}{T}$$

These relations can be taken as the definition of the angular frequency in a-c theory. It is still the custom to refer to a-c quantities in terms of their frequency (e.g., 60-cycle power), but actually it is the angular frequency which almost always appears in the theory.

When the emf of equation (41.01) is applied to a circuit, it will cause each free electron in the conductors to oscillate back and forth about a fixed average position. These oscillations are called an **alternating current** and are to be contrasted with the gradual drift of free electrons in a conductor which constitutes a direct current. Alternating and direct currents are equally useful in producing heat in resistors or mechanical power in motors, but only direct currents are useful in producing chemical effects.

A-c circuits are considerably more complex than d-c ones, principally because of the role of inductance and capacitance, and the overwhelming preference for a-c methods needs explanation. The reason lies in the increased efficiency of power transmission made possible through the

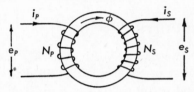

use of transformers. A **transformer** consists of a closed, soft iron ring, as shown in Figure 41.01, with two (or more) coils wound around it. The coil to which the emf is applied is usually called the **primary** and the other one the **secondary**. The subscripts P and S will be used to distinguish quantities,

Fig. 41.01. Principle of the transformer.

referring to the primary and secondary coils, respectively. Thus N_P, N_S are the number of turns of the coils and i_P, i_S the instantaneous values of the currents. If an alternating emf e is applied to the primary, there will be alternating currents in both circuits, and their combined action will produce an alternating flux ϕ in the iron core. The induced voltages in the two coils will be

$$e_P = N_P \frac{d\phi}{dt} \quad \text{and} \quad e_S = N_S \frac{d\phi}{dt} \tag{41.02}$$

assuming the flux through the two coils to be the same.

The solution of a-c circuits depends on a modification of Kirchhoff's Laws (section 34.01). The first law needs no change except to emphasize that it applies to instantaneous values of current. The second must be generalized to include other causes of potential drops beside resistance. As we have seen, both inductances (coils) and capacitances affect the potential distribution in a manner quite distinct from that of resistance. The generalized second law of Kirchhoff is that in any closed loop the net emf is equal to the algebraic sum of the potential drops, whatever their cause.

Applying this law to the primary circuit of Figure 41.01, we have

$$e = e_P + i_P R_P$$

where R_P is the resistance of the primary coil. In any practical transformer the second term is very small compared to the first. For the present the effects of the resistances of the two coils will be ignored, and to this approximation

$$e = e_P$$

From (41.02),
$$\frac{e}{e_S} = \frac{e_P}{e_S} = \frac{N_P}{N_S} \qquad (41.03)$$

and the voltage can be altered as desired by using a transformer with a suitable ratio of turns. The efficiency of transformers is very high (90% or more), and if we ignore all losses, the power from the secondary must equal the power delivered to the primary. That is,

$$e_P i_P = e_S i_S$$

and combining this with (41.03) gives

$$\frac{i_S}{i_P} = \frac{N_P}{N_S} \qquad (41.04)$$

If $N_S > N_P$, we see from (41.03) and (41.04) that the transformer produces an increased secondary voltage and a decreased secondary current. A transformer like this is called a *step-up* transformer. Conversely a *step-down* transformer lowers voltage and raises current.

It is frequently desirable to transmit electric power over distances of hundreds of miles. The principal loss involved lies in the heat produced in the transmission line. For economic reasons the wires cannot be increased beyond a certain size in order to reduce the resistance, and so the heat loss (average value of $i_S{}^2 R$) must be cut down by reducing the current, which can be done readily using a transformer. Similar changes of steady voltages and currents are difficult and costly to make, and transmission of d-c power over distances greater than a few miles is impractical. A more detailed discussion of transformers and power distribution is given in section 41.11.

In this chapter we shall consider the effect of applying a sinusoidal alternating voltage, such as given by (41.01), to circuits consisting of various combinations of resistance, inductance, and capacitance. In each case we shall find that a current of form

$$i = I_M \cos \omega t \qquad (41.05)$$

results but that, as a rule, voltage and current do not have their maximum values at the same time. Figure 41.02 illustrates graphs of e and i

plotted against ωt for some arbitrary circuit. We see that $I_M \neq E_M$ but that, apart from this scale factor, the curves are identical in form with the voltage curve shifted slightly to the left of the current curve, that is, the maxima and minima of voltage occur at earlier times than the corresponding maxima and minima of current. We say that, in this case, voltage **leads** the current in **phase.** The actual phase difference in the

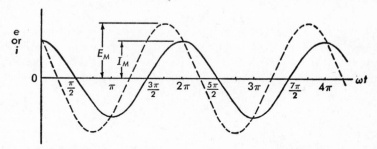

Fig. 41.02. Graphs of e (dotted line) and i (solid line) against ωt for some a-c circuit.

diagram is 45° or $\pi/4$ radians, so that the equations of the two curves plotted are

$$e = E_M \cos \left(\omega t + \frac{\pi}{4} \right)$$

and
$$i = I_M \cos \omega t$$

In general, we shall write

$$e = E_M \cos (\omega t + \phi) \tag{41.06}$$
$$i = I_M \cos \omega t \tag{41.07}$$

The phase difference ϕ may have any value between $-\pi/2$ and $+\pi/2$, depending on the constants (R, L, and C) of the circuit to which the emf is applied.

The numerical values of voltage and current are constantly changing, and it would be convenient to have a single figure to refer to as the size of an alternating voltage or current. One possibility is the maximum or **peak value** E_M (or I_M). More common, however, is the **effective** or **root-mean-square** (**rms**) value. Its advantage is that it puts alternating and direct currents on equal terms as far as delivering power is concerned. Consider the power supplied to a resistor by the current (41.07). Let a bar (horizontal line) over a symbol indicate that its average value is to be taken.

$$p = i^2 R$$

The average power is

$$P = \bar{p} = \overline{i^2 R} = \overline{i^2} R \qquad (41.08)$$

If we put $\sqrt{\overline{i^2}} = I$, I is the root-mean-square current and (41.08) becomes

$$P = I^2 R \qquad (41.09)$$

which is the same as the corresponding d-c equation. Thus numerically equal rms and direct currents supply the same amount of power to a resistor. The relation between rms and peak values is found as follows

$$i = I_M \cos \omega t$$
$$i^2 = I_M{}^2 \cos^2 \omega t$$
$$\overline{i^2} = I_M{}^2 \, \overline{\cos^2 \omega t}$$

Now
$$\sin^2 \omega t + \cos^2 \omega t = 1$$
$$\overline{\sin^2 \omega t} + \overline{\cos^2 \omega t} = 1$$

and because of the identical form of the sine and cosine curves

$$\overline{\sin^2 \omega t} = \overline{\cos^2 \omega t}$$

Therefore
$$\overline{\cos^2 \omega t} = \tfrac{1}{2}$$

and
$$\overline{i^2} = I^2 = \frac{I_M{}^2}{2}$$

or
$$I = \frac{I_M}{\sqrt{2}} \qquad (41.10)$$

The proof given above is a perfectly valid, trigonometric trick to find the average value of $\cos^2 \omega t$. An alternative proof, using a theorem from calculus, will be given in the next section. Similarly, in section 39.03 we showed from first principles that the rate of change with time of $\sin \omega t$ is $\omega \cos \omega t$, and we could just as easily prove that the rate of change with time of $\cos \omega t$ is

$$\frac{d}{dt} (\cos \omega t) = -\omega \sin \omega t$$

These differentiations occur very frequently in a-c theory, which is intimately bound up with rates of change and summations, the special fields of calculus. Because of this connection it seems fruitless to attempt a systematic development of the theory without using calculus notation. Students without training in this branch of mathematics should be able to follow most of the balance of this chapter if they keep in mind the two differentiation results just given. The trigonometry involved is extensive but fairly straightforward.

41.02 PURE RESISTANCE.   POWER

In Figure 41.03 an a-c generator G, of negligible internal resistance and emf given by (41.06), is connected to a pure resistance R.   The circle with the sine wave inside is the conventional symbol for an a-c generator. The resulting current i is shown by the arrow, although from (41.07) we see that the actual direction of current reverses every half-cycle.   At any instant the potential difference across the resistor must equal the applied emf.   Therefore

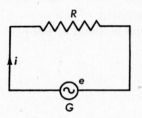

Fig. 41.03.   A-c generator connected to pure resistance.

$$e = iR$$
$$E_M \cos (\omega t + \phi) = I_M R \cos \omega t \quad (41.11)$$

Equation (41.11) must hold good for all values of time.   The simplest solution is to equate the constant terms in the equation and to equate the arguments of the two cosine functions.   This can be justified mathematically and always gives results in agreement with experiment.   Therefore

$$I_M = \frac{E_M}{R} \qquad (41.12)$$

$$\omega t + \phi = \omega t$$
$$\phi = 0 \qquad (41.13)$$

Equation (41.12) enables us to predict the maximum value of current for a given applied voltage, and (41.13) shows that e and i are in phase.

Power.   The power supplied to the resistor at any instant is

$$p = i^2 R$$

and thus fluctuates rapidly.   The quantity of interest is the average power, which we write as P.

$$P = \bar{p} = \overline{i^2 R} = \overline{i^2} R$$

since R is a constant.   Note that, while $\bar{i} = 0$, $\overline{i^2} \neq 0$ since i^2 is always zero or a positive quantity.   There is a useful theorem in calculus for finding average values of periodic functions.   If $f(x)$ is a function of x which repeats itself when x is increased by an amount x_0, then $f(x)$ is periodic in x with period x_0.

$$f(x + x_0) = f(x)$$

The theorem is

$$\overline{f(x)} = \frac{1}{x_0} \int_0^{x_0} f(x)\, dx \tag{41.14}$$

By (41.14), $$\overline{i^2} = \frac{1}{2\pi} \int_0^{2\pi} i^2\, d(\omega t)$$

since any trigonometric function has a period of 2π.

$$\overline{i^2} = \frac{1}{2\pi} \int_0^{2\pi} I_M{}^2 \cos^2 \omega t\, d(\omega t)$$

$$= \frac{I_M{}^2}{2\pi} \int_0^{2\pi} \frac{1 + \cos 2\omega t}{2}\, d(\omega t)$$

$$= \frac{I_M{}^2}{2\pi} \left[\frac{\omega t}{2} + \frac{\sin 2\omega t}{4} \right]_0^{2\pi}$$

$$= \frac{I_M{}^2}{2\pi} \left(\frac{2\pi}{2} + \frac{0}{4} - \frac{0}{2} - \frac{0}{4} \right)$$

$$= \frac{I_M{}^2}{2}$$

Therefore $$P = \frac{I_M{}^2}{2} R = I^2 R \tag{41.15}$$

where I is the rms current. It follows that equal quantities of heat will be liberated in equal resistors by a direct current of 1.000 amp or by an alternating current of the form of (41.07), whose peak value is 1.414 amp and whose rms value is $1.414/\sqrt{2} = 1.000$ amp. The use of rms values thus places direct and alternating current on the same basis with regard to their ability to deliver power, and alternating currents and voltages are almost always described in this way. The standard voltage of lighting circuits in houses is 110 v. A statement like this, made without qualification, invariably refers to rms values. The peak voltage in the circuit would be $110 \times \sqrt{2} = 155$ v. Most a-c instruments read rms values.

Power Equation. The same theorem permits us to derive a general equation for the average power expended in an a-c circuit.

$$p = ei$$

$$P = \overline{p} = \overline{ei} = \frac{1}{2\pi} \int_0^{2\pi} ei\, d(\omega t)$$

$$= \frac{1}{2\pi} \int_0^{2\pi} E_M \cos(\omega t + \phi) I_M \cos \omega t\, d(\omega t)$$

A standard result from trigonometry permits us to change from the product of two cosine functions to a sum.

$$2 \cos A \cos B = \cos (A + B) + \cos (A - B)$$

$$P = \frac{E_M I_M}{2\pi} \int_0^{2\pi} \tfrac{1}{2} \{\cos (2\omega t + \phi) + \cos \phi\} \, d(\omega t)$$

$$= \frac{E_M I_M}{4\pi} \left[\frac{\sin (2\omega t + \phi)}{2} + \omega t \cos \phi \right]_0^{2\pi}$$

$$= \frac{E_M I_M}{4\pi} \left[\frac{\sin (4\pi + \phi)}{2} + 2\pi \cos \phi - \frac{\sin \phi}{2} - 0 \cdot \cos \phi \right]$$

The first and third terms in the bracket cancel and

$$P = \frac{E_M I_M}{2} \cos \phi = \frac{E_M}{\sqrt{2}} \frac{I_M}{\sqrt{2}} \cos \phi$$

$$P = EI \cos \phi \tag{41.16}$$

where E and I are the rms voltage and current. The term $\cos \phi$ is called the **power factor**.

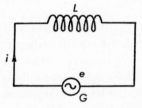

Fig. 41.04. Current through a pure inductance.

41.03 PURE INDUCTANCE

In Figure 41.04 a generator is shown connected to a pure inductance. This is a useful step in elaborating the theory, but it is impossible in practice since any inductance is made by coiling wire and must have some resistance. A varying current in an inductance induces an emf in it which opposes the change in current and hence acts in the opposite direction to the applied emf (see section 39.05). Thus the voltage drop across an inductance is $L(di/dt)$. This equals the applied emf in this circuit:

$$e = L \frac{di}{dt}$$

$$E_M \cos (\omega t + \phi) = L \frac{d}{dt} (I_M \cos \omega t)$$

$$= -\omega L I_M \sin \omega t$$

$$= \omega L I_M \cos \left(\omega t + \frac{\pi}{2} \right)$$

Equating constants and arguments of the cosine functions, we have

$$E_M = \omega L I_M$$

$$\omega t + \phi = \omega t + \frac{\pi}{2}$$

That is, $\qquad I_M = \dfrac{E_M}{\omega L} \qquad$ or $\qquad \dfrac{I_M}{E_M} = \dfrac{I_M}{\sqrt{2}}\dfrac{\sqrt{2}}{E_M} = \dfrac{I}{E} = \dfrac{1}{\omega L}$ $\qquad$ (41.17)

$$\phi = \frac{\pi}{2} \tag{41.18}$$

Since $\cos \pi/2 = 0$, $\qquad P = EI \cos \phi = 0$ $\qquad\qquad\qquad$ (41.19)

Thus inductance limits the current in a circuit, ωL playing the part of a resistance, but voltage *leads* current by 90° and consequently the inductance draws no power from the generator.

41.04 PURE CAPACITANCE

A capacitor prevents the passage of charge at a steady rate, or in other words has an infinite d-c resistance. For an alternating current of the type of (41.07), there is no net displacement of charge—the free electrons simply surge back and forth in simple harmonic motion. Thus in Figure 41.05, if at some instant the left-hand terminal of the generator is positive, electrons move around the circuit counterclockwise, accumulating negative charge on the right-hand plate of C and positive charge on the left-hand plate. Half a cycle later the emf of G is reversed and electrons move clockwise. Since this to-and-fro motion of charge *is* an alternating current, we say that a capacitor passes alternating current.

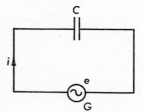

Fig. 41.05. Current through a pure capacitance.

The size of the current is found as follows:

$$e = \frac{q}{c}$$

$$\frac{de}{dt} = \frac{1}{C}\frac{dq}{dt} = \frac{i}{C}$$

since the rate of accumulation of charge is equal to the current. Using the a-c expressions for e and i, we have

$$\frac{d}{dt}\left[E_M \cos (\omega t + \phi)\right] = \frac{I_M}{C} \cos \omega t$$

$$-E_M\omega \sin (\omega t + \phi) = \frac{I_M}{C} \cos \omega t$$

$$E_M\omega \cos \left(\omega t + \phi + \frac{\pi}{2}\right) = \frac{I_M}{C} \cos \omega t$$

$$\omega E_M = \frac{I_M}{C}, \qquad \omega t + \phi + \frac{\pi}{2} = \omega t$$

Therefore $\qquad \dfrac{E_M}{I_M} = \dfrac{E}{I} = \dfrac{1}{\omega C}, \qquad \phi = -\dfrac{\pi}{2}$ \hfill (41.20)

Thus capacitance also limits current, $1/(\omega C)$ having the dimensions and role of a resistance, but in this case voltage *lags* 90° behind current, and again zero average power is drawn from the generator.

41.05 RESISTIVE-INDUCTIVE CIRCUITS. REACTANCE. IMPEDANCE

Figure 41.06 shows a circuit containing both R and L and thus is a circuit of a practical value, unlike Figure 41.04. Since at any instant

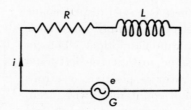

Fig. 41.06. Series R-L circuit.

the emf of the generator must equal the sum of the instantaneous voltages across the two circuit components,

$$e = Ri + L\frac{di}{dt}$$

$$E_M \cos (\omega t + \phi) = RI_M \cos \omega t + L\frac{d}{dt}(I_M \cos \omega t)$$

$$= RI_M \cos \omega t - \omega L I_M \sin \omega t \hfill (41.21)$$

Let us make the substitution:

$$\left.\begin{array}{l} R = Z \cos \alpha \\ \omega L = Z \sin \alpha \end{array}\right\} \qquad \text{where} \qquad \left.\begin{array}{l} Z = +\sqrt{R^2 + \omega^2 L^2} \\ \tan \alpha = \dfrac{\omega L}{R} \end{array}\right\} \quad (41.22)$$

The numbers Z, α can always be found from (41.22) for any numerical values of R, L, and ω. Equation (41.21) becomes

$$
\begin{aligned}
E_M \cos (\omega t + \phi) &= ZI_M \cos \omega t \cos \alpha - ZI_M \sin \omega t \sin \alpha \\
&= ZI_M (\cos \omega t \cos \alpha - \sin \omega t \sin \alpha) \\
&= ZI_M \cos (\omega t + \alpha)
\end{aligned}
$$

If this is to hold for all values of t,

$$E_M = ZI_M, \qquad \phi = \alpha$$

That is,
$$\frac{E_M}{I_M} = \frac{E}{I} = Z = + \sqrt{R^2 + \omega^2 L^2} \qquad (41.23)$$

$$\phi = \alpha = \tan^{-1} \frac{\omega L}{R} \qquad (41.24)$$

The first of these equations permits us to find the size of the current and the second the phase difference ϕ and hence the power factor $\cos \phi$. If we set $L = 0$, they reduce to equations (41.12) and (41.13); and if we set $R = 0$, we get equations (41.17) and (41.18), as of course we should since Figures 41.03 and 41.04 are special cases of Figure 41.06.

Some of these combinations occur so frequently in a-c theory that they are given special names. The quantity Z in (41.22) or (41.23) is called the **impedance** of the circuit. The middle equality of (41.23) gives

$$E = IZ \qquad (41.25)$$

which is the a-c form of Ohm's Law, with impedance replacing resistance. Equation (41.25) states that in an a-c circuit the ratio of rms voltage to rms current (or peak voltage to peak current) is a constant, independent of the size of the current *if the frequency remains unchanged*. The quantity ωL, which is the "resistive" effect of inductance, is called the **inductive reactance** and is written X_L.

Phasor Diagrams. Equations (41.06) and (41.07) are equations of simple harmonic motion and can be investigated using the technique of the circle of reference introduced in section 8.02. In Figure 41.07, circles of radii I_M and E_M are drawn about a central point O. Let OZ be a reference line which can be called the zero time line. Let a point A move with constant angular velocity ω on the circle of radius I_M in such a way that $\angle AOZ = \omega t$. Then the projection of OA on OZ is i, the instantaneous value of the current. Similarly, if $OB = E_M$ and $\angle BOZ = \omega t + \phi$, B rotates counterclockwise with angular velocity ω, and the projection of OB on OZ is e. Since the lines OA, OB rotate with the same angular velocity, the angle between them, $\angle BOA$, is constant and equals ϕ, the phase difference between e and i. Thus Figure 41.07 contains complete information about the behavior of the a-c circuit, and this information can be summarized very neatly in terms of the triangle AOB which rotates about O with angular velocity ω, maintaining the same shape and size. This triangle and modifications of it are called **phasor diagrams.**

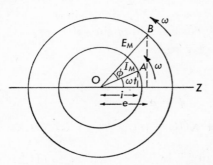

Fig. 41.07. Circles of reference for instantaneous voltage and current.

In Figure 41.08(a) AOB has been redrawn to a larger scale with a horizontal line to represent current magnitude, as is customary in dealing with series a-c circuits. Usually we work with rms quantities, so in Figure 41.08(b) $A'O'B'$ is the triangle obtained by dividing each side of AOB by $\sqrt{2}$. Thus $O'A'$ is the rms current and $O'B'$ the rms voltage. The angles of the triangle are unchanged by this scale change. Drop a

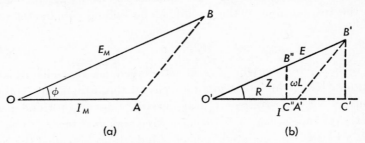

(a)   (b)

Fig. 41.08. Phasor diagrams: (a) peak voltage and current; (b) rms voltage and current.

perpendicular $B'C'$ on $O'A'$ produced. Then, if the circuit of Figure 41.06 is represented by the phasor diagram of Figure 41.08(b),

$$O'C' = O'B' \cos \phi$$

$$= E \cos \left(\tan^{-1} \frac{X_L}{R} \right) \qquad \text{[by (41.24)]}$$

$$= E \frac{R}{\sqrt{R^2 + X_L{}^2}} = E \frac{R}{Z} = IR = E_R \qquad \text{[by (41.23)]}$$

where E_R is the potential difference across the resistance R. Thus the component of E along I (the component of E in phase with I) is the potential difference across R. Similarly,

$$B'C' = E \sin \phi = IX_L = E_L$$

which by (41.17) is the potential difference across a pure inductance. These results can be summarized by the equation

$$\mathbf{E} = \mathbf{E_R} + \mathbf{E_L} \tag{41.26}$$

and, in terms of rms voltage, the applied voltage E is the geometrical (or vector) sum of the voltage drops across the components of the circuit. For this reason diagrams like Figure 41.08(b) are sometimes called vector diagrams. We prefer the word phasor as it carries no connotation of a direction in space. Since phasors are added by geometrical addition, we may use either the triangle method, as in the case just discussed, or the parallelogram method (see section 2.03).

Another modification of the phasor diagram is of interest. Divide each side of the voltage triangle $O'B'C'$ by the magnitude of the rms current. The result will be a similar triangle, shown in Figure 41.08(b) as $O'B''C''$.

$$O'B'' = \frac{E}{I} = Z$$

$$O'C'' = \frac{E \cos \phi}{I} = R$$

$$B''C'' = \frac{E \sin \phi}{I} = \omega L$$

The triangle $O'B''C''$ is called an **impedance triangle** and summarizes equation (41.22).

41.06 RESISTIVE-CAPACITIVE CIRCUITS

Figure 41.09(a) shows a circuit containing both resistance and capacitance.

$$e = \frac{q}{C} + iR$$

$$\frac{de}{dt} = \frac{i}{C} + R\frac{di}{dt}$$

$$\frac{d}{dt}[E_M \cos(\omega t + \phi)] = \frac{I_M}{C}\cos \omega t + R\frac{d}{dt}(I_M \cos \omega t)$$

$$-\omega E_M \sin(\omega t + \phi) = \frac{I_M}{C}\cos \omega t - \omega R I_M \sin \omega t$$

$$E_M \sin(\omega t + \phi) = R I_M \sin \omega t - \frac{I_M}{\omega C}\cos \omega t \tag{41.27}$$

Anticipating our final result, let us put

$$R = Z \cos \phi \left. \right\} \qquad Z = \sqrt{R^2 + \left(\frac{1}{\omega C}\right)^2} \left. \right\}$$
$$X_C = -\frac{1}{\omega C} = Z \sin \phi \left. \right\} \qquad \tan \phi = -\frac{1}{\omega CR} \left. \right\} \qquad (41.28)$$

Substituting in (41.27), we have

$$E_M \sin(\omega t + \phi) = I_M Z \sin \omega t \cos \phi + I_M Z \cos \omega t \sin \phi$$
$$= I_M Z \sin(\omega t + \phi)$$

Since the arguments of the sine functions agree and

$$Z = \frac{E_M}{I_M} = \frac{E}{I}$$

we see that equations (41.28) *do* give the impedance and phase difference.

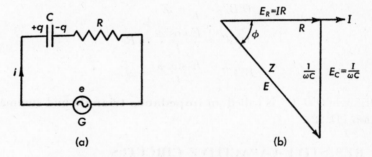

Fig. 41.09.   Series R-C circuit and phasor diagram.

Figure 41.09(b) is the phasor diagram summarizing these results. Since ϕ is a negative angle it is drawn clockwise, and current always leads voltage in an R-C circuit. The single triangle drawn represents both the voltage relations and the impedance triangle, but to different scales. The quantity X_C is called the **capacitive reactance.**

41.07 SERIES R-L-C CIRCUITS

A circuit containing all three types of electrical components is shown in Figure 41.10(a). The usual method of solution is followed.

$$e = \frac{q}{C} + Ri + L\frac{di}{dt}$$

$$\frac{de}{dt} = \frac{i}{C} + R\frac{di}{dt} + L\frac{d^2i}{dt^2}$$

$$\frac{d}{dt}\left[E_M \cos(\omega t + \phi)\right] = \frac{I_M}{C}\cos \omega t + R\frac{d}{dt}(I_M \cos \omega t) + L\frac{d^2}{dt^2}(I_M \cos \omega t)$$

That is,

$$-\omega E_M \sin(\omega t + \phi) = \frac{I_M}{C}\cos \omega t - \omega R I_M \sin \omega t - \omega^2 L I_M \cos \omega t$$

or

$$E_M \sin(\omega t + \phi) = I_M\left[R \sin \omega t + \left(\omega L - \frac{1}{\omega C}\right)\cos \omega t\right] \tag{41.29}$$

Again anticipating the final result we substitute

$$\left.\begin{aligned} R &= Z \cos \phi \\ X = \omega L - \frac{1}{\omega C} &= Z \sin \phi \end{aligned}\right]$$

where

$$\left.\begin{aligned} Z &= \sqrt{R^2 + X^2} = \sqrt{R^2 + \left(\omega L - \frac{1}{\omega C}\right)^2} \\ \tan \phi &= \frac{X}{R} = \frac{\omega L - \dfrac{1}{\omega C}}{R} \end{aligned}\right] \tag{41.30}$$

and (41.29) becomes

$$E_M \sin(\omega t + \phi) = I_M Z(\sin \omega t \cos \phi + \cos \omega t \sin \phi)$$
$$= I_M Z \sin(\omega t + \phi)$$

i.e., Z and ϕ as defined by (41.30) are the impedance and phase difference of the circuit.

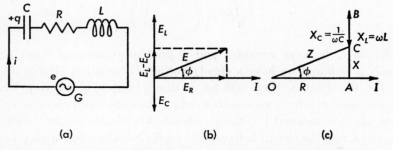

Fig. 41.10. (a) Series R-L-C circuit; (b) voltage diagram; (c) impedance diagram.

Figure 41.10(b) is the voltage diagram of the circuit, drawn as a parallelogram. The potential difference across R, E_R is in phase with the current; that across L, E_L leads I by 90°; and that across C, E_C lags I by 90°. Since E_L and E_C are 180° out of phase they are added algebraically, and the resultant $E_L - E_C$ is compounded with E_R to find the resultant rms voltage E. The impedance diagram in (c) is drawn by the method of the polygon of vectors. The diagrams are drawn for the case $E_L > E_C$, $\omega L > 1/(\omega C)$.

Reviewing the results of this chapter to date, we see that in all cases

$$\left.\begin{aligned}
I &= \frac{E}{Z} \\
Z &= (R^2 + X^2)^{\frac{1}{2}} \\
X &= X_L + X_C \\
X_L &= \omega L, \; X_C = -\frac{1}{\omega C} \\
\tan \phi &= \frac{X}{R} \\
P &= EI \cos \phi = I^2 R
\end{aligned}\right\} \tag{41.31}$$

The last of these equations can be proved readily.

$$P = EI \cos \phi = EI \frac{R}{Z} = \frac{E}{Z} IR = I^2 R$$

41.08 RESONANCE

If we write out in full the first of equations (41.31) for a series R-L-C circuit,

$$I = \frac{E}{\sqrt{R^2 + \left(\omega L - \dfrac{1}{\omega C}\right)^2}} \tag{41.32}$$

Let L and C be kept constant and ω gradually increased from zero. Initially $\omega = 0$ and we have a steady voltage. Equation (41.32) shows that $I = 0$. That is, there will be no direct current in a series circuit with a capacitor, which we know already. As ω increases through small values, ωL increases and $1/(\omega C)$ decreases but is still the larger. Thus X is negative, and the circuit behaves like an R-C combination with ϕ negative. If ω is increased sufficiently, an angular frequency ω_R will be reached at which

$$\omega_R L = \frac{1}{\omega_R C}$$

$$\omega_R = \frac{1}{\sqrt{LC}} \qquad \text{or} \qquad f_R = \frac{1}{2\pi \sqrt{LC}} \qquad (41.33)$$

At this frequency the circuit is said to be **resonant,** f_R being called the **resonant frequency.** At resonance, the effects of capacitance and inductance cancel each other out completely,

$$I = \frac{E}{R} \qquad \text{and} \qquad \phi = 0$$

If R is small, the current at resonance may be very large. Figure 41.11(a) is a graph of the current in an R-L-C circuit plotted against angular frequency. The phasor diagram at the resonant frequency is shown in (b),

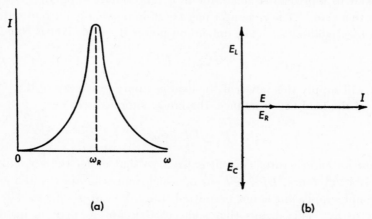

(a)   (b)

Fig. 41.11. (a) The response curve of an R-L-C circuit to a generator of fixed output voltage and variable frequency; (b) phasor diagram of an R-L-C circuit at resonance.

and it is important to note that the potential difference across the capacitor or inductor may be considerably larger than the voltage applied to the circuit by the generator.

If the frequency is increased above the resonant frequency, $\omega L > 1/\omega C$ and X is positive and increasing. Hence the current diminishes again.

Resonance is one of the most interesting of a-c phenomena. It can fairly be said to be the basis of present-day communication engineering, and resonant circuits are used in almost all electronic equipment. One example must suffice. Figure 41.11 and the discussion leading to it were based on the effect of varying the frequency. Similar effects are obtained if the frequency is kept constant and C is varied.   There will be a large current if C is given the value found from (41.33) by using the generator frequency and inductance of the circuit, and a relatively small current otherwise.   This is the method used in tuning a radio receiver to select a particular radio station.   Each station broadcasts on a particular frequency, and each station induces a small voltage in the radio receiver at this frequency.   By turning the tuning knob on the set, a capacitor is adjusted to make the first stage of the radio resonant to the frequency of the particular station desired.   The induced current at this frequency is then appreciable, but the currents due to other stations are very small. Thus the radio ignores all stations except the one to which you wish to listen.

Resonance is also important in power circuits.   Figure 41.10(a) can be taken to represent a generator in a powerhouse supplying electrical power to a load.   The generator has a certain maximum current output I and a fixed voltage E.   The maximum power it can deliver is thus

$$P_{max.} = EI$$

and it will supply this power if the load is a pure resistance of the proper size.   If the load has reactance, the power supplied will be

$$P = EI \cos \phi$$

The maximum generator current is fixed, so that under these conditions there is a difference, $EI - EI \cos \phi$, which represents power the generator could supply but is not permitted to by the nature of the load connected to it.   This means that some of the capital spent in installing the generator is going to waste, and if the power factor is too small, the results may be costly.   Consequently, power companies usually insist that purchasers of power connect loads of such a nature that $\cos \phi \geq 0.80$.

This is no problem to the householder because lights, toasters, irons, etc., which make up the bulk of the domestic load, are almost entirely resistive.   However, in an industrial plant much of the power is used to drive motors which are usually inductive, and a typical industrial load would result in a low power factor.   Steps must be taken to correct this by adding capacitance to cancel some of the inductive reactance.   This capacitance is often supplied by a special type of motor called a *synchronous motor* which under certain operating conditions has a large capacitive effect.   The electrical load of a plant is rarely brought to resonance because of the dangerously high voltages which result.

41.09 PARALLEL R-L-C CIRCUITS

The calculations involved in solving parallel a-c circuits are tedious but present no special difficulties. As an example Figure 41.12(a) shows one parallel arrangement often used, and the phasor diagram is shown in

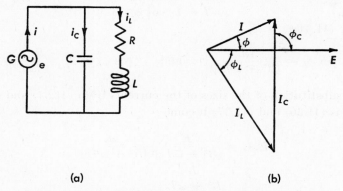

(a)   **(b)**

Fig. 41.12. Parallel *R-L-C* circuit and phasor diagram.

(b). Since the two branches are in parallel the same voltage *e* is applied to each of them. The current and phase difference in each branch are readily calculated by the methods we have already considered. The current drawn from the generator must be found by adding the rms currents geometrically for, although

$$i = i_C + i_L$$

at any instant, the rms current is

$$\mathbf{I} = \mathbf{I}_C + \mathbf{I}_L$$

$$I_L = \frac{E}{\sqrt{R^2 + \omega^2 L^2}}, \qquad \tan \phi_L = \frac{\omega L}{R} \qquad \text{(41.34)}$$

$$I_C = E\omega C, \qquad\qquad \phi_C = -\frac{\pi}{2} \qquad \text{(41.35)}$$

The total current *I* and phase difference between *E* and *I* can now be found graphically by plotting the phasor diagram to scale, or by trigonometric methods. Note that, since *E* is the quantity common to both branches, it is convenient to draw the phasor representing *E* as the horizontal or reference phasor.

From an inspection of Figure 41.12(b) it can be seen that if I_C is the right size, *I* will be in phase with *E*, and that if I_L is fixed, this particular choice of I_C results in minimum current being drawn from the generator.

A parallel circuit of this type is said to be **antiresonant** when E and I are in phase, and an antiresonant circuit behaves like a very large pure resistance. The necessary conditions are

$$\phi = 0$$
$$I_C = I_L \sin \phi_L \tag{41.36}$$
$$I = I_L \cos \phi_L \tag{41.37}$$

Now by (41.34)

$$\sin \phi_L = \frac{\omega L}{[R^2 + \omega^2 L^2]^{\frac{1}{2}}} \quad \text{and} \quad \cos \phi_L = \frac{R}{[R^2 + \omega^2 L^2]^{\frac{1}{2}}}$$

and by substitution of the sizes of the currents from (41.34) and (41.35), equations (41.36) and (41.37) become

$$E\omega C = \frac{E}{[R^2 + \omega^2 L^2]^{\frac{1}{2}}} \frac{\omega L}{[R^2 + \omega^2 L^2]^{\frac{1}{2}}}$$

that is,

$$C = \frac{L}{R^2 + \omega^2 L^2} \tag{41.38}$$

and

$$I = \frac{E}{[R^2 + \omega^2 L^2]^{\frac{1}{2}}} \frac{R}{[R^2 + \omega^2 L^2]^{\frac{1}{2}}}$$
$$= \frac{ER}{R^2 + \omega^2 L^2} = E\frac{RC}{L} \tag{41.39}$$

using (41.38).

Equation (41.38) can be used to find the capacitance value which tunes the circuit to antiresonance for a given R, L, and ω, or to find the antiresonant angular frequency for fixed R, L, and C. Solving (41.38) for ω gives

$$\omega = \left[\frac{1}{LC} - \frac{R^2}{L^2}\right]^{\frac{1}{2}} \tag{41.40}$$

In most antiresonant circuits of practical importance

$$\frac{R^2}{L^2} \ll \frac{1}{LC}$$

and (41.40) reduces to the same expression as (41.33).

Equation (41.39) gives the effective resistance of the circuit at antiresonance.

$$R_{\text{eff.}} = \frac{E}{I} = \frac{L}{RC} \tag{41.41}$$

Antiresonant circuits find extensive use in electronics.

41.10 A-C INSTRUMENTS

If there is an alternating current in the coil of a d'Arsonval galvanometer, it will show no deflection since the torque on the coil reverses as the direction of the current reverses, and the inertia of the coil is too great for it to "follow" the rapid changes of torque. Most a-c instruments operate on the **electrodynamometer** principle illustrated in Figure 41.13, where B is a fixed coil and A a coil wound on a frame pivoted at C and carrying a pointer. The coils are wound in the same sense so that if they are in series they will be attracted whether the current is from left to right or right to left. This attraction is similar to that in the current balance described in section 33.03, and as in that instrument, the force on A is proportional to the square

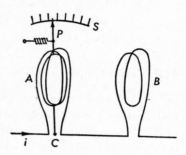

Fig. 41.13. Electrodynamometer principle used in a-c instruments.

of the current. Thus the force $F \propto i^2$. Because of the inertia of the coil A it will not respond to the rapid changes in F but will take up an average position depending on

$$\bar{F} \propto \bar{i^2} = I^2$$

Thus the meter automatically gives a reading depending on the rms current. Unfortunately the scale is not linear in I since the deflection of the coil depends on the balancing of F against the pull of the restoring spring, and F does not vary linearly with I.

The movement described briefly above can be used to measure small currents, or can be adapted with shunts and series resistors to measure larger alternating currents and voltages in the same way that d-c galvanometers are converted to ammeters and voltmeters.

In another modification of the electrodynamometer principle the coils A and B are not in series with each other, but one of them is in series with the load and the other in parallel with it. If the currents in the two coils are i_1 and i_2, respectively,

$$F \propto i_1 i_2$$

and $i_1 = i$, the load current; $i_2 \propto e$, the voltage across the load. Thus

$$F \propto ei$$
$$\bar{F} \propto \bar{ei} = EI \cos \phi = P$$

by (41.16). This instrument is called a **wattmeter** and can be used to measure power in either a-c or d-c circuits.

The electric meter on a household circuit is a **watt-hour meter** and measures the electrical energy consumed. Its principle of operation is quite different to the previous a-c instruments as it is essentially a small a-c motor whose rate of revolution is proportional to the power consumption. The number of revolutions of the motor is suitably geared down and recorded on the dials of the meter.

41.11 TRANSFORMERS. A-C POWER DISTRIBUTION

As mentioned in section 41.01, the key to the success of a-c power distribution is the transformer, and we now discuss a simplified version of its theory, assuming a purely resistive load and neglecting the resistances of the transformer windings and other sources of power losses. The core of the transformer in Figure 41.14(a) is a closed soft iron ring

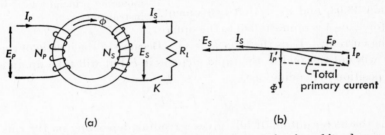

(a)   (b)

Fig. 41.14. The basic iron-cored transformer circuit and its phasor diagram.

around which two coils are wound. Let N_P and N_S be the number of turns, respectively, of the primary and secondary coils. Let an alternating voltage of rms value E_P be applied to the primary coil, and at first suppose K to be open so that there is no secondary current. Under these conditions the primary coil will act as a very large inductance since it is, in effect, an iron-cored toroid. Voltage E_P will produce a small, so-called *magnetizing* current I_P' which sets up an alternating flux ϕ in the core.

$$e_P = \sqrt{2}\, E_P \cos\left(\omega t + \frac{\pi}{2}\right) \qquad (41.42)$$

$$i_P' = \sqrt{2}\, I_P' \cos \omega t$$

Since ϕ is proportional to and in phase with i_P', if Φ is the rms flux,

$$\phi = \sqrt{2}\, \Phi \cos \omega t$$

The voltage drop across the inductance of the primary coil must equal e_P since we are neglecting the effect of the resistance of the primary.

$$e_P = N_P \frac{d\phi}{dt} = - \sqrt{2} N_P \Phi \omega \sin \omega t$$

$$= \sqrt{2}\, N_P \Phi \omega \cos \left(\omega t + \frac{\pi}{2} \right) \tag{41.43}$$

Comparing (41.42) and (41.43), we see that

$$E_P = \omega N_P \Phi \tag{41.44}$$

Since E_P is constant Φ must also be constant.

Now Φ can be calculated in another way. The mmf $\mathfrak{F} = N_P I_P{}'$, and if H is the magnetic field strength in the iron, $H = \mathfrak{F}/l$ where l is the length of the iron ring. Let A be the cross-sectional area of the ring. Then

$$\Phi = BA = \mu\mu_0 HA = \mu\mu_0 \frac{\mathfrak{F}A}{l} \tag{41.45}$$

so that if Φ is to be constant, $\mathfrak{F}$ must also be constant.

The voltage across the secondary coil is 180° out of phase with E_P and is

$$E_S = -\omega N_S \Phi \tag{41.46}$$

regardless of whether K is closed or not. If now K is closed, a secondary current I_S results, with

$$I_S = \frac{E_S}{R_L} \tag{41.47}$$

where R_L is the resistance of the load. This current I_S will be much larger than $I_P{}'$ and, by Lenz' Law, must be opposite to the primary current which produces it. This current will produce an mmf $= N_S \times I_S$ which will oppose the primary mmf. However, by (41.45) the total mmf must stay constant, and the only way this can be the case is for the primary current to increase so that

$$\mathfrak{F} = N_P I_P{}' + N_P I_P + N_S I_S = N_P I_P{}'$$

where I_P is the increase in primary current. That is, the reverse direction mmf must be cancelled out by the increased mmf of the primary current,

and

$$N_P I_P = -N_S I_S \tag{41.48}$$

The total primary current is the phasor sum of I_P and $I_P{}'$, but the second term is usually so small compared to the first as to be negligible. From (41.47), I_S is in phase with E_S, and if (41.48) is to hold, I_P and I_S must be 180° out of phase so that E_P and I_P are also in phase. Thus, when the transformer is delivering power to a resistive load it behaves as a pure resistance.

From (41.44) and (41.46),

$$\frac{E_S}{E_P} = \frac{N_S}{N_P} \tag{41.49}$$

and from (41.48)

$$\frac{I_S}{I_P} = \frac{N_P}{N_S} \tag{41.50}$$

where we have dropped the minus signs since we are interested only in magnitudes. Multiplying (41.49) and (41.50) gives

$$E_S I_S = E_P I_S \tag{41.51}$$

as was implicit in our assumption of no power losses. The losses we have neglected are the I^2R losses in the windings of the coils which must have some small resistance, hysteresis losses in the iron core, and a few other very minor items. These losses are always small, however, and big transformers have efficiencies of about 98%.

If the load connected to the secondary has any reactance, and hence an impedance Z_L, equation (41.47) is replaced by $I_S = E_S/Z_L$, and the phase angle between the secondary current and voltage is equal to the phase angle of the load. The above analysis then shows that (to the accuracy of the approximations made) the phase angle between the primary current and voltage is also equal to the phase angle of the load. Figure 41.14(b) shows the phasor diagram of the transformer for a load which is very slightly inductive.

Figure 41.15 shows a typical a-c power system. The generator is connected to a step-up transformer, and power is transmitted at high

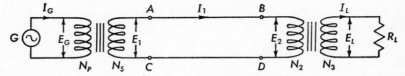

Fig. 41.15. Power transmission system.

voltage and low current along the line to the user where a transformer steps it down to a convenient low voltage and high current. The only loss in our ideal system is in the transmission line *AB*, *CD*. If the resistance of these two wires in series is R_1, this loss is $I_1^2R_1$ and in principle can be made as small as necessary by raising E_1 (and hence lowering I_1) sufficiently. If it were not for this application of transformers, the transmission of electric power over considerable distances would be impracticable because of low efficiency with line conductors of reasonable size. At present the highest transmission-line voltages used are 330 kv, and this high voltage permits electric power to be transmitted about 400 miles economically.

PROBLEMS

1. An a-c generator of negligible internal resistance has a peak voltage of 600 v. What is its rms voltage? What rms current will result if a 200-ohm resistive load is connected across the generator?

2. Frequently used alternating voltages are 220, 550, 11,000 v. What are the respective peak values?

3. In an a-c circuit rms values are 110 v and 3.00 amp. If the phase difference is 30.0°, what is the power?

4. The standard power frequency is 60.0 cycles per second. What is the corresponding angular frequency? What is the frequency in a circuit for which $\omega = 5.00 \times 10^4$ radians sec^{-1}?

5. The maximum, safe, steady voltage which may be applied to a certain capacitor is 800 v. What is the maximum rms alternating voltage it will stand safely?

   Note: A 60.0-cycle, 110-v a-c generator of negligible internal resistance supplies the power to the circuits of the following problems 6–11.

6. An inductance coil of resistance 14.0 Ω and inductance 0.360 henry is connected to the generator. Find the resulting current, phase difference, and power consumption.

7. A variable inductor has a fixed resistance of 3.00 Ω, and its inductance can be varied between 10.0 and 100 mh (millihenrys). If it is connected across the generator, what are the maximum and minimum currents attainable and what must be the setting of the inductor to give a current of 5.00 amp?

8. A series circuit consisting of a pure resistance of 10.0 Ω and an inductor of inductance 40.0 mh and resistance 2.00 Ω is connected across the generator. Find the impedance of the circuit, the resulting current, the phase difference between current and generator voltage, and the power consumption. What are the individual voltage drops across the resistor and the inductor? Draw the phasor diagram of the circuit.

9. A pure capacitor of 2.00 μf (microfarads) is connected across the generator. Calculate the current.

10. A series circuit consisting of a 25.0-Ω resistor and a capacitor is connected to the generator. A current of 1.69 amp leads the applied voltage by 67.4°. Find the capacitance.

11. A series circuit containing a 75.0-Ω resistance, 0.250-h inductance, and 40.0-μf capacitance is connected across the generator. Find the current, phase difference, power consumption, and voltages across the resistor, capacitor, and inductor. Assume the resistance of the inductor to be negligible.

12. A certain industrial plant draws its power from 2200-v, 60-cycle feeders. Under normal conditions the current is 150 amp and lags behind the voltage so that the power factor is 0.600. Find the equivalent resistance and inductance of the load. What series capacitor must be added to raise the power factor to 0.850?

13. At what angular frequency will a series a-c circuit containing a 4.00-mh inductor and a 2.50-μf capacitor be resonant? What is the resonant frequency?

14. The input circuit of a radio set has an inductance of 134 μh. What must be the range of capacitance values of the tuning capacitor in order that the set can be tuned to any frequency in the broadcast band (550–1500 kc)?

15. A series circuit has a resistance of 40.0 Ω, inductance of 16.8 mh, and capacitance of 1.40 μf. Find the resonant frequency. If an alternating voltage of 10.0 v at the resonant frequency is applied, find the current, phase angle, power consumption, and voltage across the capacitor.

16. In the circuit of problem 15, if the applied voltage is 10.0 v at an angular frequency of 4.00×10^3 radians sec^{-1}, find the current, phase angle, power consumption, and voltage across the capacitor.

17. In the circuit of Figure 41.12(a), $R = 0.500$ Ω, $L = 3.00$ mh, $C = 1.20$ μf. At what angular frequency should the generator operate for the circuit to be antiresonant? What is the effective resistance of the circuit at this frequency if the generator resistor is negligible?

18. Design an antiresonant load of the type of Figure 41.12 to have an effective resistance of 80.0 kΩ at an angular frequency of 20.0×10^6 radians sec^{-1}, if the coil to be used as an R/L ratio of 2.00×10^5 at this frequency. If the generator has an emf containing this frequency and its second and third harmonics, and if the generator has a high internal impedance, explain qualitatively why the voltage across the load contains the basic frequency only, the higher harmonics in it now being negligible.

19. In Figure 41.14 $N_P = 400$ turns, $N_S = 20$ turns, $R_L = 100$ Ω, $I_S = 5.00$ amp. If the transformer has an efficiency of 100%, find E_S, E_P, and I_P.

20. In Figure 41.15 the resistance of each of the wires AB, CD of the transmission line is 5.00 Ω. If $E_1 = 1000$ v, $I_1 = 5.00$ amp, find E_2 and the efficiency of the line.

21. The total resistance of a transmission line is 4000 Ω. If the input power is 1.00 Mw (megawatt) and an efficiency of 90% is required, what must be the input voltage and the line current?

22. In Figure 41.15 G is a resistanceless generator of emf 500 v which is supplying 5.00 kw. $N_P = 25$, $N_S = 125$, $N_2 = 400$, $N_3 = 20$ turns, and both transformers are ideal. The resistance of the transmission line is 150 Ω. Calculate the voltage and current at the load, the resistance of R_L, and the efficiency of the system.

23. In Figure 41.14 $R_L = 2000$ Ω, $N_P = 25$ turns, $N_S = 250$ turns. What is the resistance at the input terminals of the primary of the transformer? This is an additional use for transformers—to change the apparent size of a resistance or impedance.

42

Electronics

42.01 THERMIONIC EMISSION

Electronics is a part of physics and engineering which has grown to extraordinary importance during the last thirty years or so. It includes radio, television, radar, numerous applications in industrial control devices, and a wide range of applications in the technology used in all physical and most biological sciences. It is difficult to think of a branch of experimental physics in which the methods of measurement have not been revolutionized by the development of the vacuum tube. A one-sentence definition of such a diverse field is difficult to find, but there is one common, underlying factor in electronic devices and methods—they involve the separation of free electrons from matter and the subsequent control of the movement of these streams of electrons by electrostatic and magnetic fields. Electronics thus produces currents without material conductors—in fact, most of the time these currents are in the best vacua we can produce. The mass of an individual electron is so small that its inertia is usually negligible, thus permitting practically instantaneous response to orders given it by a field.

The free electrons are usually produced by raising a metallic surface to a high temperature. With certain metals this results in the emission of large numbers of free electrons. This process, called **thermionic emission,** is analogous to the escape of water-vapor molecules from the surface of liquid water.

Figure 42.01 shows the situation at the surface of a metal (in a two-dimensional section). The metal is thought to consist of an orderly array of positive ions (shown as circles with a plus sign). These ions have fixed average positions, although they are in constant, vibratory motion and have a total energy dependent on the temperature. Through this lattice the free electrons (indicated by small solid circles) move with high speeds but completely random directions. There is fairly good evidence that there are usually approximately equal numbers of positive ions and free electrons, that is, on the average each atom gives up one electron to this "gas" of free electrons. Consider one particular electron whose velocity v is normal to the surface of the metal. In position 1 this electron is strongly attracted by nearby positive ions such as A, B, C, D, but because they are arranged symmetrically on all sides of it, the net force is zero and the electron continues on its way without change in velocity. The same applies to position 2, but as the electron moves out of the metal, the positive ions are all on one side of it, producing an unbalanced force of attraction which slows it down. Usually the velocity of the electron is too small for it to escape, and in position 3 it is shown being pulled back into the metal.

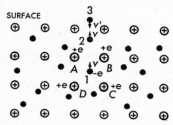

Fig. 42.01. Microscopic view of electrons in the crystal lattice of a metal.

As with the molecules in water or the molecules of a gas, the average velocity of the electrons depends on temperature, but at any temperature a small fraction of the electrons have velocities considerably above the average value, and if the fastest of these approach the surface of the metal, they may escape the electrostatic attraction of the surface layer of positive ions. The number escaping will clearly increase with temperature, but it is found that extremely high temperatures are needed if any appreciable current of electrons is to escape. In fact, for most metals the temperature needed is higher than the melting point of the substance. Electron emitters in liquid form are rarely useful (although in some tubes mercury pools serve as sources of electrons), and thus the range of materials used for thermionic emission is quite limited.

A comparison of thermionic emission and evaporation of a liquid or solid is of some interest. In solids the atoms are packed closely together, and the interatomic forces are so large that it is only rarely that an atom acquires enough kinetic energy to break away from its location and move to another one. Still, it does happen occasionally. If two dissimilar metals are clamped together and left undisturbed for some months, careful examination (using microchemical and radioactive tracer techniques) will show some diffusion of metal A into metal B and vice versa. That is, a few atoms of each metal have "wandered" across the interface. Also, it is believed that every solid has a vapor pressure, although it is measurable at room temperature by present techniques in only a few cases.

In liquids, the packing is not quite so close, and it is thought that atoms are grouped into molecules and groups of molecules. Each molecule is normally attached to a group, which forms a sort of "low-grade" crystal pattern, but owing to energy transfers in collisions, it will be a quite common event for a molecule to gain enough kinetic energy to break loose from one group and join another. If this happens to a molecule at or near the surface, it may try to escape through the surface "barrier" formed by the intermolecular forces attracting it from one side only, and some of the molecules making the attempt will succeed, that is, will evaporate.

In some ways thermionic emission is the simplest of the evaporation processes. The picture of the free electrons forming a gas is well borne out by experiment. The free electrons do move through the crystal quite easily. On the other hand, the surface barrier is relatively much higher than that holding back the surface molecules of a liquid.

Returning to the effect of temperature, a theoretical study of thermionic emission shows that the emission current depends on temperature through an equation of exponential form.

$$I \propto \epsilon^{-\frac{e\phi}{kT}} \tag{42.01}$$

where ϵ is the exponential number 2.718, e is the electronic charge, k is Boltzmann's constant, T is the temperature in degrees Kelvin, and ϕ is a property of the metal surface called the **work function**. The work function gets its name because $e\phi$ is the work required to extract an electron from the surface. Since ϕ is the work required per unit charge it is measured in volts. Now I can be made larger by increasing T or decreasing ϕ. Many different materials have been investigated to find suitable combinations of low work function and high melting point, and three have proved especially suitable. These are pure tungsten (which has the highest known melting point of any substance), a mixture of thorium and tungsten, and a mixture of barium and strontium. The temperatures at which these three substances are maintained in order to produce thermionic emission are 2400K, 2000K, and 1200K, respectively. At any of these temperatures the substance would burn up rapidly if any oxygen were present, so the emitter, usually in the form of a wire or filament, is enclosed in an airtight case or tube from which almost all the air has been removed to produce a high vacuum. Most electronic tubes are of this high-vacuum type, but a few of them contain an inert gas (such as argon) at a low pressure and are called gas-filled tubes. In these the electrons interact with the gas in a complex manner which results in quite different behavior from the high-vacuum or "hard" tubes. Gas tubes will not be considered here. Although they tend to be more sensitive than hard tubes, they are less reliable and have certain other limitations. At present their use is largely confined to rectifier tubes carrying large currents and to trigger tubes or electronic switches. Trigger tubes, such as the *thyratron*, have only two stable conditions, one in which they conduct a very small current and one with a relatively large current. A small voltage change on one of the electrodes switches the tube from one condition to the other.

42.02 DIODES. RECTIFICATION

The simplest type of vacuum tube is the diode or two-element tube which contains a hot filament and a second, cold electrode which can be used to collect the electrons. This second element is called the **plate** or anode. The conduction of electrons through a vacuum was first discovered by Thomas A. Edison (1847) and applied by Sir John Fleming (1849) to the problem of converting alternating to direct current, the problem of **rectification.** Because electrons have negative charges they will be attracted to the plate, with resulting current, if the potential of the plate is positive with respect to the filament, but if the plate is negative, there will be no current. The diode is thus a one-way street for electron conduction and for this reason is called a *thermionic valve* in England.

The current to the plate is not a linear function of the voltage either in the diode or in any vacuum tube, and because these devices do not follow Ohm's Law, most of the analytical methods of circuit analysis which we have developed do not apply to tube circuits. The alternative is a graphical approach, and the first step is to obtain experimentally the relation between voltage and current. A graph of this relation is called a **characteristic curve.** Figure 42.02(a) shows a cutaway sketch of a diode; Figure 42.02(b) shows the conventional symbol used in circuit diagrams, together with a circuit for obtaining the characteristic curve; and Figure 42.02(c) shows the resulting curve for a typical diode. In (a), E is the airtight envelope of glass or metal; F is the filament, a coil of wire to be heated; P is the plate, a nickel cylinder surrounding the filament; and B is the base. Leads to P and F are sealed through the envelope and connected to pins in the base, which usually contains four pins (one being a dummy) and fits into a standard socket.

In (b), T represents the tube; A is a milliammeter; E_F is a low-voltage battery which sends a large current through the filament to raise it to the desired temperature; and E_P is the plate battery which maintains the current I_P through the tube.   Note that I_P is shown in the conventional sense, which is opposite to the electron flow in the tube.

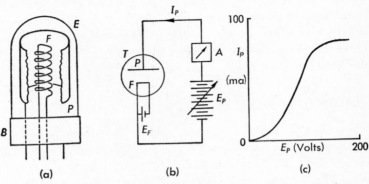

(a)   (b)   (c)

Fig. 42.02.   Diode—construction, testing circuit, and characteristic curve.

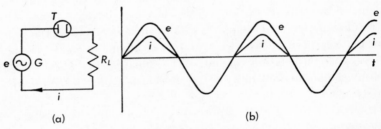

(a)   (b)

Fig. 42.03.   Half-wave rectifier circuit and wave form of current in a load.

Figure 42.03(a) shows a circuit in which a diode is used to produce rectified current.   The heating circuit for the filament is not shown, and this omission is customary in electronic circuit diagrams, unless it plays some other role beside producing electron emission.   In the figure G is an a-c generator and R_L the load to which power is supplied.   The generator voltage e and current through the load i are plotted against time in Figure 42.03(b).   The diode conducts only during each half-cycle in which the voltage on the plate is positive.   This results in a current which is zero half the time, and the circuit is called a half-wave rectifier. The current is unidirectional but far from steady.   To utilize both halves of the applied voltage and to obtain a smooth output, two diodes can be used, together with a filter circuit. This arrangement is called a *power pack* and is shown in Figure 42.04, where T_R is a transformer with two secondary windings. The a-c generator is connected to the primary, the plates of the two diodes to the ends of the high-voltage secondary winding, and the two filaments in parallel across the low-voltage winding. During half a cycle of G, the point A is positive with respect to B, and examination of the circuit will show that T_1 conducts while T_2 does not. These conditions are reversed during the other half of each cycle, resulting in a continuous unidirectional output voltage E_0 across the points J, K. Voltage E_0 fluctuates in size from zero to some maximum value with twice the frequency of G and can be considered to consist of a steady voltage (its average value) and fluctuating or a-c components.

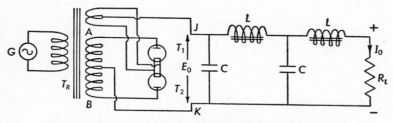

Fig. 42.04. Power pack—full-wave rectifier and filter.

The filter consists of two high-inductance, iron-cored coils (L) called *chokes* and two large capacitors (C). The chokes have very little resistance and present no appreciable obstacle to steady currents in the load. Their reactance to alternating currents is very large, however, and they tend to block off or choke any alternating current in the load. At the same time the capacitors in parallel have infinite d-c resistance and quite low reactance and serve as shunt paths for any alternating currents. The action of the filter is thus to reduce greatly any fluctuations in the load current, and the filter can be designed to give as steady an output as is desired.

A power pack (sometimes without a transformer) is a basic unit in almost any piece of electronic equipment, a radio for example, and provides the d-c power necessary for its operation. On a larger scale, rectification problems in industry are handled more and more by the use of electron tubes. Street-railway operation is a typical example. The motors used in street cars are designed for d-c operation, because d-c motors give far better speed control, and large amounts of power must be rectified. The rectifier "tubes" used are often ten feet high and four feet in diameter, but the principle employed is the same as described above.

42.03 TRIODES. AMPLIFICATION

In 1907 Lee De Forest (1873) added a third element to the tube, and the great development of electronics began. The third element is a mesh of fine, rather widely spaced wires placed between the filament and the plate and called a **grid.** Figure 42.05(a) shows a schematic picture of a three-element tube or **triode,** and the conventional symbol is shown in Figure 42.05(b). The grid is denoted G.

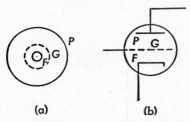
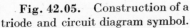

(a)   (b)

Fig. 42.05. Construction of a triode and circuit diagram symbol.

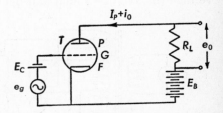

Fig. 42.06. A triode amplifier with a resistive load.

The basic property of the triode, and the one on which almost all electronic development rests, is its ability to amplify—a small change in the potential difference between the grid and filament produces the effect of a larger change in the potential difference between the plate and filament. This is readily explained in terms of the fields produced by the two pairs of electrodes. The electronic current is controlled by the electrostatic fields set up by the electrodes. The field between two electrodes increases as their spacing decreases. Hence, a small potential on the grid, which is physically closer to the filament, produces the same field as a much larger potential on the plate. At the same time the grid is mainly empty space and so intercepts little or no current from the electron stream proceeding to the plate.

Figure 42.06 is an amplifier circuit in which e_g is the a-c generator voltage which is connected between grid and filament. This generator represents the source of any fluctuating signal which we wish to amplify and may, for instance, be a microphone changing sound into an alternating voltage of small amplitude. Consider first the situation when e_g is zero. The grid is then negative by E_C volts (called the grid **bias**) with respect to the filament and opposes electron flow to the plate. The battery E_B keeps the plate sufficiently positive, however, for a steady current I_P to exist in the plate circuit. Because the grid is negative there is no current to it. This steady current is of no interest to us but is necessary if the tube is to operate under the correct conditions. Now, when e_g is turned on, the total voltage between G and F is fluctuating between $-E_C + E_M$ and $-E_C - E_M$, where E_M is the maximum voltage of the signal generator. When the grid becomes less negative $(-E_C + E_M)$, the plate battery can draw a larger current than I_P through the tube, and conversely the plate current drops below I_P when the grid becomes more strongly negative. The total plate current can be written as

$$I_P + i_0$$

where i_0 represents the a-c component, or the fluctuations about the steady current corresponding to zero signal. Similarly the voltage across the load resistor R_L is

$$V_R = (I_P + i_0)R_L = I_P R_L + e_0$$

The a-c component of this voltage, e_0, is the output voltage of the amplifier and is a more or less exact copy of e_g but increased in amplitude. The ratio of the size of e_0 to that of e_g is called the **amplification** A of the circuit. For triodes, A is usually between 5 and 15, but with tetrodes and pentodes (four and five-element tubes similar to the triode but more efficient) amplifications up to 100 or more can be obtained.

Many different amplifier circuits are in use, and the variety arises from a conflict between efficiency of operation and fidelity. One type of amplifier called a linear amplifier (Class A_1 in the jargon of electronics) gives an extremely exact copy of the signal, but the amplification and efficiency are low. Other amplifiers give higher efficiency but at the cost of a less exact copy of the signal. The signals to be amplified in radios, and even more so in radar sets, are extremely small, and many stages of amplification are necessary. That is, the output e_0 of the first amplifier stage becomes the input e_g of the second and so on. Many different and ingenious ways of connecting or "coupling" stages together have been developed, but the details belong in a course in radio engineering.

42.04 OSCILLATORS

In the circuit just discussed the a-c power delivered to R_L is $i_0^2 R_L$ if i_0 is the rms current. If the grid is kept negative at all times, no current is drawn from the signal generator, which thus supplies *no* power to the tube. The *power* amplification therefore appears to be infinite, and although a more exact discussion shows that there is actually *some* power drawn from the generator, the power amplification is still very great. Suppose now a small fraction of the power delivered to the load is diverted back to the grid circuit to be reamplified. The system could then be self-sustaining even if the original signal were withdrawn. This process is called **regeneration** and is the basis of vacuum-tube oscillators.

The need for such oscillators as sources of high-frequency a-c power is apparent when we recall that $\omega = 2\pi f$, the angular frequency of an electromagnetic generator, is also the angular velocity of the rotor or a small integral multiple of it. For mechanical reasons, angular velocities must be restricted to 300 or 400 radians/sec, but in electronics we often use angular frequencies of 10^6 or more.

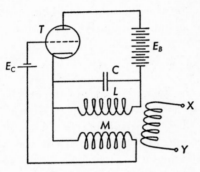

Fig. 42.07. A tuned-plate-circuit triode oscillator.

Figure 42.07 shows a simple electronic oscillator using a triode tube. In the plate circuit there is a parallel combination of a capacitor and an inductor. If C is originally charged, it starts to discharge through L, producing a current in the coil which sets up a magnetic field. When C is discharged, the energy stored in the magnetic field maintains the current until the capacitor is charged up in the opposite direction. The capacitor then starts to discharge again and the process would repeat itself indefinitely if it were not that the resistance of the coil gradually dissipates the energy as heat. The angular frequency of this oscillatory current can be shown to be

$$\omega = \frac{1}{\sqrt{LC}} \tag{42.02}$$

which is just the relation found in the preceding chapter for resonance of circuits containing inductance and capacitance. This tuned L-C circuit on the plate side of Figure 42.07 serves as the signal generator. The inductor L is coupled to the grid circuit by a mutual inductance M between L and a coil in series with the grid. The fluctuating voltage induced in M is amplified by the tube and delivers a-c power to the tuned circuit at the frequency given by (42.02). If this power is equal to or greater than the power lost as heat, self-sustaining oscillations are obtained. Alternating-current power can be drawn off this system by the third coil connected to X, Y, which is also coupled inductively to L. The original source of the power is the battery E_B, and the circuit serves to convert d-c energy to a-c at the desired frequency.

Oscillators of the type just described, or somewhat modified, can be used to generate sine-wave voltages with angular frequencies from about 300 to about 2×10^9 radians/sec. When the top of this frequency band is reached, the finite speed of travel of the electrons becomes important. The **transit time** is the time taken for an electron to go from the cathode to the anode, and when this time becomes comparable to the period of the oscillations desired, the conventional oscillatory circuits fall off so badly in efficiency as to become unusable. Electronic oscillators using types of tubes differing radically from those described above have been designed, and useful amounts of power can be generated at angular frequencies up to 2×10^{11} radians/sec or about 30,000 Mc (megacycles).

42.05 RADIO WAVES. MODULATION AND DEMODULATION

Every electrical circuit carrying an alternating current is losing energy continually in the form of waves which travel away from it at a definite speed equal to the velocity of light c. These waves consist of rapidly varying electrostatic and magnetic fields and are called **radio waves.** They differ from light waves in wavelength only, although the methods used to produce radio and light waves appear at first to have little in common. The usual connection between wavelength λ, frequency f, and velocity applies.

$$\lambda f = c \tag{42.03}$$

Since $c = 3 \times 10^8$ m sec^{-1} we can readily find the wavelengths of radiations associated with typical power, audio (sound), radio, etc., frequency currents (see Table 42.01).

TABLE 42.01 Radiation Wavelengths for Typical Frequencies.

Type of Current	Typical Frequency	Wavelength (m)
Power	60 cycles sec^{-1}	5.0×10^6
Audio	5.0 kc	6.0×10^4
Broadcast radio	1000 kc	300
Short-wave radio	10.0 Mc	30.0
Standard TV	75 Mc	4.00
Ultrahigh frequency TV	200 Mc	1.50
Radar	300 Mc	1.00
Microwave radar	1.0×10^4 Mc	3.0×10^{-2}

This radiation effect was ignored completely in discussing a-c circuits because the amount of power radiated is completely negligible unless the physical dimensions of the circuit are comparable with the wavelength corresponding to the frequency of the current. We see that if we wish to radiate appreciable power in the form of radio waves, it is necessary to construct a radiating circuit, or **antenna** as it is called, of considerable size. For broadcasting radio waves, that is, sending the waves out equally in all directions over the surface of the earth, the commonest type of antenna is a vertical wire. The antenna is preferably a full wavelength high, but must be a minimum of at least a quarter of a wavelength high for reasonably good transmission. The signals we wish to broadcast are from currents at audiofrequencies, originating in speech or music. If the signals were to be broadcast at these frequencies, a quarter-wave-length antenna for 5.0 kc would be $(6.00 \times 10^4)/4 = 15,000$ m or just over nine miles high. An antenna of this size being rather impractical, broadcasting is done at much higher frequencies called radiofrequencies, where full-wave antennas can be constructed. The range of frequencies from 550 to 1500 kc is the most widely used and is called the broadcast band.

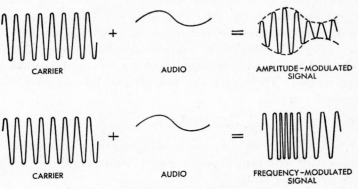

CARRIER + AUDIO = AMPLITUDE–MODULATED SIGNAL

CARRIER + AUDIO = FREQUENCY–MODULATED SIGNAL

Fig. 42.08. Amplitude- and frequency-modulated waves.

The information to be transmitted consists of sound variations turned into audiofrequency currents, and consequently the radiofrequency signal broadcast by a radio station must be **modulated,** i.e., altered in some way, by the audio signal so that this information is contained in the transmitted waves. At least six different methods of modulation are in use, but the commonest is still amplitude modulation (AM). In AM, if there is zero audio signal, the radio station broadcasts a pure sine wave at the frequency assigned to it. This sine wave is called the **carrier signal.**

To transmit information, the audio signal is used to vary the amplitude of the carrier.   A second type of modulation is frequency modulation (FM).   In this system the audio signal is used to vary slightly the frequency of the radio waves broadcast.   Both types are illustrated in Figure 42.08.

At the radio receiver a reverse process is necessary to "unscramble" the audio information from the complex radiofrequency signal.   This is called demodulation or **detection,** and the result is an audiofrequency current which can be sent through a loudspeaker to reproduce the original sounds of speech and music with some degree of fidelity.   Both modulation and demodulation are achieved through the use of electron-tube circuits, but a description of their method of operation is too lengthy to give at this point.

42.06 BLOCK DIAGRAM OF A RADIO RECEIVER

Block diagrams are useful in studying the over-all functioning of complicated circuits.   Each stage is indicated by a block with the name or function of the stage.   It is easier to see the sequence of operation in a diagram like this than in the complete circuit diagram with its maze of interconnections.   To sum up the discussion of this chapter, let us look at the block diagram of the standard, household radio receiver which is a type known as a **superheterodyne** circuit.   The diagram is shown in Figure 42.09.

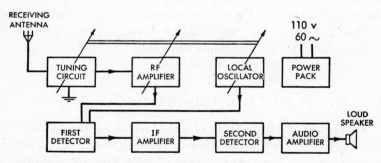

Fig. 42.09.   Block diagram of a superheterodyne receiver.

The radio waves induce voltages in the receiving antenna, and these voltages are impressed on a tuning circuit which responds most strongly with currents of one particular carrier frequency as described in section 41.07.   The chosen current is amplified by a radiofrequency (R.F.) amplifier which is also selective and can be tuned to give greater amplification to the desired frequency. As shown by the connected arrows through the first two blocks, these stages are tuned simultaneously so that they both respond to a particular broadcasting station. A local oscillator forms part of the set and can be tuned over a wide range of frequencies, its tuning being connected or "ganged" with that of the first two stages. The outputs of the local oscillator and R.F. amplifier are sent to the first detector or mixer. The frequency of the local oscillator is always tuned to be a fixed amount below the radiofrequency to which the first two stages are tuned. For example, if the set is tuned to a station whose carrier frequency is 1100 kc, the local oscillator might be tuned to 900 kc. When the output of the oscillator is mixed with the incoming signal, beats occur (see section 23.05), and the product is a signal which still contains all the audio information, but now has a "carrier" frequency of $1100 - 900 = 200$ kc. Similarly, if the set is next tuned to 800 kc, the oscillator frequency is automatically lowered to 600 kc, giving the same beat frequency of 200 kc.

The effect of this method, which is called heterodyning, is thus to supply out of the mixer a signal whose carrier frequency is constant, regardless of the frequency of the radio station to which the set is tuned. This frequency is called the intermediate frequency (I.F.), and the next stage, the I.F. amplifier, consists of a special circuit designed to amplify this frequency (actually a narrow band of frequencies centered about the I.F.) with great efficiency. The output of the I.F. amplifier goes to the second detector, which separates the audio signal from the I.F. carrier and discards the latter. The audiofrequency signal is further amplified and ultimately goes to the loudspeaker. A power pack is shown in the block diagram, but its connections have been omitted—it supplies the power to operate all the electronic stages.

42.07 CATHODE-RAY OSCILLOGRAPHS

A type of electron tube of ever-increasing importance is the cathode-ray tube (C.R.T.) which is illustrated in Figure 42.10, where G is an electron gun. It is an arrangement of a hot filament and other electrodes which produces a fine, parallel beam of electrons and directs them down the axis of the tube at a high velocity. The inside of the end of the tube is coated with a fluorescent material, such as zinc orthosilicate, which glows when struck by electrons. This screen S is viewed from the right of the diagram, and a point of light indicates where the electron beam strikes it. The beam passes symmetrically between two parallel plates V, V to which a voltage can be applied.   If the potential difference between the plates is zero, the beam strikes the center of S, but if the lower plate becomes positive with respect to the upper, the electrons are pulled slightly downward, and the spot of light is deflected as shown. A second pair of deflector plates H, H (not shown) is mounted at right angles to V, V and permits the beam to be deflected horizontally.   The glass tube T is highly evacuated.

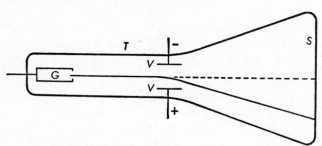

Fig. 42.10.   A cathode-ray tube.

Cathode-ray tubes have many and varied applications, only a few of which can be mentioned here.   Their most important quality is quickness of response, which follows from the extremely small mass of the electrons. The beam acts as a flexible and practically inertia-free pointer.   As an example, let us consider the study of some periodic phenomenon which varies with time.   The periodic motion is used to generate a fluctuating voltage which is applied to the vertical deflector plates.   The horizontal plates are used to supply a time base, by applying a "saw-tooth" voltage [Figure 42.11(a)] to them.   This causes the beam to move horizontally across the screen at a uniform rate.   At the end of each cycle it jumps back to the original position almost instantaneously.   The period of the saw-tooth voltage is adjusted to be equal to the period of the voltage on the vertical deflectors, and as the beam moves from left to right it is deflected vertically, the deflection being proportional to the applied voltage.   At the end of the cycle (time t_3) the voltages on each pair of plates repeat the same variations, so that the same curve is traced over and over again.   In most cases the period is so short that persistence of vision makes the figure appear stationary, and it can be photographed or measured at leisure.

Deflection of the beam in a cathode-ray tube can also be achieved using magnetic fields.   In magnetic deflection systems, coils of wire are placed on either side of the neck of the tube, and current in these coils produces a field of flux density B perpendicular to the axis of the tube. This field may occupy a region of space roughly coincident with the region occupied by the electrostatic field set up by V, V in Figure 42.10. Since the electron beam is an electric current, there will be a force on it perpendicular to both B and the direction of motion, and a deflection of the beam results. Magnetic deflection systems are superior to electrostatic ones for some purposes and are used with television tubes, for example.

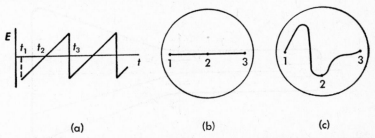

(a)   (b)   (c)

Fig. 42.11. Study of wave form with a cathode-ray tube. The way in which the voltage on the horizontal deflector plates varies with time is shown in (a). Three instants of time during a complete cycle are indicated by t_1, t_2, and t_3. If there is no vertical deflecting voltage, the beam moves horizontally from left to right, drawing a horizontal line. The position of the beam at the three times is shown by the numerals in (b). The trace obtained when some periodic voltage is applied to the vertical deflectors is shown in (c).

Another variable in a cathode-ray tube is the intensity of the beam. This can be controlled by altering one of the voltages applied to the electron gun. Even for very rapid voltage fluctuations the rate of electron emission by the gun is proportional to the voltage applied to it, and thus the brightness of the spot of light on the screen can be varied, or modulated, rapidly.

The television camera tube, or **iconoscope**, is a type of cathode-ray tube. An image of the scene to be viewed is formed optically on a special screen inside the tube. This screen is composed of millions of individual, photosensitive particles mounted on a mica sheet. When the light strikes these particles, electrons are emitted, the number given off by each particle being proportional to the intensity of the light falling on it. (This photoelectric effect will be discussed in detail in the next section.) The light-sensitive particles are insulated from each other so that they become positively charged, and the pattern of charge distribution reproduces the pattern of light intensity. Immediately behind the mica is a sheet of metal, so that each photosensitive particle forms a tiny capacitor, with the metal as the second plate and the mica as the insulator. It remains now to derive in some way from this pattern a variable electric current which will contain the so-called *video* information present on the screen. This is done with an electron beam. The camera tube uses two sets of magnetic deflection coils, and their combined action causes the electron beam to trace out a set of parallel lines covering the image to be transmitted. This process is known as **scanning** and is a type of sampling. That is, the electron beam of the camera tube does not "look" at all of the picture, but only at a set of lines forming part of the picture. The number of lines has been chosen to give a satisfactory reproduction of the details. The metal plate behind the photosensitive screen is connected through a resistor to the electron-gun anode so that a complete circuit for alternating current is formed, using the electron beam as a conductor. The current in this path will vary according to the charge on the particular capacitor forming a part of it. Hence the voltage developed across the resistor contains the video information and can be amplified. Since a complete scan contains 525 lines and 60 scans are performed per second, the agility of an electron beam is highly necessary.

The high-frequency radio wave transmitted is modulated by the signal obtained from the scanning operation. At the television receiver, the picture tube has a magnetic deflection system similar to that of the camera tube, and the electron beam sweeps across the screen of the tube in exact synchronism with the original scan. The incoming signal, after suitable amplification, is applied to the electron gun and modulates the intensity of the electron beam to reproduce the original detail observed by the camera tube.

Cathode-ray tubes are also particularly suited to the measurement of very short times of the order of microseconds and are indispensable in radar for this and other purposes.

An electron gun is an ingenious and complex device. It was one of the first achievements of a growing field called electron ballistics or electron optics. The first name comes from the resemblance between calculations on the motion of electrons and on the motion of projectiles. Problem 14 of Chapter 40 is a good example. The name electron optics arises because of a close analogy between the effect of certain configurations of electric and magnetic fields on electron paths and the effect of glass lenses on rays of light. The most striking achievement of electron optics is the electron microscope. In this instrument a beam of electrons, controlled by electric and magnetic "lenses", is projected through a thin sample to be studied. The beam is altered by the sample in such a way that when it strikes a fluorescent screen a greatly magnified image of the sample is obtained. The maximum magnification of an optical microscope is about 1500 times, whereas magnifications of over 100,000 times have been obtained with electron microscopes.

42.08 THE PHOTOELECTRIC EFFECT

If light shines on certain metal surfaces, electrons are ejected from the metal. This phenomenon has been known for over fifty years and is called the **photoelectric effect.** Investigations of it have revealed the following characteristics.

(1) The velocity of the photoelectrons ejected depends on the nature of the surface and on the wavelength or frequency of the incident light, but not on its intensity.

(2) If monochromatic light (light of a single color or wavelength) is used, the yield of photoelectrons decreases as the wavelength increases and falls to zero at a certain critical wavelength λ_c.

(3) If the wavelength of the monochromatic light $\lambda < \lambda_c$, the yield is proportional to the intensity of the light; if $\lambda > \lambda_c$, no intensity of illumination, however great, can produce any photoelectric emission.

(4) When light is first incident on the surface, the emission (if any) starts instantly.

These results are of a most revolutionary character. Prior to this it had been established that light consists of electromagnetic waves. In a wave motion the energy delivered is proportional to the square of the amplitude and is distributed uniformly across the wave front. If a light beam of known intensity strikes a surface, it is a simple matter to calculate the power incident per unit area. It is also a simple matter to calculate the average area occupied by each atom in the metal surface, using Avogadro's number and the density and atomic weight of the metal. The energy required to extract an electron from the metal is $e\phi$, where ϕ is the work function discussed in section 42.01. If all the energy falling per second on the area occupied by an atom is divided into $e\phi$, the result should be the time required for an atom to accumulate enough energy to eject an electron. This is all quite straightforward arithmetic, even if it is hard to visualize a mechanism by which the atom could "store" radiant energy until it had enough to release an electron. The difficulty is that the time calculated by this method may be seconds or even minutes for a faint light beam, but emission has been proved to start within less than 10^{-8} sec after the light first strikes. Physicists went over and over this simple argument looking for flaws, but none has been found. The classical electromagnetic theory, the crowning achievement of nineteenth century physics, simply cannot explain photoelectric emission.

About this time (around 1900) another difficulty was being studied. In section 22.11 the distribution of energy in the spectrum of black-body radiation was discussed briefly. Theoretical physicists felt it should be possible to explain the shape of this distribution curve in terms of electromagnetic theory, and many attempts were made without success, until finally Max Planck (1858) was able to derive an equation fitting the experimental results perfectly, but *only* by assuming that radiation is emitted and absorbed in discrete packages called **quanta,** the energy of a quantum being

$$E = hf \qquad (42.04)$$

where f is the frequency of the radiation and h is a constant equal to 6.62×10^{-34} joule-sec and now known as Planck's Constant. He was unable to offer any justification for this step from classical theory, and none is possible. It implies an atomicity of energy completely foreign to classical mechanics. This was the beginning of **quantum theory,** the major development of the twentieth century. This difficult and abstract theory replaces classical mechanics and electromagnetic theory and gives a satisfactory account of atomic phenomena which the classical theories fail to achieve. It yields the same results as the former theories for large-scale phenomena, so that no contradictions arise in that field, and the student need not feel that his efforts to follow Newton and Ampere have been wasted.

In 1905 Einstein extended Planck's assumption to show that quantum theory could account for the photoelectric effect. His reasoning ran somewhat as follows. The success of the wave theory in explaining interference and diffraction effects with light shows that it must have considerable validity. Let us suppose that the energy in a light beam is actually concentrated in quanta (sometimes called photons), but that the distribution of these quanta depends on the intensity of the wave. In more exact language, we assume that the probability of finding a photon in any small volume of space is proportional to the square of the amplitude of the wave at that location. We further assume that an electron can absorb the complete energy of a quantum striking it. If the energy of the quantum is sufficient, the electron is ejected, any surplus above the energy required for emission appearing as kinetic energy of the electron. In equation form,

$$\text{Max. K.E.} = \text{energy of the quantum} - \text{work of removal}$$
$$\tfrac{1}{2}mv_{\text{Max.}}^2 = hf - e\phi \tag{42.05}$$

This is Einstein's photoelectric equation. It has been completely verified by experiment, and this theory explains satisfactorily the four observations listed at the beginning of this section. The critical wavelength is found by calculating the minimum frequency for emission with zero velocity.

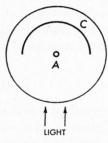

$$0 = hf_c - e\phi$$
$$f_c = \frac{e\phi}{h}$$
$$\lambda_c = \frac{c}{f_c} = \frac{hc}{e\phi} \tag{42.06}$$

Fig. 42.12. Cross-sectional view of a photocell.

The discussion of this section up to now is more closely related to the subject matter of atomic physics than to electronics, but the photoelectric effect is also very important in practice. Figure 42.12 shows one type of vacuum photocell. The cathode C is a half-cylinder, the inside of which is coated with a metal of low work function such as cesium. The anode is a wire at the axis of the cylinder and is kept at a sufficiently high potential to collect all the photoelectrons emitted from the cathode when light falls on it. The resulting current is in the microampere range but can be amplified as necessary.

A photocell can be used to measure light intensities, to count objects passing between a light source and the cell, to actuate relays operating doors, and for many similar functions. The major application is probably in connection with sound recording on film in the motion-picture industry. To record a sound track on a film, the light from a lamp is focused on the slit of a light valve. This slit consists of two metallic ribbons placed in a magnetic field. The audio currents from a microphone pass through the ribbons where they interact with the field, moving farther apart (that is, widening the slit) as the audio current increases and closer together as it decreases. The inertia of the ribbons is small enough for them to respond to the wave form of the audiofrequency current, which contains components varying with frequencies of several thousand cycles per second. The image of the slit of the light valve is focused on the film. As the film moves, a strip of film about two or three millimeters wide is exposed, forming a sound track of constant width and variable density. The density of the sound track reproduces the wave form of the audio current in both frequency and intensity. When the film is developed and printed it can be played back as follows. Light striking a very narrow, fixed slit passes through an optical system which focuses an image of the slit on the sound track. The light transmitted by the film falls on a photocell. The current in the photocell is proportional to the intensity of light striking it, which in turn is proportional to the original sound intensity, since it has passed through the variable density sound track. When the current in the cell is suitably amplified, it can be used to operate a loudspeaker, reproducing the original sound with excellent fidelity.

PROBLEMS

1. In Figure 42.02(c), explain why the characteristic curve ends in a horizontal line. This effect is called saturation.

2. Redraw Figure 42.04, tracing out the path followed by the current, (a) if $V_A > V_B$, (b) if $V_B > V_A$ where V_A is the potential of the point A.

3. In Figure 42.03(a), if G is an a-c generator supplying 120 v, $R_L = 1200$ Ω, and the maximum current through R_L is 100 ma, find the resistance of the diode when delivering this current.

4. In Figure 42.06, e_g is a sine-wave voltage generator of peak value 3.00 v. The zero-signal plate current is 12.0 ma, and when e_g is turned on, the plate current fluctuates between 8.0 and 16.0 ma. If $R_L = 10.0$ kΩ, what is the amplification of the circuit?

5. The L-C circuit of an electronic oscillator contains 20.0 μh inductance. What range of capacitance values is needed to tune the oscillator over the frequency range 300–1250 kc? If the circuit acts as the local oscillator in a broadcast-band receiver, what is the intermediate frequency of the set?

6. What is the frequency of a radio wave of wavelength 600 m? What are the wavelengths corresponding to radio waves of frequencies 300, 40×10^5, 6×10^{12} cycles sec^{-1}?

7. In optics, concentrated parallel light beams are obtained through the use of parabolic mirrors. Similar technique is used with microwave radio and radar, the output of a small source of waves being placed at the focus of a parabolic reflector. The concentration of the resulting beam depends on the ratio of the diameter of the reflector to the wavelength of the waves. If this ratio is to be ten times and the diameter of the reflector is 5.00 m, what wavelength and frequency are needed?

8. The work functions of cesium, sodium, zinc, and silver are 1.91, 2.46, 3.32, and 4.73 v, respectively. Find the critical (or cutoff) wavelength in Angstrom units for photoelectric emission from each of these metals. (1 A $= 10^{-10}$ m; $e = 1.60 \times 10^{-19}$ coulomb.)

9. A potassium surface whose work function is 2.20 v is illuminated with light of wavelength 4800 A. What is the maximum velocity of the electrons emitted? The mass of an electron is 9.11×10^{-31} kgm.

10. If the input signal to an amplifier has an amplitude of 2.00 mv and a minimum output amplitude of 40.0 v is needed, how many stages are required in the amplifier, each stage having an amplification of 12.0?

ATOMIC
PHYSICS

43

Atomic Physics

43.01 ELECTRONS AND IONS IN ELECTRIC AND MAGNETIC FIELDS

Atomic physics in the broad sense includes almost all physics, but it is usually restricted to those parts of the subject where a knowledge of the existence and properties of atoms is needed for an explanation of the observed properties of matter in bulk. Above all, atomic physics is the study of the internal structure of atoms. The word atom is derived from Greek words indicating that it is an indivisible entity; this meaning is certainly not true in the literal sense, but it is true in the sense that an atom is the ultimate unit of an element. An atom of any element can readily be divided into two or more parts, but the parts have completely different chemical and physical properties from those of the original atom.

The experimental techniques of atomic physics are primarily electrical and usually involve the control of charged particles (fragments of atoms) by electric and magnetic fields. We start by considering the action of fields on an electron or ion. Suppose an electron is released with zero velocity from a cathode and travels through a vacuum to an anode at a potential V relative to the cathode. Potential difference is work per unit charge. If the charge of the electron is e coulombs, the work done by the source of electrical energy is thus eV joules if V is in volts. This work appears as kinetic energy of the electron. When the rapidly moving electron strikes the anode its kinetic energy equals its loss of potential energy, eV.

$$\tfrac{1}{2}mv^2 = eV \tag{43.01}$$

Instead of measuring the energy gained by the electron in joules, a derived unit called the *electron volt* (ev) is widely used—it is the energy gained by a particle of charge e which is accelerated through a potential difference of 1 volt.   Since the charge e is 1.60×10^{-19} coulomb, we see from (43.01) that

$$1 \text{ ev} = 1.60 \times 10^{-19} \text{ joule}$$

Note that the energy gained by a charged particle in falling through a given potential difference depends only on the charge and not on the mass. The electron volt is a small unit of energy, but it is appropriate for energy changes in the outer atom.   Greater amounts of energy are involved in nuclear physics where the Mev (million electron volts) is used.

If the electric field strength ε is known, the force on an electron or other particle of the same charge is $e\varepsilon$.   One of the commonest cases is that of a uniform field caused by a potential difference V between parallel electrodes a distance d apart.   Then, as we have seen,

$$\varepsilon = \frac{V}{d} \qquad\qquad (43.02)$$

Turning to magnetic fields, a uniform field of flux density B has no effect on a stationary charge, but as soon as the charged particle moves

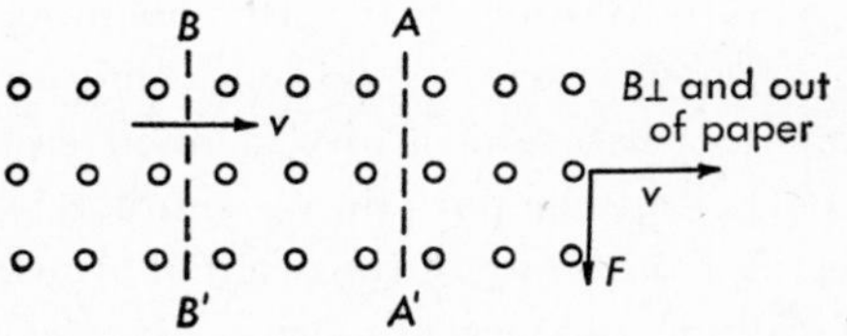

Fig. 43.01.   Force acting on a stream of charged particles.

it constitutes a current, and the component of B perpendicular to the path of the particle interacts with this current.   In Figure 43.01 a stream of particles each of charge $+e$ is moving to the right with velocity v.   The current is the charge which passes some plane perpendicular to v in one second. Let there be n particles per unit length of the stream.   If AA' and BB' are two planes a unit distance apart, there are n particles in the section of the beam cut off between these planes.   Any particle within a distance v to the left of AA' will pass this plane within one second.   Therefore

$$\text{Current } I = (nv)e$$

Suppose now a uniform magnetic field of flux density B is turned on, the direction of B being perpendicular to the plane of the figure and out from it.   The force on a length l of the beam is BIl by Ampere's Law.   Hence the force on unit length (n particles) is

$$F_n = BI \times 1 = Bnev$$

or the force per particle is

$$F = Bev \qquad (43.03)$$

and the direction of the force is as shown in the figure, by the left-hand rule.   If the particles have negative charges, the direction of the current is opposite to the direction of v, and hence the direction of the force is reversed.

In Figure 43.02, a source S emits particles of charge $+Q$ and mass m with a velocity v.   The force on each particle is

$$F = BQv$$

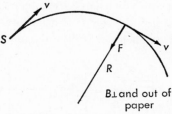

and this force is perpendicular to v. Hence the force cannot change the size of v but can and does change its direction. As the direction of the velocity changes, the direction (but not the size) of the force changes so that it is always at right angles to v.   This is just the condition for circular motion, the electromagnetic force causing the necessary centripetal acceleration.   If R is the radius of the path of the charged particle,

Fig. 43.02.   Deflection of a charged particle in a uniform magnetic field.

$$\frac{mv^2}{R} = BQv$$

$$mv = BQR \qquad (43.04)$$

If Q is known, this equation gives a method of measuring the momentum of the particles.

43.02 CHARGE-TO-MASS RATIO OF ELECTRONS

Faraday's work on electrolysis strongly indicated that discrete charges are associated with atoms, as discussed in section 35.07, and gave the equation

$$1 \text{ faraday} = 96,520 \text{ coulombs} = N_0 e \qquad (43.05)$$

where N_0 is Avogadro's number and e is the charge associated with a monovalent atom in electrolysis.   This charge was found roughly from an estimate of N_0 from kinetic theory, and the existence of a particle of charge $-e$ was postulated.   This particle was given the name **electron** about 1874.   Its existence was finally proved by J. J. Thomson (1856) in 1897.   In his original experiment he investigated the nature of the **cathode rays** which are produced in the passage of electricity through gases at low pressures.   These cathode rays appear as streamers of green light which can be deflected by electric or magnetic fields and so must consist of charged particles, now known to be electrons.   The principle of Thomson's experiment can be described with the cathode-ray tube illustrated in Figure 43.03.   The electron gun G produces an electron beam which passes between the deflector plates, P, P.   A magnetic field of flux density B can be established perpendicular to the diagram in the area enclosed by the dotted circle.   Within this area we can thus apply

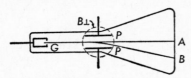

perpendicular electric and magnetic fields to the electron beam.   In the absence of either field the beam strikes the screen at A.   When the magnetic field is turned on, the beam is deflected to B, and by measuring the length AB and the geometry of the tube, the radius of curvature R of the path of the electrons in the field

Fig. 43.03.   The measurement of e/m and v for electrons in a cathode-ray tube.

can be calculated.   Next, the electric field is turned on in a direction to deflect the electrons upward, and its strength is increased until the net deflection is zero, as judged by the spot of light returning to A.

The condition for no deflection is that the two fields exert equal and opposite forces on the particles.   That is,

$$\text{Magnetic force } Bev = \text{electric force } e\mathcal{E}$$

or
$$v = \frac{\mathcal{E}}{B} \qquad (43.06)$$

Thomson found that cathode rays have velocities of the order of 10^6 or 10^7 m sec^{-1}.   If the velocity and radius R are known, equation (43.04) can be used to find the ratio of charge to mass for the particles.

$$\frac{e}{m} = \frac{BR}{v} \qquad (43.07)$$

The presently accepted value for this ratio is 1.76×10^{11} coulombs per kgm for the electron.   Thomson's value was reasonably close to this, and by combining it with the estimated size of the electronic charge, he found that the mass of a particle in a cathode ray was about one two-thousandth that of the hydrogen atom—clear proof that he was working with subatomic particles, since hydrogen is the lightest of all the elements.   It was found that particles with this charge to mass ratio could be produced from any gas by electrical discharge, from metallic substances heated to high temperatures (thermionic emission), and from some substances irradiated with light (photoelectric emission). In addition, some of the heavier elements were found to give off spontaneously very high speed particles called **β-rays**. In all cases the particles are electrons, which seem to be a universal constituent of matter.

Careful study of e/m and v for the β-rays soon revealed a surprising fact—the ratio e/m was not exactly constant but appeared to decrease slightly with velocity. This effect was observable only for velocities greater than about 10% of the velocity of light and could be accounted for exactly if the mass was assumed to depend on velocity through the equation

$$m = \frac{m_0}{\left(1 - \dfrac{v^2}{c^2}\right)^{\frac{1}{2}}} \tag{43.08}$$

where m_0 is the mass at low velocities or, strictly, of particles at rest, and c is the velocity of light. This is exactly the variation of mass with velocity predicted by the theory of relativity (see section 10.05), and this experimental confirmation of one of the predictions of the theory led to greater confidence in another of its predictions, namely, the equivalence of mass and energy ($E = mc^2$).

43.03 THE CHARGE OF THE ELECTRON

The estimate of the electronic charge obtained from kinetic theory was only approximate, and the experiments described all dealt with very large numbers of electrons, so that results were averages. In 1911 Robert Millikan (1868) completed one of the most famous experiments in physics, in which he showed that all electrons have identical charges and measured the value accurately. Though performed with many refinements, Millikan's experiment is quite simple in principle. It is sketched in Figure 43.04. The atomizer A is similar to a perfume bottle and can be used to spray very fine drops of oil into the enclosed chamber C containing air. These tiny drops fall slowly at terminal velocity, and one will soon fall through a small hole in the floor of C into the space between the insulated metal

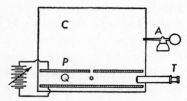

Fig. 43.04. Essentials of Millikan's oil-drop experiment for the measurement of the electronic charge.

plates P and Q. A strong light (not shown) illuminates the drop, which appears as a bright point when viewed by the telescope T. This telescope has horizontal cross hairs a known distance apart, and by timing the fall of the drop through this distance, its velocity can be measured. A theoretical study of terminal velocity (see section 11.11) shows that in this case

$$v = \tfrac{2}{9} \frac{gr^2(\rho - \rho_M)}{\eta} \tag{43.09}$$

where ρ is the density of the oil drop, ρ_M the density of the air through which it is falling, η the coefficient of viscosity of the air, and r the radius of the drop. Since everything but r is known, the size and hence the mass of the drop can be found.

When the drops are formed in the atomizer they usually acquire an electrostatic charge by friction, a charge which may, of course, be either positive or negative. If an electrostatic field $\mathcal{E}$ is applied between P and Q, the drop under study can be slowed down, and if $\mathcal{E}$ is adjusted to the right size, the drop will remain stationary, the electric force upward just balancing the net weight downward. The weight is $\tfrac{4}{3}\pi r^3 \rho g$, and the buoyancy of the air is $\tfrac{4}{3}\pi r^3 \rho_M g$ by Archimedes' Principle, so that for a balanced drop

$$\tfrac{4}{3}\pi r^3 g(\rho - \rho_M) = Q\mathcal{E} \tag{43.10}$$

where Q is the charge on the drop. In this way Millikan was able to measure the electrostatic charges on a large number of drops. The smallest he ever found was

$$e = 1.60 \times 10^{-19} \text{ coulomb}$$

and in *all* cases the charge was an *exact* integral multiple of this charge e, that is, $+3e$, $-7e$, $+4e$, etc. The same drop could be watched for several minutes or even hours. After floating at rest for some time it might suddenly start to move up or down, and a readjustment of $\mathcal{E}$ would be needed to bring it to rest again. The change in the charge on the drop was due to collisions with ions moving about in the gas which transferred charge to or from the oil drop.

43.04 RADIOACTIVITY

Another line of inquiry which has been most fruitful in the study of atomic structure started with an accidental discovery by William Roentgen (1845). Unexposed photographic plates are kept wrapped in black paper to prevent light getting at them. In 1895 Roentgen was carrying out experiments in his laboratory on the discharge of electricity through gases and discovered that some photographic plates near his equipment had become exposed while still securely wrapped. He concluded that some unknown, invisible radiation, given off by the discharge tube, had penetrated the black paper and acted on the silver bromide of the plate. He noted also that this radiation would cause a fluorescent screen to glow brightly even if a heavy, black, cardboard sheet was placed between the tube and the screen. Roentgen called this radiation **X-rays** to indicate its unknown character. X-rays were shown later to be electromagnetic waves, similar to light but much shorter in wavelength and, although important in themselves both theoretically and practically, are of interest in this section because Roentgen's discovery stimulated Henri Becquerel (1852) to search for other sources of penetrating radiation. In 1896 Becquerel found that similar darkening of a photographic plate protected from light occurred in the vicinity of a pitchblende ore, which contained *uranium*. He showed that purified uranium possessed this property more strongly than the ore, and he attributed it correctly to this element. The emission of penetrating radiations by uranium and certain other elements is called **radioactivity.**

Pierre Curie (1859) and his wife Marie (1867) studied radioactive ores and extracted from them two new elements which were much more radioactive than uranium itself. They called these elements *polonium* and *radium*. The element *thorium* was also found to have similar properties. Studies of the radiations from these elements soon showed that there were three different kinds of rays, which were labeled alpha (α), beta (β), and gamma (γ). Figure 43.05 shows an early, key experiment. A radioactive source S was placed behind a heavy lead screen L, and a collimated beam of the radiation emerged from a fine hole in L into a region with a perpendicular magnetic field B. It was found that γ-rays were not affected by the magnetic field, but

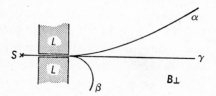

Fig. 43.05. The nature of the α-, β- and γ-rays.

α-rays were deflected in such a direction as to show that they had positive charges, and β-rays were deflected in the opposite direction, indicating negative charges. A measurement of e/m for the β-rays showed that they were very high speed electrons. The γ-rays proved to be short-wavelength electromagnetic radiation, similar to X-rays but of even shorter wavelength.

The most important of the early work on radioactivity was done at McGill University by a young New Zealand-born physicist, Ernest Rutherford (1871), and a chemist, Frederick Soddy (1877). Rutherford collected the α-rays from a source for a considerable time and was able to show spectroscopically that the α-particles were doubly charged helium ions (He^{++}). This and other experiments led him and Soddy to the theory that radioactivity is a spontaneous change or disintegration of an atom of one element into an atom of another, the difference in mass and charge being carried away as an α- or a β-particle. This was the first indication that elements are not the fixed and immutable entities that chemistry had apparently established. The theory was not received with instant acclaim—the story is told at McGill of the meeting at which Rutherford announced the conclusions he and Soddy had reached. It was a small meeting at the university, and at the conclusion of the paper one of the senior professors rose and objected to the radical and "impossible" hypothesis he had just heard advanced. Further, he hoped that this rash young man would be restrained from publishing a theory which could not fail to reflect discredit on an honored university. Fortunately his advice was not heeded.

Hydrogen is the lightest of the elements and is invariably monovalent in chemical reactions. It is plausible to suppose that it consists of a single electron together with a second particle of charge $+e$ and mass about equal to that of the hydrogen atom itself. This particle is the **proton.** Helium can be ionized and the charge-to-mass ratio measured by a modification of Thomson's experiment. The results are consistent with helium ions having masses about equal to that of the helium atom and charges $+e$ or $+2e$. Similarly, lithium atoms can be reduced to ions Li^+, Li^{++}, and Li^{+++}. Doubly ionized hydrogen, triply ionized helium, and quadruply ionized lithium are never found. It is probable therefore that neutral hydrogen contains one electron and one positively charged particle or proton, neutral helium has two electrons and two positive charges, lithium three electrons, and so on. Now if the chemical elements are listed as in the periodic table and numbered consecutively, the number is called the **atomic number** (Z) of the element. Thus for H, $Z = 1$; for He, $Z = 2$; and for Li, $Z = 3$; etc. The identification of Z with the number of electrons and the number of positive charges in the neutral atom was made early in this century and has been abundantly confirmed.

Radioactive changes are indicated by modified chemical equations. Thus the disintegrations of uranium, radium, and radium B are shown, respectively, by the equations

$$_{92}U^{238} \rightarrow {}_{90}X^{234} + {}_2He^4 + Q_1 \qquad (43.11)$$

$$_{88}Ra^{226} \rightarrow {}_{86}Y^{222} + {}_2He^4 + Q_2 \qquad (43.12)$$

$$_{82}Pb^{214} \rightarrow {}_{83}Z^{214} + \beta \qquad + Q_3 \qquad (43.13)$$

The upper right-hand number written with the chemical symbol is the **mass number** (A), the nearest integer to the atomic weight, and the lower left-hand number is Z. Note that the first two equations balance, both in mass number A and in atomic number Z. The Q's represent the energy released in the disintegrations—we shall return to this point later.

The main product of each disintegration has been shown by the symbol X, Y, or Z. In equation (43.11) the atom labeled X has an atomic number 90, which is the same as that of thorium, and chemical tests soon showed that the substance X (originally called uranium X_1) is indistinguishable, by any chemical means, from naturally occurring thorium. However, X has a mass number of 234, whereas thorium has a mass number of 232. This is an example of what are now called **isotopes,** that is, atoms having the same atomic number and the same chemical properties but different atomic weights. The study of radioactive substances reveals a large number of isotopes existing among the heavy elements $(Z \geq 81)$, most of which are radioactive.

The substance Y of equation (43.12) is very interesting because physically it is a gas under normal conditions, and so can be separated easily from the solid radium which produces it. It proves to be another new element, called *radon* (chemical symbol Rn), and is completely inert chemically, a property it shares with helium, neon, argon, krypton, and xenon. If the radon is separated from the radium, it too is observed to disintegrate, emitting an α-particle and giving rise to a solid substance which is the element polonium discovered by the Curies.

The chemical nature of the various radioelements was in doubt for some time, and a special nomenclature was developed. Thus uranium I was the label given to the isotope U^{238}. Uranium I disintegrates into uranium X_1 and it into uranium X_2 (now known to be Pa^{232}), and so on. This nomenclature is now of little interest other than historical. Equation (43.13) shows the disintegration of radium B (old name) or Pb^{214}. The β-particle has a charge of -1 so that the equation balances in the sense that the total positive charge on the left is 82 units while that on the right is $83 - 1$. This suggests that the number of *positive* charges in an atom is a more permanent property than the number of electrons, and this is borne out by the ease with which gases can be ionized, that is, the ease with which electrons can be removed temporarily. For this reason we take the atomic number to mean the number of positive charges in an atom or ion. With this interpretation of equation (43.13) the substance $_{83}Z^{214}$ should be an isotope of bismuth, and this was shown to be the case. Note that, in balancing mass numbers, the mass of the β-particle is ignored. This is permissible since its mass is so small a fraction of the mass of any atom.

The sequence of events occurring during and following the disintegration represented by equation (43.13) is worth describing in more detail. The original Pb^{214} atom is neutral, containing 82 electrons and 82 protons. When it disintegrates an additional electron is produced within it. This electron comes out of the nucleus (see section 43.06) with an enormous velocity and leaves the nucleus with an extra positive charge, so that its atomic number is now 83. Since the fast electron or β-particle has left the atom there are only 82 electrons, and the product is thus a positive ion $(_{83}Z^{214})^+$. The disintegrations going on in a sample of Pb^{214} thus result in the production of a large number of singly charged bismuth ions and an equal number of β-particles. The β-particles are slowed down by collisions with atoms, producing heat, and are eventually captured by the ions to form neutral bismuth atoms. Similar events take place in the disintegrations represented by equations (43.11) and (43.12). The α-particles $(_2He^4)$ are ejected from the nuclei as doubly charged helium ions, leaving thorium or radon atoms with two surplus electrons each. These surplus electrons are lost almost immediately by the product atoms and ultimately neutralize the helium.

Recent experiments at Oak Ridge, Tenn. by Snell (1909) and others show that the above explanation is oversimplified. The electron or α-particle leaving the nucleus may interact with other electrons on its way out of the atom, carrying some of these electrons with it, so to speak. Thus the disintegration of (43.13) may produce as many as ten free electrons and a bismuth atom short of this many electrons for neutrality, that is, bismuth in a highly ionized state. The free electrons and the bismuth ions will ultimately neutralize each other but Snell's experiments are arousing great interest because of the light they shed on the details of the disintegration process and, curiously enough, because they offer a powerful method of studying the chemical forces holding molecules together.

Equations (43.11) to (43.13) illustrate one of the early and important generalizations known as the **displacement law**: emission of an α-particle leaves an atom displaced two columns to the left in the periodic table (that is, the atomic number is reduced by two); emission of a β-particle results in a product atom displaced one column to the right.

43.05 DISINTEGRATION RATES AND HALF-LIVES

Nothing has been said as yet about the rate at which a reaction such as (43.11) or (43.12) takes place. Rutherford showed that if there were N atoms present at any time, the number of disintegrations per second was proportional to N. In mathematical terms

$$\frac{\Delta N}{\Delta t} \propto -N$$

the negative sign indicating that N is decreasing with time. In the limit as $\Delta t \to 0$ this becomes

$$\frac{dN}{dt} = -\lambda N \tag{43.14}$$

where λ is a constant called the **decay constant.** Rutherford also showed that λ could not be changed by any known physical agent, including heat, pressure, and electric or magnetic fields. Furthermore, λ is quite independent of the chemical compound of which the parent element, such as uranium in equation (43.11), may form a part. It is a very permanent and unchangeable property of the parent atom alone. Equation (43.14) is the equation of an exponential decay and can be integrated as follows:

$$\int \frac{dN}{N} = -\lambda \int dt$$
$$\ln N = -\lambda t + A$$

where A is a constant of integration. Now if there were N_0 atoms at time $t = 0$, we can substitute these values and find A.

$$\ln N_0 = -\lambda \cdot 0 + A, \qquad A = \ln N_0$$

that is,
$$\ln N - \ln N_0 = -\lambda t$$
$$N = N_0 e^{-\lambda t} \tag{43.15}$$

The rate of decay of a radioelement (a general term for radioactive substances) can be described by giving the value of λ. Another widely used method is to quote the **half-life** T, the length of time in which the amount of the radioelement present is reduced to one-half its original value. The connection between λ and T can be found from (43.15).

When $t = T$, $N = N_0/2$, so that

$$\frac{N_0}{2} = N_0 e^{-\lambda T}$$

$$e^{\lambda T} = 2$$

$$T = \frac{\ln 2}{\lambda} = \frac{0.693}{\lambda}$$

Half-lives of radioelements have a wide range of values, from more than 10^{10} years to less than a microsecond.

Radioactive Series. Theoretically an exponential decay never reaches an end because if there are N atoms originally, after a time T

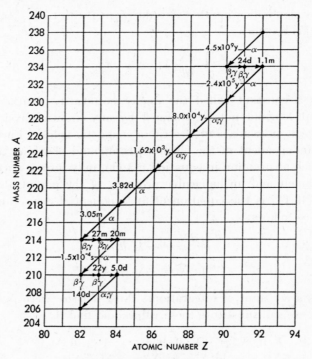

Fig. 43.06. The main features of the uranium series. The units for the half-lives are abbreviated y(years), d(days), m(minutes), and s(seconds).

there will be $N/2$ left, after another time T there will be $\frac{1}{2}(N/2)$ or $N/4$ left, and so on. However, the amount left after a long time may be too small to detect. Consider a rock weighing one kilogram. It would contain about 10^{25} atoms, of which we shall suppose 1% are radioactive, with a half-life of 1 year. After 70 years the original 10^{23} radioactive atoms would be reduced to $10^{23}/2^{70}$ or about 80 atoms. The age of the earth is estimated to be between 2.5 and 4 billion years, so that any short-lived radioelements would have long since disappeared unless the supply was constantly renewed by the decay of a long-lived element. Virtually all the naturally radioactive elements are derived from three long-lived substances: U^{238} ($T = 4.5 \times 10^9$ years) which gives rise to the uranium series, Th^{232} ($T = 1.4 \times 10^{10}$ years), and U^{235} ($T = 7.1 \times 10^8$ years). Each of these substances decays in a long and involved series of disintegrations to one of the stable isotopes of lead. The main features of the uranium series are illustrated in Figure 43.06. Each dot represents one of the atoms of the series plotted by its Z and A numbers as coordinates. The arrows show the radioactive transitions, the half-life being shown above the arrow and the types of radiations emitted being indicated below.

Since a vertical line has a constant value of Z, the figure shows the existence, in this series alone, of two isotopes of uranium ($Z = 92$), two of thorium ($Z = 90$), three of polonium ($Z = 84$), two of bismuth ($Z = 83$), and three of lead ($Z = 82$). The lowest of these lead isotopes ($A = 206$) is the stable terminal point of the uranium series. The stable lead isotopes 207 and 208 are the final products of the radioactive series that start with uranium 235 and thorium 232, respectively.

43.06 THE NUCLEAR THEORY

Rutherford went from McGill to Manchester University and from there to Cambridge University as head of the famous Cavendish Laboratory. Almost all his work was concerned with the radiations from radioactive substances (the title of his greatest book). These studies led to the explanation of radioactivity, to the discovery of the nucleus, and finally to investigations into the structure of the nucleus itself in which he succeeded in the alchemists' dream of transmuting one element into another. It is almost impossible to exaggerate the importance of the contributions made by him and by his students. He was undoubtedly the greatest experimental physicist since Faraday and throughout his life showed extraordinary ability in the formulation of new and radical theories and in the design of simple but effective experiments to test them.

The nuclear theory of the atom grew out of experiments by two of his students at Manchester on the **scattering** of α-particles by thin metal foils. If a sharply collimated beam of α-particles strikes a foil, it passes through and emerges as a slightly divergent beam. This is not surprising since the α-particles are electrically charged, and the metal atoms, although neutral, are certainly electrical in nature. Small divergences are due to the electrostatic attraction or repulsion between the α-particle and some electrified part of an atom or atoms. What is surprising is that it is found that a small fraction of the α-particles are scattered through very large angles, a few even through angles approaching 180°. In Rutherford's phrase this is as unexpected as if a 15-inch shell in full flight should bounce back from a sheet of tissue paper. He realized that the large force of repulsion needed to reflect the α-particle could be obtained electrostatically if both the α-particle and the positive charge of the atom had radii small enough to permit a close approach. This close approach is necessary since Coulomb's Law shows the force to vary inversely as the square of the distance. Mathematical study of the scattering results showed that the α-particle must approach within a distance of 10^{-14} meter of the positive center repelling it, in order to be deflected through a large angle. The experiments also indicated that the charge on this center must be $+Ze$. Rutherford suggested the nuclear theory in 1911. According to it, the atom consists of a nucleus of charge $+Ze$ and radius of the order of 10^{-15} to 10^{-14} meter, with virtually all the mass of the atom concentrated in the nucleus. The outer atom contains Z electrons. Other evidence shows that the radius of an electron is of the same order as that of the nucleus. Now an atom behaves in its relations with other atoms as if it had a radius of about 10^{-10} meter, that is, it has a radius at least ten thousand times larger than any of the less than one hundred particles of which it is constructed. Hence an atom must be almost entirely empty space, and it is not surprising that most of the bombarding α-particles sail right through the foil with little or no deflection. Rutherford's theory of the atom is now universally accepted.

The resemblance between Rutherford's nuclear atom and the solar system is close and suggests that the analogy be pushed farther. The planets move in dynamically stable orbits under the influence of the gravitational attraction of the sun. It is plausible to suggest that the electrons move in stable orbits under the influence of the electrostatic attraction of the nucleus. (A little arithmetic shows that gravitational forces between the components of an atom are negligibly small; the electrostatic attraction between a proton and an electron is more than 10^{39} times as great as the gravitational attraction between them.) Unfortunately, classical electromagnetic theory shows that it isn't as simple as this, because according to this theory, if a charged particle is accelerated, it must radiate electromagnetic waves. This is the method by which an alternating current in an antenna generates radio waves, and the production of X-rays is another example. X-rays are emitted whenever very fast electrons are slowed down abruptly by striking an anode or other solid block. An electron traveling in a circular or other curved orbit is constantly experiencing centripetal acceleration and so should radiate, thus reducing its energy. No stable orbit is possible under these circumstances. Mathematical studies indicated that no *static* arrangement of electrons about the nucleus could be stable either. The evident stability of matter was in conflict with the previous successes of electromagnetic theory. The resolution of this dilemma was the achievement of **quantum mechanics,** which will be discussed briefly later.

43.07 SPECTROSCOPY. THE BALMER SERIES

One of Newton's discoveries was that if a collimated beam of sunlight passes through a glass prism, the light is bent and separated into a band of colors which appear in the familiar order of the rainbow. Apparently "white" sunlight is a mixture of all the different colors of light, which are bent through different angles by the prism, violet light being bent through a larger angle than red. This pattern of colors is called the **spectrum** of sunlight, and the study of spectra is called **spectroscopy.** The phenomenon of dispersion and some of the optical details of spectrometers were discussed in Chapter 31 and need not be repeated here.

During the nineteenth century the spectra of various types of light sources were studied extensively. It was soon found that they consisted of two main kinds, *continuous* and *line* spectra. Continuous spectra are emitted by incandescent solids or liquids and contain all colors, just as sunlight does. Line spectra, on the other hand, contain only a limited number of distinct colors. When viewed with a spectrometer, a number of bright "lines" are seen, these lines being images, in different colors, of the collimating slit. One of the standard methods of producing a line spectrum is by an electrical discharge through gas at low pressure (1 or 2 mm Hg). Electrodes are sealed through the walls of a glass tube which is evacuated and then filled with the desired gas. When a high voltage is applied to the electrodes the tube becomes luminous. A familiar application of this phenomenon is in "neon" advertising signs (which may actually contain neon or any one of a dozen different gases to give different colors). Figure 43.07 shows the appearance of part of the spectrum obtained when the discharge tube contains hydrogen. All gases produce line spectra in a discharge tube or when heated sufficiently. This includes substances which are solid or liquid at ordinary temperatures and have been volatilized. The wavelength of the light corresponding to each line can be measured with an interferometer or a diffraction grating, and these measurements are among the most accurate in physics.

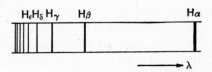

Fig. 43.07. Visible spectrum of atomic hydrogen.

Interest in line spectra intensified when it was found that the spectral pattern of each element or chemical compound is distinct and serves as an excellent identification of even a microscopic trace of the material —a sort of atomic fingerprint system. The spectra of compounds are always more complicated than those of elements, and among the elements the lower the atomic number, in general, the simpler the spectrum, atomic hydrogen having the simplest pattern of all. The interpretation of line spectra has been one of the principal tasks *and* achievements of atomic physics, and spectroscopy has proved to be the most valuable tool for the investigation of atomic structure.

The wavelengths of visible light are very short and are usually measured in *Angstrom units* (A) or microns where

$$1 \text{ A} = 10^{-10} \text{ m} = 10^{-8} \text{ cm} = 10^{-4} \mu \qquad (43.16)$$

The visible region extends for about 7600 A (red light) to about 4000 A (violet). Frequently the reciprocal of wavelength is used as a description of a line. It is called the **wave number,** σ, and is usually measured in cm^{-1}, that is, the number of waves per centimeter length in a beam of light. The wave number is closely related to the frequency f since

$$\frac{1}{\lambda} = \sigma \qquad \text{and} \qquad c = \lambda f$$

$$\frac{c}{\lambda} = f = c\sigma \qquad (43.17)$$

where c is the velocity of light. The study of spectra has resulted in wavelength tables in which λ or σ for each line in the spectrum of a substance is listed. As the experimental data accumulated, many attempts were made to systematize the information so that from a knowledge of part of the spectrum of an element (particularly one of those with a small value of Z) the rest of it could be predicted. These attempts followed from certain obvious regularities in spectra. In hydrogen (Figure 43.07) the visible spectrum has comparatively few lines, and these decrease in both intensity and spacing as λ decreases. The lines are labelled H_α, H_β, H_γ, etc., as in the figure, and the wavelengths (λ) and wave numbers (σ) are listed in Table 43.01.

TABLE 43.01   The Balmer Series in Hydrogen.

Line	λ (Angstroms)	σ (cm^{-1})	n	$R\left(\dfrac{1}{2^2} - \dfrac{1}{n^2}\right)$
H_α	6563.1	15,237	3	15,233
H_β	4860.9	20,572	4	20,565
H_γ	4340.5	23,039	5	23,033
H_δ	4101.7	24,380	6	24,373
H_ϵ	3970.1	25,188	7	25,181
.	.	.	.	.
.	.	.	.	.
.	.	.	.	.
H_∞	3646	2742×10	∞	27,420

In 1885 Balmer (1825) discovered an empirical formula for the hydrogen lines.

$$\lambda = G\,\frac{n^2 - 4}{4} \qquad (n = 3, 4, 5, \cdots)$$

which is usually written now

$$\sigma = R\left(\frac{1}{2^2} - \frac{1}{n^2}\right) \tag{43.18}$$

The value of the single constant R, called the *Rydberg Constant*, is 109,678 cm^{-1} and can be found from the experimental wave numbers. The accuracy with which this formula, with a single experimental parameter, predicts all the visible hydrogen lines is shown in the last column of Table 43.01. All the lines shown in the table or in Figure 43.07 are called the *Balmer Series*.

Similar empirical formulas, sometimes with two or three parameters, were developed to describe the line series in the alkali metals such as sodium and potassium. As in (43.18), these formulas gave the wave number of a line as the difference between two "*terms*", the terms in the Balmer series being $R/2^2$ and R/n^2. It was surmised about this time that the terms were a more direct clue to the structure of the atom than the wave numbers of the lines emitted.

43.08 BOHR'S THEORY OF THE HYDROGEN ATOM

The next step was taken in 1913 by Niels Bohr (1885), probably the greatest of living physicists. He considered the dilemma discussed at the end of section 43.06 and in particular the contrast between the continuous range of frequencies which electromagnetic theory predicts for an electron spiraling in toward the nucleus and the observed light which consists of individual discrete frequencies. He concluded that atoms *must* be able to exist in different "states" of well-defined energy and that the emission of light of a particular frequency corresponds to a change in the atom from one of these states to another of lower energy. He selected from the work of Planck and Einstein (see section 42.08) the frequency condition that

$$E_1 - E_2 = hf \tag{43.19}$$

where the E's are the energies of the two states, h is Planck's Constant, and f is the frequency emitted. Bohr next assumed a dynamical model for the hydrogen atom in which the electron moved in a circular orbit around the proton. If the centripetal force is set equal to the electrostatic attraction,

$$\frac{mv^2}{r} = \frac{e^2}{4\pi\epsilon_0 r^2} = F \tag{43.20}$$

where m, e, v, and r are the mass, charge, orbital velocity, and orbital radius of the electron, respectively, and F is the force of electrostatic attraction. From (43.20) we can find the kinetic energy of the electron.

$$\text{K.E.} = \tfrac{1}{2}mv^2 = \frac{e^2}{8\pi\epsilon_0 r} \tag{43.21}$$

We need to know the potential energy as well, and thus need some choice of zero potential. From (43.21) the kinetic energy vanishes for large r $(r \to \infty)$, and this is also a convenient choice of zero potential energy. Since the electron is attracted to the proton, the potential energy will then be negative for all finite values of r. At any distance r the electric potential caused by the proton is given by (40.15) as

$$V_r = \frac{e}{4\pi\epsilon_0 r}$$

since the charge of the proton is $+e$ and $\epsilon = 1$ in empty space. The potential energy of a charged particle in a field is its charge times the electric potential. Therefore for the electron (charge $-e$),

$$\text{P.E.} = -\frac{e^2}{4\pi\epsilon_0 r} \tag{43.22}$$

Adding (43.21) and (43.22), we get the total energy of the electron.

$$E = \text{K.E.} + \text{P.E.} = -\frac{e^2}{8\pi\epsilon_0 r} \tag{43.23}$$

As pointed out in 43.06, classical electromagnetic theory shows that orbits of the type discussed here are unstable. Bohr took the point of view that, since atoms themselves are stable, there must be something wrong with the classical theory, and some stable orbits *must* exist. He found an arbitrary stability criterion by trial and error. This criterion is that for any of the "permitted" orbits, *the angular momentum of the electron is an integral multiple of* $\mathbf{h}/2\pi$.

The dimensions of h can readily be shown to be the same as those of angular momentum, but apart from this Bohr had no justification for this assumption other than the pragmatic one—it works. In mathematical form,

$$\text{Angular momentum} = mv \times r = \frac{nh}{2\pi} \tag{43.24}$$

where $n = 1, 2, 3, \cdots$. Rearranging (43.20) gives

$$m^2v^2r^2 = \left(\frac{mv^2}{r}\right)mr^3 = \left(\frac{e^2}{4\pi\epsilon_0 r^2}\right)mr^3 = \frac{me^2r}{4\pi\epsilon_0}$$

and combining this with (43.24), we obtain

$$\frac{n^2h^2}{4\pi^2} = \frac{me^2r_n}{4\pi\epsilon_0}$$

or

$$r_n = \frac{\epsilon_0 n^2 h^2}{\pi m e^2} \tag{43.25}$$

The subscript n has been added to the radius to show that it corresponds to the particular integer n, which is called a **quantum number.** Substituting this value of r in (43.23), we find that the allowed energies of the hydrogen atom are

$$E_n = \frac{-me^4}{8\epsilon_0^2 h^2}\frac{1}{n^2} \tag{43.26}$$

By (43.19),

$$hf = E_{n_1} - E_{n_2}$$

where n_1 and n_2 are the quantum numbers of the two energy states. That is,

$$hc\sigma = \frac{me^4}{8\epsilon_0^2 h^2}\left(\frac{1}{n_2^2} - \frac{1}{n_1^2}\right)$$

$$\sigma = \frac{me^4}{8\epsilon_0^2 h^3 c}\left(\frac{1}{n_2^2} - \frac{1}{n_1^2}\right) \tag{43.27}$$

Equation (43.27) is identical with (43.18) if we take

$$\frac{me^4}{8\epsilon_0^2 h^3 c} = R, \qquad n_2 = 2, \qquad n_1 = n = 3, 4, 5, \cdots \tag{43.28}$$

Since Bohr chose his arbitrary assumptions in order to get agreement with the Balmer formula, the formal agreement between (43.18) and (43.27) is satisfactory but not too surprising. The real test of the Bohr theory is the agreement between his calculated expression for the Rydberg Constant and experiment. Before working this out, one slight modification is needed. The above derivation neglected the motion of the proton. A more detailed theory allows for this, with a resulting modification of (43.28) to

$$R = \frac{me^4}{8\epsilon_0^2 h^3 c}\frac{1}{1 + \dfrac{m}{M}} \tag{43.29}$$

where M is the mass of the proton. The currently accepted values* of the constants in (43.29) are

$$m = 9.1085 \times 10^{-31} \text{ kgm}$$
$$e = 1.6021 \times 10^{-19} \text{ coulomb}$$
$$c = 2.9979 \times 10^8 \text{ m sec}^{-1}$$
$$\epsilon_0 = \frac{1}{\mu_0 c^2} = \frac{10^7}{4\pi c^2}$$
$$= 8.8542 \times 10^{-12} \text{ farad m}^{-1}$$
$$h = 6.6252 \times 10^{-34} \text{ joule-sec}$$
$$\frac{M}{m} = 1836.1$$

Hence, from (43.29),

$$R = 1.0968 \times 10^7 \text{ m}^{-1} = 1.0968 \times 10^5 \text{ cm}^{-1}$$

in comparison with the experimental value of 109,678 cm⁻¹.

* DuMond and Cohen, Reviews of Modern Physics, 25, 706 (1953).

The normal state of a hydrogen atom will be the one of lowest energy, that is, with the quantum number $n = 1$. From (43.25) the radius of the electron orbit in this state is

$$r_1 = 0.529 \times 10^{-8} \text{ cm} \qquad (43.30)$$

which is in excellent agreement with kinetic-theory estimates for the radius of the atom. Another success of the Bohr theory is in the prediction of other series of lines besides the Balmer. If in (43.27) we put $n_2 = 1$ and $n_1 = 2, 3, 4, \cdots$, a series of frequencies or wavelengths can be calculated. The wavelengths range from 1216 A $(n_1 = 2)$ to 911 A $(n_1 = \infty)$ and are thus too short to be seen. Theodore Lyman (1874) searched for and found these lines, using an ultraviolet spectrograph. Other series, found in the infrared region, are the Paschen Series $(n_2 = 3)$, the Brackett Series $(n_2 = 4)$, and the Pfund Series $(n_2 = 5)$. All results

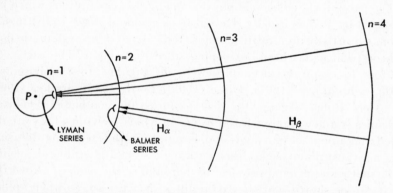

Fig. 43.08. Scale plan of Bohr orbits. The proton about which the electron revolves is marked P.

are in complete agreement with the Bohr theory. Figure 43.08 shows the arrangement of the Bohr orbits with radii in units of r_1 [equation (43.30)], the so-called *Bohr radius*. Some of the transitions giving rise to the first few members of the Lyman and Balmer Series are indicated.

43.09 QUANTUM MECHANICS

The striking success of the Bohr theory of the hydrogen atom proved beyond doubt that the quantum theory as developed by Planck, Einstein, and others must contain a great measure of truth. Its arbitrary assumptions, which were so contrary to classical mechanics and classical electrodynamics, continued to bother all physicists, however, and most hoped that some synthesis of the quantization ideas in terms of classical theories could be found. In fact, two of the most vigorous searchers for such a synthesis were Planck and Einstein. The latter to the day of his death (1955) refused to accept some of the implications of the theory he helped found.

The Bohr theory was extended rapidly by Sommerfeld (1868), Landé (1888), Goudsmit (1902), and Uhlenbeck (1900), to name only a few of the outstanding contributors. Many remarkable successes were achieved, but some outstanding failures as well. Briefly, all details of the hydrogen spectrum and of the spectra of single electron ions (He^+, Li^{++}, etc.) were accounted for quantitatively; details of the alkali metal spectra were accounted for qualitatively; but no explanation could be offered in any detail for the spectrum of neutral helium or of atoms with more than one valence electron.

The patchwork of classical physics and *ad hoc* assumptions which had developed by 1925 is usually referred to as *quantum theory* to distinguish it from **quantum mechanics,** a more radical and more systematic body of theory which has been developing since that date. The early contributors to quantum mechanics were de Broglie (1892), Heisenberg (1901), Schrodinger (1887), Dirac (1902), Born (1882), Jordan (1902), and Niels Bohr. Again, the list is far from complete. Quantum mechanics is a new approach to physics in which Newton's laws are discarded and a new set of axioms and assumptions selected. At first sight these new postulates seem either meaningless or implausible, depending on the mathematical and physical background of the reader. Nevertheless, it can be shown that they *do* result in Newton's laws when applied to the limit of macroscopic bodies, but give quite different results when applied to objects on the atomic or subatomic scale. The quantization rules follow logically from the postulates instead of being arbitrary additions as in quantum theory. Whenever a conflict has arisen between quantum theory and quantum mechanics, experiment has borne out the latter. It is fair to say that quantum mechanics has explained all phenomena concerned with the outer atom, in principle at least, and no contradictions of the results predicted by it are known. The theory is far from complete but must be characterized as extremely successful to date.

The mathematical formulation of quantum mechanics is beyond the scope of this book, but two aspects of the theory may be mentioned. In section 42.08 the duality of our present views as to the nature of light was discussed briefly. Not one, but two mental pictures are needed—sometimes we think of light as consisting of a stream of particles (quanta or photons), at other times we visualize light as a train of waves. Some indication of the reconciliation between these apparently contradictory views was also introduced. In 1924 de Broglie speculated that the duality might also apply to matter. He suggested that the motion of a material "particle", such as an electron, might be described in terms of a wave motion whose wavelength $\lambda = h/mv$, where h is Planck's Constant and mv is the momentum of the particle. Shortly after this suggestion was advanced, diffraction phenomena (the most characteristic result of wave motion) were observed for electron beams and have since been demonstrated with beams of neutrons and heavier particles. Do matter and radiation then consist of particles or waves? The answer of quantum mechanics to this question is "neither"—language was developed to describe the macroscopic world we see and is quite inadequate for the asking or answering of questions relating to the interior of atoms. Both matter and radiation will *appear* to behave as *either* wave motions *or* aggregations of particles, depending on our method of experiment. Their actual nature is probably such as our minds are incapable of visualizing. Quantum mechanics does enable us to make detailed and accurate predictions of what matter and radiation will do under chosen circumstances, and that is all we should ask of physics. Beyond that we are in the realm of philosophical speculation.

An apparently inescapable feature of quantum mechanics is the celebrated *Heisenberg Uncertainty Principle*, which may be stated briefly as follows: *It is impossible to know at the same time and with complete precision both the position and velocity of a particle.* This principle, if correct, destroys all possibility of the detailed cause-and-effect relation on which classical physics and indeed most scientific thinking have been based. The classical physicist said that if he had complete knowledge of the position and velocity of every particle in a closed system (or to be really ambitious, of the universe) he could, in principle, predict exactly the complete future history of that system. The qualification "in principle" merely admitted that the mathematical difficulties of the computations might be insuperable in the light of present knowledge of mathematics. This strict causality is impossible in the view of Heisenberg and most present-day physicists Considering a single particle, if its position at one time is known fairly accurately, its velocity cannot be known exactly, so that even if no forces act on it, we still cannot predict precisely where it will be at a future time. Most of the philosophical argument about modern physics has raged around this Heisenberg Principle. Much of the heat is misdirected because from a practical point of view causality is still very much with us. Quantum mechanics shows that we can deal only in probabilities—it is impossible to predict what one atom will do other than to say, for example, that there is a 34% chance of event A taking place and a 66% chance of event B. For this atom a certain effect does not necessarily follow a given cause. However, if we take a million atoms of the same kind (and it is extremely difficult to perform experiments with smaller samples than this), then it is a practical certainty that 340,000 events of type A will take place and 660,000 of type B. Experimentally, this kind of probability is indistinguishable from strict causality.

PROBLEMS

In the problems of this and the succeeding chapter the following values of the atomic constants are to be used.

$e = 1.602 \times 10^{-19}$ coulomb

$\dfrac{e}{m_0} = 1.759 \times 10^{11}$ coulombs/kgm

$m_0 = 9.108 \times 10^{-31}$ kgm

$N_0 = 6.025 \times 10^{23}$ molecules/gm. mole

$F = 96,520$ coulombs/gm. equivalent

$H^1 = 1.008$ amu $= 1.672 \times 10^{-27}$ kgm

$c = 2.998 \times 10^8$ meters/sec

$h = 6.625 \times 10^{-34}$ joule-sec

$\epsilon_0 = 8.854 \times 10^{-12}$ farad/meter

1. (a) What is the force on an electron situated between two parallel plates 10 cm apart at a potential difference of 450 v?
   (b) If the electron starts from rest at the cathode with what energy in electron volts will it strike the anode? What is this energy in joules?
   (c) With what velocity will it strike the anode?
   (d) What will be the transit time from cathode to anode?

2. The plate current in a vacuum tube is 10 microamp. How many electrons reach the plate per second?

3. The anode of a diode has an area of 1.5 cm² and a current of 60 ma passes through the tube when the potential difference is 150 v. What is the velocity of the electrons reaching the anode and what pressure do they exert on the anode?

4. A stream of electrons with velocity 2×10^7 m/sec enters at right angles to a uniform electric field of 10,000 v/m. Calculate the deflection of the beam in a distance of 10 cm measured along the original direction of flight.

5. An electron with a velocity of 3×10^7 m/sec moves perpendicularly to a uniform magnet field of flux density 2.0×10^{-3} weber/m². Calculate the force on the electron and the radius of the circle described by it.

6. Calculate the ratio m/m_0 for an electron moving with each of the following velocities, expressed as a decimal part of the speed of light: (a) 0.1, (b) 0.5, (c) 0.9, (d) 0.995.

7. An electron moving with a velocity of 3×10^9 cm/sec perpendicular to a magnetic field of intensity 1690 amp-turns/m describes an arc of radius 0.080 m. Calculate e/m for the electron.

8. A magnetic field of 5.0×10^{-4} weber/m² just balances a perpendicular electric field of 15,000 v/m in their effect on an electron beam passing through the two fields in a direction perpendicular to both of them. What is the speed of the electron?

9. A beam of electrons passes between two horizontal deflecting plates 1 cm long and 1 cm apart and then falls on a fluorescent screen 20 cm beyond the end of the plates. The plates are at a potential difference of 50 v, and this causes the spot on the screen to deflect 7.22 cm from its no-field position. Next, a magnetic field coincident with the electric field, but at right angles both to it and to the direction of travel of the electron beam, is turned on. It is found that a magnetic field of 1.00×10^{-3} weber/m² is required to return the spot to its zero position. Find the velocity and the e/m ratio of the electrons.

10. A small oil drop has a radius of 6×10^{-4} cm and a density of 0.851 gm/cm³. It falls freely through air at 76 cm Hg pressure and 23C temperature, under which conditions air has a viscosity of 1.832×10^{-5} mks units. Calculate the velocity with which the drop falls. Density of air at 76 cm and 23C 1.193 kgm/m³.

11. In an oil-drop experiment, the terminal velocity of the drop is measured, and its apparent mass (that is, mass reduced by buoyancy) is calculated as 3.03×10^{-15} kgm. It lies between two large horizontal condenser plates 5.00 mm apart. When the upper plate is made 232.0 v positive with respect to the lower plate, the drop is just balanced. What is the charge on the drop expressed as a multiple of the electronic charge?

12. (a) Find the energy required to release one electron from tungsten, whose work function is 4.52 v. (b) What is the minimum power which must be supplied to a tungsten filament to produce an emission current of 1 amp?

13. Mercury ultraviolet light of wavelength 2536 A is used to eject photoelectrons from a silver surface. A retarding potential of 0.11 v is sufficient to bring the ejected electrons to rest. What is the photoelectric work function of the silver?

14. Decay constants of three radioactive substances are measured as 4.63×10^{-7} sec⁻¹, 484 min⁻¹, and 6.14 yr⁻¹. Find the corresponding half-lives.

15. The thorium series starts from the decay of $_{90}Th^{232}$. Particles are emitted in the following order: α, β, β, α, α, α, α, β, β, α, yielding finally $_{82}Pb^{208}$. Construct a graph for the series similar to Figure 43.06, and write out the equations for the transformations.

16. Equation (43.29) can be generalized to cover any atom or ion with a single electron, by replacing the mass of the photon by the mass of the appropriate nucleus. Calculate the Rydberg Constant for helium.

17. Using the Bohr theory, calculate the radii of the first two circular orbits for H, He$^+$, and Li^{++}.   Note that equations (43.20) to (43.29) will need modification if the nuclear charge is $+Ze$ rather than $+e$.

18. If the helium spectrum is examined, a series called the Pickering is observed and attributed to transitions from the nth energy level of the He$^+$ atom to the fourth energy level ($n = 4$) of the atom.   Explain why alternate lines of the Pickering Series almost coincide with the Balmer Series in hydrogen.   Explain why they do not coincide exactly.

44

Nuclear Physics

44.01 ISOTOPES

In 1815 Prout (1785) offered the suggestion that hydrogen was the basic element and that other elements were groupings of integral numbers of hydrogen atoms. This hypothesis was plausible as long as the only atomic weights known with any accuracy were multiples of that of hydrogen, but as more accurate measurements of the atomic weights of more elements were made, numerous cases of nonintegral values were found. Examples of integral atomic weights are H 1.0, Be 9.0, C 12.0, N 14.0, O 16.0, F 19.0, etc.; and nonintegral ones are Li 6.9, B 10.8, Ne 20.2, Cl 35.5, etc. Inspection of the periodic table shows integral atomic weights are rare among the heavier elements. Prout's hypothesis was reluctantly set aside but not forgotten. The appeal to scientists of such a simplifying suggestion is very great.

The existence of isotopes among the radioactive elements was discussed in 43.04. The first evidence of isotopes occurring among stable elements was obtained in 1913 by J. J. Thomson, who devised an apparatus for measuring the charge-to-mass ratio (e/m) for positive ions. For positive ions of the gas neon, he found two slightly different values of e/m which gave masses of 20 and 22 when combined with Millikan's value of e. He could estimate roughly the proportion of the two masses as $9:1$, respectively, which gives an average atomic weight of

$$\frac{(20 \times 9 + 22 \times 1)}{10} = 20.2$$

in close agreement with the accurate atomic weight of 20.183.

Thomson's work was extended after the First World War by Aston (1877), Dempster (1886), Bainbridge (1904), and others, who designed instruments called **mass spectrographs** for the precise determination of the masses of ions.   Figure 44.01 illustrates the principle of Bainbridge's equipment.   Positive ions of the substance being studied are produced (often by vaporizing it and bombarding the vapor with electrons) and accelerated by an electric field.   The beam of ions is collimated by the slits S_1 and S_2 and passes between plates P_1 and P_2 where a second electric field ε exists.   A uniform magnetic field B acts perpendicular to the

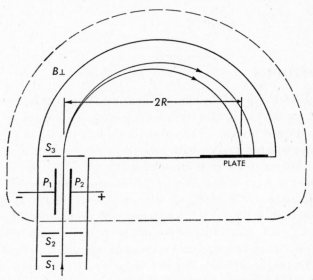

Fig. 44.01.   Mass spectrograph of Bainbridge type.

figure in the region enclosed by the dotted line, so that ions between P_1 and P_2 are subject to perpendicular magnetic and electric fields, and only those having a velocity v given by

$$BQv = Q\varepsilon$$

will pass through the slit S_3.   Note the similarity of this velocity selector to Thomson's method of measuring the velocity of cathode rays. Ions emerging from S_3 all have the same velocity and are bent in a semicircular path by the magnetic field, falling on the photographic plate. The radius of the path is given by equation (43.04) as $R = mv/(BQ)$ and thus depends on the mass of the ion.   Two separate paths are shown in the figure.   The charge Q may be a charge of $+e$, equal to the electronic charge, or a small integral multiple of this.

Work with mass spectrographs speedily showed that isotopes are the rule rather than the exception, and that nonintegral atomic weights of elements are due to mixtures of isotopes of integral (or near integral) values on the scale which makes the atomic weight of oxygen 16. The consistency of atomic weights, as measured in chemistry, is due to the fact that the proportions of the various stable isotopes in any sample of an element, regardless of the origin of the sample, is almost always the same. One of the exceptions to this is lead, because it is the end product of the various radioactive series which terminate as different isotopes of lead and thus influence the isotopic abundance of various samples of this element.

No isotope has an atomic weight differing from an integer by as much as 1%, but as the accuracy of mass spectroscopy improved, it became clear that almost all isotopes have masses differing slightly from integers. The nearest integer is called the mass number A, and Aston defined the **packing fraction (P.F.)** as a measure of the divergence from whole numbers.

$$\text{P.F.} = \frac{\text{isotopic weight} - A}{A} \times 10^4 \qquad (44.01)$$

Figure 44.02 shows a plot of packing fraction against A for stable isotopes. With the exception of He^4, C^{12}, and O^{16}, all the points lie on, or very close to, a smooth curve. A few points have been plotted to show the scatter actually obtained. Aston interpreted his results as follows. He assumed that protons and electrons are the only constituents of atoms. An atom of mass number A and atomic number Z would thus have a nucleus composed of A protons and A-Z electrons with Z extranuclear electrons. The formation of a nucleus from its components involves a loss of mass m which by the theory of relativity can be interpreted as a loss of energy $E = mc^2$. Aston thought that this loss of mass was due in some way to the tight "packing" of the protons and electrons in the nucleus—hence the name packing fraction. Whatever the cause of the loss, energy of amount E would be needed to separate the nucleus into its original components, so the larger E is, the more stable the nucleus. The energy E is called the **binding energy** of the nucleus, and E/A is the binding energy per proton in this model of the nucleus. The packing fraction is a qualitative indication of the binding energy per proton since the larger E/A is, the smaller the packing fraction is. Figure 44.02 shows that atoms in the middle region are exceptionally stable, with more possibility for instability among extremely light and extremely heavy atoms.   He⁴, C¹², and O¹⁶ are seen to be exceptionally stable compared to other atoms in the same range of masses.

The nuclear model just described was unsatisfactory from the theoretical point of view and was replaced as soon as the existence of the neutron was discovered.   The general ideas of binding energy and nuclear stability remain unchanged, however.

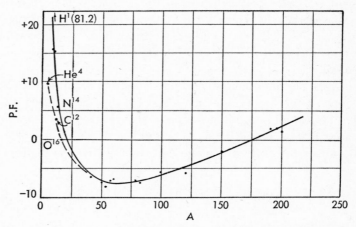

Fig. 44.02.   Aston's packing fraction curve for stable isotopes.

44.02 NEUTRONS AND NUCLEAR STRUCTURE

Rutherford and others had suggested as early as 1920 that a particle with a mass about the same as a proton but no electric charge probably existed, and the name **neutron** was given to this particle years before its existence was proved.

In 1930 and 1931 experiments on the bombardment of various light elements with alpha rays from polonium showed that a very penetrating radiation resulted, which was at first thought to be gamma radiation. Irene Curie (1896), the daughter of Marie Curie, and her husband F. Joliot (1900) showed that when this radiation struck a sheet of paraffin, high-speed protons were knocked out.   There is nothing wrong with the concept of a gamma-ray quantum colliding with a proton and transferring energy and momentum to it—similar collisions between X-ray quanta and electrons had been investigated and explained a decade earlier—but the arithmetic proved inconsistent, and the gamma-ray energies would have had to be abnormally high.   In 1932 Sir James Chadwick (1891) showed that the inconsistencies disappeared if the radiation consisted of neutrons. He proved that the reaction with beryllium is

$$_4Be^9 + {_2}He^4 \rightarrow {_6}C^{12} + {_0}n^1 \tag{44.02}$$

where n is the symbol for the neutron.

The neutron discovery immediately permitted revision of the model of the nucleus to one composed of protons and neutrons only, now referred to collectively as **nucleons.** In this model, which is widely accepted at present, A is the number of nucleons in a nucleus which thus consists of Z protons and A-Z neutrons. For example, the isotope of tin $_{50}Sn^{120}$ has a nucleus with 50 protons and 70 neutrons.

In chemical reactions it is customary to say that mass is conserved, and this is quite permissible because the mass equivalent of the energy released or absorbed in the reaction is far smaller than we can measure. In nuclear changes, however, mass is clearly not conserved, and we must apply the conservation law to the sum of mass plus energy. The success of this law in nuclear physics is abundant confirmation of the Einstein equation $E = mc^2$. In equations of radioactive decay, such as (43.11)–(43.13), the Q values (Q is the energy released in the reaction) are thus calculable if the masses are known. In calculations of this type it is vital to put all mass measurements on the same scale, normally the physical scale. Reference has been made much earlier in the book to the difference between the chemical and physical scales, but its importance warrants a brief repetition. Until 1929 all mass spectrographic results were referred to oxygen as a standard and the gram-atomic weight of oxygen was taken as 16 gm by definition, as is done in chemistry. This is known as the chemical scale. In 1929 it was shown that oxygen itself has three stable isotopes O^{16}, O^{17}, and O^{18}, with natural oxygen containing less than one-quarter of one per cent of the last two combined. This led to a new scale in which O^{16} is taken as the reference. This physical scale is fixed by defining one gram-atomic weight of pure O^{16} to have a mass of exactly 16 gm. On this scale the normal mixture of oxygen isotopes has a gram-atomic weight of 16.0044 gm. Hence masses on the physical scale are obtained from those on the chemical scale by multiplying the latter by 1.00027. This is a very small correction and indicates the accuracy with which atomic masses are known.

A very convenient scale of masses which is used in nuclear physics is defined by saying that one atom of O^{16} has a mass of exactly 16 **atomic mass units** (amu). Then 16 gm = 16 amu times Avogadro's number, N_0. The value of N_0 depends on which scale, physical or chemical, is used, but here we need the physical one in which $N_0 = 6.02472 \times 10^{23}$. Therefore

$$1 \text{ amu} = \frac{1}{N_0} \text{ gm} = 1.6598 \times 10^{-24} \text{ gm}$$

Since mass is equivalent to energy we can also express amu in joules or electron volts.

$$1 \text{ amu} = 1.660 \times 10^{-27} \text{ kgm} = 1.492 \times 10^{-10} \text{ joule} = 931.2 \text{ Mev}$$

The values accepted at present for the proton and neutron masses are

$$m_P = 1.007593 \text{ amu}; \qquad m_N = 1.008982 \text{ amu}$$

44.03 NUCLEAR PHYSICS

The first artificial transmutation of one element into another was achieved by Rutherford in 1919, and this date may conveniently be picked as the beginning of nuclear physics. Figure 44.03 shows a sketch

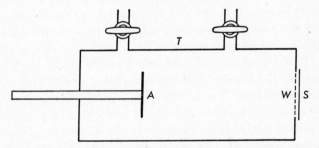

Fig. 44.03. Equipment used by Rutherford in demonstrating the disintegration of nitrogen by alpha particles.

of his equipment. A brass tube T had a small hole at one end, covered by a very thin silver foil to form a window W with a fluorescent screen S opposite the window. The tube T could be filled with any desired gas. A radioactive source A of α-particles was mounted on a sliding rod so that the distance AW could be altered as desired. Alpha-particles from a particular source have a definite range through air, at a given pressure. The source in this case was radium C' (Po^{214}), and the α-particles from radium C' travel 7 cm through air at normal temperature and pressure. The window W had a definite stopping power for α-particles, equivalent to a certain thickness of air, and when the total air equivalent between

A and S was less than 7 cm, α-particles struck the screen and could be counted, as each particle produced a tiny flash or scintillation on the screen. The scintillations were observed through a microscope.

As the air equivalent between A and S was increased to more than 7.0 cm the number of scintillations fell sharply, and the behavior at large separations of A and W depended critically on the gas in T. For air or nitrogen a few particles with ranges up to 40 cm were found, but when oxygen or carbon dioxide replaced the air none of these long-range particles were observed—apparently the nitrogen was the necessary component of air. For hydrogen a large number of long-range particles were found with ranges up to a maximum of 29 cm. These are readily explained as due to head-on collisions between α-particles and protons in the hydrogen, and the maximum range of 29 cm shows that the long-range particles obtained with nitrogen cannot be caused by hydrogen contamination. Rutherford concluded that they could only be protons resulting from the disintegration of nitrogen nuclei by α-particles according to the equation

$$_7N^{14} + {}_2He^4 \rightarrow {}_8O^{17} + {}_1H^1 \qquad (44.03)$$

He had no way of detecting the O^{17} product. Oxygen of this mass number was unknown at the time, but its existence as a stable isotope was demonstrated ten years later. Judging from the small number of long-range (over 30 cm) particles observed, he concluded that the α-particle must approach the nitrogen nucleus extremely closely for the reaction to take place. He estimated that one α-particle in every million passing through the nitrogen causes a disintegration.

Rutherford and Chadwick followed up this initial experiment, and within a few years proved that the product of the nitrogen reaction is indeed a proton, and that similar reactions occur with boron, fluorine, neon, sodium, and all the elements following in the periodic table up to and including potassium. In these reactions a proton is always produced, and this type of nuclear transformation is symbolized as (α, p). Equation (44.03) can be abbreviated to

$$N^{14}(\alpha, p)O^{17} \qquad (44.04)$$

The limit of potassium in these experiments was not believed to be caused by any unique property of the lighter elements but arose solely because the increasing charge Ze of the heavier nuclei made it more difficult for the α-particle to approach closely enough for a transmutation to occur. Accordingly, the thoughts of physicists turned toward devices for accelerating charged particles to greater speeds than those of the α-particles from radioactive substances.

44.04 ION ACCELERATORS

The first of these accelerators was produced by Cockcroft (1897) and Walton (1903) in 1932. Using ingenious electrical circuits, they were able to achieve electric potentials of several hundred thousand volts. Direct acceleration of protons resulted in energies of several hundred kev. Although this is considerably less than the several Mev of some α-particles, theoretical work in quantum mechanics by Gurney and Condon (1902) and by Gamow (1904) had indicated that protons of this energy should be effective, and this proved to be the case. Cockcroft and Walton obtained the reaction

$$_3\text{Li}^7 + {}_1\text{H}^1 \rightarrow 2 \ {}_2\text{He}^4 \tag{44.05}$$

or, in the form of (44.04)

$$\text{Li}^7(p, 2\alpha) \tag{44.06}$$

Another type of high-voltage accelerator is the van de Graaf Generator described in section 40.05, which can give potentials of up to 6 million volts. The limit is due to insulation difficulties, and it seems improbable that much higher voltages will be reached.

An accelerator of a different type is the **cyclotron** invented by Ernest Lawrence (1901). The principle of this instrument is illustrated in Figure 44.04. It consists of two hollow electrodes looking like a pillbox cut along a diameter. These **dees,** as they are called, are placed in a vacuum tank between the poles of an electromagnet which produces a uniform field. Positive ions are released from a source S at the center. Suppose D_1 is positive and D_2 is negative when a particular ion is released. The ion will be attracted to D_2

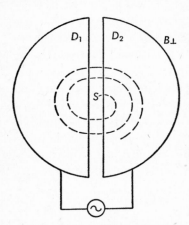

Fig. 44.04. Electrode system of a cyclotron.

and will enter the hollow electrode where there is no electric field. The magnetic field acting on the ion will cause it to move in a circular path of radius

$$R = \frac{mv}{BQ} \tag{44.07}$$

The time for the ion to describe a semicircle is

$$\frac{T}{2} = \frac{\pi R}{v} = \frac{\pi m}{BQ} \tag{44.08}$$

which is independent of both R and v. If the voltage on the dees is supplied by an a-c generator, it is possible to choose its frequency so that when the ion emerges from D_2 the potential on D_1 and D_2 is just reversed. Hence the ion is accelerated again and enters D_1. The radius of the ion's path in D_1 will be larger because of its increased kinetic energy, but by (44.07) the time to traverse a semicircle is unchanged. Hence the ion can continue on a kind of spiral path, gaining kinetic energy at each traversal of the gap between the dees, but always remaining in phase with the alternating voltage. If the peak voltage on the dees is, say, 5000 v, and a proton makes 1000 circuits before it reaches the limiting radius of the dees, it gains 5 kev of kinetic energy at each traversal of the gap and thus attains a final energy of

$$5 \text{ kev} \times 2 \times 1000 = 10 \text{ Mev}$$

This ingenious instrument thus gives the accelerating effect of 10 million volts for a maximum applied voltage of only 5000 v.

The resonant angular frequency can be calculated from (44.08) since the period of revolution T is

$$T = \frac{2\pi m}{BQ}$$

and

$$\omega = 2\pi f = \frac{2\pi}{T} = \frac{BQ}{m} \tag{44.09}$$

The dependence of energy on the radius can be found from (44.07).

$$mv = BQR$$
$$m^2 v^2 = B^2 Q^2 R^2$$
$$\text{K.E.} = \tfrac{1}{2}mv^2 = \frac{1}{2m}(m^2 v^2) = \frac{B^2 Q^2 R^2}{2m} \tag{44.10}$$

For a given type of ion, the energy attainable in a cyclotron thus increases as the square of the maximum useful radius. This radius is limited by the size of the pole pieces of the magnet supplying the magnetic field, and for this reason the custom has arisen of "rating" a cyclotron by the diameter of the pole pieces. The first one, built by Lawrence (1901) and

M. S. Livingston (1905) in 1931, was an 11-in. cyclotron giving 1.22 Mev protons. The largest, finished in 1946 at Lawrence's laboratory in Berkeley, Calif., is a 184-in. cyclotron. It has been used to accelerate protons, α-particles, and deuterons (the nuclei of the "heavy" hydrogen isotope H^2) to energies up to 350 Mev, 400 Mev, and 200 Mev, respectively.

The resonant frequency of a cyclotron is a constant, by (44.09), provided the mass of the ions does not change. The increase of mass with velocity was discussed earlier, and it was pointed out that the effect was negligible unless a velocity of about 10% of the velocity of light was involved. A proton with a velocity of $0.1c$ (c is the velocity of light) has a kinetic energy of about 47 Mev. It was at first thought that this relativistic effect would set an upper limit for energies attainable with cyclotrons, but a way out of the difficulty was found by frequency-modulating the output of the generator connected to the dees. This type of frequency-modulated, or synchro-, cyclotron starts with a frequency, given by (44.09) with the rest mass of the ion substituted, and then lowers the frequency gradually but rapidly as the ion increases in velocity and mass. This cycle is repeated many hundreds of times a second and results in pulses of ions, whose energy can still be calculated from (44.10).

The limit on cyclotron size came from the cost factor. The output energy may go up with the square of the pole-piece diameter, but the cost rises with at least the third power and a 100-in. cyclotron costs two or three million dollars to build. More economical types of ion accelerators have been designed and built for reaching very high energies. Two are in operation—the **cosmotron** at Brookhaven, N.Y., and the **bevatron** at Berkeley. The former has reached energies of over three *billion* electron volts (Bev) and the latter energies of about 7 Bev. Both machines are of the type known as proton **synchrotrons** and at least two larger ones are under construction, one in Switzerland and one in the U.S.A. These larger machines are designed to accelerate protons to energies of between 25 and 30 Bev. High-energy electron accelerators include **betatrons** and electron synchrotrons. The largest of the latter, to be built jointly by Harvard and M.I.T., will reach an energy of 6 Bev.

44.05 DETECTION EQUIPMENT

From the preceding discussion it will be seen that much of the experimental work of nuclear physics is concerned with producing, or separating from atoms, the various subatomic particles such as protons, neutrons, and α-particles. Experimental techniques are dependent on the methods used for detecting these particles, and a brief discussion of this subject is in order. Remember that no one has ever seen (or probably ever *will* see) an atom, to say nothing of a subatomic fragment. All detection methods are thus indirect, some of them depending on extremely complex sequences of events. Almost all depend on the ability of rapidly moving charged particles to ionize atoms, that is, to knock off one or more electrons from an atom, leaving electrons and positive ions.

The scintillation method used by Rutherford and his coworkers was referred to above. It was tedious and difficult. The observer had to get his eyes fully dark-adapted by sitting in pitch darkness for half an hour before starting to observe. During the twenties it was superseded by electrical methods, in particular the **Geiger counter.** This is a gas-filled tube with such a high electric field between its electrodes that it is rather unstable. If a fast charged particle enters it and produces a number of ions, the high field causes these ions to move so rapidly that they in turn ionize more atoms and rapidly produce an avalanche of charged particles which causes a measurable pulse of current. This multiplication of ions is called **ionization by collision** and is a standard feature of gas-filled tubes. In a properly designed Geiger counter the avalanche shuts itself off, and the tube is ready to "count" another incoming particle. The speed of the counter is quite remarkable—as many as 25,000 particles per minute can easily be recorded. The pulses from the counter are actually counted by electronic circuits. Counters of this type can be used to count electrons, protons, α-particles, and even γ-ray photons.

The Geiger counter, in turn, is being superseded by scintillation counters, which work essentially on the same principle as Rutherford used. Now, however, the particle strikes a crystal instead of a fluorescent screen, and the resulting flash of light is "observed" by a photoelectric cell, the output of which is amplified many times, and the results are counted electrically. The main advantages are a tenfold or better increase in speed of counting (over Geiger tubes) and a simpler method of measuring the energy of the incident particle.

Counting methods are essentially statistical. An early invention of C. T. R. Wilson (1869) permits one to see where an individual proton (say) has been, which is the next best thing to actually seeing it. This device is called a **cloud chamber** and depends on the fact that supersaturated water vapor tends to form droplets of water on any convenient particles, such as specks of dust. Ions, because of their electrical charge, serve this purpose particularly well, and if our proton flies through the chamber (full of the supersaturated vapor), water droplets form on the string of ions left by the proton and mark its trail. P. M. S. Blackett (1897) in 1925 obtained a photograph in this way of a nitrogen nucleus struck by an α-particle, with the resultant emission of a proton, confirming Rutherford's interpretation of his 1919 experiment. The tracks of the α-particle, proton, and resulting O^{17} nucleus can all be seen and

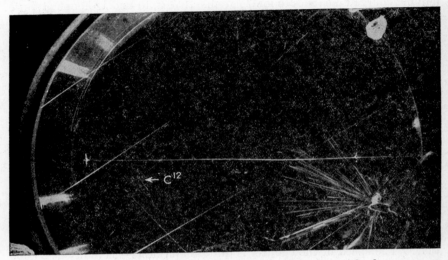

Fig. 44.05. Disintegration of a C^{12} nucleus into three particles by a neutron impact. The large number of tracks radiating from a point near the edge of the chamber are caused by α-particles (of known energy) from a polonium source. The length of these tracks serves as a calibration of the conditions in the chamber and permits a measurement of the energy of the fragments from the C^{12} nucleus. (Photograph courtesy of Dr. F. R. Terroux.)

distinguished from each other. Figure 44.05 shows a recent photograph by F. R. Terroux (1902) and D. I. Wanklyn in which a carbon nucleus is struck by a fast neutron (about 20 Mev) and shattered into three α-particles. The neutron cannot be seen because it has no charge and causes no ionization, but the tracks of the three α-particles radiating from a point can be seen.

The discovery of radiations from radioactive substances was made using photographic plates, and photographic techniques are now widely used to investigate individual events in a manner quite similar to the cloud-chamber method. A charged particle moving through the emulsion of the plate produces ions which make individual grains of the emul-

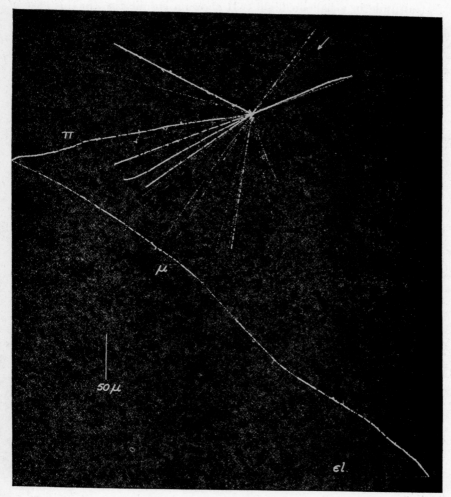

Fig. 44.06. Disintegration of a heavy nucleus by a cosmic-ray proton. Production of a π-meson and its subsequent decay into a μ-meson and then into an electron can be seen. (Photograph supplied by Dr. E. Pickup.)

sion developable just as exposure to light does. When the plate is developed, the track of the particle is visible. Ranges are very short in the high-density emulsion, and the plates are examined under a microscope. Frequently, tracings are made of the greatly enlarged image. Figure 44.06 is a tracing of a plate obtained by J. Y. Mei and E. Pickup in a study of cosmic rays, which are a mysterious high-energy radiation falling on the earth from space. The plate was exposed at about 80,000 feet altitude in a balloon flight. It shows a cosmic ray (in this case a very energetic proton) striking an Ag or Br nucleus in the emulsion. The path of the proton is marked with an arrow. The struck nucleus is shattered into many fragments, including a π-meson which decays radioactively into a μ-meson which in turn decays into an electron (the very faint track at the bottom). Actual distances in the emulsion are indicated by the scale line, which is 50 microns long. Mesons are particles with masses between those of the proton and the electron and appear to be intimately concerned with the structure of nuclei, although the details are still obscure.

44.06 NUCLEAR REACTIONS

The only types of nuclear reactions known up to 1932 were the radioactive emission ones (in which α- and β-particles and γ-rays or photons are given off spontaneously) and the $(α, p)$ type. Since that time the ever-increasing particle energies available through the use of accelerators have resulted in the discovery of almost every conceivable type of nuclear reaction, subject to the following limitations:

(1) In all reactions in which nucleons and heavier particles are emitted the total of mass plus energy is conserved.

(2) In reactions in which electrons or **positrons** (particles with the mass of an electron and a charge of $+e$) are emitted, energy does *not* appear to be conserved. This has caused much concern to physicists but has not led to the abandonment of the laws of conservation of mass and energy. It is believed that in these reactions an additional particle called a **neutrino** is emitted and carries off enough energy to balance accounts. The properties postulated for this particle (little or no mass and no charge) are such as to make the neutrino extremely difficult to detect. Over the years indirect evidence for its existence gradually accumulated, and in June 1956, the first announcement of direct detection of this particle was made by the United States Atomic Energy Commission.

(3) The number of nucleons (that is, total number of protons and neutrons) appears to be conserved. This is an empirical result.

(4) In most reactions the Z of the nucleus affected is changed by at most two units and the A by at most three or four. This limitation disappears at high energies of bombarding particles (greater than 200 Mev, say) and does not apply to fission reactions to be discussed later.

Artificial Radioactivity. Soon after the discovery of the neutron, Curie and Joliot found that light elements could become radioactive artificially in certain nuclear reactions. Their first results came from the bombardment of aluminum with α-particles when they found that both neutrons and positrons were emitted. The neutrons ceased as soon as the α-particle source was removed, but the emission of positrons continued, decaying away with a half-life of 2.5 min. These results were consistent with the equations

$$_{13}\text{Al}^{27} + {}_2\text{He}^4 \rightarrow {}_{15}\text{P}^{30} + {}_0n^1$$
$$_{15}\text{P}^{30} \rightarrow {}_{14}\text{Si}^{30} + {}_1e^0$$

and various chemical experiments confirmed that the positron activity was associated with a product behaving chemically like phosphorus. Naturally occurring phosphorus has the single isotope P^{31}, that is, P^{30} does not ordinarily exist. Its behavior is of exactly the same type as any of the β-emitting radioactive isotopes discussed earlier. Si^{30} is stable.

Literally hundreds of these radioactive isotopes have now been created in nuclear physics laboratories and have found many industrial and scientific applications. Most of them emit either electrons or positrons, and half-lives of several hundred years down to fractions of a second have been observed. Neutrons have proved very effective bombarding particles in the production of new isotopes because the absence of charge permits the neutron to approach a nucleus quite readily. Enrico Fermi (1901) and a group at Rome showed in 1935 that very slow neutrons with energies of the order of $\frac{1}{40}$ ev are particularly effective. These are called thermal neutrons because their kinetic energies are about the same as those of gas molecules at room temperature.

The type of nuclear reaction which takes place depends markedly on the energy of the bombarding particle. One example will be given to show the complexity which results. E. L. Kelly (1915) bombarded bismuth with protons whose energy was raised gradually from about 1 Mev to 40 Mev. He found the following reactions.

$$\text{Bi}^{209}(p, \gamma)\text{Po}^{210} \qquad (2\text{--}20 \text{ Mev})$$
$$\text{Bi}^{209}(p, n)\text{Po}^{209} \qquad (7\text{--}14 \text{ Mev})$$
$$\text{Bi}^{209}(p, 2n)\text{Po}^{208} \qquad (10\text{--}30 \text{ Mev})$$
$$\text{Bi}^{209}(p, 3n)\text{Po}^{207} \qquad (18 \rightarrow \text{ Mev})$$
$$\text{Bi}^{209}(p, 4n)\text{Po}^{206} \qquad (27 \rightarrow \text{ Mev})$$

The range of proton energies in which each reaction occurs is shown after the equation. It will be noted that there is considerable overlapping, that is, protons of a given energy may produce two or three different reactions on the same target.

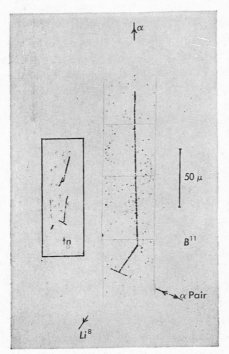

Another example illustrates the use of both nuclear plate and cloud-chamber techniques. Figure 44.07 shows an enlargement of a plate obtained by W. A. Morrison and Pickup in which a neutron strikes a B^{11} nucleus, ejecting an α-particle. The remaining Li^8 is radioactive, with a half-life of 0.88 sec, and gives off an electron to form Be^8, which is unstable and breaks up immediately (within 10^{-20} sec) into two α-particles. The reaction equations are

$$_5B^{11} + _0n^1 \rightarrow _3Li^8 + _2He^4$$
$$_3Li^8 \rightarrow _4Be^8 + _{-1}\beta^0$$
$$_4Be^8 \rightarrow 2 \ _2He^4$$

Fig. 44.07. Disintegration of B^{11} by a neutron impact. (Photograph supplied by Dr. F. R. Terroux.)

The electron track does not show up in Figure 44.07, but the Li^8 reaction is a known one and a beautiful cloud-chamber photograph of it was obtained by W. A. Fowler (1911), C. C. Lauritsen (1892), and T. Lauritsen (1915). This is shown in Figure 44.08, where the tracks of the two α-particles and the electron can be seen. The electron track is a circle because of a transverse magnetic field.

Before leaving this subject a statement of the present position of nuclear physics is in order. A tremendous amount of experimental data has accumulated, particularly since 1935. Nuclei are known to have an energy-level structure similar to that of the external electron structure of atoms, and in some cases the empirical values of the levels are well established. The basic problem remains unsolved—what holds nuclei together? They are almost certainly composed of aggregations of neutrons and protons, but the Coulomb repulsion between the protons should blow this aggregation apart. Since most nuclei are quite stable, it is clear that some new kind of attractive force must exist at close range between nucleons. No satisfactory mathematical description of this force is known, and it appears unlikely at present that it will be found until we understand more about the nature of the elementary particles. At least fifteen types of particles (neutrons, protons, mesons, and many others not mentioned in this text) are observed in high-energy nuclear reactions. It is not known which of these are "elementary", that is, which ones are the basic building-blocks of the universe; it is not even

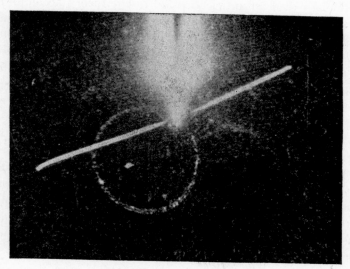

Fig. 44.08. Radioactive decay of Li⁸. The Li⁸ was produced in a cyclotron and placed in the cloud chamber on the end of a probe (which appears as a heavy, white, vertical line). (Photograph supplied by Dr. T. Lauritsen.)

clearly understood what are the significant properties of an elementary particle. Much of the effort of present-day nuclear physics is directed toward this problem, and no one can say when the answers will be found.

The reason for the drive to ever higher energies in nuclear work is clearer when we consider the remarkable process of **pair production,** discovered in 1933 by Blackett and Occhialini. They showed that a γ-ray photon, of energy 1.02 Mev or greater, occasionally disappears, being replaced by an electron-positron pair. This is a direct conversion of energy into matter. The mass of an electron or positron is 5.48×10^{-4} amu, and since 1 amu = 931 Mev, the energy equivalent of the rest mass is 0.51 Mev. This explains the lower limit on the γ-ray energy for pair formation. Two particles of equal and opposite charges must be produced to conserve electric charge and so the γ-ray must have an energy at least as great as 2×0.51 Mev. Any excess energy above this appears as kinetic energy of the particles. The reverse process in which electrons and positrons combine to yield γ-ray photons, direct conversion of mass into energy, is called **annihilation** and is also well known.

Most probably, atoms are composed of protons, neutrons, and electrons. The positron has the mass of an electron but opposite charge, and could be called an antielectron. Present theory accounts for the existence of this particle and indicates that antiprotons and antineutrons may exist also. The **antiproton** would have the mass of a proton and a charge of $-e$. The **antineutron** can have no charge but may be opposite to the neutron in some more abstruse manner, such as in magnetic properties. To produce a nucleon-antinucleon pair from a γ-ray would require an energy of almost 2 Bev since the rest mass energy of a nucleon is about 940 Mev. Such energies have not been available until recently and the discoveries (both at the University of California) of the antiproton and the antineutron were made in 1955 and 1956 respectively. Annihilation of pairs for both types of nucleons has been observed, and it seems clear that the three anti-particles now known cannot exist for more than a few microseconds in ordinary matter, so that they play no role in its structure. Nevertheless, to investigate the natures of "elementary" particles and light nuclei, energies are needed comparable to their rest mass energies, that is, up to several Bev.

44.07 FISSION, FUSION, AND NUCLEAR ENERGY

In 1939 a number of German scientists discovered that uranium when bombarded with slow neutrons breaks up into two heavy fragments with the release of from two to three fast neutrons and a large amount of energy. It was soon shown that only U^{235}, which comprises 0.7% of natural uranium, has this property and that the energy release is about 200 Mev for each U^{235} nucleus breaking up. Apparently the U^{235} absorbs the slow neutron, forming a U^{236} nucleus. From Figure 44.02 we see that all the very heavy nuclei in this region are likely to be unstable, but U^{236} is exceptionally so and breaks up almost instantly. This process is called **fission,** and the two heavy particles which result are known as **fission fragments.** Their mass numbers are around 94 and 140, where the packing is much greater than at $A = 235$. Hence the products of fission have a smaller mass than the original atom, the difference being converted into energy.

As early as 1903 Rutherford had speculated on the possibility of obtaining large amounts of energy from radioactive substances, and the release of atomic or nuclear energy remained a goal throughout the next forty years.   Uranium fission was the first practical method discovered. The key lies in the fact that one neutron falling on U^{235} produces on the average 2.5 neutrons.   It was thought that if some of these could be slowed down sufficiently to cause further fissions, the process might become self-propagating.   It was known that neutrons could be slowed down by collision with light nuclei, and if some light substance could be found which did not absorb neutrons appreciably, a self-sustaining or **chain reaction** was possible.   Figure 44.09 shows a schematic picture of such a reaction. The blocks marked M are made of the material for slowing down the neutrons. It is known technically as a **moderator**; F stands for the fission fragments and n, n are the neutrons.   The most

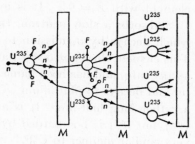

Fig. 44.09.   Mechanism of a chain reaction.

successful moderators are graphite and heavy water, that is, water in which the hydrogen is the heavy isotope H^2.

When the Second World War started in Europe in 1939 scientists were quick to recognize the possibility of a weapon in nuclear fission. American, British, and Canadian scientists worked throughout the war under extreme secrecy, and owing to wartime pressure, enormous development of the technology for the release of nuclear energy occurred in a relatively short time.   A group under Fermi constructed the first successful **nuclear reactor** in Chicago and achieved a chain reaction on December 2, 1942.   This reactor was built by piling layers of graphite blocks interspersed with lumps of uranium, and since that time reactors have popularly been called **piles**.   In a pile the release of energy is controlled by means of cadmium or boron rods which absorb neutrons strongly and which can be adjusted to maintain a certain power level automatically.   The necessity of such a control system hardly needs stressing.

Uranium consists primarily of two isotopes, U^{238} and U^{235}.   Methods have been developed for separating the isotopes so that almost pure U^{235} can be produced.   A large enough piece of U^{235} can act as its own moderator.   There is a minimum or critical size for a self-sustaining chain reaction in pure U^{235}, and if several smaller pieces are brought together to form a piece larger than the critical size, the reaction starts spontaneously (owing to the presence of a few free neutrons everywhere) and proceeds rapidly. A device of this nature is called an atomic bomb and it is well known that two atomic bombs were dropped on the Japanese cities of Hiroshima and Nagasaki in 1945, ending the Second World War. Each of these bombs had an explosive force equivalent to that of 20,000 tons of T.N.T., one of the most powerful of the chemical explosives. U^{235} is not the only isotope having fission properties, and the bomb dropped on Nagasaki was made from plutonium, an artificially produced element with $Z = 94$. It is made from U^{238} in a nuclear reactor. If U^{238} absorbs a slow neutron, the resulting U^{239} is a radioactive isotope which decays by β-emission to form an element of atomic number 93. This element does not occur naturally on the earth (at the present time at any rate) and has been named neptunium. It is a radioactive β-emitter and decays to plutonium. This element is also radioactive but with a rather long half-life. It is an α-emitter and thus decays in time to U^{235}, but if it is bombarded by slow neutrons, it undergoes fission in a very similar manner to U^{235}.

The terrible power of atomic weapons is so great that another war fought between nations possessing and using them would probably end our civilization. While desperate efforts continue to avert such a conflict, developments for the peaceful use of nuclear energy go on. The relation between living standards and energy sources was discussed in Chapter 5. Here is a great new source of energy which will certainly work changes in our manner of living at least as great as the introduction of the internal-combustion engine. Many technical problems remain to be solved, and these problems are intimately connected with the economic aspects of nuclear power. Reactors are costly to build, and the primary fuel, uranium, is scarce and expensive. At present, nuclear power cannot compete with hydroelectric power, but hydroelectric resources are limited and coal-burning generating plants are only slightly less costly than nuclear ones. It seems probable that general use of nuclear-power plants will develop within the next twenty years.

The amount of energy per uranium fission is about 200 Mev or 3.2×10^{-11} joule. Let us calculate the energy available from the fission of all the U^{235} atoms in one pound of uranium.

$$1 \text{ lb} \doteq 450 \text{ gm}$$

The atomic weight of uranium is about 238, so that

$$1 \text{ lb} = \tfrac{450}{238} = 1.9 \text{ moles}$$

and thus contains $1.9 \, N_0$ atoms, which gives

$$1 \text{ lb} = 1.9 \times 6.0 \times 10^{23} = 11.4 \times 10^{23} \text{ atoms}$$

of which $0.72\% = 8.2 \times 10^{21}$ atoms are U^{235}. The energy available is thus

$$3.2 \times 10^{-11} \times 8.2 \times 10^{21} = 2.6 \times 10^{11} \text{ joules}$$

which is approximately equal to the energy obtained from burning 10 tons of coal. Recent developments with so-called breeder reactors indicate that *all* the uranium can be used as fuel, the U^{235} directly and the U^{238} by first converting it to plutonium.

Referring again to Figure 44.02 we see that the slope of the curve for light elements is even steeper than for the very heavy elements. If a method could be found for converting hydrogen to helium, for example, the energy release per particle would be even greater than in fission. This process consists of building a heavier element out of lighter constituents and is called **fusion.** It is believed to be the source of the sun's energy. Two different sequences of reactions have been suggested as taking place in the sun.

$$
\begin{array}{ll}
{}_6C^{12} + {}_1H^1 \rightarrow {}_7N^{13} + \text{energy} & (44.11) \\
{}_7N^{13} \rightarrow {}_6C^{13} \quad\quad\quad + {}_1e^0 & \\
{}_6C^{13} + {}_1H^1 \rightarrow {}_7N^{14} + \text{energy} & \\
{}_7N^{14} + {}_1H^1 \rightarrow {}_8O^{15} + \text{energy} & \\
{}_8O^{15} \rightarrow {}_7N^{15} \quad\quad\quad + {}_1e^0 & \\
{}_7N^{15} + {}_1H^1 \rightarrow {}_6C^{12} + {}_2He^4 & (44.12)
\end{array}
$$

Adding all these reactions, we get

$$4 \, {}_1H^1 \rightarrow {}_2He^4 + 2 \, {}_1e^0 + \text{energy} \qquad (44.13)$$

This set of reactions is called the *carbon cycle*, and it will be noted that the carbon used in (44.11) is produced again in (44.12) so that it is not used up but acts in a manner similar to a chemical catalyst. The total energy released is 27 Mev.

An alternative sequence is

$$
\begin{array}{l}
2 \, {}_1H^1 + 2 \, {}_1H^1 \rightarrow 2 \, {}_1H^2 + 2 \, {}_1e^0 \\
2 \, {}_1H^2 + 2 \, {}_1H^1 \rightarrow 2 \, {}_2He^3 + \text{energy} \\
{}_2He^3 + {}_2He^3 \rightarrow {}_2He^4 + 2 \, {}_1H^1
\end{array}
$$

Adding these three reactions together gives (44.13) again. Our present knowledge of nuclear physics is sufficient to enable us to calculate the probability of these reactions taking place, and it is found that they are quite likely to occur at temperatures of several million degrees Centigrade, which almost certainly exist in the interior of stars. It is believed that both sequences described take place in the sun. The quantity of hydrogen in the sun is sufficient for it to continue to release energy at its present rate for another thirty billion years.

The temperature generated in an atomic bomb is estimated to be about ten million degrees centigrade and is thus sufficient for fusion reactions to occur. Thermonuclear weapons using atomic bombs as triggers have been developed. Many different reactions are possible, and the details of the method used are highly secret. A controlled fusion process to serve as a power source is the subject of much investigation at present. At the International Conference on the Peaceful Uses of Atomic Energy held at Geneva in 1955 it was confidently forecast that large-scale power from fusion would be available in fifty years time, or even sooner.

PROBLEMS

Masses of Light Atoms in amu

n^1 = 1.00898	**Li^6** = 6.01702	**B^{11}** = 11.01279	**N^{14}** = 14.00752
H^1 = 1.00814	**Li^7** = 7.01822	C^{11} = 11.01492	**N^{15}** = 15.00486
H^2 = 2.01473	Be^8 = 8.00785	**C^{12}** = 12.00380	**O^{16}** = 16.00000
H^3 = 3.01700	**Be^9** = 9.01504	**C^{13}** = 13.00747	**O^{17}** = 17.00453
He^3 = 3.01700	Be^{10} = 10.01671	C^{14} = 14.00768	**O^{18}** = 18.00487
He^4 = 4.00387	**B^{10}** = 10.01611	N^{13} = 13.00986	

Stable isotopes are shown in boldface type.
See values of atomic constants preceding problems in previous chapter.

1. The atomic weight of chlorine is 35.46, and there are two stable isotopes, Cl^{35} and Cl^{37}. What percentage of normal chlorine consists of the heavier isotope?

2. In the apparatus of Figure 44.01, singly ionized magnesium ions emerge from S_2. A potential difference of 3000 v is applied between the plates P_1, P_2, which are 5.000 mm apart. The magnetic field is 1.000 weber/m^2. Lines are found on the photographic plate at distances 29.84, 31.08, and 32.34 cm from S_3. Find the masses of the isotopes of magnesium in amu.

3. What is the rest mass of an electron in Mev? What is the ratio m/m_0 for an electron with a total energy of 1 Mev, 2 Mev, 50 Mev, 100 Mev?

4. Calculate the binding energy of the deuteron, the α-particle, and the O^{16} nucleus.

5. Be^8 is an inherently unstable nucleus. Explain why this is so. If it breaks up into two α-particles, what will be the kinetic energy of each of them?

6. A neutron strikes a nitrogen nucleus and projects it straight forward. The kinetic energy of the nitrogen nucleus (N^{14}), as judged from its range, is 2.5 Mev. Using the laws of conservation of energy and momentum, calculate the initial kinetic energy of the neutron.

7. The range in air of α-particles is related to their initial kinetic energy by the equation

$$\text{K.E.}(\alpha) = 2.12R^{\frac{2}{3}}$$

where kinetic energy is in Mev and R is the range in cm of air. This equation is fairly accurate for energies between about 4 and 8 Mev. For a proton the corresponding relation is

$$\text{K.E.}(p) = 0.534R^{\frac{2}{3}}$$

Find (a) The energy of the α-particles from radium C' used by Rutherford in the first disintegration experiment; (b) The maximum range of knock-on protons from these α-particles (knock-on protons are those resulting from elastic collisions between fast particles and hydrogen nuclei); (c) The energy of the 40-cm range protons observed from nitrogen.

8. The equation for the Rutherford experiment of 1919 was

$$_7N^{14} + {}_2He^4 \rightarrow {}_8O^{17} + {}_1H^1 + Q$$

The α-particles used had an energy of 8.0 Mev. Find Q. This is called an *endothermic* reaction, that is, energy must be supplied to make it "go". What minimum α-particle energy is needed?

9. In equation (44.05), if the proton energy was 400 kev, calculate the kinetic energy of the α-particles produced.

10. In a particular cyclotron the capacity of the dees is such that the maximum frequency of the generator is 25.0 megacycles. What magnetic field is required for resonance if the cyclotron is to accelerate protons? If the radius of the final orbit is 18 in., what is the maximum energy of the protons?

11. If in the cyclotron of the previous problem the relativistic corrections could be neglected, what radius of orbit would be needed to give a proton energy of 100 Mev?

12. The McGill cyclotron is frequency modulated to allow for the variation of mass, but otherwise the figures given in problems 10 and 11 describe it fairly well. The maximum dee voltage is about 6,000. What is the minimum number of turns for a proton to reach an energy of 100 Mev? Approximately how far does the proton travel during this process?

13. The McGill cyclotron accelerates protons to a kinetic energy of 100 Mev.
    (a) What is the rest mass of a proton in Mev? (b) What is the increase in
    mass of a proton of 100-Mev kinetic energy? (c) What is the velocity of such
    a proton?

14. In equation (44.13), what is the energy release in Mev per nucleus of helium
    produced? The positrons can be neglected in this calculation since they
    will encounter electrons and be "annihilated", that is, both positron and
    electron will disappear and their masses will be converted to energy. What
    energy in joules is released by converting 1 kg of hydrogen to helium?

APPENDIX A.1   Atomic Weights on the Physical Scale (1953)

Element	Symbol	Atomic Number	Atomic Weight*
Actinium	Ac**	89	227.11
Aluminum	Al	13	26.99
Americium	Am†	95	241 (Ρ)
Antimony	Sb	51	121.79
Argon	A	18	39.955
Arsenic	As	33	74.93
Astatine	At†	85	211 (Ρ)
Barium	Ba	56	137.40
Berkelium	Bk†	97	245 (Ρ)
Beryllium	Be	4	9.015
Bismuth	Bi	83	209.06
Boron	B	5	10.82
Bromine	Br	35	79.937
Cadmium	Cd	48	112.44
Calcium	Ca	20	40.09
Californium	Cf†	98	246 (Ρ)
Carbon	C	6	12.014
Cerium	Ce	58	140.17
Cesium	Cs	55	132.95
Chlorine	Cl	17	35.467
Chromium	Cr	24	52.02
Cobalt	Co	27	58.95
Copper	Cu	29	63.56
Curium	Cm†	96	242 (Ρ)
Dysprosium	Dy	66	162.50
Erbium	Er	68	167.2
Europium	Eu	63	152.0
Fluorine	F	9	19.004
Francium	Fa†	87	223 (Ρ)
Gadolinium	Gd	64	156.9
Gallium	Ga	31	69.74
Germanium	Ge	39	72.62
Gold	Au	79	197.1
Hafnium	Hf	72	178.7
Helium	He	2	4.0038

Element	Symbol	Atomic Number	Atomic Weight*
Holmium	Ho	67	164.98
Hydrogen	H	1	1.0083
Indium	In	49	114.79
Iodine	I	53	126.94
Iridium	Ir	77	192.3
Iron	Fe	26	55.87
Krypton	Kr	36	83.82
Lanthanum	La	57	138.96
Lead	Pb	82	207.27
Lithium	Li	3	6.942
Lutetium	Lu	71	175.04
Magnesium	Mg	12	24.33
Manganese	Mn	25	54.96
Mercury	Hg	80	200.67
Molybdenum	Mo	42	95.97
Neodymium	Nd	60	144.31
Neon	Ne	10	20.188
Neptunium	Np†	93	237 (?)
Nickel	Ni	28	58.71
Niobium	Nb	41	92.94
Nitrogen	N	7	14.012
Osmium	Os	76	190.3
Oxygen	O	8	16.0043
Palladium	Pd	46	106.7
Phosphorus	P	15	30.983
Platinum	Pt	78	195.29
Plutonium	Pu†	94	239
Polonium	Po**	84	210 (?)
Potassium	K	19	39.111
Praseodymium	Pr	59	140.96
Promethium	Pm†	61	145 (?)
Protoactinium	Pa**	91	231
Radium	Ra**	88	226.11
Radon	Rn**	86	222.10
Rhenium	Re	75	186.36
Rhodium	Rd	45	102.94
Rubidium	Rb	37	85.50
Ruthenium	Ru	44	101.1
Samarium	Sm	62	150.47
Scandium	Sc	21	44.97

Element	Symbol	Atomic Number	Atomic Weight*
Selenium	Se	34	78.98
Silicon	Si	14	28.09
Silver	Ag	47	107.91
Sodium	Na	11	22.997
Strontium	Sr	38	87.65
Sulphur	S	16	32.075
Tantalum	Ta	73	181.00
Technetium	Tc†	43	99(?)
Tellurium	Te	62	127.64
Terbium	Tb	55	158.97
Thallium	Tl	81	204.45
Thorium	Th**	90	232.11
Thulium	Tm	69	168.98
Tin	Sn	50	118.73
Titanium	Ti	22	47.91
Tungsten	W	74	183.97
Uranium	U	92	238.13
Vanadium	V	23	50.96
Xenon	Xe	54	131.3
Ytterbium	Yb	70	173.09
Yttrium	Y	39	88.94
Zinc	Zn	30	65.40
Zirconium	Zr	40	91.24

* Atomic weight on the physical scale = atomic weight on the chemical scale
× 1.00027.   Since the atomic weight of an element is a weighted average of the isotopic weights, the most accurate figures are often obtained from mass spectroscopy rather than chemical analysis.

** These are the major, naturally radioactive elements.

† These elements are not believed to exist naturally on the earth, but samples of all of them have been produced using the techniques of nuclear physics. These samples are all radioactive.

APPENDIX A.2 The Periodic System

Certain marked regularities appear in the chemical properties of the elements. It was recognized in the latter half of the nineteenth century that these regularities are centered around a "period" of eight, that is, that elements differing by eight in atomic number are likely to have similar properties. A periodic table is an arrangement of the elements in order of atomic number and in groups of eight, which places in vertical columns elements with similar properties. The columns are called groups, and the rows are referred to as shells, numbered one to seven. See endpaper.

Modern atomic theory has been quite successful in explaining many of the regularities displayed in the periodic table and has also accounted for many previously mysterious irregularities. A full discussion would be out of place in this book but, very briefly, the theory attributes all chemical properties to the extranuclear or "orbital" electrons. The atomic number equals the number of these electrons in a neutral atom, so that each element has one more electron than has its predecessor in the table. Certain numbers of electrons are inherently more stable, that is, chemically more inert, than others. The most stable set of electron numbers is 2, 8, 18, and 32. These numbers equals $2n^2$ where $n = 1$, 2, 3, and 4, respectively. Thus atoms with 2, $2 + 8 = 10$, $2 + 8 + 8 = 18$, $2 + 8 + 8 + 18 = 36$ electrons, etc., are the most stable of all elements. They are, respectively, helium $(Z = 2)$, neon $(Z = 10)$, argon $(Z = 18)$, krypton $(Z = 36)$, xenon $(Z = 54)$, and radon $(Z = 86)$, which are the inert gases. They take part in *no* chemical reactions and do not even form diatomic molecules as do most of the other elements which are gaseous (e.g., H_2, O_2, Cl_2, etc.). These inert elements are the last ones in each of the rows, and their electron configurations are said to form closed shells. The shells have been numbered in this periodic table but are sometimes lettered K, L, M, etc. Thus argon is the last element in the third or M shell.

If an atom contains one more electron than a closed shell, this electron is readily removed, leaving a positive ion, and the element is extremely active chemically. The elements in this category are the alkali metals, lithium, sodium, potassium, etc. They all have a valence of one. Atoms with one electron less than a closed shell very readily attach one more electron to form a closed shell and an ion with a negative charge. These elements are the halogens, fluorine, chlorine, bromine, etc. Most inorganic molecules are formed by the union of a metal from the left of the table (Groups I, II, III) and a nonmetal from the right-hand side (Groups VII, VI, V). In this union, the metallic atom gives up enough electrons for its positive ion to have a closed electron shell, and the nonmetallic atom accepts enough electrons to form a negative ion, also with a closed electron shell. The ions are held together in the molecule by electrostatic attraction. These remarks may indicate the close connection between group number and valence. Usually the commonest valence of a metal on the left of the table is its group number, and that of a nonmetal is eight minus the group number. For example, in the compound $MgCl_2$, magnesium has a valence of two and chlorine a valence of one. The magnesium atom gives up two electrons, leaving an ion with the same electron configuration as neon, and each of the chlorine atoms accepts one of them, so that each chlorine ion has the same electron configuration as argon.

Special mention should be made of the lanthanide and actinide series. The lanthanide series consists of lanthanum ($Z = 57$) and the rare earths ($Z = 58$–71). These fifteen elements are so similar chemically that they are all placed in a single space in the table. This was done empirically at first but is justified by recent atomic theory. The same arrangement holds good for actinium ($Z = 89$) and the succeeding radioactive elements thorium, protoactinium, and uranium. The artifically created elements neptunium, plutonium, etc., also belong to this actinide series.

Answers to Odd-Numbered Problems

Chapter 1

1. 4971 miles 3. 44 ft sec^{-1} 5. 5.87 × 10^{12} miles; 9.44 × 10^{12} km 7. 9.8 × 10^2 cm sec^{-2} 9. 20,000 ft^2; 0.3%; 60 ft^2 11. 0.905 m^3; 10%; 0.09 m^3 13. 1050 kgm m^{-3}; 18%; 190 kgm m^{-3} 15. 659 lb; 0.3%; 2 lb.

Chapter 2

1. 43 ft/061° 3. 55 mph; 95 mph 5. 44 miles; N 1°W 7. 44.0 m sec^{-1}; 440 m 9. 100 ft; 10.0 sec 11. 1.70 sec; −34.4 ft sec^{-2} 13. 1.29 min; 364 mph 15. 45.9 m; 3.06 sec; 30.0 m sec^{-1}; 6.12 sec 17. 2.95 sec; 74.3 ft sec^{-2} 19. 1.76 × 10^5 ft = 33.3 miles; 110 sec; 215 sec 21. 4.0 sec; 88 ft 23. 103 ft sec^{-1}; 82.5 ft 25. 112 ft 27. 20.6 m sec^{-1}; 56.3° 29. 4600 ft; 1.562 × 10^4 ft; 1732 ft sec^{-1} 31. 25.1° or 64.9°; 26.5 sec 33. 3.61 miles 35. 576 miles; 1.60 hr 37. 26.6° south of west.

Chapter 3

1. 12.0 N 3. 16.0 ft sec^{-2}; 55.0 lb-wt 5. 2.50 × 10^3 N 7. 3.00 sec 9. 225 lb-wt; 175 lb-wt 11. 10.1 tons-wt 13. 2.45 m sec^{-2}; 22.0 N 15. 32.1 ft sec^{-2} 17. 16.0 ft sec^{-2}; 11.0 lb-wt; 8.00 lb-wt 19. 11.2 sec 21. 4.5 m/sec 23. 5.56 ft sec^{-1} 25. 4.50 × 10^4 N = 4.59 × 10^3 kgm-wt 27. 1.02 × 10^4 lb-wt.

Chapter 4

1. 40.0, 80.0 lb-wt 3. 5.78, 10.6 kgm-wt 5. 12.0 ft 13. Compressions, 707 b-wt; tension, 500 lb-wt 15. 25.0, 15.0 lb-wt 17. 11.6 ft; 4.02 tons-wt.

Chapter 5

1. 400 ft-lb; 235 joules 3. 30.0 m sec^{-1} 5. 180 ft 7. 2.70 × 10^4 joules 9. 48.0 ft sec^{-1} 11. 100,000 hp 13. 16.0 ft sec^{-1} 17. 0.900, 0.750, 0.600 19. 26.0 m sec^{-1} eastward, 2.0 m sec^{-1} westward; 588 joules 21. 30.0 hp 23. 96.00; 1208 ft sec^{-1} 25. 800, 2400 ft sec^{-1}.

Chapter 6

1. 39.2 N 3. 1.93 sec 5. 0.980 m sec^{-2}; 21.6 N; 1.43 sec 7. 51.0 lb-wt; 5.88 9. 3.20 × 10^4 hp 11. 3.90 ft sec^{-2}; 47.3 hp 13. 50% 17. 57.4° 19. 1.67 ft 21. 2.50 ft.

Chapter 7

1. −2.09 radians sec^{-2} 3. 52.8 radians sec^{-1}; 1.60 radians sec^{-2} 5. 3180 rpm 7. 2.01 sec 9. 13.7 ft 11. 9.5° 13. 66.8 mph; 4.17 ft 15. 120 lb ft^2 17. 2.01 Nm 19. 100 rpm; 10.3, 51.4 ft-lb 21. 5.00 sec; T_1 = 3225 lb-wt, T_2 = 3237 lb-wt 23. 48 ft 25. 4.71 hp.

Chapter 8

1. 32.0 ft sec^{-2} 3. 1.64 sec; 0.667 m 5. 10.0, -5.88, $+5.88$ ft; 0.00, -25.4, -25.4 ft sec^{-1} 7. 11.0 sec; 12.0, 8.00 ft sec^{-2} 9. 0.305 ft-lb 11. Loses 57 sec 13. 2.08 msec; $+9.66$ cm 15. $x^2 + y^2 = 25$ 17. $y = 10.0\,e^{-t/21.7} = 10.0 \times 10^{-t/50}$ 19. 1.533 sec 13. 1.88 sec.

Chapter 9

1. 1.28×10^{-2} in. 3. 6.17 in.; 6.92×10^3 ft 5. 1.02 sec 7. 1.05 gm cm^{-3} 9. 3.33 cm 11. 0.27, 0.34, 0.35 13. 39 tons-wt.

Chapter 10

1. 1.97×10^{30} kgm 3. 382 miles sec^{-1} 5. 0.387, 0.725, 1.52, 5.21 astronomica units 7. 1.97 hr; 22,300 miles 11. 9×10^{10} joules.

Chapter 11

1. 3100 Nm^{-2} 3. 450 ft 5. 981 mb 7. 2.57 ft^3 9. 0.866 gm cm^{-3} 11. 8.32 13. 7.3 tons; 194 15. 4.4 lb in^{-2}; 36 ft 17. 103 sec 19. 25.4 cm Hg 21. 14.7 cm Hg; 22.5 miles 23. 14.9 cm 25. 0.090 mm 27. 18.3 kgm; 7.47 cm; 24.9 kgm; 0.42 cm 29. 201 centipoises 31. 8.24 poises.

Chapter 12

1. 0.578, 0.818, 0.845, 0.347, 0.451, 0.418, 0.321, 0.637, 0.478, 0.400 cal 3. 0.11 deg 5. 25.4C 7. 20C 9. $M/(M + m)$ 11. 28,650 kw 13. 874 kgm.

Chapter 13

1. 0.29F 7. -86.5C 9. 5.7% 11. 24.2 in. 13. 20.0 lit. 15. 2.234×10^{22}, 2.358 gm 17. $15.9655 + 0.0065 + 0.0320 = 16.0040$ gm 19. 3.72×10^{-23} lit. 21. 0.0067 gm, 6.39×10^{16}, 2.53×10^8 23. 1.965×10^{23} 25. -0.06, -0.67, -1.53, 0.11, 0.10, 0.04, -0.06, 0.15%.

Chapter 14

1. 2.86 sec, 98,100 dynes, 0.90 sec, 98,100 dynes 3. 20 ft 5. 0.221 atm. 7. 414×10^{-23} joule, 828×10^{-23} joule 9. 60,730 w 11. $\frac{7}{4}$ 13. 16,200 joules, 13,720 joules 15. 3.39×10^7 joules 19. 1926 m sec^{-1}, 1362 m sec^{-1} 21. 9.13×10^{-6} cm, 3.14×10^{-8} cm.

Chapter 15

3. $(\Delta P/\Delta V) = -\gamma P_0 V_0{}^\gamma/V^{\gamma+1}$ 5. $P = V$, $5P = 3V$ 7. 4.00, 2.86 cm water 9. $1.0117 V_0$ 11. 0.176 lit., 0.237 atm. 13. -43C, 382 mb 15. 1.28 atm. 17. 69.3 m 19. 5527 m, 5527 m 21. 9.78 deg km^{-1}.

Chapter 16

1. 1405 kw 3. 683 joules 5. 7.60×10^5 joules 9. 24.4×10^3, 6.11×10^3 joules 11. 3.41 joules.

Chapter 18

1. 2.82×10^{-8} cm 3. 5,835 kgm 5. 28.9×10^{-6} deg^{-1} 7. 0.29 mm 9. 7.90, 7.85 cm^3 11. 4.946 cm^3 13. 4.79×10^9, 4.28×10^9 dynes.

Chapter 19

1. 1.05×10^5 joules, 17 min 27 sec 3. 0.0067, 0.377, 8.16 mm Hg 5. 795.5 mm Hg 9. Gas 11. 12.0×10^{-8} atm.

Chapter 20

1. 2.51 gm   **5.** 802 gm   **9.** 10.56 mm Hg, 0.0104 gm lit.$^{-1}$ **11.** 3.41 × 10⁶ cal.

Chapter 21

1. 27.6 cal sec^{-1}, 115 w   **3.** 85.56C, 8.15 cal sec^{-1} **5.** 0.090 cal, 2.9 deg   **7.** (a) 2, (b) 3   **9.** 17.0 cal sec^{-1}, 4.28%.

Chapter 22

1. 401 w cm^{-2}, 0.356 cm²   **3.** 9.95 × 10^{-4} w cm^{-2} **5.** 418 w   **7.** 3.77C   **9.** 3.76 cm   **11.** 0.663 deg min^{-1} **13.** 9.36 microns.

Chapter 23

1. π radian sec^{-1}, $y = A \sin \omega t$, where $A = 3$ cm and $\omega = \pi$ sec^{-1} **3.** 0, $-3\pi^2$cm sec^{-2}, 0   **5.** 19.7 ergs   **7.** 36   **9.** $C = 8.0, 7.4, 5.8, 3.6, 2.0, 3.6, 5.8, 7.4, 8.0, \beta = 0,$ 16.5°, 31°, 36.5°, 0, −36.5°, −31°, −16.5°, 0°   **11.** $C = 10.0, 9.2, 7.1, 3.8, 0, 3.8,$ 7.1, 9.2, 10.0, $\beta = 0$, 22.5°, 45°, 67.5°, 0, −67.5°, −45.0°, −22.5°, 0.

Chapter 24

1. 5044 m sec^{-1} **3.** 104.4 m sec^{-1} **5.** Water   **9.** 3.81, 2.94   **15.** 7.96 × 10^{-11} w cm^{-2}, 0.178 dyne cm^{-2} **17.** Rises 9.54 db   **19.** 10   **21.** $AB = (n + \tfrac{1}{2})\lambda$ **27.** 450, 434 cycles sec^{-1}.

Chapter 25

1. 125, 62.5 cm   **3.** 0.2, 0.3 mm   **5.** 5/6, 36/25   **7.** 143, 429, 714, 1000, 1286 cycles sec^{-1} **9.** 286, 572, 857, 1143, 1429 cycles sec^{-1} **11.** 0.59C.

Chapter 26

1. (a) Masking, (b) masking   **3.** 20 db   **5.** (a)(i) 52.35; 52.70, 52.00 cm sec^{-1}, 1006.7, 993.3 cycles sec^{-1}; 1.34% (ii) 17.45; 17.80, 17.10 cm sec^{-1}; 1020, 980 cycle sec^{-1}; 4.08% (b) 0.125 mm   **7.** 528.0, 523.3 cycles sec^{-1} **9.** 18 sabins increase, 34 sabins decrease   **11.** $I_e/3.16$ **13.** 0.94 sec, 0.51 sec.

Chapter 27

1. 103, 35.3, 5.97.

Chapter 28

11. 6.15° = 6°9′.

Chapter 29

1. 1.26 miles (for radio 0.95 mile)   **3.** ±4.36 cm, ±4.47 cm   **5.** (a) −220 cm, (b) −60 cm, (c) −17.5 cm   **7.** 4 diopters   **9.** 10 m^{-1}, 5 m^{-1} **11.** 5.83 cm, −35.0 cm   **13.** Image distances, 3.64 cm, 6.67 cm, ∞, −3.75 cm   **15.** 39   **17.** $r, \tfrac{2}{3}r, \tfrac{3}{5}r, \tfrac{4}{7}r, \tfrac{5}{9}r$ **19.** Image distances, −1.90, −1.54, −1.25, −0.94 cm.

Chapter 30

1. 9.52 cm   **3.** Curvatures 0, −3 m^{-1}, far point, − ∞, near point, −33 cm   **5.** 0.05 mm   **7.** 24   **9.** 1.5 diopters   **11.** −2.50 cm, −2.27 cm   **13.** 11.25 mm.

Chapter 31

1. 0.0267, 0.0221 steradian   **3.** 0.194, 0.033 w   **7.** 4.78 lumens ft^{-2} **9.** 4.24 lumens   **11.** 5.13 cm, 6.00 cm, 0.055 sec   **13.** $f/5.7, f/4.6, f/4.0$ **15.** (a) $u = -1.67$ to −2.50 m, (b) $u = -1.08$ to −14.81 m.

Chapter 32

1. 4 sec   3. 12.4, 6.8, 3.9 m   7. 2.50 cm.

Chapter 33

1. 8.00×10^{-5} N   3. 2.38 ma   5. 22.0 Ω   7. 1.60×10^{-18} joule; 1.60×10^{-16} N
9. 20.0 amp; 11.0 Ω   11. 10.0 Ω, 40.0 v   13. 10.0 Ω   15. 150 v.

Chapter 34

1. 44.0 Ω; 4.0 Ω   3. 50.0 v   5. 6.28, 5.82, 3.10 v   7. 28.3 mΩ   9. 2.21 miles
11. 36.2 Ω; 150 Ω   13. 463.7 Ω   15. 1 Ω to 10 MΩ   17. 100 ma; 4 v; 80 mw; 32 ma
19. $I_1 = 6$ amp; 4 amp; 7 Ω   21. 3000 ft; 300 Ω   23. 11.4 Ω   25. Wire, 31.6 mils in
diameter; 2.75 amp.

Chapter 35

1. 25   3. 0.36 Ω; 14.4 cents: 15.8%   5. 1.6374 v; 0-2.0000 v   7. 20.01 ma;
96.02 Ω   9. 18.8 lit.   11. 1.59×10^3 amp   13. 27.7 days   15. 8.43×10^{22}; 7.42×10^{-2} mm sec⁻¹.

Chapter 36

1. 47.1 μwebers   3. 7.54×10^{-3} N   5. 260 amp m⁻¹   7. 2.00×10^{-2} Nm   9.
26.0 amp m⁻¹   11. 2120 yd from each   13. 14.3 amp m⁻¹   15. 3.94 sec.

Chapter 37

1. 39.8 amp m⁻¹   3. 754 amp   5. 800 amp m⁻¹   9. 13.0 ma   13. 9.00 amp m⁻¹.

Chapter 38

1. 40.0 N m⁻¹   3. 4.00×10^{-2} weber m⁻²; 1.95×10^{-7} Nm   5. 10.0 mΩ; 10.0
mΩ   9. 3.91 Ω, 391 mΩ, 43.5 mΩ   11. 0, 9.52, 22.2, 40.0, 66.7, 111.1, 200.0, 466.7,
∞—all in Ω   13. 800   15. 14.0 amp   17. 0.50 amp; 4.00 amp; 540 w; 400 w;
74.1%.

Chapter 39

1. 36.0 v   3. 514   5. amp   7. 503 v   9. 239.5 v; 215 v   11. 11.0 v   13. 67.5
mh   15. 1.20 amp; 40.0 μsec; 200 μsec   17. ~760 v   19. 214 v; 5.00 hp; 84.8%
21. 0.600 weber m⁻²   23. 60.0 mh.

Chapter 40

1. 4.5×10^5 N   3. 1.67×10^4 v m⁻¹   5. +2μcoulombs   7. 5.00×10^3 v m⁻¹;
36.9°   11. 2.00 μf; $V_1 = 20$ v, $V_2 = 40$ v, $V_3 = 60$ v   13. 718 cm²   15. 49.2 cm
17. 23.5 cm.

Chapter 41

1. 424 v; 212 amp   3. 286 w   5. 566 v   7. 22.8, 2.91 amp; 57.8 mh   9. 82.9
ma   11. 1.38 amp; 20.4°; 142 w; 103, 91.2, 130 v   13. 1.00×10^4 radians/sec;
1.59 kc   15. 1.04 kc; 0.250 amp; 0°; 2.50 w; 27.4 v   17. 1.67×10^4 radians sec⁻¹;
5.00 kΩ   19. 500 v; 10.0 kv; 250 ma   21. 200 kv; 5.00 amp   23. 20.0 Ω.

Chapter 42

3. 497 Ω   5. 14,100–810 μμf; 250 kc   7. 50.0 cm; 600 Mc   9. 3.68×10^5 m sec⁻¹.

Chapter 43

1. 7.2×10^{-16} N; 450 ev $= 7.2 \times 10^{-17}$ joule; 1.3×10^7 m sec^{-1}; 0.016 μsec **3.** 7.26×10^6 m sec^{-1}; 0.0165 N m^{-2} **5.** 9.6×10^{-15} N; 8.52 cm **7.** 1.76×10^{11} coulombs/kgm **9.** 5.00×10^6 m sec^{-1}; 1.76×10^{11} coulombs/kgm **11.** 4 **13.** 4.78 v **17.** H, 5.29×10^{-11}, 2.12×10^{-10} m; He$^+$, divide by 2; Li^{++}, divide by 3.

Chapter 44

1. 23% **3.** 0.511 Mev; 1.96, 3.91, 97.8, 196 **5.** 51 kev **7.** 7.76 Mev; 28.4 cm; 6.25 Mev **9.** 8.86 Mev each **11.** 34.7 in. **13.** 938 Mev; 10.7%; $\beta = v/c = 0.428$, $v = 1.28 \times 10^8$ m sec^{-1}.

Index

Aberration:
  chromatic, 542
  mirrors, 557
  spherical, 544
Absolute:
  temperature, 246
  value, 11, 12
  zero, 246
Absorption:
  coefficient, 494
  of light, 584
  of sound, 494
Absorptivity, 407
a-c, 644, 782
Acceleration, 24
  angular, 125
  as a vector, 33
  centripetal, 125
  of gravity, 25
  variable, 39, 152
Accommodation of the eye, 564
Achromatic combination, 543
Acoustics, 418, 484
Action at a distance, 44
Acuity of hearing, 486
Adhesion, 215, 357
Adiabatic:
  equation, 298
  expansion, 284, 289, 297
    microscopic picture, 272
Aerodynamics, 221
Air conditioning, 384
Aircraft, 64
  forces on, 85
  instruments, 145, 212
  jet, 64
Air resistance, 27, 39
Air-speed indicator, 213
Algebraic sum, 12
Alnico alloys, 691, 736
α-particle, 837, 838
Alternating current (a-c), 644, 782
  sinusoidal, 747
Altimeter, 212
Ammeter, 657, 728

Amorphous solids, 345
Ampere, 638
AMPERE, A. M., 688, 709
Ampere sensibility, 726
Ampere's Law, 723
Ampere-turn, 719
  per meter, 693, 719
Amperian currents, 688
Amplification, 815
Amplifier, 814
  linear, 815
Amplitude, 154
Angle:
  in radians, 124
  of incidence, 522
  of reflection, 522
  of refraction, 523
  solid, 577
Angstrom unit, 507, 828, 846
Angular acceleration, etc. See Acceleration, etc.
Angular frequency, 158, 420, 781
Anisotropic media, 622
Annihilation, 874
Anode, 672, 811
Antineutron, 874
Antinode, 464
Antiproton, 874
Antiresonant circuit, 800
Antiresonant frequency, 800
Aphelion, 154
ARCHIMEDES, 200
Archimedes' Principle, 200
ARISTOTLE, 182
Armature, 731
ARRHENIUS, SVANTE, 673
Artificial:
  disintegration of nuclei, 863
  horizon, 144
  radioactivity, 871
  satellite, 194
Astigmatism, 545, 548
  of the eye, 568
ASTON, F. W., 857
Astronomy, 181

Atmosphere, 200, 210, 301–304
Atom, 4, 249, 831
Atomic:
　energy, 91, 95, 875
　mass unit (amu), 861
　number, 838
　reactor, 195, 875
　weight, 249, 681
　　scales of, 250, 861
Attenuation, 494
Atwood's Machine, 58
Audibility, 484
Audiofrequency, 818
Automatic pilot, 146
Automobile:
　electrical system of, 676
　ignition system, 755
Average value theorem, 786
AVOGADRO, AMADEO, 250
Avogadro's Hypothesis, 252
Avogadro's Number, 250, 684

Back emf, 740, 749
Baffle, 477
BAINBRIDGE, K. T., 857
Ballistic pendulum, 103, 242
BALMER, J. J., 847
Balmer Series, 847
Banking of a roadway, 129
Bar, 199
Barkhausen Effect, 705
Barometer, 210
　aneroid, 211
　faulty, 374
Bars, vibrating, 472
Battery, 675
　charging, 677
Beats, 424, 491
BECQUEREL, HENRI, 837
Bel, 442
BERNOULLI, DANIEL, 222
Bernoulli's Theorem, 222
β-particle, 835, 837
Betatron, 866
Bevatron, 866
Binding energy, 859
BIOT, J. B., 709
Biot-Savart Law, 711
Biot's Law, 709
Birefringence, 625
Black body, 407, 581
Black-body radiation, 410, 411, 825
BLACKETT, P. M. S., 868
BOHR, NIELS, 848, 852
Boiling, 367, 370, 371
BOLTZMANN, LUDWIG, 409
Boltzmann's Constant, 255

BORN, MAX, 852
Boundary conditions, 469
Bourdon gauge, 212
Bowing a string, 475
BOYLE, ROBERT, 209, 247
Boyle's Law, 209, 247, 263, 285, 332, 372
Boyle Temperature, 333, 336
BRAHE, TYCHO, 182
Brewster's Law, 622
Bridge circuit, 660
　Kelvin double, 670
　slide-wire, 661
　Wheatstone, 660
Brush of a motor, 732
Bulk modulus, 175
Bumping of boiling water, 371
Bunsen ice calorimeter, 388
Buoyancy, 200
　center of, 201

C line, 528
C.O.P. (coefficient of performance), 323
Calorie, 233, 376
Camera, 588
　pinhole, 602
Candle, standard, 581
Capacitance, 768
　equivalent parallel, 779
　equivalent series, 779
Capacitor, 768
　blocking, 772
　energy stored in a, 769
Capillary rise, 217
Carnot:
　cycle, 319
　　efficiency, 322
　engine, 318
CARNOT, SADI, 318
Carrier signal, 818
Cartesian diver, 225
Cathode, 672
　rays, 833
Cathode-ray oscillograph, 780, 820
CAVENDISH, HENRY, 186
Cell:
　dry, 675
　Edison, 678
　lead, 676
　nickel-cadmium, 678
　primary, 675
　secondary, 675
　standard, 678
　storage, 675
CELSIUS, ANDERS, 235
Celsius scale, 235
Center:
　of buoyancy, 201

of gravity, 82
of mass, 83
Centigrade scale, 235
Centipoise, 220
Centrifugal force, 127
Centripetal:
　acceleration, 125
　force, 127
CHADWICK, SIR JAMES, 860, 863
Chain reaction, 875
Change of state, 196, 233, 235, 347, 359
Characteristic curve:
　of a tube, 811
　of photographic emulsions, 586
Charging by induction, 760
CHARLES, J. A. C., 244
Charles' Law, 244
Chemical scale of atomic weights, 250, 861
Choke coil, 813
Chromatic aberration, 542
Circle:
　of confusion, 590
　of least confusion, 545, 548
Circular:
　mil, 664
　polarization, 627
CLAPEYRON, B. P. E., 363
CLAUSIUS, R. J. E., 363
Clausius-Clapeyron Equation, 363
Clément and Désormes, experiment of, 290, 306
Closed end of a pipe, 468
Closed-loop control, 129
Closed pipe, 470
Cloud, 385
　chamber, 867
Coated lenses, 612
Cochlea, 482
COCKCROFT, SIR JOHN, 864
Coefficient of performance (C.O.P.), 323
Coefficient of restitution, 99
Cohesion, 215, 357
Collimator, 598
Collisions, 98
　elastic, 100, 238
　inelastic, 100, 238
Color, 512, 515
　temperature, 412
COLUMBUS, CHRISTOPHER, 689
Coma, 549
Commutator, 731
Compass:
　needle, 695
　rose, 698
Components of a vector, 36

Compound:
　microscope, 594
　pendulum, 160
Compressibility, 175
Compression, 57
　and rarefaction, 433
Condensation, 361
CONDON, E. U., 864
Conductance, 651
Conduction of heat, 390
　along a bare rod, 392
　along an insulated rod, 390
　through composite walls, 392
Conductivity, thermal, 391, 393
　of gases, 395
Conductors, 635
Conservation laws, 95
　angular momentum, 135
　charge, 96
　energy, 95
　mass, 95
　momentum, 63
Conservative field, 777
Consonance, 491
Contrails, 387
Convection, 390, 396
Conventional rays, 553
Conversion factors, 9, 32, 53, 89, 97
COPERNICUS, NICOLAUS, 182
CORK, JAMES M., 236, 337
Cornea, 564
Cosmic rays, 869
Cosmotron, 866
Coulomb, 642
COULOMB, C. A., 691, 762
Coulomb's Law:
　of electrostatic force, 762
　of magnetic force, 691
Couple, 81
Critical temperature, 339, 360
Crystallography, 344
Crystals, 343
CURIE, IRENE, 860, 871
CURIE, MARIE, 837
CURIE, PIERRE, 837
Curie temperature, 703
Current balance, 638
Curvature, 532
Cyclotron, 864
　frequency-modulated, 866

D line, 528
DALTON, JOHN, 253
Dalton's Law, 253
Damping, 161
d'Arsonval galvanometer, 726
db, 442

d-c, 644
DE BROGLIE, LOUIS, 852
Decay constant of radioactivity, 841
Decibel (db), 442
DE FOREST, LEE, 814
Degrees of freedom, 266
Demagnetization, 704
DEMPSTER, A. J., 857
Density, 201
    change with temperature, 352
    of water, 375
    photographic, 585
Depth of field, 589
Detection, radio, 819
Deviation by a prism, 527, 599
Devitrification, 348
Dew, 384
    point, 380
Diamagnetism, 703
Diatomic molecule, 267
Diatonic scale, 491
Dielectric, 772
    constant, 762
    strength, 765
Diffraction, 449
    at a circular aperture, 451
    at a parallel-sided slit, 451
    grating, 614
    of light, 602
    pattern of a loudspeaker, 452
Diffuse transmission and reflection, 584
Dimensional analysis, 434
Diode, 811
Diopter, 541
DIRAC, P. A. M., 852
Direct current (d-c), 644
Directional gyro, 144
Discharge:
    corona, 765
    point, 765
    spark, 765
Dispersion, 528
    angular, 529
Dispersive power, 528, 543, 561
Displacement, 11, 19
    angular, 124
Displacement law of radioactivity, 840
Dissociation, theory of, 673
Dissonance, 491
Distortion, 549
DOPPLER, CHRISTIAN J., 457
Doppler Effect, 456
Dot product, 89, 718
Double slit, 607
Dry cell, 675
Dulong and Petit's Law, 346
Dynamics, 19

Dynamic speaker, 476
Dyne, 50

e, base of logarithms, 293
Ear, 480
Earth, curvature of, 560
Ebullition. See Boiling
EDISON, THOMAS A., 811
Effective value of a-c, 784
Efficiency, 116
    effect of load on, 120
    of a heat engine, 322, 325, 329
    of a machine, 97
    of Carnot cycle, 322
    of practical heat engine, 329
EINSTEIN, ALBERT, 19, 95, 191, 825, 852
Elasticity, 78, 99, 168
Elastic limit, 170
Electric:
    charge, 634
        conservation of, 96
    current, 634
        alternating, 644
        conventional direction of, 644
        direct, 644
        effects of, 634
        hazards of, 636
    field strength, 763
    motor, 731
        shunt-wound d-c, 749
    potential difference, 640, 763, 777
    power, 644
    rating, 647, 668
Electrochemical equivalent, 681
Electrode, 672
Electrodynamics, 633
Electrodynamometer, 801
Electrolysis, 672, 683
    significance in atomic theory, 684
Electrolytic refining, 684
Electromagnet, 712
Electromagnetic:
    induction, 741
        Faraday's Law of, 743
    nature of light, 507, 776, 817
    radiation, 401
    spectrum, 402, 507
Electromotive force (emf), 652
Electron, 633
    charge, 835
    charge-to-mass ratio, 833
    gun, 780, 820
    microscope, 823
    volt, 831
Electronic:
    charge, 633, 835

tube or valve, 810
  gas-filled, 811
Electronics, 808
Electrophorus, 766
Electroplating, 683
Electroscope, 758
Electrostatics, 633
Elements, 248
emf, 652
  back, 749
  induced, 742
  thermal, 666
Emissive power, 408, 409
Emissivity, 408, 412
emu, 774
End correction of a pipe, 470
Energy, 4, 89
  atomic, 91, 95, 875
  conservation of, 95
  heat, 92, 231, 239, 316
  kinetic, 92
  of simple harmonic motion, 440
  of sound, 440
  of vibration, 421
  per degree of freedom, 269
  potential, 91
  solar, 90
Entropy, 305, 312, 325
Equation of state, 254, 255
Equilibrium, 74
  of a rigid body, 79
Equiphase lines, 442
Equivalence of mass and energy, 95
Erg, 89
Escape velocity, 67, 193
Estimated figure, 13
esu, 775
Evans, Ralph, M., 514
Evaporation, 359, 361, 365, 370, 810
Expansion:
  adiabatic, 284, 289, 297
  coefficients, 350
    apparent, 355
    relations among, 351
  isothermal, 284, 288, 297
  of liquids, 353
  of solids, 349
Experimental method, 26
Exponential decay, 162
Exposure:
  meter, 510
  photographic, 585, 588
Extraordinary radiation, 623
Eye:
  optics, 564
  ring, 596, 597
  sensitivity distribution, 507

Eyeglasses, 569
Eyepiece, 594

F line, 528
f-number, 589
Fahrenheit, Gabriel, 235
Fahrenheit scale, 235
Farad, 768
Faraday, 681
Faraday, Michael, 672, 684, 741, 749, 760
Faraday's ice-pail experiment, 760
Faraday's Law of Electromagnetic Induction, 743
Farsighted vision, 568
Feeling, threshold of, 485
Fermi, Enrico, 871, 875
Ferromagnetism, 703, 735
Field coil, 732
Filament, thermionic, 810
First law of thermodynamics, 316
Fission, 874
  fragments, 874
Fixed end of a string, 461
Fixed points, 235
Fleming, Sir John, 811
Fluid, 196
  perfect, 197
Fluorescent lamps, 512
Flux:
  luminous, 580
  radiant, 577
Focal:
  length:
    camera, 592
    lens, 540
    mirror, 557
  planes:
    lens, 551
    mirror, 557
  points of a lens, 551
Focusing:
  power, 541
  scale, 589
Fog, 385
Foot, 8
Foot-pound, 89
Foot-poundal, 89
Force, 4, 44
  centrifugal, 127
  centripetal, 127
  shear, 169
Forced vibration, 467
Fowler, W. A., 872
Frame of reference, 93, 191
Fraunhofer diffraction, 452
Free body diagram, 53

Frequency, 156
angular, 158, 420, 781
Fresnel:
Biprism, 609
diffraction, 452
Friction, 45, 105
angle of, 108
coefficient of, 107
coefficient of kinetic, 107
coefficient of rolling, 111
coefficient of static, 107
laws of, 106
limiting, 106
rolling, 111
Frost, 385
Fulcrum, 116
Fundamental:
frequency, 471
mode, 466
Fusion, 877
latent heat of, 234, 347

GALILEO GALILEI, 19, 25, 47, 55, 183,
598
GALVANI, LUIGI, 672
Galvanometer, 661
ballistic, 756
d'Arsonval, 726
shunt, 728
tangent, 721
Gamma, photographic, 586
γ-rays, 837
GAMOW, GEORGE, 864
Gas:
constant, 254
definition, 196, 361
thermometer:
constant pressure, 244
constant volume, 246
Gauge pressure, 206, 291
GAUSS, KARL F., 698
Gauss "A" and "B" positions, 698
GAY-LUSSAC, J. L., 244
Gay-Lussac's Law, 244
Geiger counter, 867
Generator:
electromagnetic, 746
excitation of a, 747
GILBERT, SIR WILLIAM, 700
Gimbals, 143
Glare, 585
GOUDSMIT, S. A., 852
Gradient, temperature, 391
Gram-atomic weight, 249, 681
Gram-molecular weight, 251
Graticule, 598
Grating, diffraction, 614

Gravitation, law of universal, 186
Grid:
bias, 814
of an electron tube, 814
Ground potential, 642
GURNEY, R. W., 864
Gyroscope, 140
artificial horizon, 144
directional, 144
gyrocompass, 144
precession of a, 141
turn indicator, 145

H.E.R. (heating energy ratio), 323
H-bomb, 878
Half-life, 841
Half-wave plate, 628
Harmonics, 427, 467, 471
Head of water, 102
Hearing, 481
acuity, 486
binaural, 487
threshold, 484
Heat, 231, 239
energy, 92, 231, 239, 316
engine, 317, 318
efficiency of, 322, 325, 329
of fusion, 234, 347
of ice, 378
of sublimation, 363
of vaporization, 233, 362, 369
of water, 378
radiant, 403
Heating energy ratio (H.E.R.), 323
HEISENBERG, WERNER, 852
Heisenberg Uncertainty Principle, 853
HELMHOLTZ, H. L. VON, 95, 491
Henry, 751
HENRY, JOSEPH, 741, 749
Hertz, 157
HIPPARCHUS, 182
HOOKE, ROBERT, 171
Hooke's Law, 155, 170, 419
Horsepower, 97
Humidifying, 384
Humidity, relative, 380
HUYGENS, CHRISTIAN, 449, 518
Huygens' Principle, 449, 518
Hydraulic:
machinery, 206
press, 206
Hydrodynamics, 197, 221
Hydrometer, 203
Hydrostatics, 197
Hygrometer, 380
Hyperfocal distance, 592
Hypermetropia, 568

Hysteresis, 736
  loop, 736

Ice:
  point, 235
  properties of, 377
Iceland spar, 623, 626
Iconoscope, 822
Ideal gas, 244
Illumination, 577
Image, 552
  distance, 540
  plane, 551
  point, 524, 533, 536, 540, 551
Images of sound sources, 500
Impedance, 791
  triangle, 793
Impulse, 62
  angular, 142
Incandescent lamp, 511
Inches of mercury, 199
Incidence, angle of, 522
Inclined plane, 118
Incoherent or discontinuous source, 423,
  607
Index of refraction, 517, 529, 561
Induced emf, 742
Inductance:
  mutual, 750
  self, 751
Inductor, 751
  earth, 756
Inertia, 47
  moment of, 133
Infrared, 513
Instantaneous center of rotation, 112
Instruments, aircraft, 145, 212
Insulator, 635
Intensity:
  level, 442
  luminous, 581
  of sound, 440, 488, 495
  radiant, 578
Interference:
  light, 607
  sound, 445
Interferometer, 613
Intermolecular attractions, 333
Inversion temperature, 337
Ion, 673
Ionization by collision, 867
Iris, 564
Irreversible process, 309, 311
Isogonal, 700
Isothermal expansion, 284, 288, 297
  microscopic picture, 272
Isotope, 249, 839, 857

JEANS, SIR JAMES, 253, 493
Jet aircraft, 64
JOLIOT, F., 860, 871
JORDAN, PASCUAL, 852
Joule, 89
JOULE, J. P., 94, 306, 338, 639
Joule's Experiment, 306, 307
Joule's Law, 639
Joule-Thomson (or Joule-Kelvin) Experi-
  ment, 337, 341

KAPITZA, PIOTR, 341
KELLY, E. L., 871
KELVIN, LORD (W. THOMSON), 246, 327,
  338, 670
Kelvin scale, 246
KEPLER, JOHANNES, 182
Kepler's Laws of Planetary Motion, 182
Kilogram, 6
Kilowatt-hour, 646
Kinematics, 19
Kinetic:
  energy of rotation, 133
  energy of translation, 92
  theory of gases, 261
Kinetics, 19
KIRCHHOFF, GUSTAV, 408, 655, 777, 782
Kirchhoff's Law (radiation), 408
Kirchhoff's Laws (electrical), 655, 777,
  782

Laminar flow, 221, 397
Lamps:
  fluorescent, 512
  incandescent, 511
LANDÉ, ALFRED, 852
LAPLACE, PIERRE SIMON MARQUIS DE,
  709
Lapse rate, 304
Latent heat:
  of fusion, 234, 347
  of sublimation, 363
  of vaporization, 233, 362, 369
Latitude, 190
LAURITSEN, C. C., 872
LAURITSEN, T., 872
LAWRENCE, ERNEST, 864
Lead cell, 676
Left-hand (motor) rule, 723
Length, 5
Lenses, 531
  coated, 612
  thick, 563
Lens relationship, 538, 562
Lenz' Law, 743
LESLIE, SIR JOHN, 405
Leslie Cube, 405, 407

Level:
  intensity, 442
  loudness, 489
Lever, 116
  optical, 168
Light-year, 181
Limit of resolution, 604
Liquefaction of gases, 341
Liquids:
  adhesion, 357
  cohesion, 357
  expansion, 353
  specific heats, 349
  tensile strength, 356
Liquid state, 196, 348
LISSAJOUS, J. A., 428
Lissajous Figures, 428, 443
Liter, 201
LIVINGSTONE, M. S., 866
Logarithmic:
  graph paper, 163
  response, 488
  scale, 292
Logarithms, abbreviation convention,
    163
Loop (antinode), 464, 469
LORENTZ, H. A., 679
Loudness, 488
  level, 489
Loudspeaker, 476
Lumen, 580
Luminosity, 580
Luminous:
  flux, 580
  intensity, 581
LYMAN, THEODORE, 851

Machine, 115
  efficiency of a, 97
  mechanical advantage of a, 115
  self-locking, 119
Mach number, 222
Macroscopic view, 240, 248, 370
Magnet, 688
Magnetic:
  axis, 690
  circuit, 736
  dip, 700
  dipole, 697
  domains, 703
  field of the earth, 700
  field strength, 693, 744
  flux, 742, 744
  flux density, 723, 744
  induction, 691
  lines of intensity, 694
  moment, 695

poles, 690
pole strength, 691
saturation, 704
variation, 689, 700
Magnetization curves, 735
Magnetometer:
  deflection, 698
  oscillation, 698
Magnetomotive force (mmf), 717
Magnification, 552
  of mirrors, 557
Magnifier, 570
Magnifying power:
  compound microscope, 594
  microscope, 570
  telescope, 597
Manometer, 211
Masking by noise, 487
Mass, 5, 47
  conservation of, 96
  number, 839
  spectrograph, 858
Mass-point, 57, 261
Matte surface, 585
MAXWELL, JAMES CLERK, 4
MAYER, J. R. VON, 95
Mean free path, 279
Mechanical advantage, 115
Medium of wave propagation, 418, 433
MEI, J. Y., 869
Melting, 347, 370
Mersenne's Laws, 466
Mesons, 870
Meter (unit), 5, 614
Method of mixtures, 237
Mev, 832
Mho, 651
MICHELSON, ALBERT A., 191, 614
Michelson-Morley Experiment, 191
Michelson's Interferometer, 613
Micron, 209, 507
Microphone, 478, 715
Microscope, 570
  compound, 594
  simple, 570
Microscopic view, 240, 248, 370
Mil, 664
Mil-ft, 664
Millibar (mb), 200, 301
MILLIKAN, R. A., 220, 685, 835
Milliliter, 375
Mirror, 555
  aberrations, 557
  ellipsoidal, 559
  magnification, 557
  paraboloidal, 559
  relation, 555

Moderator, 875
Modes of vibration, 466
Modulation:
  amplitude, 818
  frequency, 819
Modulus:
  bulk, 175, 435
  of rigidity, 176
  shear, 176
  Young's 171, 435
Molar heat:
  of a gas at constant pressure, 274
  of a gas at constant volume, 271
Mole, 251
Molecular weight, 251
Molecule, 252, 332
  diameter of, 278, 280
  diatomic, 267
  mean free path, 279
  polyatomic, 269
  speed of, 275, 437
Moment:
  of a force, 79
  of inertia, 133
  of momentum, 134
Momentum, 48
  angular, 134, 153
  conservation of, 63
  conservation of angular, 135
  moment of, 134
Monochromatic, 514
MORRISON, W. A., 872
Motion:
  angular equations, 125
  equations, constant acceleration, 27
  Newton's Laws, 47, 49, 55
  wave, 161, 431
Mutual inductance, 750
Myopia, 567

N.T.P., 260
Natural:
  law, 3, 95
  vibration, 464
Near point of the eye, 567
Nearsighted vision, 567
Negative, photographic, 586
Negative crystals, 623
"Neon" sign, 845
NERNST, WALTER, 674
Neutrino, 870
Neutron, 860
  thermal, 871
Newton, 50
NEWTON, SIR ISAAC, 47, 55, 186, 191, 195,
  219, 609, 845
Newton-meter, 132

Newton's Laws of Motion, 47, 49, 55
  suitable form of second law for angular
    motion, 130
Newton's Rings, 609
Nicol Prism, 626
Node, 464, 469
Noise, masking by, 487
Nuclear:
  emulsion, 868
  fission, 874
  reactions, 870
  reactor, 875
  theory, 843
Nuclei:
  condensation, 385
  freezing, 348, 387
Nucleon, 861
Nucleus, 844

Object, 552
  distance, 540
  plane, 551
  point, 550
Objective, microscope and telescope, 594
OERSTED, HANS C., 689, 708
Ohm, 639
Ohmmeter, 730
  shunt, 738
Ohms–circular mils per foot, 664
Ohm's Law, 645
  a-c form of, 791
Ohms-per-volt rating, 738
OLSON, HARRY F., 476, 478
Open end of a pipe, 470
Open pipe, 470
Optical:
  activity, 626
  lever, 168
Optic axis, 623
Ordinary radiation, 623
Orthochromatic, 510
Oscillator, vacuum-tube, 816
Oscillatory motion, 152
  damped, 161
Overtone, 467

Packing fraction, 859
Pair production, 873
Panchromatic, 510
Parallax, 574
Parallel:
  circuit, 650
  forces, 80
Paramagnetism, 703
Partial pressures, 253
PASCAL, BLAISE, 205
Pascal's Principle, 205

Peak value of a-c, 784
Peltier Effect, 666
Pendulum:
  ballistic, 103, 242
  compound, 160
  reversible, 167
  simple, 103, 158
  torsional, 167, 177
Perihelion, 154
Period, 154, 420
Periodic:
  system, 884
  table, 884, endpaper
Permeability, 692
  of free space, 637
  relative, 637
Permittivity:
  of free space, 762
  relative, 762
Perpetual motion, 115, 328
Phase, 156
  angle, 420
  constant, 156
  lag, 790
  lead, 784, 789
Phasor, 422, 792
  addition, 421
  diagrams, 792
Phon, 489
Photocell, 510, 826
Photoelectric effect, 824
Photographic:
  emulsions, 585
  film, 510, 585
Photography, 585
Photon, 825, 873
Photopic vision, 507
Photosynthesis, 90
Photovoltaic cell, 510
Physical scale of atomic weights, 250,
    861
PICKUP, ERIC, 869, 872
Pile, 875
Pipes, open and closed, 470
Pitch, 490
Pitch of a screw, 119
Pitot head, 213
PLANCK, MAX, 327, 825, 852
Planck's Constant, 825, 848
Planes:
  object, image, focal, 551
Planets, 181
Plasticity, 170
Plate of an electron tube, 811
Plutonium, 876
Poise, 220
POISEUILLE, J. L. M., 220

Poiseuille's Formula, 220
POISSON, S. D., 172
Poisson's Ratio, 172
Polarimeter, 626
Polarization:
  in a battery, 674
  of a dielectric, 772
  of light, 618, 621
Polaroid, 619
Pole strength, 691
Polyatomic molecules, 269
Positive crystals, 623
Positron, 870
Possible error, 14
Post Office Box, 661
Potential:
  divider, 680
  drop, 653
  electric, 640, 777
  energy, 91
    graph, 153
Potentiometer, 679
  direct-reading, 686
Pound, 8
Poundal, 52
Pound-weight, 50
Power, 96
  electric, 644
  equation, 644, 787
  factor, 788
  factor, correction of, 798
  of a lens, 541
  pack, 813
  rating, 647, 668
Precession, 141
  of the equinoxes, 188
Precipitation, 387
Presbyopia, 567
Pressure, 108, 197
  absolute, 206
  excess, in a bubble, 218
  excess, in a drop, 217
  gauge, 206, 291
  hydrostatic, 197
  of sound, 440
  partial, 253
  variation in a sound wave, 484
  variation with height, 301
Primary coil, 742, 782
Principal rays, 553
Prisms, 526
  spectrometer, 599
  thin, 528
Projectile, 37
Projectors, slide and film, 592
Proton, 633, 838
PROUT, WILLIAM, 857

Psychrometer. *See* Hygrometer
Psychrometric tables, 383
Ptolemy, 182
Pulley, 117
  differential, 118
Pump:
  diffusion, 208
  filter, 223
  fore, 209
  suction, 207
  vacuum, 208
  Venturi, 223
Pumping speed, 225

Quantum, 825
  mechanics, 845, 852
  number, 849
  theory, 825, 852
Quarter-wave plate, 628

Radial field, 725
Radian measure, 124
Radiant:
  flux, 577
  heat, 403
  intensity, 578
Radiation, thermal, 401, 404
Radio:
  superheterodyne, 819
  wave, 817
Radioactive:
  decay constant, 841
  half-life, 841
  series, 842
Radioactivity, 91, 837
  artificial, 871
Radiofrequency, 818
Radius:
  of curvature, 532
  vector, 422
Rain, 387
Rarefaction, 433
Rate-of-climb indicator, 213
Rationalized mksa system of units, 637
Ratio of specific heats, 274
Ratios of the electrical units, 776
Rays, 523
  conventional, 553
  principal, 553
Reactance:
  capacitive, 794
  inductive, 791
Reaction motor, 64
Reactor:
  breeder, 877
  nuclear, 875

Rectification, 747, 811
Reference circle, 155, 420
Reflected wave, 464
Reflection:
  angle of, 522
  total, 525
Reflectivity, 408
Refraction, angle of, 523
Refractive index, 517, 561
Relative humidity, 380
Relativity, theory of, 93, 191, 835
Relay, 713
Resistance, 639
  temperature coefficient of, 665
  thermometer, 666
  variation with temperature, 664
Resistivity, 663
Resolution, limit of, 604
Resolution of a vector, 35
Resolving power, 606
Resonance, 464
  electrical, 796, 800
Resonant:
  circuit, 797
  frequency, 797
  vibration, 464, 467
Restitution, coefficient of, 99
Retina, 564, 566
Reverberation, 498, 502
  time, 498
Reversible process, 309
REYNOLDS, OSBORNE, 221
Reynolds Number, 221
Rheostat, 658
Right-hand rule:
  current, 709
  generator, 743
rms (root mean square), 276
  value of a-c, 784
Rocket, 64, 66
  mass ratio of a, 66
ROENTGEN, WILLIAM, 836
Root mean square, 276
  value of a-c, 784
Rotation, 123
  instantaneous center of, 112
rpm, rps (revs per min, per sec), 126
RUMFORD, COUNT (BENJAMIN THOMPSON), 94
RUTHERFORD, LORD (ERNEST), 838, 841, 843, 860, 862
Rydberg Constant, 847, 850

Sabin, 495
SABINE, WALLACE C., 495
Satellite, artificial, 194
SAVART, FELIX, 709

Scalar:
  product, 89
  quantity, 20
Scale:
  diatonic, 491
  musical, 491
  of equal temperament, 493
Scanning, 823
Scattering:
  of α-particles, 843
  of light, 620
Schmidt telescope, 560
SCHRODINGER, ERWIN, 852
Scotopic vision, 507
Screws, 119
Search coil, 756
Second, 6
Secondary coil, 742, 782
Second law of thermodynamics, 327
Seebeck Effect, 666
Self inductance, 751
Semiconductor, 664
Semitone, 492
Series circuit, 649
Servomechanism, 129
Shear, 169, 176
  modulus, 176
Shock wave, 456
Shunt, 728
  Ayrton-Mather, 729
Sign convention, 533
  mirrors, 555
Significant figures, 15
Simple harmonic:
  motion, 154, 419
    circle of reference, 155, 420
    damped, 161
  waves, 161, 437
Simple pendulum, 103, 158
Singing of a kettle, 369
Sink (heat), 319
Sinusoidal a-c voltage, 747
Siphon, 207
Slip ring, 747
Slug, 51
SNELL, A. H., 840
Snow, 387
SODDY, FREDERICK, 838
Solar:
  constant, 413
  energy, 90, 877
Solenoid, 711, 720
Solid:
  angle, 577
  state, 196, 342
Solids, 342
  crystalline nature, 345

expansion, 349
  specific heat, 345
SOMMERFELD, ARNOLD, 852
Sone, 490
Sonic barrier, 455
Sounding boards and boxes, 473
Sound-level meter, 489
Sound recording, on film, 826
Sound waves in gases, speed, 436
Sources:
  heat, 319
  light, 510, 578
Speaker, dynamic or direct-radiator, 476
Specific:
  gravity, 202
  heat, 232, 376
    of a gas at constant pressure, 274
    of a gas at constant volume, 271
    of ice, 377
    of liquids, 349
    of solids, 345
    of water, 376
  volume, 375
Spectacles, 569
Spectra, continuous and line, 845
Spectrograph, 599
Spectrometer, 598, 614
Spectroscopy, 845
Specular transmission and reflection, 583
Speech, 479, 486, 499
Speed:
  of light, 507, 517
  of sound, 436
  of waves, 434
Spherical aberration, 544
Stadia rod, 552, 598
Standard:
  atmosphere, 200, 302
  candle, 581
  cell, 678
  meter, 5, 614
Standing waves, 464
  longitudinal, 468
State:
  change of, 196, 233, 235, 347, 359
  gaseous, 196, 243–341, 361
  liquid, 196, 348
  solid, 196, 342
Statics, 19, 74
Steam point, 235
STEFAN, JOSEPH, 409
Stefan-Boltzmann:
  constant, 409
  Law, 409
Steiner's Parallel Axes Theorem, 151
Steradian, 577
Stereoscopic vision, 575

STOKES, SIR GEORGE G., 220
Stokes' Law, 220
Strain, 91, 170
    optical study of, 629
Streamlines, 221
Stress, 169
    and temperature, 355
Stroboscope, 461
Sublimation, 361
    latent heat of, 363
Supercooling, 348, 376
Surface:
    tension, 214
    waves, 433
Synchrotron, 866
Systems of units, 7
    cgs, 8
    emu, 774
    esu, 775
    fps (British), 8
    mksa, 7
    rationalized mksa, 637

Tables:
    atomic weights, physical scale, 881
    Balmer series in hydrogen, 847
    camera, f-numbers and exposures, 589
    conductivities, thermal, 393, 394, 395
    crystals, uniaxial, indices of, 623
    densities and molecular weights of
        gases, 260
    dielectric constants, 762
    elastic properties, 175
    electrical units, definitions, 646
    electromagnetic units—relations to
        mks units, 774
    electrostatic units—relations to mks
        units, 775
    eye, dimensions and indices, 565
    force units, 53
    free fall, speeds and distances, 27
    incandescent lamp, efficiency, 512
    kinetic-molecular theory, symbols, 256
    masses of light atoms in amu, 878
    metric units, nomenclature, 7
    molecular weights, 251
    musical scales, intervals, 493
    ratios of specific heats of gases, 282
    refractive indices, 561
    resistivities and temperature coeffi-
        cients, 665
    sound absorption coefficients, 494
    specific gravities and densities, 205
    surface tensions, 219
    vapor pressure of water, 389
    viscosities, 221
Telegraph, 715

Telephone, 476, 715
Telescope, 596
    Galilean, 598
Teletype, 715
Television:
    camera tube, 822
    receiver, 823
Temperature, 232, 270
Tensile strength, 171
    of liquids, 356
Tension, 57
    surface, 214
Tephigram, 305
Terminal velocity, 27, 220
TERROUX, F. R., 868
Thermal:
    emf, 666
    radiation, 404
Thermionic:
    emission, 808
    tube, 810
    valve, 811
Thermocouple, 404, 667
Thermometer, 234
    platinum resistance, 666
Thermometric properties, 234, 243
Thermopile, 404, 508, 667
Thermostat, 129
Thin lens:
    equation of, 537
    relationship, 538
THOMSON, J. J., 833, 857
THOMSON, WILLIAM (LORD KELVIN), 338
Threshold:
    of hearing, 484
    of feeling, 485
THRING, M. W., 329
Throttling, 309, 335, 339
Thyratron, 811
Timbre, 475
Time, 5
Time constant, 752
Tones, 492
TORICELLI, E., 210
Toroid, 711, 719
Torque, 78
    of a couple, 82
Torsion:
    balance, 186
    pendulum, 167, 177
Transducer, 476
Transformer, 742, 802
    iron-cored, 742, 782
    phasor diagram of a, 804
    step-down, 783
    step-up, 783
Transit time, in an electron-tube, 817

Translation, 123
Trichromatic theory, 514
Triode, 814
Truss, 86
Tuning a radio receiver, 798
Tuning fork, 472
Turbulent flow, 221, 397
Turn indicator, 145

Uhlenbeck, G. E., 852
Ultraviolet, 513
Universal gas constant, 254

Valence, 681, 884
van de Graaf generator, 767, 864
van der Waals, 334
van der Waals' equation, 334
Vapor, definition, 361
Vaporization, latent heat of, 233, 362, 369
Vapor pressure, equilibrium, 360
    determination of, 372
        ice, 378
        water, 378, 389
Vector addition, 22
    by parallelogram law, 22
    by polygon of vectors, 23
    by triangle of vectors, 22
Vector quantities, 20
    components, 36
    resolution, 35
Velocity, 23
    angular, 124, 419
    angular, as a vector, 142
    escape, 67, 193
    molecular, 275, 437
    of light, 507, 517, 776
    of sound, 436
    terminal, 27, 220
Vibrating system, 418
Vibration, 417
Video, 823
Virial coefficients, 350
Virtual image, 536, 540
Viscosity, 197, 219
    coefficient of, 220, 279
Vocal cords, 479
Voice, 479
Voice-coil, 476
Volt, 642
    per meter, 764

Volta, Count Alessandro, 672
Voltmeter, 657, 729

Walton, E. T. S., 864
Wanklyn, D. I., 868
Watt, 96
Watt, James, 97
Watt-hour meter, 802
Wattmeter, 802
Watt's Governor, 128
Wave:
    fronts, 442
    motion, 161, 417
    number, 846
Wavelength, 438
Waves:
    capillary, 435
    gravity, 435
    longitudinal, 432, 439
    on water, 433
    speed of, 434
    standing, 464
    surface, 433
    transverse, 431
Weber, 692, 743
    per square meter, 724
Weight, 44
Wet-and-dry-bulb hygrometer, 381
Wheatstone, Sir Charles, 661
Wheatstone Bridge, 661
Wiedemann-Franz Law, 393
Wien, Wilhelm, 411
Wien's Displacement Law, 411
Wilson, C. T. R., 867
Wimshurst machine, 767
Wind instruments, 475
Wood, Alexander, 479
Work, 88
    function, 810
    on an indicator diagram, 299
Working substance, 318
Wow, 491, 503

X-rays, 837

Young, Thomas, 171
Young's Experiment, 607
Young's Modulus, 171, 435

Zemansky, Mark W., 327, 341